Selected Books

Selected Books

THE FOUR LOVES

THE PILGRIM'S REGRESS

MERE CHRISTIANITY

THE PROBLEM OF PAIN

PRAYER: LETTERS TO MALCOLM

REFLECTIONS ON THE PSALMS

THE SCREWTAPE LETTERS

SCREWTAPE PROPOSES A TOAST

TILL WE HAVE FACES

THE GREAT DIVORCE

MIRACLES

SURPRISED BY JOY

C.S. Lewis

HarperCollins*Publishers*

HarperCollins*Religious*
Part of HarperCollins*Publishers*
77–85 Fulham Palace Road, London W6 8JB

Contents

THE FOUR LOVES

That our affections kill us not, nor dye.

DONNE

Contents

I

INTRODUCTION

'God is love,' says St John. When I first tried to write this book I thought that his maxim would provide me with a very plain highroad through the whole subject. I thought I should be able to say that human loves deserved to be called loves at all just in so far as they resembled that Love which is God. The first distinction I made was therefore between what I called Gift-love and Need-love. The typical example of Gift-love would be that love which moves a man to work and plan and save for the future well-being of his family which he will die without sharing or seeing; of the second, that which sends a lonely or frightened child to its mother's arms.

There was no doubt which was more like Love Himself. Divine Love is Gift-love. The Father gives all He is and has to the Son. The Son gives Himself back to the Father, and gives Himself to the world, and for the world to the Father, and thus gives the world (in Himself) back to the Father too.

And what, on the other hand, can be less like anything we believe of God's life than Need-love? He lacks nothing, but our Need-love, as Plato saw, is 'the son of Poverty'. It is the accurate reflection in consciousness of our actual nature. We are born helpless. As soon as we are fully conscious we discover loneliness. We need others physically, emotionally, intellectually; we need them if we are to know anything, even ourselves.

I was looking forward to writing some fairly easy panegyrics on the first sort of love and disparagements of the second. And much of what I was going to say still seems to me to be true. I still think that if all we mean by our love is a craving to be loved, we are in a very deplorable state. But I would not now say (with my master, MacDonald) that if we mean only this craving we are mistaking for love something that is not love at all. I cannot now deny the name *love* to Need-love. Every time I have tried to think the thing out along those lines I have ended in puzzles and contradictions. The reality is more complicated than I supposed.

First of all, we do violence to most languages, including our own, if we do not call Need-love 'love'. Of course language is not an infallible guide, but it contains, with all its defects, a good deal of stored insight and experience. If you begin by flouting it, it has a way of avenging itself later on. We had better not follow Humpty Dumpty in making words mean whatever we please.

Secondly, we must be cautious about calling Need-love 'mere selfishness'. *Mere* is always a dangerous word. No doubt Need-love, like all our impulses, can be selfishly indulged. A tyrannous and gluttonous demand for affection can be a horrible thing. But in ordinary life no one calls a child selfish because it turns for comfort to its mother; nor an adult who turns to his fellow 'for company'. Those, whether children or adults, who do so least are not usually the most selfless. Where Need-love is felt there may be reasons for denying or totally mortifying it; but not to feel it is in general the mark of the cold egoist. Since we do in reality need one another ('it is not good for man to be alone'), then the failure of this need to appear as Need-love in consciousness – in other words, the illusory feeling that it *is* good for us to be alone – is a bad spiritual symptom; just as lack of appetite is a bad medical symptom because men do really need food.

But thirdly, we come to something far more important. Every Christian would agree that a man's spiritual health is exactly proportional to his love for God. But man's love for God, from the very nature of the case, must always be very largely, and must often be entirely, a Need-love. This is obvious when we implore forgiveness for our sins or support in our tribulations. But in the long run it is perhaps even more apparent in our growing – for it ought to be growing – awareness that our whole being by its very nature is one vast need; incomplete, preparatory, empty yet cluttered, crying out for Him who can untie things that are now knotted together and tie up things that are still dangling loose. I do not say that man can never bring to God anything at all but sheer Need-love. Exalted souls may tell us of a reach beyond that. But they would also, I think, be the first to tell us that those heights would cease to be true Graces, would become Neo-Platonic or finally diabolical illusions, the moment a man dared to think that he could live on them and henceforth drop out the element of need. 'The highest,' says the *Imitation*, 'does not stand without the lowest.' It would be a bold and silly creature that came before its Creator with the boast 'I'm no beggar. I love you disinterestedly.' Those who come nearest to a Gift-love for God will next moment, even at the very same moment, be beating their breasts with the publican and laying their indigence before the only real Giver. And God will have it so. He addresses our Need-love; 'Come unto me all ye that travail and are heavy-laden,' or, in the Old Testament, 'Open your mouth wide and I will fill it.'

Thus one Need-love, the greatest of all, either coincides with or at least makes a main ingredient in man's highest, healthiest, and most realistic spiritual condition. A very strange corollary follows. Man approaches God most nearly when he is in one sense least like God. For what can be more unlike than fullness and need, sovereignty and humility, righteousness and penitence, limitless power and a cry for help? This paradox staggered me when I first ran into it; it also wrecked all my previous attempts to write about love. When we face it, something like this seems to result.

We must distinguish two things which might both possibly be called 'nearness to God'. One is likeness to God. God has impressed some sort of likeness to Himself, I suppose, in all that He has made. Space and time, in their own fashion, mirror His greatness; all life, His fecundity; animal life, His activity. Man has a more important likeness than these by being rational. Angels, we believe, have likenesses which Man lacks; immortality and intuitive knowledge. In that way all men, whether good or bad, all angels including those that fell, are more like God than the animals are. Their natures are in this sense 'nearer' to the Divine Nature. But, secondly, there is what we may call nearness of approach. If this is what we mean, the states in which a man is 'nearest' to God are those in which he is most surely and swiftly approaching his final union with God, vision of God and enjoyment of God. And as soon as we distinguish nearness-by-likeness and nearness-of-approach, we see that they do not necessarily coincide. They may or may not.

Perhaps an analogy may help. Let us suppose that we are doing a mountain walk to the village which is our home. At mid-day we come to the top of a cliff where we are, in space, very near it because it is just below us. We could drop a stone into it. But as we are no cragsmen we can't get down. We must go a long way round; five miles, maybe. At many points during that *détour* we shall, statically, be far further from the village than we were when we sat above the cliff. But only statically. In terms of progress we shall be far 'nearer' our baths and teas.

Since God is blessed, omnipotent, sovereign and creative, there is obviously a sense in which happiness, strength, freedom and fertility (whether of mind or body), wherever they appear in human life, constitute likenesses, and in that way proximities, to God. But no one supposes that the possession of these gifts has any necessary connection with our sanctification. No kind of riches is a passport to the Kingdom of Heaven.

At the cliff's top we are near the village, but however long we sit there we shall never be any nearer to our bath and our tea. So here the likeness, and in that sense nearness, to Himself which God has conferred upon certain creatures and certain states of those creatures is something finished, built in. What is near Him by likeness is never, by that fact alone, going to be any nearer. But nearness of approach is, by definition, increasing nearness. And whereas the likeness is given to us – and can be received with or without thanks, can be used or abused – the approach, however initiated and supported by Grace, is something we must do. Creatures are made in their varying ways images of God without their own collaboration or even consent. It is not so that they become sons of God. And the likeness they receive by sonship is not that of images or portraits. It is in one way more than likeness, for it is unison or unity with God in will; but this is consistent with all the differences we have been considering. Hence, as a better writer has said, our imitation of God in this life – that is, our willed imitation as distinct from any of the likenesses which He has impressed upon our natures or states – must be an imitation of God incarnate: our model is the Jesus, not only of Calvary, but of the workshop, the roads, the crowds, the clamorous demands and surly oppositions, the lack of all peace and privacy, the interruptions. For this, so strangely unlike anything we can attribute to the Divine life in itself, is apparently not only like, but is, the Divine life operating under human conditions.

I must now explain why I have found this distinction necessary to any treatment of our loves. St John's saying that God is love has long been balanced in my mind against the remark of a modern author (M. Denis de Rougemont) that 'love ceases to be a demon only when he ceases to be a god'; which of course can be re-stated in the form 'begins to be a demon the moment he begins to be a god'. This balance seems to me an indispensable safeguard. If we ignore it the truth that God is love may slyly come to mean for us the converse, that love is God.

I suppose that everyone who has thought about the matter will see what M. de Rougemont meant. Every human love, at its height, has a tendency to claim for itself a divine authority. Its voice tends to sound as if it were the will of God Himself. It tells us not to count the cost, it demands of us a total commitment, it attempts to override all other claims and insinuates that any action which is sincerely done 'for love's sake' is thereby lawful and even meritorious. That erotic love and love of one's country may thus attempt to 'become gods' is generally recognised. But family affection may do the same. So, in a different way, may friendship. I shall not here elaborate the point, for it will meet us again and again in later chapters.

Now it must be noticed that the natural loves make this blasphemous claim not when they are in their worst, but when they are in their best, natural condition; when they are what our grandfathers called 'pure' or 'noble'. This is especially obvious in the erotic sphere. A faithful and genuinely self-sacrificing passion will speak to us with what seems the voice of God. Merely animal or frivolous lust will not. It will corrupt its addict in a dozen ways, but not in that way; a man may act upon such feelings but he cannot revere them any more than a man who scratches reveres the itch. A silly woman's temporary indulgence, which is really self-indulgence, to a spoiled child – her living doll while the fit lasts – is much less likely to 'become a god' than the deep, narrow devotion of a woman who (quite really) 'lives for her son'. And I am inclined to think that the sort of love for a man's country which is worked up by beer and brass bands will not lead him to do much harm (or much good) for her sake. It will probably be fully discharged by ordering another drink and joining in the chorus.

And this of course is what we ought to expect. Our loves do not make their claim to divinity until the claim becomes plausible. It does not become plausible until there is in them a real resemblance to God, to Love Himself. Let us here make no mistake. Our Gift-loves are really God-like; and among our Gift-loves those are most God-like which are most boundless and unwearied in giving. All the things the poets say about them are true. Their joy, their energy, their patience, their readiness to forgive, their desire for the good of the beloved – all this is a real and all but adorable image of the Divine life. In its presence we are right to thank God 'who has given such power to men'. We may say, quite truly and in an intelligible sense, that those who love greatly are 'near' to God. But of course it is 'nearness by likeness'. It will not of itself produce 'nearness of approach'. The likeness has been given us. It has no necessary connection with that slow and painful approach which must be our own (though by no means our unaided) task. Meanwhile, however, the likeness is a splendour. That is why we may mistake Like for Same. We may give our human loves the unconditional allegiance which we owe only to God. Then they become gods: then they become demons. Then they will destroy us, and also destroy themselves. For natural loves that are allowed to become gods do not remain loves. They are still called so, but can become in fact complicated forms of hatred.

Our Need-loves may be greedy and exacting but they do not set up to be gods. They are not near enough (by likeness) to God to attempt that.

It follows from what has been said that we must join neither the idolaters nor the 'debunkers' of human love. Idolatry both of erotic love and of 'the domestic affections' was the great error of nineteenth-century literature. Browning, Kingsley, and Patmore sometimes talk as if they thought that falling in love was the same thing as sanctification; the novelists habitually oppose to 'the World' not the Kingdom of Heaven but the home. We live in the reaction against this. The debunkers stigmatise as slush and sentimentality a very great deal of what their fathers said in praise of love. They are always pulling up and exposing the grubby roots of our natural loves. But I take it we must listen neither 'to the over-wise nor to the over-foolish giant'. The highest does not stand without the lowest. A plant must have roots below as well as sunlight above and roots must be grubby. Much of the grubbiness is clean dirt if only you will leave it in the garden and not keep on sprinkling it over the library table. The human loves can be glorious images of Divine love. No less than that: but also no more – proximities of likeness which in one instance may help, and in another may hinder, proximity of approach. Sometimes perhaps they have not very much to do with it either way.

2

LIKINGS AND LOVES FOR

THE SUB-HUMAN

Most of my generation were reproved as children for saying that we 'loved' strawberries, and some people take a pride in the fact that English has the two verbs *love* and *like* while French has to get on with *aimer* for both. But French has a good many other languages on its side. Indeed it very often has actual English usage on its side too. Nearly all speakers, however pedantic or however pious, talk every day about 'loving' a food, a game, or a pursuit. And in fact there is a continuity between our elementary likings for things and our loves for people. Since 'the highest does not stand without the lowest' we had better begin at the bottom, with mere likings; and since to 'like' anything means to take some sort of pleasure in it, we must begin with pleasure.

Now it is a very old discovery that pleasures can be divided into two classes; those which would not be pleasures at all unless they were preceded by desire, and those which are pleasures in their own right and need no such preparation. An example of the first would be a drink of water. This is a pleasure if you are thirsty and a great one if you are very thirsty. But probably no one in the world, except in obedience to thirst or to a doctor's orders, ever poured himself out a glass of water and drank it just for the fun of the thing. An example of the other class would be the unsought and unexpected pleasures of smell – the breath from a bean-field or a row of sweet-peas meeting you on your morning walk. You were in want of nothing, completely contented, before it; the pleasure, which may be very great, is an unsolicited, super-added gift. I am taking very simple instances for clarity's sake, and of course there are many complications. If you are given a coffee or beer where you expected (and would have been satisfied with) water, then of course you get a pleasure of the first kind (allaying of thirst) and one of the second (a nice taste) at the same time. Again, an addiction may turn what was once a pleasure of the second kind into one of the first. For the temperate man an occasional glass of wine is a treat – like the smell of the bean-field. But to the alcoholic, whose palate and digestion have long since been destroyed, no liquor gives any pleasure except that of relief from an unbearable craving. So far as he can still discern tastes at all, he rather dislikes it; but it is better than the misery of remaining sober. Yet through all their permutations and combinations the distinction between the two classes remains tolerably clear. We may call them Need-pleasures and Pleasures of Appreciation.

The resemblance between these Need-pleasures and the 'Need-loves' in my first chapter will occur to everyone. But there, you remember, I confessed that I had had to resist a tendency to disparage the Need-loves or even to say they were not loves at all. Here, for most people, there may be an opposite inclination. It would be very easy to spread ourselves in laudation of the Need-pleasures and to frown upon those that are Appreciatives: the one so natural (a word to conjure with), so necessary, so shielded from excess by their very naturalness, the other unnecessary and opening the door to every kind of luxury and vice. If we were short of matter on this theme we could turn on the tap by opening the works of the Stoics and it would run till we had a bathful. But throughout this inquiry we must be careful never to adopt prematurely a moral or evaluating attitude. The human mind is generally far more eager to praise and dispraise than to describe and define. It wants to make every distinction a distinction of value; hence those fatal critics who can never point out the differing quality of two poets without putting them in an order of preference as if they were candidates for a prize. We must do nothing of the sort about the pleasures. The reality is too complicated. We are already warned of this by the fact that Need-pleasure is the state in which Appreciative pleasures end up when they go bad (by addiction).

For us at any rate the importance of the two sorts of pleasure lies in the extent to which they foreshadow characteristics in our 'loves' (properly so called).

The thirsty man who has just drunk off a tumbler of water may say, 'By Jove, I *wanted* that.' So may the alcoholic who has just had his 'nip'. The man who passes the sweet-peas in his morning walk is more likely to say, 'How lovely the smell *is*.' The connoisseur after his first sip of the famous claret, may similarly say, 'This *is* a great wine.' When Need-pleasures are in question we tend to make statements about ourselves in the past tense; when Appreciative pleasures are in question we tend to make statements about the object in the present tense. It is easy to see why.

Shakespeare has described the satisfaction of a tyrannous lust as something

Past reason hunted and, no sooner had,
Past reason hated.

But the most innocent and necessary of Need-pleasures have about them something of the same character – only something, of course. They are not hated once we have had them, but they certainly 'die on us' with extraordinary abruptness, and completely. The scullery tap and the tumbler are very attractive indeed when we come in parched from mowing the grass; six seconds later they are emptied of all interest. The smell of frying food is very different before and after breakfast. And, if you will forgive me for citing the most extreme instance of all, have there not for most of us been moments (in a strange town) when the sight of the word GENTLEMEN over a door has roused a joy almost worthy of celebration in verse?

Pleasures of Appreciation are very different. They make us feel that something has not merely gratified our senses in fact but claimed our appreciation by right. The connoisseur does not merely enjoy his claret as he might enjoy warming his feet when they were cold. He feels that here is a wine that deserves his full attention; that justifies all the tradition and skill that have gone to its making and all the years of training that have made his own palate fit to judge it. There is even a glimmering of unselfishness in his attitude. He wants the wine to be preserved and kept in good condition, not entirely for his own sake. Even if he were on his death-bed and was never going to drink wine again, he would be horrified at the thought of this vintage being spilled or spoiled or even drunk by clods (like myself) who can't tell a good claret from a bad. And so with the man who passes the sweet-peas. He does not simply enjoy, he feels that this fragrance somehow deserves to be enjoyed. He would blame himself if he went past inattentive and undelighted. It would be blockish, insensitive. It would be a shame that so fine a thing should have been wasted on him. He will remember the delicious moment years hence. He will be sorry when he hears that the garden past which his walk led him that day has now been swallowed up by cinemas, garages and the new bypass.

Scientifically both sorts of pleasures are, no doubt, relative to our organisms. But the Need-pleasures loudly proclaim their relativity not only to the human frame but to its momentary condition, and outside that relation have no meaning or interest for us at all. The objects which afford pleasures of appreciation give us the feeling – whether irrational or not – that we somehow owe it to them to savour, to attend to and praise it. 'It would be a sin to set a wine like that before Lewis,' says the expert in claret. 'How can you walk past this garden taking no notice of the smell?' we ask. But we should never feel this about a Need-pleasure: never blame ourselves or others for not having been thirsty and therefore walking past a well without taking a drink of water.

How the Need-pleasures foreshadow our Need-loves is obvious enough. In the latter the beloved is seen in relation to our own needs, just as the scullery tap is seen by the thirsty man or the glass of gin by the alcoholic. And the Need-love, like the Need-pleasure, will not last longer than the need. This does not, fortunately, mean that all affections which begin in Need-love are transitory. The need itself may be permanent or recurrent. Another kind of love may be grafted on the Need-love. Moral principles (conjugal fidelity, filial piety, gratitude, and the like) may preserve the relationship for a lifetime. But where Need-love is left unaided we can hardly expect it not to 'die on us' once the need is no more. That is why the world rings with the complaints of mothers whose grown-up children neglect them and of forsaken mistresses whose lovers' love was pure need – which they have satisfied. Our Need-love for God is in a different position because our need of Him can never end either in this world or in any other. But our awareness of it can, and then the Need-love dies too. 'The Devil was sick, the Devil a monk would be.' There seems no reason for describing as hypocritical the short-lived piety of those whose religion fades away once they have emerged from 'danger, necessity, or tribulation'. Why should they not have been sincere? They were desperate and they howled for help. Who wouldn't?

What Appreciative pleasure foreshadows is not so quickly described.

First of all, it is the starting point for our whole experience of beauty. It is impossible to draw a line below which such pleasures are 'sensual' and above which they are 'aesthetic'. The experiences of the expert in claret already contain elements of concentration, judgment and disciplined perceptiveness, which are not sensual; those of the musician still contain elements which are. There is no frontier – there is seamless continuity – between the sensuous pleasure of garden smells and an enjoyment of the countryside (or 'beauty') as a whole, or even our enjoyment of the painters and poets who treat it.

And, as we have seen, there is in these pleasures from the very beginning a shadow or dawn of, or an invitation to, disinterestedness. Of course in one way we can be disinterested or unselfish, and far more heroically so, about the Need-pleasures: it is a cup of water that the wounded Sidney sacrifices to the dying soldier. But that is not the sort of disinterestedness I now mean. Sidney loves his neighbour. But in the Appreciative pleasures, even at their lowest, and more and more as they grow up into the full appreciation of all beauty, we get something that we can hardly help calling *love* and hardly help calling *disinterested*, towards the object itself. It is the feeling which would make a man unwilling to deface a great picture even if he were the last man left alive and himself about to die; which makes us glad of unspoiled forests that we shall never see; which makes us anxious that the garden or bean-field should continue to exist. We do not merely like the things; we pronounce them, in a momentarily God-like sense, 'very good'.

And now our principle of starting at the lowest – without which 'the highest does not stand' – begins to pay a dividend. It has revealed to me a deficiency in our previous classification of the loves into those of Need and those of Gift. There is a third element in love, no less important than these, which is foreshadowed by our appreciative pleasures. This judgment that the object is very good, this attention (almost homage) offered to it as a kind of debt, this wish that it should be and should continue being what it is even if we were never to enjoy it, can go out not only to things but to persons. When it is offered to a woman we call it admiration; when to a man, hero-worship; when to God, worship simply.

Need-love cries to God from our poverty; Gift-love longs to serve, or even to suffer for, God; Appreciative love says: 'We give thanks to thee for thy great glory.' Need-love says of a woman 'I cannot live without her'; Gift-love longs to give her happiness, comfort, protection – if possible, wealth; Appreciative love gazes and holds its breath and is silent, rejoices that such a wonder should exist even if not for him, will not be wholly dejected by losing her, would rather have it so than never to have seen her at all.

We murder to dissect. In actual life, thank God, the three elements of love mix and succeed one another, moment by moment. Perhaps none of them except Need-love ever exists alone, in 'chemical' purity, for more than a few seconds. And perhaps that is because nothing about us except our neediness is, in this life, permanent.

Two forms of love for what is not personal demand special treatment.

For some people, perhaps especially for Englishmen and Russians, what we call 'the love of nature' is a permanent and serious sentiment. I mean here that love of nature which cannot be adequately classified simply as an instance of our love for beauty. Of course many natural objects – trees, flowers and animals – are beautiful. But the nature-lovers whom I have in mind are not very much concerned with individual beautiful objects of that sort. The man who is distracts them. An enthusiastic botanist is for them a dreadful companion on a ramble. He is always stopping to draw their attention to particulars. Nor are they looking for 'views' or landscapes. Wordsworth, their spokes-man, strongly deprecates this. It leads to 'a comparison of scene with scene', makes you 'pamper' yourself with 'meagre novelties of colour and proportion'. While you are busying yourself with this critical and discriminating activity you lose what really matters – the 'moods of time and season', the 'spirit' of the place. And of course Wordsworth is right. That is why, if you love nature in his fashion, a landscape painter is (out of doors) an even worse companion than a botanist.

It is the 'moods' or the 'spirit' that matter. Nature-lovers want to receive as fully as possible whatever nature, at each particular time and place, is, so to speak, saying. The obvious richness, grace and harmony of some scenes are no more precious to them than the grimness, bleakness, terror, monotony, or 'visionary dreariness' of others. The featureless itself gets from them a willing response. It is one more word uttered by nature. They lay themselves bare to the sheer quality of every countryside every hour of the day. They want to absorb it into themselves, to be coloured through and through by it.

This experience, like so many others, after being lauded to the skies in the nineteenth century, has been debunked by the moderns. And one must certainly concede to the debunkers that Wordsworth, not when he was communicating it as a poet, but when he was merely talking about it as a philosopher (or philosophaster), said some very silly things. It is silly, unless you have found any evidence, to believe that flowers enjoy the air they breathe, and sillier not to add that, if this were true, flowers would undoubtedly have pains as well as pleasures. Nor have many people been taught moral philosophy by an 'impulse from a vernal wood'.

If they were, it would not necessarily be the sort of moral philosophy Wordsworth would have approved. It might be that of ruthless competition. For some moderns I think it is. They love nature in so far as, for them, she calls to 'the dark gods in the blood'; not although, but because, sex and hunger and sheer power there operate without pity or shame.

If you take nature as a teacher she will teach you exactly the lessons you had already decided to learn; this is only another way of saying that nature does not teach. The tendency to take her as a teacher is obviously very easily grafted on to the experience we call 'love of nature'. But it is only a graft. While we are actually subjected to them, the 'moods' and 'spirits' of nature point no morals. Overwhelming gaiety, insupportable grandeur, sombre desolation are flung at you. Make what you can of them, if you must make at all. The only imperative that nature utters is, 'Look. Listen. Attend.'

The fact that this imperative is so often misinterpreted and sets people making theologies and pantheologies and antitheologies – all of which can be debunked – does not really touch the central experience itself. What nature-lovers – whether they are Wordsworthians or people with 'dark gods in their blood' – get from nature is an iconography, a language of images. I do not mean simply visual images; it is the 'moods' or 'spirits' themselves – the powerful expositions of terror, gloom, jocundity, cruelty, lust, innocence, purity – that are the images. In them each man can clothe his own belief. We must learn our theology or philosophy elsewhere (not surprisingly, we often learn them from theologians and philosophers).

But when I speak of 'clothing' our belief in such images I do not mean anything like using nature for similes or metaphors in the manner of the poets. Indeed I might have said 'filling' or 'incarnating' rather than clothing. Many people – I am one myself – would never, but for what nature does to us, have had any content to put into the words we must use in confessing our faith. Nature never taught me that there exists a God of glory and of infinite majesty. I had to learn that in other ways. But nature gave the word *glory* a meaning for me. I still do not know where else I could have found one. I do not see how the 'fear' of God could have ever meant to me anything but the lowest prudential efforts to be safe, if I had never seen certain ominous ravines and unapproachable crags. And if nature had never awakened certain longings in me, huge areas of what I can now mean by the 'love' of God would never, so far as I can see, have existed.

Of course the fact that a Christian can so use nature is not even the beginning of a proof that Christianity is true. Those suffering from Dark Gods can equally use her (I suppose) for their creed. That is precisely the point. Nature does not teach. A true philosophy may sometimes validate an experience of nature; an experience of nature cannot validate a philosophy. Nature will not verify any theological or metaphysical proposition (or not in the manner we are now considering); she will help to show what it means.

And not, on the Christian premises, by accident. The created glory may be expected to give us hints of the uncreated; for the one is derived from the other and in some fashion reflects it.

In some fashion. But not perhaps in so direct and simple a fashion as we at first might suppose. For of course all the facts stressed by nature-lovers of the other school are facts too; there are worms in the belly as well as primroses in the wood. Try to reconcile them, or to show that they don't really need reconciliation, and you are turning from direct experience of nature – our present subject – to metaphysics or theodicy or something of that sort. That may be a sensible thing to do; but I think it should be kept distinct from the love of nature. While we are on that level, while we are still claiming to speak of what nature has directly 'said' to us, we must stick to it. We have seen an image of glory. We must not try to find a direct path through it and beyond it to an increasing knowledge of God. The path peters out almost at once. Terrors and mysteries, the whole depth of God's counsels and the whole tangle of the history of the universe, choke it. We can't get through; not that way. We must make a *détour* – leave the hills and woods and go back to our studies, to church, to our Bibles, to our knees. Otherwise the love of nature is beginning to turn into a nature religion. And then, even if it does not lead us to the Dark Gods, it will lead us to a great deal of nonsense.

But we need not surrender the love of nature – chastened and limited as I have suggested – to the debunkers. Nature cannot satisfy the desires she arouses nor answer theological questions nor sanctify us. Our real journey to God involves constantly turning our backs on her; passing from the dawn-lit fields into some poky little church, or (it might be) going to work in an East End parish. But the love of her has been a valuable and, for some people, an indispensable initiation.

I need not say 'has been'. For in fact those who allow no more than this to the love of nature seem to be those who retain it. This is what one should expect. This love, when it sets up as a religion, is beginning to be a god – therefore to be a demon. And demons never keep their promises. Nature 'dies on' those who try to live for a love of nature. Coleridge ended by being insensible to her; Wordsworth, by lamenting that the glory had passed away. Say your prayers in a garden early, ignoring steadfastly the dew, the birds and the flowers, and you will come away overwhelmed by its freshness and joy; go there in order to be overwhelmed and, after a certain age, nine times out of ten nothing will happen to you.

I turn now to the love of one's country. Here there is no need to labour M. de Rougemont's maxim; we all know now that this love becomes a demon when it becomes a god. Some begin to suspect that it is never anything but a demon. But then they have to reject half the high poetry and half the heroic action our race has achieved. We cannot keep even Christ's lament over Jerusalem. He too exhibits love for His country.

Let us limit our field. There is no need here for an essay on international ethics. When this love becomes demoniac it will of course produce wicked acts. But others, more skilled, may say what acts between nations are wicked. We are only considering the sentiment itself in the hope of being able to distinguish its innocent from its demoniac condition. Neither of these is the efficient cause of national behaviour. For strictly speaking it is rulers, not nations, who behave internationally. Demoniac patriotism in their subjects – I write only for subjects – will make it easier for them to act wickedly; healthy patriotism may make it harder: when they are wicked they may by propaganda encourage a demoniac condition of our sentiments in order to secure our acquiescence in their wickedness. If they are good, they could do the opposite. That is one reason why we private persons should keep a wary eye on the health or disease of our own love for our country. And that is what I am writing about.

How ambivalent patriotism is may be gauged by the fact that no two writers have expressed it more vigorously than Kipling and Chesterton. If it were one element two such men could not both have praised it. In reality it contains many ingredients, of which many different blends are possible.

First, there is love of home, of the place we grew up in or the place, perhaps many, which have been our homes; and of all places fairly near these and fairly like them; love of old acquaintances, of familiar sights, sounds and smells. Note that at its largest this is, for us, a love of England, Wales, Scotland, or Ulster. Only foreigners and politicians talk about 'Britain'. Kipling's 'I do not love my empire's foes' strikes a ludicrously false note. *My* empire! With this love for the place there goes a love for the way of life; for beer and tea and open fires, trains with compartments in them and an unarmed police force and all the rest of it; for the local dialect and (a shade less) for our native language. As Chesterton says, a man's reasons for not wanting his country to be ruled by foreigners are very like his reasons for not wanting his house to be burned down; because he 'could not even begin' to enumerate all the things he would miss.

It would be hard to find any legitimate point of view from which this feeling could be condemned. As the family offers us the first step beyond self-love, so this offers us the first step beyond family selfishness. Of course it is not pure charity; it involves love of our neighbours in the local, not of our Neighbour, in the Dominical, sense. But those who do not love the fellow-villagers or fellow-townsmen whom they *have* seen are not likely to have got very far towards loving 'Man' whom they have not. All natural affections, including this, can become rivals to spiritual love: but they can also be preparatory imitations of it, training (so to speak) of the spiritual muscles which Grace may later put to a higher service; as women nurse dolls in childhood and later nurse children. There may come an occasion for renouncing this love; pluck out your right eye. But you need to have an eye first: a creature which had none – which had only got so far as a 'photosensitive' spot – would be very ill employed in meditation on that severe text.

Of course patriotism of this kind is not in the least aggressive. It asks only to be let alone. It becomes militant only to protect what it loves. In any mind which has a pennyworth of imagination it produces a good attitude towards foreigners. How can I love my home without coming to realise that other men, no less rightly, love theirs? Once you have realised that the Frenchmen like *café complet* just as we like bacon and eggs – why, good luck to them and let them have it. The last thing we want is to make everywhere else just like our own home. It would not be home unless it were different.

The second ingredient is a particular attitude to our country's past. I mean to that past as it lives in popular imagination; the great deeds of our ancestors. Remember Marathon. Remember Waterloo. 'We must be free or die who speak the tongue that Shakespeare spoke.' This past is felt both to impose an obligation and to hold out an assurance; we must not fall below the standards our fathers set us, and because we are their sons there is good hope we shall not.

This feeling has not quite such good credentials as the sheer love of home. The actual history of every country is full of shabby and even shameful doings. The heroic stories, if taken to be typical, give a false impression of it and are often themselves open to serious historical criticism. Hence a patriotism based on our glorious past is fair game for the debunker. As knowledge increases it may snap and be converted into disillusioned cynicism, or may be maintained by a voluntary shutting of the eyes. But who can condemn what clearly makes many people, at many important moments, behave so much better than they could have done without its help?

I think it is possible to be strengthened by the image of the past without being either deceived or puffed up. The image becomes dangerous in the precise degree to which it is mistaken, or substituted, for serious and systematic historical study. The stories are best when they are handed on and accepted as stories. I do not mean by this that they should be handed on as mere fictions (some of them are after all true). But the emphasis should be on the tale as such, on the picture which fires the imagination, the example that strengthens the will. The schoolboy who hears them should dimly feel – though of course he cannot put it into words – that he is hearing *saga*. Let him be thrilled – preferably 'out of school' – by the 'Deeds that won the Empire'; but the less we mix this up with his 'history lessons' or mistake it for a serious analysis – worse still, a justification – of imperial policy, the better. When I was a child I had a book full of coloured pictures called *Our Island Story*. That title has always seemed to me to strike exactly the right note. The book did not look at all like a text-book either. What does seem to me poisonous, what breeds a type of patriotism that is pernicious if it lasts but not likely to last long in an educated adult, is the perfectly serious indoctrination of the young in knowably false or biased history – the heroic legend drably disguised as text-book fact. With this creeps in the tacit assumption that other nations have not equally their heroes; perhaps even the belief – surely it is very bad biology – that we can literally 'inherit' a tradition. And these almost inevitably lead on to a third thing that is sometimes called patriotism.

This third thing is not a sentiment but a belief; a firm, even prosaic belief that our own nation, in sober fact, has long been, and still is markedly superior to all others. I once ventured to say to an old clergyman who was voicing this sort of patriotism, 'But, sir, aren't we told that *every* people thinks its own men the bravest and its own women the fairest in the world?' He replied with total gravity – he could not have been graver if he had been saying the Creed at the altar – 'Yes, but in England it's true.' To be sure, this conviction had not made my friend (God rest his soul) a villain; only an extremely lovable old ass. It can however produce asses that kick and bite.

On the lunatic fringe it may shade off into that popular Racialism which Christianity and science equally forbid.

This brings us to the fourth ingredient. If our nation is really so much better than others it may be held to have either the duties or the rights of a superior being towards them. In the nineteenth century the English became very conscious of such duties: the 'white man's burden'. What we called *natives* were our wards and we their self-appointed guardians. This was not all hypocrisy. We did do them some good. But our habit of talking as if England's motive for acquiring an empire (or any youngster's motives for seeking a job in the Indian Civil Service) had been mainly altruistic nauseated the world. And yet this showed the sense of superiority working at its best. Some nations who have also felt it have stressed the rights not the duties. To them, some foreigners were so bad that one had the right to exterminate them. Others, fitted only to be hewers of wood and drawers of water to the chosen people, had better be made to get on with their hewing and drawing. Dogs, know your betters! I am far from suggesting that the two attitudes are on the same level. But both are fatal. Both demand that the area in which they operate should grow 'wider still and wider'. And both have about them this sure mark of evil: only by being terrible do they avoid being comic. If there were no broken treaties with Redskins, no extermination of the Tasmanians, no gas-chambers and no Belsen, no Amritsar, Black and Tans or Apartheid, the pomposity of both would be roaring farce.

Finally we reach the stage where patriotism in its demoniac form unconsciously denies itself. Chesterton picked on two lines from Kipling as the perfect example. It was unfair to Kipling, who knew – wonderfully, for so homeless a man – what the love of home can mean. But the lines, in isolation, can be taken to sum up the thing. They run:

If England was what England seems
'Ow quick we'd drop 'er. But she ain't!

Love never spoke that way. It is like loving your children only 'if they're good', your wife only while she keeps her looks, your husband only so long as he is famous and successful. 'No man,' said one of the Greeks, 'loves his city because it is great, but because it is his.' A man who really loves his country will love her in her ruin and degeneration – 'England, with all thy faults, I love thee still.' She will be to him 'a poor thing but mine own'. He may think her good and great, when she is not, because he loves her; the delusion is up to a point pardonable. But Kipling's soldier reverses it; he loves her because he thinks her good and great – loves her on her merits. She is a fine going concern and it gratifies his pride to be in it. How if she ceased to be such? The answer is plainly given: ''Ow quick we'd drop 'er.' When the ship begins to sink he will leave her. Thus that kind of patriotism which sets off with the greatest swagger of drums and banners actually sets off on the road that can lead to Vichy. And this is a phenomenon which will meet us again. When the natural loves become lawless they do not merely do harm to other loves; they themselves cease to be the loves they were – to be loves at all.

Patriotism has then, many faces. Those who would reject it entirely do not seem to have considered what will certainly step – has already begun to step – into its place. For a long time yet, or perhaps forever, nations will live in danger. Rulers must somehow nerve their subjects to defend them or at least to prepare for their defence. Where the sentiment of patriotism has been destroyed this can be done only by presenting every international conflict in a purely ethical light. If people will spend neither sweat nor blood for 'their country' they must be made to feel that they are spending them for justice, or civilisation, or humanity. This is a step down, not up. Patriotic sentiment did not of course need to disregard ethics. Good men needed to be convinced that their country's cause was just; but it was still their country's cause, not the cause of justice as such. The difference seems to me important. I may without self-righteousness or hypocrisy think it just to defend my house by force against a burglar; but if I start pretending that I blacked his eye purely on moral grounds – wholly indifferent to the fact that the house in question was mine – I become insufferable. The pretence that when England's cause is just we are on England's side – as some neutral Don Quixote might be – for that reason alone, is equally spurious. And nonsense draws evil after it. If our country's cause is the cause of God, wars must be wars of annihilation. A false transcendence is given to things which are very much of this world.

The glory of the old sentiment was that while it could steel men to the utmost endeavour, it still knew itself to be a sentiment. Wars could be heroic without pretending to be Holy Wars. The hero's death was not confused with the martyr's. And (delightfully) the same sentiment which could be so serious in a rearguard action, could also in peacetime, take itself as lightly as all happy loves often do. It could laugh at itself. Our older patriotic songs cannot be sung without a twinkle in the eye; later ones sound more like hymns. Give me 'The British Grenadiers' (*with a tow-row-row-row*) any day rather than 'Land of Hope and Glory'.

It will be noticed that the sort of love I have been describing, and all its ingredients, can be for something other than a country: for a school, a regiment, a great family, or a class. All the same criticisms will still apply. It can also be felt for bodies that claim more than a natural affection: for a Church or (alas) a party in a Church, or for a religious order. This terrible subject would require a book to itself. Here it will be enough to say that the Heavenly Society is also an earthly society. Our (merely natural) patriotism towards the latter can very easily borrow the transcendent claims of the former and use them to justify the most abominable actions. If ever the book which I am not going to write is written it must be the full confession by Christendom of Christendom's specific contribution to the sum of human cruelty and treachery. Large areas of 'the World' will not hear us till we have publicly disowned much of our past. Why should they? We have shouted the name of Christ and enacted the service of Moloch.

It may be thought that I should not end this chapter without a word about our love for animals. But that will fit in better in the next. Whether animals are in fact sub-personal or not, they are never loved as if they were. The fact or the illusion of personality is always present, so that love for them is really an instance of that Affection which is the subject of the following chapter.

3

AFFECTION

I begin with the humblest and most widely diffused of loves, the love in which our experience seems to differ least from that of the animals. Let me add at once that I do not on that account give it a lower value. Nothing in Man is either worse or better for being shared with the beasts. When we blame a man for being 'a mere animal', we mean not that he displays animal characteristics (we all do) but that he displays these, and only these, on occasions where the specifically human was demanded. (When we call him 'brutal' we usually mean that he commits cruelties impossible to most real brutes; they're not clever enough.)

The Greeks called this love *storge* (two syllables and the g is 'hard'). I shall here call it simply Affection. My Greek Lexicon defines *storge* as 'affection, especially of parents to offspring'; but also of offspring to parents. And that, I have no doubt, is the original form of the thing as well as the central meaning of the word. The image we must start with is that of a mother nursing a baby, a bitch or a cat with a basketful of puppies or kittens; all in a squeaking, nuzzling heap together; purrings, lickings, baby-talk, milk, warmth, the smell of young life.

The importance of this image is that it presents us at the very outset with a certain paradox. The Need and Need-love of the young is obvious; so is the Gift-love of the mother. She gives birth, gives suck, gives protection. On the other hand, she must give birth or die. She must give suck or suffer. That way, her Affection too is a Need-love. There is the paradox. It is a Need-love but what it needs is to give. It is a Gift-love but it needs to be needed. We shall have to return to this point.

But even in animal life, and still more in our own, Affection extends far beyond the relation of mother and young. This warm comfortableness, this satisfaction in being together, takes in all sorts of objects. It is indeed the least discriminating of loves. There are women for whom we can predict few wooers and men who are likely to have few friends. They have nothing to offer. But almost anyone can become an object of Affection; the ugly, the stupid, even the exasperating. There need be no apparent fitness between those whom it unites. I have seen it felt for an imbecile not only by his parents but by his brothers. It ignores the barriers of age, sex, class and education. It can exist between a clever young man from the university and an old nurse, though their minds inhabit different worlds. It ignores even the barriers of species. We see it not only between dog and man but, more surprisingly, between dog and cat. Gilbert White claims to have discovered it between a horse and a hen.

Some of the novelists have seized this well. In *Tristram Shandy* 'my father' and Uncle Toby are so far from being united by any community of interests or ideas that they cannot converse for ten minutes without cross-purposes; but we are made to feel their deep mutual affection. So with Don Quixote and Sancho Panza, Pickwick and Sam Weller, Dick Swiveller and the Marchioness. So too, though probably without the author's conscious intention, in *The Wind in the Willows*; the quaternion of Mole, Rat, Badger and Toad suggests the amazing heterogeneity possible between those who are bound by Affection.

But Affection has its own criteria. Its objects have to be familiar. We can sometimes point to the very day and hour when we fell in love or began a new friendship. I doubt if we ever catch Affection beginning. To become aware of it is to become aware that it has already been going on for some time. The use of 'old' or *vieux* as a term of Affection is significant. The dog barks at strangers who have never done it any harm and wags its tail for old acquaintances even if they never did it a good turn. The child will love a crusty old gardener who has hardly ever taken any notice of it and shrink from the visitor who is making every attempt to win its regard. But it must be an *old* gardener, one who has 'always' been there – the short but seemingly immemorial 'always' of childhood.

Affection, as I have said, is the humblest love. It gives itself no airs. People can be proud of being 'in love', or of friendship. Affection is modest – even furtive and shame-faced. Once when I had remarked on the affection quite often found between cat and dog, my friend replied, 'Yes. But I bet no dog would ever confess it to the other dogs.' That is at least a good caricature of much human Affection. 'Let homely faces stay at home,' says Comus. Now Affection has a very homely face. So have many of those for whom we feel it. It is no proof of our refinement or perceptiveness that we love them; nor that they love us. What I have called Appreciative Love is no basic element in Affection. It usually needs absence or bereavement to set us praising those to whom only Affection binds us. We take them for granted: and this taking for granted, which is an outrage in erotic love, is here right and proper up to a point. It fits the comfortable, quiet nature of the feeling. Affection would not be affection if it was loudly and frequently expressed; to produce it in public is like getting your household furniture out for a move. It did very well in its place, but it looks shabby or tawdry or grotesque in the sunshine. Affection almost slinks or seeps through our lives. It lives with humble, un-dress, private things; soft slippers, old clothes, old jokes, the thump of a sleepy dog's tail on the kitchen floor, the sound of a sewing-machine, a gollywog left on the lawn.

But I must at once correct myself. I am talking of Affection as it is when it exists apart from the other loves. It often does so exist; often not. As gin is not only a drink in itself but also a base for many mixed drinks, so Affection, besides being a love itself, can enter into the other loves and colour them all through and become the very medium in which from day to day they operate. They would not perhaps wear very well without it. To make a friend is not the same as to become affectionate. But when your friend has become an old friend, all those things about him which had originally nothing to do with the friendship become familiar and dear with familiarity. As for erotic love, I can imagine nothing more disagreeable than to experience it for more than a very short time without this homespun clothing of affection. That would be a most uneasy condition, either too angelic or too animal or each by turn; never quite great enough or little enough for man. There is indeed a peculiar charm, both in friendship and in Eros, about those moments when Appreciative Love lies, as it were, curled up asleep, and the mere ease and ordinariness of the relationship (free as solitude, yet neither is alone) wraps us round. No need to talk. No need to make love. No needs at all except perhaps to stir the fire.

This blending and overlapping of the loves is well kept before us by the fact that at most times and places all three of them had in common, as their expression, the kiss. In modern England friendship no longer uses it, but Affection and Eros do. It belongs so fully to both that we cannot now tell which borrowed it from the other or whether there were borrowing at all. To be sure, you may say that the kiss of Affection differs from the kiss of Eros. Yes; but not all kisses between lovers are lovers' kisses. Again, both these loves tend – and it embarrasses many moderns – to use a 'little language' or 'baby-talk'. And this is not peculiar to the human species. Professor Lorenz has told us that when jackdaws are amorous their calls 'consist chiefly of infantile sounds reserved by adult jackdaws for these occasions' (*King Solomon's Ring*, p. 158). We and the birds have the same excuse. Different sorts of tenderness are both tenderness and the language of the earliest tenderness we have ever known is recalled to do duty for the new sort.

One of the most remarkable by-products of Affection has not yet been mentioned. I have said that is not primarily an Appreciative Love. It is not discriminating. It can 'rub along' with the most unpromising people.

Yet oddly enough this very fact means that it can in the end make appreciations possible which, but for it, might never have existed. We may say, and not quite untruly, that we have chosen our friends and the woman we love for their various excellencies – for beauty, frankness, goodness of heart, wit, intelligence, or what not. But it had to be the particular kind of wit, the particular kind of beauty, the particular kind of goodness that we like, and we have our personal tastes in these matters. That is why friends and lovers feel that they were 'made for one another'. The especial glory of Affection is that it can unite those who most emphatically, even comically, are not; people who, if they had not found themselves put down by fate in the same household or community, would have had nothing to do with each other. If Affection grows out of this – of course it often does not – their eyes begin to open. Growing fond of 'old so-and-so', at first simply because he happens to be there, I presently begin to see that there is 'something in him' after all. The moment when one first says, really meaning it, that though he is not 'my sort of man' he is a very good man 'in his own way' is one of liberation. It does not feel like that; we may feel only tolerant and indulgent. But really we have crossed a frontier. That 'in his own way' means that we are getting beyond our own idiosyncracies, that we are learning to appreciate goodness or intelligence in themselves, not merely goodness or intelligence flavoured and served to suit our own palate.

'Dogs and cats should always be brought up together,' said someone, 'it broadens their minds so.' Affection broadens ours; of all natural loves it is the most catholic, the least finical, the broadest. The people with whom you are thrown together in the family, the college, the mess, the ship, the religious house, are from this point of view a wider circle than the friends, however numerous, whom you have made for yourself in the outer world. By having a great many friends I do not prove that I have a wide appreciation of human excellence. You might as well say I prove the width of my literary taste by being able to enjoy all the books in my own study. The answer is the same in both cases – 'You chose those books. You chose those friends. Of course they suit you.' The truly wide taste in reading is that which enables a man to find something for his needs on the sixpenny tray outside any secondhand bookshop. The truly wide taste in humanity will similarly find something to appreciate in the cross-section of humanity whom one has to meet every day. In my experience it is Affection that creates this taste, teaching us first to notice, then to endure, then to smile at, then to enjoy, and finally to appreciate, the people who 'happen to be there'. Made for us? Thank God, no. They are themselves, odder than you could have believed and worth far more than we guessed.

And now we are drawing near the point of danger. Affection, I have said, gives itself no airs; charity, said St Paul, is not puffed up. Affection can love the unattractive: God and His saints love the unlovable. Affection 'does not expect too much', turns a blind eye to faults, revives easily after quarrels; just so charity suffers long and is kind and forgives. Affection opens our eyes to goodness we could not have seen, or should not have appreciated without it. So does humble sanctity. If we dwelled exclusively on these resemblances we might be led on to believe that this Affection is not simply one of the natural loves but is Love Himself working in our human hearts and fulfilling the law. Were the Victorian novelists right after all? Is love (of this sort) really enough? Are the 'domestic affections', when in their best and fullest development, the same thing as the Christian life? The answer to all these questions, I submit, is certainly No.

I do not mean simply that those novelists sometimes wrote as if they had never heard the text about 'hating' wife and mother and one's own life also. That of course is true. The rivalry between all natural loves and the love of God is something a Christian dare not forget. God is the great Rival, the ultimate object of human jealousy; that beauty, terrible as the Gorgon's, which may at any moment steal from me – or it seems like stealing to me – my wife's or husband's or daughter's heart. The bitterness of some unbelief, though disguised even from those who feel it an anti-clericalism or hatred of superstition, is really due to this. But I am not at present thinking of that rivalry; we shall have to face it in a later chapter. For the moment our business is more 'down to earth'.

How many of these 'happy homes' really exist? Worse still; are all the unhappy ones unhappy because Affection is absent? I believe not. It can be present, causing the unhappiness. Nearly all the characteristics of this love are ambivalent. They may work for ill as well as for good. By itself, left simply to follow its own bent, it can darken and degrade human life. The debunkers and anti-sentimentalists have not said all the truth about it, but all they have said is true.

Symptomatic of this, perhaps, is the odiousness of nearly all those treacly tunes and saccharine poems in which popular art expresses Affection. They are odious because of their falsity. They represent as a ready-made recipe for bliss (and even for goodness) what is in fact only an opportunity. There is no hint that we shall have to do anything: only let Affection pour over us like a warm shower-bath and all, it is implied, will be well.

Affection, we have seen, includes both Need-love and Gift-love. I begin with the Need – our craving for the Affection of others.

Now there is a clear reason why this craving, of all love-cravings, easily becomes the most unreasonable. I have said that almost anyone may be the object of Affection. Yes; and almost everyone expects to be. The egregious Mr Pontifex in *The Way of all Flesh* is outraged to discover that his son does not love him; it is 'unnatural' for a boy not to love his own father. It never occurs to him to ask whether, since the first day the boy can remember, he has ever done or said anything that could excite love. Similarly, at the beginning of *King Lear* the hero is shown as a very unlovable old man devoured with a ravenous appetite for Affection. I am driven to literary examples because you, the reader, and I, do not live in the same neighbourhood; if we did, there would unfortunately be no difficulty about replacing them with examples from real life. The thing happens every day. And we can see why. We all know that we must do something if not to merit, at least to attract, erotic love or friendship. But Affection is often assumed to be provided, ready made, by nature; 'built-in', 'laid-on', 'on the house'. We have a right to expect it. If the others do not give it, they are 'unnatural'.

This assumption is no doubt the distortion of a truth. Much has been 'built-in'. Because we are a mammalian species, instinct will provide at least some degree, often a high one, of maternal love. Because we are a social species familiar association provides a *milieu* in which, if all goes well, Affection will arise and grow strong without demanding any very shining qualities in its objects. If it is given us it will not necessarily be given us on our merits; we may get it with very little trouble. From a dim perception of the truth (many are loved with Affection far beyond their deserts) Mr Pontifex draws the ludicrous conclusion, 'Therefore I, without desert, have a right to it.' It is as if, on a far higher plane, we argued that because no man by merit has a right to the Grace of God, I, having no merit, am entitled to it. There is no question of rights in either case. What we have is not 'a right to expect' but a 'reasonable expectation' of being loved by our intimates if we, and they, are more or less ordinary people. But we may not be. We may be intolerable. If we are, 'nature' will work against us. For the very same conditions of intimacy which make Affection possible also – and no less naturally – make possible a peculiarly incurable distaste; a hatred as immemorial, constant, unemphatic, almost at times unconscious, as the corresponding form of love. Siegfried, in the opera, could not remember a time before every shuffle, mutter and fidget of his dwarfish foster-father had become odious. We never catch this kind of hatred, any more than Affection, at the moment of its beginning. It was always there before. Notice that *old* is a term of wearied loathing as well as of endearment: 'at his old tricks', 'in his old way', 'the same old thing'.

It would be absurd to say that Lear is lacking in Affection. In so far as Affection is Need-love he is half-crazy with it. Unless, in his own way, he loved his daughters he would not so desperately desire their love. The most unlovable parent (or child) may be full of such ravenous love. But it works to their own misery and everyone else's. The situation becomes suffocating. If people are already unlovable a continual demand on their part (as of right) to be loved – their manifest sense of injury, their reproaches, whether loud and clamorous or merely implicit in every look and gesture of resentful self-pity – produce in us a sense of guilt (they are intended to do so) for a fault we could not have avoided and cannot cease to commit. They seal up the very fountain for which they are thirsty. If ever, at some favoured moment, any germ of Affection for them stirs in us, their demand for more and still more, petrifies us again. And of course such people always desire the same proof of our love; we are to join their side, to hear and share their grievance against someone else. If my boy really loved me he would see how selfish his father is ... if my brother loved me he would make a party with me against my sister ... if you loved me you wouldn't let me be treated like this ...

And all the while they remain unaware of the real road. 'If you would be loved, be lovable,' said Ovid. That cheery old reprobate only meant, 'If you want to attract the girls you must be attractive,' but his maxim has a wider application. The amorist was wiser in his generation than Mr Pontifex and King Lear.

The really surprising thing is not that these insatiable demands made by the unlovable are sometimes made in vain, but that they are so often met. Sometimes one sees a woman's girlhood, youth and long years of her maturity up to the verge of old age all spent in tending, obeying, caressing, and perhaps supporting, a maternal vampire who can never be caressed and obeyed enough. The sacrifice – but there are two opinions about that – may be beautiful; the old woman who exacts it is not.

The 'built-in' or unmerited character of Affection thus invites a hideous misinterpretation. So does its ease and informality.

We hear a great deal about the rudeness of the rising generation. I am an oldster myself and might be expected to take the oldsters' side, but in fact I have been far more impressed by the bad manners of parents to children than by those of children to parents. Who has not been the embarrassed guest at family meals where the father or mother treated their grown-up offspring with an incivility which, offered to any other young people, would simply have terminated the acquaintance? Dogmatic assertions on matters which the children understand and their elders don't, ruthless interruptions, flat contradictions, ridicule of things the young take seriously – sometimes of their religion – insulting references to their friends, all provide an easy answer to the question 'Why are they always out? Why do they like every house better than their home?' Who does not prefer civility to barbarism?

If you asked any of these insufferable people – they are not all parents of course – why they behaved that way at home, they would reply, 'Oh, hang it all, one comes home to relax. A chap can't be always on his best behaviour. If a man can't be himself in his own house, where can he? Of course we don't want Company Manners at home. We're a happy family. We can say *anything* to one another here. No one minds. We all understand.'

Once again it is so nearly true yet so fatally wrong. Affection is an affair of old clothes, and ease, of the unguarded moment, of liberties which would be ill-bred if we took them with strangers. But old clothes are one thing; to wear the same shirt till it stank would be another. There are proper clothes for a garden party; but the clothes for home must be proper too, in their own different way. Similarly there is a distinction between public and domestic courtesy. The root principle of both is the same: 'that no one give any kind of preference to himself.' But the more public the occasion, the more our obedience to this principle has been 'taped' or formalised. There are 'rules' of good manners. The more intimate the occasion, the less the formalisation; but not therefore the less need of courtesy. On the contrary, Affection at its best practises a courtesy which is incomparably more subtle, sensitive and deep than the public kind. In public a ritual would do. At home you must have the reality which that ritual represented, or else the deafening triumphs of the greatest egoist present. You must really give no kind of preference to yourself; at a party it is enough to conceal the preference. Hence the old proverb 'come live with me and you'll know me.' Hence a man's familiar manners first reveal the true value of his (significantly odious phrase!) 'Company' or 'Party' manners. Those who leave their manners behind them when they come home from the dance or the sherry party have no real courtesy even there. They were merely aping those who had.

'We can say *anything* to one another.' The truth behind this is that Affection at its best can say whatever Affection at its best wishes to say, regardless of the rules that govern public courtesy; for Affection at its best wishes neither to wound nor to humiliate nor to domineer. You may address the wife of your bosom as 'Pig!' when she has inadvertently drunk your cocktail as well as her own. You may roar down the story which your father is telling once too often. You may tease and hoax and banter. You can say 'Shut up. I want to read.' You can do anything in the right tone and at the right moment – the tone and moment which are not intended to, and will not, hurt. The better the Affection the more unerringly it knows which these are (every love has its *art of love*). But the domestic Rudesby means something quite different when he claims liberty to say 'anything'. Having a very imperfect sort of Affection himself, or perhaps at that moment none, he arrogates to himself the beautiful liberties which only the fullest Affection has a right to or knows how to manage. He then uses them spitefully in obedience to his resentments; or ruthlessly in obedience to his egoism; or at best stupidly, lacking the art. And all the time he may have a clear conscience. He knows that Affection takes liberties. He is taking liberties. Therefore (he concludes) he is being affectionate. Resent anything and he will say that the defect of love is on your side. He is hurt. He has been misunderstood.

He then sometimes avenges himself by getting on his high horse and becoming elaborately 'polite'. The implication is of course, 'Oh! So we are not to be intimate? We are to behave like mere acquaintances? I had hoped – but no matter. Have it your own way.' This illustrates prettily the difference between intimate and formal courtesy. Precisely what suits the one may be a breach of the other. To be free and easy when you are presented to some eminent stranger is bad manners; to practise formal and ceremonial courtesies at home ('public faces in private places') is – and is always intended to be – bad manners. There is a delicious illustration of really good domestic manners in *Tristram Shandy*. At a singularly unsuitable moment Uncle Toby has been holding forth on his favourite theme of fortification. 'My Father', driven for once beyond endurance, violently interrupts. Then he sees his brother's face; the utterly unretaliating face of Toby, deeply wounded, not by the slight to himself – he would never think of that – but by the slight to the noble art. My Father at once repents. There is an apology, a total reconciliation. Uncle Toby, to show how complete is his forgiveness, to show that he is not on his dignity, resumes the lecture on fortification.

But we have not yet touched on jealousy. I suppose no one now believes that jealousy is especially connected with erotic love. If anyone does the behaviour of children, employees and domestic animals, ought soon to undeceive him. Every kind of love, almost every kind of association, is liable to it. The jealousy of Affection is closely connected with its reliance on what is old and familiar. So also with the total, or relative, unimportance for Affection of what I call Appreciative love. We don't want the 'old, familiar faces' to become brighter or more beautiful, the old ways to be changed even for the better, the old jokes and interests to be replaced by exciting novelties. Change is a threat to Affection.

A brother and sister, or two brothers – for sex here is not at work – grow to a certain age sharing everything. They have read the same comics, climbed the same trees, been pirates or spacemen together, taken up and abandoned stamp-collecting at the same moment. Then a dreadful thing happens. One of them flashes ahead – discovers poetry or science or serious music or perhaps undergoes a religious conversion. His life is flooded with the new interest. The other cannot share it; he is left behind. I doubt whether even the infidelity of a wife or husband raises a more miserable sense of desertion or a fiercer jealousy than this can sometimes do. It is not yet jealousy of the new friends whom the deserter will soon be making. That will come; at first it is jealousy of the thing itself – of this science, this music, of God (always called 'religion' or 'all this religion' in such contexts). The jealousy will probably be expressed by ridicule. The new interest is 'all silly nonsense', contemptibly childish (or contemptibly grown-up), or else the deserter is not really interested in it at all – he's showing off, swanking; it's all affectation. Presently the books will be hidden, the scientific specimens destroyed, the radio forcibly switched off the classical programmes. For Affection is the most instinctive, in that sense the most animal, of the loves; its jealousy is proportionately fierce. It snarls and bares its teeth like a dog whose food has been snatched away. And why would it not? Something or someone has snatched away from the child I am picturing his life-long food, his second self. His world is in ruins.

But it is not only children who react thus. Few things in the ordinary peacetime life of a civilised country are more nearly fiendish than the rancour with which a whole unbelieving family will turn on the one member of it who has become a Christian, or a whole lowbrow family on the one who shows signs of becoming an intellectual. This is not, as I once thought, simply the innate and, as it were, disinterested hatred of darkness for light. A church-going family in which one has gone atheist will not always behave any better. It is the reaction to a desertion, even to robbery. Someone or something has stolen 'our' boy (or girl). He who was one of Us has become one of Them. What right had anybody to do it? He is *ours*. But once change has thus begun, who knows where it will end? (And we all so happy and comfortable before and doing no harm to no one!)

Sometimes a curious double jealousy is felt, or rather two inconsistent jealousies which chase each other round in the sufferer's mind. On the one hand 'This' is 'All nonsense, all bloody high-brow nonsense, all canting humbug'. But on the other, 'Supposing – it can't be, it mustn't be, but just supposing there were something in it?' Supposing there really were anything in literature, or in Christianity? How if the deserter has really entered a new world which the rest of us never suspected? But, if so, how unfair! Why him? Why was it never opened to us? 'A chit of a girl – a whipper-snapper of a boy – being shown things that are hidden from their elders?' And since that is clearly incredible and unendurable, jealousy returns to the hypothesis 'All nonsense'.

Parents in this state are much more comfortably placed than brothers and sisters. Their past is unknown to their children. Whatever the deserter's new world is, they can always claim that they have been through it themselves and come out the other end. 'It's a phase,' they say, 'It'll blow over.' Nothing could be more satisfactory. It cannot be there and then refuted, for it is a statement about the future. It stings, yet – so indulgently said – is hard to resent. Better still, the elders may really believe it. Best of all, it may finally turn out to have been true. It won't be their fault if it doesn't.

'Boy, boy, these wild courses of yours will break your mother's heart.' That eminently Victorian appeal may often have been true. Affection was bitterly wounded when one member of the family fell from the homely *ethos* into something worse – gambling, drink, keeping an opera girl. Unfortunately it is almost equally possible to break your mother's heart by rising above the homely *ethos*. The conservative tenacity of Affection works both ways. It can be a domestic counterpart to that nationally suicidal type of education which keeps back the promising child because the idlers and dunces might be 'hurt' if it were undemocratically moved into a higher class than themselves.

All these perversions of Affection are mainly connected with Affection as a Need-love. But Affection as a Gift-love has its perversions too.

I am thinking of Mrs Fidget, who died a few months ago. It is really astonishing how her family have brightened up. The drawn look has gone from her husband's face; he begins to be able to laugh. The younger boy, whom I had always thought an embittered, peevish little creature, turns out to be quite human. The elder, who was hardly ever at home except when he was in bed, is nearly always there now and has begun to reorganise the garden. The girl, who was always supposed to be 'delicate' (though I never found out what exactly the trouble was), now has the riding lessons which were once out of the question, dances all night, and plays any amount of tennis. Even the dog who was never allowed out except on a lead is now a well-known member of the Lamp-post Club in their road.

Mrs Fidget very often said that she lived for her family. And it was not untrue. Everyone in the neighbourhood knew it. 'She lives for her family,' they said; 'what a wife and mother!' She did all the washing; true, she did it badly, and they could have afforded to send it out to a laundry, and they frequently begged her not to do it. But she did. There was always a hot lunch for anyone who was at home and always a hot meal at night (even in midsummer). They implored her not to provide this. They protested almost with tears in their eyes (and with truth) that they liked cold meals. It made no difference. She was living for her family. She always sat up to 'welcome' you if you were out late at night; two or three in the morning, it made no odds; you would always find the frail, pale, weary face awaiting you, like a silent accusation. Which meant of course that you couldn't with any decency go out very often. She was always making things too; being in her own estimation (I'm no judge myself) an excellent amateur dressmaker and a great knitter. And of course, unless you were a heartless brute, you had to wear the things. (The Vicar tells me that, since her death, the contributions of that family alone to 'sales of work' outweigh those of all his other parishioners put together.) And then her care for their health! She bore the whole burden of that daughter's 'delicacy' alone. The Doctor – an old friend, and it was not being done on National

Health – was never allowed to discuss matters with his patient. After the briefest examination of her, he was taken into another room by the mother. The girl was to have no worries, no responsibility for her own health. Only loving care; caresses, special foods, horrible tonic wines and breakfast in bed. For Mrs Fidget, as she so often said, would 'work her fingers to the bone' for her family. They couldn't stop her. Nor could they – being decent people – quite sit still and watch her do it. They had to help. Indeed they were always having to help. That is, they did things for her to help her to do things for them which they didn't want done. As for the dear dog, it was to her, she said, 'just like one of the children'. It was in fact as like one of them as she could make it. But since it had no scruples it got on rather better than they, and though vetted, dieted and guarded within an inch of its life, contrived sometimes to reach the dustbin or the dog next door.

The Vicar says Mrs Fidget is now at rest. Let us hope she is. What's quite certain is that her family are.

It is easy to see how liability to this state is, so to speak, congenital in the maternal instinct. This, as we saw, is a Gift-love, but one that needs to give; therefore needs to be needed. But the proper aim of giving is to put the recipient in a state where he no longer needs our gift. We feed children in order that they may soon be able to feed themselves; we teach them in order that they may soon not need our teaching. Thus a heavy task is laid upon this Gift-love. It must work towards its own abdication. We must aim at making ourselves superfluous. The hour when we can say 'They need me no longer' should be our reward. But the instinct, simply in its own nature, has no power to fulfil this law. The instinct desires the good of its object, but not simply; only the good it can itself give. A much higher love – a love which desires the good of the object as such, from whatever source that good comes – must step in and help or tame the instinct before it can make the abdication. And of course it often does. But where it does not, the ravenous need to be needed will gratify itself either by keeping its objects needy or by inventing for them imaginary needs. It will do this all the more ruthlessly because it thinks (in one sense truly) that it is a Gift-love and therefore regards itself as 'unselfish'.

It is not only mothers who can do this. All those other Affections which, whether by derivation from parental instinct or by similarity of function, need to be needed may fall into the same pit. The Affection of patron for *protégé* is one. In Jane Austen's novel, Emma intends that Harriet Smith should have a happy life; but only the sort of happy life which Emma herself has planned for her. My own profession – that of a university teacher – is in this way dangerous. If we are any good we must always be working towards the moment at which our pupils are fit to become our critics and rivals. We should be delighted when it arrives, as the fencing master is delighted when his pupil can pink and disarm him. And many are.

But not all. I am old enough to remember the sad case of Dr Quartz. No university boasted a more effective or devoted teacher. He spent the whole of himself on his pupils. He made an indelible impression on nearly all of them. He was the object of much well-merited hero-worship. Naturally, and delightfully, they continued to visit him after the tutorial relation had ended – went round to his house of an evening and had famous discussions. But the curious thing is that this never lasted. Sooner or later – it might be within a few months or even a few weeks – came the fatal evening when they knocked on his door and were told that the Doctor was engaged. After that he would always be engaged. They were banished from him forever. This was because, at their last meeting, they had rebelled. They had asserted their independence – differed from the master and supported their own view, perhaps not without success. Faced with that very independence which he had laboured to produce and which it was his duty to produce if he could, Dr Quartz could not bear it. Wotan had toiled to create the free Siegfried; presented with the free Siegfried, he was enraged. Dr Quartz was an unhappy man.

This terrible need to be needed often finds its outlet in pampering an animal. To learn that someone is 'fond of animals' tells us very little until we know in what way. For there are two ways. On the one hand the higher and domesticated animal is, so to speak, a 'bridge' between us and the rest of nature. We all at times feel somewhat painfully our human isolation from the sub-human world – the atrophy of instinct which our intelligence entails, our excessive self-consciousness, the innumerable complexities of our situation, our inability to live in the present. If only we could shuffle it all off! We must not – and incidentally we can't – become beasts. But we can be *with* a beast. It is personal enough to give the word *with* a real meaning; yet it remains very largely an unconscious little bundle of biological impulses. It has three legs in nature's world and one in ours. It is a link, an ambassador. Who would not wish, as Bosanquet put it, 'to have a representative at the court of Pan'? Man with dog closes a gap in the universe. But of course animals are often used in a worse fashion. If you need to be needed and if your family, very properly, decline to need you, a pet is the obvious substitute. You can keep it all its life in need of you. You can keep it permanently infantile, reduce it to permanent invalidism, cut it off from all genuine animal well-being, and compensate for this by creating needs for countless little indulgences which only you can grant. The unfortunate creature thus becomes very useful to the rest of the household; it acts as a sump or drain – you are too busy spoiling a dog's life to spoil theirs. Dogs are better for this purpose than cats: a monkey, I am told, is best of all. Also it is more like the real thing. To be sure, it's all very bad luck for the animal. But probably it cannot fully realise the wrong you have done it. Better still, you would never know if it did. The most down-trodden human, driven too far, may one day turn and blurt out a terrible truth. Animals can't speak.

Those who say 'The more I see of men the better I like dogs' – those who find in animals a *relief* from the demands of human companionship – will be well advised to examine their real reasons.

I hope I am not being misunderstood. If this chapter leads anyone to doubt that the lack of 'natural affection' is an extreme depravity I shall have failed. Nor do I question for a moment that Affection is responsible for nine-tenths of whatever solid and durable happiness there is in our natural lives. I shall therefore have some sympathy with those whose comment on the last few pages takes the form 'Of course. Of course. These things do happen. Selfish or neurotic people can twist anything, even love, into some sort of misery or exploitation. But why stress these marginal cases? A little common sense, a little give and take, prevents their occurrence among decent people.' But I think this comment itself needs a commentary.

Firstly, as to *neurotic*. I do not think we shall see things more clearly by classifying all these maleficial states of Affection as pathological. No doubt there are really pathological conditions which make the temptation to these states abnormally hard or even impossible to resist for particular people. Send those people to the doctors by all means. But I believe that everyone who is honest with himself will admit that he has felt these temptations. Their occurrence is not a disease; or if it is, the name of that disease is Being a Fallen Man. In ordinary people the yieldings to them – and who does not sometimes yield? – is not disease, but sin. Spiritual direction will here help us more than medical treatment. Medicine labours to restore 'natural' struc-ture or 'normal' function. But greed, egoism, self-deception and self-pity are not unnatural or abnormal in the same sense as astigmatism or a floating kidney. For who, in Heaven's name, would describe as natural or normal the man from whom these failings were wholly absent? 'Natural', if you like, in a quite different sense; archnatural, unfallen. We have seen only one such Man. And He was not at all like the psychologist's picture of the integrated, bal-anced, adjusted, happily married, employed, popular citizen. You can't really be very well 'adjusted' to your world if it says you 'have a devil' and ends by nailing you up naked to a stake of wood.

But secondly, the comment in its own language admits the very thing I am trying to say. Affection produces happiness if – and only if – there is common sense and give and take and 'decency'. In other words, only if something more, and other, than Affection is added. The mere feeling is not enough. You need 'common sense', that is, reason. You need 'give and take'; that is, you need justice, continually stimulating mere Affection when it fades and restraining it when it forgets or would defy the *art* of love. You need 'decency'. There is no disguising the fact that this means goodness; patience, self-denial, humility, and the continual intervention of a far higher sort of love than Affection, in itself, can ever be. That is the whole point. If we try to live by Affection alone, Affection will 'go bad on us'.

How bad, I believe we seldom recognise. Can Mrs Fidget really have been quite unaware of the countless frustrations and miseries she inflicted on her family? It passes belief. She knew – of course she knew – that it spoiled your whole evening to know that when you came home you would find her uselessly, accusingly, 'sitting up for you'. She continued all these practices because if she had dropped them she would have been faced with the fact that she was determined not to see; would have known that she was not necessary. That is the first motive. Then too, the very laboriousness of her life silenced her secret doubts as to the quality of her love. The more her feet burned and her back ached, the better, for this pain whispered in her ear 'How much I must love them if I do all this!' That is the second motive. But I think there is a lower depth. The unappreciativeness of the others, those terrible, wounding words – anything will 'wound' a Mrs Fidget – in which they begged her to send the washing out, enabled her to feel ill-used, therefore, to have a continual grievance, to enjoy the pleasures of resentment. If anyone says he does not know those pleasures, he is a liar or a saint. It is true that they are pleasures only to those who hate. But then a love like Mrs Fidget's contains a good deal of hatred. It was of erotic love that the Roman poet said, 'I love and hate,' but other kinds of love admit the same mixture. They carry in them the seeds of hatred. If Affection is made the absolute sovereign of a human life the seeds will germinate. Love, having become a god, becomes a demon.

4

FRIENDSHIP

When either Affection or Eros is one's theme, one finds a prepared audience. The importance and beauty of both have been stressed and almost exaggerated again and again. Even those who would debunk them are in conscious reaction against this laudatory tradition and, to that extent, influenced by it. But very few modern people think Friendship a love of comparable value or even a love at all. I cannot remember that any poem since *In Memoriam*, or any novel, has celebrated it. Tristan and Isolde, Antony and Cleopatra, Romeo and Juliet, have innumerable counterparts in modern literature: David and Jonathan, Pylades and Orestes, Roland and Oliver, Amis and Amile, have not. To the Ancients, Friendship seemed the happiest and most fully human of all loves; the crown of life and the school of virtue. The modern world, in comparison, ignores it. We admit of course that besides a wife and family a man needs a few 'friends'. But the very tone of the admission, and the sort of acquaintanceships which those who make it would describe as 'friendships', show clearly that what they are talking about has very little to do with that *Philia* which Aristotle classified among the virtues or that *Amicitia* on which Cicero wrote a book. It is something quite marginal; not a main course in life's banquet; a diversion; something that fills up the chinks of one's time. How has this come about?

The first and most obvious answer is that few value it because few experience it. And the possibility of going through life without the experience is rooted in that fact which separates Friendship so sharply from both the other loves. Friendship is – in a sense not at all derogatory to it – the least *natural* of loves; the least instinctive, organic, biological, gregarious and necessary. It has least commerce with our nerves; there is nothing throaty about it; nothing that quickens the pulse or turns you red and pale. It is essentially between individuals; the moment two men are friends they have in some degree drawn apart together from the herd. Without Eros none of us would have been begotten and without Affection none of us would have been reared; but we can live and breed without Friendship. The species, biologically considered, has no need of it. The pack or herd – the community – may even dislike and distrust it. Its leaders very often do. Headmasters and Headmistresses and Heads of religious communities, colonels and ships' captains, can feel uneasy when close and strong friendships arise between little knots of their subjects.

This (so to call it) 'non-natural' quality in Friendship goes far to explain why it was exalted in ancient and medieval times and has come to be made light of in our own. The deepest and most permanent thought of those ages was ascetic and world-renouncing. Nature and emotion and the body were feared as dangers to our souls, or despised as degradations of our human status. Inevitably that sort of love was most prized which seemed most independent, or even defiant, of mere nature. Affection and Eros were too obviously connected with our nerves, too obviously shared with the brutes. You could feel these tugging at your guts and fluttering in your diaphragm. But in Friendship – in that luminous, tranquil, rational world of relationships freely chosen – you got away from all that. This alone, of all the loves, seemed to raise you to the level of gods or angels.

But then came Romanticism and 'tearful comedy' and the 'return to nature' and the exaltation of Sentiment; and in their train all that great wallow of emotion which, though often criticised, has lasted ever since. Finally, the exaltation of instinct, the dark gods in the blood; whose hierophants may be incapable of male friendship. Under this new dispensation all that had once commended this love now began to work against it. It had not tearful smiles and keepsakes and baby-talk enough to please the sentimentalists. There was not blood and guts enough about it to attract the primitivists. It looked thin and etiolated; a sort of vegetarian substitute for the more organic loves.

Other causes have contributed. To those – and they are now the majority – who see human life merely as a development and complication of animal life all forms of behaviour which cannot produce certificates of an animal origin and of survival value are suspect. Friendship's certificates are not very satisfactory. Again, that outlook which values the collective above the individual necessarily disparages Friendship; it is a relation between men at their highest level of individuality. It withdraws men from collective 'togetherness' as surely as solitude itself could do; and more dangerously, for it withdraws them by twos and threes. Some forms of democratic sentiment are naturally hostile to it because it is selective and an affair of the few. To say 'These are my friends' implies 'Those are not'. For all these reasons if a man believes (as I do) that the old estimate of Friendship was the correct one, he can hardly write a chapter on it except as a rehabilitation.

This imposes on me at the outset a very tiresome bit of demolition. It has actually become necessary in our time to rebut the theory that every firm and serious friendship is really homosexual.

The dangerous word *really* is here important. To say that every Friendship is consciously and explicitly homosexual would be too obviously false; the wiseacres take refuge in the less palpable charge that it is *really* – unconsciously, cryptically, in some Pickwickian sense – homosexual. And this, though it cannot be proved, can never of course be refuted. The fact that no positive evidence of homosexuality can be discovered in the behaviour of two Friends does not disconcert the wiseacres at all: 'That,' they say gravely, 'is just what we should expect.' The very lack of evidence is thus treated as evidence; the absence of smoke proves that the fire is very carefully hidden. Yes – if it exists at all. But we must first prove its existence. Otherwise we are arguing like a man who should say 'If there were an invisible cat in that chair, the chair would look empty; but the chair does look empty; therefore there is an invisible cat in it.'

A belief in invisible cats cannot perhaps be logically disproved, but it tells us a good deal about those who hold it. Those who cannot conceive Friendship as a substantive love but only as a disguise or elaboration of Eros betray the fact that they have never had a Friend. The rest of us know that though we can have erotic love and friendship for the same person yet in some ways nothing is less like a Friendship than a love-affair. Lovers are always talking to one another about their love; Friends hardly ever about their Friendship. Lovers are normally face to face, absorbed in each other; Friends, side by side, absorbed in some common interest. Above all, Eros (while it lasts) is necessarily between two only. But two, far from being the necessary number for Friendship, is not even the best. And the reason for this is important.

Lamb says somewhere that if, of three friends (A, B, and C), A should die, then B loses not only A but 'A's part in C', while C loses not only A but 'A's part in B'. In each of my friends there is something that only some other friend can fully bring out. By myself I am not large enough to call the whole man into activity; I want other lights than my own to show all his facets. Now that Charles is dead, I shall never again see Ronald's reaction to a specifically Caroline joke. Far from having more of Ronald, having him 'to myself' now that Charles is away, I have less of Ronald. Hence true Friendship is the least jealous of loves. Two friends delight to be joined by a third, and three by a fourth, if only the newcomer is qualified to become a real friend. They can then say, as the blessed souls say in Dante, 'Here comes one who will augment our loves.' For in this love 'to divide is not to take away'. Of course the scarcity of kindred souls – not to mention practical considerations about the size of rooms and the audibility of voices – set limits to the enlargement of the circle; but within those limits we possess each friend not less but more as the number of those with whom we share him increases. In this, Friendship exhibits a glorious 'nearness by resemblance' to Heaven itself where the very multitude of the blessed (which no man can number) increases the fruition which each has of God. For every soul, seeing Him in her own way, doubt-less communicates that unique vision to all the rest. That, says an old author, is why the Seraphim in Isaiah's vision are crying 'Holy, Holy, Holy' *to one another* (Isaiah 6:3). The more we thus share the Heavenly Bread between us, the more we shall all have.

The homosexual theory therefore seems to me not even plausible. This is not to say that Friendship and abnormal Eros have never been combined. Certain cultures at certain periods seem to have tended to the contamina-tion. In war-like societies it was, I think, especially likely to creep into the relation between the mature Brave and his young armour-bearer or squire. The absence of the women while you were on the warpath had no doubt something to do with it. In deciding, if we think we need or can decide, where it crept in and where it did not, we must surely be guided by the evi-dence (when there is any) and not by an *a priori* theory. Kisses, tears and embraces are not in themselves evidence of homosexuality. The implications would be, if nothing else, too comic. Hrothgar embracing Beowulf, Johnson embracing Boswell (a pretty flagrantly heterosexual couple) and all those hairy old toughs of centurions in Tacitus, clinging to one another and begging for last kisses when the legion was broken up ... all pansies? If you can believe that you can believe anything. On a broad historical view it is, of course, not the demonstrative gestures of Friendship among our ances-tors but the absence of such gestures in our own society that calls for some special explanation. We, not they, are out of step.

I have said that Friendship is the least biological of our loves. Both the individual and the community can survive without it. But there is some-thing else, often confused with Friendship, which the community does need; something which, though not Friendship, is the matrix of Friendship.

In early communities the co-operation of the males as hunters or fighters was no less necessary than the begetting and rearing of children. A tribe where there was no taste for the one would die no less surely than a tribe where there was no taste for the other. Long before history began we men have got together apart from the women and done things. We had to. And to like doing what must be done is a characteristic that has survival value. We not only had to do the things, we had to talk about them. We had to plan the hunt and the battle. When they were over we had to hold a *post mortem* and draw conclusions for future use. We liked this even better. We ridiculed or punished the cowards and bunglers, we praised the star-performers. We rev-elled in technicalities. ('He might have known he'd never get near the brute, not with the wind that way' ... 'You see, I had a lighter arrowhead; that's what did it' ... 'What I always say is –' ... 'stuck him just like that, see? Just the way I'm holding this stick' ...) In fact, we talked shop. We enjoyed one another's society greatly: we Braves, we hunters, all bound together by shared skill, shared dangers and hardships, esoteric jokes – away from the women and children. As some wag has said, palaeolithic man may or may not have had a club on his shoulder but he certainly had a club of the other sort. It was probably part of his religion; like that sacred smoking-club where the savages in Melville's *Typee* were 'famously smug' every evening of their lives.

What were the women doing meanwhile? How should I know? I am a man and never spied on the mysteries of the Bona Dea. They certainly often had rituals from which men were excluded. When, as sometimes happened, agriculture was in their hands, they must, like the men, have had common skills, toils and triumphs. Yet perhaps their world was never as emphatically feminine as that of their men-folk was masculine. The children were with them; perhaps the old men were there too. But I am only guessing. I can trace the pre-history of Friendship only in the male line.

This pleasure in co-operation, in talking shop, in the mutual respect and understanding of men who daily see one another tested, is biologically valuable. You may, if you like, regard it as a product of the 'gregarious instinct'. To me that seems a roundabout way of getting at something which we all understand far better already than anyone has ever understood the word *instinct* – something which is going on at this moment in dozens of ward-rooms, bar-rooms, common-rooms, messes and golf-clubs. I prefer to call it Companionship – or Clubbableness.

This Companionship is, however, only the matrix of Friendship. It is often called Friendship, and many people when they speak of their 'friends' mean only their companions. But it is not Friendship in the sense I give to the word. By saying this I do not at all intend to disparage the merely Clubbable relation. We do not disparage silver by distinguishing it from gold.

Friendship arises out of mere Companionship when two or more of the companions discover that they have in common some insight or interest or even taste which the others do not share and which, till that moment, each believed to be his own unique treasure (or burden). The typical expression of opening Friendship would be something like, 'What? You too? I thought I was the only one.' We can imagine that among those early hunters and warriors single individuals – one in a century? one in a thousand years? – saw what others did not; saw that the deer was beautiful as well as edible, that hunting was fun as well as necessary, dreamed that his gods might be not only powerful but holy. But as long as each of these percipient persons dies without finding a kindred soul, nothing (I suspect) will come of it; art or sport or spiritual religion will not be born. It is when two such persons discover one another, when, whether with immense difficulties and semi-articulate fumblings or with what would seem to us amazing and elliptical speed, they share their vision – it is then that Friendship is born. And instantly they stand together in an immense solitude.

Lovers seek for privacy. Friends find this solitude about them, this barrier between them and the herd, whether they want it or not. They would be glad to reduce it. The first two would be glad to find a third.

In our own time Friendship arises in the same way. For us of course the shared activity and therefore the companionship on which Friendship supervenes will not often be a bodily one like hunting or fighting. It may be a common religion, common studies, a common profession, even a common recreation. All who share it will be our companions; but one or two or three who share something more will be our Friends. In this kind of love, as Emerson said, *Do you love me?* means *Do you see the same truth?* – Or at least, 'Do you *care about* the same truth?' The man who agrees with us that some question, little regarded by others, is of great importance, can be our Friend. He need not agree with us about the answer.

Notice that Friendship thus repeats on a more individual and less socially necessary level the character of the Companionship which was its matrix. The Companionship was between people who were doing something together – hunting, studying, painting or what you will. The Friends will still be doing something together, but something more inward, less widely shared and less easily defined; still hunters, but of some immaterial quarry; still collaborating, but in some work the world does not, or not yet, take account of; still travelling companions, but on a different kind of journey. Hence we picture lovers face to face but Friends side by side; their eyes look ahead.

That is why those pathetic people who simply 'want friends' can never make any. The very condition of having Friends is that we should want something else besides Friends. Where the truthful answer to the question *Do you see the same truth?* would be 'I see nothing and I don't care about the truth; I only want a Friend', no Friendship can arise – though Affection of course may. There would be nothing for the Friendship to be *about*; and Friendship must be about something, even if it were only an enthusiasm for dominoes or white mice. Those who have nothing can share nothing; those who are going nowhere can have no fellow-travellers.

When the two people who thus discover that they are on the same secret road are of different sexes, the friendship which arises between them will very easily pass – may pass in the first half-hour – into erotic love. Indeed, unless they are physically repulsive to each other or unless one or both already loves elsewhere, it is almost certain to do so sooner or later. And conversely, erotic love may lead to Friendship between the lovers. But this, so far from obliterating the distinction between the two loves, puts it in a clearer light. If one who was first, in the deep and full sense, your Friend, is then gradually or suddenly revealed as also your lover you will certainly not want to share the Beloved's erotic love with any third. But you will have no jealousy at all about sharing the Friendship. Nothing so enriches an erotic love as the discovery that the Beloved can deeply, truly and spontaneously enter into Friendship with the Friends you already had: to feel that not only are we two united by erotic love but we three or four or five are all travellers on the same quest, have all a common vision.

The co-existence of Friendship and Eros may also help some moderns to realise that Friendship is in reality a love, and even as great a love as Eros. Suppose you are fortunate enough to have 'fallen in love with' and married your Friend. And now suppose it possible that you were offered the choice of two futures: '*Either* you two will cease to be lovers but remain forever joint seekers of the same God, the same beauty, the same truth, *or else*, losing all that, you will retain as long as you live the raptures and ardours, all the wonder and the wild desire of Eros. Choose which you please.' Which should we choose? Which choice should we not regret after we had made it?

I have stressed the 'unnecessary' character of Friendship, and this of course requires more justification than I have yet given it.

It could be argued that Friendships are of practical value to the Community. Every civilised religion began in a small group of friends. Mathematics effectively began when a few Greek friends got together to talk about numbers and lines and angles. What is now the Royal Society was originally a few gentlemen meeting in their spare time to discuss things which they (and not many others) had a fancy for. What we now call 'the Romantic Movement' once *was* Mr Wordsworth and Mr Coleridge talking incessantly (at least Mr Coleridge was) about a secret vision of their own. Communism, Tractarianism, Methodism, the movement against slavery, the Reformation, the Renaissance, might perhaps be said, without much exaggeration, to have begun in the same way.

There is something in this. But nearly every reader would probably think some of these movements good for society and some bad. The whole list, if accepted, would tend to show, at best, that Friendship is both a possible benefactor and a possible danger to the community. And even as a benefactor it would have, not so much survival value, as what we may call 'civilisation value'; would be something (in Aristotelian phrase) which helps the community not to live but to live well. Survival value and civilisation value coincide at some periods and in some circumstances, but not in all. What at any rate seems certain is that when Friendship bears fruit which the community can use it has to do so accidentally, as a by-product. Religions devised for a social purpose, like Roman emperor-worship or modern attempts to 'sell' Christianity as a means of 'saving civilisation', do not come to much. The little knots of Friends who turn their backs on the 'World' are those who really transform it. Egyptian and Babylonian Mathematics were practical and social, pursued in the service of Agriculture and Magic. But the free Greek Mathematics, pursued by Friends as a leisure occupation, have mattered to us more.

Others again would say that Friendship is extremely useful, perhaps necessary for survival, to the individual. They could produce plenty of authority: 'bare is back without brother behind it' and 'there is a friend that sticketh closer than a brother'. But when we speak thus we are using *friend* to mean 'ally'. In ordinary usage *friend* means, or should mean, more than that. A Friend will, to be sure, prove himself to be also an ally when alliance becomes necessary; will lend or give when we are in need, nurse us in sickness, stand up for us among our enemies, do what he can for our widows and orphans. But such good offices are not the stuff of Friendship. The occasions for them are almost interruptions. They are in one way relevant to it, in another not. Relevant, because you would be a false friend if you would not do them when the need arose; irrelevant, because the role of benefactor always remains accidental, even a little alien, to that of Friend. It is almost embarrassing. For Friendship is utterly free from Affection's need to be needed. We are sorry that any gift or loan or night-watching should have been necessary – and now, for heaven's sake, let us forget all about it and go back to the things we really want to do or talk of together. Even gratitude is no enrichment to this love. The stereotyped 'Don't mention it' here expresses what we really feel. The mark of perfect Friendship is not that help will be given when the pinch comes (of course it will) but that, having been given, it makes no difference at all. It was a distraction, an anomaly. It was a horrible waste of the time, always too short, that we had together. Perhaps we had only a couple of hours in which to talk and, God bless us, twenty minutes of it has had to be devoted to *affairs*.

For of course we do not want to know our Friend's affairs at all. Friendship, unlike Eros, is uninquisitive. You become a man's Friend without knowing or caring whether he is married or single or how he earns his living. What have all these 'unconcerning things, matters of fact' to do with the real question, *Do you see the same truth?* In a circle of true Friends each man is simply what he is: stands for nothing but himself. No one cares twopence about anyone else's family, profession, class, income, race, or previous history. Of course you will get to know about most of these in the end. But casually. They will come out bit by bit, to furnish an illustration or an analogy, to serve as pegs for an anecdote; never for their own sake. That is the kingliness of Friendship. We meet like sovereign princes of independent states, abroad, on neutral ground, freed from our contexts. This love (essentially) ignores not only our physical bodies but that whole embodiment

46

which consists of our family, job, past and connections. At home, besides being Peter or Jane, we also bear a general character; husband or wife, brother or sister, chief, colleague or subordinate. Not among our Friends. It is an affair of disentangled, or stripped minds. Eros will have naked bodies; Friendship naked personalities.

Hence (if you will not misunderstand me) the exquisite arbitrariness and irresponsibility of this love. I have no duty to be anyone's Friend and no man in the world has a duty to be mine. No claims, no shadow of necessity. Friendship is unnecessary, like philosophy, like art, like the universe itself (for God did not need to create). It has no survival value; rather it is one of those things which give value to survival.

When I spoke of Friends as side by side or shoulder to shoulder I was pointing a necessary contrast between their posture and that of the lovers whom we picture face to face. Beyond that contrast I do not want the image pressed. The common quest or vision which unites Friends does not absorb them in such a way that they remain ignorant or oblivious of one another. On the contrary it is the very medium in which their mutual love and knowledge exist. One knows nobody so well as one's 'fellow'. Every step of the common journey tests his metal; and the tests are tests we fully understand because we are undergoing them ourselves. Hence, as he rings true time after time, our reliance, our respect and our admiration blossom into an Appreciative Love of a singularly robust and well-informed kind. If, at the outset, we had attended more to him and less to the thing our Friendship is 'about', we should not have come to know or love him so well. You will not find the warrior, the poet, the philosopher or the Christian by staring in his eyes as if he were your mistress: better fight beside him, read with him, argue with him, pray with him.

In a perfect Friendship this Appreciative Love is, I think, often so great and so firmly based that each member of the circle feels, in his secret heart, humbled before all the rest. Sometimes he wonders what he is doing there among his betters. He is lucky beyond desert to be in such company. Especially when the whole group is together, each bringing out all that is best, wisest, or funniest in all the others. Those are the golden sessions; when four or five of us after a hard day's walking have come to our inn; when our slippers are on, our feet spread out towards the blaze and our drinks at our elbows; when the whole world, and something beyond the world, opens itself to our minds as we talk; and no one has any claim on or any responsibility for another, but all are freemen and equals as if we had first met an hour ago, while at the same time an Affection mellowed by the years enfolds us. Life – natural life – has no better gift to give. Who could have deserved it?

From what has been said it will be clear that in most societies at most periods Friendships will be between men and men or between women and women. The sexes will have met one another in Affection and in Eros but not in this love. For they will seldom have had with each other the companionship in common activities which is the matrix of Friendship. Where men are educated and women not, where one sex works and the other is idle, or where they do totally different work, they will usually have nothing to be Friends about. But we can easily see that it is this lack, rather than anything in their natures, which excludes Friendship; for where they can be companions they can also become Friends. Hence in a profession (like my own) where men and women work side by side, or in the mission field, or among authors and artists, such Friendship is common. To be sure, what is offered as Friendship on one side may be mistaken for Eros on the other, with painful and embarrassing results. Or what begins as Friendship in both may become also Eros. But to say that something can be mistaken for, or turn into, something else is not to deny the difference between them. Rather it implies it; we should not otherwise speak of 'turning into' or being 'mistaken for'.

In one respect our own society is unfortunate. A world where men and women never have common work or a common education can probably get along comfortably enough. In it men turn to each other, and only to each other, for Friendship, and they enjoy it very much. I hope the women enjoy their feminine Friends equally. Again, a world where all men and women had sufficient common ground for this relationship could also be comfortable. At present, however, we fall between two stools. The necessary common ground, the matrix, exists between the sexes in some groups but not in others. It is notably lacking in many residential suburbs. In a plutocratic neighbourhood where the men have spent their whole lives in acquiring money some at least of the women have used their leisure to develop an intellectual life – have become musical or literary. In such places the men appear among the women as barbarians among civilised people. In another neighbourhood you will find the situation reversed. Both sexes have, indeed, 'been to school'. But since then the men have had a much more serious education; they have become doctors, lawyers, clergymen, architects, engineers, or men of letters. The women are to them as children to adults. In neither neighbourhood is real Friendship between the sexes at all probable. But this, though an impoverishment, would be tolerable if it were admitted and accepted. The peculiar trouble of our own age is that men and women in this situation, haunted by rumours and glimpses of happier groups where no such chasm between the sexes exists, and bedevilled by the egalitarian idea that what is possible for some ought to be (and therefore is) possible to all, refuse to acquiesce in it. Hence, on the one hand, we get the wife as school-marm, the 'cultivated' woman who is always trying to bring her husband 'up to her level'. She drags him to concerts and would like him to learn morris-dancing and invites 'cultivated' people to the house. It often does surprisingly little harm. The middle-aged male has great powers of passive resistance and (if she but knew) of indulgence; 'women will have their fads.' Something much more painful happens when it is the men who are civilised and the women not, and when all the women, and many of the men too, simply refuse to recognise the fact.

When this happens we get a kind, polite, laborious and pitiful pretence. The women are 'deemed' (as lawyers say) to be full members of the male circle. The fact – in itself not important – that they now smoke and drink like the men seems to simple-minded people a proof that they really are. No stag-parties are allowed. Wherever the men meet, the women must come too. The men have learned to live among ideas. They know what discussion, proof and illustration mean. A woman who has had merely school lessons and has abandoned soon after marriage whatever tinge of 'culture' they gave her – whose reading is the Women's Magazines and whose general conversation is almost wholly narrative – cannot really enter such a circle. She can be locally and physically present with it in the same room. What of that? If the men are ruthless, she sits bored and silent through a conversation which means nothing to her. If they are better bred, of course, they try to bring her in. Things are explained to her: people try to sublimate her irrelevant and blundering observations into some kind of sense. But the efforts soon fail and, for manners' sake, what might have been a real discussion is deliberately diluted and peters out in gossip, anecdotes and jokes. Her presence has thus destroyed the very thing she was brought to share. She can never really enter the circle because the circle ceases to be itself when she enters it – as the horizon ceases to be the horizon when you get there. By learning to drink and smoke and perhaps to tell *risqué* stories, she has not, for this purpose, drawn an inch nearer to the men than her grandmother. But her grand-mother was far happier and more realistic. She was at home talking real women's talk to other women and perhaps doing so with great charm, sense and even wit. She herself might be able to do the same. She may be quite as clever as the men whose evening she has spoiled, or cleverer. But she is not really interested in the same things, nor mistress of the same methods. (We all appear as dunces when feigning an interest in things we care nothing about.)

The presence of such women, thousands strong, helps to account for the modern disparagement of Friendship. They are often completely victorious. They banish male companionship, and therefore male Friendship, from whole neighbourhoods. In the only world they know, an endless prattling 'Jolly' replaces the intercourse of minds. All the men they meet talk like women while women are present.

49

This victory over Friendship is often unconscious. There is, however, a more militant type of woman who plans it. I have heard one say 'Never let two men sit together or they'll get talking about some *subject* and then there'll be no fun.' Her point could not have been more accurately made. Talk, by all means; the more of it the better; unceasing cascades of the human voice; but not, please, a subject. The talk must not be about anything.

This gay lady – this lively, accomplished, 'charming', unendurable bore – was seeking only each evening's amusement, making the meeting 'go'. But the conscious war against Friendship may be fought on a deeper level. There are women who regard it with hatred, envy and fear as the enemy of Eros and, perhaps even more, of Affection. A woman of that sort has a hundred arts to break up her husband's Friendships. She will quarrel with his Friends herself or, better still, with their wives. She will sneer, obstruct and lie. She does not realise that the husband whom she succeeds in isolating from his own kind will not be very well worth having; she has emasculated him. She will grow to be ashamed of him herself. Nor does she remember how much of his life lies in places where she cannot watch him. New Friendships will break out, but this time they will be secret. Lucky for her, and lucky beyond her deserts, if there are not soon other secrets as well.

All these, of course, are silly women. The sensible women who, if they wanted, would certainly be able to qualify themselves for the world of discussion and ideas, are precisely those who, if they are not qualified, never try to enter it or to destroy it. They have other fish to fry. At a mixed party they gravitate to one end of the room and talk women's talk to one another. They don't want us, for this sort of purpose, any more than we want them. It is only the riff-raff of each sex that wants to be incessantly hanging on the other. Live and let let live. They laugh at us a good deal. That is just as it should be. Where the sexes, having no real shared activities, can meet only in Affection and Eros – cannot be Friends – it is healthy that each should have a lively sense of the other's absurdity. Indeed it is always healthy. No one ever really appreciated the other sex – just as no one really appreciates children or animals – without at times feeling them to be funny. For both sexes are. Humanity is tragi-comical; but the division into sexes enables each to see in the other the joke that often escapes it in itself – and the pathos too.

I gave warning that this chapter would be largely a rehabilitation. The preceding pages have, I hope, made clear why to me at least it seems no wonder if our ancestors regarded Friendship as something that raised us almost above humanity. This love, free from instinct, free from all duties but those which love has freely assumed, almost wholly free from jealousy, and free without qualification from the need to be needed, is eminently spiritual. It is the sort of love one can imagine between angels. Have we here found a natural love, which is Love itself?

Before we rush to any such conclusion let us beware of the ambiguity in the word *spiritual*. There are many New Testament contexts in which it means 'pertaining to the (Holy) Spirit', and in such contexts the spiritual is, by definition, good. But when *spiritual* is used simply as the opposite of corporeal, or instinctive, or animal, this is not so. There is spiritual evil as well as spiritual good. There are unholy, as well as holy, angels. The worst sins of men are spiritual. We must not think that in finding Friendship to be *spiritual* we have found it to be in itself holy or inerrant. Three significant facts remain to be taken into account.

The first, already mentioned, is the distrust which Authorities tend to have of close Friendships among their subjects. It may be unjustified; or there may be some basis for it.

Secondly, there is the attitude of the majority towards all circles of close Friends. Every name they give such a circle is more or less derogatory. It is at best a 'set'; lucky if not a *coterie*, a 'gang', a 'little senate', or a 'mutual admiration society'. Those who in their own lives know only Affection, Companionship and Eros, suspect Friends to be 'stuck-up prigs who think themselves too good for us'. Of course this is the voice of Envy. But Envy always brings the truest charge, or the charge nearest to the truth, that she can think up; it hurts more. This charge, therefore, will have to be considered.

Finally, we must notice that Friendship is very rarely the image under which Scripture represents the love between God and Man. It is not entirely neglected; but far more often, seeking a symbol for the highest love of all, Scripture ignores this seemingly almost angelic relation and plunges into the depth of what is most natural and instinctive. Affection is taken as the image when God is represented as our Father; Eros, when Christ is represented as the Bridegroom of the Church.

Let us begin with the suspicions of those in Authority. I think there is a ground for them and that a consideration of this ground brings something important to light. Friendship, I have said, is born at the moment when one man says to another 'What! You too? I thought that no one but myself ...' But the common taste or vision or point of view which is thus discovered need not always be a nice one. From such a moment art, or philosophy, or an advance in religion or morals might well take their rise; but why not also torture, cannibalism, or human sacrifice? Surely most of us have experienced the ambivalent nature of such moments in our own youth? It was wonderful when we first met someone who cared for our favourite poet. What we had hardly understood before now took clear shape. What we had been half ashamed of we now freely acknowledged. But it was no less delightful when we first met someone who shared with us a secret evil. This too became far more palpable and explicit; of this too, we ceased to be ashamed. Even now, at whatever age, we all know the perilous charm of a shared hatred or grievance. (It is difficult not to hail as a Friend the only other man in College who really sees the faults of the Sub-Warden.)

Alone among unsympathetic companions, I hold certain views and standards timidly, half ashamed to avow them and half doubtful if they can after all be right. Put me back among my Friends and in half an hour – in ten minutes – these same views and standards become once more indisputable. The opinion of this little circle, while I am in it, outweighs that of a thousand outsiders: as Friendship strengthens, it will do this even when my Friends are far away. For we all wish to be judged by our peers, by the men 'after our own heart'. Only they really know our mind and only they judge it by standards we fully acknowledge. Theirs is the praise we really covet and the blame we really dread. The little pockets of early Christians survived because they cared exclusively for the love of 'the brethren' and stopped their ears to the opinion of the Pagan society all round them. But a circle of criminals, cranks, or perverts survives in just the same way; by becoming deaf to the opinion of the outer world, by discounting it as the chatter of outsiders who 'don't understand', of the 'conventional', 'the bourgeois', the 'Establishment', of prigs, prudes and humbugs.

It is therefore easy to see why Authority frowns on Friendship. Every real Friendship is a sort of secession, even a rebellion. It may be a rebellion of serious thinkers against accepted clap-trap or of faddists against accepted good sense; of real artists against popular ugliness or of charlatans against civilised taste; of good men against the badness of society or of bad men against its goodness. Whichever it is, it will be unwelcome to Top People. In each knot of Friends there is a sectional 'public opinion' which fortifies its members against the public opinion of the community in general. Each therefore is a pocket of potential resistance. Men who have real Friends are less easy to manage or 'get at'; harder for good Authorities to correct or for bad Authorities to corrupt. Hence if our masters, by force or by propaganda about 'Togetherness' or by unobtrusively making privacy and unplanned leisure impossible, ever succeed in producing a world where all are Companions and none are Friends, they will have removed certain dangers, and will also have taken from us what is almost our strongest safeguard against complete servitude.

But the dangers are perfectly real. Friendship (as the ancients saw) can be a school of virtue; but also (as they did not see) a school of vice. It is ambivalent. It makes good men better and bad men worse. It would be a waste of time to elaborate the point. What concerns us is not to expatiate on the badness of bad Friendships but to become aware of the possible danger in good ones. This love, like the other natural loves, has its congenital liability to a particular disease.

It will be obvious that the element of secession, of indifference or deafness (at least on some matters) to the voices of the outer world, is common to all Friendships, whether good, bad, or merely innocuous. Even if the common ground of the Friendship is nothing more momentous than stamp-collecting, the circle rightly and inevitably ignores the views of the millions who think it a silly occupation and of the thousands who have merely dabbled in it. The founders of meteorology rightly and inevitably ignored the views of the millions who still attributed storms to witchcraft. There is no offence in this. As I know that I should be an Outsider to a circle of golfers, mathematicians, or motorists, so I claim the equal right of regarding them as Outsiders to mine. People who bore one another should meet seldom; people who interest one another, often.

The danger is that this partial indifference or deafness to outside opinion, justified and necessary though it is, may lead to a wholesale indifference or deafness. The most spectacular instances of this can be seen not in a circle of friends but in a Theocratic or aristocratic class. We know what the Priests in Our Lord's time thought of the common people. The Knights in Froissart's chronicles had neither sympathy nor mercy for the 'outsiders', the churls or peasantry. But this deplorable indifference was very closely intertwined with a good quality. They really had, among themselves, a very high standard of valour, generosity, courtesy and honour. This standard the cautious, close-fisted churl would have thought merely silly. The Knights, in maintaining it, were, and had to be be, wholly indifferent to his views. They 'didn't give a damn' what he thought. If they had, our own standard today would be the poorer and the coarser for it. But the habit of 'not giving a damn' grows on a class. To discount the voice of the peasant where it really ought to be discounted makes it easier to discount his voice when he cries for justice or mercy. The partial deafness which is noble and necessary encourages the wholesale deafness which is arrogant and inhuman.

A circle of friends cannot of course oppress the outer world as a powerful social class can. But it is subject, on its own scale, to the same danger. It can come to treat as 'outsiders' in a general (and derogatory) sense those who were quite properly outsiders for a particular purpose. Thus, like an aristocracy, it can create around it a vacuum across which no voice will carry. The literary or artistic circle which began by discounting, perhaps rightly, the plain man's ideas about literature or art may come to discount equally his idea that they should pay their bills, cut their nails and behave civilly. Whatever faults the circle has – and no circle is without them – thus become incurable. But that is not all. The partial and defensible deafness was based on some kind of superiority – even if it were only a superior knowledge about stamps. The sense of superiority will then get itself attached to the total deafness. The group will disdain as well as ignore those outside it. It will, in effect, have turned itself into something very like a class. A *coterie* is a self-appointed aristocracy.

I said above that in a good Friendship each member often feels humility towards the rest. He sees that they are splendid and counts himself lucky to be among them. But unfortunately the *they* and *them* are also, from another point of view *we* and *us*. Thus the transition from individual humility to corporate pride is very easy.

I am not thinking of what we should call a social or snobbish pride: a delight in knowing, and being known to know, distinguished people. That is quite a different thing. The snob wishes to attach himself to some group because it is already regarded as an *élite*; friends are in danger of coming to regard themselves as an *élite* because they are already attached. We seek men after our own heart for their own sake and are then alarmingly or delightfully surprised by the feeling that we have become an aristocracy. Not that we'd call it that. Every reader who has known Friendship will probably feel inclined to deny with some heat that his own circle was ever guilty of such an absurdity. I feel the same. But in such matters it is best not to begin with ourselves. However it may be with us, I think we have all recognised some such tendency in those other circles to which we are Outsiders.

I was once at some kind of conference where two clergymen, obviously close friends, began talking about 'uncreated energies' other than God. I asked how there could be any uncreated things except God if the Creed was right in calling Him the 'maker of all things visible and invisible'. Their reply was to glance at one another and laugh. I had no objection to their laughter, but I wanted an answer in words as well. It was not at all a sneering or unpleasant laugh. It expressed very much what Americans would express by saying 'Isn't he cute?' It was like the laughter of jolly grown-ups when an *enfant terrible* asks the sort of question that is never asked. You can hardly imagine how inoffensively it was done, nor how clearly it conveyed the impression that they were fully aware of living habitually on a higher plane than the rest of us, that they came among us as Knights among churls or as grown-ups among children. Very possibly they had an answer to my question and knew that I was too ignorant to follow it. If they had said in so many words 'I'm afraid it would take too long to explain', I would not be attributing to them the pride of Friendship. The glance and the laugh are the real point – the audible and visible embodiment of a corporate superiority taken for granted and unconcealed. The almost complete inoffensiveness, the absence of any apparent wish to wound or exult (they were very nice young men) really underline the Olympian attitude. Here was a sense of superiority so secure that it could afford to be tolerant, urbane, unemphatic.

This sense of corporate superiority is not always Olympian; that is, tranquil and tolerant. It may be Titanic; restive, militant and embittered. Another time, when I had been addressing an undergraduate society and some discussion (very properly) followed my paper, a young man with an expression as tense as that of a rodent so dealt with me that I had to say, 'Look, sir. Twice in the last five minutes you have as good as called me a liar. If you cannot discuss a question of criticism without that kind of thing I must leave.' I expected he would do one of two things; lose his temper and redouble his insults, or else blush and apologise. The startling thing is that he did neither. No new perturbation was added to the habitual *malaise* of his expression. He did not repeat the Lie Direct; but apart from that he went on just as before. One had come up against an iron curtain. He was forearmed against the risk of any strictly personal relation, either friendly or hostile, with such as me. Behind this, almost certainly, there lies a circle of the Titanic sort – self-dubbed Knights Templar perpetually in arms to defend a critical Baphomet. We – who are *they* to them – do not exist as persons at all. We are specimens; specimens of various Age Groups, Types, Climates of Opinion, or Interests, to be exterminated. Deprived of one weapon, they coolly take up another. They are not, in the ordinary human sense, meeting us at all; they are merely doing a job of work – spraying (I have heard one use that image) insecticide.

My two nice young clergymen and my not so nice Rodent were on a high intellectual level. So were that famous set who in Edwardian times reached the sublime fatuity of calling themselves 'the Souls'. But the same feeling of corporate superiority can possess a group of much more commonplace friends. It will then be flaunted in a cruder way. We have all seen this done by the 'old hands' at school talking in the presence of a new boy, or two Regulars in the Army talking before a 'Temporary'; sometimes by very loud and vulgar friends to impress mere strangers in a bar or a railway carriage. Such people talk very intimately and esoterically in order to be overheard. Everyone who is not in the circle must be shown that he is not in it. Indeed the Friendship may be 'about' almost nothing except the fact that it excludes. In speaking to an Outsider each member of it delights to mention the others by their Christian names or nicknames; not although, but because, the Outsider won't know who he means. A man I once knew was even subtler. He simply referred to his friends as if we all knew, certainly ought to know, who they were. 'As Richard Button once said to me ...' he would begin. We were all very young. We never dared to admit that we hadn't heard of Richard Button. It seemed so obvious that to everyone who was anyone he must be a household word; 'not to know him argued ourselves unknown.' Only much later did we come to realise that no one else had heard of him either. (Indeed I now have a suspicion that some of these Richard Buttons, Hezekiah Cromwells and Eleanor Forsyths had no more existence than Mrs Harris. But for a year or so we were completely over-awed.)

We can thus detect the pride of Friendship – whether Olympian, Titanic, or merely vulgar – in many circles of Friends. It would be rash to assume that our own is safe from its danger; for of course it is in our own that we should be slowest to recognise it. The danger of such pride is indeed almost inseparable from Friendly love. Friendship must exclude. From the innocent and necessary act of excluding to the spirit of exclusiveness is an easy step; and thence to the degrading pleasure of exclusiveness. If that is once admitted the downward slope will grow rapidly steeper. We may never perhaps become Titans or plain cads; we might – which is in some ways worse – become 'Souls'. The common vision which first brought us together may fade quite away. We shall be a *coterie* that exists for the sake of being a *coterie*; a little self-elected (and therefore absurd) aristocracy, basking in the moonshine of our collective self-approval.

Sometimes a circle in this condition begins to dabble in the world of practice. Judiciously enlarging itself to admit recruits whose share in the original common interest is negligible but who are felt to be (in some undefined sense) 'sound men', it becomes a power in the land. Membership of it comes to have a sort of political importance, though the politics involved may be only those of a regiment, a college, or a cathedral close. The manipulation of committees, the capture of jobs (for sound men) and the united front against the Have-nots now become its principal occupation, and those who once met to talk about God or poetry now meet to talk about lectureships or livings. Notice the justice of their doom. 'Dust thou art and unto dust shalt thou return,' said God to Adam. In a circle which has thus dwindled into a coven of wanglers Friendship has sunk back again into the mere practical Companionship which was its matrix. They are now the same sort of body as the primitive horde of hunters. Hunters, indeed, is precisely what they are; and not the kind of hunters I most respect.

The mass of the people, who are never quite right, are never quite wrong. They are hopelessly mistaken in their belief that every knot of friends came into existence for the sake of the pleasures of conceit and superiority. They are, I trust, mistaken in their belief that every Friendship actually indulges in these pleasures. But they would seem to be right in diagnosing pride as the danger to which Friendships are naturally liable. Just because this is the most spiritual of loves the danger which besets it is spiritual too. Friendship is even, if you like, angelic. But man needs to be triply protected by humility if he is to eat the bread of angels without risk.

Perhaps we may now hazard a guess why Scripture uses Friendship so rarely as an image of the highest love. It is already, in actual fact, too spiritual to be a good symbol of Spiritual things. The highest does not stand without the lowest. God can safely represent Himself to us as Father and Husband because only a lunatic would think that He is physically our sire or that His marriage with the Church is other than mystical. But if Friendship were used for this purpose we might mistake the symbol for the thing symbolised. The danger inherent in it would be aggravated. We might be further encouraged to mistake that nearness (by resemblance) to the heavenly life which Friendship certainly displays for a nearness of approach.

Friendship, then, like the other natural loves, is unable to save itself. In reality, because it is spiritual and therefore faces a subtler enemy, it must, even more wholeheartedly than they, invoke the divine protection if it hopes to remain sweet. For consider how narrow its true path is. It must not become what the people call a 'mutual admiration society'; yet if it is not full of mutual admiration, of Appreciative love, it is not Friendship at all. For unless our lives are to be miserably impoverished it must be for us in our Friendships as it was for Christiana and her party in *The Pilgrim's Progress*:

> *They seemed to be a terror one to the other, for that they could not see that glory each one on herself which they could see in each other. Now therefore they began to esteem each other better than themselves. For you are fairer than I am, said one; and you are more comely than I am, said another.*

There is in the long run only one way in which we can taste this illustrious experience with safety. And Bunyan has indicated it in the same passage. It was in the House of the Interpreter, after they had been bathed, sealed and freshly clothed in 'White Raiment' that the women saw one another in this light. If we remember the bathing, sealing and robing, we shall be safe. And the higher the common ground of the Friendship is, the more necessary the remembrance. In an explicitly religious Friendship, above all, to forget it would be fatal.

For then it will seem to us that we – we four or five – have chosen one another, the insight of each finding the intrinsic beauty of the rest, like to like, a voluntary nobility; that we have ascended above the rest of mankind by our native powers. The other loves do not invite the same illusion. Affection obviously requires kinship or at least proximities which never depended on our own choice. And as for Eros, half the love songs and half the love poems in the world will tell you that the Beloved is your fate or destiny, no more your choice than a thunderbolt, for 'it is not in our power to love or hate'. Cupid's archery, genes – anything but ourselves. But in Friendship, being free of all that, we think we have chosen our peers. In reality, a few years' difference in the dates of our births, a few more miles between certain houses, the choice of one university instead of another, posting to different regiments, the accident of a topic being raised or not raised at a first meeting – any of these chances might have kept us apart. But, for a Christian, there are, strictly speaking, no chances. A secret Master of the Ceremonies has been at work. Christ, who said to the disciples 'Ye have not chosen me, but I have chosen you,' can truly say to every group of Christian friends 'You have not chosen one another but I have chosen you for one another.' The Friendship is not a reward for our discrimination and good taste in finding one another out. It is the instrument by which God reveals to each the beauties of all the others. They are no greater than the beauties of all the others. They are no greater than the beauties of a thousand other men; by Friendship God opens our eyes to them. They are, like all beauties, derived from Him, and then, in a good Friendship, increased by Him through the Friendship itself, so that it is His instrument for creating as well as for revealing. At this feast it is He who has spread the board and it is He who has chosen the guests. It is He, we may dare to hope, who sometimes does, and always should, preside. Let us not reckon without our Host.

Not that we must always partake of it solemnly. 'God who made good laughter' forbid. It is one of the difficult and delightful subtleties of life that we must deeply acknowledge certain things to be serious and yet retain the power and will to treat them often as lightly as a game. But there will be a time for saying more about this in the next chapter. For the moment I will only quote Dunbar's beautifully balanced advice:

Man, please thy Maker, and be merry,
And give not for this world a cherry.

5

EROS

B y *Eros* I mean of course that state which we call 'being in love'; or, if you prefer, that kind of love which lovers are 'in'. Some readers may have been surprised when, in an earlier chapter, I described Affection as the love in which our experience seems to come closest to that of the animals. Surely, it might be asked, our sexual functions bring us equally close? This is quite true as regards human sexuality in general. But I am not going to be concerned with human sexuality simply as such. Sexuality makes part of our subject only when it becomes an ingredient in the complex state of 'being in love'. That sexual experience can occur without Eros, without being 'in love', and that Eros includes other things besides sexual activity, I take for granted. If you prefer to put it that way, I am inquiring not into the sexuality which is common to us and the beasts or even common to all men but into one uniquely human variation of it which develops within 'love' – what I call Eros. The carnal or animally sexual element within Eros, I intend (following an old usage) to call Venus. And I mean by Venus what is sexual not in some cryptic or rarified sense – such as a depth-psychologist might explore – but in a perfectly obvious sense; what is known to be sexual by those who experience it; what could be proved to be sexual by the simplest observations.

Sexuality may operate without Eros or as part of Eros. Let me hasten to add that I make the distinction simply in order to limit our inquiry and without any moral implications. I am not at all subscribing to the popular idea that it is the absence or presence of Eros which makes the sexual act 'impure' or 'pure', degraded or fine, unlawful or lawful. If all who lay together without being in the state of Eros were abominable, we all come of tainted stock. The times and places in which marriage depends on Eros are in a small minority. Most of our ancestors were married off in early youth to partners chosen by their parents on grounds that had nothing to do with Eros. They went to the act with no other 'fuel', so to speak, than plain animal desire. And they did right; honest Christian husbands and wives, obeying their fathers and mothers, discharging to one another their 'marriage debt', and bringing up families in the fear of the Lord. Conversely, this act, done under the influence of a soaring and iridescent Eros which reduces the role of the senses to a minor consideration, may yet be plain adultery, may involve breaking a wife's heart, deceiving a husband, betraying a friend, polluting hospitality and deserting your children. It has not pleased God that the distinction between a sin and a duty should turn on fine feelings. This act, like any other, is justified (or not) by far more prosaic and definable criteria; by the keeping or breaking of promises, by justice or injustice, by charity or selfishness, by obedience or disobedience. My treatment rules out mere sexuality – sexuality without Eros – on grounds that have nothing to do with morals; because it is irrelevant to our purpose.

To the evolutionist Eros (the human variation) will be something that grows out of Venus, a late complication and development of the immemorial biological impulse. We must not assume, however, that this is necessarily what happens within the consciousness of the individual. There may be those who have first felt mere sexual appetite for a woman and then gone on at a later stage to 'fall in love with her'. But I doubt if this is at all common. Very often what comes first is simply a delighted pre-occupation with the Beloved – a general, unspecified pre-occupation with her in her totality. A man in this state really hasn't leisure to think of sex. He is too busy thinking of a person. The fact that she is a woman is far less important than the fact that she is herself. He is full of desire, but the desire may not be sexually toned. If you asked him what he wanted, the true reply would often be, 'To go on thinking of her.' He is love's contemplative. And when at a later stage the explicitly sexual element awakes, he will not feel (unless scientific theories are influencing him) that this had all along been the root of the whole matter. He is more likely to feel that the incoming tide of Eros, having demolished many sand-castles and made islands of many rocks, has now at last with a triumphant seventh wave flooded this part of his nature also – the little pool of ordinary sexuality which was there on his beach before the tide came in. Eros enters him like an invader, taking over and reorganising, one by one, the institutions of a conquered country. It may have taken over many others before it reaches the sex in him; and it will reorganise that too.

No one has indicated the nature of that reorganisation more briefly and accurately than George Orwell, who disliked it and preferred sexuality in its native condition, uncontaminated by Eros. In *Nineteen-Eighty-Four* his dreadful hero (how much less human than the four-footed heroes of his excellent *Animal Farm*!), before towsing the heroine, demands a reassurance, 'You like doing this?', he asks, 'I don't mean simply me; I mean the thing in itself.' He is not satisfied till he gets the answer, 'I adore it.' This little dialogue defines the reorganisation. Sexual desire, without Eros, wants *it*, the *thing in itself*; Eros wants the Beloved.

The *thing* is a sensory pleasure; that is, an event occurring within one's own body. We use a most unfortunate idiom when we say, of a lustful man prowling the streets, that he 'wants a woman'. Strictly speaking, a woman is just what he does not want. He wants a pleasure for which a woman happens to be the necessary piece of apparatus. How much he cares about the woman as such may be gauged by his attitude to her five minutes after fruition (one does not keep the carton after one has smoked the cigarettes). Now Eros makes a man really want, not a woman, but one particular woman. In some mysterious but quite indisputable fashion the lover desires the Beloved herself, not the pleasure she can give. No lover in the world ever sought the embraces of the woman he loved as the result of a calcula-tion, however unconscious, that they would be more pleasurable than those of any other woman. If he raised the question he would, no doubt, expect that this would be so. But to raise it would be to step outside the world of Eros altogether. The only man I know of who ever did raise it was Lucretius, and he was certainly not in love when he did. It is interesting to note his answer. That austere voluptuary gave it as his opinion that love actually impairs sexual pleasure. The emotion was a distraction. It spoiled the cool and critical receptivity of his palate. (A great poet; but 'Lord, what beastly fellows these Romans were!')

The reader will notice that Eros thus wonderfully transforms what is *par excellence* a Need-pleasure into the most Appreciative of all pleasures. It is the nature of a Need-pleasure to show us the object solely in relation to our need, even our momentary need. But in Eros, a Need, at its most intense, sees the object most intensely as a thing admirable in herself, important far beyond her relation to the lover's need.

If we had not all experienced this, if we were mere logicians, we might boggle at the conception of desiring a human being, as distinct from desiring any pleasure, comfort, or service that human being can give. And it is cer-tainly hard to explain. Lovers themselves are trying to express part of it (not much) when they say they would like to 'eat' one another. Milton has expressed more when he fancies angelic creatures with bodies made of light who can achieve total interpenetration instead of our mere embraces. Charles Williams has said something of it in the words, 'Love you? I *am* you.'

Without Eros sexual desire, like every other desire, is a fact about our-selves. Within Eros it is rather about the Beloved. It becomes almost a mode of perception, entirely a mode of expression. It feels objective; something outside us, in the real world. That is why Eros, though the king of pleasures, always (at his height) has the air of regarding pleasure as a by-product. To think about it would plunge us back in ourselves, in our own nervous system. It would kill Eros, as you can 'kill' the finest mountain prospect by locating it all in your own retina and optic nerves. Anyway, whose pleasure? For one of the first things Eros does is to obliterate the distinction between giving and receiving.

Hitherto I have been trying merely to describe, not to evaluate. But certain moral questions now inevitably arise, and I must not conceal my own view of them. It is submitted rather than asserted, and of course open to correction by better men, better lovers and better Christians.

It has been widely held in the past, and is perhaps held by many unsophisticated people today, that the spiritual danger of Eros arises almost entirely from the carnal element within it; that Eros is 'noblest' or 'purest' when Venus is reduced to the minimum. The older moral theologians certainly seem to have thought that the danger we chiefly had to guard against in marriage was that of a soul-destroying surrender to the senses. It will be noticed, however, that this is not the Scriptural approach. St Paul, dissuading his converts from marriage, says nothing about that side of the matter except to discourage prolonged abstinence from Venus (1 Corinthians 7:5). What he fears is pre-occupation, the need of constantly 'pleasing' – that is, considering – one's partner, the multiple distractions of domesticity. It is marriage itself, not the marriage bed, that will be likely to hinder us from waiting uninterruptedly on God. And surely St Paul is right? If I may trust my own experience, it is (within marriage as without) the practical and prudential cares of this world, and even the smallest and most prosaic of those cares, that are the great distraction. The gnat-like cloud of petty anxieties and decisions about the conduct of the next hour have interfered with my prayers more often than any passion or appetite whatever. The great, permanent temptation of marriage is not to sensuality but (quite bluntly) to avarice. With all proper respect to the medieval guides, I cannot help remembering that they were all celibates, and probably did not know what Eros does to our sexuality; how, far from aggravating, he reduces the nagging and addictive character of mere appetite. And that not simply by satisfying it. Eros, without diminishing desire, makes abstinence easier. He tends, no doubt, to a pre-occupation with the Beloved which can indeed be an obstacle to the spiritual life; but not chiefly a sensual pre-occupation.

The real spiritual danger in Eros as a whole lies, I believe, elsewhere. I will return to the point. For the moment, I want to speak of the danger which at present, in my opinion, especially haunts the act of love. This is a subject on which I disagree, not with the human race (far from it), but with many of its gravest spokesmen. I believe we are all being encouraged to take Venus too seriously; at any rate, with a wrong kind of seriousness. All my life a ludicrous and portentous solemnisation of sex has been going on.

One author tells us that Venus should recur through the married life in 'a solemn, sacramental rhythm'. A young man to whom I had described as 'pornographic' a novel that he much admired, replied with genuine bewilderment, 'Pornographic? But how can it be? It treats the whole thing so seriously' – as if a long face were a sort of moral disinfectant. Our friends who harbour Dark Gods, the 'pillar of blood' school, attempt seriously to restore something like the Phallic religion. Our advertisements, at their sexiest, paint the whole business in terms of the rapt, the intense, the swoony-devout; seldom a hint of gaiety. And the psychologists have so bedevilled us with the infinite importance of complete sexual adjustment and the all but impossibility of achieving it, that I could believe some young couples now go to it with the complete works of Freud, Kraft-Ebbing, Havelock Ellis and Dr Stopes spread out on bed-tables all round them. Cheery old Ovid, who never either ignored a molehill or made a mountain of it, would be more to the point. We have reached the stage at which nothing is more needed than a roar of old-fashioned laughter.

But, it will be replied, the thing *is* serious. Yes; quadruply so. First, theologically, because this is the body's share in marriage which, by God's choice, is the mystical image of the union between God and Man. Secondly, as what I will venture to call a sub-Christian, or Pagan or natural sacrament, our human participation in, and exposition of, the natural forces of life and fertility – the marriage of Sky-Father and Earth-Mother. Thirdly, on the moral level, in view of the obligations involved and the incalculable momentousness of being a parent and ancestor. Finally it has (sometimes, not always) a great emotional seriousness in the minds of the participants.

But eating is also serious; theologically, as the vehicle of the Blessed Sacrament; ethically in view of our duty to feed the hungry; socially, because the table is from time immemorial the place for talk; medically, as all dyspeptics know. Yet we do not bring bluebooks to dinner nor behave there as if we were in church. And it is *gourmets*, not saints, who come nearest to doing so. Animals are always serious about food.

We must not be totally serious about Venus. Indeed we can't be totally serious without doing violence to our humanity. It is not for nothing that every language and literature in the world is full of jokes about sex. Many of them may be dull or disgusting and nearly all of them are old. But we must insist that they embody an attitude to Venus which in the long run endangers the Christian life far less than a reverential gravity. We must not attempt to find an absolute in the flesh. Banish play and laughter from the bed of love and you may let in a false goddess. She will be even falser than the Aphrodite of the Greeks; for they, even while they worshipped her, knew that she was 'laughter-loving'. The mass of the people are perfectly right in their conviction that Venus is a partly comic spirit. We are under no obligation at all to sing all our love-duets in the throbbing, world-without-end, heart-breaking manner of Tristan and Isolde; let us often sing like Papageno and Papagena instead.

Venus herself will have a terrible revenge if we take her (occasional) seriousness at its face value. And that in two ways. One is most comically – though with no comic intention – illustrated by Sir Thomas Browne when he says that her service is 'the foolishest act a wise man commits in all his life, nor is there anything that will more deject his cool'd imagination, when he shall consider what an odd and unworthy piece of folly he had committed'. But if he had gone about that act with less solemnity in the first place he would not have suffered this 'dejection'. If his imagination had not been misled, its cooling would have brought no such revulsion. But Venus has another and worse revenge.

She herself is a mocking, mischievous spirit, far more elf than deity, and makes game of us. When all external circumstances are fittest for her service she will leave one or both the lovers totally indisposed for it. When every overt act is impossible and even glances cannot be exchanged – in trains, in shops and at interminable parties – she will assail them with all her force. An hour later, when time and place agree, she will have mysteriously withdrawn; perhaps from only one of them. What a pother this must raise – what resentments, self-pities, suspicions, wounded vanities and all the current chatter about 'frustration' – in those who have deified her! But sensible lovers laugh. It is all part of the game; a game of catch-as-catch-can, and the escapes and tumbles and head-on collisions are to be treated as a romp.

For I can hardly help regarding it as one of God's jokes that a passion so soaring, so apparently transcendent, as Eros, should thus be linked in incongruous symbiosis with a bodily appetite which, like any other appetite, tactlessly reveals its connections with such mundane factors as weather, health, diet, circulation, and digestion. In Eros at times we seem to be flying; Venus gives us the sudden twitch that reminds us we are really captive balloons. It is a continual demonstration of the truth that we are composite creatures, rational animals, akin on one side to the angels, on the other to tom-cats. It is a bad thing not to be able to take a joke. Worse, not to take a divine joke; made, I grant you, at our expense, but also (who doubts it?) for our endless benefit.

Man has held three views of his body. First there is that of those ascetic Pagans who called it the prison or the 'tomb' of the soul, and of Christians like Fisher to whom it was a 'sack of dung', food for worms, filthy, shameful, a source of nothing but temptation to bad men and humiliation to good ones. Then there are the Neo-Pagans (they seldom know Greek), the nudists and the sufferers from Dark Gods, to whom the body is glorious. But thirdly we have the view which St Francis expressed by calling his body

'Brother Ass'. All three may be – I am not sure – defensible; but give me St Francis for my money.

Ass is exquisitely right because no one in his senses can either revere or hate a donkey. It is a useful, sturdy, lazy, obstinate, patient, lovable and infuriating beast; deserving now the stick and now a carrot; both pathetically and absurdly beautiful. So the body. There's no living with it till we recognise that one of its functions in our lives is to play the part of buffoon. Until some theory has sophisticated them, every man, woman and child in the world knows this. The fact that we have bodies is the oldest joke there is. Eros (like death, figure-drawing and the study of medicine) may at moments cause us to take it with total seriousness. The error consists in concluding that Eros should always do so and permanently abolish the joke. But this is not what happens. The very faces of all the happy lovers we know make it clear. Lovers, unless their love is very short-lived, again and again feel an element not only of comedy, not only of play, but even of buffoonery, in the body's expression of Eros. And the body would frustrate us if this were not so. It would be too clumsy an instrument to render love's music unless its very clumsiness could be felt as adding to the total experience its own grotesque charm – a sub-plot or antimasque miming with its own hearty rough-and-tumble what the soul enacts in statelier fashion. (Thus in old comedies the lyric loves of the hero and heroine are at once parodied and corroborated by some much more earthy affair between a Touchstone and an Audrey or a valet and a chambermaid.) The highest does not stand without the lowest. There is indeed at certain moments a high poetry in the flesh itself; but also, by your leave, an irreducible element of obstinate and ludicrous un-poetry. If it does not make itself felt on one occasion, it will on another. Far better plant it foursquare within the drama of Eros as comic relief than pretend you haven't noticed it.

For indeed we require this relief. The poetry is there as well as the un-poetry; the gravity of Venus as well as her levity, the *gravis ardor* or burning weight of desire. Pleasure, pushed to its extreme, shatters us like pain. The longing for a union which only the flesh can mediate while the flesh, our mutually excluding bodies, renders it forever unattainable, can have the grandeur of a metaphysical pursuit. Amorousness as well as grief can bring tears to the eyes. But Venus does not always come thus 'entire fastened to her prey', and the fact that she sometimes does so is the very reason for preserving always a hint of playfulness in our attitude to her. When natural things look most divine, the demoniac is just round the corner.

This refusal to be quite immersed – this recollection of the levity even when, for the moment, only the gravity is displayed – is especially relevant to a certain attitude which Venus, in her intensity, evokes from most (I believe, not all) pairs of lovers. This act can invite the man to an extreme, though short-lived, masterfulness, to the dominance of a conqueror or a captor, and the woman to a correspondingly extreme abjection and surrender. Hence the roughness, even fierceness, of some erotic play; the 'lover's pinch which hurts and is desired'. How should a sane couple think of this? or a Christian couple permit it?

I think it is harmless and wholesome on one condition. We must recognise that we have here to do with what I called 'the Pagan sacrament' in sex. In Friendship, as we noticed, each participant stands for precisely himself – the contingent individual he is. But in the act of love we are not merely ourselves. We are also representatives. It is here no impoverishment but an enrichment to be aware that forces older and less personal than we work through us. In us all the masculinity and femininity of the world, all that is assailant and responsive, are momentarily focused. The man does play the Sky-Father and the woman the Earth-Mother; he does play Form, and she Matter. But we must give full value to the word *play*. Of course neither 'plays a part' in the sense of being a hypocrite. But each plays a part or role in – well, in something which is comparable to a mystery-play or ritual (at one extreme) and to a masque or even a charade (at the other).

A woman who accepted as literally her own this extreme self-surrender would be an idolatress offering to a man what belongs only to God. And a man would have to be the coxcomb of all coxcombs, and indeed a blasphemer, if he arrogated to himself, as the mere person he is, the sort of sovereignty to which Venus for a moment exalts him. But what cannot lawfully be yielded or claimed can be lawfully enacted. Outside this ritual or drama he and she are two immortal souls, two free-born adults, two citizens. We should be much mistaken if we supposed that those marriages where this mastery is most asserted and acknowledged in the act of Venus were those where the husband is most likely to be dominant in the married life as a whole; the reverse is perhaps more probable. But within the rite or drama they become a god and goddess between whom there is no equality – whose relations are asymmetrical.

Some will think it strange I should find an element of ritual or masquerade in that action which is often regarded as the most real, the most unmasked and sheerly genuine, we ever do. Are we not our true selves when naked? In a sense, no. The word *naked* was originally a past participle; the naked man was the man who had undergone the process of *naking*, that is, of stripping or peeling (you used the verb of nuts and fruit). Time out of mind the naked man has seemed to our ancestors not the natural but the abnormal man; not the man who has abstained from dressing but the man who has been for some reason undressed. And it is a simple fact – anyone can observe it at a men's bathing place – that nudity emphasises common humanity and soft-pedals what is individual. In that way we are 'more ourselves' when clothed. By nudity the lovers cease to be solely John and Mary; the universal He and She are emphasised. You could almost say they *put on* nakedness as a ceremonial robe – or as the costume for a charade. For we must still beware – and never more than when we thus partake of the Pagan sacrament in our love-passages – of being serious in the wrong way. The Sky-Father himself is only a Pagan dream of One far greater than Zeus and far more masculine than the male. And a mortal man is not even the Sky-Father, and cannot really wear his crown. Only a copy of it, done in tinselled paper. I do not call it this in contempt. I like ritual; I like private theatricals; I even like charades. Paper crowns have their legitimate, and (in the proper context) their serious, uses. They are not in the last resort much flimsier ('if imagination mend them') than all earthly dignities.

But I dare not mention this Pagan sacrament without turning aside to guard against any danger of confusing it with an incomparably higher mystery. As nature crowns man in that brief action, so the Christian law has crowned him in the permanent relationship of marriage, bestowing – or should I say, inflicting? – a certain 'headship' on him. This is a very different coronation. And as we could easily take the natural mystery too seriously, so we might take the Christian mystery not seriously enough. Christian writers (notably Milton) have sometimes spoken of the husband's headship with a complacency to make the blood run cold. We must go back to our Bibles. The husband is the head of the wife just in so far as he is to her what Christ is to the Church. He is to love her as Christ loved the Church – read on – *and gave his life for her* (Ephesians 5:25). This headship, then, is most fully embodied not in the husband we should all wish to be but in him whose marriage is most like a crucifixion; whose wife receives most and gives least, is most unworthy of him, is – in her own mere nature – least lovable. For the Church has no beauty but what the Bridegroom gives her; he does not find, but makes her, lovely. The chrism of this terrible coronation is to be seen not in the joys of any man's marriage but in its sorrows, in the sickness and sufferings of a good wife or the faults of a bad one, in his unwearying (never paraded) care or his inexhaustible forgiveness: forgiveness, not acquiescence. As Christ sees in the flawed, proud, fanatical or lukewarm Church on earth that Bride who will one day be without spot or wrinkle, and labours to produce the latter, so the husband whose headship is Christ-like (and he is allowed no other sort) never despairs. He is a King Cophetua who after twenty years still hopes that the beggar-girl will one day learn to speak the truth and wash behind her ears.

To say this is not to say that there is any virtue or wisdom in making a marriage that involves such misery. There is no wisdom or virtue in seeking unnecessary martyrdom or deliberately courting persecution; yet it is, none the less, the persecuted or martyred Christian in whom the pattern of the

Master is most unambiguously realised. So, in these terrible marriages, once they have come about, the 'headship' of the husband, if only he can sustain it, is most Christ-like.

The sternest feminist need not grudge my sex the crown offered to it either in the Pagan or in the Christian mystery. For the one is of paper and the other of thorns. The real danger is not that husbands may grasp the latter too eagerly; but that they will allow or compel their wives to usurp it.

From Venus, the carnal ingredient within Eros, I now turn to Eros as a whole. Here we shall see the same pattern repeated. As Venus within Eros does not really aim at pleasure, so Eros does not aim at happiness. We may think he does, but when he is brought to the test it proves otherwise. Everyone knows that it is useless to try to separate lovers by proving to them that their marriage will be an unhappy one. This is not only because they will disbelieve you. They usually will, no doubt. But even if they believed, they would not be dissuaded. For it is the very mark of Eros that when he is in us we had rather share unhappiness with the Beloved than be happy on any other terms. Even if the two lovers are mature and experienced people who know that broken hearts heal in the end and can clearly foresee that, if they once steeled themselves to go through the present agony of parting, they would almost certainly be happier ten years hence than marriage is at all likely to make them – even then, they would not part. To Eros all these calculations are irrelevant – just as the coolly brutal judgment of Lucretius is irrelevant to Venus. Even when it becomes clear beyond all evasion that marriage with the Beloved cannot possibly lead to happiness – when it cannot even profess to offer any other life than that of tending an incurable invalid, of hopeless poverty, of exile, or of disgrace – Eros never hesitates to say, 'Better this than parting. Better to be miserable with her than happy without her. Let our hearts break provided they break together.' If the voice within us does not say this, it is not the voice of Eros.

This is the grandeur and terror of love. But notice, as before, side by side with this grandeur, the playfulness. Eros, as well as Venus, is the subject of countless jokes. And even when the circumstances of the two lovers are so tragic that no bystander could keep back his tears, they themselves – in want, in hospital wards, on visitors' days in jail – will sometimes be surprised by a merriment which strikes the onlooker (but not them) as unbearably pathetic. Nothing is falser than the idea that mockery is necessarily hostile. Until they have a baby to laugh at, lovers are always laughing at each other.

It is in the grandeur of Eros that the seeds of danger are concealed. He has spoken like a god. His total commitment, his reckless disregard of happiness, his transcendence of self-regard, sound like a message from the eternal world.

And yet it cannot, just as it stands, be the voice of God Himself. For Eros, speaking with that very grandeur and displaying that very transcendence of self, may urge to evil as well as to good. Nothing is shallower than the belief that a love which leads to sin is always qualitatively lower – more animal or more trivial – than one which leads to faithful, fruitful and Christian marriage. The love which leads to cruel and perjured unions, even to suicide-pacts and murder, is not likely to be wandering lust or idle sentiment. It may well be Eros in all his splendour; heartbreakingly sincere; ready for every sacrifice except renunciation.

There have been schools of thought which accepted the voice of Eros as something actually transcendent and tried to justify the absoluteness of his commands. Plato will have it that 'falling in love' is the mutual recognition on earth of souls which have been singled out for one another in a previous and celestial existence. To meet the Beloved is to realise 'We loved before we were born.' As a myth to express what lovers feel this is admirable. But if one accepted it literally one would be faced by an embarrassing conse-quence. We should have to conclude that in that heavenly and forgotten life affairs were no better managed than here. For Eros may unite the most unsuitable yoke-fellows; many unhappy, and predictably unhappy, mar-riages were love-matches.

A theory more likely to be accepted in our own day is what we may call Shavian – Shaw himself might have said 'metabiological' – Romanticism. According to Shavian Romanticism the voice of Eros is the voice of the *élan vital* or Life Force, the 'evolutionary appetite'. In overwhelming a particular couple it is seeking parents (or ancestors) for the superman. It is indifferent both to their personal happiness and to the rules of morality because it aims at something which Shaw thinks very much more important: the future perfection of our species. But if all this were true it hardly makes clear whether – and if so, why – we should obey it. All pictures yet offered us of the superman are so unattractive that one might well vow celibacy at once to avoid the risk of begetting him. And secondly, this theory surely leads to the conclusion that the Life Force does not very well understand its (or her? or his?) own business. So far as we can see the existence or intensity of Eros between two people is no warrant that their offspring will be especially satis-factory, or even that they will have offspring at all. Two good 'strains' (in the stockbreeders' sense), not two good lovers, is the recipe for fine children. And what on earth was the Life Force doing through all those countless gen-erations when the begetting of children depended very little on mutual Eros and very much on arranged marriages, slavery and rape? Has it only just thought of this bright idea for improving the species?

Neither the Platonic nor the Shavian type of erotic transcendentalism can help a Christian. We are not worshippers of the Life Force and we know nothing of previous existences. We must not give unconditional obedience to the voice of Eros when he speaks most like a god. Neither must we ignore or attempt to deny the god-like quality. This love is really and truly like Love Himself. In it there is a real nearness to God (by Resemblance); but not, therefore and necessarily, a nearness of Approach. Eros, honoured so far as love of God and charity to our fellows will allow, may become for us a means of Approach. His total commitment is a paradigm or example, built into our natures, of the love we ought to exercise towards God and Man. As Nature, for the Nature-lover, gives a content to the word *glory*, so this gives a content to the word *Charity*. It is as if Christ said to us through Eros, 'Thus – just like this – with this prodigality – not counting the cost – you are to love me and the least of my brethren.' Our conditional honour to Eros will of course vary with our circumstances. Of some a total renunciation (but not a contempt) is required. Others, with Eros as their fuel and also as their model, can embark on the married life. Within which Eros, of himself, will never be enough – will indeed survive only in so far as he is continually chastened and corroborated by higher principles.

But Eros, honoured without reservation and obeyed unconditionally, becomes a demon. And this is just how he claims to be honoured and obeyed. Divinely indifferent to our selfishness, he is also demoniacally rebellious to every claim of God or Man that would oppose him. Hence as the poet says:

People in love cannot be moved by kindness,
And opposition makes them feel like martyrs.

Martyrs is exactly right. Years ago when I wrote about medieval love poetry and described its strange, half make-believe, 'religion of love', I was blind enough to treat this as an almost purely literary phenomenon. I know better now. Eros by his nature invites it. Of all loves he is, at his height, most god-like; therefore most prone to demand our worship. Of himself he always tends to turn 'being in love' into a sort of religion.

Theologians have often feared, in this love, a danger of idolatry. I think they meant by this that the lovers might idolise one another. That does not seem to me to be the real danger; certainly not in marriage. The deliciously plain prose and business-like intimacy of married life render it absurd. So does the Affection in which Eros is almost invariably clothed. Even in courtship I question whether anyone who has felt the thirst for the Uncreated, or even dreamed of feeling it, ever supposed that the Beloved could satisfy it. As a fellow-pilgrim pierced with the very same desire, that is, as a Friend, the Beloved may be gloriously and helpfully relevant; but as an object for it – well (I would not be rude), ridiculous. The real danger seems to me not that the lovers will idolise each other but that they will idolise Eros himself.

I do not of course mean that they will build altars or say prayers to him. The idolatry I speak of can be seen in the popular misinterpretation of Our Lord's words 'Her sins, which are many, are forgiven her, for she loved much' (Luke 7:47). From the context, and especially from the preceding parable of the debtors, it is clear that this must mean: 'The greatness of her love for Me is evidence of the greatness of the sins I have forgiven her.' (The *for* here is like the *for* in 'He can't have gone out, *for* his hat is still hanging in the hall'; the presence of the hat is not the cause of his being in the house but a probable proof that he is.) But thousands of people take it quite differently. They first assume, with no evidence, that her sins were sins against chastity, though, for all we know, they may have been usury, dishonest shopkeeping, or cruelty to children. And they then take Our Lord to be saying, 'I forgive her unchastity because she was so much in love.' The implication is that a great Eros extenuates – almost sanctions – almost sanctifies – any actions it leads to.

When lovers say of some act that we might blame, 'Love made us do it,' notice the tone. A man saying, 'I did it because I was frightened,' or 'I did it because I was angry,' speaks quite differently. He is putting forward an excuse for what he feels to require excusing. But the lovers are seldom doing quite that. Notice how tremulously, almost how devoutly, they say the word *love*, not so much pleading an 'extenuating circumstance' as appealing to an authority. The confession can be almost a boast. There can be a shade of defiance in it. They 'feel like martyrs'. In extreme cases what their words really express is a demure yet unshakable allegiance to the god of love.

'These reasons in love's law have passed for good,' says Milton's Dalila. That is the point; *in love's law*. 'In love', we have our own 'law', a religion of our own, our own god. Where a true Eros is present resistance to his commands feels like apostasy, and what are really (by the Christian standard) temptations speak with the voice of duties – quasi-religious duties, acts of pious zeal to Love. He builds his own religion round the lovers. Benjamin Constant has noticed how he creates for them, in a few weeks or months, a joint past which seems to them immemorial. They recur to it continually with wonder and reverence, as the Psalmists recur to the history of Israel. It is in fact the Old Testament of Love's religion; the record of love's judgments and mercies towards his chosen pair up to the moment when they first knew they were lovers. After that, its New Testament begins. They are now under a new law, under what corresponds (in this religion) to Grace. They are new creatures. The 'spirit' of Eros supersedes all laws, and they must not 'grieve' it.

It seems to sanction all sorts of actions they would not otherwise have dared. I do not mean solely, or chiefly, acts that violate chastity. They are just as likely to be acts of injustice or uncharity against the outer world. They will seem like proofs of piety and zeal towards Eros. The pair can say to one another in an almost sacrificial spirit, 'It is for love's sake that I have neglected my parents – left my children – cheated my partner – failed my friend at his greatest need.' These reasons in love's law have passed for good. The votaries may even come to feel a particular merit in such sacrifices; what costlier offering can be laid on love's altar than one's conscience?

And all the time the grim joke is that this Eros whose voice seems to speak from the eternal realm is not himself necessarily even permanent. He is notoriously the most mortal of our loves. The world rings with complaints of his fickleness. What is baffling is the combination of this fickleness with his protestations of permanency. To be in love is both to intend and to promise lifelong fidelity. Love makes vows unasked; can't be deterred from making them. 'I will be ever true,' are almost the first words he utters. Not hypocritically but sincerely. No experience will cure him of the delusion. We have all heard of people who are in love again every few years; each time sincerely convinced that '*this* time it's the real thing', that their wanderings are over, that they have found their true love and will themselves be true till death.

And yet Eros is in a sense right to make this promise. The event of falling in love is of such a nature that we are right to reject as intolerable the idea that it should be transitory. In one high bound it has overleaped the massive wall of our selfhood; it has made appetite itself altruistic, tossed personal happiness aside as a triviality and planted the interests of another in the centre of our being. Spontaneously and without effort we have fulfilled the law (towards one person) by loving our neighbour as ourselves. It is an image, a foretaste, of what we must become to all if Love Himself rules in us without a rival. It is even (well used) a preparation for that. Simply to relapse from it, merely to 'fall out of' love again, is – if I may coin the ugly word – a sort of *disredemption*. Eros is driven to promise what Eros of himself cannot perform.

Can we be in this selfless liberation for a lifetime? Hardly for a week. Between the best possible lovers this high condition is intermittent. The old self soon turns out to be not so dead as he pretended – as after a religious conversion. In either he may be momentarily knocked flat; he will soon be up again; if not on his feet, at least on his elbow, if not roaring, at least back to his surly grumbling or his mendicant whine. And Venus will often slip back into mere sexuality.

But these lapses will not destroy a marriage between two 'decent and sensible' people. The couple whose marriage will certainly be endangered by them, and possibly ruined, are those who have idolised Eros. They thought he had the power and truthfulness of a god. They expected that mere feeling would do for them, and permanently, all that was necessary. When this expectation is disappointed they throw the blame on Eros or, more usually, on their partners. In reality, however, Eros, having made his gigantic promise and shown you in glimpses what its performance would be like, has 'done his stuff'. He, like a godparent, makes the vows; it is we who must keep them. It is we who must labour to bring our daily life into even closer accordance with what the glimpses have revealed. We must do the works of Eros when Eros is not present. This all good lovers know, though those who are not reflective or articulate will be able to express it only in a few conventional phrases about 'taking the rough along with the smooth', not 'expecting too much', having 'a little common sense', and the like. And all good Christian lovers know that this programme, modest as it sounds, will not be carried out except by humility, charity and divine grace; that it is indeed the whole Christian life seen from one particular angle.

Thus Eros, like the other loves, but more strikingly because of his strength, sweetness, terror and high port, reveals his true status. He cannot of himself be what, nevertheless, he must be if he is to remain Eros. He needs help; therefore needs to be ruled. The god dies or becomes a demon unless he obeys God. It would be well if, in such case, he always died. But he may live on, mercilessly chaining together two mutual tormentors, each raw all over with the poison of hate-in-love, each ravenous to receive and implacably refusing to give, jealous, suspicious, resentful, struggling for the upper hand, determined to be free and to allow no freedom, living on 'scenes'. Read *Anna Karenina*, and do not fancy that such things happen only in Russia. The lovers' old hyperbole of 'eating' each other can come horribly near to the truth.

6

CHARITY

William Morris wrote a poem called *Love is Enough* and someone is said to have reviewed it briefly in the words 'It isn't'. Such has been the burden of this book. The natural loves are not self-sufficient. Something else, at first vaguely described as 'decency and common sense', but later revealed as goodness, and finally as the whole Christian life in one particular relation, must come to the help of the mere feeling if the feeling is to be kept sweet.

To say this is not to belittle the natural loves but to indicate where their real glory lies. It is no disparagement to a garden to say that it will not fence and weed itself, nor prune its own fruit trees, nor roll and cut its own lawns. A garden is a good thing but that is not the sort of goodness it has. It will remain a garden, as distinct from a wilderness, only if someone does all these things to it. Its real glory is of quite a different kind. The very fact that it needs constant weeding and pruning bears witness to that glory. It teems with life. It glows with colour and smells like heaven and puts forward at every hour of a summer day beauties which man could never have created and could not even, on his own resources, have imagined. If you want to see the difference between its contribution and the gardener's, put the commonest weed it grows side by side with his hoes, rakes, shears and packet of weed killer; you have put beauty, energy and fecundity beside dead, sterile things. Just so, our 'decency and common sense' show grey and deathlike beside the geniality of love. And when the garden is in its full glory the gardener's contributions to that glory will still have been in a sense paltry compared with those of nature. Without life springing from the earth, without rain, light and heat descending from the sky, he could do nothing. When he has done all, he has merely encouraged here and discouraged there, powers and beauties that have a different source. But his share, though small, is indispensable and laborious. When God planted a garden He set a man over it and set the man under Himself. When He planted the garden of our nature and caused the flowering, fruiting loves to grow there, He set our will to 'dress' them. Compared with them it is dry and cold.

And unless His grace comes down, like the rain and the sunshine, we shall use this tool to little purpose. But its laborious – and largely negative – services are indispensable. If they were needed when the garden was still Paradisal, how much more now when the soil has gone sour and the worst weeds seem to thrive on it best? But heaven forbid we should work in the spirit of prigs and Stoics. While we hack and prune we know very well that what we are hacking and pruning is big with a splendour and vitality which our rational will could never of itself have supplied. To liberate that splendour, to let it become fully what it is trying to be, to have tall trees instead of scrubby tangles, and sweet apples instead of crabs, is part of our purpose.

But only part. For now we must face a topic that I have long postponed. Hitherto hardly anything has been said in this book about our natural loves as rivals to the love of God. Now the question can no longer be avoided. There were two reasons for my delay.

One – already hinted – is that this question is not the place at which most of us need begin. It is seldom, at the outset, 'addressed to our condition'. For most of us the true rivalry lies between the self and the human Other, not yet between the human Other and God. It is dangerous to press upon a man the duty of getting beyond earthly love when his real difficulty lies in getting so far. And it is no doubt easy enough to love the fellow-creature less and to imagine that this is happening because we are learning to love God more, when the real reason may be quite different. We may be only 'mistaking the decays of nature for the increase of Grace'. Many people do not find it really difficult to hate their wives or mothers. M. Mauriac, in a fine scene, pictures the other disciples stunned and bewildered by this strange command, but not Judas. He laps it up easily.

But to have stressed the rivalry earlier in this book would have been premature in another way also. The claim to divinity which our loves so easily make can be refuted without going so far as that. The loves prove that they are unworthy to take the place of God by the fact that they cannot even remain themselves and do what they promise to do without God's help. Why prove that some petty princeling is not the lawful Emperor when without the Emperor's support he cannot even keep his subordinate throne and make peace in his little province for half a year? Even for their own sakes the loves must submit to be second things if they are to remain the things they want to be. In this yoke lies their true freedom; they 'are taller when they bow'. For when God rules in a human heart, though He may sometimes have to remove certain of its native authorities altogether, He often continues others in their offices and, by subjecting their authority to His, gives it for the first time a firm basis. Emerson has said, 'When half-gods go, the gods arrive.' That is a very doubtful maxim. Better say, 'When God arrives (and only then) the half-gods can remain.' Left to themselves they either vanish or become demons. Only in His name can they with beauty and security 'wield their little tridents'. The rebellious slogan 'All for love' is really love's death warrant (date of execution, for the moment, left blank).

But the question of the Rivalry, for these reasons long postponed, must now be treated. In any earlier period, except the Nineteenth Century, it would have loomed large throughout a book on this subject. If the Victorians needed the reminder that love is not enough, older theologians were always saying very loudly that (natural) love is likely to be a great deal too much. The danger of loving our fellow creatures too little was less present to their minds than that of loving them idolatrously. In every wife, mother, child and friend they saw a possible rival to God. So of course does Our Lord (Luke 14:26).

There is one method of dissuading us from inordinate love of the fellow-creature which I find myself forced to reject at the very outset. I do so with trembling, for it met me in the pages of a great saint and a great thinker to whom my own glad debts are incalculable.

In words which can still bring tears to the eyes, St Augustine describes the desolation in which the death of his friend Nebridius plunged him (*Confessions* IV, 10). Then he draws a moral. This is what comes, he says, of giving one's heart to anything but God. All human beings pass away. Do not let your happiness depend on something you may lose. If love is to be a blessing, not a misery, it must be for the only Beloved who will never pass away.

Of course this is excellent sense. Don't put your goods in a leaky vessel. Don't spend too much on a house you may be turned out of. And there is no man alive who responds more naturally than I to such canny maxims. I am a safety-first creature. Of all arguments against love none makes so strong an appeal to my nature as 'Careful! This might lead you to suffering.'

To my nature, my temperament, yes. Not to my conscience. When I respond to that appeal I seem to myself to be a thousand miles away from Christ. If I am sure of anything I am sure that His teaching was never meant to confirm my congenital preference for safe investments and limited liabilities. I doubt whether there is anything in me that pleases Him less. And who could conceivably begin to love God on such a prudential ground – because the security (so to speak) is better? Who could even include it among the grounds for loving? Would you choose a wife or a Friend – if it comes to that, would you choose a dog – in this spirit? One must be outside the world of love, of all loves, before one thus calculates. Eros, lawless Eros, preferring the Beloved to happiness, is more like Love Himself than this.

I think that this passage in the *Confessions* is less a part of St Augustine's Christendom than a hangover from the high-minded Pagan philosophies in which he grew up. It is closer to Stoic 'apathy' or neo-

Platonic mysticism than to charity. We follow One who wept over Jerusalem and at the grave of Lazarus, and, loving all, yet had one disciple whom, in a special sense, he 'loved'. St Paul has a higher authority with us than St Augustine – St Paul who shows no sign that he would not have suffered like a man, and no feeling that he ought not so to have suffered, if Epaphroditus had died (Philippians 2:27).

Even if it were granted that insurances against heartbreak were our highest wisdom, does God Himself offer them? Apparently not. Christ comes at last to say 'Why hast thou forsaken me?'

There is no escape along the lines St Augustine suggests. Nor along any other lines. There is no safe investment. To love at all is to be vulnerable. Love anything, and your heart will certainly be wrung and possibly be broken. If you want to make sure of keeping it intact, you must give your heart to no one, not even to an animal. Wrap it carefully round with hobbies and little luxuries; avoid all entanglements; lock it up safe in the casket or coffin of your selfishness. But in that casket – safe, dark, motionless, airless – it will change. It will not be broken; it will become unbreakable, impenetrable, irredeemable. The alternative to tragedy, or at least to the risk of tragedy, is damnation. The only place outside Heaven where you can be perfectly safe from all the dangers and perturbations of love is Hell.

I believe that the most lawless and inordinate loves are less contrary to God's will than a self-invited and self-protective lovelessness. It is like hiding the talent in a napkin and for much the same reason. 'I knew thee that thou wert a hard man.' Christ did not teach and suffer that we might become, even in the natural loves, more careful of our own happiness. If a man is not uncalculating towards the earthly beloveds whom he has seen, he is none the more likely to be so towards God whom he has not. We shall draw nearer to God, not by trying to avoid the sufferings inherent in all loves, but by accepting them and offering them to Him; throwing away all defensive armour. If our hearts need to be broken, and if He chooses this as the way in which they should break, so be it.

It remains certainly true that all natural loves can be inordinate. *Inordinate* does not mean 'insufficiently cautious'. Nor does it mean 'too big'. It is not a quantitative term. It is probably impossible to love any human being simply 'too much'. We may love him too much *in proportion to* our love for God; but it is the smallness of our love for God, not the greatness of our love for the man, that constitutes the inordinacy. But even this must be refined upon. Otherwise we shall trouble some who are very much on the right road but alarmed because they cannot feel towards God so warm a sensible emotion as they feel for the earthly Beloved. It is much to be wished – at least I think so – that we all, at all times, could. We must pray that this gift should be given us. But the question whether we are loving God or the earthly Beloved 'more' is not, so far as concerns our Christian duty, a question about the comparative intensity of two feelings. The real question is, which (when the alternative comes) do you serve, or choose, or put first? To which claim does your will, in the last resort, yield?

As so often, Our Lord's own words are both far fiercer and far more tolerable than those of the theologians. He says nothing about guarding against earthly loves for fear we might be hurt; He says something that cracks like a whip about trampling them all under foot the moment they hold us back from following Him. 'If any man come to me and hate not his father and mother and wife ... and his own life also, he cannot be my disciple' (Luke 14:26).

But how are we to understand the word *hate*? That Love Himself should be commanding what we ordinarily mean by hatred – commanding us to cherish resentment, to gloat over another's misery, to delight in injuring him – is almost a contradiction in terms. I think Our Lord, in the sense here intended, 'hated' St Peter when he said, 'Get thee behind me.' To hate is to reject, to set one's face against, to make no concession to, the Beloved when the Beloved utters, however sweetly and however pitiably, the suggestions of the Devil. A man, said Jesus, who tries to serve two masters, will 'hate' the one and 'love' the other. It is not, surely, mere feelings of aversion and liking that are here in question. He will adhere to, consent to, work for, the one and not the other. Consider again, 'I loved Jacob and I *hated* Esau' (Malachi 1:2–3). How is the thing called God's 'hatred' of Esau displayed in the actual story? Not at all as we might expect. There is of course no ground for assuming that Esau made a bad end and was a lost soul; the Old Testament, here as elsewhere, has nothing to say about such matters. And, from all we are told, Esau's earthly life was, in every ordinary sense, a good deal more blessed than Jacob's. It is Jacob who has all the disappointments, humiliations, terrors and bereavements. But he has something which Esau has not. He is a patriarch. He hands on the Hebraic tradition, transmits the vocation and the blessing, becomes an ancestor of Our Lord. The 'loving' of Jacob seems to mean the acceptance of Jacob for a high (and painful) vocation; the 'hating' of Esau, his rejection. He is 'turned down', fails to 'make the grade', is found useless for the purpose. So, in the last resort, we must turn down or disqualify our nearest and dearest when they come between us and our obedience to God. Heaven knows, it will seem to them sufficiently like hatred. We must not act on the pity we feel; we must be blind to tears and deaf to pleadings.

I will not say that this duty is hard; some find it too easy; some, hard almost beyond endurance. What is hard for all is to know when the occasion for such 'hating' has arisen. Our temperaments deceive us. The meek and tender – uxorious husbands, submissive wives, doting parents, dutiful children – will not easily believe that it has ever arrived. Self-assertive people, with a dash of the bully in them, will believe it too soon. That is why it is of such extreme importance so to order our loves that it is unlikely to arrive at all.

How this could come about we may see on a far lower level when the Cavalier poet, going to the wars, says to his mistress:

I could not love thee, dear, so much
Loved I not honour more.

There are women to whom the plea would be meaningless. *Honour* would be just one of those silly things that Men talk about; a verbal excuse for, therefore an aggravation of, the offence against 'love's law' which the poet is about to commit. Lovelace can use it with confidence because his lady is a Cavalier lady who already admits, as he does, the claims of Honour. He does not need to 'hate' her, to set his face against her, because he and she acknowledge the same law. They have agreed and understood each other on this matter long before. The task of converting her to a belief in Honour is not now – now, when the decision is upon them – to be undertaken. It is this prior agreement which is so necessary when a far greater claim than that of Honour is at stake. It is too late, when the crisis comes, to begin telling a wife or husband or mother or friend, that your love all along had a secret reservation – 'under God' or 'so far as a higher Love permits'. They ought to have been warned; not, to be sure, explicitly, but by the implication of a thousand talks, by the principle revealed in a hundred decisions upon small matters. Indeed, a real disagreement on this issue should make itself felt early enough to prevent a marriage or a Friendship from existing at all. The best love of either sort is not blind. Oliver Elton, speaking of Carlyle and Mill, said that they differed about justice, and that such a difference was naturally fatal 'to any friendship worthy of the name'. If 'All' – quite seriously all – 'for love' is implicit in the Beloved's attitude, his or her love is not worth having. It is not related in the right way to Love Himself.

And this brings me to the foot of the last steep ascent this book must try to make. We must try to relate the human activities called 'loves' to that Love which is God a little more precisely than we have yet done. The precision can, of course, be only that of a model or a symbol, certain to fail us in the long run and, even while we use it, requiring correction from other models. The humblest of us, in a state of Grace, can have some 'knowledge-by-acquaintance' (*connaître*), some 'tasting', of Love Himself; but man even at his highest sanctity and intelligence has no direct 'knowledge about' (*savoir*) the ultimate Being – only analogies. We cannot see light, though by light we can see things. Statements about God are extrapolations from the knowledge of other things which the divine illumination enables us to know. I labour these deprecations because, in what follows, my efforts to be clear (and not intolerably lengthy) may suggest a confidence which I by no means feel. I should be mad if I did. Take it as one man's reverie, almost one man's myth. If anything in it is useful to you, use it; if anything is not, never give it a second thought.

God is love. Again, 'Herein is love, not that we loved God but that He loved us' (1 John 4:10). We must not begin with mysticism, with the creature's love for God, or with the wonderful foretastes of the fruition of God vouchsafed to some in their earthly life. We begin at the real beginning, with love as the Divine energy. This primal love is Gift-love. In God there is no hunger that needs to be filled, only plenteousness that desires to give. The doctrine that God was under no necessity to create is not a piece of dry scholastic speculation. It is essential. Without it we can hardly avoid the conception of what I can only call a 'managerial' God; a Being whose function or nature is to 'run' the universe, who stands to it as a headmaster to a school or a hotelier to a hotel. But to be sovereign of the universe is no great matter to God. In Himself, at home in 'the land of the Trinity', he is Sovereign of a far greater realm. We must keep always before our eyes that vision of Lady Julian's in which God carried in His hand a little object like a nut, and that nut was 'all that is made'. God, who needs nothing, loves into existence wholly superfluous creatures in order that He may love and perfect them. He creates the universe, already foreseeing – or should we say 'seeing'? there are no tenses in God – the buzzing cloud of flies about the cross, the flayed back pressed against the uneven stake, the nails driven through the mesial nerves, the repeated incipient suffocation as the body droops, the repeated torture of back and arms as it is time after time, for breath's sake, hitched up. If I may dare the biological image, God is a 'host' who deliberately creates His own parasites; causes us to be that we may exploit and 'take advantage of' Him. Herein is love. This is the diagram of Love Himself, the inventor of all loves.

God, as Creator of nature, implants in us both Gift-loves and Need-loves. The Gift-loves are natural images of Himself; proximities to Him by resemblance which are not necessarily and in all men proximities of approach. A devoted mother, a beneficent ruler or teacher, may give and give, continually exhibiting the likeness, without making the approach. The Need-loves, so far as I have been able to see, have no resemblance to the Love which God is. They are rather correlatives, opposites; not as evil is the opposite of good, of course, but as the form of the blancmange is an opposite to the form of the mould.

But in addition to these natural loves God can bestow a far better gift; or rather, since our minds must divide and pigeon-hole, two gifts.

He communicates to men a share of His own Gift-love. This is different from the Gift-loves He has built into their nature. These never quite seek simply the good of the loved object for the object's own sake. They are biased in favour of those goods they can themselves bestow, or those which they would like best themselves, or those which fit in with a pre-conceived picture of the life they want the object to lead. But Divine Gift-love – Love Himself working in a man – is wholly disinterested and desires what is simply best for the beloved. Again, natural Gift-love is always directed to objects which the lover finds in some way intrinsically lovable – objects to which Affection or Eros or a shared point of view attracts him, or, failing that, to the grateful and the deserving, or perhaps to those whose helplessness is of a winning and appealing kind. But Divine Gift-love in the man enables him to love what is not naturally lovable; lepers, criminals, enemies, morons, the sulky, the superior and the sneering. Finally, by a high paradox, God enables men to have a Gift-love towards Himself. There is of course a sense in which no one can give to God anything which is not already His; and if it is already His, what have you given? But since it is only too obvious that we can withhold ourselves, our wills and hearts, from God, we can, in that sense, also give them. What is His by right and would not exist for a moment if it ceased to be His (as the song is the singer's), He has nevertheless made ours in such a way that we can freely offer it back to Him. 'Our wills are ours to make them Thine.' And as all Christians know there is another way of giving to God; every stranger whom we feed or clothe is Christ. And this apparently is Gift-love to God whether we know it or not. Love Himself can work in those who know nothing of Him. The 'sheep' in the parable had no idea either of the God hidden in the prisoner whom they visited or of the God hidden in themselves when they made the visit. (I take the whole parable to be about the judgment of the heathen. For it begins by saying, in the Greek, that the Lord will summon all 'the nations' before Him – presumably, the Gentiles, the *Goyim*.)

That such a Gift-love comes by Grace and should be called Charity, everyone will agree. But I have to add something which will not perhaps be so easily admitted. God, as it seems to me, bestows two other gifts; a supernatural Need-love of Himself and a supernatural Need-love of one another. By the first I do not mean the Appreciative love of Himself, the gift of adoration. What little I have to say on that higher – that highest – subject will come later. I mean a love which does not dream of disinterestedness, a bottomless indigence. Like a river making its own channel, like a magic wine which in being poured out should simultaneously create the glass that was to hold it, God turns our need of Him into Need-love of Him. What is stranger still is that he creates in us a more than natural receptivity of Charity from our fellow men. Need is so near greed and we are so greedy already that it seems a strange grace. But I cannot get it out of my head that this is what happens.

Let us consider first this supernatural Need-love of Himself, bestowed by Grace. Of course the Grace does not create the need. That is there already; 'given' (as the mathematicians say) in the mere fact of our being creatures, and incalculably increased by our being fallen creatures. What the Grace gives is the full recognition, the sensible awareness, the complete acceptance – even, with certain reservations, the glad acceptance – of this Need. For, without Grace, our wishes and our necessities are in conflict.

All those expressions of unworthiness which Christian practice puts into the believer's mouth seem to the outer world like the degraded and insincere grovellings of a sycophant before a tyrant, or at best a *façon de parler* like the self-depreciation of a Chinese gentleman when he calls himself 'this coarse and illiterate person'. In reality, however, they express the continually renewed, because continually necessary, attempt to negate that misconception of ourselves and of our relation to God which nature, even while we pray, is always recommending to us. No sooner do we believe that God loves us than there is an impulse to believe that He does so, not because He is Love, but because we are intrinsically lovable. The Pagans obeyed this impulse unabashed; a good man was 'dear to the gods' because he was good. We, being better taught, resort to subterfuge. Far be it from us to think that we have virtues for which God could love us. But then, how magnificently we have repented! As Bunyan says, describing his first and illusory conversion, 'I thought there was no man in England that pleased God better than I.' Beaten out of this, we next offer our own humility to God's admiration. Surely He'll like *that*? Or if not that, our clear-sighted and humble recognition that we still lack humility. Thus, depth beneath depth and subtlety within subtlety, there remains some lingering idea of our own, our very own, attractiveness. It is easy to acknowledge, but almost impossible to realise for long, that we are mirrors whose brightness, if we are bright, is wholly derived from the sun that shines upon us. Surely we must have a little – however little – native luminosity? Surely we can't be *quite* creatures?

For this tangled absurdity of a Need, even a Need-love, which never fully acknowledges its own neediness, Grace substitutes a full, childlike and delighted acceptance of our Need, a joy in total dependence. We become 'jolly beggars'. The good man is sorry for the sins which have increased his Need. He is not entirely sorry for the fresh Need they have produced. And he is not sorry at all for the innocent Need that is inherent in his creaturely condition. For all the time this illusion to which nature clings as her last treasure, this pretence that we have anything of our own or could for one hour retain by our own strength any goodness that God may pour into us, has kept us from being happy. We have been like bathers who want to keep their feet – or one foot – or one toe – on the bottom, when to lose that foothold would be to surrender themselves to a glorious tumble in the surf. The consequences of parting with our last claim to intrinsic freedom, power, or worth, are real freedom, power and worth, really ours just because God gives them and because we know them to be (in another sense) not 'ours'. Anodos has got rid of his shadow.

But God also transforms our Need-love for one another, and it requires equal transformation. In reality we all need at times, some of us at most times, that Charity from others which, being Love Himself in them, loves the unlovable. But this, though a sort of love we need, is not the sort we want. We want to be loved for our cleverness, beauty, generosity, fairness, usefulness. The first hint that anyone is offering us the highest love of all is a terrible shock. This is so well recognised that spiteful people will pretend to be loving us with Charity precisely because they know that it will wound us. To say to one who expects a renewal of Affection, Friendship, or Eros, 'I forgive you as a Christian' is merely a way of continuing the quarrel. Those who say it are of course lying. But the thing would not be falsely said in order to wound unless, if it were true, it would be wounding.

How difficult it is to receive, and to go on receiving, from others a love that does not depend on our own attraction, can be seen from an extreme case. Suppose yourself a man struck down shortly after marriage by an incurable disease which may not kill you for many years; useless, impotent, hideous, disgusting; depending on your wife's earnings; impoverishing where you hoped to enrich; impaired even in intellect and shaken by gusts of uncontrollable temper, full of unavoidable demands. And suppose your wife's care and pity to be inexhaustible. The man who can take this sweetly, who can receive all and give nothing without resentment, who can abstain even from those tiresome self-depreciations which are really only a demand for petting and reassurance, is doing something which Need-love in its merely natural condition could not attain. (No doubt such a wife will also be doing something beyond the reach of a natural Gift-love, but that is not the point at present.) In such a case to receive is harder and perhaps more blessed than to give. But what the extreme example illustrates is universal. We are all receiving Charity. There is something in each of us that cannot be naturally loved. It is no one's fault if they do not so love it. Only the lovable can be naturally loved. You might as well ask people to like the taste of rotten bread or the sound of a mechanical drill. We can be forgiven, and pitied, and loved in spite of it, with Charity; no other way. All who have good parents, wives, husbands, or children, may be sure that at some times – and perhaps at all times in respect of some one particular trait or habit –

they are receiving Charity, are not loved because they are lovable but because Love Himself is in those who love them.

Thus God, admitted to the human heart, transforms not only Gift-love but Need-love; not only our Need-love of Him, but our Need-love of one another. This is of course not the only thing that can happen. He may come on what seems to us a more dreadful mission and demand that a natural love be totally renounced. A high and terrible vocation, like Abraham's, may constrain a man to turn his back on his own people and his father's house. Eros, directed to a forbidden object, may have to be sacrificed. In such instances, the process, though hard to endure, is easy to understand. What we are more likely to overlook is the necessity for a transformation even when the natural love is allowed to continue.

In such a case the Divine Love does not *substitute* itself for the natural – as if we had to throw away our silver to make room for the gold. The natural loves are summoned to become modes of Charity while also remaining the natural loves they were.

One sees here at once a sort of echo or rhyme or corollary to the Incarnation itself. And this need not surprise us, for the Author of both is the same. As Christ is perfect God and perfect Man, the natural loves are called to become perfect Charity and also perfect natural loves. As God becomes Man 'Not by conversion of the Godhead into flesh, but by taking of the Manhood into God', so here; Charity does not dwindle into merely natural love but natural love is taken up into, made the tuned and obedient instrument of, Love Himself.

How this can happen, most Christians know. All the activities (sins only excepted) of the natural loves can in a favoured hour become works of the glad and shameless and grateful Need-love or of the selfless, unofficious Gift-love, which are both Charity. Nothing is either too trivial or too animal to be thus transformed. A game, a joke, a drink together, idle chat, a walk, the act of Venus – all these can be modes in which we forgive or accept forgiveness, in which we console or are reconciled, in which we 'seek not our own'. Thus in our very instincts, appetites and recreations, Love has prepared for Himself 'a body'.

But I said 'in a favoured hour'. Hours soon pass. The total and secure transformation of a natural love into a mode of Charity is a work so difficult that perhaps no fallen man has ever come within sight of doing it perfectly. Yet the law that loves must be so transformed is, I suppose, inexorable.

One difficulty is that here, as usual, we can take a wrong turn. A Christian – a somewhat too vocally Christian – circle or family, having grasped this principle, can make a show, in their overt behaviour and especially in their words, of having achieved the thing itself – an elaborate, fussy, embarrassing and intolerable show. Such people make every trifle a matter of explicitly spiritual importance – out loud and to one another (to God, on their knees, behind a closed door, it would be another matter). They are always unnecessarily asking, or insufferably offering, forgiveness. Who would not rather live with those ordinary people who get over their tantrums (and ours) unemphatically, letting a meal, a night's sleep, or a joke mend all? The real work must be, of all our works, the most secret. Even as far as possible secret from ourselves. Our right hand must not know what our left is doing. We have not got far enough if we play a game of cards with the children 'merely' to amuse them or to show that they are forgiven. If this is the best we can do we are right to do it. But it would be better if a deeper, less conscious, Charity threw us into a frame of mind in which a little fun with the children was the thing we should at that moment like best.

We are, however, much helped in this necessary work by that very feature of our experience at which we most repine. The invitation to turn our natural loves into Charity is never lacking. It is provided by those frictions and frustrations that meet us in all of them; unmistakable evidence that (natural) love is not going to be 'enough' – unmistakable, unless we are blinded by egotism. When we are, we use them absurdly. 'If only I had been more fortunate in my children (that boy gets more like his father every day) I could have loved them perfectly.' But every child is sometimes infuriating; most children are not infrequently odious. 'If only my husband were more considerate, less lazy, less extravagant' ... 'If only my wife had fewer moods and more sense, and were less extravagant' ... 'If my father wasn't so infernally prosy and close-fisted.' But in everyone, and of course in ourselves, there is that which requires forbearance, tolerance, forgiveness. The necessity of practising these virtues first sets us, forces us, upon the attempt to turn – more strictly, to let God turn – our love into Charity. These frets and rubs are beneficial. It may even be that where there are fewest of them the conversion of natural love is most difficult. When they are plentiful the necessity of rising above it is obvious. To rise above it when it is as fully satisfied and as little impeded as earthly conditions allow – to see that we must rise when all seems so well already – this may require a subtler conversion and a more delicate insight. In this way also it may be hard for 'the rich' to enter the Kingdom.

And yet, I believe, the necessity for the conversion is inexorable; at least, if our natural loves are to enter the heavenly life. That they can enter it most of us in fact believe. We may hope that the resurrection of the body means also the resurrection of what may be called our 'greater body'; the general fabric of our earthly life with its affections and relationships. But only on a condition; not a condition arbitrarily laid down by God, but one necessarily inherent in the character of Heaven: nothing can enter there which cannot become heavenly. 'Flesh and blood', mere nature, cannot inherit that

Kingdom. Man can ascend to Heaven only because the Christ, who died and ascended to Heaven, is 'formed in him'. Must we not suppose that the same is true of a man's loves? Only those into which Love Himself has entered will ascend to Love Himself. And these can be raised with Him only if they have, in some degree and fashion, shared His death; if the natural element in them has submitted – year after year, or in some sudden agony – to transmutation. The fashion of this world passes away. The very name of nature implies the transitory. Natural loves can hope for eternity only in so far as they have allowed themselves to be taken into the eternity of Charity; have at least allowed the process to begin here on earth, before the night comes when no man can work. And the process will always involve a kind of death. There is no escape. In my love for wife or friend the only eternal element is the transforming presence of Love Himself. By that presence, if at all, the other elements may hope, as our physical bodies hope, to be raised from the dead. For this only is holy in them, this only is the Lord.

Theologians have sometimes asked whether we shall 'know one another' in Heaven, and whether the particular love-relations worked out on earth would then continue to have any significance. It seems reasonable to reply: 'It may depend what kind of love it had become, or was becoming, on earth.' For, surely, to meet in the eternal world someone for whom your love in this, however strong, had been merely natural, would not be (on that ground) even interesting. Would it not be like meeting in adult life someone who had seemed to be a great friend at your preparatory school solely because of common interests and occupations? If there was nothing more, if he was not a kindred soul, he will now be a total stranger. Neither of you now plays conkers. You no longer want to swop your help with his French exercise for his help with your arithmetic. In Heaven, I suspect, a love that had never embodied Love Himself would be equally irrelevant. For Nature has passed away. All that is not eternal is eternally out of date.

But I must not end on this note, I dare not – and all the less because longings and terrors of my own prompt me to do so – leave any bereaved and desolate reader confirmed in the widespread illusion that reunion with the loved dead is the goal of the Christian life. The denial of this may sound harsh and unreal in the ears of the broken hearted, but it must be denied.

'Thou hast made us for thyself,' said St Augustine, 'and our heart has no rest till it comes to Thee.' This, so easy to believe for a brief moment before the altar or, perhaps, half-praying, half-meditating in an April wood, sounds like mockery beside a deathbed. But we shall be far more truly mocked if, casting this away, we pin our comfort on the hope – perhaps even with the aid of *séance* and necromancy – of some day, this time forever, enjoying the earthly Beloved again, and no more. It is hard not to imagine that such an endless prolongation of earthly happiness would be completely satisfying.

But, if I may trust my own experience, we get at once a sharp warning that there is something wrong. The moment we attempt to use our faith in the other world for this purpose, that faith weakens. The moments in my life when it was really strong have all been moments when God Himself was central in my thoughts. Believing in Him, I could then believe in Heaven as a corollary. But the reverse process – believing first in reunion with the Beloved, and then, for the sake of that reunion, believing in Heaven, and finally, for the sake of Heaven, believing in God – this will not work. One can of course imagine things. But a self-critical person will soon be increasingly aware that the imagination at work is his own; he knows he is only weaving a fantasy. And simpler souls will find the phantoms they try to feed on void of all comfort and nourishment, only to be stimulated into some semblance of reality by pitiful efforts of self-hypnotism, and perhaps by the aid of ignoble pictures and hymns and (what is worse) witches.

We find thus by experience that there is no good applying to Heaven for earthly comfort. Heaven can give heavenly comfort; no other kind. And earth cannot give earthly comfort either. There is no earthly comfort in the long run.

For the dream of finding our end, the thing we were made for, in a Heaven of purely human love could not be true unless our whole Faith were wrong. We were made for God. Only by being in some respect like Him, only by being a manifestation of His beauty, lovingkindness, wisdom or goodness, has any earthly Beloved excited our love. It is not that we have loved them too much, but that we did not quite understand what we were loving. It is not that we shall be asked to turn from them, so dearly familiar, to a Stranger. When we see the face of God we shall know that we have always known it. He has been a party to, has made, sustained and moved moment by moment within, all our earthly experiences of innocent love. All that was true love in them was, even on earth, far more His than ours, and ours only because His. In Heaven there will be no anguish and no duty of turning away from our earthly Beloved. First, because we shall have turned already; from the portraits to the Original, from the rivulets to the Fountain, from the creatures He made lovable to Love Himself. But secondly, because we shall find them all in Him. By loving Him more than them we shall love them more than we now do.

But all that is far away in 'the land of the Trinity', not here in exile, in the weeping valley. Down here it is all loss and renunciation. The very purpose of the bereavement (so far as it affects ourselves) may have been to force this upon us. We are then compelled to try to believe, what we cannot yet feel, that God is our true Beloved. That is why bereavement is in some ways easier for the unbeliever than for us. He can storm and rage and shake his fist at the universe, and (if he is a genius) write poems like Housman's or Hardy's. But we, at our lowest ebb, when the least effort seems too much for us, must begin to attempt what seem impossibilities.

'Is it easy to love God?' asks an old author. 'It is easy,' he replies, 'to those who do it.' I have included two Graces under the word Charity. But God can give a third. He can awake in man, towards Himself, a supernatural Appreciative Love. This is of all gifts the most to be desired. Here, not in our natural loves, nor even in ethics, lies the true centre of all human and angelic life. With this all things are possible.

And with this, where a better book would begin, mine must end. I dare not proceed. God knows, not I, whether I have ever tasted this love. Perhaps I have only imagined the tasting. Those like myself whose imagination far exceeds their obedience are subject to a just penalty; we easily imagine conditions far higher than any we have really reached. If we describe what we have imagined we may make others, and make ourselves, believe that we have really been there. And if I have only imagined it, is it a further delusion that even the imagining has at some moments made all other objects of desire – yes, even peace, even to have no more fears – look like broken toys and faded flowers? Perhaps. Perhaps, for many of us, all experience merely defines, so to speak, the shape of that gap where our love of God ought to be. It is not enough. It is something. If we cannot 'practise the presence of God', it is something to practise the absence of God, to become increasingly aware of our unawareness till we feel like men who should stand beside a great cataract and hear no noise, or like a man in a story who looks in a mirror and finds no face there, or a man in a dream who stretches out his hand to visible objects and gets no sensation of touch. To know that one is dreaming is to be no longer perfectly asleep. But for news of the fully waking world you must go to my betters.

THE PILGRIM'S REGRESS

An allegorical apology
for Christianity,
Reason and Romanticism

As cold waters to a thirsty soul,
so is good news from a far country.
PROVERBS

MAPPA MUNDI

SENSIBLE

BROAD

Shires

I	Puritania	XI	Zeitgeistheim
II	Carimonia	XII	Crudsland
III	Orgiastica	XIII	Pagus
IV	Quietismus	XIV	Hegeliana
V	Behmenheim	XV	Anthroposophia
VI	Glamaria	XVI	Wisland
VII	Occultica	XVII	Naughtstow
VIII	Goinesshire	XVIII	Dialectica
IX	Trineland	XIX	The Tableland
X	Aesthetica		

To Arthur Greeves

PREFACE TO THE

THIRD EDITION

On re-reading this book ten years after I wrote it, I find its chief faults to be those two which I myself least easily forgive in the books of other men: needless obscurity, and an uncharitable temper.

There were two causes, I now realise, for the obscurity. On the intellectual side my own progress had been from 'popular realism' to Philosophical Idealism; from Idealism to Pantheism; from Pantheism to Theism; and from Theism to Christianity. I still think this a very natural road, but I now know that it is a road very rarely trodden. In the early thirties I did not know this. If I had had any notion of my own isolation, I should either have kept silent about my journey or else endeavoured to describe it with more consideration for the reader's difficulties. As things were, I committed the same sort of blunder as one who should narrate his travels through the Gobi Desert on the assumption that this route was as familiar to the British public as the line from Euston to Crewe. And this original blunder was soon aggravated by a profound change in the philosophical thought of our age. Idealism itself went out of fashion. The dynasty of Green, Bradley, and Bosanquet fell, and the world inhabited by philosophical students of my own generation became as alien to our successors as if not years but centuries had intervened.

The second cause of obscurity was the (unintentionally) 'private' meaning I then gave to the word 'Romanticism'. I would not now use this word to describe the experience which is central in this book. I would not, indeed, use it to describe anything, for I now believe it to be a word of such varying senses that it has become useless and should be banished from our vocabulary. Even if we exclude the vulgar sense in which a 'romance' means simply 'a love affair' (Peer and Film Star Romance) I think we can distinguish at least seven kinds of things which are called 'romantic'.

1. Stories about dangerous adventure – particularly, dangerous adventure in the past or in remote places – are 'romantic'. In this sense Dumas is a typically 'romantic' author, and stories about sailing ships, the Foreign Legion, and the rebellion of 1745, are usually 'romantic'.

2. The marvellous is 'romantic', provided it does not make part of the believed religion. Thus magicians, ghosts, fairies, witches, dragons, nymphs, and dwarfs are 'romantic'; angels, less so. Greek gods are 'romantic' in Mr James Stephens or Mr Maurice Hewlett; not so in Homer and Sophocles. In this sense Malory, Boiardo, Ariosto, Spenser, Tasso, Mrs Radcliffe, Shelley, Coleridge, William Morris, and Mr E. R. Eddison are 'romantic' authors.

3. The art dealing with 'Titanic' characters, emotions strained beyond the common pitch, and high-flown sentiments or codes of honour is 'romantic'. (I welcome the growing use of the word 'Romanesque' to describe this type.) In this sense Rostand and Sidney are 'romantic', and so (though unsuccessfully) are Dryden's Heroic Dramas, and there is a good deal of 'romanticism' in Corneille. I take it that Michelangelo is, in this sense, a 'romantic' artist.

4. 'Romanticism' can also mean the indulgence in abnormal, and finally in anti-natural, moods. The macabre is 'romantic', and so is an interest in torture, and a love of death. This, if I understand them, is what M. Mario Praz and M. D. de Rougemont would mean by the word. In this sense *Tristan* is Wagner's most 'romantic' opera; Poe, Baudelaire, and Flaubert, are 'romantic' authors; Surrealism is 'romantic'.

5. Egoism and Subjectivism are 'romantic'. In this sense the typically 'romantic' books are *Werther* and Rousseau's *Confessions*, and the works of Byron and Proust.

6. Every revolt against existing civilisation and conventions whether it looks forward to revolution, or backward to the 'primitive' is called 'romantic' by some people. Thus pseudo-Ossian, Epstein, D. H. Lawrence, Walt Whitman, and Wagner are 'romantic'.

7. Sensibility to natural objects, when solemn and enthusiastic, is 'romantic'. In this sense *The Prelude* is the most 'romantic' poem in the world: and there is much 'romanticism' in Keats, Shelley, de Vigny, de Musset, and Goethe.

It will be seen, of course, that many writers are 'romantic' on more than one account. Thus Morris comes in my first class as well as my second, Mr Eddison in my second as well as my third, Rousseau in my sixth as well as my fifth, Shelley in my sixth and fifth, and so on. This may suggest some common root, whether historical or psychological, for all seven: but the real qualitative difference between them is shown by the fact that a liking for any one does not imply liking for the others. Though people who are 'romantic' in different senses may turn to the same books, they turn to them for different reasons and one half of William Morris's readers do not know how the other half live. It makes all the difference in the world whether you like Shelley because he provides a mythology or because he promises a revolution. Thus I myself always loved the second kind of

Romanticism and detested the fourth and fifth kinds; I liked the first very little and the third only after I was grown-up – as an acquired taste.

But what I meant by 'Romanticism' when I wrote *The Pilgrim's Regress* – and what I would still be taken to mean on the title page of this book – was not exactly any one of these seven things. What I meant was a particular recurrent experience which dominated my childhood and adolescence and which I hastily called 'Romantic' because inanimate nature and marvellous literature were among the things that evoked it. I still believe that the experience is common, commonly misunderstood, and of immense importance: but I know now that in other minds it arises under other *stimuli* and is entangled with other irrelevancies and that to bring it into the forefront of consciousness is not so easy as I once supposed. I will now try to describe it sufficiently to make the following pages intelligible.

The experience is one of intense longing. It is distinguished from other longings by two things. In the first place, though the sense of want is acute and even painful, yet the mere wanting is felt to be somehow a delight. Other desires are felt as pleasures only if satisfaction is expected in the near future: hunger is pleasant only while we know (or believe) that we are soon going to eat. But this desire, even when there is no hope of possible satisfaction, continues to be prized, and even to be preferred to anything else in the world, by those who have once felt it. This hunger is better than any other fullness; this poverty better than all other wealth. And thus it comes about, that if the desire is long absent, it may itself be desired, and that new desiring becomes a new instance of the original desire, though the subject may not at once recognise the fact and thus cries out for his lost youth of soul at the very moment in which he is being rejuvenated. This sounds complicated, but it is simple when we live it. 'Oh to feel as I did then!' we cry; not noticing that even while we say the words the very feeling whose loss we lament is rising again in all its old bitter-sweetness. For this sweet Desire cuts across our ordinary distinctions between wanting and having. To have it is, by definition, a want: to want it, we find, is to have it.

In the second place, there is a peculiar mystery about the *object* of this Desire. Inexperienced people (and inattention leaves some inexperienced all their lives) suppose, when they feel it, that they know what they are desiring. Thus if it comes to a child while he is looking at a far off hillside he at once thinks 'if only I were there'; if it comes when he is remembering some event in the past, he thinks 'if only I could go back to those days'. If it comes (a little later) while he is reading a 'romantic' tale or poem of 'perilous seas and faerie lands forlorn', he thinks he is wishing that such places really existed and that he could reach them. If it comes (later still) in a context with erotic suggestions he believes he is desiring the perfect beloved. If he falls upon literature (like Maeterlinck or the early Yeats) which treats of spirits and the like with some show of serious belief, he may think that he is hankering for real magic and occultism. When it darts out upon him from his studies in history or science, he may confuse it with the intellectual craving for knowledge.

But every one of these impressions is wrong. The sole merit I claim for this book is that it is written by one who has proved them all to be wrong. There is no room for vanity in the claim: I know them to be wrong not by intelligence but by experience, such experience as would not have come my way if my youth had been wiser, more virtuous, and less self-centred than it was. For I have myself been deluded by every one of these false answers in turn, and have contemplated each of them earnestly enough to discover the cheat. To have embraced so many false Florimels is no matter for boasting: it is fools, they say, who learn by experience. But since they do at last learn, let a fool bring his experience into the common stock that wiser men may profit by it.

Every one of these supposed *objects* for the Desire is inadequate to it. An easy experiment will show that by going to the far hillside you will get either nothing, or else a recurrence of the same desire which sent you thither. A rather more difficult, but still possible, study of your own memories, will prove that by returning to the past you could not find, as a possession, that ecstasy which some sudden reminder of the past now moves you to desire. Those remembered moments were either quite commonplace at the time (and owe all their enchantment to memory) or else were themselves moments of desiring. The same is true of the things described in the poets and marvellous romancers. The moment we endeavour to think out seriously what it would be like if they were actual, we discover this. When Sir Arthur Conan Doyle claimed to have photographed a fairy, I did not, in fact, believe it: but the mere making of the claim – the approach of the fairy to within even that hailing distance of actuality – revealed to me at once that if the claim had succeeded it would have chilled rather than satisfied the desire which fairy literature had hitherto aroused. Once grant your fairy, your enchanted forest, your satyr, faun, wood-nymph and well of immortality *real*, and amidst all the scientific, social and practical interest which the discovery would awake, the Sweet Desire would have disappeared, would have shifted its ground, like the cuckoo's voice or the rainbow's end, and be now calling us from beyond a *further* hill. With Magic in the darker sense (as it has been and is actually practised) we should fare even worse. How if one had gone that way – had actually called for something and it had come? What would one feel? Terror, pride, guilt, tingling excitement ... but what would all that have to do with our Sweet Desire? It is not at Black Mass or seance that the Blue Flower grows. As for the sexual answer, that I suppose to be the most obviously false Florimel of all. On whatever plane you take it, it is not what we were looking for. Lust can be gratified. Another personality can become to us 'our America, our New-found-land'. A happy marriage can be achieved. But what has any of the three, or any mixture of the three, to do with that unnameable something, desire for which pierces us like a rapier at the smell of a bonfire, the sound of wild ducks flying overhead, the title of *The Well at the World's End*, the opening lines of *Kubla Khan*, the morning cobwebs in late summer, or the noise of falling waves?

It appeared to me therefore that if a man diligently followed this desire, pursuing the false objects until their falsity appeared and then resolutely abandoning them, he must come out at last into the clear knowledge that the human soul was made to enjoy some object that is never fully given – nay, cannot even be imagined as given – in our present mode of subjective and spatio-temporal experience. This Desire was, in the soul, as the Siege Perilous in Arthur's castle – the chair in which only one could sit. And if nature makes nothing in vain, the One who can sit in this chair must exist. I knew only too well how easily the longing accepts false objects and through what dark ways the pursuit of them leads us: but I also saw that the Desire itself contains the corrective of all these errors. The only fatal error was to pretend that you had passed from desire to fruition, when, in reality, you had found either nothing, or desire itself, or the satisfaction of some different desire. The dialectic of Desire, faithfully followed, would retrieve all mistakes, head you off from all false paths, and force you not to propound, but to live through, a sort of ontological proof. This lived dialectic, and the merely argued dialectic of my philosophical progress, seemed to have converged on one goal; accordingly I tried to put them both into my allegory which thus became a defence of Romanticism (in my peculiar sense) as well as of Reason and Christianity.

After this explanation the reader will more easily understand (I do not ask him to condone) the bitterness of certain pages in this book. He will realise how the Post-War period must have looked to one who had followed such a road as mine. The different intellectual movements of that time were hostile to one another; but the one thing that seemed to unite them all was their common enmity to 'immortal longings'. The direct attack carried out on them from below by those who followed Freud or D. H. Lawrence, I think I could have borne with some temper; what put me out of patience was the scorn which claimed to be from above, and which was voiced by the American 'Humanists', the Neo-Scholastics, and some who wrote for *The Criterion*. These people seemed to me to be condemning what they did not understand. When they called Romanticism 'nostalgia' I, who had rejected long ago the illusion that the desired object was in the past, felt that they had not even crossed the *Pons Asinorum*. In the end I lost my temper.

If I were now writing a book I could bring the question between those thinkers and myself to a much finer point. One of them described Romanticism as 'spilled religion'. I accept the description. And I agree that he who has religion ought not to spill it. But does it follow that he who finds it spilled should avert his eyes? How if there is a man to whom those bright drops on the floor are the beginning of a trail which, duly followed, will lead him in the end to taste the cup itself? How if no other trail, humanly speaking, were possible? Seen in this light my ten-years-old quarrel both with the counter-Romantics on the one hand and with the sub-Romantics on the other (the apostles of instinct and even of gibberish) assumes, I trust, a certain permanent interest. Out of this double quarrel came the dominant image of my allegory – the barren, aching rocks of its 'North', the foetid swamps of its 'South', and between them the Road on which alone mankind can safely walk.

The things I have symbolised by North and South, which are to me equal and opposite evils, each continually strengthened and made plausible by its critique of the other, enter our experience on many different levels. In agriculture we have to fear both the barren soil and the soil which is irresistibly fertile. In the animal kingdom, the crustacean and the jellyfish represent two low solutions of the problem of existence. In our eating, the palate revolts both from excessive bitter and excessive sweet. In art, we find on the one hand, purists and doctrinaires, who would rather (like Scaliger) lose a hundred beauties than admit a single fault, and who cannot believe anything to be good if the unlearned spontaneously enjoy it: on the other hand, we find the uncritical and slovenly artists who will spoil the whole work rather than deny themselves any indulgence of sentiment or humour or sensationalism. Everyone can pick out among his own acquaintance the Northern and Southern types – the high noses, compressed lips, pale complexions, dryness and taciturnity of the one, the open mouths, the facile laughter and tears, the garrulity and (so to speak) general greasiness of the others. The Northerners are the men of rigid systems whether sceptical or dogmatic, Aristocrats, Stoics, Pharisees, Rigorists, signed and sealed members of highly organised 'Parties'. The Southerners are by their very nature less definable; boneless souls whose doors stand open day and night to almost every visitant, but always with readiest welcome for those, whether Maenad or Mystagogue, who offer some sort of intoxication. The delicious tang of the forbidden and the unknown draws them on with fatal attraction; the smudging of all frontiers, the relaxation of all resistances, dream, opium, darkness, death, and the return to the womb. Every feeling is justified by the mere fact that it is felt: for a Northerner, every feeling on the same ground is suspect. An arrogant and hasty selectiveness on some narrow *a priori* basis cuts him off from the sources of life. In Theology also there is a North and South. The one cries 'Drive out the bondmaid's son', and the other 'Quench not the smoking flax'. The one exaggerates the distinctness between Grace and Nature into a sheer opposition and by vilifying the higher levels of Nature (the real *praeparatio evangelica* inherent in certain immediately sub-Christian experiences) makes the way hard for those who are at the point of coming in. The other blurs the distinction altogether, flatters mere kindliness into thinking it is charity and vague optimisms or pantheisms into thinking that they are Faith, and makes the way out fatally easy and imperceptible for the budding apostate. The two extremes do not coincide with Romanism (to the North) and Protestantism (to the South). Barth might well have been placed among my Pale Men, and Erasmus might have found himself at home with Mr Broad.

I take our own age to be predominantly Northern – it is two great 'Northern' powers that are tearing each other to pieces on the Don while I write. But the matter is complicated, for the rigid and ruthless system of the Nazis has 'Southern' and swamp-like elements at its centre: and when our age is 'Southern' at all, it is excessively so. D. H. Lawrence and the Surrealists have perhaps reached a point further 'South' than humanity ever reached before. And this is what one would expect. Opposite evils, far from balancing, aggravate each other. 'The heresies that men leave are hated most'; widespread drunkenness is the father of Prohibition and Prohibition of widespread drunkenness. Nature, outraged by one extreme, avenges herself by flying to the other. One can even meet adult males who are not ashamed to attribute their own philosophy to 'Reaction' and do not think the philosophy thereby discredited.

With both the 'North' and the 'South' a man has, I take it, only one concern – to avoid them and hold the Main Road. We must not 'hearken to the over-wise or to the over-foolish giant'. We were made to be neither cerebral men nor visceral men, but Men. Not beasts nor angels but Men – things at once rational and animal.

The fact that, if I say anything in explanation of my North and South, I have to say so much, serves to underline a rather important truth about symbols. In the present edition I have tried to make the book easier by a running headline. But I do so with great reluctance. To supply a 'key' to an allegory may encourage that particular misunderstanding of allegory which, as a literary critic, I have elsewhere denounced. It may encourage people to suppose that allegory is a disguise, a way of saying obscurely what could have been said more clearly. But in fact all good allegory exists not to hide but to reveal; to make the inner world more palpable by giving it an (imagined) concrete embodiment. My headline is there only because my allegory failed – partly through my own fault (I am now heartily ashamed of the preposterous allegorical filigree on p.199), and partly because modern readers are unfamiliar with the method. But it remains true that wherever the symbols are best, the key is least adequate. For when allegory is at its best, it approaches myth, which must be grasped with the imagination, not with the intellect. If, as I still sometimes hope, my North and South and my Mr Sensible have some touch of mythical life, then no amount of 'explanation' will quite catch up with their meaning. It is the sort of thing you cannot learn from definition: you must rather get to know it as you get to know a smell or a taste, the 'atmosphere' of a family or a country town, or the personality of an individual.

Three other cautions remain to be given. 1. The map on the end leaves has puzzled some readers because, as they say, 'it marks all sorts of places not mentioned in the text'. But so do all maps in travel books. John's route is marked with a dotted line: those who are not interested in the places off that route need not bother about them. They are a half whimsical attempt to fill in the 'Northern' and 'Southern' halves of the world with the spiritual phenomena appropriate to them. Most of the names explain themselves. *Wanhope* is Middle English for Despair; *Woodey* and *Lyssanesos* mean 'Isle of Insanity'; *Behmenheim* is named, unfairly, after Jakob Boehme or Behmen; *Golnesshire* (Anglo-Saxon *Gál*) is the county of Lechery; in *Trine*land one feels 'in tune with the infinite'; and *Zeitgeistheim*, of course, is the habitat of the *Zeitgeist* or Spirit of the Age. *Naughtstow* is 'a place that is no good at all'. The two military railways were meant to symbolise the double attack from Hell on the two sides of our nature. It was hoped that the roads spreading out from each of the enemy railheads would look rather like claws or tentacles reaching out into the country of Man's Soul. If you like to put little black arrows pointing South on the seven Northern roads (in the fashion of the newspaper war maps) and others pointing North on the six southern roads, you would get a clear picture of the Holy War as I see it. You might amuse yourself by deciding where to put them – a question that admits different answers. On the Northern front, for example, I should represent the enemy in occupation of Cruelsland and Superbia, and thus threatening the Pale Men with a pincer movement. But I don't claim to know; and doubtless the position shifts every day. 2. The name *Mother Kirk* was chosen because 'Christianity' is not a very convincing name. Its defect was that it not unnaturally led the reader to attribute to me a much more definite *Ecclesiastical* position than I could really boast of. The book is concerned solely with Christianity as against unbelief. 'Denominational' questions do not come in. 3. In this preface the autobiographical element in John has had to be stressed because the source of the obscurities lay there. But you must not assume that everything in the book is autobiographical. I was attempting to generalise, not to tell people about my own life.

C. S. LEWIS

Contents

BOOK 7 – SOUTHWARD ALONG THE CANYON

BOOK 8 – AT BAY

BOOK I

THE DATA

*This every soul seeketh and for the sake of
this doth all her actions, having an inkling
that it is; but what it is she cannot sufficiently
discern, and she knoweth not her way, and
concerning this she hath no constant assurance
as she hath of other things.*

PLATO

*Whose souls, albeit in a cloudy memory, yet
seek back their good, but, like drunk men,
know not the road home.*

BOETHIUS

*Somewhat it seeketh, and what that is
directly it knoweth not, yet very intentive
desire thereof doth so incite it, that all other
known delights and pleasures are laid aside,
they give place to the search of this but only
suspected desire.*

HOOKER

THE RULES

*Knowledge of broken law precedes all other
religious experiences – John receives his first
religious instruction –
Did the instructors really mean it?*

I dreamed of a boy who was born in the land of Puritania and his name was John. And I dreamed that when John was able to walk he ran out of his parents' garden on a fine morning on to the road. And on the other side of the road there was a deep wood, but not thick, full of primroses and soft green moss. When John set eyes on this he thought he had never seen anything so beautiful: and he ran across the road and into the wood, and was just about to go down on his hands and knees and to pull up the primroses by handfuls, when his mother came running out of the garden gate, and she also ran across the road, and caught John up, and smacked him soundly and told him he must never go into the wood again. And John cried, but he asked no questions, for he was not yet at the age for asking questions. Then a year went past. And then, another fine morning, John had a little sling and he went out into the garden and he saw a bird sitting on a branch. And John got his sling ready and was going to have a shot at the bird, when the cook came running out of the garden and caught John up and smacked him soundly and told him he must never kill any of the birds in the garden.

'Why?' said John.

'Because the Steward would be very angry,' said cook.

'Who is the Steward?' said John.

'He is the man who makes rules for all the country round here,' said cook.

'Why?' said John.

'Because the Landlord set him to do it.'

'Who is the Landlord?' said John.

'He owns all the country,' said the cook.

'Why?' said John.

And when he asked this, the cook went and told his mother. And his mother sat down and talked to John about the Landlord all afternoon: but John took none of it in, for he was not yet at the age for taking it in. Then a year went past, and one dark, cold, wet morning John was made to put on new clothes. They were the ugliest clothes that had ever been put upon him, which John did not mind at all, but they also caught him under the chin, and were tight under the arms, which he minded a great deal, and they made him itch all over. And his father and mother took him out along the road, one holding him by each hand (which was uncomfortable, too, and very unnecessary), and told him they were taking him to see the Steward. The Steward lived in a big dark house of stone on the side of the road. The father and mother went in to talk to the Steward first, and John was left sitting in the hall on a chair so high that his feet did not reach the floor. There were other chairs in the hall where he could have sat in comfort, but his father had told him that the Steward would be very angry if he did not sit absolutely still and be very good: and John was beginning to be afraid, so he sat still in the high chair with his feet dangling, and his clothes itching all over him, and his eyes starting out of his head. After a very long time his parents came back again, looking as if they had been with the doctor, very grave. Then they said that John must go in and see the Steward too. And when John came into the room, there was an old man with a red, round face, who was very kind and full of jokes, so that John quite got over his fears, and they had a good talk about fishing tackle and bicycles. But just when the talk was at its best, the Steward got up and cleared his throat. He then took down a mask from the wall with a long white beard attached to it and suddenly clapped it on his face, so that his appearance was awful. And he said, 'Now I am going to talk to you about the Landlord. The Landlord owns all the country, and it is *very, very* kind of him to allow us to live on it at all – very, very kind.' He went on repeating 'very kind' in a queer sing-song voice so long that John would have laughed, but that now he was beginning to be frightened again. The Steward then took down from a peg a big card with small print all over it, and said, 'Here is a list of all the things the Landlord says you must not do. You'd better look at it.' So John took the card: but half the rules seemed to forbid things he had never heard of, and the other half forbade things he was doing every day and could not imagine not doing: and the number of the rules was so enormous that he felt he could never remember them all. 'I hope,' said the Steward, 'that you have not already broken any of the rules?' John's heart began to thump, and his eyes bulged more and more, and he was at his wit's end when the Steward took the mask off and looked at John with his real face and said, 'Better tell a lie, old chap, better tell a lie. Easiest for all concerned,' and popped the mask on his face all in a flash. John gulped and said quickly, 'Oh, no, sir.' 'That is just as well,' said the steward through the mask. 'Because, you know, if you did break any of them and the Landlord got to know of it, do you know what he'd do to you?' 'No, sir,' said John: and the Steward's eyes seemed to be twinkling dreadfully through the holes of the mask. 'He'd take you and shut you up for ever and ever in a black hole full of snakes and scorpions as large as lobsters – for ever and ever. And besides that, he is such a kind, good man, so very, very kind, that I am sure you would never *want* to displease him.' 'No, sir,' said John. 'But, please, sir ...' 'Well,' said the Steward. 'Please, sir, supposing I did break one, one little one, just by accident, you know. Could nothing stop the snakes and lobsters?' 'Ah!...' said the Steward; and then he sat down and talked for a long time, but John could not understand a single syllable. However, it all ended with pointing out that the Landlord was quite extraordinarily kind and good to his tenants, and would certainly torture most of them to death the moment he had the slightest pretext. 'And you can't blame him,' said the Steward. 'For after all, it *is* his land, and it is so very good of him to let us live here at all – people like us, you know.' Then the Steward took off the mask and had a nice, sensible chat with John again, and gave him a cake and brought him out to his father and mother. But just as they were going he bent down and whispered in John's ear, 'I shouldn't bother about it all too much if I were you.' At the same time he slipped the card of the rules into John's hand and told him he could keep it for his own use.

2

THE ISLAND

He is more serious than the instructors: and
discovers the other Law in his members – He
awakes to Sweet Desire; and almost at once
mixes his own fantasies with it

Now the days and the weeks went on again, and I dreamed that John had little peace either by day or night for thinking of the rules and the black hole full of snakes. At first he tried very hard to keep them all, but when it came to bedtime he always found that he had broken far more than he had kept: and the thought of the horrible tortures to which the good, kind Landlord would put him became such a burden that next day he would become quite reckless and break as many as he possibly could; for oddly enough this eased his mind for the moment. But then after a few days the fear would return and this time it would be worse than before because of the dreadful number of rules that he had broken during the interval. But what puzzled him most at this time was a discovery which he made after the rules had been hanging in his bedroom for two or three nights: namely, that on the other side of the card, on the back, there was quite a different set of rules. There were so many that he never read them all through and he was always finding new ones. Some of them were very like the rules on the front of the card, but most of them were just the opposite. Thus whereas the front of the card said that you must be always examining yourself to see how many rules you had broken, the back of the card began like this:

Rule 1
   Put the whole thing out of your head
   The moment you get into bed.

Or again, whereas the front said that you must always go and ask your elders what the rule about a certain thing was, if you were in the least doubt, the back said:

Rule 2
   Unless they saw you do it,
   Keep quiet or else you'll rue it.

And so on. And now I dreamed that John went out one morning and tried to play in the road and to forget his troubles; but the rules kept coming back into his head so that he did not make much of it. However, he went on always a few yards further till suddenly he looked up and saw that he was so far away from home that he was in a part of the road he had never seen before. Then came the sound of a musical instrument, from behind it seemed, very sweet and very short, as if it were one plucking of a string or one note of a bell, and after it a full, clear voice – and it sounded so high and strange that he thought it was very far away, further than a star. The voice said, Come. Then John saw that there was a stone wall beside the road in that part: but it had (what he had never seen in a garden wall before) a window. There was no glass in the window and no bars; it was just a square hole in the wall. Through it he saw a green wood full of primroses: and he remembered suddenly how he had gone into another wood to pull primroses, as a child, very long ago – so long that even in the moment of remembering the memory seemed still out of reach. While he strained to grasp it, there came to him from beyond the wood a sweetness and a pang so piercing that instantly he forgot his father's house, and his mother, and the fear of the Landlord, and the burden of the rules. All the furniture of his mind was taken away. A moment later he found that he was sobbing, and the sun had gone in: and what it was that had happened to him he could not quite remember, nor whether it had happened in this wood, or in the other wood when he was a child. It seemed to him that a mist which hung at the far end of the wood had parted for a moment, and through the rift he had seen a calm sea, and in the sea an island, where the smooth turf sloped down unbroken to the bays, and out of the thickets peeped the pale, small-breasted Oreads, wise like gods, unconscious of themselves like beasts, and tall enchanters, bearded to their feet, sat in green chairs among the forests. But even while he pictured these things he knew, with one part of his mind, that they were not like the things he had seen – nay, that what had befallen him was not seeing at all. But he was too young to heed the distinction: and too empty, now that the unbounded sweetness passed away, not to seize greedily whatever it had left behind. He had no inclination yet to go into the wood: and presently he went home, with a sad excitement upon him, repeating to himself a thousand times, 'I know now what I want'. The first time that he said it, he was aware that it was not entirely true: but before he went to bed he was believing it.

3

THE EASTERN MOUNTAINS

He hears of Death and what his elders
pretend to believe about it – An
uncomfortable funeral, lacking both Pagan
fortitude and Christian hope – Everyone
except John cheers up on the way home

John had a disreputable old uncle who was the tenant of a poor little farm beside his father's. One day when John came in from the garden, he found a great hubbub in the house. His uncle was sitting there with his cheeks the colour of ashes. His mother was crying. His father was sitting very still with a solemn face. And there, in the midst of them, was the Steward with his mask on. John crept round to his mother and asked her what the matter was.

'Poor Uncle George has had notice to quit,' she said.

'Why?' said John.

'His lease is up. The Landlord has sent him notice to quit.'

'But didn't you know how long the lease was for?'

'Oh, no, indeed we did not. We thought it was for years and years more. I am sure the Landlord never gave us any idea he was going to turn him out at a moment's notice like this.'

'Ah, but it doesn't need any notice,' broke in the Steward. 'You know he always retains the right to turn anyone out whenever he chooses. It is very good of him to let any of us stay here at all.'

'To be sure, to be sure,' said the mother.

'That goes without saying,' said the father.

'I'm not complaining,' said Uncle George. 'But it seems cruelly hard.'

'Not at all,' said the Steward. 'You've only got to go to the Castle and knock at the gate and see the Landlord himself. You know that he's only turning you out of here to make you much more comfortable somewhere else. Don't you?'

Uncle George nodded. He did not seem able to get his voice.

Suddenly the father looked at his watch. Then he looked up at the Steward and said:

'Well?'

'Yes,' said the Steward.

Then John was sent up to his bedroom and told to put on the ugly and uncomfortable clothes; and when he came downstairs, itching all over, and tight under the arms, he was given a little mask to put on, and his parents put masks on too. Then I thought in my dream that they wanted to put a mask on Uncle George, but he was trembling so that it would not stay on. So they had to see his face as it was; and his face became so dreadful that everyone looked in a different direction and pretended not to see it. They got Uncle George to his feet with much difficulty, and then they all came out on to the road. The sun was just setting at one end of the road, for the road ran east and west. They turned their backs on the dazzling western sky and there John saw ahead of them the night coming down over the eastern mountains. The country sloped down and eastward to a brook, and all this side of the brook was green and cultivated: on the other side of the brook a great black moor sloped upward, and beyond that were the crags and chasms of the lower mountains, and high above them again the bigger mountains: and on top of the whole waste was one mountain so big and black that John was afraid of it. He was told that the Landlord had his castle up there.

He trudged on eastward, a long time, always descending, till they came to the brook. They were so slow now that the sunset behind them was out of sight. Before them, all was growing darker every minute, and the cold east wind was blowing out of the darkness, right from the mountain tops. When they had stood for a little, Uncle George looked round on them all once or twice, and said, 'Oh, dear! Oh, dear!' in a funny small voice like a child's. Then he stepped over the brook and began to walk away up the moor. It was now so dark and there were so many ups and downs in the moorland that they lost sight of him almost at once. Nobody ever saw him again.

'Well,' said the Steward, untying his mask as they turned homeward. 'We've all got to go when our time comes.'

'That's true,' said the father, who was lighting his pipe. When it was lit he turned to the Steward and said: 'Some of those pigs of George's have won prizes.'

'I'd keep 'em if I were you,' said the Steward. 'It's no time for selling now.'

'Perhaps you're right,' said the father.

John walked behind with his mother.

'Mother.'

'Well, dear?'

'Could any of us be turned out without notice like that any day?'

'Well, yes. But it is very unlikely.'

'But we *might* be?'

'You oughtn't to be thinking of that sort of thing at your age.'

'Why oughtn't I?'

'It's not healthy. A boy like you.'

'Mother.'

'Yes?'

'Can *we* break off the lease without notice too?'

'How do you mean?'

'Well, the Landlord can turn us out of the farm whenever he likes. Can we leave the farm whenever we like?'

'No, certainly not.'

'Why not?'

'That's in the lease. We must go when he likes, and stay as long as he likes.'

'Why?'

'I suppose because he makes the leases.'

'What would happen if we did leave?'

'He would be very angry.'

'Would he put us in the black hole?'

'Perhaps.'

'Mother.'

'Well, dear?'

'Will the Landlord put Uncle George in the black hole?'

'How dare you say such a thing about your poor uncle? Of course he won't.'

'But hasn't Uncle George broken all the rules?'

'Broken all the rules? Your Uncle George was a very good man.'

'You never told me that before,' said John.

4

LEAH FOR RACHEL

Greed to recover Desire hides the real offer
of its return – John tries to force himself to
feel it, but finds (and accepts) Lust instead

Then I turned over in my sleep and began to dream deeper still: and I dreamed that I saw John growing tall and lank till he ceased to be a child and became a boy. The chief pleasure of his life in these days was to go down the road and look through the window in the wall in the hope of seeing the beautiful Island. Some days he saw it well enough, especially at first, and heard the music and the voice. At first he would not look through the window into the wood unless he had heard the music. But after a time both the sight of the Island, and the sounds, became very rare. He would stand looking through the window for hours, and seeing the wood, but no sea or Island beyond it, and straining his ears but hearing nothing except the wind in the leaves. And the yearning for that sight of the Island and the sweet wind blowing over the water from it, though indeed these themselves had given him only yearning, became so terrible that John thought he would die if he did not have them again soon. He even said to himself, 'I would break every rule on the card for them if I could only get them. I would go down into the black hole for ever if it had a window from which I could see the Island.' Then it came into his head that perhaps he ought to explore the wood and thus he might find his way down to the sea beyond it: so he determined that the next day, whatever he saw or heard at the window, he would go through and spend the whole day in the wood. When the morning came, it had been raining all night and a south wind had blown the clouds away at sunrise, and all was fresh and shining. As soon as he had had his breakfast John was out on the road. With the wind and the birds, and country carts passing, there were many noises about that morning, so that when John heard a strain of music long before he had reached the wall and the window – a strain like that which he desired, but coming from an unexpected quarter – he could not be absolutely certain that he had not imagined it. It made him stand still in the road for a minute, and in my dream I could hear him thinking – like this: 'If I go after that sound – away off the road, up yonder – it is all luck whether I shall find anything at all. But if I go on to the window, there I *know* I shall reach the wood, and there I can have a good hunt for the shore and the Island. In fact, I shall *insist* on finding it. I am determined to. But if I go a new way I shall not be able to insist: I shall just have to take what comes.' So he went on to the place he knew and climbed through the window into the wood. Up and down and to and fro among the trees he walked, looking this way and that: but he found no sea and no shore, and indeed no end to the wood in any direction. When it came to the middle of the day he was so hot that he sat down and fanned himself. Often, of late, when the sight of the Island had been withheld, he had felt sad and despairing: but what he felt now was more like anger. 'I must have it,' he kept on saying to himself, and then, 'I must have something.' Then it occurred to him that at least he had the wood, which he would once have loved, and that he had not given it a thought all morning. Very well, thought John, I will enjoy the wood: I *will* enjoy it. He set his teeth and wrinkled his forehead and sat still until the sweat rolled off him in an effort to enjoy the wood. But the more he tried the more he felt that there was nothing to enjoy. There was the grass and there were the trees: 'But what am I to *do* with them?' said John. Next it came into his head that he might perhaps get the old feeling – for what, he thought, had the Island ever given him but a *feeling*? – by imagining. He shut his eyes and set his teeth again and made a picture of the Island in his mind: but he could not keep his attention on the picture because he wanted all the time to watch some other part of his mind to see if the *feeling* were beginning. But no feeling began: and then, just as he was opening his eyes he heard a voice speaking to him. It was quite close at hand, and very sweet, and not at all like the old voice of the wood. When he looked round he saw what he had never expected, yet he was not surprised. There in the grass beside him sat a laughing brown girl of about his own age, and she had no clothes on.

'It was me you wanted,' said the brown girl. 'I am better than your silly Islands.'

And John rose and caught her, all in haste, and committed fornication with her in the wood.

5

ICHABOD

*The deception does not last: but it leaves a
habit of sin behind it*

After that John was always going to the wood. He did not always have
his pleasure of her in the body, though it often ended that way: sometimes he would talk to her about himself, telling her lies about his courage
and his cleverness. All that he told her she remembered, so that on other
days she could tell it over to him again. Sometimes, even, he would go with
her through the wood looking for the sea and the Island, but not often.
Meanwhile the year went on and the leaves began to fall in the wood and
the skies were more often grey: until now, as I dreamed, John had slept in
the wood, and he woke up in the wood. The sun was low and a blustering
wind was stripping the leaves from the branches. The girl was still there
and the appearance of her was hateful to John: and he saw that she knew
this, and the more she knew it the more she stared at him, smiling. He
looked round and saw how small the wood was after all – a beggarly strip
of trees between the road and a field that he knew well. Nowhere in sight
was there anything that he liked at all.

'I shall not come back here,' said John. 'What I wanted is not here. It
wasn't you I wanted, you know.'

'Wasn't it?' said the brown girl. 'Then be off. But you must take your
family with you.'

With that she put up her hands to her mouth and called. Instantly from
behind every tree there slipped out a brown girl: each of them was just like
herself: the little wood was full of them.

'What are these?'

'Our daughters,' said she. 'Did you not know you were a father? Did
you think I was barren, you fool? And now, children,' she added, turning
to the mob, 'go with your father.'

Suddenly John became very much afraid and leaped over the wall into
the road. There he ran home as fast as he could.

6

QUEM QUAERITIS IN SEPULCHRO? NON EST HIC

*Sin and the Law torment John, each
aggravating the other – Sweet Desire
returns and he resolves to make it the object
of his life*

From that day forth until he left his home John was not happy. First of all
the weight of all the rules that he had broken descended upon him: for
while he was going daily to the wood he had almost forgotten the Landlord,
and now suddenly the whole reckoning was to pay. In the second place, his
last sight of the Island was now so long ago that he had forgotten how to
wish for it even, and almost how to set about looking for it. At first he feared
to go back to the window in the wall, lest he should meet the brown girl: but
he soon found that her family were so constantly with him that place made
no difference. Wherever he sat down to rest on a walk, there sooner or later,
would be a little brown girl beside him. When he sat of an evening with his
father and mother, a brown girl, visible only to him, would sidle in and sit at
his feet: and sometimes his mother would fix her eyes on him and even ask
him what he was staring at. But most of all they plagued him whenever he
had a fit of fright about the Landlord and the black hole. It was always the
same. He would wake one morning full of fear, and take down his card and
read it – the front of it – and determine that today he would really begin to
keep the rules. And for that day he would, but the strain was intolerable. He
used to comfort himself by saying, It will get more easy as I go on. Tomorrow
it will be easier. But tomorrow was always harder, and on the third day it was
worst of all. And on that third day when he crept away to bed, tired to death
and raw in his soul, always he would be sure to find a brown girl waiting for
him there: and on such a night he had no spirit to resist her blandishments.

But when he perceived that no place was more, or less, haunted than
another, then he came sidling back to the window in the wall. He had little

hopes of it. He visited it more as a man visits a grave. It was full winter now, and the grove was naked and dark, the trees dripped in it, and the stream – he saw now that it was little more than a gutter – was full of dead leaves and mud. The wall, too, was broken where he had jumped over it. Yet John stood there a long time, many a winter evening, looking in. And he seemed to himself to have reached the bottom of misery.

One night he was trudging home from it, when he began to weep. He thought of that first day when he had heard the music and seen the Island: and the longing, not now for the Island itself, but for that moment when he had so sweetly longed for it, began to swell up in a warm wave, sweeter, sweeter, till he thought he could bear no more, and then yet sweeter again, till on the top of it, unmistakably, there came the short sound of music, as if a string had been plucked or a bell struck once. At the same moment a coach had gone past him. He turned and looked after it, in time to see a head even then being withdrawn from the window: and he thought he heard a voice say, Come. And far beyond the coach, among the hills of the western horizon, he thought that he saw a shining sea, and a faint shape of an Island, not much more than a cloud. It was nothing compared with what he had seen the first time: it was so much further away. But his mind was made up. That night he waited till his parents were asleep, and then, putting some few needments together, he stole out by the back door and set his face to the West to seek for the Island.

BOOK 2

THRILL

*Thou shalt not make to thyself any graven
image, nor the likeness of anything that is in
the heaven above.*

EXODUS

*The soul of man, therefore, desiring to learn
what manner of things these are, casteth her
eyes upon objects akin to herself, whereof
none sufficeth. And then it is that she saith,
'With the Lord and with the things whereof
I spoke, there is nothing in that likeness;
what then is it like?' This is the question, oh
son of Dionysius, that is the cause of all evils
– or rather the travail wherein the soul
travaileth about it.*

PLATO[1]

*Following false copies of the good, that no
Sincere fulfilment of their promise make.*

DANTE

*In hand she boldly took
To make another like the former dame,
Another Florimell in shape and look
So lively and so like that many it mistook.*

SPENSER

[1] Some think it wrongly attributed to him.

DIXIT INSIPIENS

*John begins to think for himself and meets
Nineteenth Century Rationalism, which can
explain away religion by any number of
methods – 'Evolution' and 'Comparative
Religion', and all the guess-work which
masquerades as 'Science'*

Still I lay dreaming in bed, and looked, and I saw John go plodding along the road westward in the bitter black of a frosty night. He walked so long that the morning broke. Then presently John saw a little inn by the side of the road and a woman with a broom who had opened the door and was sweeping out the rubbish. So he turned in there and called for a breakfast, and while it was cooking he sat down in a hard chair by the newly-lit fire and fell asleep. When he woke the sun was shining in through the window and there was his breakfast laid. Another traveller was already eating: he was a big man with red hair and a red stubble on all his three chins, buttoned up very tight. When they had both finished the traveller rose and cleared his throat and stood with his back to the fire. Then he cleared his throat again and said:

'A fine morning, young sir.'

'Yes, sir,' said John.

'You are going West, perhaps, young man?'

'I – I think so.'

'It is possible that you don't know me.'

'I am a stranger here.'

'No offence,' said the stranger. 'My name is Mr Enlightenment, and I believe it is pretty generally known. I shall be happy to give you my assistance and protection as far as our ways lie together.'

John thanked him very much for this and when they went out from the inn there was a neat little trap waiting, with a fat little pony between the shafts: and its eyes were so bright and its harness was so well polished that it was difficult to say which was twinkling the keener in the morning sunshine. They both got into the trap and Mr Enlightenment whipped up the fat little pony and they went bowling along the road as if nobody had a care in the world. Presently they began to talk.

'And where might you come from, my fine lad?' said Mr Enlightenment.

'From Puritania, sir,' said John.

'A good place to leave, eh?'

'I am so glad you think that,' cried John. 'I was afraid –'

'I hope I am a man of the world,' said Mr Enlightenment. 'Any young fellow who is anxious to better himself may depend on finding sympathy and support in me. Puritania! Why, I suppose you have been brought up to be afraid of the Landlord.'

'Well, I must admit I sometimes *do* feel rather nervous.'

'You may make your mind easy, my boy. There is no such person.'

'There is no Landlord?'

'There is absolutely no such thing – I might even say no such *entity* – in existence. There never has been and never will be.'

'And this is absolutely certain?' cried John; for a great hope was rising in his heart.

'Absolutely certain. Look at me, young man. I ask you – do I look as if I was easily taken in?'

'Oh, no,' said John hastily. 'I was just wondering, though. I mean – how did they all come to think there was such a person?'

'The Landlord is an invention of those Stewards. All made up to keep the rest of us under their thumb: and of course the Stewards are hand in glove with the police. They are a shrewd lot, those Stewards. They know which side their bread is buttered on, all right. Clever fellows. Damn me, I can't help admiring them.'

'But do you mean that the Stewards don't believe it themselves?'

'I dare say they do. It is just the sort of cock and bull story they would believe. They are simple old souls most of them – just like children. They have no knowledge of modern science and they would believe anything they were told.'

John was silent for a few minutes. Then he began again:

'But how do you *know* there is no Landlord?'

'Christopher Columbus, Galileo, the earth is round, invention of printing, gunpowder!!' exclaimed Mr Enlightenment in such a loud voice that the pony shied.

'I beg your pardon,' said John.

'Eh?' said Mr Enlightenment.

'I didn't quite understand,' said John.

'Why, it's as plain as a pikestaff,' said the other. 'Your people in Puritania believe in the Landlord because they have not had the benefits of a scientific training. For example, now, I dare say it would be news to you to hear that the earth was round – round as an orange, my lad!'

'Well, I don't know that it would,' said John, feeling a little disappointed. 'My father always said it was round.'

'No, no, my dear boy,' said Mr Enlightenment, 'you must have misunderstood him. It is well known that everyone in Puritania thinks the earth flat. It is not likely that I should be mistaken on such a point. Indeed, it is out of the question. Then again, there is the palaeontological evidence.'

'What's that?'

'Why, they tell you in Puritania that the Landlord made all these roads. But that is quite impossible for old people can remember the time when the roads were not nearly so good as they are now. And what is more, scientists have found all over the country the traces of *old* roads running in quite different directions. The inference is obvious.'

John said nothing.

'I said,' repeated Mr Enlightenment, 'that the inference was obvious.'

'Oh, yes, yes, of course,' said John hastily, turning a little red.

'Then again, there is anthropology.'

'I'm afraid I don't know –'

'Bless me, of course you don't. They don't mean you to know. An anthropologist is a man who goes round your backward villages in these parts, collecting the odd stories that the country people tell about the Landlord. Why, there is one village where they think he has a trunk like an elephant. Now anyone can see that that couldn't be true.'

'It is very unlikely.'

'And what is better still, we know how the villagers came to think so. It all began by an elephant escaping from the local zoo; and then some old villager – he was probably drunk – saw it wandering about on the mountain one night, and so the story grew up that the Landlord had a trunk.'

'Did they catch the elephant again?'

'Did who?'

'The anthropologists.'

'Oh, my dear boy, you are misunderstanding. This happened long before there were any anthropologists.'

'Then how do they know?'

'Well, as to that ... I see that you have a very crude notion of how science actually works. To put it simply – for, of course, you could not understand the *technical* explanation – to put it simply, they know that the escaped elephant must have been the source of the trunk story because they know that an escaped snake must have been the source of the snake story in the next village – and so on. This is called the inductive method. Hypothesis, my dear young friend, establishes itself by a cumulative process: or, to use popular language, if you make the same guess often enough it ceases to be a guess and becomes a Scientific Fact.'

After he had thought for a while, John said:

'I think I see. Most of the stories about the Landlord are probably untrue; therefore the rest are probably untrue.'

'Well, that is as near as a beginner can get to it, perhaps. But when you have had a scientific training you will find that you can be quite certain about all sorts of things which now seem to you only probable.'

By this time the fat little pony had carried them several miles, and they had come to a place where a by-road went off to the right. 'If you are going West, we must part here,' said Mr Enlightenment, drawing up. 'Unless perhaps you would care to come home with me. You see that magnificent city?' John looked down by the by-road and saw in a flat plain without any trees a huge collection of corrugated iron huts, most of which seemed rather old and rusty.

'That,' said Mr Enlightenment, 'is the city of Claptrap. You will hardly believe me when I say that I can remember it as a miserable village. When I first came here it had only forty inhabitants: it now boasts a population of twelve million, four hundred thousand, three hundred and sixty-one souls, who include, I may add, the majority of our most influential publicists and scientific popularisers. In this unprecedented development I am proud to say that I have borne no small part: but it is no mock modesty to add that the invention of the printing press has been more important than any merely personal agency. If you would care to join us –'

'Well, thank you,' said John, 'but I think I will keep to the main road a little longer.'

He got out of the trap and turned to bid good-bye to Mr Enlightenment. Then a sudden thought came into his head, and he said:

'I am not sure that I have really understood all your arguments, sir. Is it absolutely certain that there is no Landlord?'

'Absolutely. I give you my word of honour.'

With these words they shook hands. Mr Enlightenment turned the pony's head up the by-road, gave it a touch with the whip, and in a few moments was out of sight.

2

THE HILL

*John abandons his religion with profound
relief – And forthwith has his first explicitly
moral experience*

Then I saw John bounding forward on his road so lightly that before he
knew it he had come to the top of a little hill. It was not because the
hill had tired him that he stopped there, but because he was too happy to
move. 'There is no Landlord,' he cried. Such a weight had been lifted from
his mind that he felt he could fly. All round him the frost was gleaming like
silver; the sky was like blue glass; a robin sat in the hedge beside him; a cock
was crowing in the distance. 'There is no Landlord.' He laughed when he
thought of the old card of rules hung over his bed in the bedroom, so low
and dark, in his father's house. 'There is no Landlord. There is no black
hole.' He turned and looked back on the road he had come by: and when he
did so he gasped with joy. For there in the East, under the morning light, he
saw the mountains heaped up to the sky like clouds, green and violet and
dark red; shadows were passing over the big rounded slopes, and water
shone in the mountain pools, and up at the highest of all the sun was smiling steadily on the ultimate crags. These crags were indeed so shaped that
you could easily take them for a castle: and now it came into John's head
that he had never looked at the mountains before, because as long as he
thought that the Landlord lived there, he had been afraid of them. But now
that there was no Landlord he perceived that they were beautiful. For a
moment he almost doubted whether the Island could be more beautiful,
and whether he would not be wiser to go East, instead of West. But it did
not seem to him to matter, for he said, 'If the world has the mountains at
one end and the Island at the other, then every road leads to beauty, and the
world is a glory among glories.'

At that moment he saw a man walking up the hill to meet him. Now I
knew in my dream that this man's name was Mr Vertue, and he was about
of an age with John, or a little older.

'What is the name of this place?' said John.

'It is called Jehovah-Jirah,' said Mr Vertue.

Then they both turned and continued their journey to the West. After they had gone a little way Mr Vertue stole a glance at John's face and then he smiled a little.

'Why do you smile?' said John.

'I was thinking that you looked very glad.'

'So would you be if you had lived in the fear of a Landlord all your life and had just discovered that you were a free man.'

'Oh, it's that, is it?'

'You don't believe in the Landlord, do you?'

'I know nothing about him – except by hearsay like the rest of us.'

'You wouldn't like to be under his thumb.'

'Wouldn't like? I wouldn't *be* under anyone's thumb.'

'You might have to, if he had a black hole.'

'I'd let him put me in the black hole sooner than take orders if the orders were not to my mind.'

'Why, I think you are right. I can hardly believe it yet – that I need not obey the rules. There's that robin again. To think that I could have a shot at it if I liked and no one would interfere with me!'

'Do you want to?'

'I'm not sure that I do,' said John, fingering his sling. But when he looked round on the sunshine and remembered his great happiness and looked twice at the bird, he said, 'No, I don't. There is nothing I want less. Still – I could if I liked.'

'You mean you could if you chose.'

'Where's the difference?'

'All the difference in the world.'

3

A LITTLE SOUTHWARD

The Moral Imperative does not fully
understand itself – John decides that
Aesthetic Experience is the thing to pursue

I thought that John would have questioned him further, but now they came in sight of a woman who was walking slower than they so that presently they came up with her and wished her good-day. When she turned, they saw that she was young and comely, though a little dark of complexion. She was friendly and frank, but not wanton like the brown girls, and the whole world became pleasanter to the young men because they were travelling the same way with her. But first they told her their names, and she told them hers, which was Media Halfways.

'And where are you travelling to, Mr Vertue?' she asked.

'To travel hopefully is better than to arrive,' said Vertue.

'Do you mean you are just out for a walk, just for exercise?'

'Certainly not,' said Vertue, who was becoming a little confused. 'I am on a pilgrimage. I must admit, now that you press me, I have not a very clear idea of the end. But that is not the important question. These speculations don't make one a better walker. The great thing is to do one's thirty miles a day.'

'Why?'

'Because that is the rule.'

'Ho-ho!' said John. 'So you *do* believe in the Landlord after all.'

'Not at all. I didn't say it was the Landlord's rule.'

'Whose is it then?'

'It is my own rule. I made it myself.'

'But why?'

'Well, that again is a speculative question. I have made the best rules I can. If I find any better ones I shall adopt them. In the meantime, the great thing is to have rules of some sort and to keep them.'

'And where are you going?' said Media, turning to John.

Then John began to tell his companions about the Island, and how he had first seen it, and was determined to give up everything for the hope of finding it.

'Then you had better come and see my father,' said she. 'He lives in the city of Thrill, and at the bottom of this hill there is a turn to the left which will bring us there in half an hour.'

'Has your Father been to the Island? Does he know the way?'

'He often talks about something very like it.'

'You had better come with us, Vertue,' said John, 'since you do not know where you are going and there can be no place better to go than the Island.'

'Certainly not,' said Vertue. 'We must keep to the road. We must keep on.'

'I don't see why,' said John.

'I dare say you don't,' said Vertue.

All this time they were going down the hill, and now they came to a little grassy lane on the left which went off through a wood. Then I thought that John had a little hesitation: but partly because the sun was now hot and the hard metal of the road was becoming sore to his feet, and partly because he felt a little angry with Vertue, and most of all because Media was going that way, he decided to turn down the lane. They said good-bye to Vertue, and he went on his way stumping up the next hill without ever looking back.

4

SOFT GOING

When they were in the lane they walked more gently. The grass was soft under their feet, and the afternoon sun beating down on the sheltered place made it warm. And presently they heard a sound of sweet and melancholy chimes.

'Those are the bells of the city,' said Media.

As they went on they walked closer together, and soon they were walking arm in arm. Then they kissed each other: and after that they went on their way kissing and talking in slow voices, of sad and beautiful things. And the shadow of the wood and the sweetness of the girl and the sleepy sound of the bells reminded John a little bit of the Island, and a little bit of the brown girls.

'This is what I have been looking for all my life,' said John. 'The brown girls were too gross and the Island was too fine. This is the real thing.'

'This is Love,' said Media with a deep sigh. 'This is the way to the *real* Island.'

Then I dreamed that they came in sight of the city, very old, and full of spires and turrets, all covered with ivy, where it lay in a little grassy valley, built on both sides of a lazy, winding river. And they passed the gate in the ruinous old city wall and came and knocked at a certain door and were let in. Then Media brought him in to a darkish room with a vaulted roof and windows of stained glass, and exquisite food was brought to them. With the food came old Mr Halfways. He was a gliding gentleman with soft, silver hair and a soft, silver voice, dressed in flowing robes: and he was so solemn, with his long beard, that John was reminded of the Steward with his mask on. 'But it is much better than the Steward,' thought John, 'because there is nothing to be afraid of. Also, he doesn't need a mask: his face is really like that.'

LEAH FOR RACHEL

*'Romantic' poetry professes to give what
hitherto John has only desired – For a
moment it seems to have kept its promise –
The rapture does not last but dwindles into
technical appreciation and sentiment*

As they ate John told him about the Island.

'You will find your Island here,' said Mr Halfways, looking into John's eyes.

'But how can it be here in the middle of the city?'

'It needs no place. It is everywhere and nowhere. It refuses entry to none who asks. It is an Island of the Soul,' said the old gentleman. 'Surely even in Puritania they told you that the Landlord's castle was within you?'

'But I don't want the castle,' said John. 'And I don't believe in the Landlord.'

'What is truth?' said the old man. 'They were mistaken when they told you of the Landlord: and yet they were not mistaken. What the imagination seizes as beauty must be truth, whether it existed before or not. The Landlord they dreamed to find, we find in our hearts: the Island you seek for, you already inhabit. The children of that country are never far from their fatherland.'

When the meal was ended the old gentleman took a harp, and at the first sweep of his hand across the strings John began to think of the music that he had heard by the window in the wall. Then came the voice: and it was no longer merely silver sweet and melancholy like Mr Halfways' speaking voice, but strong and noble and full of strange overtones, the noise of the sea, and of all birds, and sometimes of wind and thunder. And John began to see a picture of the Island with his eyes open: but it was more than a picture, for he sniffed the spicy smell and the sharp brine of the sea mixed with it. He seemed to be in the water, only a few yards from the sand of the Island. He could see more than he had ever seen before. But just as he had put down his feet and touched a sandy bottom and was beginning to wade ashore, the song ceased. The whole vision went away. John found himself back in the dusky room, seated on a low divan, with Media by his side.

'Now I shall sing you something else,' said Mr Halfways.

'Oh, no,' cried John, who was sobbing. 'Sing the same again. Please sing it again.'

'You had better not hear it twice in the same evening. I have plenty of other songs.'

'I would die to hear the first one again,' said John.

'Well, well,' said Mr Halfways, 'perhaps you know best. Indeed, what does it matter? It is as short to the Island one way as another.' Then he smiled indulgently and shook his head, and John could not help thinking that his talking voice and talking manner were almost silly after the singing. But as soon as the great deep wall of the music began again it swept everything else from his mind. It seemed to him that this time he got more pleasure from the first few notes, and even noticed delicious passages which had escaped him at the first hearing; and he said to himself, 'This is going to be even better than the other. I shall keep my head this time and sip all the pleasure at my ease.' I saw that he settled himself more comfortably to listen and Media slipped her hand into his. It pleased him to think that they were going to the Island together. Now came the vision of the Island again: but this time it was changed, for John scarcely noticed the Island because of a lady with a crown on her head who stood waiting for him on the shore. She was fair, divinely fair. 'At last,' said John, 'a girl with no trace of brown.' And he began again to wade ashore holding out his arms to embrace that queen: and his love for her appeared to him so great and so pure, and they had been parted for so long, that his pity for himself and her almost overwhelmed him. And as he was about to embrace her the song stopped.

'Sing it again, sing it again,' cried John, 'I liked it better the second time.'

'Well, if you insist,' said Mr Halfways with a shrug. 'It is nice to have a really appreciative audience.' So he sang it the third time. This time John noticed yet more about the music. He began to see how several of the effects were produced and that some parts were better than others. He wondered if it were not a trifle too long. The vision of the Island was a little shadowy this time, and he did not take much notice of it. He put his arm round Media and they lay cheek to cheek. He began to wonder if Mr Halfways would never end: and when at last the final passage closed, with a sobbing break in the singer's voice, the old gentleman looked up and saw how the young people lay in one another's arms. Then he rose and said:

'You have found your Island – you have found it in one another's hearts.'

Then he tiptoed from the room, wiping his eyes.

6

ICHABOD

Rapture would finally turn into Lust, but
that in the nick of time the 'modern' literary
movement offers to 'debunk' it

'Media, I love you,' said John.

'We have come to the *real* Island,' said Media.

'But oh, alas!' said he, 'so long our bodies why do we forbear?'

'Else a great prince in prison lies,' sighed she.

'No one else can understand the mystery of our love,' said he.

At that moment a brisk, hobnailed step was heard and a tall young man strode into the room carrying a light in his hand. He had coal-black hair and a straight mouth like the slit in a pillar-box, and he was dressed in various kinds of metal wire. As soon as he saw them he burst into a great guffaw. The lovers instantly sprang up and apart.

'Well, Brownie,' said he, 'at your tricks again?'

'Don't call me that name,' said Media, stamping her foot, 'I have told you before not to call me that.'

The young man made an obscene gesture at her, and then turned to John, 'I see that old fool of a father of mine has been at you?'

'You have no right to speak that way of Father,' said Media. Then, turning to John, her cheeks flaming, her breast heaving, she said, 'All is over. Our dream – is shattered. Our mystery – is profaned. I would have taught you all the secrets of love, and now you are lost to me for ever. We must part. I shall go and kill myself,' and with that she rushed from the room.

7

NON EST HIC

'Don't bother about her,' said the young man. 'She has threatened that a hundred times. She is only a brown girl, though she doesn't know it.'

'A brown girl!' cried John, 'And your father ...'

'My father has been in the pay of the Brownies all his life. He doesn't know it, the old chuckle-head. Calls them the Muses, or the Spirit, or some rot. In actual fact, he is by profession a pimp.'

'And the Island?' said John.

'We'll talk about it in the morning. Ain't the kind of Island you're thinking of. Tell you what. I don't live with my father and my precious sister. I live in Eschropolis and I am going back tomorrow. I'll take you down to the laboratory and show you some *real* poetry. Not fantasies. The real thing.'

'Thank you very much,' said John.

Then young Mr Halfways found his room for him and the whole of that household went to bed.

8

GREAT PROMISES

*The poetry of the Machine Age is so
very pure*

Gus Halfways was the name of Mr Halfways' son. As soon as he rose
in the morning he called John down to breakfast with him so that
they might start on their journey. There was no one to hinder them, for old
Halfways was still asleep and Media always had breakfast in bed. When
they had eaten, Gus brought him into a shed beside his father's house and
showed him a machine on wheels.

'What is this?' said John.

'My old bus,' said young Halfways. Then he stood back with his head on
one side and gazed at it for a bit: but presently he began to speak in a
changed and reverent voice.

'She is a poem. She is the daughter of the spirit of the age. What was the
speed of Atlanta to her speed? The beauty of Apollo to her beauty?'

Now beauty to John meant nothing save glimpses of his Island, and the
machine did not remind him of his Island at all: so he held his tongue.

'Don't you see?' said Gus. 'Our fathers made images of what they called
gods and goddesses; but they were really only brown girls and brown boys
whitewashed – as anyone found out by looking at them too long. All self-
deception and phallic sentiment. But here you have the real art. Nothing
erotic about *her*, eh?'

'Certainly not,' said John, looking at the cog-wheels and coils of wire, 'it
is certainly not at all like a brown girl.' It was, in fact, more like a nest of
hedgehogs and serpents.

'I should say not,' said Gus. 'Sheer power, eh? Speed, ruthlessness, austerity, significant form, eh? Also' (and here he dropped his voice) 'very
expensive indeed.'

Then he made John sit in the machine and he himself sat beside him.
Then he began pulling the levers about and for a long time nothing happened: but at last there came a flash and a roar and the machine bounded
into the air and then dashed forward. Before John had got his breath they
had flashed across a broad thoroughfare which he recognised as the main

road, and were racing through the country to the north of it – a flat country of square stony fields divided by barbed wire fences. A moment later they were standing still in a city where all the houses were built of steel.

BOOK 3

THROUGH DARKEST

ZEITGEISTHEIM

And every shrewd turn was exalted among
men ... and simple goodness, wherein nobility
doth ever most participate, was mocked away
and clean vanished.
THUCYDIDES

Now live the lesser, as lords of the world,
The busy troublers. Banished is our glory,
The earth's excellence grows old and sere.
ANON

The more ignorant men are, the more
convinced are they that their little parish and
their little chapel is an apex to which
civilisation and philosophy has painfully
struggled up.
SHAW

ESCHROPOLIS

*The poetry of the Silly Twenties – The
'Courage' and mutual loyalty of Artists*

Then I dreamed that he led John into a big room rather like a bathroom: it was full of steel and glass and the walls were nearly all window, and there was a crowd of people there, drinking what looked like medicine and talking at the tops of their voices. They were all either young, or dressed up to look as if they were young. The girls had short hair and flat breasts and flat buttocks so that they looked like boys: but the boys had pale, egg-shaped faces and slender waists and big hips so that they looked like girls – except for a few of them who had long hair and beards.

'What are they so angry about?' whispered John.

'They are not angry,' said Gus; 'they are talking about Art.'

Then he brought John into the middle of the room and said:

'Say! Here's a guy who has been taken in by my father and wants some real hundred per cent music to clean him out. We had better begin with something neo-romantic to make the transition.'

Then all the Clevers consulted together and presently they all agreed that Victoriana had better sing first. When Victoriana rose John at first thought that she was a school-girl: but after he had looked at her again he perceived that she was in fact about fifty. Before she began to sing she put on a dress which was a sort of exaggerated copy of Mr Halfways' robes, and a mask which was like the Steward's mask except that the nose had been painted bright red and one of the eyes had been closed in a permanent wink.

'Priceless!' exclaimed one half of the Clevers, 'too Puritanian.'

But the other half, which included all the bearded men, held their noses in the air and looked very stiff. Then Victoriana took a little toy harp and began. The noises of the toy harp were so strange that John could not think of them as music at all. Then, when she sang, he had a picture in his mind which was a little like the Island, but he saw at once that it was not the Island. And presently he saw people who looked rather like his father, and the Steward and old Mr Halfways, dressed up as clowns and doing a stiff sort of dance. Then there was a columbine, and some sort of love-story. But suddenly the whole Island turned into an aspidistra in a pot and the song was over.

'Priceless,' said the Clevers.

'I hope you like it,' said Gus to John.

'Well,' began John doubtfully, for he hardly knew what to say: but he got no further, for at that moment he had a very great surprise. Victoriana had thrown her mask away and walked up to him and slapped him in the face twice, as hard as she could.

'That's right,' said the Clevers, 'Victoriana has *courage*. We may not all agree with you, Vikky dear, but we admire your courage.'

'You may persecute me as much as you like,' said Victoriana to John. 'No doubt to see me thus with my back to the wall, wakes the hunting lust in you. You will always follow the cry of the majority. But I will fight to the end. So there,' and she began to cry.

'I am extremely sorry,' said John. 'But –'

'And I *know* it was a good song,' sobbed Victoriana, 'because all great singers are persecuted in their lifetime – and I'm per-persecuted – and therefore I *must* be a great singer.'

'She has you there,' said the Clevers, as Victoriana left the laboratory.

'Well, I must admit,' said one of the Clevers, 'now that she has gone, that I think that stuff of hers rather *vieux jeu*.'

'Can't stand it myself,' said another.

'I think it was *her* face that needed slapping,' said a third.

'She's been spoiled and flattered all her life,' said a fourth. 'That's what's the matter with her.'

'Quite,' said the rest in chorus.

2

A SOUTH WIND

The swamp-literature of the Dirty Twenties
– It was a low-brow blunder to mention the
most obvious thing about it

'Perhaps,' said Gus, 'someone else would give us a song.'

'I will,' cried thirty voices all together: but one cried much louder than the others and its owner had stepped into the middle of the room before anyone could do anything about it. He was one of the bearded men and wore nothing but a red shirt and a cod-piece made of the skins of crocodiles: and suddenly he began to beat on an African tom-tom and to croon with his voice, swaying his lean, half-clad body to and fro and staring at them all, out of eyes which were like burning coals. This time John saw no picture of an Island at all. He seemed to be in a dark green place full of tangled roots and hairy vegetable tubes: and all at once he saw in it shapes moving and writhing that were not vegetable but human. And the dark green grew darker, and a fierce heat came out of it: and suddenly all the shapes that were moving in the darkness came together to make a single obscene image which dominated the whole room. And the song was over.

'Priceless,' said the Clevers. 'Too stark! Too virile.'

John blinked and looked round and when he saw all the Clevers as cool as cucumbers, smoking their cigarettes and drinking the drinks that looked like medicines, all as if nothing remarkable had happened, he was troubled in his mind; for he thought that the song must have meant something different to them, and 'If so,' he argued, 'what very pure-minded people they must be.' Feeling himself among his betters, he became ashamed.

'You like it, *hein*?' said the bearded singer.

'I – I don't think I understood it,' said John.

'I make you like it, *hein*,' said the singer, snatching up his tom-tom again. 'It was what you *really* wanted all the time.'

'No, no,' cried John. 'I know you are wrong there. I grant you, that – that sort of thing – is what I always get if I think too long about the Island. But it can't be what I *want*.'

'No? Why not?'

'If it is what I wanted, why am I so disappointed when I get it? If what a man really wanted was food, how could he be disappointed when the food arrived? As well, I don't understand –'

'What you not understand? I explain to you.'

'Well, it's like this. I thought that you objected to Mr Halfways' singing because it led to brown girls in the end.'

'So we do.'

'Well, why is it better to lead to black girls in the beginning?'

A low whistle ran round the whole laboratory. John knew he had made a horrible blunder.

'Look here,' said the bearded singer in a new voice, 'what do you mean? You are not suggesting that there is anything of that kind about my singing, are you?'

'I – I suppose – perhaps it was my fault,' stammered John.

'In other words,' said the singer, 'you are not yet able to distinguish between art and pornography!' and advancing towards John very deliberately, he spat in his face and turned to walk out of the room.

'That's right, Phally,' cried the Clevers, 'serve him right.'

'Filthy-minded little beast,' said one.

'Yah! Puritanian!' said a girl.

'I expect he's impotent,' whispered another.

'You mustn't be too hard on him,' said Gus. 'He is full of inhibitions and everything he says is only a rationalisation of them. Perhaps he would get on better with something more formal. Why don't you sing, Glugly?'

3

FREEDOM OF THOUGHT

The gibberish-literature of the Lunatic
Twenties – John abandons 'the Movement',
though a little damaged by it

Glugly instantly rose. She was very tall and as lean as a post: and her mouth was not quite straight in her face. When she was in the middle of the room, and silence had been obtained, she began to make gestures. First of all she set her arms a-kimbo and cleverly turned her hands the wrong way so that it looked as if her wrists were sprained. Then she waddled to and fro with her toes pointing in. After that she twisted herself to make it look as if her hip bone was out of joint. Finally she made some grunts, and said:

'Globol abol ookle ogle globol gloogle gloo,' and ended by pursing up her lips and making a vulgar noise such as children make in their nurseries. Then she went back to her place and sat down.

'Thank you very much,' said John politely.

But Glugly made no reply, for Glugly could not talk, owing to an accident in infancy.

'I hoped you liked it,' said young Halfways.

'I didn't understand her.'

'Ah,' said a woman in spectacles who seemed to be Glugly's nurse or keeper, 'that is because you are looking for beauty. You are still thinking of your Island. You have got to realise that satire is the moving force in modern music.'

'It is the expression of a savage disillusionment,' said someone else.

'Reality has broken down,' said a fat boy who had drunk a great deal of the medicine and was lying flat on his back, smiling happily.

'Our art *must* be brutal,' said Glugly's nurse.

'We lost our ideals when there was a war in this country,' said a very young Clever, 'they were ground out of us in the mud and the flood and the blood. That is why we have to be so stark and brutal.'

'But, look here,' cried John, 'that war was years ago. It was your fathers who were in it: and they are all settled down and living ordinary lives.'

'Puritanian! Bourgeois!' cried the Clevers. Everyone seemed to have risen.

'Hold your tongue,' whispered Gus in John's ear. But already someone had struck John on the head, and as he bowed under the blow someone else hit him from behind.

'It was the mud and the blood,' hissed the girls all round him.

'Well,' said John, ducking to avoid a retort that had been flung at him, 'If you are really old enough to remember that war, why do you pretend to be so young?'

'We are young,' they howled; 'we are the new movement; we are the revolt.'

'We have got over humanitarianism,' bellowed one of the bearded men, kicking John on the kneecap.

'And prudery,' said a thin little old maid trying to wrench his clothes off from the neck. And at the same moment six girls leaped at his face with their nails, and he was kicked in the back and the belly, and tripped up so that he fell on his face, and hit again as he rose, and all the glass in the world seemed breaking round his head as he fled for his life from the laboratory. And all the dogs of Eschropolis joined in the chase as he ran along the street, and all the people followed pelting him with ordure, and crying:

'Puritanian! Bourgeois! Prurient!'

4

THE MAN BEHIND THE GUN

What did the Revolutionary Intellectuals
live on?

When John could run no further he sat down. The noise of the pursuers had died away and, looking back, he could see no sign of Eschropolis. He was covered with filth and blood, and his breathing hurt him. There seemed to be something wrong with one of his wrists. As he was too tired to walk he sat still and thought for a while. And first he thought that he would like to go back to Mr Halfways. 'It is true,' he said, 'that if you listened to him too long it would lead you to Media – and she *had* a trace of brown in her. But then you had a glimpse of the Island first. Now the Clevers took you straight to brown girls – or worse – without even a glimpse of the Island. I wonder would it be possible to keep always at the Island stage with Mr Halfways? Must it always end like that?' Then it came into his head that after all he did not want Mr Halfways' songs, but the Island itself: and that this was the only thing he wanted in the world. And when he remembered this he rose very painfully to continue his journey, looking round for the West. He was still in the flat country, but there seemed to be mountains ahead, and above them the sun was setting. A road ran towards them: so he began to limp along it. Soon the sunset disappeared and the sky was clouded over and a cold rain began.

When he had limped about a mile he passed a man who was mending the fence of his field and smoking a big cigar. John stopped and asked him if he knew the way to the sea.

'Nope,' said the man without looking up.

'Do you know of any place in this country where I could get a night's lodging?'

'Nope,' said the man.

'Could you give me a piece of bread?' said John.

'Certainly not,' said Mr Mammon, 'it would be contrary to all economic laws. It would pauperise you.' Then, when John lingered, he added, 'Move on. I don't want any loiterers about here.'

John limped on for about ten minutes. Suddenly he heard Mr Mammon calling out to him. He stopped and turned round.

'What do you want?' shouted John.

'Come back,' said Mr Mammon.

John was so tired and hungry that he humbled himself to walk back (and the way seemed long) in the hope that Mammon had relented. When he came again to the place where they had talked before, the man finished his work without speaking and then said:

'Where did you get your clothes torn?'

'I had a quarrel with the Clevers in Eschropolis.'

'Clevers?'

'Don't you know them?'

'Never heard of them.'

'You know Eschropolis?'

'Know it? I *own* Eschropolis.'

'How do you mean?'

'What do you suppose they live on?'

'I never thought of that.'

'Every man of them earns his living by writing for me or having shares in my land. I suppose the "Clevers" is some nonsense they do in their spare time – when they're not beating up tramps,' and he glanced at John. Then he resumed his work.

'You needn't wait,' he said presently.

5

UNDER ARREST

*John is hindered from pursuing his quest by
the Intellectual climate of the Age*

Then I turned round and immediately began to dream again and I saw John plodding westward in the dark and the rain, in great distress, because he was too tired to go on and too cold to stop. And after a time there came a north wind that drove the rain away and skinned the puddles with ice and set the bare boughs clashing in the trees. And the moon came out. Now John looked up with his teeth chattering and saw that he was entering into a long valley of rocks with high cliffs on the right and the left. And the far end of the valley was barred with a high cliff all across except for one narrow pass in the middle. The moonlight lay white on this cliff and right amidst it was a huge shadow like a man's head. John glanced over his shoulder and saw that the shadow was thrown by a mountain behind him, which he had passed in the darkness.

It was far too cold for a man to stay in the wind, and I dreamed of John going stumblingly forward up the valley till now he had come to the rock-wall and was about to enter the pass. But just as he rounded a great boulder and came full in sight of the pass he saw some armed men sitting in it by a brazier; and immediately they sprang up and barred his way.

'You can't pass here,' said their leader.

'Where can I pass?' said John.

'Where are you going to?'

'I am going to find the sea in order to set sail for an Island that I have seen in the West.'

'Then you cannot pass.'

'By whose orders?'

'Do you not know that all this country belongs to the Spirit of the Age?'

'I am sorry,' said John, 'I didn't know. I have no wish to trespass, I will go round some other way. I will not go through his country at all.'

'You fool,' said the captain, 'you are in his country *now*. This pass is the way out of it, not the way into it. He welcomes strangers. His quarrel is with runaways.' Then he called to one of his men and said, 'Here, Enlightenment, take this fugitive to our Master.'

A young man stepped out and clapped fetters upon John's hands: then putting the length of chain over his own shoulder and giving it a jerk he began to walk down the valley dragging John after him.

6

POISONING THE WELLS

John is hindered especially by Freudianism –
All is only Wish-Fulfilment – A doctrine
which leads to the giant's prison

Then I saw them going down the valley, the way John had come up, with the moon full in their faces: and up against the moon was the mountain which had cast the shadow, and now it looked more like a man than before.

'Mr Enlightenment,' said John at last. 'Is it really you?'

'Why should it not be?' said the guard.

'You looked so different when I met you before.'

'We have never met before.'

'What? Did you not meet me at the inn on the borders of Puritania and drive me five miles in your pony trap?'

'Oh, *that*?' said the other. 'That must have been my father, old Mr Enlightenment. He is a vain and ignorant old man, almost a Puritanian, and we never mention him in the family. I am Sigismund Enlightenment and I have long since quarrelled with my father.'

They went on in silence for a bit. Then Sigismund spoke again.

'It may save trouble if I tell you at once the best reason for not trying to escape: namely, that there is nowhere to escape to.'

'How do you know there is no such place as my Island?'

'Do you wish very much that there was?'

'I do.'

'Have you never before imagined anything to be true because you greatly wished for it?'

John thought for a little, and then he said, 'Yes.'

'And your Island is *like* an imagination – isn't it?'

'I suppose so.'

'It is just the sort of thing you *would* imagine merely through wanting it – the whole thing is very suspicious. But answer me another question. Have you ever – ever once yet – had a vision of the Island that did not end in brown girls?'

'I don't know that I have. But they weren't what I wanted.'

'No. What you wanted was to have them, and with them, the satisfaction of feeling that you were good. Hence the Island.'

'You mean –'

'The Island was the pretence that you put up to conceal your own lusts from yourself.'

'All the same – I was disappointed when it ended like that.'

'Yes. You were disappointed at finding that you could not have it both ways. But you lost no time in having it the way you could: you did not reject the brown girls.'

They went on in silence for a time and always the mountain with its odd shape grew bigger in front of them; and now they were in its shadow. Then John spoke again, half in his sleep, for he was very tired.

'After all, it isn't only my Island. I might go back – back East and try the mountains.'

'The mountains do not exist.'

'How do you know?'

'Have you ever been there? Have you ever seen them except at night or in a blaze of sunrise?'

'No.'

'And your ancestors must have enjoyed thinking that when their leases were out they would go up to the mountains and live in the Landlord's castle. It is a more cheerful prospect than going nowhere.'

'I suppose so.'

'It is clearly one more of the things people *wish* to believe.'

'But do we never do anything else? Are all the things I see at this moment there, only because I wish to see them.'

'Most of them,' said Sigismund. 'For example – you would like that thing in front of us to be a mountain; that is why you think it is a mountain.'

'Why?' cried John. 'What is it?'

And then in my nightmare I thought John became like a terrified child and put his hands over his eyes not to see the giant; but young Mr Enlightenment tore his hands away and forced his face round and made him see the Spirit of the Age where it sat like one of the stone giants, the size of a mountain, with its eyes shut. Then Mr Enlightenment opened a little door among the rocks and flung John into a pit made in the side of the hill, just opposite the giant, so that the giant could look into it through its gratings.

'He will open his eyes presently,' said Mr Enlightenment. Then he locked the door and left John in prison.

7

FACING THE FACTS

John sees all humanity as bundles of
complexes

John lay in his fetters all night in the cold and stench of the dungeon. And when morning came there was a little light at the grating, and looking round, John saw that he had many fellow prisoners, of all sexes and ages. But instead of speaking to him, they all huddled away from the light and drew as far back into the pit, away from the grating, as they could. But John thought that if he could breathe a little fresh air he would be better, and he crawled up to the grating. But as soon as he looked out and saw the giant, it crushed the heart out of him: and even as he looked, the giant began to open his eyes and John, without knowing why he did it, shrank from the grating. Now I dreamed that the giant's eyes had this property, that whatever they looked on became transparent. Consequently, when John looked round into the dungeon, he retreated from his fellow prisoners in terror, for the place seemed to be thronged with demons. A woman was seated near him, but he did not know it was a woman, because, through the face, he saw the skull and through that the brain and the passages of the nose, and the larynx, and the saliva moving in the glands and the blood in the veins: and lower down the lungs panting like sponges and the liver, and the intestines like a coil of snakes. And when he averted his eyes from her they fell on an old man, and this was worse for the old man had a cancer. And when John sat down and drooped his head, not to see the horrors, he saw only the working of his own innards. Then I dreamed of all these creatures living in that hole under the giant's eye for many days and nights. And John looked round on it all and suddenly he fell on his face and thrust his hands into his eyes and cried out, 'It is the black hole. There may be no Landlord, but it is true about the black hole. I am mad. I am dead. I am in hell for ever.'

8

PARROT DISEASE

At last John's commonsense revolts

Every day a jailor brought the prisoners their food, and as he laid down the dishes he would say a word to them. If their meal was flesh he would remind them that they were eating corpses, or give them some account of the slaughtering: or, if it was the innards of some beast, he would read them a lecture in anatomy and show the likeness of the mess to the same parts in themselves – which was the more easily done because the giant's eyes were always staring into the dungeon at dinner time. Or if the meal were eggs he would recall to them that they were eating the menstruum of a verminous fowl, and crack a few jokes with the female prisoners. So he went on day by day. Then I dreamed that one day there was nothing but milk for them, and the jailor said as he put down the pipkin:

'Our relations with the cow are not delicate – as you can easily see if you imagine eating any of her other secretions.'

Now John had been in the pit a shorter time than any of the others: and at these words something seemed to snap in his head and he gave a great sigh and suddenly spoke out in a loud, clear voice:

'Thank heaven! Now at last I know that you are talking nonsense.'

'What do you mean?' said the jailor, wheeling round upon him.

'You are trying to pretend that unlike things are like. You are trying to make us think that milk is the same sort of thing as sweat or dung.'

'And pray, what difference is there except by custom?'

'Are you a liar or only a fool, that you see no difference between that which Nature casts out as refuse and that which she stores up as food?'

'So Nature is a person, then, with purposes and consciousness,' said the jailor with a sneer. 'In fact, a Landlady. No doubt it comforts you to imagine you can believe that sort of thing'; and he turned to leave the prison with his nose in the air.

'I know nothing about that,' shouted John after him. 'I am talking of what happens. Milk does feed calves and dung does not.'

'Look here,' cried the jailor, coming back, 'we have had enough of this. It is high treason and I shall bring you before the Master.' Then he jerked John up by his chain and began to drag him towards the door; but John as he was being dragged, cried out to the others, 'Can't you see it's all a cheat?' Then the jailor struck him in the teeth so hard that his mouth was filled with blood and he became unable to speak: and while he was silent the jailor addressed the prisoners and said:

'You see he is trying to argue. Now tell me, someone, what is argument?'

There was a confused murmur.

'Come, come,' said the jailor. 'You must know your catechisms by now. You, there' (and he pointed to a prisoner little older than a boy whose name was Master Parrot), 'what is argument?'

'Argument,' said Master Parrot, 'is the attempted rationalisation of the arguer's desires.'

'Very good,' replied the jailor, 'but you should turn out your toes and put your hands behind your back. That is better. Now: what is the proper answer to an argument proving the existence of the Landlord?'

'The proper answer is, "You say that because you are a Steward."'

'Good boy. But hold your head up. That's right. And what is the answer to an argument proving that Mr Phally's songs are just as brown as Mr Halfways'?'

'There are two only generally necessary to damnation,' said Master Parrot. 'The first is, "You say that because you are a Puritanian," and the second is, "You say that because you are a sensualist."'

'Good. Now just one more. What is the answer to an argument turning on the belief that two and two make four?'

'The answer is, "You say that because you are a mathematician."'

'You are a very good boy,' said the jailor. 'And when I come back I shall bring you something nice. And now for *you*,' he added, giving John a kick and opening the grating.

9

THE GIANT SLAYER

*The spell begins to break – Once rational
argument is allowed a hearing the giant
is lost*

When they came out into the air John blinked a little, but not much, for
they were still only in a half-light under the shadow of the giant, who
was very angry, with smoke coming from his mouth, so that he looked
more like a volcano than an ordinary mountain. And now John gave himself up for lost, but just as the jailor had dragged him up to the giant's feet,
and had cleared his throat, and begun 'The case against this prisoner –' there
was a commotion and a sound of a horse's hoofs. The jailor looked round,
and even the giant took his terrible eyes off John and looked round: and last
of all, John himself looked round too. They saw some of the guard coming
towards them leading a great black stallion, and on it was seated a figure
wound in a cloak of blue which was hooded over the head and came down
concealing the face.

'Another prisoner, Lord,' said the leader of the guards.

Then very slowly the giant raised his great, heavy finger and pointed to
the mouth of the dungeon.

'Not yet,' said the hooded figure. Then suddenly it stretched out its
hands with the fetters on them and made a quick movement of the wrists.
There was a tinkling sound as the fragments of the broken chain fell on the
rock at the horse's feet: and the guardsmen let go the bridle and fell back,
watching. Then the rider threw back the cloak and a flash of steel smote
light into John's eyes and on the giant's face. John saw that it was a woman
in the flower of her age: she was so tall that she seemed to him a Titaness, a
sun-bright virgin clad in complete steel, with a sword naked in her hand.
The giant bent forward in his chair and looked at her.

'Who are you?' he said.

'My name is Reason,' said the virgin.

'Make out her passport quickly,' said the giant in a low voice. 'And let
her go through our dominion and be off with all the speed she wishes.'

'Not yet,' said Reason. 'I will ask you three riddles before I go, for a
wager.'

'What is the pledge?' said the giant.

'Your head,' said Reason.

There was silence for a time among the mountains.

'Well,' said the giant at last, 'what must be, must be. Ask on.'

'This is my first riddle,' said Reason. 'What is the colour of things in dark places, of fish in the depth of the sea, or of the entrails in the body of man?'

'I cannot say,' said the giant.

'Well,' said Reason. 'Now hear my second riddle. There was a certain man who was going to his own house and his enemy went with him. And his house was beyond a river too swift to swim and too deep to wade. And he could go no faster than his enemy. While he was on his journey his wife sent to him and said, You know that there is only one bridge across the river: tell me, shall I destroy it that the enemy may not cross, or shall I leave it standing that you may cross? What should this man do?'

'It is too hard for me,' said the giant.

'Well,' said Reason. 'Try now to answer my third riddle. By what rule do you tell a copy from an original?'

The giant muttered and mumbled and could not answer, and Reason set spurs in her stallion and it leaped up on to the giant's mossy knees and galloped up his foreleg, till she plunged her sword into his heart. Then there was a noise and a crumbling like a landslide and the huge carcass settled down: and the Spirit of the Age became what he had seemed to be at first, a sprawling hummock of rock.

BOOK 4

BACK TO THE ROAD

*Doth any man doubt, that if there were
taken out of men's minds vain opinions,
flattering hopes, false valuations,
imaginations as one would, and the like: but
it would leave the minds of a number of men
poor shrunken things: full of melancholy and
indisposition, and unpleasing to themselves?*

BACON

I

LET GRILL BE GRILL

Those who have been Freudianised too long
are incurable

The guards had fled. Reason dismounted from her horse and wiped her sword clean on the moss of the foot hills which had been the giant's knees. Then she turned to the door of the pit and struck it so that it broke and she could look into the darkness of the pit and smell the filth.

'You can all come out,' she said.

But there was no movement from within: only, John could hear the prisoners wailing together and saying:

'It is one more wish-fulfilment dream: it is one more wish-fulfilment dream. Don't be taken in again.'

But presently Master Parrot came to the mouth of the pit and said, 'There is no good trying to fool us. Once bit twice shy.' Then he put out his tongue and retired.

'This psittacosis is a very obstinate disorder,' said Reason. And she turned to mount the black horse.

'May I come with you, lady?' said John.

'You may come until you are tired,' said Reason.

ARCHETYPE AND ECTYPE

*A question-begging argument exposed – The
sciences bring to the 'facts' the philosophy
they claim to derive from them*

In my dream I saw them set off together, John walking by the lady's stirrup: and I saw them go up the rocky valley where John had gone on the night of his capture. They found the pass unguarded and it gave back an echo to the horse's hoofs and then in a moment they were out of the mountain country and going down a grassy slope into the land beyond. There were few trees and bare, and it was cold: but presently John looked aside and saw a crocus in the grass. For the first time for many days the old sweetness pierced through John's heart: and the next moment he was trying to call back the sound of the birds wheeling over the Island and the green of the waves breaking on its sand – for they had all flashed about him so quickly that they were gone before he knew. His eyes were wet.

He turned to Reason and spoke.

'You can tell me, lady. Is there such a place as the Island in the West, or is it only a feeling of my own mind?'

'I cannot tell you,' said she, 'because you do not know.'

'But you know.'

'But I can tell you only what *you* know. I can bring things out of the dark part of your mind into the light part of it. But now you ask me what is not even in the dark part of your mind.'

'Even if it were only a feeling in my own mind, would it be a bad feeling?'

'I have nothing to tell you of good and bad.'

'I mean this,' said John. 'And this you can tell me. Is it true that it must always end in brown girls, or rather, that it really *begins* from brown girls? They say it is all a pretence, all a disguise for lust.'

'And what do you think of that saying?'

'It is very like that,' said John. 'Both are sweet. Both are full of longing. The one runs into the other. They *are* very alike.'

'Indeed they are,' said the lady. 'But do you not remember my third riddle?'

'About the copy and the original? I could not understand it.'

'Well, now you shall. The people in the country we have just left have seen that your love for the Island is very like your love for the brown girls. Therefore they say that one is a copy of the other. They would also say that you have followed me because I am like your mother, and that your trust in me is a copy of your love for your mother. And then they would say again that your love for your mother is a copy of your love for the brown girls; and so they would come full circle.'

'And what should I answer them?'

'You would say, perhaps one is a copy of the other. But which is the copy of which?'

'I never thought of that.'

'You are not yet of an age to have thought much,' said Reason. 'But you must see that if two things are alike, then it is a further question whether the first is copied from the second, or the second from the first, or both from a third.'

'What would the third be?'

'Some have thought that all these loves were copies of our love for the Landlord.'

'But surely they have considered that and rejected it. Their sciences have disproved it.'

'They could not have, for their sciences are not concerned at all with the general relations of this country to anything that may lie East of it or West of it. They indeed will tell you that their researches have proved that if two things are similar, the fair one is always the copy of the foul one. But their only reason to say so is that they have already decided that the fairest things of all – that is the Landlord, and, if you like, the mountains and the Island – are a mere copy of *this* country. They pretend that their researches lead to that doctrine: but in fact they assume that doctrine first and interpret their researches by it.'

'But they have reasons for assuming it.'

'They have none, for they have ceased to listen to the only people who can tell them anything about it.'

'Who are they?'

'They are younger sisters of mine, and their names are Philosophy and Theology.'

'Sisters! Who is your father?'

'You will know sooner than you wish.'

And now the evening was falling and they were near a little farm, so they turned in there and asked a night's lodging of the farmer, which was readily given them.

3

ESSE IS PERCIPI

*The Reason's duty not (even for life's sake)
to decide without evidence – Why all
accounts of the Unconscious are misleading –
Though they also have their use*

Next morning they continued their journey together. In my dream I saw them go through a country of little hills where the road was always winding to conform to the lie of the valleys: and John walked at the lady's stirrup. The fetter of his hands had broken at the moment when she killed the giant, but the handcuffs were still on his wrists. One half of the broken chain hung down from each hand. There was a greater mildness in the air this day and the buds were fully formed in the hedges.

'I have been thinking, lady,' said John, 'of what you said yesterday and I think I understand that though the Island is very like the place where I first met the brown girl, yet she might be the shadow and the Island the reality. But there is one thing that troubles me.'

'What is that?' said Reason.

'I cannot forget what I have seen in the giant's prison. If we are really like that inside, whatever we imagine must be abominable however innocent it looks. It may be true in general that the foul thing is not always the original and the fair thing not always the copy. But when we have to do with human imaginations, with things that come out of *us*, surely then the giant is right? There at least it is much more likely that whatever seems good is only a veil for the bad – only a part of our skin that has so far escaped the giant's eyes and not yet become transparent.'

'There are two things to be said about that,' replied the lady, 'and the first is this. Who told you that the Island was an imagination of yours?'

'Well, you would not assure me that it was anything real.'

'Nor that it was not.'

'But I must think it is one or the other.'

'By my father's soul, you must *not* – until you have some evidence. Can you not remain in doubt?'

'I don't know that I have ever tried.'

'You must learn to, if you are to come far with me. It is not hard to do it. In Eschropolis, indeed, it is impossible, for the people who live there have to give an opinion once a week or once a day, or else Mr Mammon would soon cut off their food. But out here in the country you can walk all day and all the next day with an unanswered question in your head: you need never speak until you have made up your mind.'

'But if a man wanted to know so badly that he would die unless the question was decided – and no more evidence turned up.'

'Then he would die, that would be all.'

They went on in silence for a while.

'You said there were two things to say,' said John. 'What was the second?'

'The second was this. Did you think that the things you saw in the dungeon were *real*: that we really are like that?'

'Of course I did. It is only our skin that hides them.'

'Then I must ask you the same question that I asked the giant. What is the colour of things in the dark?'

'I suppose, no colour at all.'

'And what of their shape? Have you any notion of it save as what could be seen or touched, or what you could collect from many seeings and touchings?'

'I don't know that I have.'

'Then do you not see how the giant has deceived you?'

'Not quite clearly.'

'He showed you by a trick what our innards *would* look like if they were visible. That is, he showed you something that is not, but something that would be if the world were made all other than it is. But in the real world our innards are invisible. They are not coloured shapes at all, they are feelings. The warmth in your limbs at this moment, the sweetness of your breath as you draw it in, the comfort in your belly because we breakfasted well, and your hunger for the next meal – these are the reality: all the sponges and tubes that you saw in the dungeon are the lie.'

'But if I cut a man open I should see them in him.'

'A man cut open is, so far, not a man: and if you did not sew him up speedily you would be seeing not organs, but death. I am not denying that death is ugly: but the giant made you believe that life is ugly.'

'I cannot forget the man with the cancer.'

'What you saw was unreality. The ugly lump was the giant's trick: the reality was pain, which has no colour or shape.'

'Is that much better?'

'That depends on the man.'

'I think I begin to see.'

'Is it surprising that things should look strange if you see them as they are not? If you take an organ out of a man's body – or a longing out of the dark part of a man's mind – and give to the one the shape and colour, and to the other the self-consciousness, which they never have in reality, would you expect them to be other than monstrous?'

'Is there, then, no truth at all in what I saw under the giant's eyes?'

'Such pictures are useful to physicians.'

'Then I really am clean,' said John. 'I am not – like those.'

Reason smiled. 'There, too,' she said, 'there is truth mixed up with the giant's conjuring tricks. It will do you no harm to remember from time to time the ugly sights inside. You come of a race that cannot afford to be proud.'

As she spoke John looked up, in doubt of her meaning: and for the first time since he came into her company he felt afraid. But the impression lasted only for a moment. 'Look,' said John, 'here is a little inn. Is it not time that we rested and ate something?'

4

ESCAPE

*If Religion is a Wish-fulfilment dream,
whose wishes does it fulfil? – Certainly not
John's! – He decides to stop reasoning at
this point*

In the warmth of the afternoon they went on again, and it came into John's mind to ask the lady the meaning of her second riddle.

'It has two meanings,' said she, 'and in the first the bridge signifies Reasoning. The Spirit of the Age wishes to allow argument and not to allow argument.'

'How is that?'

'You heard what they said. If anyone argues with them they say that he is rationalising his own desires, and therefore need not be answered. But if anyone listens to them they will then argue themselves to show that their own doctrines are true.'

'I see. And what is the cure for this?'

'You must ask them whether any reasoning is valid or not. If they say no, then their own doctrines, being reached by reasoning, fall to the ground. If they say yes, then they will have to examine your arguments and refute them on their merits: for if some reasoning is valid, for all they know, your bit of reasoning may be one of the valid bits.'

'I see,' said John. 'But what was the second interpretation?'

'In the second,' said Reason, 'the bridge signifies the giant's own favourite doctrine of the wish-fulfilment dream. For this also he wishes to use and not to use.'

'I don't see how he wishes *not* to use it.'

'Does he not keep on telling people that the Landlord is a wish-fulfilment dream?'

'Yes; surely that is true – the only true thing he did say.'

'Now think. Is it really true that the giant and Sigismund, and the people in Eschropolis, and Mr Halfways, are going about filled with a longing that there should be a Landlord, and cards of rules, and a mountain land beyond the brook, with a possibility of a black hole?'

Then John stood still on the road to think. And first he gave a shake of his shoulders, and then he put his hands to his sides, and then he began to laugh till he was almost shaken to pieces. And when he had nearly finished, the vastness and impudence and simplicity of the fraud which had been practised came over him all again, and he laughed harder. And just when he had nearly recovered and was beginning to get his breath again, suddenly he had a picture in his mind of Victoriana and Glugly and Gus Halfways and how they would look if a rumour reached them that there *was* a Landlord and he was coming to Eschropolis. This was too much for him, and he laughed so hard that the broken chains of the Spirit of the Age fell off his wrists altogether. But all the while Reason sat and watched him.

'You had better hear the rest of the argument,' she said at last. 'It may not be such a laughing matter as you suppose.'

'Oh, yes – the argument,' said John, wiping his eyes.

'You see now the direction in which the giant does *not* want the wish-fulfilment theory used?'

'I'm not sure that I do,' said John.

'Don't you see what follows if you adopt his own rules?'

'No,' said John, very loudly: for a terrible apprehension was stealing over him.

'But you must see,' said Reason, 'that for him and all his subjects *disbelief* in the Landlord is a wish-fulfilment dream.'

'I shall not adopt his rules.'

'You would be foolish not to have profited *at all* by your stay in his country,' said Reason. 'There is some force in the wish-fulfilment doctrine.'

'Some, perhaps, but very little.'

'I only wanted to make it clear that whatever force it had was in favour of the Landlord's existence, not against it – specially in your case.'

'Why specially in mine?' said John sulkily.

'Because the Landlord is the thing you have been most afraid of all your life. I do not say that any theory should be accepted because it is disagreeable, but if any should, then belief in the Landlord should be accepted first.'

As Reason said these words they had reached the top of a little hill, and John begged for a halt, being out of breath. He looked back and saw beyond the green, rolling country the dark line of mountains which was the frontier of the giant's land: but behind them, and far bigger, rose the old mountains of the East, picked out in the rays of the declining sun against a dark sky. They seemed no smaller than when John had looked at them long ago from Puritania.

'I do not know where you are leading me,' he said at last, 'and among all these winding roads I have lost my sense of direction. As well, I find the pace of your horse fatiguing. If you will excuse me, I think I will henceforth pursue my journey alone.'

'As you wish,' said Reason. 'But I would strongly advise you to take this turn to the left.'

'Where does it go to?' asked John suspiciously.

'It takes you back to the main road,' said Reason.

'That will do well enough,' said John. 'And now, lady, give me your blessing before I go.'

'I have no blessing to give,' said the Virgin. 'I do not deal in blessings and cursings.'

Then John bade her good-bye and took the road she had pointed out to him. As soon as she was out of sight, I dreamed that he put down his head and ran; for the silly fellow supposed that she might follow him. And he continued running until he found that he was going up a hill – a hill so steep that it left him no breath for running – and at the very top his road cut into another which ran left and right along the ridge. Then John looked one way along it to the East and the other way along it to the West, and saw that it was indeed the main road. He stayed for a minute to mop his brow. Then he turned to the right, with his face towards the setting sun, and resumed his journey.

BOOK 5

THE GRAND CANYON

Not by road and foot nor by sail and ocean
Shalt thou find any course that reaches
The world beyond the North.
PINDAR

The ephemerals have no help to give. Behold them;
They are deedless and cripple, like to
A dream. The kind of mortals
Is bound with a chain and their eyes are in darkness.
AESCHYLUS

Alas, what can they teach and not mislead,
Ignorant of themselves, of God much more,
And how the world began, and how man fell.
MILTON

THE GRAND CANYON

*John decides to live virtuously but at once
meets an obstacle – Conscience tells him he
can and must pass it by his own efforts –
Traditional Christianity says he cannot*

The main road soon began to ascend and after a short climb John found
himself on a bleak tableland which continued to rise before him, but at
a gentler angle. After he had walked a mile or so he saw the figure of a man
ahead, outlined against the setting sun. At first the figure stood still: then it
took a few paces to the left and to the right as if in indecision. Then it
turned about to face him, and to his surprise hailed him as an old acquaintance. Because of the light in his face John could not at first see who it was,
and they had joined hands before he knew that it was Vertue.

'What can have delayed you?' cried John, 'I thought by your pace when I
left you that you would have been a week's journey ahead of me by now.'

'If you think that,' said Vertue, 'your way must have been easier than
mine. Have you not crossed mountains?'

'I came through a pass,' said John.

'The main road took them without a bend,' said Vertue. 'And
I often made scarcely ten miles a day. But that does not signify: I have
learned something of climbing and sweated off a good deal of soft flesh.
What has really delayed me is this – I have been here for several days.'

With that he motioned John to proceed and they went forward together
to the brow of the slope. Then I saw John start back a pace or so with a cry,
for he had found that he stood on the edge of a precipice. Then presently he
re-approached it with caution and looked.

He saw that the road ran up without warning to the edge of a great gorge
or chasm and ended in the air, as if it had been broken off. The chasm might
be seven miles wide and as for its length, it stretched southward on his left
and northward on his right as far as he could see. The sun shining in his face
cast all the further side into shadow, so that he could not see much of it
clearly. It seemed to him, however, a rich country from the verdure and the
size of the trees.

'I have been exploring the cliffs,' said Vertue. 'And I think we could get
half-way down. Come a little nearer. You see that ledge?'

'I have a very poor head for heights,' said John.

'That one,' said Vertue, pointing to a narrow strip of greenery a thousand feet below them.

'I could never reach it.'

'Oh, you could reach *that* easily enough. The difficulty is to know what happens beyond it. I am inclined to think that it overhangs: and though we could get down to it, I am not sure that we could get back if the rest of the descent was impracticable.'

'Then it would be madness to trust ourselves so far.'

'I don't know about that. It would be in accordance with the rule.'

'What rule?'

'The rule is,' said Vertue, 'that if we have one chance out of a hundred of surviving, we must attempt it: but if we have none, absolutely none, then it would be self-destruction, and we need not.'

'It is no rule of mine,' said John.

'But it is. We all have the same set of rules, really, you know.'

'If it is a rule of mine, it is one that I cannot obey.'

'I don't think I understand you,' said Vertue. 'But of course you may be such a bad climber that *you* wouldn't have even one chance ... that would make a difference, I allow.'

Then a third voice spoke.

'You have neither of you any chance at all unless I carry you down.'

Both the young men turned at the sound. An old woman was seated in a kind of rocky chair at the very edge of the precipice.

'Oh, it's you, Mother Kirk, is it?' said Vertue, and added in an undertone to John, 'I have seen her about the cliffs more than once. Some of the country people say she is second-sighted, and some that she is crazy.'

'I shouldn't trust her,' said John in the same tone. 'She looks to me much more like a witch.' Then he turned to the old woman and said aloud: 'And how could you carry us down, mother? We would be more fit to carry you.'

'I could do it, though,' said Mother Kirk, 'by the power that the Landlord has given me.'

'So you believe in the Landlord, too?' said John.

'How can I not, dear,' said she, 'when I am his own daughter-in-law?'

'He does not give you very fine clothes,' said John, glancing at the old woman's country cloak.

'They'll last my time,' said the old woman placidly.

'We ought to try her,' whispered Vertue to John. 'As long as there is any chance we are not allowed to neglect it.' But John frowned at him to be silent and addressed the old woman again.

'Do you not think this Landlord of yours is a very strange one?' he said.

'How so?' said she.

'Why does he make a road like this running up to the very edge of a precipice – unless it is to encourage travellers to break their necks in the dark?'

'Oh, bless you, he never left it like that,' said the old woman. 'It was a good road all round the world when it was new, and all this gorge is far later than the road.'

'You mean,' said Vertue, 'that there has been some sort of catastrophe.'

'Well,' said Mother Kirk, 'I see there will be no getting you down tonight, so I may as well tell you the story. Come and sit down by me. You are neither of you so wise that you need be ashamed of listening to an old wives' tale.'

2

MOTHER KIRK'S STORY

*The Sin of Adam – Because of it all his
posterity find a chasm across their road*

When they were seated, the old woman told the following story:
'You must know that once upon a time there were no tenants in this
country at all, for the Landlord used to farm it himself. There were only the
animals and the Landlord used to look after them, he and his sons and
daughters. Every morning they used to come down from the mountains
and milk the cows and lead out the sheep to pasture. And they needed less
watching, for all the animals were tamer then: and there were no fences
needed, for if a wolf got in among the flocks he would do them no harm.
And one day the Landlord was going home from his day's work when he
looked round on the country, and the beasts, and saw how the crops were
springing, and it came into his head that the whole thing was too good to
keep to himself. So he decided to let the country to tenants, and his first
tenant was a young married man. But first the Landlord made a farm in the
very centre of the land where the soil was the best and the air most wholesome, and that was the very spot where you are sitting now. They were to
have the whole land, but that was too much for them to keep under cultivation. The Landlord's idea was that they could work the farm and leave the
rest as a park for the time being: but later they could divide the park up into
holdings for their children. For you must know that he drew up a very
different lease from the kind you have nowadays. It was a lease in
perpetuity on his side, for he promised never to turn them out; but on their
side, they could leave when they chose, as long as one of their sons was
there, to take the farm on, and then they could go up to live with him in the
mountains. He thought that would be a good thing because it would
broaden the minds of his own mountain children to mix with strangers.
And they thought so too. But before he put the tenants in possession there
was one thing he had to do. Up to this time the country had been full of a
certain fruit which the Landlord had planted for the refreshment of himself
and his children, if they were thirsty during the day as they worked down
here. It was a very good fruit and up in the mountains they say it is even

more plentiful: but it is very strong and only those who are mountain-bred ought to eat it, for only they can digest it properly. Hitherto, while there were only beasts in the land, it had done no harm for these mountain-apples to be growing in every thicket; for you know that an animal will eat nothing but what is good for it. But now that there were to be men in the land, the Landlord was afraid that they might do themselves an injury; yet it was not to be thought of that he should dig up every sapling of that tree and make the country into a desert. So he decided that it was best to be frank with the young people, and when he found a great big mountain-apple tree growing in the very centre of the farm he said, "So much the better. If they are to learn sense, they may as well learn it from the beginning: and if they will not, there's no help for it. For if they did not find mountain-apples on the farm, they would soon find them somewhere else." So he left the apple tree standing, and put the man and his wife into their farm: but before he left them he explained the whole affair to them – as much of it as could be explained – and warned them on no account to eat any of the apples. Then he went home. And for a time the young man and his wife behaved very well, tending the animals and managing their farm, and abstaining from the mountain-apples; and for all I know they might never have done otherwise if the wife had not somehow made a new acquaintance. This new acquaintance was a landowner himself. He had been born in the mountains and was one of our Landlord's own children, but he had quarrelled with his father and set up on his own, and now had built up a very considerable estate in another country. His estate marches, however, with this country: and as he was a great land-grabber he always wanted to take this bit in – and he has very nearly succeeded.'

'I've never met any tenants of his,' said John.

'Not tenants in chief, my dear,' said the old woman. 'And so you didn't know them. But you may have met the Clevers, who are the tenants of Mr Mammon: and he is a tenant of the Spirit of the Age: who holds directly of the Enemy.'

'I am sure the Clevers would be very surprised,' said John, 'to hear that they had a Landlord at all. They would think this enemy, as you call him, no less a superstition than *your* Landlord.'

'But that is how business is managed,' said Mother Kirk. 'The little people do not know the big people to whom they belong. The big people do not intend that they should. No important transference of property could be carried out if all the small people at the bottom knew what was really happening. But this is not part of my story. As I was saying, the enemy got to know the farmer's wife: and, however he did it, or whatever he said to her, it wasn't long before he persuaded her that the one thing she needed was a nice mountain-apple. And she took one and ate it. And then – you know how it is with husbands – she made the farmer come round to her mind. And at the moment he put out his hand and plucked the fruit there was an earthquake, and the country cracked open all the way across from North to South; and ever since, instead of the farm, there has been this gorge, which the country people call the Grand Canyon. But in my language its name is *Peccatum Adae*.'

3

THE SELF-SUFFICIENCY

OF VERTUE

*Fear is too suspicious, and the natural
conscience too proud, to accept help –
Rejecting Christianity, John turns to
cultured Worldliness*

'And I suppose,' said John sourly, 'the Landlord was so annoyed that it was he who invented the rules and the black hole?'

'The story is not quite so simple as that,' said the old woman, 'so many things happened after the eating of the apple. For one thing, the taste created such a craving in the man and the woman that they thought they could never eat enough of it; and they were not content with all the wild apple trees, but planted more and more, and grafted mountain-apple on to every other kind of tree so that every fruit should have a dash of that taste in it. They succeeded so well that the whole vegetable system of the country is now infected: and there is hardly a fruit or a root in the land – certainly none this side of the canyon – that has not a little mountain-apple in it. You have never tasted anything that was quite free from it.'

'And what has that got to do with the card of rules?' said John.

'Everything,' said Mother Kirk. 'In a country where all the food is more or less poisoned – but some of it very much less than more – you need very complicated rules indeed to keep healthy.'

'Meanwhile,' said Vertue, 'we are not getting on with our journey.'

'I will carry you down in the morning, if you like,' said Mother Kirk. 'Only mind you, it is a dangerous place, and you must do exactly as I tell you.'

'If the place is so dangerous –' began John, when Vertue, who had been struck by the woman's last words, suddenly broke in:

'I am afraid it is no use, mother,' he said; 'I cannot put myself under anyone's orders. I must be the captain of my soul and the master of my fate. But thank you for your offer.'

'You are right,' said John hastily, and added in a whisper, 'The old creature is clearly insane. Our real business is to explore this chasm North and South until we find some place where the descent *is* practicable.'

Vertue had risen.

'We are thinking, mother,' he said, 'that we should like to make sure for ourselves that there is no place where we cannot get down without being carried. You see my own legs have served me so far – and I should not like to start being carried now.'

'It will do you no harm to try,' answered Mother Kirk. 'And I should not wonder if you find a way down. Getting up the other side is another question, to be sure; but perhaps we shall meet again when it comes to that.'

By this time it was quite dark. The two young men bade good night to the woman and drew back along the main road to discuss their plans. Two by-roads branched off from it about a quarter of a mile from the precipice: and as that which went to the north seemed rather the better, and also pointed a little backward and away from the cliffs (which John was anxious not to skirt in the darkness), they turned northward. It was a fine starlit night and grew colder as they proceeded.

4

MR SENSIBLE

*The pretentiousness and cold frivolity of
cultured Worldliness – Far from attacking
the spiritual life, the cultured World
patronises it – 'The philosophy of all sensible
men' – Its hatred of all systematic reasoning
– Its ignorant and dilettante scepticism*

When they had walked rather more than a mile John drew Vertue's attention to a light a little back from the road: and I saw them follow it till they came to a gateway and after that to a door, and there they knocked.

'Whose house is this?' said Vertue when the servant opened to them.

'This is Mr Sensible's house,' said the servant. 'And if you are benighted travellers he will receive you gladly.'

Then he brought them into a room where a lamp was burning clearly, but not very brightly, and an old gentleman was seated by a blazing wood fire with his dog at his feet and his book on his knees and a jig-saw puzzle at one side of him spread out on a wooden frame, and on the other a chessboard with the pieces set for a problem. He rose to greet them very cordially but not hastily.

'You are very welcome, gentlemen,' said Mr Sensible. 'Pray come and warm yourselves. Drudge' (and here he called to the servant) 'make some supper ready for three: the usual supper, Drudge. I shall not be able to offer you luxury, gentlemen. The wine of my own country, cowslip wine, shall be your drink. It will be rough to your palates, but to mine the draught that I owe to my own garden and my own kitchen will always have a flavour beyond Hippocrene. The radishes, also of my own growing, I think I may venture to praise. But I see by your looks that I have already betrayed my foible. I confess that my garden is my pride. But what then? We are all children, and I reckon him the wisest among us that can make most sport out of the toys suitable to that condition, without seeking to go beyond it. *Regum æquabit opes animis.* Contentment, my friends, contentment is the best riches. Do not let the dog tease you, sir. He has mange. Down, Rover! Alas, Rover! thou little knowest that sentence is passed upon thee.'

'You are surely not going to destroy him, sir?' said John.

'He begins to ail,' said Mr Sensible. 'And it would be foolish to keep him longer. What would you? *Omnes eodem cogimur*. He has lain in the sun and hunted fleas enough, and now, poor fellow, he must go *quo dives Tullus et Ancus*. We must take life on the terms it is given us.'

'You will miss your old companion.'

'Why, as to that you know, the great art of life is to moderate our passions. Objects of affection are like other belongings. We must love them enough to enrich our lives while we have them – not enough to impoverish our lives when they are gone. You see this puzzle here. While I am engaged on it it seems to me of sovereign importance to fit the pieces together: when it is done I think of it no more: and if I should fail to do it, why I should not break my heart. Confound that Drudge. Hi! whoreson, are we to wait all night for our supper?'

'Coming, sir,' said Drudge from the kitchen.

'I think the fellow goes to sleep over his pots and pans,' said Mr Sensible, 'but let us occupy the time by continuing our conversation. Good conversation I reckon among the finer sweets of life. But I would not include diatribe or lecturing or persistent discussion under that head. Your doctrinaire is the bane of all talk. As I sit here listening to your opinions – *nullius addictus* – and following the ball wherever it rolls, I defy system. I love to explore your minds *en déshabille*. Nothing comes amiss – *j'aime le jeu, l'amour, les livres, la musique, la ville et la champagne – enfin tout*! Chance is, after all, our best guide – need I call a better witness than the fortunate cast of the dice which has brought you beneath my roof tonight?'

'It wasn't exactly chance,' said Vertue, who had been restlessly waiting to speak. 'We are on a journey and we are looking for a way to cross the Grand Canyon.'

'*Haud equidem invideo*,' said the old gentleman. 'You do not insist on my accompanying you?'

'We hadn't thought of it,' said John.

'Why then I am very willing that you should go!' cried Mr Sensible with a burst of melodious laughter. 'And yet to what end? I often amuse myself with speculating on that curious restlessness in the mind which drives us, specially in youth, to climb up a mountain merely in order that we may then climb down, or to cross the seas in order that we may pay an inn-keeper for setting before us worse cheer than we might eat in our own house. *Caelum non animum mutamus*. Not that I would repress the impulse, you understand, any more than I would starve any other part of my nature. Here again, the secret of happiness lies in knowing where to stop. A moderate allowance of travelling – enough to quiet, without satiating, a liberal curiosity – is very well. One brings back a few rarities to store in one's inner cabinet against a dull day. But the Grand Canyon – surely a modest tour along the cliffs on *this* side of it would give you much the same sort of scenery, and save your necks.'

'It wasn't scenery we were looking for,' said John. 'I am trying to find the Island in the West.'

'You refer, no doubt, to some aesthetic experience. There again – I would not urge a young man to shut his eyes to that sort of thing. Who has not felt immortal longings at the lengthening of the shadow or the turning of the leaf? Who not stretched out his hands for the ulterior shore? *Et ego in Arcadia*! We have all been fools once – aye, and are glad to have been fools too. But our imaginations, like our appetites, need discipline: not, heaven help us, in the interest of any transcendental ethic, but in the interests of our own solid good. That wild impulse must be tasted, not obeyed. The bees have stings, but we rob them of their honey. To hold all that urgent sweetness to our lips in the cup of one perfect moment, missing no faintest ingredient in the flavour of its μονόχρονος ἡδονή, yet ourselves, in a sense, unmoved – this is the true art. This tames in the service of the reasonable life even those pleasures whose loss might seem to be the heaviest, yet necessary, price we paid for rationality. Is it an audacity to hint that for the corrected palate the taste of the draught even owes its last sweetness to the knowledge that we have wrested it from an unwilling source? To cut off pleasures from the consequences and conditions which they have by nature, detaching, as it were, the precious phrase from its irrelevant context, is what distinguishes the man from the brute and the citizen from the savage. I cannot join with those moralists who inveigh against the Roman emetics in their banquets: still less with those who would forbid the even more beneficient contraceptive devices of our later times. That man who can eat as taste, not nature, prompts him and yet fear no aching belly, or who can indulge in Venus and fear no impertinent bastard, is a civilized man. In him I recognize Urbanity – the note of the centre.'

'Do you know of any way across the canyon?' said Vertue abruptly.

'I do not,' said their host, 'for I have never made inquiries. The proper study of mankind is man, and I have always left useless speculations alone. Suppose that there were a way across, to what purpose should I use it? Why should I scramble down this side and up the other to find after my labours the same soil still beneath me and the same heaven above? It would be laughable to suppose that the country beyond the gorge can be any different from the country on this side of it. *Eadem sunt omnia semper.* Nature has already done all she can for our comfort and amusement, and the man who does not find content at home will seek it vainly abroad. Confound that fellow! Drudge!! Will you bring us our supper or do you prefer to have every bone in your body broken?'

'Coming, sir,' said Drudge from the kitchen.

'There might be different *people* on the other side of the canyon,' suggested John in the momentary pause that followed.

'That is even less likely,' said Mr Sensible. 'Human nature is always the same. The dress and the manners may vary, but I detect the unchanging heart beneath the shifting disguises. If there are men beyond the canyon, rest assured that we know them already. They are born and they die: and in the interval between they are the same lovable rascals that we know at home.'

'Still,' said John, 'you can't really be certain that there is no such place as my Island. Reason left it an open question.'

'Reason!' exclaimed Mr Sensible. 'Do you mean the mad woman who goes riding about the country dressed up in armour? I trust that when I spoke of the reasonable life you did not think that I meant anything under *her* auspices? There is a strange confusion in our language here, for the reasonableness which I commend has no more dangerous enemy than Reason. Perhaps I should drop the use of the name altogether, and say that my deity is not reason but *le bon sens*.'

'What is the difference?' said Vertue.

'Sense is easy, Reason is hard. Sense knows where to stop with gracious inconsistency, while Reason slavishly follows an abstract logic whither she knows not. The one seeks comfort and finds it, the other seeks truth and is still seeking. *Le bon sens* is the father of a flourishing family: Reason is barren and a virgin. If I had my way I should clap this Reason of yours in the bridewell to pursue her meditations in the straw. The baggage has a pretty face, I allow: but she leads us from our true aim – joy, pleasure, ease, content, whate'er the name! She is a fanatic who has never learned from my master to pursue the golden mean, and, being a mortal, to think mortal thoughts. *Auream quis quis –*'

'It is very odd that you should say that,' interrupted Vertue, 'for I also was brought up on Aristotle. But I think my text must have differed from yours. In mine, the doctrine of the Mean does not bear the sense you have given it at all. He specially says that there is no excess of goodness. You cannot go too far in the right direction. The line that we should follow may start from a middle point in the base of a triangle: but the further off the apex is, the better. In that dimension –'

'*Do manus!*' broke out Mr Sensible. 'Spare us the rest, young man. We are not at a lecture, and I readily admit that your scholarship is more recent than mine. Philosophy should be our mistress, not our master: and the pursuit of a pedantic accuracy amidst the freedom of our social pleasures is as unwelcome as –'

'And the bit about thinking mortal thoughts,' continued Vertue, whose social experience, as I dreamed, was not extensive, 'the bit about mortal thoughts was quoted by Aristotle to say that he disagreed with it. He held that the end of mortal life was to put on immortality as much as might be. And he also said that the most useless of studies was the noblest.'

'I see you are letter-perfect, young man,' said Mr Sensible, with a rather chilly smile, 'and I am sure these pieces of information, if repeated to your teachers, would win the applause they deserve. Here, if you will forgive me, they are a little out of place. A gentleman's knowledge of the ancient authors is not that of a pedant: and I think you have misunderstood the place which philosophy ought to hold in the reasonable life. We do not memorise *systems*. What system can stand? What system does not leave us with the old refrain – *que sais-je?* It is in her power to remind us of the strangeness of things – in the brown charm of her secluded meditations – above all, in her decorative function – that philosophy becomes instrumental to the good life. We go to the Porch and the Academy to be spectators, not partisans. Drudge!!'

'Dinner is served, sir,' said Drudge, appearing at the door.

Then I dreamed that they went into the dining room and so to table.

5

TABLE TALK

The cultured World's unacknowledged
dependences – 'The religion of all
sensible men'

The cowslip wine came with the oysters. It was a little rough, as the old gentleman had prophesied, and the glasses were so very small that Vertue drained his at once. John was afraid that there might be no more to come and therefore dallied over his, partly because he feared that he might put his host out of countenance and partly because he disliked the taste. But his precautions were needless, for with the soup came sherry.

'*Dapibus mensas onerabat inemptis*!' said Mr Sensible. 'I hope that this wild garden vintage is not unpleasing to an unspoiled palate.'

'You don't mean to say that you have vines?' exclaimed John.

'I was referring to the cowslip wine,' said Mr Sensible. 'I hope to have some good vines soon, but at present I still rely a little on my neighbours. Is this our own sherry, Drudge?'

'No, sir,' said Drudge. 'This is that lot that Mr Broad sent.'

'Halibut!' said John. 'You surely don't –'

'No,' said Mr Sensible. 'Sea fish, I confess, I must get from my friends on the coast.'

As the meal went on, John's good manners forbade him to make further inquiries, and when a salad came with one or two very small radishes in it he was positively relieved that his host should be able to claim them as his own produce ('His humble sauce a radish or an egg,' said Mr Sensible). But in my dream I was privileged to know the sources of the whole meal. The cowslip wine and the radishes were home-grown; the joint had been a present from Mr Mammon: the entrées and savouries came from Eschropolis: the champagne and ices from old Mr Halfways. Some of the food was part of the stores which Mr Sensible had taken over when he came to live there, from his predecessors who had occupied this house before him: for on that table-land, and especially to the North of the main road, the air is so light and cold that things keep for a long time. The bread, the salt, and the apples had been left by Epicurus who was the builder of the house and its first inhabitant. Some very fine hock had belonged to Horace. The claret and also (as I remember) most of the silver, were Montaigne's. But the port, which was one in a thousand and the best thing on that table, had once belonged to Rabelais, who in his turn had it as a present from old Mother Kirk when they were friends. Then I dreamed that after dinner old Mr Sensible stood up and made a little speech in Latin thanking the Landlord for all they had received.

'What?' said John. 'Do *you* believe in the Landlord?'

'No part of our nature is to be suppressed,' said Mr Sensible. 'Least of all a part that has enshrined itself in beautiful traditions. The Landlord has his function like everything else as one element in the good life.'

Then presently Mr Sensible, who was turning very red, fixed his eyes intently on John and repeated:

'As one element. As one element.'

'I see,' said John, and there was a long silence.

'As well,' began Mr Sensible, with great energy some ten minutes later, 'it is part of good manners. Αθανάτους μὲν πρῶτα θεούς νόμῳ ὡς διάκειται– Τμα. My dear Mr Vertue, my dear young friend, your glass is quite empty. I mean absolutely empty. *Cras ingens iterabimus.*'

There was another and longer pause. John began to wonder whether Mr Sensible were not asleep, when suddenly Mr Sensible said with great conviction:

'*Pellite cras ingens tum-tum* νόμῳ ὡς διάκειται.'

Then he smiled at them and finally went to sleep. And presently Drudge came in looking old and thin and dirty in the pale morning light – for I thought that the dawn was just then beginning to show through the chinks of the shutters – to carry his master to bed. Then I saw him come back and lead the guests to their beds. And then the third time I saw him come back into the dining-room and pour out the remains of the claret into a glass and drink it off. Then he stood for a moment or so blinking his red eyes and rubbing his bony, stubbly chin. At last he yawned and set about tidying the room for breakfast.

6

DRUDGE

The 'sensible' men are parasitic –
Their culture is precarious

I dreamed that John awoke feeling cold. The chamber in which he lay was luxuriously furnished and all the house was silent, so that John thought it would be useless to rise, and he piled all his clothes on him and tried to sleep again. But he only grew colder. Then he said to himself, 'Even if there is no chance of breakfast, I may save myself from freezing by walking about.' So he rose and huddled on all his clothes and went down into the house, but the fires were not yet lit. Finding the back door open he went out. It was full morning of a grey, sunless day. There were dark clouds, fairly low, and as John came out one snowflake fell at his feet, but no more. He found that he was in Mr Sensible's garden, but it was more of a yard than a garden. A high wall ran all about it and all within the wall was dry, brown earth, with a few stony paths. Dibbling the earth with his foot, John found that the soil was only half an inch deep: under it was solid rock. A little way from the house he found Drudge down on his hands and knees scraping together what seemed to be a little pile of dust, but it was in fact the soil of the garden. The little pile had been got together at the cost of leaving the rock uncovered for a big circle – like a bald patch – all round Drudge.

'Good morning, Drudge,' said John. 'What are you making?'

'Radish beds, sir.'

'Your master is a great gardener.'

'Talks about it, sir.'

'Does he not work in the garden himself?'

'No, sir.'

'It is a poor soil here. Does he manage to feed himself on his own produce in a good year?'

'Feeds me on it, sir.'

'What does the garden grow – besides radishes?'

'Nothing, sir.'

John passed on to the end of the garden and looked over the wall, which was lower here. He drew back with a little start for he found that he was

188

looking down an abyss: the garden was perched on the edge of the Grand Canyon. Below John's feet, at the bottom of the gorge, lay the forest, and on the opposite side he saw a mixture of wood and cliff. The cliffs were all shaggy with trailing and hanging greenery and streams, rendered immovable to sight by their distance, came down from the land beyond. Even on that cold morning the farther side looked richer and warmer than his own.

'We must get out of this,' said John. At that moment Drudge called to him.

'I shouldn't lean on that wall, sir,' he said. 'There's frequent landslides.'

'Landslides?'

'Yes, sir. I've rebuilt that wall a dozen times. The house used to be right out there – half-way across the gorge.'

'The canyon is getting wider, then?'

'At this point, sir. In Mr Epicurus' time –'

'You have been employed here under other masters, then?'

'Yes, sir. I've seen a good many of them. Whoever has lived here has always needed me. Choregia they used to call me in the old days, but now they just call me Drudge.'

'Tell me about your old masters,' said John.

'Mr Epicurus was the first. Mental case he was, poor gentleman: he had a chronic fear of the black hole. Something dreadful. I never had a better employer, though. Nice, kind, quiet-spoken sort of a man. I was very sorry when he went down the cliff –'

'Goodness me!' exclaimed John. 'Do you mean that some of your masters have lost their lives in these landslides?'

'Most of them, sir.'

At that moment a leonine roar came from one of the upper windows of the house.

'Drudge! Son of a bitch! Hot water.'

'Coming, sir,' said Drudge, rising very deliberately from his knees and giving a finishing pat to his heap of dust. 'I shall be leaving here soon,' he continued to John. 'I am thinking of going further North.'

'Further North?'

'Yes, sir. There are openings with Mr Savage up in the mountains. I was wondering if you and Mr Vertue were going that way –'

'Drudge!' bellowed Mr Sensible's voice from the house.

'Coming, sir,' said Drudge, beginning to untie two pieces of string with which he had confined his trousers beneath his knees. 'So you see, Mr John, I should be greatly obliged if you would allow me to travel with you.'

'Drudge! Am I to call you again?' shouted Mr Sensible.

'Coming, sir. If you was to agree I would give Mr Sensible notice this morning.'

'We are certainly going North for a bit,' said John. 'And I should have no objection, provided Mr Vertue agrees.'

'Very kind of you, I am sure, sir,' said Drudge. Then he turned and walked slowly into the house.

7

THE GAUCHERIE OF VERTUE

Take away the cultured World's power
of commanding labour – And the whole
thing collapses

M r Sensible was not in good humour when they met at breakfast. 'That ungrateful blockhead of a servant of mine is leaving me in the lurch,' he said, 'and for the next few days we must shift for ourselves. I fear I am a wretched cook. Perhaps, Vertue, you would indulge me so far as to take the cooking on yourself until I get a new man? I dare say you could enable the three of us to live a very tolerable sort of picnic life for three days?'

The two young men informed him that they were continuing their journey after breakfast.

'This,' said Mr Sensible, 'is getting really serious. Do you mean to say that you are going to desert me? I am to be reduced to absolute solitude – deprived of the common decencies of life – compelled to spend my day in menial offices? Very well, sir, I am unacquainted with modern manners: no doubt this is the way in which young men now return hospitality.'

'I beg your pardon, sir,' said Vertue. 'I had not seen it in that light. I will certainly act as our servant for a day or so if you wish it. I had not understood that it would be such a burden to you to cook for yourself. I don't remember that you said anything about servants when you were outlining the good life last night.'

'Why, sir,' said Mr Sensible. 'When I outline the principles of the steam engine I do not explicitly state that I expect fire to burn or the laws of gravity to operate. There are certain things that one always takes for granted. When I speak of the art of life I presuppose the ordinary conditions of life which that art utilises.'

'Such as wealth,' said Vertue.

'A competence, a competence,' said Mr Sensible.

'And health, too?' said Vertue.

'Moderate health,' said Mr Sensible.

'Your art, then,' said Vertue, 'seems to teach men that the best way of being happy is to enjoy unbroken good fortune in every respect. They would not all find the advice helpful. And now, if Drudge will show me his scullery, I will wash up the breakfast things.'

'You may save yourself the trouble, sir,' said Mr Sensible drily. 'I cannot pretend to your intensity, and I do not choose to be lectured at the breakfast table. When you have mixed more with the world you will learn not to turn the social board into a school room. In the meantime, forgive me if I feel that I should find your continued society a little fatiguing. Conversation should be like the bee which darts to the next flower before the last has ceased swaying from its airy visit: you make it more like a wood beetle eating its way through a table.'

'As you wish,' said Vertue, 'but how will you do?'

'I shall shut up the house,' said Mr Sensible, 'and practise αὐτάρκεια in a hotel until I have fitted this place up with such mechanical devices as will henceforth render me wholly independent. I see that I have let myself get behind the times. I should have listened more to certain good friends of mine in the city of Claptrap who have kept abreast of modern invention. They assure me that machinery will soon put the good life beyond the reach of chance: and if mechanism alone will not do it I know a eugenist who promises to breed us a race of peons who will be psychologically incapable of playing me a trick like this of Drudge's.'

So it fell out that all four left the house together. Mr Sensible was astonished to find that Drudge (who parted from his employer very civilly) was accompanying the young men. He only shrugged his shoulders, however, and said, '*Vive la bagatelle*! You have stayed in my house which is called Thelema, and its motto is *Do what you will*. So many men, so many minds. I hope I can tolerate anything except intolerance.' Then he went his way and they saw him no more.

BOOK 6

NORTHWARD ALONG

THE CANYON

For being unlike the magnanimous man,
they yet ape him; and that in such particulars
as they can.
ARISTOTLE

Much of the soul they talk, but all awry,
And in themselves seek virtue.
MILTON

I do not admire the excess of some one virtue
unless I am shewn at the same time the
excess of the opposite virtue. A man does not
prove his greatness by standing at an
extremity, but by touching both extremities
at once and filling all that lies between them.
PASCAL

Contempt is a well-recognized defensive
reaction.
I. A. RICHARDS

FIRST STEPS TO THE NORTH

Accompanied by poverty and virtue – John
travels into sterner regions of the mind

'It is of no use keeping to the road,' said Vertue. 'We must explore the cliff-edge as we go along and make trial descents from point to point.'

'Begging your pardon, sir,' said Drudge, 'I know these parts very well and there is no way down, at least within thirty miles. You'll miss nothing by keeping to the road for today at any rate.'

'How do you know?' asked Vertue. 'Have you ever tried?'

'Oh, bless you, yes,' said Drudge. 'I've often tried to get across the canyon when I was a youngster.'

'Clearly we had better follow the road,' said John.

'I do not feel quite satisfied,' said Vertue. 'But we can always take the cliffs on the way back. I have an idea that if there is a way down it will be at the extreme north where this gorge opens on the sea: or failing everything, we might manipulate the mouth of the gorge by boat. In the meantime I dare say we might do worse than press on by road.'

'I quite agree,' said John.

Then I saw the three set forward on a more desolate march than I had yet beheld. On every side of them the tableland seemed perfectly flat, but their muscles and lungs soon told them that there was a slight but continuous rise. There was little vegetation – here a shrub, and there some grass: but the most of it was brown earth and moss and rock, and the road beneath them was stone. The grey sky was never broken and I do not remember that they saw a single bird: and it was so bleak that if they stopped at any time to rest, the sweat grew cold on them instantly.

Vertue never abated his pace and Drudge kept even with him though always a respectful yard behind: but I saw that John grew footsore and began to lag. For some hours he was always inventing pretexts to stop and finally he said, 'Friends, it is no use, I can go no further.'

'But you must,' said Vertue.

'The young gentleman is soft, sir, very soft,' said Drudge. 'He is not used to this sort of thing. We'll have to help him along.'

So they took him, one by each arm, and helped him along for a few hours. They found nothing to eat or drink in the waste. Towards evening they heard a desolate voice crying 'Maiwi-maiwi', and looked up, and there was a seagull hanging in the currents of the wind as though it sauntered an invisible stair towards the low rain-clouds.

'Good!' cried Vertue. 'We are nearing the coast.'

'It's a good step yet, sir,' said Drudge. 'These gulls come forty miles inland and more in bad weather.'

Then they plodded on for many more miles. And the sky began to turn from sunless grey to starless black. And they looked and saw a little shanty by the roadside and there they knocked on the door.

THREE PALE MEN

*Counter-romanticism makes strange
bedfellows – Modern thought begets
Freudianism on baser, Negativism on
finer, souls – These men are interested
in everything not for what it is
but for what it is not*

When they were let in they found three young men, all very thin and pale, seated by a stove under the low roof of the hut. There was some sacking on a bench along one wall and little comfort else.

'You will fare badly here,' said one of the three men. 'But I am a Steward and it is my duty according to my office to share my supper with you. You may come in.' His name was Mr Neo-Angular.

'I am sorry that my convictions do not allow me to repeat my friend's offer,' said one of the others. 'But I have had to abandon the humanitarian and egalitarian fallacies.' His name was Mr Neo-Classical.

'I hope,' said the third, 'that your wanderings in lonely places do not mean that you have any of the romantic virus still in your blood.' His name was Mr Humanist.

John was too tired and Drudge too respectful to reply: but Vertue said to Mr Neo-Angular, 'You are very kind. You are saving our lives.'

'I am not kind at all,' said Mr Neo-Angular with some warmth. 'I am doing my duty. My ethics are based on dogma, not on feeling.'

'I understand you very well,' said Vertue. 'May I shake hands with you?'

'Can it be,' said the other, 'that you are one of us? You are a Catholic? A scholastic?'

'I know nothing about that,' said Vertue, 'but I know that the rule is to be obeyed because it is a rule and not because it appeals to my feelings at the moment.'

'I see you are not one of us,' said Angular, 'and you are undoubtedly damned. *Virtutes paganorum splendida vitia.* Now let us eat.'

Then I dreamed that the three pale men produced three tins of bully beef and six biscuits, and Angular shared his with the guests. There was very little for each and I thought that the best share fell to John and Drudge, for Vertue and the young Steward entered into a kind of rivalry over who should leave most for the others.

'Our fare is simple,' said Mr Neo-Classical. 'And perhaps unwelcome to palates that have been reared on the kickshaws of lower countries. But you see the perfection of form. This beef is a perfect cube: this biscuit a true square.'

'You will admit,' said Mr Humanist, 'that, at least, our meal is quite free from any lingering flavour of the old romantic sauces.'

'Quite free,' said John, staring at the empty tin.

'It's better than radishes, sir,' said Drudge.

'Do you *live* here, gentlemen?' said Vertue when the empty tins had been removed.

'We do,' said Mr Humanist. 'We are founding a new community. At present we suffer the hardships of pioneers and have to import our food: but when we have brought the country under cultivation we shall have plenty – as much as is needed for the practice of temperance.'

'You interest me exceedingly,' said Vertue. 'What are the principles of this community?'

'Catholicism, Humanism, Classicism,' said all three.

'Catholicism! Then you are all Stewards?'

'Certainly not,' said Classical and Humanist.

'At least you all believe in the Landlord?'

'I have no interest in the question,' said Classical.

'And I,' said Humanist, 'know perfectly well that the Landlord is a fable.'

'And I,' said Angular, 'know perfectly well that he is a fact.'

'This is very surprising,' said Vertue. 'I do not see how you have come together, or what your common principles can possibly be.'

'We are united by a common antagonism to a common enemy,' said Humanist. 'You must understand that we are three brothers, the sons of old Mr Enlightenment of the town of Claptrap.'

'I know him,' said John.

'Our father was married, twice,' continued Humanist. 'Once to a lady named Epichaerecacia, and afterwards to Euphuia. By his first wife he had a son called Sigismund who is thus our step-brother.'

'I know him too,' said John.

'We are the children of his second marriage,' said Humanist.

'Then,' cried Vertue, 'we are related – if you care to acknowledge the kinship. You have probably heard that Euphuia had a child before she married your father. I was that child – though I confess that I never discovered who my father was and enemies have hinted that I am a bastard.'

'You have said quite sufficient,' replied Angular. 'You can hardly expect that the subject should be agreeable to us. I might add that my office, if there were nothing else, sets me apart even from my legitimate relations.'

'And what about the common antagonism?' said John.

'We were all brought up,' said Humanist, 'by our step-brother in the university at Eschropolis, and we learned there to see that whoever stays with Mr Halfways must either come on to Eschropolis or else remain at Thrill as the perpetual minion of his brown daughter.'

'You had not been with Mr Halfways yourselves, then?' asked John.

'Certainly not. We learned to hate him from watching the effect which his music had on other people. Hatred of him is the first thing that unites us. Next, we discovered how residence in Eschropolis inevitably leads to the giant's dungeon.'

'I know all about that too,' said John.

'Our common hatred therefore links us together against the giant, against Eschropolis, and against Mr Halfways.'

'But specially against the latter,' said Classical.

'I should rather say,' remarked Angular, 'against half measures and compromises of all sorts – against any pretence that there is any kind of goodness or decency, any even tolerable temporary resting place, on this side of the Grand Canyon.'

'And that,' said Classical, 'is why Angular is for me, in one sense, the enemy, but, in another, *the* friend. I cannot agree with his notions about the other side of the canyon: but just because he relegates his delusions to the *other* side, he is free to agree with me about this side and to be an implacable exposer (like myself) of all attempts to foist upon us any transcendental, romantic, optimistic trash.'

'My own feeling,' said Humanist, 'is rather that Angular is with me in guarding against any confusion of the *levels* of experience. He *canalises* all the mystical nonsense – the *sehnsucht* and *Wanderlust* and Nympholepsy – and transfers them to the far side: that prevents their drifting about on this side and hindering our real function. It leaves us free to establish a really tolerable and even comfortable civilisation here on the plateau; a culture based alike on those truths which Mr Sensible acknowledges and on those which the giant reveals, but throwing over both alike a graceful veil of illusion. And that way we shall remain human: we shall not become beasts with the giant nor abortive angels with Mr Halfways.'

'The young gentleman is asleep, sir,' said Drudge: and indeed John had sunk down some time ago.

'You must excuse him,' said Vertue. 'He found the road long today.'

Then I saw that all six men lay down together in the sacking. The night was far colder than the night they passed in Mr Sensible's house: but as there was here no pretence of comfort and they lay huddled together in the narrow hut, John slept warmer here than at Thelema.

3

NEO-ANGULAR

The men talk as if they had 'seen through'
things they have not even seen

When they rose in the morning John was so footsore and his limbs ached so that he knew not how to continue his journey. Drudge assured them that the coast could not now be very far. He thought that Vertue could reach it and return in a day and that John might await him in the hut. As for John himself, he was loth to burden hosts who lived in such apparent poverty: but Mr Angular constrained him to stay, when he had explained that the secular virtue of hospitality was worthless and care for the afflicted a sin if it proceeded from humanitarian sentiment, but that he was obliged to act as he did by the rules of his order. So, in my dream, I saw Drudge and Vertue set out northwards alone, while John remained with the three pale men.

In the forenoon he had a conversation with Angular.

'You believe then,' said John, 'that there is a way across the canyon?'

'I know there is. If you will let me take you to Mother Kirk she will carry you over in a moment.'

'And yet, I am not sure that I am not sailing under false colours. When I set out from home, crossing the canyon was never in my thoughts – still less was Mother Kirk.'

'It does not matter in the least what was in your thoughts.'

'It does, to me. You see, my only motive for crossing, is the hope that something I am looking for may be on the other side.'

'That is a dangerous, subjective motive. What is this something?'

'I saw an Island –'

'Then you must forget it as soon as you can. Islands are the Halfways' concern. I assure you, you must eradicate every trace of that nonsense from your mind before I can help you.'

'But how can you help me after removing the only thing that I want to be helped to? What is the use of telling a hungry man that you will grant him his desires, provided there is no question of eating?'

'If you do not *want* to cross the canyon, there is no more to be said. But, then, you must realise where you are. Go on with your Island, if you like, but do not pretend that it is anything but a part of the land of destruction this side of the canyon. If you are a sinner, for heaven's sake have the grace to be a cynic too.'

'But how can you say that the Island is all bad, when it is longing for the Island, and nothing else, that has brought me this far?'

'It makes no difference. All on this side of the canyon is much of a muchness. If you confine yourself to this side, then the Spirit of the Age is right.'

'But this is not what Mother Kirk said. She particularly insisted that some of the food was much less poisonous than the rest.'

'So you have met Mother Kirk? No wonder that you are confused. You had no business to talk to her except through a qualified Steward. Depend upon it, you have misunderstood every word she said.'

'Then there was Reason, too. She refused to say that the Island was an illusion. But perhaps, like Mr Sensible, you have quarrelled with Reason.'

'Reason is divine. But how should you understand her? You are a beginner. For you, the only safe commerce with Reason is to learn from your superiors the dogmata in which her deliverances have been codified for general use.'

'Look here,' said John. 'Have you ever seen my Island?'

'God forbid.'

'And you have never heard Mr Halfways either.'

'Never. And I never will. Do you take me for an escapist?'

'Then there is at least one object in the world of which I know more than you. I have *tasted* what you call romantic trash; you have only talked about it. You need not tell me that there is a danger in it and an element of evil. Do you suppose that I have not felt that danger and that evil a thousand times more than you? But I know also that the evil in it is not what I went to it to find, and that I should have sought nothing and found nothing without it. I know this by experience as I know a dozen things about it of which you betray your ignorance as often as you speak. Forgive me if I am rude: but how is it possible that you can advise me in this matter? Would you recommend a eunuch as confessor to a man whose difficulties lay in the realm of chastity? Would a man born blind be my best guide against the lust of the eye? But I am getting angry. And you have shared your biscuit with me. I ask your pardon.'

'It is part of my office to bear insults with patience,' said Mr Angular.

4

HUMANIST

They boast of rejecting what was never in
fact within their reach

In the afternoon Mr Humanist took John out to show him the garden, by whose produce, in time, the new culture was to become self-supporting. As there was no human, or indeed animal, habitation within sight, no wall or fence had been deemed necessary but the area of the garden had been marked out by a line of stones and sea-shells alternately arranged: and this was necessary as the garden would else have been indistinguishable from the waste. A few paths, also marked by stones and shells, were arranged in a geometrical pattern.

'You see,' said Mr Humanist, 'we have quite abandoned the ideas of the old romantic landscape gardeners. You notice a certain severity. A landscape gardener would have had a nodding grove over there on the right, and a mound on the left, and winding paths, and a pond, and flower-beds. He would have filled the obscurer parts with the means of sensuality – the formless potato and the romantically irregular cabbage. You see, there is nothing of the sort here.'

'Nothing at all,' said John.

'At present, of course, it is not very fruitful. But we are pioneers.'

'Do you ever try *digging* it?' suggested John.

'Why, no,' said Mr Humanist, 'you see, it is pure rock an inch below the surface, so we do not disturb the soil. That would remove the graceful veil of illusion which is so necessary to the *human* point of view.'

5

FOOD FROM THE NORTH

This region has no strength to resist
philosophies more inhuman than its own

L ate that evening the door of the hut opened and Vertue staggered in and
dropped to a sitting position by the stove. He was very exhausted and
it was long before he had his breath to talk. When he had, his first words
were:

'You must leave this place, gentlemen. It is in danger.'

'Where is Drudge?' said John.

'He stayed there.'

'And what is this danger?' asked Mr Humanist.

'I'm going to tell you. By the by, there's no way over the gorge northward.'

'We have been on a fool's errand, then,' said John, 'ever since we left the
main road.'

'Except that now we know,' replied Vertue. 'But I must eat before I can
tell my story. Tonight I am able to return our friends' hospitality,' and with
that he produced from various parts of his clothing the remains of a handsome cold pie, two bottles of strong beer and a little flask of rum. For
some time there was silence in the hut, and when the meal was finished and
a little water had been boiled so that each had a glass of hot grog, Vertue
began his story.

6

FURTHEST NORTH

The revolutionary sub-men, whether of
the Left or the Right – Who are all alike
vassals of cruelty – Heroic Nihilism laughs
at the less thoroughgoing forms of Tough-
Mindedness

'It is all like this as far as the mountains – about fifteen miles – and there is nothing to tell of our journey except rock and moss and a few gulls. The mountains are frightful as you approach them, but the road runs up to a pass and we had not much difficulty. Beyond the pass you get into a little rocky valley and it was here that we first found any signs of habitation. The valley is a regular warren of caves inhabited by dwarfs. There are several species of them, I gather, though I only distinguished two – a black kind with black shirts and a red kind who call themselves Marxomanni. They are all very fierce and apparently quarrel a good deal but they all acknowledge some kind of vassalage to this man Savage. At least they made no difficulty in letting me through when they heard that I wanted to see him – beyond insisting on giving me a guard. It was there I lost Drudge. He said he had come to join the red dwarfs and would I mind going on alone. He was just the same up to the end – civil as ever – but he was down one of their burrows and apparently quite at home before I could get in a word. Then my dwarfs took me on. I didn't care for the arrangements much. They were not men, you know, not dwarf men, but real dwarfs – trolls. They could talk, and they walk on two legs, but the structure must be quite different from ours. I felt all the time that if they killed me it wouldn't be murder, any more than if a crocodile or a gorilla killed me. It *is* a different species – however it came there. Different faces.

'Well, they kept taking me up and up. It was all rocky zig-zags, round and round. Fortunately, I do not get giddy. My chief danger was the wind whenever we got on a ridge – for of course my guides, being only some three feet high, did not offer it the same target. I had one or two narrow escapes. Savage's nest is a terrifying place. It is a long hall like a barn and when I first caught sight of it – half-way up the sky from where they were leading me – I thought to myself that wherever else we were going it could not be *there*; it looked so inaccessible. But on we went.

'One thing you must get into your heads is that there are caves all the way up, all inhabited. The whole mountain must be honeycombed. I saw thousands of the dwarfs. Like an ant-hill – and not a man in the place except me.

'From Savage's nest you look straight down to the sea. I should think it is the biggest sheer drop on any coast. It was from there that I saw the mouth of the gorge. The mouth is only a lowering of the cliff: from the lowest part of the opening it is still thousands of feet to the sea. There is no conceivable landing. It is no use to anyone but seagulls.

'But you want to hear about Savage. He sat on a high chair at the end of his barn – a very big man, almost a giant. When I say that I don't mean his height: I had the same feeling about him that I had about the dwarfs. That doubt about the *species*. He was dressed in skins and had an iron helmet on his head with horns stuck in it.

'He had a woman there, too, a great big woman with yellow hair and high cheek-bones. Grimhild her name is. And the funny thing is that she is the sister of an old friend of yours, John. She is Mr Halfways' elder daughter. Apparently Savage came down to Thrill and carried her off: and what is stranger still, both the girl and the old gentleman were rather pleased about it than otherwise.

'As soon as the dwarfs brought me in, Savage rapped on the table and bellowed out, "Lay the board for us men," and she set about laying it. He didn't say anything to me for a long time. He just sat and looked and sang. He had only one song and he was singing it off and on all the time I was there. I remember bits of it.

Wind age, wolf age,
Ere the world crumbles:
Shard age, spear age,
Shields are broken...

'Then there was another bit began:

East sits the Old 'Un
In Iron-forest;
Feeds amidst it
Fenris' children...

'I sat down after a bit, for I did not want him to think I was afraid of him. When the food was on the table he asked me to have some, so I had it. He offered me a sweet drink, very strong, in a horn, so I drank it. Then he shouted and drank himself and said that mead in a horn was all he could offer me at present: "But soon," he said, "I shall drink the blood of men from skulls." There was a lot of this sort of stuff. We ate roast pork, with our fingers. He kept on singing his song and shouting. It was only after dinner that he began to talk connectedly. I wish I could remember it all. This is the important part of my story.

'It is hard to understand it without being a biologist. These dwarfs *are* a different species and an older species than ours. But, then, the specific variation is always liable to reappear in human children. They revert to the dwarf. Consequently, they are multiplying very fast; they are being increased both by ordinary breeding among themselves and also from without by those hark-backs or changelings. He spoke of lots of sub-species besides the Marxomanni – Mussolimini, Swastici, Gangomanni ... I can't remember them all. For a long time I couldn't see where he himself came in.

'At last he told me. He is breeding and training them for a descent on this country. When I tried to find out why, for a long time he would only stare at me and sing his song. Finally – as near as I could get it – his theory seemed to be that fighting was an end in itself.

'Mind you, he was not drunk. He said that he could understand old-fashioned people who believed in the Landlord and kept the rules and hoped to go up and live in the Landlord's castle when they had to leave this country. "They have something to live for," he said. "And if their belief was true, their behaviour would be perfectly sensible. But as their belief is not true, there remains only one way of life fit for a man." This other way of life was something called Heroism, or Master-Morality, or Violence. "All the other people in between," he said, "are ploughing the sand." He went on railing at the people in Claptrap for ages, and also at Mr Sensible. "These are the dregs of man," he said. "They are always thinking of happiness. They are scraping together and storing up and trying to *build*. Can they not see that the law of the world is against them? Where will any of them be a hundred years hence?" I said they might be building for posterity. "And who will posterity build for?" he asked. "Can't you see that it is all bound to come to nothing in the end? And the end may come tomorrow: and however late it comes, to those who look back all their 'happiness' will seem but a moment that has slipped away and left nothing behind. You can't gather happiness. Do you go to bed with any more in hand on the day you have had a thousand pleasures?" I asked if his "Heroism" left anything behind it either: but he said it did. "The excellent deed," he said, "is eternal. The hero alone has this privilege, that death for him is not defeat, and the lamenting over him and the memory is part of the good he aimed for; and the moment of battle fears nothing from the future because it has already cast security away."

'He talked a lot like that. I asked him what he thought of the Eschropolitans and he roared with laughter and said: "When the Cruels meet the Clevers there will not be even the ghost of a tug of war." Then I asked him if he knew you three and he laughed louder still. He said that Angular might turn out an enemy worth fighting when he grew up. "But I don't know," he said. "Likely enough he is only an Eschropolitan turned inside-out – poacher turned gamekeeper. As for the other pair, they are the last even of the last men." I asked him what he meant. "The men of Claptrap," he said, "may have some excuse for their folly, for they at least still believe that your country is a place where Happiness is possible. But your two friends are madmen without qualification. They claim to have reached rock-bottom, they talk of being disillusioned. They think that they have reached the furthest North – as if I were not here to the North of them. They live on a rock that will never feed man, between a chasm that they cannot cross and the home of a giant to whom they dare not return: and still they maunder of a culture and a security. If all men who try to build are but polishing the brasses on a sinking ship, then your pale friends are the supreme fools who polish with the rest though they know and admit that the ship is sinking. Their Humanism and what not is but the old dream with a new name. The rot in the world is too deep and the leak in the world is too wide. They may patch and tinker as they please, they will not save it. Better give in. Better cut the wood with the grain. If I am to live in a world of destruction let me be its agent and not its patient."

'In the end he said: "I will make this concession to your friends. They do live further North than anyone but me. They are more like men than any of their race. They shall have this honour when I lead the dwarfs to war, that Humanist's skull shall be the first from which I drink the blood of a man: and Grimhild here shall have Classical's."

'That was about all he said. He made me go out on the cliffs with him. It was all I could do to keep my footing. He said, "This wind blows straight from the pole; it will make a man of you." I think he was trying to frighten me. In the end I got away. He loaded me with food for myself and you. "Feed them up," he said. "There is not enough blood in them at present to quench the thirst of a dwarfish sword." Then I came away. And I am very tired.'

7

FOOL'S PARADISE

The sub-men have no answer to it

'I should like to meet this Savage,' said Angular. 'He seems to be a very clear-headed man.'

'I don't know about that,' said Humanist. 'He and his dwarfs seem to me to be just the thing I am fighting against – the logical conclusion of Eschropolis against which I raise the banner of Humanism. All the wild atavistic emotions which old Halfways sets free under false pretences – I am not at all surprised that he likes a valkyrie for a daughter – and which young Halfways unmasks, but cherishes when he has unmasked them; where can they end but in a complete abandonment of the *human*? I am glad to hear of him. He shows how necessary I am.'

'I agree,' said John in great excitement, 'but how are you going to fight? Where are your troops? Where is your base of supplies? You can't feed an army on a garden of stones and sea-shells.'

'It is intelligence that counts,' said Humanist.

'It moves nothing,' said John. 'You see that Savage is scalding hot and you are cold. You must get heat to rival his heat. Do you think you can rout a million armed dwarfs by being "not romantic"?'

'If Mr Vertue will not be offended,' said Classical, 'I would suggest that he dreamed the whole thing. Mr Vertue is romantic: he is paying for his wish-fulfilment dreams as he will always pay – with a fear-fulfilment dream. It is well-known that nobody lives further North than we.' But Vertue was too tired to defend his story and soon all the occupants of the hut were asleep.

BOOK 7

SOUTHWARD ALONG
THE CANYON

*Now is the seventh winter since Troy fell,
and we*
*Still search beneath unfriendly stars, through
every sea*
And desert isle, for Italy's retreating strand.
*But here is kinsman's country and Acestes'
land;*
*What hinders here to build a city and
remain?*
*Oh fatherland, oh household spirits
preserved in vain*
*From the enemy, shall no new Troy arise?
Shall no*
*New Simois there, re-named for Hector's
memory, flow?*
*Rather, come! – burn with me the boats that
work us harm!*

VIRGIL

*Through this and through no other fault
we fell,*
Nor, being fallen, bear other pain than this,
– Always without hope in desire to dwell.

DANTE

*Some also have wished that the next way to
their Father's house were here that they
might be troubled no more with either Hills
or Mountains to go over; but the way is the
way, there's an end.*

BUNYAN

I

VERTUE IS SICK

In the presence of these thoughts traditional
morality falters – Without Desire it finds no
motive: with Desire, no morality

I saw the two travellers get up from their sacking and bid good-bye to their hosts, and set out southwards. The weather had not changed, nor did I ever see any other weather over that part of the country than clouds and wind without rain. Vertue himself was out of sorts and made haste without the spirit of haste. Then at last he opened his mind to his companion and said, 'John, I do not know what is coming over me. Long ago you asked me – or was it Media asked me – where I was going and why: and I remember that I brushed the question aside. At that time it seemed to me so much more important to keep my rules and do my thirty miles a day. But I am beginning to find that it will not do. In the old days it was always a question of doing what I chose instead of what I wanted: but now I am beginning to be uncertain what it is I choose.'

'How has this come about?' said John.

'Do you know that I nearly decided to stay with Savage?'

'With Savage?'

'It sounds like raving, but think it over. Supposing there is no Landlord, no mountains in the East, no Island in the West, nothing but this country. A few weeks ago I would have said that all those things made no difference. But now – I don't know. It is quite clear that all the ordinary ways of living in the country lead to something which I certainly do *not* choose. I know that, even if I don't know what I *do* choose. I know that I don't want to be a Halfways, or a Clever, or a Sensible. Then there is the life I have been leading myself – marching on I don't know where. I can't see that there is any other good in it except the mere fact of imposing my will on my inclinations. And that seems to be good *training*, but training for what? Suppose after all it was training for battle? Is it so absurd to think that that might be the thing we were born for? A fight in a narrow place, life or death; – that must be the final act of will – the conquest of the deepest inclination of all.'

'I think my heart will break,' said John after they had gone many paces in silence. 'I came out to find my Island. I am not high-minded like you,

Vertue: it was never anything but sweet desire that led me. I have not smelled the air from that Island since – since – it is so long that I cannot remember. I saw more of it at home. And now my only friend talks of selling himself to the dwarfs.'

'I am sorry for you,' said Vertue, 'and I am sorry for myself. I am sorry for every blade of grass and for this barren rock we are treading and the very sky above us. But I have no help to give you.'

'Perhaps,' said John, 'there are things East and West of this country after all.'

'Do you still understand me so little as that!' cried Vertue, turning on him. 'Things East and West! Don't you see that that is the other fatal possibility? Don't you see that I am caught either way?'

'Why?' said John: and then, 'Let us sit down. I am tired and we have nowhere to hurry to – not now.'

Vertue sat down as one not noticing that he did it.

'Don't you see?' he said. 'Suppose there is anything East and West. How can that give me a motive for going on? Because there is something pleasant ahead? That is a bribe. Because there is something dreadful behind? That is a threat. I meant to be a free man. I meant to choose things because I chose to choose them – not because I was paid for it. Do you think I am a child to be scared with rods and baited with sugar plums? It was for this reason that I never even enquired whether the stories about the Landlord were true; I saw that his castle and his black hole were there to corrupt my will and kill my freedom. If it was true it was a truth an honest man must not know.'

Evening darkened on the tableland and they sat for a long time, immovable.

'I believe that I am mad,' said Vertue presently. 'The world cannot be as it seems to me. If there is something to go to, it is a bribe, and I cannot go to it: if I can go, then there is nothing to go to.'

'Vertue,' said John, 'give in. For once yield to desire. Have done with your choosing. *Want* something.'

'I cannot,' said Vertue. 'I must choose because I choose because I choose: and it goes on for ever, and in the whole world I cannot find a reason for rising from this stone.'

'Is it not reason enough that the cold will presently kill us here?'

It had grown quite dark, and Vertue made no reply.

'Vertue!' said John, and then suddenly again in a louder voice, frightened, 'Vertue!!' But there was no answer. He groped for his friend in the dark and touched the cold dust of the tableland. He rose on his hands and knees and groped all about, calling. But he was confused and could not even find again the place whence he had risen himself. He could not tell how often he might have groped over the same ground or whether he was getting further and further from their resting-place. He could not be still; it was too cold. So all that night he rummaged to and fro in the dark, calling out Vertue's name: and often it came into his head that Vertue had been all along one of the phantoms of a dream and that he had followed a shade.

2

JOHN LEADING

*Conscience can guide John no longer. 'Sick,
wearied out with contrarieties, he yields up
moral questions in despair'*

I dreamed that morning broke over the plateau, and I saw John rise up, white and dirty, in the new twilight. He looked all round him and saw nothing but the heath. Then he walked this way and that, still looking, and so for a long time. And at last he sat down and wept: that also for a long time. And when he had wept enough he rose like a man determined and resumed his journey southward.

He had hardly gone twenty paces when he stopped with a cry, for there lay Vertue at his feet. I understood in my dream that during his groping in the darkness he had unwittingly gone further and further from the place where they had first sat down.

In a moment John was on his knees and feeling for Vertue's heart. It beat still. He laid his face to Vertue's lips. They breathed still. He caught him by the shoulder and shook him.

'Wake up,' he cried, 'the morning is here.'

Then Vertue opened his eyes and smiled at John, a little foolishly.

'Are you well?' said John. 'Are you fit to travel?'

But Vertue only smiled. He was dumb. Then John held out his hands and pulled Vertue to his feet: and Vertue stood up uncertainly, but as soon as he made a stride he stumbled and fell, for he was blind. It was long before John understood. Then at last I saw him take Vertue by the hand and, leading him, resume their journey to the South. And there fell upon John that last loneliness which comes when the comforter himself needs comforting, and the guide is to be guided.

3

THE MAIN ROAD AGAIN

They found Mr Sensible's house empty, as John had expected, with the shutters up and the chimneys smokeless. John decided to push on to the main road and then, if the worst came to the worst, they could go to Mother Kirk: but he hoped it would not come to that.

All their journey South had been a descent, from the northern mountains to Mr Sensible's: but after his house it began to rise again a little to the main road, which ran along a low ridge, so that, when they had gained the road, the country South of it was suddenly all opened before them. At the same moment there came a gleam of sunshine, the first for many days. The road was unfenced to the heath on its northern side, but on its southern side there was a hedge with a gate in it: and the first thing John saw through the gate was a long low mound of earth. He had not been a farmer's son for nothing. Having led Vertue to the bank of the road and seated him, he lost no time in climbing the gate and digging with both hands into the earthen mound. It contained, as he had expected, turnips; and in a minute he was seated by Vertue, cutting a fine root into chunks, feeding the blind man and teaching him how to feed himself. The sun grew warmer every moment. The spring seemed further on in this place, and the hedge behind them was already more green than brown. Among many notes of birds John thought he could distinguish a lark. They had breakfasted well, and as the warmth increased pleasantly over their aching limbs, they fell asleep.

4

GOING SOUTH

John looks longingly towards less comfortless
modes of thought

When John awoke his first look was towards Vertue, but Vertue was still sleeping. John stretched himself and rose: he was warm and well, but a little thirsty. It was a four-cross-road where they had been sitting, for the northern road, at which John looked with a shudder, was but the continuation of a road from the South. He stood and looked down the latter. To his eyes, long now accustomed to the dusty flats of the northern plateau, the country southward was as a rich counterpane. The sun had passed noon by an hour or so, and the slanting light freckled with rounded shadows a green land, that fell ever away before him, opening as it sank into valleys, and beyond them into deeper valleys again, so that places on the same level where now he stood, yonder were mountain tops. Nearer at hand were fields and hedgerows, ruddy ploughland, winding woods, and frequent farm-houses white among their trees. He went back and raised Vertue and was about to show it all to him when he remembered his blindness. Then, sighing, he took him by the hand and went down the new road.

Before they had gone far he heard a bubbling sound by the roadside, and found a little spring pouring itself into a stream that ran henceforth with the road, now at the left, now at the right, and often crossed their way. He filled his hat with water and gave Vertue to drink. Then he drank himself and they went on, always downhill. The road nestled deeper each half-mile between banks of grass. There were primroses, first one or two, then clustered, then innumerable. From many turns of the road John caught sight of the deeper valleys to which they were descending, blue with distance and rounded with the weight of trees: but often a little wood cut off all remoter prospect.

The first house they came to was a red house, old and ivied, and well back from the road, and John thought it had the look of a Steward's house: as they came nearer, there was the Steward himself, without his mask, pottering about at some light gardening labour on the sunny side of the hedge. John leaned over the gate and asked for hospitality, explaining at the same time his friend's condition.

'Come in, come in,' said the Steward. 'It will be a great pleasure.'

Now I dreamed that this Steward was the same Mr Broad who had sent a case of sherry to Mr Sensible. He was about sixty years of age.

5

TEA ON THE LAWN

*John meets Broad Church, modernising,
'religion' – It is friends with the World
and goes on no pilgrimage – It is fond of
wild-flowers*

'It is almost warm enough to have tea on the lawn,' said Mr Broad. 'Martha, I think we will have tea on the lawn.'

Chairs were set and all three sat down. On the smooth lawn, surrounded by laurels and laburnum, it was even warmer than in the road, and suddenly a sweet bird-note shot out from the thickets.

'Listen!' said Mr Broad, 'it is a thrush. I really believe it is a thrush.'

Maidservants in snowy aprons opened the long windows of the library and came over the grass carrying tables and trays, the silver teapot and the stand of cakes. There was honey for tea. Mr Broad asked John some questions about his travels.

'Dear me,' he said, when he heard of Mr Savage, 'dear me! I ought to go and see him. And such a clever man, too, by your account ... it is very sad.'

John went on to describe the three pale men.

'Ah, to be sure,' said Mr Broad. 'I knew their father very well. A very able man. I owed a good deal to him at one time. Indeed, as a young man, he formed my mind. I suppose I ought to go and see his boys. Young Angular I *have* met. He is a dear, good fellow – a little narrow; I would venture to say, even a little old-fashioned, though of course I wouldn't for the world – the two brothers are doing splendidly I have no doubt. I really ought to go and see them. But I am getting on, and I confess it never suits me up there.'

'It is a very different climate from this,' said John.

'I always think it is possible for a place to be *too* bracing. They call it the land of the Tough-minded – tough-skinned would be a better name. If one has a tendency to lumbago – But, dear me, if you have come from there you must have met my old friend Sensible?'

'You know him too?'

'Know him? He is my oldest friend. He is a kind of connection of mine, and then, you know, we are quite near neighbours. He is only a mile north of the road and I am about a mile south of it. I should think I did know him. I have passed many, many happy hours in his house. The dear old man. Poor Sensible, he is ageing fast. I don't think he has ever quite forgiven me for having kept most of my hair!'

'I should have thought his views differed from yours a good deal.'

'Ah, to be sure, to be sure! He is not very orthodox, perhaps, but as I grow older, I am inclined to set less and less store by mere orthodoxy. So often the orthodox view means the lifeless view, the barren formula. I am coming to look more and more at the language of the heart. Logic and definition divide us: it is those things which draw us together that I now value most – our common affections, our common struggle towards the light. Sensible's heart is in the right place.'

'I wonder,' said John, 'if he treats that servant of his very well.'

'His language is a little bit rough, I suppose. One must be charitable. You young people are so hard. Dear me, I remember when I was a boy myself ... And then a man of Sensible's age suffers a good deal. We are none of us perfect. Will you not have a little more tea?'

'Thank you,' said John, 'but if you can give me some directions I think I would like to continue my journey. I am trying to find an Island in the West –'

'That is a beautiful idea,' said Mr Broad. 'And if you will trust an older traveller, the seeking is the finding. How many happy days you have before you!'

'And I want to know,' continued John, 'whether it is really necessary to cross the canyon.'

'To be sure you do. I wouldn't for the world hold you back. At the same time, my dear boy, I think there is a very real danger at your age of trying to make these things too definite. That has been the great error of my profession in past ages. We have tried to enclose everything in formulae, to turn poetry into logic, and metaphor into dogma; and now that we are beginning to realise our mistake we find ourselves shackled by the formulae of dead men. I don't say that they were not adequate once: but they have ceased to be adequate for us with our wider knowledge. When I became a man, I put away childish things. These great truths need re-interpretation in every age.'

'I am not sure that I quite understand,' said John. 'Do you mean that I must cross the canyon or that I must not?'

'I see you want to pin me down,' said Mr Broad, with a smile, 'and I love to see it. I was like that myself once. But one loses faith in abstract logic as one grows older. Do you never feel that the truth is so great and so simple that no mere words can contain it? The heaven and the heaven of heavens ... how much less this house that I have builded.'

'Well, anyway,' said John, deciding to try a new question. 'Supposing a man *did* have to cross the canyon. Is it true that he would have to rely on Mother Kirk?'

'Ah, Mother Kirk! I love and honour her from the bottom of my heart, but I trust that loving her does not mean being blind to her faults. We are none of us infallible. If I sometimes feel that I must differ from her at present, it is because I honour all the more the *idea* that she stands for, the thing she may yet become. For the moment, there is no denying that she has let herself get a little out of date. Surely, for many of our generation, there is a truer, a more acceptable, message in all this beautiful world around us? I don't know whether you are anything of a botanist. If you would care –'

'I want my Island,' said John. 'Can you tell me how to reach it? I am afraid I am not specially interested in botany.'

'It would open a new world to you,' said Mr Broad. 'A new window on the Infinite. But perhaps this is not in your line. We must all find our own key to the mystery after all. I wouldn't for the world ...'

'I think I must be going,' said John. 'And I have enjoyed myself very much. If I follow this road, shall I find anywhere that will give me a night's lodging in a few miles?'

'Oh, easily,' said Mr Broad. 'I should be very glad to have you here if you would care to stay. But if not, there is Mr Wisdom within an easy walk. You will find him a delightful man. I used to go and see him quite often when I was younger, but it is a little too far for me now. A dear, good fellow – a *little* persistent, perhaps ... I sometimes wonder if he is really quite free from a trace of narrow-mindedness ... You should hear what Sensible says about him! But there: we are none of us perfect, and he is a very good sort of man on the whole. You will like him very much.'

The old Steward bade goodbye to John with almost fatherly kindness, and John, still leading Vertue, pursued his journey.

6

THE HOUSE OF WISDOM

John takes up the study of Metaphysics

The stream that they had followed to the Steward's house was now no longer a brook by the roadside, but a river that sometimes approached, sometimes receded from the road, sliding in swift amber reaches and descending silver rapids. The trees grew more thickly hereabouts and were of larger kinds – and as the valley deepened, tiers of forest rose one above the other on each side. They walked in shadow. But far above their heads the sun was still shining on the mountain tops, beyond the forest slopes and beyond the last steep fields, where there were domed summits of pale grass and winding water-glens, and cliffs the colour of doves, and cliffs the colour of wine. The moths were already flying when they reached an open place. The valley widened and a loop of the river made room for a wide and level lawn between its banks and the wooded mountains. Amidst the lawn stood a low, pillared house approachable by a bridge, and the door stood open. John led the sick man up to it and saw that the lamps were already lit within; and then he saw Wisdom sitting among his children, like an old man.

'You may stay here as long as you wish,' he said in answer to John's question. 'And it may be that we shall heal your friend if his sickness is not incurable. Sit and eat, and when you have eaten you shall tell us your story.'

Then I saw that chairs were brought for the travellers and some of the young men of the house carried water to them to wash. And when they had washed, a woman set a table before them and laid on it a loaf, and cheese, and a dish of fruit, with some curds, and butter-milk in a pitcher: 'For we can get no wine here,' said the old man with a sigh.

When the meal was over there was silence in the house, and John saw that they waited for his story. So he collected himself and cast back in his mind, a long time, in silence; and when at last he spoke he told the whole thing in order, from the first sight he had had of the Island down to his arrival among them.

Then Vertue was led away from John, and he himself was brought into a cell where there was a bed, and a table, and a pitcher of water. He lay on the bed, and it was hard, but not lumpy, and he was immediately in a deep sleep.

7

ACROSS THE CANYON

BY MOONLIGHT

John's imagination re-awakes

In the middle of the night he opened his eyes and saw the full moon, very large and low, shining at his window: and beside his bed stood a woman darkly clothed, who held up her hand for silence when he would have spoken.

'My name is Contemplation,' she said, 'and I am one of the daughters of Wisdom. You must rise and follow me.'

Then John rose and followed her out of the house on to the grassy lawn in the moonlight. She led him across it to its westward edge where the mountain began to rise under its cloak of forest. But as they came right up to the eaves of the forest he saw that there was a crack or crevasse in the earth between them and it, to which he could find no bottom, and though it was not very wide, it was too wide to jump.

'It is too wide a jump by day,' said the Lady, 'but in the moonlight you can jump it.'

John felt no doubt of her and gathered himself together and leaped. His leap carried him further than he had intended – though he felt no surprise – and he found himself flying over the tree tops and the steep fields, and he never alighted till he reached the mountain top; and the Lady was there by his side.

'Come,' she said, 'we have still far to go.'

Then they went on together over hills and dales, very fast, in the moonlight, till they came to the edge of a cliff, and he looked down and saw the sea below him: and out in the sea lay the Island. And because it was moonlight and night John could not see it so well as he had sometimes seen it, but either for that reason, or for some other, it seemed to him the more real.

'When you have learned to fly further, we can leap from here right into the Island,' said the Lady. 'But for this night, it is enough.'

As John turned to answer her, the Island and the sea and the Lady herself vanished, and he was awake, in daylight, in his cell in the house of Wisdom, and a bell was ringing.

8

THIS SIDE BY SUNLIGHT

*Idealist Philosophy rejects the literal truth of
religion – But also rejects Materialism – The
chasm is still not crossed – But this
Philosophy, while denying the Hope yet
spares the Desire, to cross it*

On the next day Mr Wisdom caused John and Vertue both to sit by him
in a porch of his house looking westward. The wind was in the south
and the sky was a little clouded and over the western mountains there was a
delicate mist, so that they had the air of being in another world, though
they were not more than a mile away. And Mr Wisdom instructed them.

'As to this Island in the West, and those eastern mountains, and as
touching the Landlord also and the Enemy, there are two errors, my sons,
which you must equally conquer, and pass right between them, before you
can become wise. The first error is that of the southern people, and it consists in holding that these eastern and western places are real places – real
as this valley is real, and places as this valley is a place. If any such thought
lingers in your minds, I would have you root it out utterly, and give no
quarter to that thought, whether it threatens you with fears, or tempts you
with hopes. For this is Superstition, and all who believe it will come in the
end to the swamps and the jungles of the far South, where they will live in
the city of Magicians, transported with delight in things that help not, and
haunted with terror of that which cannot hurt. And it is part of the same
error to think that the Landlord is a real man: real as I am real, man as I am
man. That is the first error. And the second is the opposite of it, and is
chiefly current to the North of the road: it is the error of those who say
that the eastern and western things are merely illusions in our own minds.
This also it is my will that you should utterly reject: and you must be on
your guard lest you ever embrace this error in your fear of the other, or
run to and fro between the two as your hearts will prompt you to do, like
some who will be Materialists (for that is the name of the second error)
when the story of the black hole frightens them for their lawless living, or
even when they are afraid of spectres, and then another day will believe in
the Landlord and the castle because things in this country go hard with
them, or because the lease of some dear friend is running out and they

would gladly hope to meet him again. But the wise man, ruling his passions with reason and disciplined imagination, withdraws himself to the middle point between these two errors, having found that the truth lies there, and remains fixed immovably. But what that truth is you shall learn tomorrow; and for the present this sick man will be cared for, and you who are whole may do as you will.'

Then I saw Mr Wisdom rise and leave them, and Vertue was taken to another place. John spent the most part of that day walking in the neighbourhood of the house. He crossed the level grass of the valley and came to its western edge where the mountain began to rise under its cloak of forest. But as he came under the forest eaves, he saw that between him and the first trees there was a crack or crevasse in the earth to which he could find no bottom. It was very narrow, but not quite narrow enough to jump. There seemed also to be some vapour rising from it which made the further side indistinct: but the vapour was not so thick nor the chasm so wide but that he could see here a spray of foliage and there a stone with deep moss, and in one place falling water that caught the sunlight. His desire to pass and to go on to the Island was sharp, but not to the degree of pain. Mr Wisdom's words that the eastern and western things were neither wholly real nor wholly illusion, had spread over his mind a feeling of intent, yet quiet, comfort. Some fear was removed: the suspicion, never before wholly laid at rest, that his wanderings might lead him soon or late into the power of the Landlord, had passed away, and with it the gnawing anxiety lest the Island had never existed. The world seemed full of expectation, even as the misty veil between him and the forest seemed both to cover and discover sublimities that were without terror and beauties without sensuality; and every now and then a strengthening of the south wind would make a moment's clearness and show him, withdrawn in unexpected depth, remote reaches of the mountain valleys, desolate fields of flowers, the hint of snow beyond. He lay down in the grass. Presently one of the young men of the house passed that way and stopped to talk with him. They spoke of this and that, lazily, and at long intervals. Sometimes they discussed the regions further South where John had not been; sometimes, his own travels. The young man told him that if he had followed the road a few miles beyond the valley he would have come to a fork. The left hand turn would lead you, by a long way round, to the parts about Claptrap: the right went on to the southern forests, to the city of the Magicians and the country of Nycteris, 'and beyond that it is all swamp and sugar cane,' said he, 'and crocodiles and venomous spiders until the land sinks away altogether into the final salt swamp which becomes at last the southern ocean. There are no settlements there except a few lake-dwellers, Theosophists and what not, and it is very malarial.'

While they were speaking of the parts that John already knew, he asked his informant whether they in the House of Wisdom knew anything of the Grand Canyon or of the way down into it.

'Do you not know,' said the other, 'that we are in the bottom of the canyon here?' Then he made John sit up and showed him the lie of the land. The sides of the valley drew together northward, and at the same time grew more precipitous, so that at last they came together into a great V. 'And that V is the canyon, and you are looking into it endways from the southern end. The eastern face of the canyon is gentle and you were walking down into it all day yesterday, though you did not notice it.'

'So I am in the bottom of it already,' said John. 'And now there is nothing to prevent me from crossing it.'

The young man shook his head.

'There is no crossing it,' he said. 'When I told you we were now at the bottom, I meant the lowest point that can be reached by man. The real bottom is, of course, the bottom of this crevasse which we are sitting by: and that, of course – well, it would be a misunderstanding to talk of getting down it. There is no question of crossing or of getting to what you see over there.'

'Could it not be bridged?' said John.

'In a sense there is nothing to bridge – there is nowhere for this bridge to *arrive at*. You must not take literally the show of forest and mountain which we seem to see as we look across.'

'You don't mean that it is an illusion?'

'No. You will understand better when you have been longer with my father. It is not an illusion, it is an appearance. It is a true appearance, too, in a sense. You *must* see it as a mountain-side or the like – a continuation of the world we *do* know – and it does not mean that there is anything wrong with your eyes or any better way of seeing it to which you can attain. But don't think you can get there. Don't think there is any meaning in the idea of you (a man) going "there", as if it were really a place.'

'What? And the Island too! You would have me give up my heart's desire?'

'I would not. I would not have you cease to fix all your desires on the far side, for to wish to cross is simply to be a man, and to lose that wish is to be a beast. It is not desire that my father's doctrine kills: it is only hope.'

'And what is this valley called?'

'We call it now simply Wisdom's Valley: but the oldest maps mark it as the Valley of Humiliation.'

'The grass is quite wet,' said John, after a pause. 'The dew is beginning.'

'It is time that we went to supper,' said the young man.

WISDOM — EXOTERIC

*Whence come logical categories? Whence
come moral values? – Philosophy says that
the existence of God would not answer the
question – Philosophy will not explain away
John's glimpse of the Transcendent –
The Desired is real just because it is never
an experience*

Next day, as before, Wisdom had John and Vertue into the porch and continued to instruct them:

'You have heard what you are not to think of the eastern and western things, and now let us discover, as far as the imperfection of our faculty allows, what may rightly be thought. And first, consider this country in which we live. You see that it is full of roads, and no man remembers the making of these roads: neither have we any way to describe and order the land in our minds except by reference to them. You have seen how we determine the position of every other place by its relation to the main road: and though you may say that we have maps, you are to consider that the maps would be useless without the roads, for we find where we are on the map by the skeleton of roads which is common to it and to the country. We see that we have just passed such a turn to the right or the left, or that we are approaching such a bend in the road, and thus we know that we are near to some other place on the map which is not yet visible on the countryside. The people, indeed, say that the Landlord made these roads: and the Claptrapians say that we first made them on the map and have projected them, by some strange process, from it to the country. But I would have you hold fast to the truth, that we find them and do not make them: but also that no *man* could make them. For to make them he would need a bird's-eye view of the whole country, which he could have only from the sky. But no man could live in the sky. Again, this country is full of rules. The Claptrapians say that the Stewards made the rules. The servants of the giant say that we made them ourselves in order to restrain by them the lusts of our neighbours and to give a pompous colouring to our own. The people say that the Landlord made them.

'Let us consider these doctrines one by one. The Stewards made them? How then came they to be Stewards, and why did the rest of us consent to their rules? As soon as we ask this question, we are obliged to ask another. How comes it that those who have rejected the Stewards immediately set about making new rules of their own, and that these new rules are substantially the same as the old? A man says, "I have finished with rules: henceforth I will do what I want": but he finds that his deepest want, the only want that is constant through the flux of his appetites and despondencies, his moments of calm and of passion, is to keep the rules. Because these rules are a disguise for his desires, say the giant's following. But, I ask, what desires? Not any and every desire: the rules are frequently denials of these desires. The desire for self-approbation, shall we say? But why should we approve ourselves for keeping the rules unless we already thought that the rules were good? A man may find pleasure in supposing himself swifter or stronger than he really is, but only if he already loves speed or strength. The giant's doctrine thus destroys itself. If we wish to give a seemly colouring to our lusts we have already the idea of the seemly, and the seemly turns out to be nothing else than that which is according to the rules. The want to obey the rules is thus presupposed in every doctrine which describes our obedience to them, or to the rules themselves, as a self-flattery. Let us turn then to the old tale of the Landlord. Some mighty man beyond this country has made the rules. Suppose he has: then why do we obey them?'

Mr Wisdom turned to Vertue and said, 'This part is of great concern to you and to your cure,' then he continued:

'There can be only two reasons. Either because we respect the power of the Landlord, and are moved by fear of the penalties and hopes of the rewards with which he sanctions the rules: or else, because we freely agree with the Landlord, because we also think good the things that he thinks good. But neither explanation will serve. If we obey through hope and fear, in that very act we disobey: for the rule which we reverence most, whether we find it in our own hearts or on the Steward's card, is that rule which says that a man must act disinterestedly. To obey the Landlord thus, would be to disobey. But what if we obey freely, because we agree with him? Alas, this is even worse. To say that we agree, and obey because we agree, is only to say again that we find the same rule written in our hearts and obey *that*. If the Landlord enjoins *that*, he enjoins only what we already purposed to do, and his voice is idle: if he enjoins anything else, his voice again is idle, for we shall disobey him. In either case the mystery of the rules remains unsolved, and the Landlord is a meaningless addition to the problem. If he spoke, the rules were there before he spoke. If we and he agree about them, where is the common original which he and we both copy: what is the thing about which his doctrine and ours are both true?

'Of the rules, then as of the roads, we must say that indeed we find them and do not make them, but that it helps us not at all to assume a Landlord for their maker. And there is a third thing also' (here he looked to John) 'which specially concerns you. What of the Island in the West? The People in our age have all but forgotten it. The giant would say that it is, again, a delusion in your own mind trumped up to conceal lust. Of the Stewards, some do not know that there is such a thing: some agree with the giant, denouncing your Island as wickedness: some say that it is a blurred and confused sight from far off of the Landlord's castle. They have no common doctrine: but let us consider the question for ourselves.

'And first I would have you set aside all suspicion that the giant is right: and this will be the easier for you because you have already talked with Reason. They say it is there to conceal lust. But it does not conceal lust. If it is a screen, it is a very bad screen. The giant would make the dark part of our mind so strong and subtle that we never escape from its deceptions: and yet when this omnipotent conjuror has done all that he can, he produces an illusion which a solitary boy, in the fancies of his adolescence, can expose and see through in two years. This is but wild talk. There is no man and no nation at all capable of seeing the Island, who have not learned by experience, and that soon, how easily the vision ends in lust: and there is none also, not corrupted, who has not felt the disappointment of that ending, who has not known that it is the breaking of the vision, not its consummation. The words between you and Reason were true. What does not satisfy when we find it, was not the thing we were desiring. If water will not set a man at ease, then be sure it was not thirst, or not thirst only, that tormented him: he wanted drunkenness to cure his dullness, or talk to cure his solitude, or the like. How, indeed, do we know our desires save by their satisfaction? When do we know them until we say, "Ah, *this* was what I wanted"? And if there were any desire which it was natural for man to feel but impossible for man to satisfy, would not the nature of this desire remain to him always ambiguous? If old tales were true, if a man without putting off humanity could indeed pass the frontiers of our country, if he could be, and yet be a man, in that fabled East and fabled West, then indeed at the moment of fruition, the raising of the cup, the assumption of the crown, the kiss of the spouse – then first, to his backward glance, the long roads of desire that he had trodden would become plain in all their winding, and when he found, he would know what it was that he had sought. I am old and full of tears, and I see that you also begin to feel the sorrow that is born with us. Abandon hope: do not abandon desire. Feel no wonder that these glimpses of your Island so easily confuse themselves with viler things, and are so easily blasphemed. Above all, never try to keep them, never try to revisit the same place or time wherein the vision was accorded to you. You will pay the penalty of all who would bind down to one place or time within our country that which our country cannot contain. Have you not heard from the Stewards of the sin of idolatry, and how, in their old chronicles, the manna turned to worms if any tried to hoard it? Be not greedy, be not passionate; you will but crush dead on your own breast with hot, rough hands the thing you loved. But if ever you incline to doubt that the thing you long for is something real, remember what your own experience has taught you. Think that it is a *feeling*, and at once the feeling has no value. Stand sentinel at your own mind, watching for that feeling, and you will find – what shall I say? – a flutter in the heart, an image in the head, a sob in the throat; and was *that* your desire? You know that it was not, and that no feeling whatever will appease you; that *feeling*, refine it as you will, is but one more spurious claimant – spurious as the gross lusts of which the giant speaks. Let us conclude then that what you desire is no state of yourself at all, but something, for that very reason, Other and Outer. And knowing this you will find tolerable the truth that you cannot attain it. That the thing should *be* is so great a good that when you remember "it is" you will forget to be sorry that you can never have it. Nay, anything that you could have would be so much less than this that its fruition would be immeasurably below the mere hunger for this. Wanting is better than having. The glory of any world wherein you can live is in the end appearance: but then, as one of my sons has said, that leaves the world more glorious yet.'

10

WISDOM — ESOTERIC

*John finds that the real strength in the lives
of the Philosophers comes from sources
better, or worse, than any their philosophies
acknowledge – Marx really a Dwarf;
Spinoza a Jew; Kant a Puritan*

That day John spent as he had spent the other, wandering and often sleeping in the fields. In this valley the year came on with seven-leagued boots. Today the riverside was thick with fritillaries, the kingfisher flew, the dragon-flies darted, and when he sat it was in the shade. A pleasing melancholy rested upon him, and a great indolence. He talked that day with many of the people of the house, and when he went that night to his cell his mind was full of their resigned voices, and of their faces, so quiet and yet so alert, as though they waited in hourly expectation of something that would never happen. When next he opened his eyes moonlight filled his cell; and as he lay waking heard a low whistle from without his window. He put out his head. A dark figure stood in the shadow of the house. 'Come out and play,' said he. At the same time there came a sound of suppressed laughter from an angle of deeper shadow beyond the speaker.

'This window is too high for me to jump from,' said John.

'You forget that it is by moonlight,' said the other, and held up his hands. 'Jump!' he said.

John cast some clothes about him and bounded from the window. To his surprise, he reached the ground with no hurt or shock, and a moment later he found himself progressing over the lawn in a series of great leaps amidst a laughing crowd of the sons and daughters of the house: so that the valley in the moonlight, if any had watched, would have looked like nothing so much as a great salver which had been made into the arena for a troupe of performing fleas. Their dance or race led them to the dark border of a neighbouring wood and as John tumbled down breathless at the foot of a hawthorn, he heard with surprise all around him the sounds of silver and glass, of hampers opening, and bottles uncorking.

'My father's ideas of feeding are a little strict,' explained his host, 'and we younger ones have found it necessary to supplement the household meals a bit.'

'Here is champagne, from Mr Halfways,' said one.

'Cold chicken and tongue from Mr Mammon. What should we do without our friends?'

'Hashish from the south. Nycteris sent it up herself.'

'This claret,' said a girl beside him rather shyly, 'is from Mother Kirk.'

'I don't think we ought to drink that,' said another voice, 'that is really going a bit too far.'

'No further than your caviare from the Theosophists,' said the first girl, 'and anyway, I need it. It is only this that keeps me alive.'

'Try some of my brandy,' said another voice. 'All made by Savage's dwarfs.'

'I don't know how you can drink that stuff, Karl.[1] Plain, honest food from Claptrap is what you need.'

'So *you* say, Herbert,'[2] retorted a new speaker. 'But some of us find it rather heavy. For me, a morsel of lamb from the Shepherd's Country and a little mint sauce – that is really all you need to add to our Father's table.'

'We all know what you like, Benedict,'[3] said several.

'I have finished,' announced Karl, 'and now for a night with the dwarfs. Anyone come with me?'

'Not there,' cried another. 'I'm going South tonight to the magicians.'

'You had much better not, Rudolph,'[4] said someone. 'A few quiet hours in Puritania with me would be much better for you – much better.'

'Chuck it, Immanuel,'[5] said another. 'You might as well go to Mother Kirk straight away.'

'Bernard[6] does,' said the girl, who had contributed the claret.

By this time the party was rapidly decreasing, for most of the young people, after trying in vain to win converts to their several schemes of pleasure, had bounded off alone, plunging from treetop to treetop, and soon even the thin silvery sound of their laughter had died away. Those who were left swarmed round John soliciting his attention now for this, now for that, amusement. Some sat down beyond the shadow of the wood to work out puzzles in the light of the moon: others settled to serious leap-frog; the more frivolous ran to and fro chasing the moths, wrestling with and tickling one another, giggling and making giggle, till the wood rang with their shrill squeals of glee. It seemed to go on for a long time and if there was any more in that dream John did not remember it when he woke.

[1]Marx [2]Spencer [3]Spinoza [4]Steiner [5]Kant [6]Bosanquet

11

MUM'S THE WORD

At breakfast on the following morning John stole many furtive glances at the sons and daughters of Wisdom, but he could see no sign that they were conscious of having met him in such different guise during the night. Indeed, neither then, nor at any other time during his stay in the valley, did he find evidence that they were aware of their nocturnal holidays: and a few tentative questions assured him that, unless they were liars, they all believed themselves to be living exclusively on the spare diet of the house. Immanuel indeed admitted, as a speculative truth, that there were such things as dreams, and that he conceivably dreamed himself: but then he had a complex proof (which John never quite grasped) that no one could possibly remember a dream: and though his appearance and constitution were those of a prize-fighter he attributed this all to the excellent quality of the local fruit. Herbert was a lumpish sort of man who never could muster any appetite for his meals: but John discovered that Herbert put this down to his liver and had no notion that he had been stuffing himself with Claptrapian steak and gravy all night as hard as he could. Another of the family, Bernard by name, was in radiant health. John had seen him drinking Mother Kirk's wine with great relish and refreshment by moonlight: but the waking Bernard maintained that Mother Kirk's wine was merely a bad, early attempt at the admirable barley-water which his father sometimes brought out on birthdays and great occasions; and 'to this barley-water,' he said, 'I owe my health. It has made me what I am.' Still less could John discover, by all the traps that he laid for them, whether the younger members of the household had any recollection of their nightly leap-frog and other gambols. He was forced at last to conclude that either the whole thing had been a private dream of his own or else the secret was very well kept. A little irritation which some displayed when he questioned them, seemed to favour the second hypothesis.

12

MORE WISDOM

*John is taught that the finite self cannot
enter the Noumenal World – The doctrine of
the Absolute or Mind-as-such covers more of
the facts than any doctrine John has yet
encountered*

When they were seated in the porch, Wisdom continued his discourse.
'You have learned that there are these three things, the Island, the
Roads, and the Rules: that they are certainly in some way real and that we
have not made them; and further that it does not help us to invent a
Landlord. Nor is it possible that there should really be a castle at one end of
the world and an island at the other: for the world is round and we are
everywhere at the end of the world, since the end of a sphere is its surface.
The world is *all* end: but we can never pass beyond that end. And yet these
things which our imagination impossibly places as a world beyond the
world's end are, we have seen, in some sense real.

'You have told me how Reason refuted the lies of the giant by asking
what was the colour of things in dark places. You learned from her that
there is no colour without seeing, no hardness without touching: no *body*,
to say all, save in the minds of those who perceive it. It follows, then, that
all this choir of heaven and furniture of earth are imaginations: not your
imaginations nor mine, for here we have met in the same world, which
could not be if the world was shut up within my mind or yours. Without
doubt, then, all this show of sky and earth floats within some mighty
imagination. If you ask Whose, again the Landlord will not help you. He is
a man: make him as great as you will, he still is other than we and his imagining inaccessible to us, as yours would be to me. Rather we must say that
the world is not in this mind, or in that, but in Mind itself, in that impersonal principle of consciousness which flows eternally through us, its
perishable forms.

'You see how this explains all the questions that have lain on our knees
since we began. We find the roads, the reasonable skeleton in the countryside,
the guiding-lines that enable us both to make maps and to use them when we
have made them, because our country is the offspring of the rational.
Consider also the Island. All that you know of it comes at last to this: that

234

your first sight of it was yearning or wanting and that you have never ceased to want that first sight back, as though you wanted a wanting, as though the wanting were the having, and the having a wanting. What is the meaning of this hungry fruition and this emptiness which is the best filling? Surely, it becomes plain when you have learned that no man says "I" in an unambiguous sense. I am an old man who must soon go over the brook and be seen no more: I am eternal Mind in which time and place themselves are contained. I am the Imaginer: I am one of his imaginations. The Island is nothing else than that perfection and immortality which I possess as Spirit eternal, and vainly crave as mortal soul. Its voices sound at my very ear and are further than the stars; it is under my hand and will never be mine: I have it and lo! the very having is the losing: because at every moment I, as Spirit, am indeed abandoning my rich estate to become that perishing and imperfect creature in whose repeated deaths and births stands my eternity. And I as man in every moment still enjoy the perfection I have lost, since still, so far as I am at all, I am Spirit, and only by being Spirit maintain my short vitality as soul. See how life subsists by death and each becomes the other: for Spirit lives by dying perpetually into such things as we, and we also attain our truest life by dying to our mortal nature and relapsing, as far as may be, into the impersonality of our source: for this is the final meaning of all moral precepts, and the goodness of temperance and justice and of love itself is that they plunge the red heat of our separate and individual passions back in the ice brook of the Spirit, there to take eternal temper, though not endless duration.

'What I tell you is the *evangelium eternum*. This has been known always: ancients and moderns bear witness to it. The stories of the Landlord in our own time are but a picture-writing which show to the people as much of the truth as they can understand. Stewards must have told you – though it seems that you neither heeded nor understood them – the legend of the Landlord's Son. They say that after the eating of the mountain-apple and the earthquake, when things in our country had gone all awry, the Landlord's Son himself became one of his Father's tenants and lived among us, for no other purpose than that he should be killed. The Stewards themselves do not know clearly the meaning of their story: hence, if you ask them how the slaying of the Son should help us, they are driven to monstrous answers. But to us the meaning is clear and the story is beautiful. It is a picture of the life of Spirit itself. What the Son is in the legend, every man is in reality: for the whole world is nothing else than the Eternal thus giving itself to death that it may live – that we may live. Death is life's mode, and the increase of life is through repeated death.

'And what of the rules? You have seen that it is idle to make them the arbitrary commands of a Landlord: yet those who do so were not altogether astray, for it is equally an error to think that they are each man's

personal choice. Remember what we have said of the Island. Because I
am and am not Spirit, therefore I have and have not my desire. The same
double nature of the word "I", explains the rules. I am the lawgiver: but I
am also the subject. I, the Spirit, impose upon the soul which I become, the
laws she must henceforth obey: and every conflict between the rules and
our inclinations is but a conflict of the wishes of my mortal and apparent
self against those of my real and eternal. "I ought but I do not wish" –
how meaningless the words are, how close to saying, "I want and I do
not want." But once we have learned to say "I, and yet not I, want," the
mystery is plain.

'And now your sick friend is almost whole, and it is nearly noon.'

BOOK 8

AT BAY

He that hath understanding in himself is best;
He that lays up his brother's wisdom in his breast
Is good. But he that neither knoweth, nor will be taught
By the instruction of the wise – this man is naught.

HESIOD

Persons without education certainly do not
want either acuteness or strength of mind in
what concerns themselves, or in things
immediately within their observation; but
they have no power of abstraction – they see
their objects always near, never in the
horizon.

HAZLITT

TWO KINDS OF MONIST

But supposing one tries to live by Pantheistic
philosophy – does it lead to a complacent
Hegelian optimism? Or to Oriental
pessimism and self-torture? – Adjustment
between the two views seems impossible

That afternoon as John was walking in the water meadow he saw a man coming towards him who walked blunderingly like one whose legs were not his own. And as the man came nearer he saw that it was Vertue, with his face very pale.

'What,' cried John, 'are you cured? Can you see? Can you speak?'

'Yes,' said Vertue in a weak voice. 'I suppose I can see.' And he leaned heavily on a stile and breathed hard.

'You have walked too far,' said John. 'Are you ill?'

'I am still weak. It is nothing. I shall get my breath in a moment.'

'Sit down by me,' said John. 'And when you have rested we will go gently back to the house.'

'I am not going back to the house.'

'Not going back? You are not fit to travel – and where are you going?'

'I am not fit for anything, apparently,' said Vertue. 'But I must go on.'

'Go on where? You are not still hoping to cross the canyon? Do you not believe what Wisdom has told us?'

'I do. That is why I am going on.'

'Sit down at least for a moment,' said John, 'and explain yourself.'

'It is plain enough!'

'It isn't plain at all.'

Vertue spoke impatiently.

'Did you not hear what Wisdom said about the rules?' he asked.

'Of course I did,' said John.

'Well, then, he has given me back the rules. *That* puzzle is solved. The rules have to be obeyed, as I always thought. I know that now better than I have ever known it before.'

'Well?'

'And didn't you see what all the rest came to? The rules are from this Spirit or whatever he calls it, which is somehow also me. And any disinclination to

239

obey the rules is the other part of me – the moral part. Does it not follow from that, and from everything else he said, that the real disobedience to the rules begins with being in this country at all? This country is simply *not* the Island, *not* the rules: that is its definition. My mortal self – that is, for all practical purposes, myself – can be defined, only as the part of me that is against the rules. Just as the Spirit answers to the Landlord, so this whole world answers to the black hole.'

'I take it all exactly the other way,' said John. 'Rather this world corresponds to the Landlord's castle. Everything is this Spirit's imagination, and therefore everything, properly understood, is good and happy. That the glory of this world in the end is appearance, leaves the world more glorious yet. I quite agree that the rules – the authority of the rules – becomes stronger than ever: but their content must be – well, easier. Perhaps I should say richer – more concrete.'

'Their content must become harsher. If the real good is simply "what is not here" and *here* means simply "the place where the good is not", what can the real rule be except to live here as little as possible, to commit ourselves as little as we can to the system of this world? I used to talk of innocent pleasures, fool that I was – as if anything could be innocent for us whose mere existence is a fall – as if all that a man eats or drinks or begets were not propagated curse.'

'Really, Vertue, this is a very strange view. The effect of Mr Wisdom's lessons on me has been just the opposite. I have been thinking how much of the Puritanian virus there must still be in me, to have held me back so long from the blameless generosity of Nature's breasts. Is not the meanest thing, in its degree, a mirror of the One; the lightest or the wildest pleasure as necessary to the perfection of the whole as the most heroic sacrifice? I am assured that in the Absolute, every flame even of carnal passion burns on –'

'Can even eating, even the coarsest food and the barest pittance, be justified? The flesh is but a living corruption –'

'There was a great deal to be said for Media after all –'

'I see that Savage was wiser than he knew –'

'It is true she had a dark complexion. And yet – is not brown as necessary to the spectrum as any other colour?'

'Is not every colour equally a corruption of the white radiance?'

'What we call evil – our greatest wickednesses – seen in the true setting is an element in the good. I am the doubter and the doubt.'

'What we call our righteousness is filthy rags. You are a fool, John, and I am going. I am going up into the rocks till I find where the wind is coldest and the ground hardest and the life of man furthest away. My notice to quit has not yet come, and I must be stained a while longer with the dye of our country. I shall still be part of that dark cloud which offends the white light:

but I shall make that part of the cloud which is called Me as thin, as nearly not a cloud, as I can. Body and mind shall pay for the crime of their existence. If there is any fasting, or watching, any mutilation or self-torture more harsh to nature than another, I shall find it out.'

'Are you mad?' said John.

'I have just become sane,' said Vertue. 'Why are you staring at me thus? I know I am pale and my pulse beats like a hammer. So much the saner! Disease is better than health and sees clearer, for it is one degree nearer to the Spirit, one degree less involved in the riot of our animal existence. But it will need stronger pains than this to kill the obscene thirst for life which I drank in with my mother's milk.'

'Why should we leave this pleasant valley?' John began, but Vertue cut him short.

'Who spoke of We? Do you think that I asked or expected *you* to accompany me? *You* to sleep on thorns and eat sloes?'

'You don't mean that we are to part?' said John.

'Pah!' said Vertue. 'You could not do the things I intend to do: and if you could, I would have none of you. Friendship – affection – what are these but the subtlest chains that tie us to our present country? He would be a fool indeed who mortified the body and left the mind free to be happy and thus still to affirm – to wallow in – her finite will. It is not this pleasure or that, but *all* that are to be cut off. No knife will cut deep enough to end the cancer. But I'll cut as deep as I can.'

He rose, still swaying, and continued his way over the meadow northward. He held his hand to his side as though he was in pain. Once or twice he nearly fell.

'What are you following me for?' he shouted to John. 'Go back.'

John stopped for a moment, checked by the hatred in his friend's face. Then, tentatively, he went on again. He thought that Vertue's illness had harmed his brain and had some indistinct hope that he might find means to humour him and bring him back. Before they had gone many paces, however, Vertue turned again and lifted a stone in his hand. 'Be off,' he said, 'or I'll throw it. We have nothing to do with one another, you and I. My own body and my own soul are enemies, and do you think I will spare *you*?'

John halted, undetermined, and then ducked, for the other had hurled the stone. I saw them go on like this for some way, John following at a distance, and stopping, and then continuing again, while Vertue every now and then stoned him and reviled him. But at last the distance between them was too great either for voice or stone to carry.

JOHN LED

John would turn back. Christ forces him on

As they went on thus John saw that the valley narrowed and the sides of it grew steeper. At the same time, the crevasse on his left hand which separated him from the western forest, became wider and wider; so that, what with that, and with the narrowing of the valley as a whole, the level piece where they were travelling was constantly diminished. Soon it was no longer the floor of the valley but only a ledge on its eastern side: and the crevasse revealed itself as being not a slot in the floor but the very floor. John saw that he was, in fact, walking on a shelf half-way down one side of the Grand Canyon. The cliff towered above him.

Presently a kind of spur or root of rock came out from the cliff and barred their way – crossing the ledge with a ruin of granite. And as Vertue began to scramble about the bases of this ascent, trying this grip and that to go up, John gained on him and came again within earshot. Before he came to the foot of the crags, however, Vertue had begun to climb. John heard his gasping as he struggled from hold to hold. Once he slipped back and left a little trail of blood where the rock skinned his ankle: but he went on again, and soon John saw him stand up, shaking and wiping the sweat out of his eyes, apparently at the top. He looked down and made gestures threateningly, and shouted, but he was too far for John to hear his words. Next moment John leaped aside to save his limbs, for Vertue had sent a great boulder rolling down: and as its thunder ceased echoing in the gorge and John looked up again, Vertue had gone over the spur out of sight and he saw no more of him.

John sat down in the desolate place. The grass here was finer and shorter, such grass as sheep love, which grows in the quiet intervals between the rocks. The windings of the gorge had already shut off the sight of Wisdom's Valley: yet I saw that John had no thought save of going back. There was indeed a confusion of shame and sorrow and bewilderment in his mind, but he put it all aside and held fast to his fear of the rocks and of meeting Vertue, now mad, in some narrow place whence he could not retreat. He thought,

'I will sit here and rest, till I get my wind, and then I will go back. I must live out the rest of my life as best I can.' Then suddenly he heard himself hailed from above. A Man was descending where Vertue had gone up.

'Hi!' shouted the Man. 'Your friend has gone on. Surely you will follow him?'

'He is mad, sir,' said John.

'No madder than you, and no saner,' said the Man. 'You will both recover if only you will keep together.'

'I cannot get up the rocks,' said John.

'I will give you a hand,' said the Man. And he came down till he was within reach of John, and held out his hand. And John grew pale as paper and nausea came upon him.

'It's now or never,' said the Man.

Then John set his teeth and took the hand that was offered him. He trembled at the very first grip he was made to take but he could not go back for they were speedily so high that he dared not attempt the return alone: and what with pushing and pulling the Man got him right up to the top and there he fell down on his belly in the grass to pant and to groan at the pains in his chest. When he sat up the Man was gone.

3

JOHN FORGETS HIMSELF

*As soon as he attempts seriously to live by
Philosophy, it turns into Religion*

John looked back and turned away with a shudder. All thought of descending again must be put aside at once and for ever. 'That fellow has left me in a nice fix,' he said bitterly. Next, he looked ahead. The cliffs still rose high above him and dropped far below him: but there was a ledge on a level with him, a narrow ledge, ten feet broad at its best and two at its worst, winding away along the cliff till it became but a green thread. His heart failed him. Then he tried to recall the lessons of Mr Wisdom, whether they would give him any strength. 'It is only myself,' he said. 'It is I myself, eternal Spirit, who drive this Me, the slave, along that ledge. I ought not to care whether he falls and breaks his neck or not. It is not he that is real, it is I – I – I. Can I remember that?' But then he felt so different from the eternal Spirit that he could call it 'I' no longer. 'It is all very well for *him*,' said John, 'but why does he give me no help? I want help. Help.' Then he gazed up at the cliffs and the narrow sky, blue and remote, between them, and he thought of that universal mind and of the shining tranquillity hidden somewhere behind the colours and the shapes, the pregnant silence under all the sounds, and he thought, 'If one drop of all that ocean would flow into me now – if I, the mortal, could but realise that I *am* that, all would be well. I know there is something there. I know the sensuous curtain is not a cheat.' In the bitterness of his soul he looked up again, saying: 'Help. Help. I want help.'

But as soon as the words were out of his mouth, a new fear, far deeper than his fear of the cliffs, sprang at him from the hiding-place, close to the surface, where it had lain against this moment. As a man in a dream talks without fear to his dead friend, and only afterwards bethinks himself, 'It was a ghost! I have talked with a ghost!' and wakes screaming: even so John sprang up as he saw what he had done.

'I have been *praying*,' he said. 'It is the Landlord under a new name. It is the rules and the black hole and the slavery dressed out in a new fashion to catch me. And I am caught. Who would have thought the old spider's web was so subtle?'

But this was insupportable to him and he said that he had only fallen into a metaphor. Even Mr Wisdom had confessed that Mother Kirk and the Stewards gave an account of the truth in picture-writing. And one must use metaphors. The feelings and the imagination needed that support. 'The great thing,' said John, 'is to keep the intellect free from them: to remember that they *are* metaphors.'

4

JOHN FINDS HIS VOICE

From Pantheism to Theism.
The transcendental I *becomes* Thou

He was much comforted by this idea of metaphor, and as he was now also rested, he began his journey along the cliff path with some degree of timid resolution. But it was very dreadful to him in the narrower places: and his courage seemed to him to decrease rather than to grow as he proceeded. Indeed he soon found that he could go forward at all only by remembering Mr Wisdom's Absolute incessantly. It was necessary by repeated efforts of the will to turn thither, consciously to draw from that endless reservoir the little share of vitality that he needed for the next narrow place. He knew now that he was praying, but he thought that he had drawn the fangs of that knowledge. In a sense, he said, Spirit is not. I am it, but I am not the whole of it. When I turn back to that part of it which is not I – that far greater part which my soul does not exhaust – surely that part is to me an Other. It must become, for my imagination, not really 'I' but 'Thou'. A metaphor – perhaps more than a metaphor. Of course there is no need at all to confuse it with the *mythical* Landlord ... However I think of it, I think of it inadequately.

Then a new thing happened to John, and he began to sing: and this is as much of his song as I remember from my dream:

He whom I bow to only knows to whom I bow
When I attempt the ineffable name, murmuring Thou;
And dream of Pheidian fancies and embrace in heart
Meanings, I know, that cannot be the thing thou art.
All prayers always, taken at their word, blaspheme,
Invoking with frail imageries a folk-lore dream;
And all men are idolaters, crying unheard
To senseless idols, if thou take them at their word,
And all men in their praying, self-deceived, address
One that is not (so saith that old rebuke) unless
Thou, of mere grace, appropriate, and to thee divert

Men's arrows, all at hazard aimed, beyond desert.
Take not, oh Lord, our literal sense, but in thy great,
Unbroken speech our halting metaphor translate.

When he came to think over the words that had gone out of him he began
once more to be afraid of them. Day was declining and in the narrow chasm
it was already almost dark.

5

FOOD AT A COST

John must accept God's grace or die –
Having accepted His grace, he must
acknowledge His existence

For a while he went on cautiously, but he was haunted by a picture in his mind of a place where the path would break off short when it was too dark for him to see, and he would step on air. This fear made him halt more and more frequently to examine his ground: and when he went on it was each time more slowly: till at last he came to a standstill. There seemed to be nothing for it but to rest where he was. The night was warm, but he was both hungry and thirsty. And he sat down. It was quite dark now.

Then I dreamed that once more a Man came to him in the darkness and said, 'You must pass the night where you are, but I have brought you a loaf and if you crawl along the ledge ten paces more you will find that a little fall of water comes down the cliff.'

'Sir,' said John. 'I do not know your name and I cannot see your face, but I thank you. Will you not sit down and eat, yourself?'

'I am full and not hungry,' said the Man. 'And I will pass on. But one word before I go. You cannot have it both ways.'

'What do you mean, sir?'

'Your life has been saved all this day by crying out to something which you call by many names, and you have said to yourself that you used metaphors.'

'Was I wrong, sir?'

'Perhaps not. But you must play fair. If its help is not a metaphor, neither are its commands. If it can answer when you call, then it can speak without your asking. If you can go to it, it can come to you.'

'I think I see, sir. You mean that I am not my own man: in some sense I have a Landlord after all?'

'Even so. But what is it that dismays you? You heard from Wisdom how the rules were yours and not yours. Did you not mean to keep them? And if so, can it scare you to know that there is one who will make you able to keep them?'

248

'Well,' said John. 'I suppose you have found me out. Perhaps I did not fully mean to keep them – not all – or not all the time. And yet, in a way, I think I did. It is like a thorn in your finger, sir. You know when you set about taking it out yourself – you mean to get it out – you know it will hurt – and it does hurt – but somehow it is not very serious business – well, I suppose, because you feel that you always *could* stop if it was very bad. Not that you intend to stop. But it is a very different thing to hold your hand out to a surgeon to be hurt as much as *he* thinks fit. And at *his* speed.'

The Man laughed. 'I see you understand me very well,' He said. 'But the great thing is to get the thorn out.' And then He went away.

6

CAUGHT

The terror of the Lord –
Where now is Sweet Desire?

John had no difficulty in finding the stream and when he had drunk he sat by it and ate. The bread had a rather flat taste which was somehow familiar and not very agreeable, but he was in no position to be dainty. Extreme weariness prevented him from thinking much of the conversation that had just passed. At the bottom of John's heart the stranger's words lay like a cold weight that he must some day take up and carry: but his mind was full of the pictures of cliff and chasm, of wondering about Vertue, and of smaller fears for the morrow and the moment, and, above all, the blessedness of food and of sitting still; and all these jumbled themselves together in an even dimmer confusion till at last he could no longer remember which he had been thinking of the moment before: and then he knew that he was sleeping: and last he was in deep sleep and knew nothing.

In the morning it was not so. With his first waking thought the full-grown horror leaped upon him. The blue sky above the cliffs was watching him: the cliffs themselves were imprisoning him: the rocks behind were cutting off his retreat: the path ahead was ordering him on. In one night the Landlord – call Him by what name you would – had come back to the world, and filled the world, quite full without a cranny. His eyes stared and His hand pointed and His voice commanded in everything that could be heard or seen, even from this place where John sat, to the end of the world: and if you passed the end of the world He would be there too. All things were indeed one – more truly one than Mr Wisdom dreamed – and all things said one word: CAUGHT – Caught into slavery again, to walk warily and on sufferance all his days, never to be alone; never the master of his own soul, to have no privacy, no corner whereof you could say to the whole universe: This is my own, here I can do as I please. Under that universal and inspecting gaze, John cowered like some small animal caught up in a giant's hands and held beneath a magnifying-glass.

When he had drunk and splashed his face in the stream he continued his way, and presently he made this song:

You rest upon me all my days
The inevitable Eye,
Dreadful and undeflected as the blaze
Of some Arabian sky;

Where, dead still, in their smothering tent
Pale travellers crouch, and, bright
About them, noon's long-drawn Astonishment
Hammers the rocks with light.

Oh, for but one cool breath in seven,
One air from northern climes,
The changing and the castle-clouded heaven
Of my old Pagan times!

But you have seized all in your rage
Of Oneness. Round about,
Beating my wings, all ways, within your cage,
I flutter, but not out.

And as he walked on, all day, in the strength of the bread he had eaten, not daring often to look down into the gulf and keeping his head mostly turned a little inward to the cliff, he had time to turn his trouble over in his mind and discover new sides to it. Above all it grew upon him that the return of the Landlord had blotted out the Island: for if there still were such a place he was no longer free to spend his soul in seeking it, but must follow whatever designs the Landlord had for him. And at the very best it now seemed that the last of things was at least more like a person than a place, so that the deepest thirst within him was not adapted to the deepest nature of the world. But sometimes he comforted himself by saying that this new and real Landlord must yet be very different from him whom the Stewards proclaimed and indeed from all images that men could make of him. There might still hang about him some of that promising darkness which had covered the Absolute.

7

THE HERMIT

John begins to learn something of the history
of human thought – History has seen people
like the Counter-Romantics in many ages

Presently he heard a bell struck, and he looked and saw a little chapel in a
cave of the cliff beside him; and there sat a hermit whose name was
History, so old and thin that his hands were transparent and John thought
that a little wind would have blown him away.

'Turn in, my son,' said the hermit, 'and eat bread and then you shall go
on your journey.' John was glad to hear the voice of a man among the
rocks and he turned in and sat. The hermit gave him bread and water but
he himself ate no bread and drank a little wine.

'Where are you going, son?' he said.

'It seems to me, Father, that I am going where I do not wish; for I set out
to find an Island and I have found a Landlord instead.'

And the hermit sat looking at him, nodding almost imperceptibly with
the tremors of age.

'The Clevers were right and the pale men were right,' said John, thinking
aloud, 'since the world holds no allaying for the thirst I was born with, and
seemingly the Island was an illusion after all. But I forget, Father, that you
will not know these people.'

'I know all parts of this country,' said the hermit, 'and the genius of
places. Where do these people live?'

'To the North of the road. The Clevers are in the country of Mammon,
where a stone giant is the lord of the soil, and the pale men are on the
Tableland of the Tough-Minded.'

'I have been in these countries a thousand times, for in my young days I
was a pedlar and there is no land I have not been in. But tell me, do they
still keep their old customs?'

'What customs were those?'

'Why, they all sprang from the ownership of the land there, for more
than half of the country North of the road is now held by the Enemy's tenants. Eastward it was the giant, and under him Mammon and some others.
But westward, on the Tableland, it was two daughters of the Enemy – let

me see – yes, Ignorantia and Superbia. They always did impose strange customs on the smaller tenants. I remember many tenants there – Stoics and Manichees, Spartiates, and all sorts. One time they had a notion to eat better bread than is made of wheat. Another time their very nurses took up a strange ritual of always emptying the baby out along with the bath. Then once the Enemy sent a fox without a tail among them and it persuaded them that all animals should be without tails and they docked all their dogs and horses and cows. I remember they were very puzzled how to apply any corresponding treatment to themselves, until at last a wise man suggested that they could cut off their noses. But the strangest custom of all was one that they practised all the time through all their other changes of customs. It was this – that they never set anything to rights but destroyed it instead. When a dish was dirty they did not wash it, they broke it; and when their clothes were dirty they burned them.'

'It must have been a very expensive custom.'

'It was ruinous, and it meant, of course, that they were constantly importing new clothes and new crockery. But indeed they had to import everything, for that is the difficulty of the Tableland. It never has been able to support life and it never will. Its inhabitants have always lived on their neighbours.'

'They must always have been very rich men.'

'They always *were* very rich men. I don't think I remember a single case of a poor or a common person going there. When humble people go wrong they generally go South. The Tough-Minded nearly always go to the Tableland as colonists from Mammon's country. I would guess that your pale men are reformed Clevers.'

'In a kind of way I believe they are. But can you tell me, Father, why these Tough-Minded people behave so oddly?'

'Well, for one thing, they *know* very little. They never travel and consequently never learn anything. They really do not know that there are any places outside Mammon's country and their own Tableland – except that they have heard exaggerated rumours about the Southern swamps, and suppose that everything is swamp a few miles South of themselves. Thus, their disgust with bread came about through sheer ignorance. At home in Mammon's country they knew only the standard bread that Mammon makes, and a few sweet, sticky cakes which Mammon imported from the South – the only kind of Southern product that Mammon would be likely to let in. As they did not like either of these, they invented a biscuit of their own. It never occurred to them to walk a mile off the Tableland into the nearest cottage and try what an honest loaf tasted like. The same with the babies. They disliked babies because babies meant to them the various deformities spawned in the brothels of Mammon: again, a moderate walk would have shown them healthy children at play in the lanes. As for their poor noses – on the Tableland there is nothing to smell, good, bad, or indifferent, and in Mammon's land whatever does not reek of scent reeks of ordure. So they saw no good in noses, though five miles away from them the hay was being cut.'

'And what about the Island, Father?' said John. 'Were they equally wrong about that?'

'That is a longer story, my son. But I see it is beginning to rain, so perhaps you may as well hear it.'

John went to the mouth of the cave and looked out. The sky had grown dark while they talked and a warm rain, blotting out the cliffs like a steam, was descending as far as his eye could reach.

8

HISTORY'S WORDS

There was a really Divine element in John's
Romanticism – For Morality is by no means
God's only witness in the sub-Christian world
– Even Pagan mythology contained a Divine
call – But the Jews, instead of a mythology,
had the Law – Conscience and Sweet Desire
must come together to make a Whole Man

When John had returned and seated himself, the hermit resumed: 'You may be sure that they make the same mistake about the Island that they make about everything else. But what is the current lie at present?'

'They say it is all a device of Mr Halfways – who is in the pay of the Brown Girls.'

'Poor Halfways! They treat him very unfairly – as if he were anything more than the local representative of a thing as widespread and as necessary (though, withal, as dangerous) as the sky! Not a bad representative, either, if you take his songs in your stride and use them as they are meant to be used: of course people who go to him in cold blood to get as much *pleasure* as they can, and therefore hear the same song over and over again, have only themselves to thank if they wake in the arms of Media.'

'That is very true, Father. But they wouldn't believe that I had seen and longed for the Island before I met Mr Halfways – before I ever heard a song at all. They insist on treating it as his invention.'

'That is always the way with stay-at-homes. If they like something in their own village they take it for a thing universal and eternal, though perhaps it was never heard of five miles away; if they dislike something, they say it is a local, backward, provincial convention, though, in fact, it may be the law of nations.'

'Then it is really true that all men, all nations, have had this vision of an Island?'

'It does not always come in the form of an Island: and to some men, if they inherit particular diseases, it may not come at all.'

'But what *is* it, Father? And has it anything to do with the Landlord? I do not know how to fit things together.'

'It comes from the Landlord. We know this by its results. It has brought you to where you now are: and nothing leads back to him which did not at first proceed from him.'

'But the Stewards would say that it was the Rules which come from him.'

'Not all Stewards are equally travelled men. But those who are, know perfectly well that the Landlord has circulated other things besides the Rules. What use are Rules to people who cannot read?'

'But nearly everyone can.'

'No one is born able to read: so that the starting point for all of us must be a picture and not the Rules. And there are more than you suppose who are illiterate all their lives or who, at the best, never learn to read well.'

'And for these people the pictures are the right thing?'

'I would not quite say that. The pictures alone are dangerous, and the Rules alone are dangerous. That is why the best thing of all is to find Mother Kirk at the very beginning, and to live from infancy with a third thing which is neither the Rules nor the pictures and which was brought into the country by the Landlord's Son. That, I say, is the best: never to have known the quarrel between the Rules and the pictures. But it very rarely happens. The Enemy's agents are everywhere at work, spreading illiteracy in one district and blinding men to the pictures in another. Even where Mother Kirk is nominally the ruler men can grow old without knowing how to read the Rules. Her empire is always crumbling. But it never quite crumbles: for as often as men become Pagans again, the Landlord again sends them pictures and stirs up sweet desire and so leads them back to Mother Kirk even as he led the actual Pagans long ago. There is, indeed, no other way.'

'Pagans?' said John. 'I do not know that people.'

'I forgot that you had travelled so little. It may well be that you were never in the country of Pagus in the flesh, though in another sense, you have lived there all your life. The curious thing about Pagus was that the people there had not heard of the Landlord.'

'Surely, a great many other people don't know either?'

'Oh, a great many *deny* his existence. But you have to be told about a thing before you can deny it. The peculiarity of the Pagans was that they had not been told: or if they had, it is so long ago that the tradition had died out. You see, the Enemy had practically supplanted the Landlord, and he kept a sharp watch against any news from that quarter reaching the tenants.'

'Did he succeed?'

'No. It is commonly thought that he did, but that is a mistake. It is commonly thought that he fuddled the tenants by circulating a mass of false stories about the Landlord. But I have been through Pagus in my rounds too often to think it was quite so simple. What really happened was this: the Landlord succeeded in getting a lot of messages through.'

'What sort of messages?'

'Mostly pictures. You see, the Pagans couldn't read, because the Enemy shut up the schools as soon as he took over Pagus. But they had pictures. The moment you mentioned your Island I knew what you were at. I have seen that Island dozens of times in those pictures.'

'And what happened then?'

'Almost certainly the same thing has happened to you. These pictures woke desire. You understand me?'

'Very well.'

'And then the Pagans made mistakes. They would keep on trying to get the same picture again: and if it didn't come, they would make copies of it for themselves. Or even if it did come they would try to get out of it not desire but satisfaction. But you must know all this.'

'Yes, yes, indeed. But what came of it?

'They went on making up more and more stories for themselves about the pictures, and then pretending the stories were true. They turned to brown girls and tried to believe that that was what they wanted. They went far South, some of them and became magicians, and tried to believe it was that. There was no absurdity and no indecency they did not commit. But however far they went, the Landlord was too much for them. Just when their own stories seemed to have completely overgrown the original messages and hidden them beyond recovery, suddenly the Landlord would send them a new message and all their stories would look stale. Or just when they seemed to be growing really contented with lust or mystery mongering, a new message would arrive and the old desire, the real one, would sting them again, and they would say "Once more it has escaped us".'

'I know. And then the whole cycle would begin over again.'

'Yes. But all the while there was one people that could read. You have heard of the Shepherd People?'

'I had been hoping you would not come to that, Father. I have heard the Stewards talk of them and I think it is that more than anything else that sickened me of the whole story. It is so clear that the Shepherd People are just one of these Pagan peoples – and a peculiarly unattractive one. If the whole thing is hobbled by one leg to that special People...'

'This is merely a blunder,' said History. 'You, and those whom you trust, have not *travelled*. You have never been in Pagus, nor among the Shepherds. If you had lived on the roads as I have, you would never say that they were the same. The Shepherds could read: that is the thing to remember about them. And because they could read, they had from the Landlord, not pictures but Rules.'

'But who wants Rules instead of Islands?'

'That is like asking who wants cooking instead of dinner. Do you not see that the Pagans, because they were under the Enemy, were beginning at the wrong end? They were like lazy schoolboys attempting eloquence before they learn grammar. They had pictures for their eyes instead of roads for their feet, and that is why most of them could do nothing but desire and then, through starved desire, become corrupt in their imaginations, and so awake and despair, and so desire again. Now the Shepherds, because they were under the Landlord, were made to begin at the right end. Their feet were set on a road: and as the Landlord's Son once said, if the feet have been put right the hands and the head will come right sooner or later. It won't work the other way.'

'You know so much, Father,' said John, 'that I do not know how to answer you. But this is all unlike the accounts I have heard of those countries. Surely some of the Pagans did get somewhere.'

'They did. They got to Mother Kirk. That is the definition of a Pagan – a man so travelling that if all goes well he arrives at Mother Kirk's chair and is carried over this gorge. I saw it happen myself. But we define a thing by its perfection. The trouble about Pagus is that the perfect, and in that sense typical, Pagan, is so uncommon there. It must be so, must it not? These pictures – this ignorance of writing – this endless desire which so easily confuses itself with other desires and, at best, remains pure only by knowing what it does *not* want – you see that it is a starting point from which *one* road leads home and a thousand roads lead into the wilderness.'

'But were the Shepherds not just as bad in their own way? Is it not true that they were illiberal, narrow, bigoted?'

'They *were* narrow. The thing they had charge of was narrow: it was the Road. They found it. They sign-posted it. They kept it clear and repaired it. But you must not think I am setting them up against the Pagans. The truth is that a Shepherd is only half a man, and a Pagan is only half a man, so that neither people was well without the other, nor could either be healed until the Landlord's Son came into the country. And even so, my son, you will not be well until you have overtaken your fellow-traveller who slept in my cell last night.'

'Do you mean Vertue?' said John.

'That was his name. I knew him though he did not tell me, for I know his family; and his father, whom he does not know, was called Nomos and lived among the Shepherds. You will never do anything until you have sworn blood brotherhood with him: nor can he do anything without you.'

'I would gladly overtake him,' said John, 'but he is so angry with me that I am afraid to come near him. And even if we made it up, I don't see how we could help falling out again. Somehow we have never been able to be quite comfortable together for very long.'

'Of yourselves you never will. It is only a third that can reconcile you.'

'Who is that?'

'The same who reconciled the Shepherds and the Pagans. But you must go to Mother Kirk to find him.'

'It is raining harder than ever,' said John from the mouth of the cave.

'It will not stop tonight,' said Father History. 'You must stay with me till the morning.'

9

MATTER OF FACT

It is dangerous to welcome Sweet Desire, but
fatal to reject it – Whether it comes as
Courtly Love in the Middle Ages – Or
nature-worship in the Nineteenth Century –
Every form has its proper corruption: but
'de-bunking' is not the cure

'I see,' said John presently, 'that this question is harder than the Clevers and the pale men suppose. But they were right in distrusting the Island. From all that you have told me, it is a very dangerous thing.'

'There is no avoiding danger in our country,' said History. 'Do you know what happens to people who set about learning to skate with a determination to get no falls? They fall as often as the rest of us, and they cannot skate in the end.'

'But it is more than dangerous. You said it was beginning at the wrong end, while the Shepherd people began at the right end.'

'That is true. But if you are a Pagan by birth or by nature, you have no choice. It is better to begin at the wrong end than not to begin at all. And the most part of men are always Pagans. Their first step will always be the desire born of the pictures: and though that desire hides a thousand false trails it also hides the only true one for them, and those who preach down the desire under whatever pretext – Stoic, Ascetic, Rigorist, Realist, Classicist – are on the Enemy's side whether they know it or not.'

'Then there is always need for the Island?'

'It does not always take the form of an Island, as I have said. The Landlord sends pictures of many different kinds. What is universal is not the particular picture, but the arrival of some message, not perfectly intelligible, which wakes this desire and sets men longing for something East or West of the world: something possessed, if at all, only in the act of desiring it, and lost so quickly that the craving itself becomes craved; something that tends inevitably to be confused with common or even with vile satisfactions lying close to hand, yet which is able, if any man faithfully live through the dialectic of its successive births and deaths, to lead him at last where true joys are to be found. As for the shapes in which it comes, I have seen many in my travels. In Pagus it was sometimes, as I said, an Island. But it was often, too, a picture of people, stronger and fairer than we are. Sometimes it was a picture telling a story. The strangest shape it ever took was in Medium Aevum – that was a master stroke of the Landlord's diplomacy; for of course, since the Enemy has been in the country, the Landlord has had to become a politician. Medium Aevum was first inhabited by colonists from Pagus. They came there at the very worst period in the history of Pagus, when the enemy seemed to have succeeded completely in diverting all the desires that the Landlord could arouse into nothing but lust. These poor colonists were in such a state that they could not let their fancies wander for a minute without seeing images of black, craving eyes, and breasts, and gnawing kisses. It seemed hopeless to do anything with them. Then came the Landlord's crowning audacity. The very next picture he sent them was a picture of a Lady! Nobody had ever had the idea of a Lady before: and yet a Lady is a woman: so this was a new thing, which took the Enemy off his guard, and yet at the same time it was an old thing – in fact, the very thing which he was reckoning on as his strongest point. He got the shock of his life. The people went mad over the new picture, and made songs that are sung still, and looked away from the picture at the real women around them and saw them quite differently – so that ordinary love for women became, for a time, itself a form of the real desire, and not merely one of the spurious satisfactions offered to it. Of course the Landlord was playing a dangerous game (nearly all his games *are* dangerous) and the Enemy managed to mix up and corrupt the new message – as usual – but not so much as he wished, or as people afterwards said: and before he had recovered himself, one at least[1] of the tenants had carried this new form of the desire right up to its natural conclusion and found what he had really been wanting. He wrote it all down in what he called a *Comedy*.'

'And what about Mr Halfways?' said John. 'Where did his kind of song begin?'

'That was the last big arrival of new messages that we had,' said History. 'And it happened just before I retired from the world. It was in the land of Mr Enlightenment, but he was very different then. I do not know any man who has deteriorated so with advancing years. In those days Claptrap had not been built. The Enemy had agents in the country but did not come there often himself: it must have been just about that time that Mammon was taking it over, and building new towns and turning the people out of the fields into the factories. One of the results was a great deal of anaemia – though there were other causes for that too – and weak hearts. This time the Landlord did a curious thing: he sent them pictures of the country they were actually living in – as if he had sent them a number of mirrors. You

[1] Dante

see, he always does the last thing the Enemy is expecting. And just as the pictures of the Lady in Medium Aevum had made the real women look different, so when men looked at these pictures of the country and then turned to the real landscape, it was all changed. And a new idea was born in their minds, and they saw something – the old something, the Island West of the world, the Lady, the heart's desire – as it were hiding, yet not quite hidden, like something even more about to be, in every wood and stream and under every field. And because they saw this, the land seemed to be coming to life, and all the old stories of the Pagans came back to their minds and meant more than the Pagans themselves ever knew: and because women also were in the landscape, the old idea of the Lady came back too. For this is part of the Landlord's skill, that when one message has died he brings it to life again in the heart of the next. But out of this third revelation, which they called Romantic, so many songs were made that I cannot remember all of them: and many deeds were done, too, and many, through the usual false starts and disillusions and re-beginnings of desire, found their way home. Your Mr Halfways is one of the later and weaker followers of that school.'

'I don't think that the history of the Romantic pictures is quite as clear as the other histories. What exactly was the Landlord doing? And what did the Enemy do?'

'I thought you would have seen. This third stroke of policy was in a way one of the greatest. All the previous pictures had been of something that was *not there* in the world around you. This gave the Enemy the chance of making people believe that you *had* it in the picture, and *lacked* it elsewhere – in other words that the picture itself was the thing you wanted. And that, as you know, means idolatry, and then, when the idol disappoints you (as it must) there is an easy passage to all the spurious satisfactions. But this weapon was knocked out of the Enemy's hand when once the thing in the picture was the very same thing that you saw all round you. Even the stupidest tenant could see that you *had* the landscape, in the only sense in which it could be had, already: and still you *wanted*: therefore the landscape was not what you wanted. Idolatry became impossible. Of course the Enemy, when he had recovered himself, found a new method of defence. Just because the new message could not be idolised, it could be easily belittled. The desire awakened thus between the picture and the countryside could be confused with the ordinary *pleasure* that any healthy man feels in moving about out-of-doors: and when it had been so confused, the Enemy could pretend that the Romantics had made a great pother about nothing. And you can imagine that all the people who had not had pictures sent to them, and therefore not felt the desire, and therefore were itching with envy, would welcome this explanation.'

'I see,' said John. 'But still – on your own showing, all these messages get blurred and corrupted in the end, and then, surely, the thing to do is to look out for the new one. These pale men might be quite right to occupy themselves in cleaning away the rubbish of the old revelation. That might be the way to get ready for the next.'

'That is another notion they have which a little travel would soon blow to pieces. They think that the Landlord works like the factories in Claptrap, inventing every day a new machine which supersedes the old. As machines are among the very few things that they do know something about, they cannot help thinking that everything is like them. But this leads them into two mistakes. First of all, they have no conception how slowly the Landlord acts – the enormous intervals between these big changes in his type of picture. And secondly, they think that the new thing refutes and cancels the old, whereas, in reality it brings it to a fuller life. I have never known a case where the man who was engaged in ridiculing or rejecting the old message became the receiver of the new. For one thing it all takes so long. Why, bless my soul, I remember Homer in Pagus ridiculing some of the story pictures: but they had thousands of years to run still and thousands of souls were to get nourishment out of them. I remember Clopinel[2] in Medium Aevum, jeering at the pictures of the Lady before they had reached half his countrymen. But his jeer was no spell to evoke a new message, nor was he helping any cause but the Enemy's.'

[2] Jean de Meung

ARCHETYPE AND ECTYPE

We know that the object of Sweet Desire is
not subjective – Nay, even the Desire ceases
to be our Desire – No matter; for it is God's
love, not ours, that moves us and all things

There was a long silence in the cave except for the sound of the rain. Then John began once more:

'And yet ...' he said, 'and yet, Father, I am terribly afraid. I am afraid that the things the Landlord really intends for me may be utterly unlike the things he has taught me to desire.'

'They will be very unlike the things you imagine. But you already know that the objects which your desire imagines are always inadequate to that desire. Until you have it you will not know what you wanted.'

'I remember that Wisdom said that too. And I understand that. Perhaps what troubles me is a fear that my desires, after all you have said, do not really come from the Landlord – that there is some older and rival Beauty in the world which the Landlord will not allow me to get. How can we *prove* that the Island comes from him? Angular would say it did not.'

'You have proved it for yourself: you have *lived* the proof. Has not every object which fancy and sense suggested for the desire, proved a failure, confessed itself, after trial, not to be what you wanted? Have you not found by elimination that this desire is the perilous siege in which only One can sit?'

'But then,' said John, 'the very quality of it is so – so unlike what we think of the Landlord. I will confess to you what I had hoped to keep secret. It has been with me almost a bodily desire. There have been times ... I have felt the sweetness flow over from the soul into the body ... pass through me from head to foot. It's quite true, what the Clevers say. It *is* a thrill – a physical sensation.'

'That is an old story. You must fear thrills, but you must not fear them too much. It is only a foretaste of that which the real Desirable will be when you have found it. I remember well what an old friend of mine in Medium Aevum once said to me – "Out of the soul's bliss," he said, "there shall be a flowing over into the flesh."'

'Did he say that? I did not suppose that anyone except the Clevers knew it.

Do not laugh at me Father – or laugh if you will – I am indeed very ignorant and I have listened to people more ignorant still.'

Twilight, hastened by the rain, had fallen on the canyon, and in the cave it was quite dark. John heard the old man moving to and fro and presently there came the flame of a little lamp lighting up his pale bird-like face. He set food for supper before his guest and bade him eat and then sleep.

'Gladly, Father,' said John, 'for I am very tired. I do not know why I have plagued you with questions about the Island. It is all a story of what happened to me long ago. It was long ago that I saw it clearly. The visions, ever since the first one, have grown rarer, the desires fainter. I have been talking as if I still craved it, but I do not think I can find any craving in my heart now at all.'

The old man sat still, nodding a little as before.

Suddenly John spoke again.

'Why should it *wear out* if it is from the Landlord? It doesn't last, you know. Isn't it that which gives away the whole case?'

'Have you not heard men say, or have you forgotten, that it is like human love?' asked the hermit.

'What has that to do with it?'

'You would not ask if you had been married, or even if you had studied generation among the beasts. Do you not know how it is with love? First comes delight: then pain: then fruit. And then there is joy of the fruit, but that is different again from the first delight. And mortal lovers must not try to remain at the first step: for lasting passion is the dream of a harlot and from it we wake in despair. You must not try to keep the raptures: they have done their work. Manna kept, is worms. But you are full of sleep and we had better talk no more.'

Then I dreamed that John lay down on a hard bed in the cave; and as he lay between waking and sleeping, the hermit, as he thought, lit two candles at the back of the cave on an altar and went to and fro doing and saying his holy things. And on the very borders of sleep John heard him begin to sing, and this was the song:

My heart is empty. All the fountains that should run
*   With longing, are in me*
Dried up. In all my countryside there is not one
*   That drips to find the sea.*
I have no care for anything thy love can grant
*   Except the moment's vain*
And hardly noticed filling of the moment's want
*   And to be free from pain.*
Oh, thou that art unwearying, that dost neither sleep

Nor slumber, who didst take
All care for Lazarus in the careless tomb, oh keep
   Watch for me till I wake.
If thou think for me what I cannot think, if thou
   Desire for me what I
Cannot desire, my soul's interior Form, though now
   Deep-buried, will not die,
– No more than the insensible dropp'd seed which grows
   Through winter ripe for birth
Because, while it forgets, the heaven remembering throws
   Sweet influence still on earth,
– Because the heaven, moved moth-like by thy beauty, goes
   Still turning round the earth.

BOOK 9

ACROSS THE CANYON

Sholde nevere whete wexe bote whete
fyrste deyde;
And other sedes also, in the same wyse,
Thae ben leide on louh erthe, ylore as
hit were,
And thorwh the grete grace of God, of
greyn ded in erthe
Atte last launceth up wher-by we liven alle.
LANGLAND

You will not sleep, if you lie there a thousand
years, until you have opened your hand and
yielded that which is not yours to give or to
withhold. You may think you are dead, but
it will be only a dream; you may think you
have come awake, but it will still be only a
dream. Open your hand, and you will sleep
indeed – then wake indeed.
GEORGE MACDONALD

You may as well come quiet.
POLICE MAXIM

ACROSS THE CANYON BY

THE INNER LIGHT

*John realises that he is in imminent danger
of becoming a Christian – He struggles to
withdraw*

When John opened his eyes the day was still far off but there was light in the cave as though from a hundred candles. The hermit lay fast asleep by one wall of the cell as John lay by the other, and between them stood a woman, something like Reason and something like Mother Kirk, very bright.

'I am Contemplation,' she said. 'Rise and come with me.'

'You are not like the Contemplation that I know,' said John.

'It is one of my shadows whom you have met,' said the Lady. 'And there is little good in them and less harm. But rise and come.'

Then John rose and the Lady took him by the hand and led him out on to the ledge before the cave. And the night was still black with thunderous rain, but the Lady and he were in a sphere of light, so that the raindrops as they passed out of the darkness into it became bright like diamonds in the centre of the sphere and iridescent at the circumference. Held by the Lady's hand he crossed the chasm and passed up the glens of the mountains on the other side. When they had travelled a long way (and still the darkness lay everywhere save where they trod) they came to the sea. And they crossed the sea also, gliding a little above the water, and the water also was dark until it reached their light, but within that it was blue as though it lay in Mediterranean sunshine. But presently the surrounding darkness vanished away and the drop of light in which they had journeyed entered an ocean of light and was swallowed up. The sky was visible above them and it seemed to be early morning, for it was cool and dew soaked their feet. And John looked and saw fields going up before him and the light ran down as a river in the midst of the fields, singing with a voice like a river but more articulate and very loud, too bright to look at. There were many people with them. And as John looked round upon the people he saw that they were approaching some high walls and great gates. And, at the shape of the tower clustered above him, a memory, very deeply buried, stirred in his mind, first sweet, then uneasy, then spreading through the pool of his mind in widening circles of dismay, till at last with certainty, inevitable, unbearable, there flashed before him the picture of those turreted crags seen long ago from Puritania at the summit of the Eastern mountains, and he saw where he was – beyond the brook – where Uncle George had vanished – at the Landlord's castle – the good kind Landlord with the black hole. He began to draw his hand out of the Lady's hand. He could not get it free. She was leading him on to the castle gates and all the crowd of people were moving on in the same direction, with a sinister happiness on their faces. He struggled with Contemplation and screamed: and with that and the struggling he awoke.

2

THIS SIDE BY LIGHTNING

Reason will not let him withdraw

It was now pitchy black in the cave. Only the quiet breathing of the hermit recalled to John where he was: and with the first return of the knowledge he was already creeping out of the cave to dare the black night and the narrow ledge, to crawl the skin off his hands and his knees, to do and suffer anything so long as he was going back and not on – on in this direction where the next turning might lead him into the heart of his adversary's power. The rain fell in torrents and thunder echoed among the rocks: but the cool moisture on his back was better than the hot moisture on his forehead. He did not dare to stand up and walk, for the new terrors had not driven out the old, but rather joined with them in a phantasmagoric harmony, so that all in one moment his inner eye saw the black hole full of the spiders and scorpions – the narrow, narrow ledge sloping horribly the wrong way – the drop into the darkness and his own body bounced from crag to crag – the terrible face of Uncle George when the mask would not stay on it. And as the flashes came faster and the thunder followed faster on each flash, a new fear joined the dance: and in each flash the timeless unforgettable sight of the cliffs, lit up from end to end, gave a new edge to the old fear of climbing: and that again brought back the fear of Uncle George's face (so will mine look when I lie broken at the bottom of the gorge), until at last, when the complexity of fears seemed to admit no increase, a sharp, commanding voice out of the darkness suddenly startled him with such a shock that he seemed not to have been frightened till then.

'Back!' said the voice.

John crouched motionless from the balance of fears. He was not even sure that he *could* turn on this bit of the ledge.

'Back,' said the voice, 'or else show that you're the better man.'

The lightning tore open the darkness and flung it to again. But John had seen his enemy. It was Reason, this time on foot, but still mailed, and her sword drawn in her hand.

'Do you want to fight?' she said in the darkness.

John had a wild thought of catching one of the mailed ankles from where he crouched: but when he had a picture of Reason falling into the gulf he could not get it clear of another picture in which he fell with her.

'I can't turn here,' he said: but the steel was at his throat and turn he did. He shuffled along at a surprising speed, still on his hands and knees, till he had passed the cave again. It was no longer a question of plans or of ultimate escape. The hunted animal's impulse to prolong the chase kept him ragingly on the move. The flashes were growing rare and a star or two showed ahead. Then all of a sudden a wind shook the last raindrops fiercely in his face and there was moonlight all about him. But he drew back with a groan.

3

THIS SIDE BY THE DARKNESS

*John sees the face of Death and learns that
dying is the only escape from it*

Within an inch of him he had seen a face. Now a cloud crossed the
moon and the face was no longer visible, but he knew that it was still
looking at him – an aged, appalling face, crumbling and chaotic, larger than
human. Presently its voice began:

'Do you still think it is the black hole you fear? Do you not know even
now the deeper fear whereof the black hole is but the veil? Do you not
know why they would all persuade you that there is nothing beyond the
brook and that when a man's lease is out his story is done? Because, if this
were true, they could in their reckoning make me equal to nought, therefore not dreadful: could say that where I am they are not, that while they
are, I am not. They have prophesied soft things to you. I am no negation,
and the deepest of your heart acknowledges it. Else why have you buried
the memory of your uncle's face so carefully that it has needed all these
things to bring it up? Do not think that you can escape me; do not think
you can call me Nothing. To you I am not Nothing; I am the being blind-
folded, the losing all power of self-defence, the surrender, not because any
terms are offered, but because resistance is gone: the step into the dark: the
defeat of all precautions: utter helplessness turned out to utter risk: the final
loss of liberty. The Landlord's Son who feared nothing, feared me.'

'What am I to do?' said John.

'Which you choose,' said the voice. 'Jump, or be thrown. Shut your eyes
or have them bandaged by force. Give in or struggle.'

'I would sooner do the first, if I could.'

'Then I am your servant and no more your master. The cure of death is
dying. He who lays down his liberty in that act receives it back. Go down
to Mother Kirk.'

John looked about him when next the moon shone. The bottom of the
chasm was level far below him, and there he saw what seemed a concourse
of dark figures. Amidst them they had left an open space, where there was
a glimmer as of water: and near the water there was someone standing.

It seemed to him that he was waited for, and he began to explore the face of the cliff below him. To his surprise it was no longer sheer and smooth. He tried a few footholds and got five feet below the ledge. Then he sat down again, sick. But the kind of fear which he now suffered was cold and leaden: there was no panic in it: and soon he continued his descent.

4

SECURUS TE PROJICE

John returns to the Church of Christ –
Though all the states of mind through which
he has ever passed rise up to dissuade him

On the floor of *Peccatum Adae* stood Mother Kirk crowned and sceptred in the midst of the bright moonlit circle left by the silent people. All their faces were turned towards her, and she was looking eastward to where John slowly descended the cliff. Not far from her sat Vertue, mother-naked. They were both on the margin of a large pool which lay in a semicircle against the western cliff. On the far side of the water that cliff rose sheer to the edge of the canyon. There was deep silence for about half an hour.

At last the small, drooping figure of a man detached itself from the shadow of the crags and advanced towards them through the open moonlight. It was John.

'I have come to give myself up,' he said.

'It is well,' said Mother Kirk. 'You have come a long way round to reach this place, whither I would have carried you in a few moments. But it is very well.'

'What must I do?' said John.

'You must take off your rags,' said she, 'as your friend has done already, and then you must dive into this water.'

'Alas,' said he, 'I have never learned to dive.'

'There is nothing to learn,' said she. 'The art of diving is not to do anything new but simply to cease doing something. You have only to let yourself go.'

'It is only necessary,' said Vertue, with a smile, 'to abandon all efforts at self-preservation.'

'I think,' said John, 'that if it is all one, I would rather jump.'

'It is not all one,' said Mother Kirk. 'If you jump, you will be trying to save yourself and you may be hurt. As well, you would not go deep enough. You must dive so that you can go right down to the bottom of the pool: for you are not to come up again on this side. There is a tunnel in the cliff, far beneath the surface of the water, and it is through that that you must pass so that you may come up on the far side.'

'I see,' thought John to himself, 'that they have brought me here to kill me,' but he began, nevertheless, to take off his clothes. They were little loss to him, for they hung in shreds, plastered with blood and with the grime of every shire from Puritania to the canyon: but they were so stuck to him that they came away with pain and a little skin came with them. When he was naked Mother Kirk bade him come to the edge of the pool, where Vertue was already standing. It was a long way down to the water, and the reflected moon seemed to look up at him from the depth of a mine. He had had some thought of throwing himself in, with a run, the very instant he reached the edge, before he had time to be afraid. And the making of that resolution had seemed to be itself the bitterness of death, so that he half believed the worst must be over and that he would find himself in the water before he knew. But lo! he was still standing on the edge, still on this side. Then a stranger thing came to pass. From the great concourse of spectators, shadowy people came stealing out to his side, touching his arm and whispering to him: and every one of them appeared to be the wraith of some old acquaintance.

First came the wraith of old Enlightenment and said, 'There's still time. Get away and come back to me and all this will vanish like a nightmare.'

Then came the wraith of Media Halfways and said, 'Can you really risk losing me for ever? I know you do not desire me at this moment. But for ever? Think. Don't burn your boats.'

And the wraith of old Halfways said, 'After all – has this anything to do with the Island as you used to imagine it? Come back and hear my songs instead. You *know* them.'

The wraith of young Halfways said, 'Aren't you ashamed? Be a man. Move with the times and don't throw your life away for an old wives' tale.'

The wraith of Sigismund said, 'You know what this is, I suppose. Religious melancholia. Stop while there is time. If you dive, you dive into insanity.'

The wraith of Sensible said, 'Safety first. A touch of rational piety adds something to life: but this salvationist business ... well! Who knows where it will end? Never accept unlimited liabilities.'

The wraith of Humanist said, 'Mere atavism. You are diving to escape your real duties. All this emotionalism, after the first plunge, is so much *easier* than virtue in the classical sense.'

The wraith of Broad said, 'My dear boy, you are losing your head. These sudden conversions and violent struggles don't achieve anything. We have had to discard so much that our ancestors thought necessary. It is all far easier, far more gracious and beautiful than they supposed.'

But at that moment the voice of Vertue broke in:

'Come on, John,' he said, 'the longer we look at it the less we shall like it.' And with that he took a header into the pool and they saw him no more.

And how John managed it or what he felt I did not know, but he also rubbed his hands, shut his eyes, despaired, and let himself go. It was not a good dive, but, at least, he reached the water head first.

ACROSS THE CANYON

*John comes where Philosophy said no man
could come – The goal is, and is not, what he
had always Desired*

My dream grew darker so that I have a sense, but little clear memory of the things that John experienced both in the pool and in great catacombs, paved sometimes with water, sometimes with stone, and upon winding stairways in the live rocks, whereby he and Vertue ascended through the inwards of the mountain to the land beyond *Peccatum Adae*. He learned many mysteries in the earth and passed through many elements, dying many deaths. One thing has come through into my waking memory. Of all the people he had met in his journey only Wisdom appeared to him in the caverns, and troubled him by saying that no man could really come where he had come and that all his adventures were but figurative, for no professed experience of these places could be anything other than mythology. But then another voice spoke to him from behind him, saying:

'Child, if you will, it *is* mythology. It is but truth, not fact: an image, not the very real. But then it is My mythology. The words of Wisdom are also myth and metaphor: but since they do not know themselves for what they are, in them the hidden myth is master, where it should be servant: and it is but of man's inventing. But this is My inventing, this is the veil under which I have chosen to appear even from the first until now. For this end I made your senses and for this end your imagination, that you might see My face and live. What would you have? Have you not heard among the Pagans the story of Semele? Or was there any age in any land when men did not know that corn and wine were the blood and body of a dying and yet living God?'

And not long after that the light and colour, as with the sound of a trumpet, rushed back upon my dreaming eyes, and my ears were full of the sound of birds and the rustle of leaves, for John and Vertue had come up out of the earth into the green forests of the land beyond the canyon. Then I saw that they were received into a great company of other pilgrims who had all descended like them into the water and the earth and again come up, and now took their march westward along the banks of a clear river. All kinds of men were among them. And during the whole of this part of their journey Reason rode with the company, talking to them at will and not visiting them any longer by sudden starts, nor vanishing suddenly. It was a wonder to John to find so many companions: nor could he conceive how he had failed to run across them in the earlier parts of his journey.

I watched this journey in my dream a long time. At the outset their goal was heard of only by rumours as of something very far off: then, by continuous marching, winding their way among the peaked and valleyed lands, I saw where they came down to the white beaches of a bay of the sea, the western end of the world; a place very ancient, folded many miles deep in the silence of forests; a place, in some sort, lying rather at the world's beginning, as though men were born travelling away from it. It was early in the morning when they came there and heard the sound of the waves; and looking across the sea – at that hour still almost colourless – all these thousands became still. And what the others saw I do not know: but John saw the Island. And the morning wind, blowing off-shore from it, brought the sweet smell of its orchards to them, but rarefied and made faint with the thinness and purity of early air, and mixed with a little sharpness of the sea. But for John, because so many thousands looked at it with him, the pain and the longing were changed and all unlike what they had been of old: for humility was mixed with their wildness, and the sweetness came not with pride and with the lonely dreams of poets nor with the glamour of a secret, but with the homespun truth of folk-tales, and with the sadness of graves and freshness as of earth in the morning. There was fear in it also, and hope: and it began to seem well to him that the Island should be different from his desires, and so different that, if he had known it, he would not have sought it.

6

NELLA SUA VOLUNTADE

And the Christian life still to begin

How it fared with the other pilgrims I did not see, but presently a comely person took John and Vertue apart and said that he had been appointed to be their Guide. I dreamed that he was one born in the Mountain and they called him Slikisteinsauga because his sight was so sharp that the sight of any other who travelled with him would be sharpened by his company.

'Thank you,' said John. 'Pray, do we take ship from here?'

But Slikisteinsauga shook his head: and he asked them to look at the Island again and specially to consider the shape of the crags, or the castle (for they could not well see which at that distance) to which it rose at its highest point.

'I see,' said John presently.

'What do you see?' said the Guide.

'They are the very same shape as that summit of the Eastern Mountain which we called the Landlord's castle as we saw it from Puritania.'

'They are not only the same shape. They are the same.'

'How can that be?' said John with a sinking heart, 'for those mountains were in the extreme East, and we have been travelling West ever since we left home.'

'But the world is round,' said the Guide, 'and you have come nearly round it. The Island is the Mountains: or, if you will, the Island is the other side of the Mountains, and not, in truth, an Island at all.'

'And how do we go on from here?'

The Guide looked at him as a merciful man looks on an animal which he must hurt.

'The way to go on,' he said at last, 'is to go back. There are no ships. The only way is to go East again and cross the brook.'

'What must be must be,' said John. 'I deserve no better. You mean that I have been wasting my labour all my life, and I have gone half-round the world to reach what Uncle George reached in a mile or so.'

'Who knows what your uncle has reached, except the Landlord? Who knows what you would have reached if you had crossed the brook without ever leaving home? You may be sure the Landlord has brought you the shortest way: though I confess it would look an odd journey on a map.'

'How does it strike you, friend?' said John to Vertue.

'It cannot be helped,' said Vertue. 'But indeed, after the water and the earth, I thought we had already crossed the brook in a sense.'

'You will be always thinking that,' said the Guide. 'We call it Death in the Mountain language. It is too tough a morsel to eat at one bite. You will meet that brook more often than you think: and each time you will suppose that you have done with it for good. But some day you really will.'

They were all silent for a while.

'Come,' said the Guide at last, 'if you are ready let us start East again. But I should warn you of one thing – the country will look very different on the return journey.'

BOOK 10

THE REGRESS

*And if, when he returned into the cave, he
were constrained once more to contend with
those that had always there been prisoners, in
judgment of the said shadows, would they not
mock him, and say of him that by going up out
of the cave he had come down again with his
eyes marred for his pains, and that it was lost
labour for any so much as to try that ascent?*

PLATO

*First I must lead the human soul through all
the range
Of heaven, that she may learn
How fortunate hath the turning of the wheel
of change
How fate will never turn.*

BERNARDUS SILVESTRIS

*Let us suppose a person destitute of that
knowledge which we have from our senses
… Let it be supposed that in his drought he
puts golden dust into his eyes; when his eyes
smart, he puts wine into his ears; that in his
hunger, he puts gravel into his mouth; that
in pain, he loads himself with the iron chains;
that feeling cold, he puts his feet in the
water; that being frighted at the fire, he runs
away from it; that being weary, he makes a
seat of his bread … Let us suppose that some
good being came to him, and showed him
the nature and use of all the things that were
about him.*

LAW

THE SAME YET DIFFERENT

John now first sees the real shape of the
world we live in – How we walk on a knife-
edge between Heaven and Hell

Then I dreamed that the Guide armed John and Vertue at all points and led them back through the country they had just been travelling, and across the canyon again into this country. And they came up out of the canyon at the very place where the main road meets it by Mother Kirk's chair. I looked forward in the same direction where they were looking, expecting to see on my left the bare tableland rising to the North with Sensible's house a little way off, and on my right the house of Mr Broad and the pleasant valleys southward. But there was nothing of the kind: only the long straight road, very narrow, and on the left crags rising within a few paces of the road into ice and mist and, beyond that, black cloud: on the right, swamps and jungle sinking almost at once into black cloud. But, as it happens in dreams, I never doubted that this was the same country which I had seen before, although there was no similarity. John and Vertue came to a stand with their surprise.

'Courage,' said Slikisteinsauga, 'you are seeing the land as it really is. It is long but very narrow. Beyond these crags and cloud on the North it sinks immediately into the Arctic Sea, beyond which again lies the Enemy's country. But the Enemy's country is joined up with ours on the North by a land bridge called the Isthmus Sadisticus and right amid that Isthmus sits the cold dragon, the cold, costive, crustacean dragon who wishes to enfold all that he can get within the curl of his body and then to draw his body tighter round it so as to have it all inside himself. And you, John, when we pass the Isthmus must go up and contend with him that you may be hardened. But on the South, as soon as it passes into these swamps and this other cloud, the land sinks into the Southern Sea: and across that sea also there comes a land bridge, the Isthmus Mazochisticus, where the hot dragon crawls, the expansive, invertebrate dragon whose fiery breath makes all that she touches melt and corrupt. And to her you, Vertue, must go down that you may steal her heat and be made malleable.'

'Upon my soul,' said John, 'I think Mother Kirk treats us very ill. Since we have followed her and eaten her food the way seems twice as narrow and twice as dangerous as it did before.'

'You all know,' said the Guide, 'that security is mortals' greatest enemy.'

'It will do very well,' said Vertue, 'let us begin.'

Then they set out on their journey and Vertue sang this song:

'Thou only art alternative to God, oh, dark
And burning island among spirits, tenth hierarch,
Wormwood, immortal Satan, Ahriman, alone
Second to Him to whom no second else were known,
Being essential fire, sprung of His fire, but bound
Within the lightless furnace of thy Self, bricked round
To rage in the reverberated heat from seven
Containing walls: hence power thou hast to rival heaven.
Therefore, except the temperance of the eternal love
Only thy absolute lust is worth the thinking of.
All else is weak disguisings of the wishful heart,
All that seemed earth is Hell, or Heaven. God is: thou art:
The rest, illusion. How should man live save as glass
To let the white light without flame, the Father, pass
Unstained: or else – opaque, molten to thy desire,
Venus infernal starving in the strength of fire!'

'Lord, open not too often my weak eyes to this.'

2

THE SYNTHETIC MAN

*'The World of all Sensible Men' becomes
invisible*

As they went on, Vertue glanced to the side of the road to see if there were any trace of Mr Sensible's house, but there was none.

'It is just as it was when you passed it before,' said the Guide, 'but your eyes are altered. You see nothing now but realities: and Mr Sensible was so near to nonentity – so shadowy even as an appearance – that he is now invisible to you. That mote will trouble your eyes no longer.'

'I am very surprised,' said Vertue, 'I should have thought that even if he was bad he was a singularly solid and four-square kind of evil.'

'All that solidity,' said the Guide, 'belonged not to him but to his predecessors in that house. There was an appearance of temperance about him, but it came from Epicurus. There was an appearance of poetry, but it came from Horace. A trace of old Pagan dignities lingered in his house – it was Montaigne's. His heart seemed warm for a moment, but the warmth was borrowed from Rabelais. He was a man of shreds and patches, and when you have taken from him what was not his own, the remainder equals nought.'

'But surely,' said Vertue, 'these things were not the less his own because he learned them from others.'

'He did not learn them. He learned only catchwords from them. He could talk like Epicurus of spare diet, but he was a glutton. He had from Montaigne the language of friendship, but no friend. He did not even know what these predecessors had really said. He never read one ode of Horace seriously in his life. And for his Rabelais, he can quote *Do what you will*. But he has no notion that Rabelais gave that liberty to his Thelemites on the condition that they should be bound by Honour, and for this reason alone free from laws positive. Still less does he know that Rabelais himself was following a great Steward of the olden days who said *Habe caritatem et fac quod vis*: and least of all that this Steward in his turn was only reducing to an epigram the words of his Master, when He said, "On these two commandments hang all the law and the prophets."'

3

LIMBO

God's mercy on philosophical Despair

Then I dreamed that John looked aside on the right hand of the road and saw a little island of willow trees amid the swamps, where ancient men sat robed in black, and the sound of their sighing reached his ears.

'That place,' said the Guide, 'is the same which you called the Valley of Wisdom when you passed it before: but now that you are going East you may call it Limbo, or the twilit porches of the black hole.'

'Who lives there?' asked John, 'and what do they suffer?'

'Very few live there, and they are all men like old Mr Wisdom – men who have kept alive and pure the deep desire of the soul but through some fatal flaw, of pride or sloth or, it may be, timidity, have refused till the end the only means to its fulfilment; taking huge pains, often, to prove to themselves that the fulfilment is impossible. They are very few because old Wisdom has few sons who are true to him, and the most part of those who come to him either go on and cross the canyon, or else, remaining his sons in name, secretly slip back to feed on worse fare than his. To stay long where he lives requires both a strange strength and a strange weakness. As for their sufferings, it is their doom to live for ever in desire without hope.'

'Is it not rather harsh of the Landlord to make them suffer at all?'

'I can answer that only by hearsay,' returned the Guide, 'for pain is a secret which he has shared with your race and not with mine; and you would find it as hard to explain suffering to me as I should find it to reveal to you the secrets of the Mountain people. But those who know best say this, that any liberal man would choose the pain of this desire, even for ever, rather than the peace of feeling it no longer: and that though the best thing is to have, the next best is to want, and the worst of all is not to want.'

'I see that,' said John. 'Even the wanting, though it is pain too, is more precious than anything else we experience.'

'It is as I foresaw, and you understand it already better than I can. But there is this also. The Landlord does not condemn them to lack of hope: they have done that themselves. The Landlord's interference is all on the other side. Left to itself, the desire without the hope would soon fall back to spurious satisfactions, and these souls would follow it of their own free will into far darker regions at the very bottom of the black hole. What the Landlord has done is to fix it forever: and by his art, though unfulfilled, it is uncorrupted. Men say that his love and his wrath are one thing. Of some places in the black hole you cannot see this, though you can believe it: but of that Island yonder under the willows, you can see it with your own eyes.'

'I see it very well,' said John.

Then the Guide sang:

'God in His mercy made
The fixèd pains of Hell.
That misery might be stayed,
God in His mercy made
Eternal bounds and bade
Its waves no further swell.
God in his mercy made
The fixèd pains of Hell.'

4

THE BLACK HOLE

The Divine Justice – Hell as a tourniquet –
Human choice

'Then there is, after all,' said John, 'a black hole such as my old Steward described to me.'

'I do not know what your Steward described. But there is a black hole.'

'And still the Landlord is "so kind and good"!'

'I see you have been among the Enemy's people. In these latter days there is no charge against the Landlord which the Enemy brings so often as cruelty. That is just like the Enemy: for he is, at bottom, very dull. He has never hit on the one slander against the Landlord which would be really plausible. Anyone can refute the charge of cruelty. If he really wants to damage the Landlord's character, he has a much stronger line than that to take. He ought to say that the Landlord is an inveterate gambler. That would not be true, but it would be plausible, for there is no denying that the Landlord does take risks.'

'But what about the charge of cruelty?'

'I was just coming to that. The Landlord has taken the risk of working the country with free tenants instead of slaves in chain gangs: and as they are free there is no way of making it impossible for them to go into forbidden places and eat forbidden fruits. Up to a certain point he can doctor them even when they have done so, and break them of the habit. But beyond that point – you can see for yourself. A man can go on eating mountain-apple so long that *nothing* will cure his craving for it: and the very worms it breeds inside him will make him more certain to eat more. You must not try to fix the point after which a return is impossible, but you can see that there will be such a point somewhere.'

'But surely the Landlord can do anything?'

'He cannot do what is contradictory: or, in other words, a meaningless sentence will not gain meaning simply because someone chooses to prefix to it the words "the Landlord can". And it is meaningless to talk of forcing a man to do freely what a man has freely made impossible for himself.'

'I see. But at least these poor creatures are unhappy enough: there is no need to add a black hole.'

'The Landlord does not make the blackness. The blackness is there already wherever the taste of mountain-apple has created the vermiculate will. What do you mean by a hole? Something that ends. A black hole is blackness enclosed, limited. And in that sense the Landlord *has* made the black hole. He has put into the world a Worst Thing. But evil of itself would never reach a worst: for evil is fissiparous and could never in a thousand eternities find any way to arrest its own reproduction. If it could, it would be no longer evil: for Form and Limit belong to the good. The walls of the black hole are the tourniquet on the wound through which the lost soul else would bleed to a death she never reached. It is the Landlord's last service to those who will let him do nothing better for them.'

Then the Guide sang:

'Nearly they stood who fall;
Themselves as they look back
See always in the track
The one false step, where all
Even yet, by lightest swerve
Of foot not yet enslaved,
By smallest tremor of the smallest nerve,
Might have been saved.

'Nearly they fell who stand,
And with cold after fear
Look back to mark how near
They grazed the Sirens' land,
Wondering that subtle fate,
By threads so spidery fine,
The choice of ways so small, the event so great,
Should thus entwine.

'Therefore oh, man, have fear
Lest oldest fears be true,
Lest thou too far pursue
The road that seems so clear,
And step, secure, a hair's
Breadth past the hair-breadth bourne,
Which, being once crossed forever unawares,
Denies return.'

5

SUPERBIA

*Tough-mindedness revealed as a form of
Pride – As virtue increases so does the
temptation to Pride – The vision of God is
the fountain of Humility*

Then they went further and saw in the rocks beside them on the left
what seemed at first sight a skeleton, but as they drew nearer they
saw that there was indeed skin stretched over its bones and eyes flaming
in the sockets of its skull. And it was scrabbling and puddering to and fro
on what appeared to be a mirror; but it was only the rock itself scraped
clean of every speck of dust and fibre of lichen and polished by the continued activity of this famished creature.

'This is one of the Enemy's daughters,' said the Guide, 'and her name is
Superbia. But when you last saw her, perhaps she wore the likeness of three
pale men.'

As they passed her she began to croak out her song.

*'I have scraped clean the plateau from the filthy earth,
Earth the unchaste, the fruitful, the great grand maternal,
Sprawling creature, lolling at random and supine,
The broad-faced, sluttish helot, the slave wife
Grubby and warm, who opens unashamed
Her thousand wombs unguarded to the lickerous sun.
Now I have scoured my rock clean from the filthy earth,
On it no root can strike and no blade come to birth,
And though I starve of hunger it is plainly seen
That I have eaten nothing common or unclean.*

*'I have by fasting purged away the filthy flesh,
Flesh the hot, moist, salt scum, the obscenity
And parasitic tetter, from my noble bones.
I have torn from my breasts – I was an udder'd beast –
My child, for he was fleshly. Flesh is caught
By a contagion carried from impure
Generation to generation through the body's sewer.*

And now though I am barren, yet no man can doubt
I am clean and my iniquities are blotted out.

'I have made my soul (once filthy) a hard, pure, bright
Mirror of steel: no damp breath breathes upon it
Warming and dimming: it would freeze the finger
If any touched it. I have a mineral soul.
Minerals eat no food and void no excrement.
So I, borrowing nothing and repaying
Nothing, neither growing nor decaying,
Myself am to myself, a mortal God, a self-contained
Unwindowed monad, unindebted and unstained.'

John and the Guide were hurrying past, but Vertue hesitated.

'Her means may be wrong,' he said, 'but there is something to be said for her idea of the End.'

'What idea?' said the Guide.

'Why – self-sufficiency, integrity. Not to commit herself, you know. All said and done, there *is* something foul about all these natural processes.'

'You had better be careful of your thoughts here,' said the Guide. 'Do not confuse Repentance with Disgust: for the one comes from the Landlord and the other from the Enemy.'

'And yet disgust has saved many a man from worse evils.'

'By the power of the Landlord it may be so – now and then. But don't try to play that game for yourself. Fighting one vice with another is about the most dangerous strategy there is. You know what happens to kingdoms that use alien mercenaries.'

'I suppose you are right,' said Vertue, 'and yet this feeling goes very deep. Is it wholly wrong to be ashamed of being in the body?'

'The Landlord's Son was not. You know the verses – "When thou took-est upon thee to deliver man".'

'That was a special case.'

'It was a special case because it was the archetypal case. Has no one told you that that Lady spoke and acted for all that bears, in the presence of all that begets: for this country as against the things East and West: for matter as against form and patiency against agency? Is not the very word Mother akin to Matter? Be sure that the whole of this land, with all its warmth and wetness and fecundity, with all the dark and the heavy and the multitudinous for which you are too dainty, spoke through her lips when she said that He had regarded the lowliness of His hand-maiden. And if that Lady was a maid though a mother, you need not doubt that the nature which is, to human sense, impure, is also pure.'

'Well,' said Vertue, turning away from Superbia, 'I will think this over.'

'One thing you may as well know,' remarked the Guide, 'whatever virtues you may attribute to the Landlord, decency is not one of them. That is why so few of your national jokes have any point in my country.'

And as they continued their journey, Vertue sang:

'Because of endless pride
Reborn with endless error,
Each hour I look aside
Upon my secret mirror
Trying all postures there
To make my image fair.

'Thou givest grapes, and I,
Though starving, turn to see
How dark the cool globes lie
In the white hand of me,
And linger gazing thither
Till the live clusters wither.

'So should I quickly die
Narcissus-like of want,
But, in the glass, my eye
Catches such forms as haunt
Beyond nightmare, and make
Pride humble for pride's sake.

'Then and then only turning
The stiff neck round, I grow
A molten man all burning
And look behind and know
Who made the glass, whose light makes dark, whose fair
Makes foul, my shadowy form reflected there
That Self-Love, brought to bed of Love may die and bear
Her sweet son in despair.'

6

IGNORANTIA

*The change from classical to scientific
education strengthens our Ignorance –
Though the Machine Age, for good or ill,
will do less than is expected of it*

Still I lay dreaming and saw these three continue their journey through
that long and narrow land with the rocks upon their left and the swamp
on their right. They had much talk on the way of which I have remembered
only snatches since I woke. I remember that they passed Ignorantia some
miles beyond her sister Superbia and that led the pilgrims to question their
Guide as to whether the Ignorance of the Tough-minded and the Clevers
would some day be cured. He said there was less chance of that now than
there had ever been: for till recently the Northern people had been made to
learn the languages of Pagus 'and that meant', said the Guide, 'that at least
they started no further from the light than the old Pagans themselves and
had therefore the chance to come at last to Mother Kirk. But now they are
cutting themselves off even from that roundabout route.'

'Why have they changed?' asked one of the others.

'Why did the shadow whom you call Sensible leave his old house and go
to practise αὐτάρκεια in a hotel? Because his Drudge revolted. The same
thing is happening all over the plateau and in Mammon's country: their
slaves are escaping further north and becoming dwarfs, and therefore the
masters are turning all their attention to machinery, by which they hope to
be able to lead their old life without slaves. And this seems to them so
important that they are suppressing every kind of knowledge except
mechanical knowledge. I am speaking of the sub-tenants. No doubt the
great landowners in the background have their own reasons for encouraging this movement.'

'There must be a good side somewhere to this revolution,' said Vertue. 'It
is too solid – it looks too lasting – to be a mere evil. I cannot believe that the
Landlord would otherwise allow the whole face of nature and the whole
structure of life to be so permanently and radically changed.'

The Guide laughed. 'You are falling into their own error,' he said. 'The
change is not radical, nor will it be permanent. That idea depends on a
curious disease which they have all caught – an inability to dis-believe

advertisements. To be sure, if the machines did what they promised, the change would be very deep indeed. Their next war, for example, would change the state of their country from disease to death. They are afraid of this themselves – though most of them are old enough to know by experience that a gun is no more likely than a toothpaste or a cosmetic to do the things its makers say it will do. It is the same with all their machines. Their labour-saving devices multiply drudgery; their aphrodisiacs make them impotent: their amusements bore them: their rapid production of food leaves half of them starving, and their devices for saving time have banished leisure from their country. There will be no radical change. And as for permanence – consider how quickly all machines are broken and obliterated. The black solitudes will some day be green again and of all cities that I have seen these iron cities will break most suddenly.'

And the Guide sang:

'Iron will eat the world's old beauty up.
Girder and grid and gantry will arise,
   Iron forest of engines will arise,
   Criss-cross of iron crotchet. For your eyes
   No green or growth. Over all, the skies
   Scribbled from end to end with boasts and lies.
(When Adam ate the irrevocable apple, Thou
Saw'st beyond death the resurrection of the dead.)

   'Clamour shall clean put out the voice of wisdom,
   The printing-presses with their clapping wings,
   Fouling your nourishment. Harpy wings,
   Filling your minds all day with foolish things,
   Will tame the eagle Thought: till she sings
   Parrot-like in her cage to please dark kings.
(When Israel descended into Egypt, Thou
Didst purpose both the bondage and the coming out.)

   'The new age, the new art, the new ethic and thought,
   And fools crying, Because it has begun
   It will continue as it has begun!
   The wheel runs fast, therefore the wheel will run
   Faster for ever. The old age is done,
   We have new lights and see without the sun.
(Though they lay flat the mountains and dry up the sea,
Wilt Thou yet change, as though God were a god?)'

7

LUXURIA

*Lechery means not simply forbidden
pleasure, but loss of the man's unity – Its
supreme mode of temptation is to make all
else insipid*

After this, John looked up and saw that they were approaching a con-course of living creatures beside the road. Their way was so long and desolate (and he was footsore too) that he welcomed any diversion, and he cast his eyes curiously upon this new thing. When he was nearer he saw that the concourse was of men, but they lay about in such attitudes and were so disfigured that he had not recognised them for men: moreover, the place was to the south of the road, and therefore the ground was very soft and some of them were half under water and some hidden in the reeds. All seemed to be suffering from some disease of a crumbling and disintegrating kind. It was doubtful whether all the life that pulsated in their bodies was their own: and soon John was certain, for he saw what seemed to be a growth on a man's arm slowly detach itself under his eyes and become a fat reddish creature, separable from the parent body, though it was in no hurry to separate itself. And once he had seen that, his eyes were opened and he saw the same thing happening all round him, and the whole assembly was but a fountain of writhing and reptilian life quickening as he watched and sprouting out of the human forms. But in each form the anguished eyes were alive, sending to him unutterable messages from the central life which survived, self-conscious, though the self were but a fountain of vermin. One old cripple, whose face was all gone but the mouth and eyes, was sitting up to receive drink from a cup which a woman held to his lips. When he had as much as she thought good, she snatched the cup from his hands and went on to her next patient. She was dark but beautiful.

'Don't lag,' said the Guide, 'this is a very dangerous place. You had better come away. This is Luxuria.'

But John's eyes were caught by a young man to whom the witch had just come in her rounds. The disease, by seeming, had hardly begun with him: there was an unpleasant suspicion about his fingers – something a little too supple for joints – a little independent of his other movements – but, on the whole, he was still a well-looking person. And as the witch came to him the hands shot out to the cup, and the man drew them back again: and the hands went crawling out for the cup a second time, and again the man wrenched them back, and turned his face away, and cried out:

'Quick! The black, sulphurous, never quenched,
Old festering fire begins to play
Once more within. Look! By brute force I have wrenched
Unmercifully my hands the other way.

'Quick, Lord! On the rack thus, stretched tight,
Nerves clamouring as at nature's wrong.
Scorched to the quick, whipp'd raw – Lord, in this plight
You see, you see no man can suffer long.

'Quick, Lord! Before new scorpions bring
New venom – ere fiends blow the fire
A second time – quick, show me that sweet thing
Which, 'spite of all, more deeply I desire.'

And all the while the witch stood saying nothing, but only holding out the cup and smiling kindly on him with her dark eyes and her dark, red mouth. Then, when she saw that he would not drink, she passed on to the next: but at the first step she took, the young man gave a sob and his hands flew out and grabbed the cup and he buried his head in it: and when she took it from him, his lips clung to it as a drowning man to a piece of wood. But at last he sank down in the swamp with a groan. And the worms where there should have been fingers were unmistakable.

'Come on,' said Vertue.

They resumed their journey, John lagging a bit. I dreamed that the witch came to him walking softly in the marshy ground by the roadside and holding out the cup to him also: when he went faster she kept pace with him.

'I will not deceive you,' she said. 'You see there is no pretence. I am not trying to make you believe that this cup will take you to your Island. I am not saying it will quench your thirst for long. But taste it, none the less, for you are very thirsty.'

But John walked forward in silence.

'It is true,' said the witch, 'that you never can tell when you have reached the point beyond which there is no return. But that cuts both ways. If you can never be certain that one more taste is safe, neither can you be certain that one more taste is fatal. But you can be certain that you are terribly thirsty.'

But John continued as before.

'At least,' said the witch, 'have one more taste of it, before you abandon it for ever. This is a bad moment to choose for resistance, when you are tired and miserable and have already listened to me too long. Taste this once, and I will leave you. I do not promise never to come back: but perhaps when I come again, you will be strong and happy and well able to resist me – not as you are now.'

And John continued as before.

'Come,' said the witch. 'You are only wasting time. You know you will give in, in the end. Look ahead at the hard road and the grey sky. What other pleasure is there in sight?'

So she accompanied him for a long way, till the weariness of her importunity tempted him far more than any positive desire. But he forced his mind to other things and kept himself occupied for a mile or so by making the following verses:

> When Lilith means to draw me
> Within her secret bower,
> She does not overawe me
> With beauty's pomp and power,
> Nor, with angelic grace
> Of courtesy, and the pace
> Of gliding ships, comes veiled at evening hour.

> Eager, unmasked, she lingers
> Heart-sick and hunger sore;
> With hot, dry, jewelled fingers
> Stretched out, beside her door,
> Offering with gnawing haste
> Her cup, whereof who taste,
> (She promises no better) thirst far more.

> What moves me, then, to drink it?
> – Her spells, which all around
> So change the land, we think it
> A great waste where a sound
> Of wind like tales twice told
> Blusters, and cloud is rolled
> Always above yet no rain falls to ground.

> Across drab iteration
> Of bare hills, line on line,
> The long road's sinuation

> *Leads on. The witch's wine,*
> *Though promising nothing, seems*
> *In that land of no streams,*
> *To promise best – the unrelished anodyne.*

And by the time he had reached the word *'anodyne'* the witch was gone. But he had never in his life felt more weary, and for a while the purpose of his pilgrimage woke no desire in him.

8

THE NORTHERN DRAGON

*The Northern and Southern diseases of the
Soul – The Northern tension, hardness,
possessiveness, coldness, anaemia – John
overcomes it – and wins from it some of the
needful hardness he lacked*

'Now,' said the Guide, 'our time is come.'
They looked at him inquiringly.

'We are come,' said he, 'to that point of the road which lies midway between the two land bridges that I spoke of. The cold dragon is here on our left, and the hot dragon on our right. Now is the time to show what you are made of. Wolf is waiting in the wood southward: in the rocks northward, raven wheeling, in hope of carrion. Behoves you both be on guard quickly. God defend you.'

'Well,' said Virtue. And he drew his sword and slung his shield round from his back. Then he held out his hand first to the Guide, and then to John. 'So long,' he said.

'Go where it is least green,' said the Guide, 'for there the ground is firmest. And good luck.'

Virtue left the road and began to pick his way cautiously southward, feeling out the fen-paths. The Guide turned to John.

'Have you any practice with a sword?' he said.

'None, sir,' answered John.

'None is better than a smattering. You must trust to mother-wit. Aim at his belly – an upward jab. I shouldn't try cutting, if I were you: you don't know enough.'

'I will do the best I can,' said John. And then, after a pause: 'There is only one dragon, I suppose. I don't need to guard my back.'

'Of course there is only one, for he has eaten all the others. Otherwise he would not be a dragon. You know the maxim – *serpens nisi serpentem comederit –*'

Then I saw John also settle his gear and step off the road to the left. The ascent began at once, and before he was ten yards from the road he was six feet above it: but the formation of the rocks was such that it was like mounting a huge stair, and was tiring rather than difficult. When he first

301

stopped to wipe the sweat out of his eyes the mist was already so dense that he could hardly see the road beneath him. Ahead the grey darkness shaded quickly into black. Then suddenly John heard a dry, rattling sound in front of him, and a little above. He got a better grip on his sword, and took one pace towards it, listening intently. Then came the sound again: and after that he heard a croaking voice, as of a gigantic frog. The dragon was singing to himself:

'Once the worm-laid egg broke in the wood.
I came forth shining into the trembling world,
The sun was on my scales, dew upon the grasses,
The cool, sweet grasses and the budding leaves.
I wooed my speckled mate. We played at druery
And sucked warm milk dropping from the goats' teats.

'Now I keep watch on the gold in my rock cave
In a country of stones: old, deplorable dragon,
Watching my hoard. In winter night the gold
Freezes through toughest scales my cold belly.
The jagged crowns and twisted cruel rings
Knobbly and icy are old dragon's bed.

'Often I wish I hadn't eaten my wife,
Though worm grows not to dragon till he eat worm.
She could have helped me, watch and watch about,
Guarding the hoard. Gold would have been the safer.
I could uncoil my weariness at times and take
A little sleep, sometimes when she was watching.

'Last night under the moonset a fox barked,
Woke me. Then I knew I had been sleeping.
Often an owl flying over the country of stones
Startles me, and I think I must have slept.
Only a moment. That very moment a man
Might have come out of the cities, stealing, to get my gold.

'They make plots in the towns to steal my gold.
They whisper of me in a low voice, laying plans,
Merciless men. Have they not ale upon the benches,
Warm wife in bed, singing, and sleep the whole night?
But I leave not the cave but once in winter
To drink of the rock pool: in summer twice.

'They feel no pity for the old, lugubrious dragon.
Oh, Lord, that made the dragon, grant me Thy peace!
But ask not that I should give up the gold,
Nor more, nor die; others would get the gold.
Kill, rather, Lord, the men and the other dragons
That I may sleep, go when I will to drink.'

As John listened to this song he forgot to be afraid. Disgust first, and then pity, chased fear from his mind: and after them came a strange desire to speak with the dragon and to suggest some sort of terms and division of the spoil: not that he desired the gold, but it seemed to him a not all ignoble desire to surround and contain so much within oneself. But while these things passed through his imagination, his body took care of him, keeping his grip steady on the sword hilt, his eyes strained into the darkness, and his feet ready to spring: so that he was not taken by surprise when he saw that in the rolling of the mist above him something else was rolling, and rolling round him to enclose him. But still he did not move. The dragon was paying its body out like a rope from a cave just above him. At first it swayed, the great head bobbing vertically, as a caterpillar sways searching for a new grip with half its length while the other half rests still on the leaf. Then the head dived and went behind him. He kept turning round to watch it, and it led the volume of the dragon's body round in a circle and finally went back into the cave, leaving a loop of dragon all round the man. Still John waited till the loop began to tighten, about on a level with his chest. Then he ducked and came up again with a jab of his sword into the under-side of the brute. It went in to the hilt, but there was no blood. At once the head came twisting back out of the cave. Eyes full of cruelty – cold cruelty without a spark of rage in it – stared into his face. The mouth was wide open – it was not red within, but grey like lead – and the breath of the creature was freezing cold. As soon as it touched John's face, everything was changed. A corselet of ice seemed to be closed about him, seemed to shut in his heart, so that it could never again flutter with panic or with greed. His strength was multiplied. His arms seemed to him iron. He found he was laughing and making thrust after thrust into the brute's throat. He found that the struggle was already over – perhaps hours ago. He was standing unwearied in a lonely place among rocks with a dead reptile at his feet. He remembered that he had killed it. And the time before he had killed it seemed very long ago.

9

THE SOUTHERN DRAGON

*Meanwhile John's Moral Self must meet the
Southern evil – And take into him its heat,
which will make Virtue itself henceforth
a passion*

John came leaping down the rocks into the road, whistling a tune. The
Guide came to greet him, but before they had spoken a word, they both
turned round in wonder at a great cry from the South. The sun had come out
so that the whole marsh glittered like dirty copper: and at first they thought
that it was the sun upon his arms that made Vertue flash like flame as he came
leaping, running, and dancing towards them. But as he drew nearer they saw
that he was veritably on fire. Smoke came from him, and where his feet
slipped into the bog holes there were little puffs of steam. Hurtless flames ran
up and down his sword and licked over his hand. His breast heaved and he
reeled like a drunk man. They made towards him, but he cried out:

*'I have come back with victory got –
But stand away – touch me not
Even with your clothes. I burn red-hot.*

*'The worm was bitter. When she saw
My shield glitter beside the shaw
She spat flame from her golden jaw.*

*'When on my sword her vomit spilt
The blade took fire. On the hilt
Beryl cracked, and bubbled gilt.*

*'When sword and sword arm were all flame
With the very heat that came
Out of the brute, I flogged her tame.*

*'In her own spew the worm died.
I rolled her round and tore her wide
And plucked the heart from her boiling side.*

304

'When my teeth were in the heart
I felt a pulse within me start
As though my breast would break apart.

'It shook the hills and made them reel
And spun the woods round like a wheel.
The grass singed where I set my heel.

'Behemoth is my serving man!
Before the conquered hosts of Pan
Riding tamed Leviathan,
Loud I sing for well I can
RESVRGAM and IO PAEAN;
IO, IO, IO, PAEAN!!

'Now I know the stake I played for,
Now I know what a worm's made for!'

10

THE BROOK

Death is at hand. Morality still seeks no
reward and desires no resurrection –
But Faith, being humbler, asks more –
The Angel sings

My dream was full of light and noise. I thought they went on their way singing and laughing like schoolboys. Vertue lost all his dignity, and John was never tired: and for ten miles or so they picked up an old fiddler who was going that way, who played them such jigs and they danced more than they walked. And Vertue invented doggerels to his tunes to mock the old Pagan virtues in which he had been bred.

But in the midst of all this gaiety, suddenly John stood still and his eyes filled with tears. They had come to a little cottage, beside a river, which was empty and ruinous. Then they all asked John what ailed him.

'We have come back to Puritania,' he said, 'and that was my father's house. I see that my father and mother are gone already beyond the brook. I had much I would have said to them. But it is no matter.'

'No matter indeed,' said the Guide, 'since you will cross the brook your-self before nightfall.'

'For the last time?' said Vertue.

'For the last time,' said the Guide, 'all being well.'

And now the day was declining and the Eastern Mountains loomed big and black ahead of them. Their shadows lengthened as they went down towards the brook.

'I am cured of playing the Stoic,' said Vertue, 'and I confess that I go down in fear and sadness. I also – there were many people I would have spoken to. There were many years I would call back. Whatever there is beyond the brook, it cannot be the same. Something is being ended. It is a real brook.'

'I am not one that easily flits past in thought
The ominous stream, imagining death made for nought.
This person, mixed of body and breath, to which concurred
Once only one articulation of thy word,
Will be resolved eternally: nor can time bring

(Else time were vain) once back again the self-same thing.
Therefore among the riddles that no man has read
I put thy paradox, Who liveth and was dead.
As Thou hast made substantially, thou wilt unmake
In earnest and for everlasting. Let none take
Comfort in frail supposal that some hour and place
To those who mourn recovers the wished voice and face.
Whom Thy great Exit banishes, no after age
Of epilogue leads back upon the lighted stage.
Where is Prince Hamlet when the curtain's down? Where fled
Dreams at the dawn, or colours when the light is sped?
We are thy colours, fugitive, never restored,
Never repeated again. Thou only art the Lord,
Thou only art holy. In the shadowy vast
Of thine Osirian wings Thou dost enfold the past.
There sit in throne antediluvian, cruel kings,
There the first nightingale that sang to Eve yet sings,
There are the irrecoverable guiltless years,
There, yet unfallen, Lucifer among his peers.
For thou art also a deity of the dead, a god
Of graves, with necromancies in thy potent rod;
Thou art Lord of the unbreathable transmortal air
Where mortal thinking fails: night's nuptial darkness, where
All lost embraces intermingle and are bless'd.
And all die, but all are, while Thou continuest.'

The twilight was now far advanced and they were in sight of the brook. And John said, 'I thought all those things when I was in the house of Wisdom. But now I think better things. Be sure it is not for nothing that the Landlord has knit our hearts so closely to time and place – to one friend rather than another and one shire more than all the land.

'Passing today by a cottage, I shed tears
When I remembered how once I had dwelled there
With my mortal friends who are dead. Years
Little had healed the wound that was laid bare.

'Out, little spear that stabs. I, fool, believed
I had outgrown the local, unique sting,
I had transmuted away (I was deceived)
Into love universal the lov'd thing.

'But Thou, Lord, surely knewest Thine own plan
When the angelic indifferences with no bar
Universally loved but Thou gav'st man
The tether and pang of the particular;

'Which, like a chemic drop, infinitesimal,
Plashed into pure water, changing the whole,
Embodies and embitters and turns all
Spirit's sweet water to astringent soul.

'That we, though small, may quiver with fire's same
Substantial form as Thou – not reflect merely,
As lunar angel, back to thee, cold flame.
Gods we are, Thou has said: and we pay dearly.'

And now they were already at the brook, and it was so dark that I did not see them go over. Only, as my dream ended, and the voice of the birds at my window began to reach my ear (for it was a summer morning), I heard the voice of the Guide, mixed with theirs and not unlike them, singing this song:

'I know not, I,
   What the men together say,
How lovers, lovers die
   And youth passes away.

'Cannot understand
   Love that mortal bears
For native, native land
   – All lands are theirs.

'Why at grave they grieve
   For one voice and face,
And not, and not receive
   Another in its place.

'I, above the cone
   Of the circling night
Flying, never have known
   More or lesser light.

'Sorrow it is they call
   This cup: whence my lip,
Woe's me, never in all
   My endless days must sip.'

MERE CHRISTIANITY

A revised and amplified edition, with a new
introduction, of the three books *Broadcast Talks,
Christian Behaviour* and *Beyond Personality*

PREFACE

The contents of this book were first given on the air, and then published in three separate parts as *Broadcast Talks* (1942), *Christian Behaviour* (1943) and *Beyond Personality* (1944). In the printed versions I made a few additions to what I had said at the microphone, but otherwise left the text much as it had been. A 'talk' on the radio should, I think, be as like real talk as possible, and should not sound like an essay being read aloud. In my talks I had therefore used all the contractions and colloquialisms I ordinarily use in conversation. In the printed version I reproduced this, putting *don't* and *we've* for *do not* and *we have*. And wherever, in the talks, I had made the importance of a word clear by the emphasis of my voice, I printed it in italics. I am now inclined to think that this was a mistake – an undesirable hybrid between the art of speaking and the art of writing. A talker ought to use variations of voice for emphasis because his medium naturally lends itself to that method: but a writer ought not to use italics for the same purpose. He has his own, different, means of bringing out the key words and ought to use them. In this edition I have expanded the contractions and replaced most of the italics by a recasting of the sentences in which they occurred: but without altering, I hope, the 'popular' or 'familiar' tone which I had all along intended. I have also added and deleted where I thought I understood any part of my subject better now than ten years ago or where I knew that the original version had been misunderstood by others.

The reader should be warned that I offer no help to anyone who is hesitating between two Christian 'denominations'. You will not learn from me whether you ought to become an Anglican, a Methodist, a Presbyterian, or a Roman Catholic. This omission is intentional (even in the list I have just given the order is alphabetical). There is no mystery about my own position. I am a very ordinary layman of the Church of England, not especially 'high', nor especially 'low', nor especially anything else. But in this book I am not trying to convert anyone to my own position. Ever since I became a Christian I have thought that the best, perhaps the only, service I could do for my unbelieving neighbours was to explain and defend the belief that has been common to nearly all Christians at all times. I had more than one reason for thinking this. In the first place, the questions which divide Christians from one another often involve points of high Theology or even of ecclesiastical history, which ought never to be treated except by real experts. I should have been out of my depth in such waters: more in need of help myself than able to help others. And secondly, I think we must admit that the discussion of these disputed points has no tendency at all to bring an outsider into the Christian fold. So long as we write and talk about them we are much more likely to deter him from entering any Christian communion than to draw him into our own. Our divisions should never be discussed except in the presence of those who have already come to believe that there is one God and that Jesus Christ is His only Son. Finally, I got the impression that far more, and more talented, authors were already engaged in such controversial matters than in the defence of what Baxter calls 'mere' Christianity. That part of the line where I thought I could serve best was also the part that seemed to be thinnest. And to it I naturally went.

So far as I know, these were my only motives, and I should be very glad if people would not draw fanciful inferences from my silence on certain disputed matters.

For example, such silence need not mean that I myself am sitting on the fence. Sometimes I am. There are questions at issue between Christians to which I do not think we have been told the answer. There are some to which I may never know the answer: if I asked them, even in a better world, I might (for all I know) be answered as a far greater questioner was answered: 'What is that to thee? Follow thou Me.' But there are other questions as to which I am definitely on one side of the fence, and yet say nothing. For I am not writing to expound something I could call 'my religion', but to expound 'mere' Christianity, which is what it is and what it was long before I was born and whether I like it or not.

Some people draw unwarranted conclusions from the fact that I never say more about the Blessed Virgin Mary than is involved in asserting the Virgin Birth of Christ. But surely my reason for not doing so is obvious? To say more would take me at once into highly controversial regions. And there is no controversy between Christians which needs to be so delicately touched as this. The Roman Catholic beliefs on that subject are held not only with the ordinary fervour that attaches to all sincere religious belief, but (very naturally) with the peculiar and, as it were, chivalrous sensibility that a man feels when the honour of his mother or his beloved is at stake. It is very difficult so to dissent from them that you will not appear to them a cad as well as a heretic. And contrariwise, the opposed Protestant beliefs on this subject call forth feelings which go down to the very roots of all

Monotheism whatever. To radical Protestants it seems that the distinction between Creator and creature (however holy) is imperilled: that Polytheism is risen again. Hence it is hard so to dissent from them that you will not appear something worse than a heretic – a Pagan. If any topic could be relied upon to wreck a book about 'mere' Christianity – if any topic makes utterly unprofitable reading for those who do not yet believe that the Virgin's son is God – surely this is it.

Oddly enough, you cannot even conclude, from my silence on disputed points, either that I think them important or that I think them unimportant. For this is itself one of the disputed points. One of the things Christians are disagreed about is the importance of their disagreements. When two Christians of different denominations start arguing, it is usually not long before one asks whether such-and-such a point 'really matters' and the other replies: 'Matter? Why, it's absolutely essential.'

All this is said simply in order to make clear what kind of book I was trying to write; not in the least to conceal or evade responsibility for my own beliefs. About those, as I said before, there is no secret. To quote Uncle Toby: 'They are written in the Common-Prayer Book.'

The danger clearly was that I should put forward as common Christianity anything that was peculiar to the Church of England or (worse still) to myself. I tried to guard against this by sending the original script of what is now Book II to four clergymen (Anglican, Methodist, Presbyterian, Roman Catholic) and asking for their criticism. The Methodist thought I had not said enough about Faith, and the Roman Catholic thought I had gone rather too far about the comparative unimportance of theories in explanation of the Atonement. Otherwise all five of us were agreed. I did not have the remaining books similarly 'vetted' because in them, though differences might arise among Christians, these would be differences between individuals or schools of thought, not between denominations.

So far as I can judge from reviews and from the numerous letters written to me, the book, however faulty in other respects, did at least succeed in presenting an agreed, or common, or central, or 'mere' Christianity. In that way it may possibly be of some help in silencing the view that, if we omit the disputed points, we shall have left only a vague and bloodless H.C.F. The H.C.F. turns out to be something not only positive but pungent; divided from all non-Christian beliefs by a chasm to which the worst divisions inside Christendom are not really comparable at all. If I have not directly helped the cause of reunion, I have perhaps made it clear why we ought to be reunited. Certainly I have met with little of the fabled *odium theologicum* from convinced members of communions different from my own. Hostility has come more from borderline people whether within the

Church of England or without it: men not exactly obedient to any communion. This I find curiously consoling. It is at her centre, where her truest children dwell, that each communion is really closest to every other in spirit, if not in doctrine. And this suggests that at the centre of each there is a something, or a Someone, who against all divergencies of belief, all differences of temperament, all memories of mutual persecution, speaks with the same voice.

So much for my omissions on doctrine. In Book III, which deals with morals, I have also passed over some things in silence, but for a different reason. Ever since I served as an infantryman in the First World War I have had a great dislike of people who, themselves in ease and safety, issue exhortations to men in the front line. As a result I have a reluctance to say much about temptations to which I myself am not exposed. No man, I suppose, is tempted to every sin. It so happens that the impulse which makes men gamble has been left out of my make-up; and, no doubt, I pay for this by lacking some good impulse of which it is the excess or perversion. I therefore did not feel myself qualified to give advice about permissible and impermissible gambling: if there is any permissible, for I do not claim to know even that. I have also said nothing about birth-control. I am not a woman nor even a married man, nor am I a priest. I did not think it my place to take a firm line about pains, dangers and expenses from which I am protected; having no pastoral office which obliged me to do so.

Far deeper objections may be felt – and have been expressed – against my use of the word *Christian* to mean one who accepts the common doctrines of Christianity. People ask: 'Who are you, to lay down who is, and who is not a Christian?' : or 'May not many a man who cannot believe these doctrines be far more truly a Christian, far closer to the spirit of Christ, than some who do?' Now this objection is in one sense very right, very charitable, very spiritual, very sensitive. It has every available quality except that of being useful. We simply cannot, without disaster, use language as these objectors want us to use it. I will try to make this clear by the history of another, and very much less important, word.

The word *gentleman* originally meant something recognisable; one who had a coat of arms and some landed property. When you called someone 'a gentleman' you were not paying him a compliment, but merely stating a fact. If you said he was not 'a gentleman' you were not insulting him, but giving information. There was no contradiction in saying that John was a liar and a gentleman; any more than there now is in saying that James is a fool and an M.A. But then there came people who said – so rightly, charitably, spiritually, sensitively, so anything but usefully – 'Ah, but surely the important thing about a gentleman is not the coat of arms and the land, but the behaviour? Surely he is the true gentleman who behaves as a gentleman should? Surely in that sense Edward is far more truly a gentle-man than John?' They meant well. To be honourable and courteous and brave is of course a far better thing than to have a coat of arms. But it is not the same thing. Worse still, it is not a thing everyone will agree about. To call a man 'a gentleman' in this new, refined sense, becomes, in fact, not a way of giving information about him, but a way of praising him: to deny that he is 'a gentleman' becomes simply a way of insulting him. When a word ceases to be a term of description and becomes merely a term of praise, it no longer tells you facts about the object: it only tells you about the speaker's attitude to that object. (A 'nice' meal only means a meal the speaker likes.) A *gentle-man*, once it has been spiritualised and refined out of its old coarse, objective sense, means hardly more than a man whom the speaker likes. As a result, *gentleman* is now a useless word. We had lots of terms of approval already, so it was not needed for that use; on the other hand if anyone (say, in a historical work) wants to use it in its old sense, he cannot do so without explanations. It has been spoiled for that purpose.

Now if once we allow people to start spiritualising and refining, or as they might say 'deepening', the sense of the word *Christian*, it too will speedily become a useless word. In the first place, Christians themselves will never be able to apply it to anyone. It is not for us to say who, in the deepest sense, is or is not close to the spirit of Christ. We do not see into men's hearts. We cannot judge, and are indeed forbidden to judge. It would be wicked arrogance for us to say that any man is, or is not, a Christian in this refined sense. And obviously a word which we can never apply is not going to be a very useful word. As for the unbelievers, they will no doubt cheer-fully use the word in the refined sense. It will become in their mouths simply a term of praise. In calling anyone a Christian they will mean that they think him a good man. But that way of using the word will be no enrichment of the language, for we already have the word *good*. Meanwhile, the word *Christian* will have been spoiled for any really useful purpose it might have served.

We must therefore stick to the original, obvious meaning. The name *Christians* was first given at Antioch (Acts 11:26) to 'the disciples', to those who accepted the teaching of the apostles. There is no question of its being restricted to those who profited by that teaching as much as they should have. There is no question of its being extended to those who in some refined, spiritual, inward fashion were 'far closer to the spirit of Christ' than the less satisfactory of the disciples. The point is not a theological or moral one. It is only a question of using words so that we can all understand what is being said. When a man who accepts the Christian doctrine lives un-worthily of it, it is much clearer to say he is a bad Christian than to say he is not a Christian.

I hope no reader will suppose that 'mere' Christianity is here put forward as an alternative to the creeds of the existing communions – as if a man could adopt it in preference to Congregationalism or Greek Orthodoxy or anything else. It is more like a hall out of which doors open into several rooms. If I can bring anyone into that hall I shall have done what I attempted. But it is in the rooms, not in the hall, that there are fires and chairs and meals. The hall is a place to wait in, a place from which to try the various doors, not a place to live in. For that purpose the worst of the rooms (whichever that may be) is, I think, preferable. It is true that some people may find they have to wait in the hall for a considerable time, while others feel certain almost at once which door they must knock at. I do not know why there is this difference, but I am sure God keeps no one waiting unless He sees that it is good for him to wait. When you do get into your room you will find that the long wait has done you some kind of good which you would not have had otherwise. But you must regard it as waiting, not as camping. You must keep on praying for light: and, of course, even in the hall, you must begin trying to obey the rules which are common to the whole house. And above all you must be asking which door is the true one; not which pleases you best by its paint and panelling. In plain language, the question should never be: 'Do I like that kind of service?' but 'Are these doctrines true: Is holiness here? Does my conscience move me towards this? Is my reluctance to knock at this door due to my pride, or my mere taste, or my personal dislike of this particular door-keeper?'

When you have reached your own room, be kind to those who have chosen different doors and to those who are still in the hall. If they are wrong they need your prayers all the more; and if they are your enemies, then you are under orders to pray for them. That is one of the rules common to the whole house.

Contents

BOOK 4 — BEYOND PERSONALITY: OR FIRST STEPS IN THE DOCTRINE OF THE TRINITY

BOOK I

RIGHT AND WRONG AS A CLUE TO THE MEANING OF THE UNIVERSE

I

THE LAW OF HUMAN NATURE

Every one has heard people quarrelling. Sometimes it sounds funny and sometimes it sounds merely unpleasant; but however it sounds, I believe we can learn something very important from listening to the kind of things they say. They say things like this: 'How'd you like it if anyone did the same to you?' – 'That's my seat, I was there first' – 'Leave him alone, he isn't doing you any harm' – 'Why should you shove in first?' – 'Give me a bit of your orange, I gave you a bit of mine' – 'Come on, you promised.' People say things like that every day, educated people as well as uneducated, and children as well as grown-ups.

Now what interests me about all these remarks is that the man who makes them is not merely saying that the other man's behaviour does not happen to please him. He is appealing to some kind of standard of behaviour which he expects the other man to know about. And the other man very seldom replies: 'To hell with your standard.' Nearly always he tries to make out that what he has been doing does not really go against the standard, or that if it does there is some special excuse. He pretends there is some special reason in this particular case why the person who took the seat first should not keep it, or that things were quite different when he was given the bit of orange, or that something has turned up which lets him off keeping his promise. It looks, in fact, very much as if both parties had in mind some kind of Law or Rule of fair play or decent behaviour or morality or whatever you like to call it, about which they really agreed. And they have. If they had not, they might, of course, fight like animals, but they could not quarrel in the human sense of the word. Quarrelling means trying to show that the other man is in the wrong. And there would be no sense in trying to do that unless you and he had some sort of agreement as to what Right and Wrong are; just as there would be no sense in saying that a footballer had committed a foul unless there was some agreement about the rules of football.

Now this Law or Rule about Right and Wrong used to be called the Law of Nature. Nowadays, when we talk of the 'laws of nature' we usually mean things like gravitation, or heredity, or the laws of chemistry. But when the older thinkers called the Law of Right and Wrong 'the Law of Nature', they really meant the Law of Human Nature. The idea was that, just as all bodies are governed by the law of gravitation, and organisms by biological laws, so the creature called man also had his law – with this great difference, that a body could not choose whether it obeyed the law of gravitation or not, but a man could choose either to obey the Law of Human Nature or to disobey it.

We may put this in another way. Each man is at every moment subjected to several different sets of law but there is only one of these which he is free to disobey. As a body, he is subjected to gravitation and cannot disobey it; if you leave him unsupported in mid-air, he has no more choice about falling than a stone has. As an organism, he is subjected to various biological laws which he cannot disobey any more than an animal can. That is, he cannot disobey those laws which he shares with other things; but the law which is peculiar to his human nature, the law he does not share with animals or vegetables or inorganic things, is the one he can disobey if he chooses.

This law was called the Law of Nature because people thought that every one knew it by nature and did not need to be taught it. They did not mean, of course, that you might not find an odd individual here and there who did not know it, just as you find a few people who are colour-blind or have no ear for a tune. But taking the race as a whole, they thought that the human idea of decent behaviour was obvious to every one. And I believe they were right. If they were not, then all the things we said about the war were nonsense. What was the sense in saying the enemy were in the wrong unless Right is a real thing which the Nazis at bottom knew as well as we did and ought to have practised? If they had had no notion of what we mean by right, then, though we might still have had to fight them, we could no more have blamed them for that than for the colour of their hair.

I know that some people say the idea of a Law of Nature or decent behaviour known to all men is unsound, because different civilisations and different ages have had quite different moralities.

But this is not true. There have been differences between their moralities, but these have never amounted to anything like a total difference. If anyone will take the trouble to compare the moral teaching of, say, the ancient Egyptians, Babylonians, Hindus, Chinese, Greeks and Romans, what will really strike him will be how very like they are to each other and to our own. Some of the evidence for this I have put together in the appendix of another book called *The Abolition of Man*; but for our present purpose I need only ask the reader to think what a totally different morality would mean. Think of a country where people were admired for running away in battle, or where a man felt proud of double-crossing all the people who had been kindest to him. You might just as well try to imagine a country where two and two made five. Men have differed as regards what people you ought to be unselfish to – whether it was only your own family, or your fellow countrymen, or every one. But they have always agreed that you ought not to put yourself first. Selfishness has never been admired. Men have differed as to whether you should have one wife or four. But they have always agreed that you must not simply have any woman you liked.

But the most remarkable thing is this. Whenever you find a man who says he does not believe in a real Right and Wrong, you will find the same man going back on this a moment later. He may break his promise to you, but if you try breaking one to him he will be complaining 'It's not fair' before you can say Jack Robinson. A nation may say treaties don't matter; but then, next minute, they spoil their case by saying that the particular treaty they want to break was an unfair one. But if treaties do not matter, and if there is no such thing as Right and Wrong – in other words, if there is no Law of Nature – what is the difference between a fair treaty and an unfair one? Have they not let the cat out of the bag and shown that, whatever they say, they really know the Law of Nature just like anyone else?

It seems, then, we are forced to believe in a real Right and Wrong. People may be sometimes mistaken about them, just as people sometimes get their sums wrong; but they are not a matter of mere taste and opinion any more than the multiplication table. Now if we are agreed about that, I go on to my next point, which is this. None of us are really keeping the Law of Nature. If there are any exceptions among you, I apologise to them. They had much better read some other book, for nothing I am going to say concerns them. And now, turning to the ordinary human beings who are left:

I hope you will not misunderstand what I am going to say. I am not preaching, and Heaven knows I do not pretend to be better than anyone else. I am only trying to call attention to a fact; the fact that this year, or this month, or, more likely, this very day, we have failed to practise ourselves the kind of behaviour we expect from other people. There may be all sorts of excuses for us. That time you were so unfair to the children was when you were very tired. That slightly shady business about the money – the one you have almost forgotten – came when you were very hard-up. And what you promised to do for old So-and-so and have never done – well, you never would have promised if you had known how frightfully busy you were going to be. And as for your behaviour to your wife (or husband) or sister (or brother) if I knew how irritating they could be, I would not wonder at it – and who the dickens am I, anyway? I am just the same. That is to say, I do not succeed in keeping the Law of Nature very well, and the moment anyone tells me I am not keeping it, there starts up in my mind a string of excuses as long as your arm. The question at the moment is not whether they are good excuses. The point is that they are one more proof of how deeply, whether we like it or not, we believe in the Law of Nature. If we do not believe in decent behaviour, why should we be so anxious to make excuses for not having behaved decently? The truth is, we believe in decency so much – we feel the Rule of Law pressing on us so – that we cannot bear to face the fact that we are breaking it, and consequently we try to shift the responsibility. For you notice that it is only for our bad behaviour that we find all these explanations. It is only our bad temper that we put down to being tired or worried or hungry; we put our good temper down to ourselves.

These, then, are the two points I wanted to make. First, that human beings, all over the earth, have this curious idea that they ought to behave in a certain way, and cannot really get rid of it. Secondly, that they do not in fact behave in that way. They know the Law of Nature; they break it. These two facts are the foundation of all clear thinking about ourselves and the universe we live in.

2

SOME OBJECTIONS

If they are the foundation, I had better stop to make that foundation firm before I go on. Some of the letters I have had show that a good many people find it difficult to understand just what this Law of Human Nature, or Moral Law, or Rule of Decent Behaviour is.

For example, some people wrote to me saying, 'Isn't what you call the Moral Law simply our herd instinct and hasn't it been developed just like all our other instincts?' Now I do not deny that we may have a herd instinct: but that is not what I mean by the Moral Law. We all know what it feels like to be prompted by instinct – by mother love, or sexual instinct, or the instinct for food. It means that you feel a strong want or desire to act in a certain way. And, of course, we sometimes do feel just that sort of desire to help another person: and no doubt that desire is due to the herd instinct. But feeling a desire to help is quite different from feeling that you ought to help whether you want to or not. Supposing you hear a cry for help from a man in danger. You will probably feel two desires – one a desire to give help (due to your herd instinct), the other a desire to keep out of danger (due to the instinct for self-preservation). But you will find inside you, in addition to these two impulses, a third thing which tells you that you ought to follow the impulse to help, and suppress the impulse to run away. Now this thing that judges between two instincts, that decides which should be encouraged, cannot itself be either of them. You might as well say that the sheet of music which tells you, at a given moment, to play one note on the piano and not another, is itself one of the notes on the keyboard. The Moral Law tells us the tune we have to play: our instincts are merely the keys.

Another way of seeing that the Moral Law is not simply one of our instincts is this. If two instincts are in conflict, and there is nothing in a creature's mind except those two instincts, obviously the stronger of the two must win. But at those moments when we are most conscious of the Moral Law, it usually seems to be telling us to side with the weaker of the two impulses. You probably *want* to be safe much more than you want to help the man who is drowning: but the Moral Law tells you to help him all the same. And surely it often tells us to try to make the right impulse stronger than it naturally is? I mean, we often feel it our duty to stimulate the herd instinct, by waking up our imaginations and arousing our pity and so on, so as to get up enough steam for doing the right thing. But clearly we are not acting *from* instinct when we set about making an instinct stronger than it is. The thing that says to you, 'Your herd instinct is asleep. Wake it up,' cannot itself *be* the herd instinct. The thing that tells you which note on the piano needs to be played louder cannot itself be that note.

Here is a third way of seeing it. If the Moral Law was one of our instincts, we ought to be able to point to some one impulse inside us which was always what we call 'good,' always in agreement with the rule of right behaviour. But you cannot. There is none of our impulses which the Moral Law may not sometimes tell us to suppress, and none which it may not sometimes tell us to encourage. It is a mistake to think that some of our impulses – say mother love or patriotism – are good, and others, like sex or the fighting instinct, are bad. All we mean is that the occasions on which the fighting instinct or the sexual desire need to be restrained are rather more frequent than those for restraining mother love or patriotism. But there are situations in which it is the duty of a married man to encourage his sexual impulse and of a soldier to encourage the fighting instinct. There are also occasions on which a mother's love for her own children or a man's love for his own country have to be suppressed or they will lead to unfairness towards other people's children or countries. Strictly speaking, there are no such things as good and bad impulses. Think once again of a piano. It has not got two kinds of notes on it, the 'right' notes and the 'wrong' ones. Every single note is right at one time and wrong at another. The Moral Law is not any one instinct or set of instincts: it is something which makes a kind of tune (the tune we call goodness or right conduct) by directing the instincts.

By the way, the point is of great practical consequence. The most dangerous thing you can do is to take any one impulse of your own nature and set it up as the thing you ought to follow at all costs. There is not one of them which will not make us into devils if we set it up as an absolute guide. You might think love of humanity in general was safe, but it is not. If you leave out justice you will find yourself breaking agreements and faking evidence in trials 'for the sake of humanity', and become in the end a cruel and treacherous man.

Other people wrote to me saying, 'Isn't what you call the Moral Law just a social convention, something that is put into us by education?' I think there is a misunderstanding here. The people who ask that question are usually taking it for granted that if we have learned a thing from parents and teachers, then that thing must be merely a human invention. But, of course, that is not so. We all learned the multiplication table at school. A child who grew up alone on a desert island would not know it. But surely it does not follow that the multiplication table is simply a human convention, something human beings have made up for themselves and might have made different if they had liked? I fully agree that we learn the Rule of Decent Behaviour from parents and teachers, and friends and books, as we learn everything else. But some of the things we learn are mere conventions which might have been different – we learn to keep to the left of the road, but it might just as well have been the rule to keep to the right – and others of them, like mathematics, are real truths. The question is to which class the Law of Human Nature belongs.

There are two reasons for saying it belongs to the same class as mathematics. The first is, as I said in the first chapter, that though there are differences between the moral ideas of one time or country and those of another, the differences are not really very great – not nearly so great as most people imagine – and you can recognise the same law running through them all: whereas mere conventions, like the rule of the road or the kind of clothes people wear, may differ to any extent. The other reason is this. When you think about these differences between the morality of one people and another, do you think that the morality of one people is ever better or worse than that of another? Have any of the changes been improvements? If not, then of course there could never be any moral progress. Progress means not just changing, but changing for the better. If no set of moral ideas were truer or better than any other, there would be no sense in preferring civilised morality to savage morality, or Christian morality to Nazi morality. In fact, of course, we all do believe that some moralities are better than others. We do believe that some of the people who tried to change the moral ideas of their own age were what we would call Reformers or Pioneers – people who understood morality better than their neighbours did. Very well then. The moment you say that one set of moral ideas can be better than another, you are, in fact, measuring them both by a standard, saying that one of them conforms to that standard more nearly than the other. But the standard that measures two things is something different from either. You are, in fact, comparing them both with some Real Morality, admitting that there is such a thing as a real Right, independent of what people think, and that some people's ideas get nearer to that real Right than others. Or put it this way. If your moral ideas can be truer, and those of the Nazis less true, there must be something – some Real Morality – for them to be true about. The reason why your idea of New York can be truer or less true than mine is that New York is a real place, existing quite apart from what either of us thinks. If when each of us said 'New York' each means merely 'The town I am imagining in my own head', how could one of us have truer ideas than the other? There would be no question of truth or falsehood at all. In the same way, if the Rule of Decent Behaviour meant simply 'whatever each nation happens to approve', there would be no sense in saying that any one nation had ever been more correct in its approval than any other; no sense in saying that the world could ever grow morally better or morally worse.

I conclude then, that though the difference between people's ideas of Decent Behaviour often make you suspect that there is no real natural Law of Behaviour at all, yet the things we are bound to think about these differences really prove just the opposite. But one word before I end. I have met people who exaggerate the differences, because they have not distinguished between differences of morality and differences of belief about facts. For example, one man said to me, 'Three hundred years ago people in England were putting witches to death. Was that what you call the Rule of Human Nature or Right Conduct?' But surely the reason we do not execute witches is that we do not believe there are such things. If we did – if we really thought that there were people going about who had sold themselves to the devil and received supernatural powers from him in return and were using these powers to kill their neighbours or drive them mad or bring bad weather – surely we would all agree that if anyone deserved the death penalty, then these filthy quislings did? There is no difference of moral principle here: the difference is simply about matter of fact. It may be a great advance in knowledge not to believe in witches: there is no moral advance in not executing them when you do not think they are there. You would not call a man humane for ceasing to set mousetraps if he did so because he believed there were no mice in the house.

3

THE REALITY OF

THE LAW

I now go back to what I said at the end of the first chapter, that there were two odd things about the human race. First, that they were haunted by the idea of a sort of behaviour they ought to practise, what you might call fair play, or decency, or morality, or the Law of Nature. Second, that they did not in fact do so. Now some of you may wonder why I called this odd. It may seem to you the most natural thing in the world. In particular, you may have thought I was rather hard on the human race. After all, you may say, what I call breaking the Law of Right and Wrong or of Nature, only means that people are not perfect. And why on earth should I expect them to be? That would be a good answer if what I was trying to do was to fix the exact amount of blame which is due to us for not behaving as we except others to behave. But that is not my job at all. I am not concerned at present with blame; I am trying to find out truth. And from that point of view the very idea of something being imperfect, of its not being what it ought to be, has certain consequences.

If you take a thing like a stone or a tree, it is what it is and there seems no sense in saying it ought to have been otherwise. Of course you may say a stone is 'the wrong shape' if you want to use it for a rockery, or that a tree is a bad tree because it does not give you as much shade as you expected. But all you mean is that the stone or the tree does not happen to be convenient for some purpose of your own. You are not, except as a joke, blaming them for that. You really know, that, given the weather and the soil, the tree could not have been any different. What we, from our point of view, call a 'bad' tree is obeying the laws of its nature just as much as a 'good' one.

Now have you noticed what follows? It follows that what we usually call the laws of nature – the way weather works on a tree for example – may not really be *laws* in the strict sense, but only in a manner of speaking. When you say that falling stones always obey the law of gravitation, is not this much the same as saying that the law only means 'what stones always do'? You do not really think that when a stone is let go, it suddenly remembers that it is under orders to fall to the ground. You only mean that, in fact, it does fall. In other words, you cannot be sure that there is anything over and above the facts themselves, any law about what ought to happen, as distinct from what does happen. The laws of nature, as applied to stones or trees, may only mean 'what Nature, in fact, does'. But if you turn to the Law of Human Nature, the Law of Decent Behaviour, it is a different matter. That law certainly does not mean 'what human beings, in fact, do'; for as I said before, many of them do not obey this law at all, and none of them obey it completely. The law of gravity tells you what stones do if you drop them; but the Law of Human Nature tells you what human beings ought to do and do not. In other words, when you are dealing with humans, something else comes in above and beyond the actual facts. You have the facts (how men do behave) and you also have something else (how they ought to behave). In the rest of the universe there need not be anything but the facts. Electrons and molecules behave in a certain way, and certain results follow, and that may be the whole story.* But men behave in a certain way and that is not the whole story, for all the time you know that they ought to behave differently.

Now this is really so peculiar that one is tempted to try to explain it away. For instance, we might try to make out that when you say a man ought not to act as he does, you only mean the same as when you say that a stone is the wrong shape; namely, that what he is doing happens to be inconvenient to you. But that is simply untrue. A man occupying the corner seat in the train because he got there first, and a man who slipped into it while my back was turned and removed my bag, are both equally inconvenient. But I blame the second man and do not blame the first. I am not angry – except perhaps for a moment before I come to my senses – with a man who trips me up by accident; I am angry with a man who tries to trip me up even if he does not succeed. Yet the first has hurt me and the second has not. Sometimes the behaviour which I call bad is not inconvenient to me at all, but the very opposite. In war, each side may find a traitor on the other side very useful. But though they use him and pay him they regard him as human vermin. So you cannot say that what we call decent behaviour in others is simply the behaviour that happens to be useful to us. And as for decent behaviour in ourselves, I suppose it is pretty obvious that it does not mean the behaviour that pays. It means things like being content with thirty shillings when you might have got three pounds, doing school work honestly when it would be easy to cheat, leaving a girl alone when you would like to make love to her, staying in dangerous places when you would rather go somewhere safer, keeping promises you would rather not keep, and telling the truth even when it makes you look a fool.

Some people say that though decent conduct does not mean what pays

---

* I do not think it is the whole story, as you will see later. I mean that, as far as the argument has gone up to date, it may be.

each particular person at a particular moment, still, it means what pays the human race as a whole; and that consequently there is no mystery about it. Human beings, after all, have some sense; they see that you cannot have any real safety or happiness except in a society where every one plays fair, and it is because they see this that they try to behave decently. Now, of course, it is perfectly true that safety and happiness can only come from individuals, classes, and nations being honest and fair and kind to each other. It is one of the most important truths in the world. But as an explanation of why we feel as we do about Right and Wrong it just misses the point. If we ask: 'Why ought I to be unselfish?' and you reply 'Because it is good for society,' we may then ask, 'Why should I care what's good for society except when it happens to pay *me* personally?' and then you will have to say, 'Because you ought to be unselfish' – which simply brings us back to where we started. You are saying what is true, but you are not getting any further. If a man asked what was the point of playing football, it would not be much good saying 'in order to score goals', for trying to score goals is the game itself, not the reason for the game, and you would really only be saying that football was football – which is true, but not worth saying. In the same way, if a man asks what is the point of behaving decently, it is no good replying, 'in order to benefit society', for trying to benefit society, in other words being unselfish (for 'society' after all only means 'other people'), is one of the things decent behaviour consists in; all you are really saying is that decent behaviour is decent behaviour. You would have said just as much if you had stopped at the statement, 'Men ought to be unselfish.'

And that is where I do stop. Men ought to be unselfish, ought to be fair. Not that men are unselfish, not that they like being unselfish, but that they ought to be. The Moral Law, or Law of Human Nature, is not simply a fact about human behaviour in the same way as the Law of Gravitation is, or may be, simply a fact about how heavy objects behave. On the other hand, it is not a mere fancy, for we cannot get rid of the idea, and most of the things we say and think about men would be reduced to nonsense if we did. And it is not simply a statement about how we should like men to behave for our own convenience; for the behaviour we call bad or unfair is not exactly the same as the behaviour we find inconvenient, and may even be the opposite. Consequently, this Rule of Right and Wrong, or Law of Human Nature, or whatever you call it, must somehow or other be a real thing – a thing that is really there, not made up by ourselves. And yet it is not a fact in the ordinary sense, in the same way as our actual behaviour is a fact. It begins to look as if we shall have to admit that there is more than one kind of reality; that, in this particular case, there is something above and beyond the ordinary facts of men's behaviour, and yet quite definitely real – a real law, which none of us made, but which we find pressing on us.

4

WHAT LIES BEHIND
THE LAW

Let us sum up what we have reached so far. In the case of stones and trees and things of that sort, what we call the Laws of Nature may not be anything except a way of speaking. When you say that nature is governed by certain laws, this may only mean that nature does, in fact, behave in a certain way. The so-called laws may not be anything real – anything above and beyond the actual facts which we observe. But in the case of Man, we saw that this will not do. The Law of Human Nature, or of Right and Wrong, must be something above and beyond the actual facts of human behaviour. In this case, besides the actual facts, you have something else – a real law which we did not invent and which we know we ought to obey.

I now want to consider what this tells us about the universe we live in. Ever since men were able to think they have been wondering what this universe really is and how it came to be there. And, very roughly, two views have been held. First, there is what is called the materialist view. People who take that view think that matter and space just happen to exist, and always have existed, nobody knows why; and that the matter, behaving in certain fixed ways, has just happened, by a sort of fluke, to produce creatures like ourselves who are able to think. By one chance in a thousand something hit our sun and made it produce the planets; and by another thousandth chance the chemicals necessary for life, and the right temperature, occurred on one of these planets, and so some of the matter on this earth came alive; and then, by a very long series of chances, the living creatures developed into things like us. The other view is the religious view.* According to it, what is behind the universe is more like a mind than it is like anything else we know. That is to say, it is conscious, and has purposes, and prefers one thing to another. And on this view it made the universe, partly for purposes we do not know, but partly, at any rate, in order to produce creatures like itself – I mean, like itself to the extent of having minds. Please do not think that one of these

* See Note at the end of this chapter.

views was held a long time ago and that the other has gradually taken its place. Wherever there have been thinking men both views turn up. And note this too. You cannot find out which view is the right one by science in the ordinary sense. Science works by experiments. It watches how things behave. Every scientific statement in the long run, however complicated it looks, really means something like, 'I pointed the telescope to such and such a part of the sky at 2.20 a.m. on January 15th and saw so-and-so,' or, 'I put some of this stuff in a pot and heated it to such-and-such a temperature and it did so-and-so.' Do not think I am saying anything against science: I am only saying what its job is. And the more scientific a man is, the more (I believe) he would agree with me that this is the job of science – and a very useful and necessary job it is too. But why anything comes to be there at all, and whether there is anything behind the things science observes – something of a different kind – this is not a scientific question. If there is 'Something Behind', then either it will have to remain altogether unknown to men or else make itself known in some different way. The statement that there is any such thing, and the statement that there is no such thing, are neither of them statements that science can make. And real scientists do not usually make them. It is usually the journalists and popular novelists who have picked up a few odds and ends of half-baked science from textbooks who go in for them. After all, it is really a matter of common sense. Supposing science ever became complete so that it knew every single thing in the whole universe. Is it not plain that the questions, 'Why is there a universe?' 'Why does it go on as it does?' 'Has it any meaning?' would remain just as they were?

Now the position would be quite hopeless but for this. There is one thing, and only one, in the whole universe which we know more about than we could learn from external observation. That one thing is Man. We do not merely observe men, we *are* men. In this case we have, so to speak, inside information; we are in the know. And because of that, we know that men find themselves under a moral law, which they did not make, and cannot quite forget even when they try, and which they know they ought to obey. Notice the following point. Anyone studying Man from the outside as we study electricity or cabbages, not knowing our language and consequently not able to get any inside knowledge from us, but merely observing what we did, would never get the slightest evidence that we had this moral law. How could he? for his observations would only show what we did, and the moral law is about what we ought to do. In the same way, if there were anything above or behind the observed facts in the case of stones or the weather, we, by studying them from outside, could never hope to discover it.

The position of the question, then, is like this. We want to know whether the universe simply happens to be what it is for no reason or whether there is a power behind it that makes it what it is. Since that power, if it exists, would be not one of the observed facts but a reality which makes them, no mere observation of the facts can find it. There is only one case in which we can know whether there is anything more, namely our own case. And in that one case we find there is. Or put it the other way round. If there was a controlling power outside the universe, it could not show itself to us as one of the facts inside the universe – no more than the architect of a house could actually be a wall or staircase or fireplace in that house. The only way in which we could expect it to show itself would be inside ourselves as an influence or a command trying to get us to behave in a certain way. And that is just what we do find inside ourselves. Surely this ought to arouse our suspicions? In the only case where you can expect to get an answer, the answer turns out to be Yes; and in the other cases, where you do not get an answer, you see why you do not. Suppose someone asked me, when I see a man in blue uniform going down the street leaving little paper packets at each house, why I suppose that they contain letters? I should reply, 'Because whenever he leaves a similar little packet for me I find it does contain a letter.' And if he then objected – 'But you've never seen all these letters which you think the other people are getting,' I should say, 'Of course not, and I shouldn't expect to, because they're not addressed to me. I'm explaining the packets I'm not allowed to open by the ones I am allowed to open.' It is the same about this question. The only packet I am allowed to open is Man. When I do, especially when I open that particular man called Myself, I find that I do not exist on my own, that I am under a law; that somebody or something wants me to behave in a certain way. I do not, of course, think that if I could get inside a stone or a tree I should find exactly the same thing, just a I do not think all the other people in the street get the same letters as I do. I should expect, for instance, to find that the stone had to obey the law of gravity – that whereas the sender of the letters merely tells me to obey the law of my human nature, he compels the stone to obey the laws of its stony nature. But I should expect to find that there was, so to speak, a sender of letters in both cases, a Power behind the facts, a Director, a Guide.

Do not think I am going faster than I really am. I am not yet within a hundred miles of the God of Christian theology. All I have got to is a Something which is directing the universe, and which appears in me as a law urging me to do right and making me feel responsible and uncomfortable when I do wrong. I think we have to assume it is more like a mind than it is like anything else we know – because after all the only other thing we know is matter and you can hardly imagine a bit of matter giving instructions. But, of course, it need not be very like a mind, still less like a person. In the next chapter we shall see if we can find out anything more about it. But one word of warning. There has been a great deal of soft soap talked about God for the last hundred years. That is not what I am offering. You can cut all that out.

NOTE:– In order to keep this section short enough when it was given on the air, I mentioned only the Materialist view and the Religious view. But to be complete I ought to mention the In-between view called Life-Force philosophy, or Creative Evolution, or Emergent Evolution. The wittiest expositions of it come in the works of Bernard Shaw, but the most profound ones in those of Bergson. People who hold this view say that the small variations by which life on this planet 'evolved' from the lowest forms to Man were not due to chance but to the 'striving' or 'purposiveness' of a Life-Force. When people say this we must ask them whether by Life-Force they mean something with a mind or not. If they do, then 'a mind bringing life into existence and leading it to perfection' is really a God, and their view is thus identical with the Religious. If they do not, then what is the sense in saying that something without a mind 'strives' or has 'purposes'? This seems to me fatal to their view. One reason why many people find Creative Evolution so attractive is that it gives one much of the emotional comfort of believing in God and none of the less pleasant consequences. When you are feeling fit and the sun is shining and you do not want to believe that the whole universe is a mere mechanical dance of atoms, it is nice to be able to think of this great mysterious Force rolling on through the centuries and carrying you on its crest. If, on the other hand, you want to do something rather shabby, the Life-Force, being only a blind force, with no morals and no mind, will never interfere with you like that troublesome God we learned about when we were children. The Life-Force is a sort of tame God. You can switch it on when you want, but it will not bother you. All the thrills of religion and none of the cost. Is the Life-Force the greatest achievement of wishful thinking the world has yet seen?

5

WE HAVE CAUSE TO

BE UNEASY

I ended my last chapter with the idea that in the Moral Law somebody or something from beyond the material universe was actually getting at us. And I expect when I reached that point some of you felt a certain annoyance. You may even have thought that I had played a trick on you – that I had been carefully wrapping up to look like philosophy what turns out to be one more 'religious jaw'. You may have felt you were ready to listen to me as long as you thought I had anything new to say; but if it turns out to be only religion, well, the world has tried that and you cannot put the clock back. If anyone is feeling that way I should like to say three things to him.

First, as to putting the clock back. Would you think I was joking if I said that you can put a clock back, and that if the clock is wrong it is often a very sensible thing to do? But I would rather get away from that whole idea of clocks. We all want progress. But progress means getting nearer to the place where you want to be. And if you have taken a wrong turning, then to go forward does not get you any nearer. If you are on the wrong road, progress means doing an about-turn and walking back to the right road; and in that case the man who turns back soonest is the most progressive man. We have all seen this when doing arithmetic. When I have started a sum the wrong way, the sooner I admit this and go back and start again, the faster I shall get on. There is nothing progressive about being pig-headed and refusing to admit a mistake. And I think if you look at the present state of the world, it is pretty plain that humanity has been making some big mistake. We are on the wrong road. And if that is so, we must go back. Going back is the quickest way on.

Then, secondly, this has not yet turned exactly into a 'religious jaw'. We have not yet got as far as the God of any actual religion, still less the God of that particular religion called Christianity. We have only got as far as a Somebody of Something behind the Moral Law. We are not taking anything from the Bible or the Churches, we are trying to see what we can find out about this Somebody on our own steam. And I want to make it quite clear that what we find out on our own steam is something that gives us a shock. We have two bits of evidence about the Somebody. One is the universe He has made. If we used that as our only clue, then I think we should have to conclude that He was a great artist (for the universe is a very beautiful place), but also that He is quite merciless and no friend to man (for the universe is a very dangerous and terrifying place). The other bit of evidence is that Moral Law which He has put into our minds. And this is a better bit of evidence than the other, because it is inside information. You find out more about God from the Moral Law than from the universe in general just as you find out more about a man by listening to his conversation than by looking at a house he has built. Now, from this second bit of evidence we conclude that the Being behind the universe is intensely interested in right conduct – in fair play, unselfishness, courage, good faith, honesty and truthfulness. In that sense we should agree with the account given by Christianity and some other religions, that God is 'good'. But do not let us go too fast here. The Moral Law does not give us any grounds for thinking that God is 'good' in the sense of being indulgent, or soft, or sympathetic. There is nothing indulgent about the Moral Law. It is as hard as nails. It tells you to do the straight thing and it does not seem to care how painful, or dangerous, or difficult it is to do. If God is like the Moral Law, then He is not soft. It is no use, at this stage, saying that what you mean by a 'good' God is a God who can forgive. You are going too quickly. Only a Person can forgive. And we have not yet got as far as a personal God – only as far as a power, behind the Moral Law, and more like a mind than it is like anything else. But it may still be very unlike a Person. If it is pure impersonal mind, there may be no sense in asking it to make allowances for you or let you off, just as there is no sense in asking the multiplication table to let you off when you do your sums wrong. You are bound to get the wrong answer. And it is no use either saying that if there is a God of that sort – an impersonal absolute goodness – then you do not like Him and are not going to bother about Him. For the trouble is that one part of you is on His side and really agrees with his disapproval of human greed and trickery and exploitation. You may want Him to make an exception in your own case, to let you off this one time; but you know at bottom that unless the power behind the world really and unalterably detests that sort of behaviour, then He cannot be good. On the other hand, we know that if there does exist an absolute goodness it must hate most of what we do. This is the terrible fix we are in. If the universe is not governed by an absolute goodness, then all our efforts are in the long run hopeless. But if it is, then we are making ourselves enemies to that goodness every day, and are not in the least likely to do any better tomorrow, and so our case is hopeless again. We cannot do without it, and we cannot do with it. God is the only comfort, He is also the supreme terror: the thing we most need and the thing we most want to hide from. He is our only possible ally, and we have made ourselves His enemies. Some people talk as if meeting the gaze of absolute goodness would be fun. They need to think again. They are still only playing with religion. Goodness is either the great safety or the great danger – according to the way you react to it. And we have reacted the wrong way.

Now my third point. When I chose to get to my real subject in this roundabout way, I was not trying to play any kind of trick on you. I had a different reason. My reason was that Christianity simply does not make sense until you have faced the sort of facts I have been describing. Christianity tells people to repent and promises them forgiveness. It therefore has nothing (as far as I know) to say to people who do not know they have done anything to repent of and who do not feel that they need any forgiveness. It is after you have realised that there is a real Moral Law, and a Power behind the law, and that you have broken that law and put yourself wrong with that Power – it is after all this, and not a moment sooner, that Christianity begins to talk. When you know you are sick, you will listen to the doctor. When you have realised that our position is nearly desperate you will begin to understand what the Christians are talking about. They offer an explanation of how we got into our present state of both hating goodness and loving it. They offer an explanation of how God can be this impersonal mind at the back of the Moral Law and yet also a Person. They tell you how the demands of this law, which you and I cannot meet, have been met on our behalf, how God Himself becomes a man to save man from the disapproval of God. It is an old story and if you want to go into it you will no doubt consult people who have more authority to talk about it than I have. All I am doing is to ask people to face the facts – to understand the questions which Christianity claims to answer. And they are very terrifying facts. I wish it was possible to say something more agreeable. But I must say what I think true. Of course, I quite agree that the Christian religion is, in the long run, a thing of unspeakable comfort. But it does not begin in comfort; it begins in the dismay I have been describing, and it is no use at all trying to go on to that comfort without first going through that dismay. In religion, as in war and everything else, comfort is the one thing you cannot get by looking for it. If you look for truth, you may find comfort in the end: if you look for comfort you will not get either comfort or truth – only soft soap and wishful thinking to begin with and, in the end, despair. Most of us have got over the pre-war wishful thinking about international politics. It is time we did the same about religion.

BOOK 2

WHAT CHRISTIANS
BELIEVE

I

THE RIVAL CONCEPTIONS

OF GOD

I have been asked to tell you what Christians believe, and I am going to begin by telling you one thing that Christians do not need to believe. If you are a Christian you do not have to believe that all the other religions are simply wrong all through. If you are an atheist you do have to believe that the main point in all the religions of the whole world is simply one huge mistake. If you are a Christian, you are free to think that all those religions, even the queerest ones, contain at least some hint of the truth. When I was an atheist I had to try to persuade myself that most of the human race have always been wrong about the question that mattered to them most; when I became a Christian I was able to take a more liberal view. But, of course, being a Christian does mean thinking that where Christianity differs from other religions, Christianity is right and they are wrong. As in arithmetic – there is only one right answer to a sum, and all other answers are wrong; but some of the wrong answers are much nearer being right than others.

The first big division of humanity is into the majority, who believe in some kind of God or gods, and the minority who do not. On this point, Christianity lines up with the majority – lines up with ancient Greeks and Romans, modern savages, Stoics, Platonists, Hindus, Mohammedans, etc., against the modern Western European materialist.

Now I go on to the next big division. People who all believe in God can be divided according to the sort of God they believe in. There are two very different ideas on this subject. One of them is the idea that He is beyond good and evil. We humans call one thing good and another thing bad. But according to some people that is merely our human point of view. These people would say that the wiser you become the less you would want to call anything good or bad, and the more clearly you would see that everything is good in one way and bad in another, and that nothing could have been different. Consequently, these people think that long before you got anywhere near the divine point of view the distinction would have disappeared altogether. We call a cancer bad, they would say, because it kills a man; but you might just as well call a successful surgeon bad because he kills a cancer. It all depends on the point of view. The other and opposite idea is that God is quite definitely 'good' or 'righteous', a God who takes sides, who loves love and hates hatred, who wants us to behave in one way and not in another. The first of these views – the one that thinks God beyond good and evil – is called Pantheism. It was held by the great Prussian philosopher Hegel and, as far as I can understand them, by the Hindus. The other view is held by Jews, Mohammedans and Christians.

And with this big difference between Pantheism and the Christian idea of God, there usually goes another. Pantheists usually believe that God, so to speak, animates the universe as you animate your body: that the universe almost *is* God, so that if it did not exist He would not exist either, and anything you find in the universe is a part of God. The Christian idea is quite different. They think God invented and made the universe – like a man making a picture or composing a tune. A painter is not a picture, and he does not die if his picture is destroyed. You may say, 'He's put a lot of himself into it,' but you only mean that all its beauty and interest has come out of his head. His skill is not in the picture in the same way that it is in his head, or even in his hands. I expect you see how this difference between Pantheists and Christians hangs together with the other one. If you do not take the distinction between good and bad very seriously, then it is easy to say that anything you find in this world is a part of God. But, of course, if you think some things really bad, and God really good, then you cannot talk like that. You must believe that God is separate from the world and that some of the things we see in it are contrary to His will. Confronted with a cancer or a slum the Pantheist can say, 'If you could only see it from the divine point of view, you would realise that this also is God.' The Christian replies, 'Don't talk damned nonsense.'* For Christianity is a fighting religion. It thinks God made the world – that space and time, heat and cold, and all the colours and tastes, and all the animals and vegetables, are things that God 'made up out of His head' as a man makes up a story. But it also thinks that a great many things have gone wrong with the world that God made and that God insists, and insists very loudly, on our putting them right again.

And, of course, that raises a very big question. If a good God made the world why has it gone wrong? And for many years I simply refused to listen to the Christian answers to this question, because I kept on feeling 'whatever you say, and however clever your arguments are, isn't it much simpler and easier to say that the world was not made by any intelligent power?

---

* One listener complained of the word *damned* as frivolous swearing. But I mean exactly what I say – nonsense that is *damned* is under God's curse, and will (apart from God's grace) lead those who believe it to eternal death.

Aren't all your arguments simply a complicated attempt to avoid the obvious?' But then that threw me back into another difficulty.

My argument against God was that the universe seemed so cruel and unjust. But how had I got this idea of *just* and *unjust*? A man does not call a line crooked unless he has some idea of a straight line. What was I comparing this universe with when I called it unjust? If the whole show was bad and senseless from A to Z, so to speak, why did I, who was supposed to be part of the show, find myself in such violent reaction against it? A man feels wet when he falls into water, because man is not a water animal: a fish would not feel wet. Of course I could have given up my idea of justice by saying it was nothing but a private idea of my own. But if I did that, then my argument against God collapsed too – for the argument depended on saying that the world was really unjust, not simply that it did not happen to please my fancies. Thus in the very act of trying to prove that God did not exist – in other words, that the whole of reality was senseless – I found I was forced to assume that one part of reality – namely my idea of justice – was full of sense. Consequently atheism turns out to be too simple. If the whole universe has no meaning, we should never have found out that it has no meaning: just as, if there were no light in the universe and therefore no creatures with eyes, we should never know it was dark. *Dark* would be a word without meaning.

2

THE INVASION

Very well then, atheism is too simple. And I will tell you another view that is also too simple. It is the view I call Christianity-and-water, the view which simply says there is a good God in Heaven and everything is all right – leaving out all the difficult and terrible doctrines about sin and hell and the devil, and the redemption. Both these are boys' philosophies.

It is no good asking for a simple religion. After all, real things are not simple. They look simple, but they are not. The table I am sitting at looks simple: but ask a scientist to tell you what it is really made of – all about the atoms and how the light waves rebound from them and hit my eye and what they do to the optic nerve and what it does to my brain – and, of course, you find that what we call 'seeing a table' lands you in mysteries and complications which you can hardly get to the end of. A child saying a child's prayer looks simple. And if you are content to stop there, well and good. But if you are not – and the modern world usually is not – if you want to go on and ask what is really happening – then you must be prepared for something difficult. If we ask for something more than simplicity, it is silly then to complain that the something more is not simple.

Very often, however, this silly procedure is adopted by people who are not silly, but who, consciously or unconsciously, want to destroy Christianity. Such people put up a version of Christianity suitable for a child of six and make that the object of their attack. When you try to explain the Christian doctrine as it is really held by an instructed adult, they then complain that you are making their heads turn round and that it is all too complicated and that if there really were a God they are sure He would have made 'religion' simple, because simplicity is so beautiful, etc. You must be on your guard against these people for they will change their ground every minute and only waste your time. Notice, too, their idea of God 'making religion simple'; as if 'religion' were something God invented, and not His statement to us of certain quite unalterable facts about His own nature.

Besides being complicated, reality, in my experience, is usually odd. It is not neat, not obvious, not what you expect. For instance, when you have grasped that the earth and the other planets all go round the sun, you would naturally expect that all the planets were made to match – all at equal distances from each other, say, or distances that regularly increased, or all the same size, or else getting bigger or smaller as you go further from the sun. In fact, you find no rhyme or reason (that we can see) about either the sizes or the distances; and some of them have one moon, one has four, one has two, some have none, and one has a ring.

Reality, in fact, is usually something you could not have guessed. That is one of the reasons I believe Christianity. It is a religion you could not have guessed. If it offered us just the kind of universe we had always expected, I should feel we were making it up. But, in fact, it is not the sort of thing anyone would have made up. It has just that queer twist about it that real things have. So let us leave behind all these boys' philosophies – these over-simple answers. The problem is not simple and the answer is not going to be simple either.

What is the problem? A universe that contains much that is obviously bad and apparently meaningless, but containing creatures like ourselves who know that it is bad and meaningless. There are only two views that face all the facts. One is the Christian view that this is a good world that has gone wrong, but still retains the memory of what it ought to have been. The other is the view called Dualism. Dualism means the belief that there are two equal and independent powers at the back of everything, one of them good and the other bad, and that this universe is the battlefield in which they fight out an endless war. I personally think that next to Christianity Dualism is the manliest and most sensible creed on the market. But it has a catch in it.

The two powers, or spirits, or gods – the good one and the bad one – are supposed to be quite independent. They both existed from all eternity. Neither of them made the other, neither of them has any more right than the other to call itself God. Each presumably thinks it is good and thinks the other bad. One of them likes hatred and cruelty, the other likes love and mercy, and each backs its own view. Now what do we mean when we call one of them the Good Power and the other the Bad Power? Either we are merely saying that we happen to prefer the one to the other – like preferring beer to cider – or else we are saying that, whatever the two powers think about it, and whichever we humans, at the moment, happen to like, one of them is actually wrong, actually mistaken, it regarding itself as good. Now if we mean merely that we happen to prefer the first, then we must give up talking about good and evil at all. For good means what you ought to prefer quite regardless of what you happen to like at any given moment. If 'being good' meant simply joining the side you happened to fancy, for no real reason, then good would not deserve to be called good. So we must mean that one of the two powers is actually wrong and the other actually right.

But the moment you say that, you are putting into the universe a third thing in addition to the two Powers: some law or standard or rule of good which one of the powers conforms to and the other fails to conform to. But since the two powers are judged by this standard, then this standard, or the Being who made this standard, is farther back and higher up than either of them, and He will be the real God. In fact, what we meant by calling them good and bad turns out to be that one of them is in a right relation to the real ultimate God and the other in a wrong relation to Him.

The same point can be made in a different way. If Dualism is true, then the bad Power must be a being who likes badness for its own sake. But in reality we have no experience of anyone liking badness just because it is bad. The nearest we can get to it is in cruelty. But in real life people are cruel for one of two reasons – either because they are sadists, that is, because they have a sexual perversion which makes cruelty a cause of sensual pleasure to them, or else for the sake of something they are going to get out of it – money, or power, or safety. But pleasure, money, power, and safety are all, as far as they go, good things. The badness consists in pursuing them by the wrong method, or in the wrong way, or too much. I do not mean, of course, that the people who do this are not desperately wicked. I do mean that wickedness, when you examine it, turns out to be the pursuit of some good in the wrong way. You can be good for the mere sake of goodness: you cannot be bad for the mere sake of badness. You can do a kind action when you are not feeling kind and when it gives you no pleasure, simply because kindness is right; but no one ever did a cruel action simply because cruelty is wrong – only because cruelty was pleasant or useful to him. In other words badness cannot succeed even in being bad in the same way in which goodness is good. Goodness is, so to speak, itself: badness is only spoiled goodness. And there must be something good first before it can be spoiled. We called sadism a sexual perversion; but you must first have the idea of a normal sexuality before you can talk of its being perverted; and you can see which is the perversion, because you can explain the perverted from the normal, and cannot explain the normal from the perverted. It follows that this Bad Power, who is supposed to be on an equal footing with the Good Power, and to love badness in the same way as the Good Power loves goodness, is a mere bogy. In order to be bad he must have good things to want and then to pursue in the wrong way: he must have impulses which were originally good in order to be able to pervert them. But if he is bad he cannot supply himself either with good things to desire or with good impulses to pervert. He must be getting both from the Good Power. And if so, then he is not independent. He is part of the Good Power's world: he was made either by the Good Power or by some power above them both.

Put it more simply still. To be bad, he must exist and have intelligence and will. But existence, intelligence and will are in themselves good. Therefore he must be getting them from the Good Power: even to be bad he must borrow or steal from his opponent. And do you now begin to see why Christianity has always said that the devil is a fallen angel? That is not a mere story for the children. It is a real recognition of the fact that evil is a parasite, not an original thing. The powers which enable evil to carry on are powers given it by goodness. All the things which enable a bad man to be effectively bad are in themselves good things – resolution, cleverness, good looks, existence itself. That is why Dualism, in a strict sense, will not work.

But I freely admit that real Christianity (as distinct from Christianity-and-water) goes much nearer to Dualism than people think. One of the things that surprised me when I first read the New Testament seriously was that it talked so much about a Dark Power in the universe – a mighty evil spirit who was held to be the Power behind death and disease, and sin. The difference is that Christianity thinks this Dark Power was created by God, and was good when he was created, and went wrong. Christianity agrees with Dualism that this universe is at war. But it does not think this is a war between independent powers. It thinks it is a civil war, a rebellion, and that we are living in a part of the universe occupied by the rebel.

Enemy-occupied territory – that is what this world is. Christianity is the story of how the rightful king has landed, you might say landed in disguise, and is calling us all to take part in a great campaign of sabotage. When you go to church you are really listening-in to the secret wireless from our friends: that is why the enemy is so anxious to prevent us from going. He does it by playing on our conceit and laziness and intellectual snobbery. I know someone will ask me, 'Do you really mean, at this time of day, to re-introduce our old friend the devil – hoofs and horns and all?' Well, what the time of day has to do with it I do not know. And I am not particular about the hoofs and horns. But in other respects my answer is 'Yes, I do.' I do not claim to know anything about his personal appearance. If anybody really wants to know him better I would say to that person, 'Don't worry. If you really want to, you will. Whether you'll like it when you do is another question.'

3

THE SHOCKING

ALTERNATIVE

Christians, then, believe that an evil power has made himself for the present the Prince of this World. And, of course, that raises problems. Is this state of affairs in accordance with God's will, or not? If it is, He is a strange God, you will say: and if it is not, how can anything happen contrary to the will of a being with absolute power?

But anyone who has been in authority knows how a thing can be in accordance with your will in one way and not in another. It may be quite sensible for a mother to say to the children, 'I'm not going to go and make you tidy the schoolroom every night. You've got to learn to keep it tidy on your own.' Then she goes up one night and finds the Teddy bear and the ink and the French Grammar all lying in the grate. That is against her will. She would prefer the children to be tidy. But on the other hand, it is her will which has left the children free to be untidy. The same thing arises in any regiment, or trade union, or school. You make a thing voluntary and then half the people do not do it. That is not what you willed, but your will has made it possible.

It is probably the same in the universe. God created things which had free will. That means creatures which can go either wrong or right. Some people think they can imagine a creature which was free but had no possibility of going wrong; I cannot. If a thing is free to be good it is also free to be bad. And free will is what has made evil possible. Why, then, did God give them free will? Because free will, though it makes evil possible, is also the only thing that makes possible any love or goodness or joy worth having. A world of automata – of creatures that worked like machines – would hardly be worth creating. The happiness which God designs for His higher creatures is the happiness of being freely, voluntarily united to Him and to each other in an ecstasy of love and delight compared with which the most rapturous love between a man and a woman on this earth is mere milk and water. And for that they must be free.

Of course God knew what would happen if they used their freedom the wrong way: apparently He thought it worth the risk. Perhaps we feel inclined to disagree with Him. But there is a difficulty about disagreeing with God. He is the source from which all your reasoning power comes: you could not be right and He wrong any more than a stream can rise higher that its own source. When you are arguing against Him you are arguing against the very power that makes you able to argue at all: it is like cutting off the branch you are sitting on. If God thinks this state of war in the universe a price worth paying for free will – that is, for making a live world in which creatures can do real good or harm and something of real importance can happen, instead of a toy world which only moves when He pulls the strings – then we may take it it is worth paying.

When we have understood about free will, we shall see how silly it is to ask, as somebody once asked me: 'Why did God make a creature of such rotten stuff that it went wrong?' The better stuff a creature is made of – the cleverer and stronger and freer it is – then the better it will be if it goes right, but also the worse it will be if it goes wrong. A cow cannot be very good or very bad; a dog can be both better and worse; a child better and worse still; an ordinary man, still more so; a man of genius, still more so; a superhuman spirit best – or worst – of all.

How did the Dark Power go wrong? Here, no doubt, we ask a question to which human beings cannot give an answer with any certainty. A reasonable (and traditional) guess, based on our own experiences of going wrong, can, however, be offered. The moment you have a self at all, there is a possibility of putting yourself first – wanting to be the centre – wanting to be God, in fact. That was the sin of Satan: and that was the sin he taught the human race. Some people think the fall of man had something to do with sex, but that is a mistake. (The story in the Book of Genesis rather suggests that some corruption in our sexual nature followed the fall and was its result, not its cause.) What Satan put into the heads of our remote ancestors was the idea that they could 'be like gods' – could set up on their own as if they had created themselves – be their own masters – invent some sort of happiness for themselves outside God, apart from God. And out of that hopeless attempt has come nearly all that we call human history – money, poverty, ambition, war, prostitution, classes, empires, slavery – the long terrible story of man trying to find something other than God which will make him happy.

The reason why it can never succeed is this. God made us: invented us as a man invents an engine. A car is made to run on petrol, and it would not run properly on anything else. Now God designed the human machine to run on Himself. He Himself is the fuel our spirits were designed to burn, or the food our spirits were designed to feed on. There is no other. That is why it is just no good asking God to make us happy in our own way without bothering about religion. God cannot give us a happiness and peace apart from Himself, because it is not there. There is no such thing.

That is the key to history. Terrific energy is expended – civilisations are built up – excellent institutions devised; but each time something goes wrong. Some fatal flaw always brings the selfish and cruel people to the top and it all slides back into misery and ruin. In fact, the machine conks. It seems to start up all right and runs a few yards, and then it breaks down. They are trying to run it on the wrong juice. That is what Satan has done to us humans.

And what did God do? First of all He left us conscience, the sense of right and wrong: and all through history there have been people trying (some of them very hard) to obey it. None of them ever quite succeeded. Secondly, He sent the human race what I call good dreams: I mean those queer stories scattered all through the heathen religions about a god who dies and comes to life again and, by his death, has somehow given new life to men. Thirdly, He selected one particular people and spent several centuries hammering into their heads the sort of God He was – that there was only one of Him and that He cared about right conduct. Those people were the Jews, and the Old Testament gives an account of the hammering process.

Then comes the real shock. Among these Jews there suddenly turns up a man who goes about talking as if He was God. He claims to forgive sins. He says He has always existed. He says He is coming to judge the world at the end of time. Now let us get this clear. Among Pantheists, like the Indians, anyone might say that he was a part of God, or one with God: there would be nothing very odd about it. But this man, since He was a Jew, could not mean that kind of God. God, in their language, meant the Being outside the world, who had made it and was infinitely different from anything else. And when you have grasped that, you will see that what this man said was, quite simply, the most shocking thing that has ever been uttered by human lips.

One part of the claim tends to slip past us unnoticed because we have heard it so often that we no longer see what it amounts to. I mean the claim to forgive sins: any sins. Now unless the speaker is God, this is really so preposterous as to be comic. We can all understand how a man forgives offences against himself. You tread on my toes and I forgive you, you steal my money and I forgive you. But what should we make of a man, himself unrobbed and untrodden on, who announced that he forgave you for treading on other men's toes and stealing other men's money? Asinine fatuity is the kindest description we should give of his conduct. Yet this is what Jesus did. He told people that their sins were forgiven, and never waited to consult all the other people whom their sins had undoubtedly injured. He unhesitatingly behaved as if He was the party chiefly concerned, the person chiefly offended in all offences. This makes sense only if He really was the God whose laws are broken and whose love is wounded in every sin. In the mouth of any speaker who is not God, these words would imply what I can only regard as a silliness and conceit unrivalled by any other character in history.

Yet (and this is the strange, significant thing) even His enemies, when they read the Gospels, do not usually get the impression of silliness and conceit. Still less do unprejudiced readers. Christ says that He is 'humble and meek' and we believe Him; not noticing that, if He were merely a man, humility and meekness are the very last characteristics we could attribute to some of His sayings.

I am trying here to prevent anyone saying the really foolish thing that people often say about Him: 'I'm ready to accept Jesus as a great moral teacher, but I don't accept His claim to be God.' That is the one thing we must not say. A man who was merely a man and said the sort of things Jesus said would not be a great moral teacher. He would either be a lunatic – on a level with the man who says he is a poached egg – or else he would be the Devil of Hell. You must make your choice. Either this man was, and is, the Son of God: or else a madman or something worse. You can shut Him up for a fool, you can spit at Him and kill Him as a demon; or you can fall at His feet and call Him Lord and God. But let us not come with any patronising nonsense about His being a great human teacher. He has not left that open to us. He did not intend to.

4

THE PERFECT PENITENT

We are faced, then, with a frightening alternative. This man we are talking about either was (and is) just what He said or else a lunatic, or
something worse. Now it seems to me obvious that He was neither a lunatic
nor a fiend: and consequently, however strange or terrifying or unlikely it
may seem, I have to accept the view that He was and is God. God has landed
on this enemy-occupied world in human form.

And now, what was the purpose of it all? What did he come to do? Well,
to teach, of course; but as soon as you look into the New Testament or any
other Christian writing you will find they are constantly talking about
something different – about His death and His coming to life again. It is
obvious that Christians think the chief point of the story lies there. They
think the main thing He came to earth to do was to suffer and be killed.

Now before I became a Christian I was under the impression that the first
thing Christians had to believe was one particular theory as to what the
point of this dying was. According to that theory God wanted to punish
men for having deserted and joined the Great Rebel, but Christ volunteered
to be punished instead, and so God let us off. Now I admit that even this
theory does not seem to me quite so immoral and so silly as it used to; but
that is not the point I want to make. What I came to see later on was that
neither this theory nor any other is Christianity. The central Christian belief
is that Christ's death has somehow put us right with God and given us a
fresh start. Theories as to how it did this are another matter. A good many
different theories have been held as to how it works; what all Christians are
agreed on is that it does work. I will tell you what I think it is like. All sensible people know that if you are tired and hungry a meal will do you good.
But the modern theory of nourishment – all about the vitamins and proteins
– is a different thing. People ate their dinners and felt better long before the
theory of vitamins was ever heard of: and if the theory of vitamins is some
day abandoned they will go on eating their dinners just the same.
Theories about Christ's death are not Christianity: they are explanations

about how it works. Christians would not all agree as to how important those theories are. My own church – the Church of England – does not lay down any one of them as the right one. The Church of Rome goes a bit further. But I think they will all agree that the thing itself is infinitely more important than any explanations that theologians have produced. I think they would probably admit that no explanation will ever be quite adequate to the reality. But as I said in the preface to this book, I am only a layman, and at this point we are getting into deep water. I can only tell you, for what it is worth, how I, personally, look at the matter.

In my view the theories are not themselves the thing you are asked to accept. Many of you no doubt have read Jeans or Eddington. What they do when they want to explain the atom, or something of that sort, is to give you a description out of which you can make a mental picture. But then they warn you that this picture is not what the scientists actually believe. What the scientists believe is a mathematical formula. The pictures are there only to help you to understand the formula. They are not really true in the way the formula is; they do not give you the real thing but only something more or less like it. They are only meant to help, and if they do not help you can drop them. The thing itself cannot be pictured, it can only be expressed mathematically. We are in the same boat here. We believe that the death of Christ is just that point in history at which something absolutely unimaginable from outside shows through into our own world. And if we cannot picture even the atoms of which our own world is built, of course we are not going to be able to picture this. Indeed, if we found that we could fully understand it, that very fact would show it was not what it professes to be – the inconceivable, the uncreated, the thing from beyond nature, striking down into nature like lightning. You may ask what good it will be to us if we do not understand it. But that is easily answered. A man can eat his dinner without understanding exactly how food nourishes him. A man can accept what Christ has done without knowing how it works: indeed, he certainly would not know how it works until he has accepted it.

We are told that Christ was killed for us, that His death has washed out our sins, and that by dying He disabled death itself. That is the formula. That is Christianity. That is what has to be believed. Any theories we build up as to how Christ's death did all this are, in my view, quite secondary: mere plans or diagrams to be left alone if they do not help us, and, even if they do help us, not to be confused with the thing itself. All the same, some of these theories are worth looking at.

The one most people have heard is the one I mentioned before – the one about our being let off because Christ has volunteered to bear a punishment instead of us. Now on the face of it that is a very silly theory. If God was prepared to let us off, why on earth did He not do so? And what possible point could there be in punishing an innocent person instead? None at all that I can see, if you are thinking of punishment in the police-court sense. On the other hand, if you think of a debt, there is plenty of point in a person who has some assets paying it on behalf of someone who has not. Or if you take 'paying the penalty', not in the sense of being punished, but in the more general sense of 'standing the racket' or 'footing the bill', then, of course, it is a matter of common experience that, when one person has got himself into a hole, the trouble of getting him out usually falls on a kind friend.

Now what was the sort of 'hole' man had got himself into? He had tried to set up on his own, to behave as if he belonged to himself. In other words, fallen man is not simply an imperfect creature who needs improvement: he is a rebel who must lay down his arms. Laying down your arms, surrendering, saying you are sorry, realising that you have been on the wrong track and getting ready to start life over again from the ground floor – that is the only way out of our 'hole'. This process of surrender – this movement full speed astern – is what Christians call repentance. Now repentance is no fun at all. It is something much harder than merely eating humble pie. It means unlearning all the self-conceit and self-will that we have been training ourselves into for thousands of years. It means killing part of yourself, undergoing a kind of death. In fact, it needs a good man to repent. And here comes the catch. Only a bad person needs to repent: only a good person can repent perfectly. The worse you are the more you need it and the less you can do it. The only person who could do it perfectly would be a perfect person – and he would not need it.

Remember, this repentance, this willing submission to humiliation and a kind of death, is not something God demands of you before He will take you back and which He could let you off if He chose: it is simply a description of what going back to Him is like. If you ask God to take you back without it, you are really asking Him to let you go back without going back. It cannot happen. Very well, then, we must go through with it. But the same badness which makes us need it, makes us unable to do it. Can we do it if God helps us? Yes, but what do we mean when we talk of God helping us? We mean God putting into us a bit of Himself, so to speak. He lends us a little of His reasoning powers and that is how we think: He puts a little of His love into us and that is how we love one another. When you teach a child writing, you hold its hand while it forms the letters: that is, it forms the letters because you are forming them. We love and reason because God loves and reasons and holds our hand while we do it. Now if we had not fallen, that would be all plain sailing. But unfortunately we now need God's help in order to do something which God, in His own nature, never does at all – to surrender, to suffer, to submit, to die. Nothing in God's nature corresponds to this process at all. So that the one road for which we now need God's leadership most of all is a road God, in His own nature, has never walked. God can share only what He has: this thing, in His own nature, He has not.

But supposing God became a man – suppose our human nature which can suffer and die was amalgamated with God's nature in one person – then that person could help us. He could surrender His will, and suffer and die, because He was man; and He could do it perfectly because He was God. You and I can go through this process only if God does it in us; but God can do it only if He becomes man. Our attempts at this dying will succeed only if we men share in God's dying, just as our thinking can succeed only because it is a drop out of the ocean of His intelligence: but we cannot share God's dying unless God dies; and He cannot die except by being a man. That is the sense in which He pays our debt, and suffers for us what He Himself need not suffer at all.

I have heard some people complain that if Jesus was God as well as man, then His sufferings and death lose all value in their eyes, 'because it must have been so easy for Him': Others may (very rightly) rebuke the ingratitude and ungraciousness of this objection; what staggers me is the misunderstanding it betrays. In one sense, of course, those who make it are right. They have even understated their own case. The perfect submission, the perfect suffering, the perfect death were not only easier to Jesus because He was God, but were possible only because He was God. But surely that is a very odd reason for not accepting them? The teacher is able to form the letters for the child because the teacher is grown-up and knows how to write. That, of course, makes it easier for the teacher; and only because it is easier for him can he help the child. If it rejected him because 'it's easy for grown-ups' and waited to learn writing from another child who could not write itself (and so had no 'unfair' advantage), it would not get on very quickly. If I am drowning in a rapid river, a man who still has one foot on the bank may give me a hand which saves my life. Ought I to shout back (between my gasps) 'No, it's not fair! You have an advantage! You're keeping one foot on the bank'? That advantage – call it 'unfair' if you like – is the only reason why he can be of any use to me. To what will you look for help if you will not look to that which is stronger than yourself?

Such is my own way of looking at what Christians call the Atonement. But remember this is only one more picture. Do not mistake it for the thing itself: and if it does not help you, drop it.

5

THE PRACTICAL

CONCLUSION

The perfect surrender and humiliation were undergone by Christ: perfect because He was God, surrender and humiliation because He was man. Now the Christian belief is that if we somehow share the humility and suffering of Christ we shall also share in His conquest of death and find a new life after we have died and in it become perfect, and perfectly happy, creatures. This means something much more than our trying to follow His teaching. People often ask when the next step in evolution – the step to something beyond man – will happen. But on the Christian view, it has happened already. In Christ a new kind of man appeared: and the new kind of life which began in Him is to be put into us.

How is this to be done? Now, please remember how we acquired the old, ordinary kind of life. We derived it from others, from our father and mother and all our ancestors, without our consent – and by a very curious process, involving pleasure, pain, and danger. A process you would never have guessed. Most of us spend a good many years in childhood trying to guess it: and some children, when they are first told, do not believe it – and I am not sure that I blame them, for it is very odd. Now the God who arranged that process is the same God who arranges how the new kind of life – the Christ-life – is to be spread. We must be prepared for it being odd too. He did not consult us when He invented sex: He has not consulted us either when He invented this.

There are three things that spread the Christ life to us: baptism, belief, and that mysterious action which different Christians call by different names – Holy Communion, the Mass, the Lord's Supper. At least, those are the three ordinary methods. I am not saying there may not be special cases where it is spread without one or more of these. I have not time to go into special cases, and I do not know enough. If you are trying in a few minutes to tell a man how to get to Edinburgh you will tell him the trains: he can, it is true, get there by boat or by a plane, but you will hardly bring that in. And I am not saying anything about which of these three things is the most essential. My

Methodist friend would like me to say more about belief and less (in proportion) about the other two. But I am not going into that. Anyone who professes to teach you Christian doctrine will, in fact, tell you to use all three, and that is enough for our present purpose.

I cannot myself see why these things should be the conductors of the new kind of life. But then, if one did not happen to know, I should never have seen any connection between a particular physical pleasure and the appearance of a new human being in the world. We have to take reality as it comes to us: there is no good jabbering about what it ought to be like or what we should have expected it to be like. But though I cannot see why it should be so, I can tell you why I believe it is so. I have explained why I have to believe that Jesus was (and is) God. And it seems plain as a matter of history that He taught His followers that the new life was communicated in this way. In other words, I believe it on His authority. Do not be scared by the word authority. Believing things on authority only means believing them because you have been told them by someone you think trustworthy. Ninety-nine per cent of the things you believe are believed on authority. I believe there is such a place as New York. I have not seen it myself. I could not prove by abstract reasoning that there must be such a place. I believe it because reliable people have told me so. The ordinary man believes in the Solar System, atoms, evolution, and the circulation of the blood on authority – because the scientists say so. Every historical statement in the world is believed on authority. None of us has seen the Norman Conquest or the defeat of the Armada. None of us could prove them by pure logic as you prove a thing in mathematics. We believe them simply because people who did see them have left writings that tell us about them: in fact, on authority. A man who jibbed at authority in other things as some people do in religion would have to be content to know nothing all his life.

Do not think I am setting up baptism and belief and the Holy Communion as things that will do instead of your own attempts to copy Christ. Your natural life is derived from your parents; that does not mean it will stay there if you do nothing about it. You can lose it by neglect, or you can drive it away by committing suicide. You have to feed it and look after it: but always remember you are not making it, you are only keeping up a life you got from someone else. In the same way a Christian can lose the Christ-life which has been put into him, and he has to make efforts to keep it. But even the best Christian that ever lived is not acting on his own steam – he is only nourishing or protecting a life he could never have acquired by his own efforts. And that has practical consequences. As long as the natural life is in your body, it will do a lot towards repairing that body. Cut it, and up to a point it will heal, as a dead body would not. A live body is not one that never gets hurt, but one that can to some extent repair itself. In the same way a Christian is not a man who never goes wrong, but a man who is enabled to repent and pick himself up and begin over again after each stumble – because the Christ-life is inside him, repairing him all the time, enabling him to repeat (in some degree) the kind of voluntary death which Christ Himself carried out.

That is why the Christian is in a different position from other people who are trying to be good. They hope, by being good, to please God if there is one; or – if they think there is not – at least they hope to deserve approval from good men. But the Christian thinks any good he does comes from the Christ-life inside him. He does not think God will love us because we are good, but that God will make us good because He loves us; just as the roof of a greenhouse does not attract the sun because it is bright, but becomes bright because the sun shines on it.

And let me make it quite clear that when Christians say the Christ-life is in them, they do not mean simply something mental or moral. When they speak of being 'in Christ' or of Christ being 'in them', this is not simply a way of saying that they are thinking about Christ or copying Him. They mean that Christ is actually operating through them; that the whole mass of Christians are the physical organism through which Christ acts – that we are His fingers and muscles, the cells of His body. And perhaps that explains one or two things. It explains why this new life is spread not only by purely mental acts like belief, but by bodily acts like baptism and Holy Communion. It is not merely the spreading of an idea; it is more like evolution – a biological or super-biological fact. There is no good trying to be more spiritual than God. God never meant man to be a purely spiritual creature. That is why He uses material things like bread and wine to put the new life into us. We may think this rather crude and unspiritual. God does not: He invented eating. He likes matter. He invented it.

Here is another thing that used to puzzle me. Is it not frightfully unfair that this new life should be confined to people who have heard of Christ and been able to believe in Him? But the truth is God has not told us what His arrangements about the other people are. We do know that no man can be saved except through Christ; we do not know that only those who know Him can be saved through Him. But in the meantime, if you are worried about the people outside, the most unreasonable thing you can do is to remain outside yourself. Christians are Christ's body, the organism through which He works. Every addition to that body enables Him to do more. If you want to help those outside you must add your own little cell to the body of Christ who alone can help them. Cutting off a man's fingers would be an odd way of getting him to do more work.

Another possible objection is this. Why is God landing in this enemy-occupied world in disguise and starting a sort of secret society to undermine the devil? Why is He not landing in force, invading it? Is it that He is not strong enough? Well, Christians think He is going to land in force; we do not know when. But we can guess why He is delaying. He wants to give us the chance of joining His side freely. I do not suppose you and I would have thought much of a Frenchman who waited till the Allies were marching into Germany and then announced he was on our side. God will invade. But I wonder whether people who ask God to interfere openly and directly in our world quite realise what it will be like when He does. When that happens, it is the end of the world. When the author walks on to the stage the play is over. God is going to invade, all right: but what is the good of saying you are on His side then, when you see the whole natural universe melting away like a dream and something else – something it never entered your head to conceive – comes crashing in; something so beautiful to some of us and so terrible to others that none of us will have any choice left? For this time it will be God without disguise; something so overwhelming that it will strike either irresistible love or irresistible horror into every creature. It will be too late then to choose your side. There is no use saying you choose to lie down when it has become impossible to stand up. That will not be the time for choosing: it will be the time when we discover which side we really have chosen, whether we realised it before or not. Now, to-day, this moment, is our chance to choose the right side. God is holding back to give us that chance. It will not last for ever. We must take it or leave it.

BOOK 3

CHRISTIAN BEHAVIOUR

I

THE THREE PARTS OF
MORALITY

There is a story about a schoolboy who was asked what he thought God was like. He replied that, as far as he could make out, God was 'the sort of person who is always snooping around to see if anyone is enjoying himself and then trying to stop it'. And I am afraid that is the sort of idea that the word Morality raises in a good many people's minds: something that interferes, something that stops you having a good time. In reality, moral rules are directions for running the human machine. Every moral rule is there to prevent a breakdown, or a strain, or a friction, in the running of that machine. That is why these rules at first seem to be constantly interfering with our natural inclinations. When you are being taught how to use any machine, the instructor keeps on saying, 'No, don't do it like that,' because, of course, there are all sorts of things that look all right and seem to you the natural way of treating the machine, but do not really work.

Some people prefer to talk about moral 'ideals' rather than moral rules and about moral 'idealism' rather than moral obedience. Now it is, of course, quite true that moral perfection is an 'ideal' in the sense that we cannot achieve it. In that sense every kind of perfection is, for us humans, an ideal; we cannot succeed in being perfect car drivers or perfect tennis players or in drawing perfectly straight lines. But there is another sense in which it is very misleading to call moral perfection an ideal. When a man says that a certain woman, or house, or ship, or garden is 'his ideal' he does not mean (unless he is rather a fool) that everyone else ought to have the same ideal. In such matters we are entitled to have different tastes and, therefore, different ideals. But it is dangerous to describe a man who tries very hard to keep the moral law as a 'man of high ideals', because this might lead you to think that moral perfection was a private taste of his own and that the rest of us were not called on to share it. This would be a disastrous mistake. Perfect behaviour may be as unattainable as perfect gear-changing when we drive; but it is a necessary ideal prescribed for all men by the very nature of the human machine just as perfect gear-changing is an ideal prescribed for all drivers by the very nature of cars. And it would be even more dangerous to think of oneself as a person 'of high ideals' because one is trying to tell no lies at all (instead of only a few lies) or never to commit adultery (instead of commiting it only seldom) or not to be a bully (instead of being only a moderate bully). It might lead you to become a prig and to think you were rather a special person who deserved to be congratulated on his 'idealism'. In reality you might just as well expect to be congratulated because, whenever you do a sum, you try to get it quite right. To be sure, perfect arithmetic is 'an ideal'; you will certainly make some mistakes in some calculations. But there is nothing very fine about trying to be quite accurate at each step in each sum. It would be idiotic not to try; for every mistake is going to cause you trouble later on. In the same way every moral failure is going to cause trouble, probably to others and certainly to yourself. By talking about rules and obedience instead of 'ideals' and 'idealism' we help to remind ourselves of these facts.

Now let us go a step further. There are two ways in which the human machine goes wrong. One is when human individuals drift apart from one another, or else collide with one another and do one another damage, by cheating or bullying. The other is when things go wrong inside the individual – when the different parts of him (his different faculties and desires and so on) either drift apart or interfere with one another. You can get the idea plain if you think of us as a fleet of ships sailing in formation. The voyage will be a success only, in the first place, if the ships do not collide and get in one another's way; and, secondly, if each ship is seaworthy and has her engines in good order. As a matter of fact, you cannot have either of these two things without the other. If the ships keep on having collisions they will not remain seaworthy very long. On the other hand, if their steering gears are out of order they will not be able to avoid collisions. Or, if you like, think of humanity as a band playing a tune. To get a good result, you need two things. Each player's individual instrument must be in tune and also each must come in at the right moment so as to combine with all the others.

But there is one thing we have not yet taken into account. We have not asked where the fleet is trying to get to, or what piece of music the band is trying to play. The instruments might be all in tune and might all come in at the right moment, but even so the performance would not be a success if they had been engaged to provide dance music and actually played nothing but Dead Marches. And however well the fleet sailed, its voyage would be a failure if it were meant to reach New York and actually arrived at Calcutta.

Morality, then, seems to be concerned with three things. Firstly, with fair play and harmony between individuals. Secondly, with what might be called tidying up or harmonising the things inside each individual. Thirdly, with the general purpose of human life as a whole: what man was made for: what course the whole fleet ought to be on: what tune the conductor of the band wants it to play.

You may have noticed that modern people are nearly always thinking about the first thing and forgetting the other two. When people say in the newspapers that we are striving for Christian moral standards, they usually mean that we are striving for kindness and fair play between nations, and classes, and individuals; that is, they are thinking only of the first thing. When a man says about something he wants to do, 'It can't be wrong because it doesn't do anyone else any harm,' he is thinking only of the first thing. He is thinking it does not matter what his ship is like inside provided that he does not run into the next ship. And it is quite natural, when we start thinking about morality, to begin with the first thing, with social relations. For one thing, the results of bad morality in that sphere are so obvious and press on us every day: war and poverty and graft and lies and shoddy work. And also, as long as you stick to the first thing, there is very little disagreement about morality. Almost all people at all times have agreed (in theory) that human beings ought to be honest and kind and helpful to one another. But though it is natural to begin with all that, if our thinking about morality stops there, we might just as well not have thought at all. Unless we go on to the second thing – the tidying up inside each human being – we are only deceiving ourselves.

What is the good of telling the ships how to steer so as to avoid collisions if, in fact, they are such crazy old tubs that they cannot be steered at all? What is the good of drawing up, on paper, rules for social behaviour, if we know that, in fact, our greed, cowardice, ill temper, and self-conceit are going to prevent us from keeping them? I do not mean for a moment that we ought not to think, and think hard, about improvements in our social and economic system. What I do mean is that all that thinking will be mere moonshine unless we realise that nothing but the courage and unselfishness of individuals is ever going to make any system work properly. It is easy enough to remove the particular kinds of graft or bullying that go on under the present system: but as long as men are twisters or bullies they will find some new way of carrying on the old game under the new system. You cannot make men good by law: and without good men you cannot have a good society. That is why we must go on to think of the second thing: of morality inside the individual.

But I do not think we can stop there either. We are now getting to the point at which different beliefs about the universe lead to different behaviour. And it would seem, at first sight, very sensible to stop before we got there, and just carry on with those parts of morality that all sensible people agree about. But can we? Remember that religion involves a series of statements about facts, which must be either true or false. If they are true, one set of conclusions will follow about the right sailing of the human fleet: if they are false, quite a different set. For example, let us go back to the man who says that a thing cannot be wrong unless it hurts some other human being. He quite understands that he must not damage the other ships in the convoy, but he honestly thinks that what he does to his own ship is simply his own business. But does it not make a great difference whether his ship is his own property or not? Does it not make a great difference whether I am, so to speak, the landlord of my own mind and body, or only a tenant, responsible to the real landlord? If somebody else made me, for his own purposes, then I shall have a lot of duties which I should not have if I simply belonged to myself.

Again, Christianity asserts that every individual human being is going to live for ever, and this must be either true of false. Now there are a good many things which would not be worth bothering about if I were going to live only seventy years, but which I had better bother about very seriously if I am going to live for ever. Perhaps my bad temper or my jealousy are gradually getting worse – so gradually that the increase in seventy years will not be very noticeable. But it might be absolute hell in a million years: in fact, if Christianity is true, Hell is the precisely correct technical term for what it would be. And immortality makes this other difference, which, by the by, has a connection with the difference between totalitarianism and democracy. If individuals live only seventy years, then a state, or a nation, or a civilisation, which may last for a thousand years, is more important than an individual. But if Christianity is true, then the individual is not only more important but incomparably more important, for he is everlasting and the life of a state or a civilisation, compared with his, is only a moment.

It seems, then, that if we are to think about morality, we must think of all three departments: relations between man and man: things inside each man: and relations between man and the power that made him. We can all co-operate in the first one. Disagreements begin with the second and become more serious with the third. It is dealing with the third that the main differences between Christian and non-Christian morality come out. For the rest of this book I am going to assume the Christian point of view, and look at the whole picture as it will be if Christianity is true.

2

THE 'CARDINAL VIRTUES'

The previous section was originally composed to be given as a short talk on the air.

If you are allowed to talk for only ten minutes, pretty well everything else has to be sacrificed to brevity. One of my chief reasons for dividing morality up into three parts (with my picture of the ships sailing in convoy) was that this seemed the shortest way of covering the ground. Here I want to give some idea of another way in which the subject has been divided by old writers, which was too long to use in my talk, but which is a very good one.

According to this longer scheme there are seven 'virtues'. Four of them are called 'Cardinal' virtues, and the remaining three are called 'Theological' virtues. The 'Cardinal' ones are those which all civilised people recognise: the 'Theological' are those which, as a rule, only Christians know about. I shall deal with the Theological ones later on: at present I am talking about the four Cardinal virtues. (The word 'cardinal' has nothing to do with 'Cardinals' in the Roman Church. It comes from a Latin word meaning 'the hinge of a door'. These were called 'cardinal' virtues because they are, as we should say, 'pivotal'.) They are PRUDENCE, TEMPERANCE, JUSTICE and FORTITUDE.

Prudence means practical common sense, taking the trouble to think out what you are doing and what is likely to come of it. Nowadays most people hardly think of Prudence as one of the 'virtues'. In fact, because Christ said we could only get into His world by being like children, many Christians have the idea that, provided you are 'good', it does not matter being a fool. But that is a misunderstanding. In the first place, most children show plenty of 'prudence' about doing the things they are really interested in, and think them out quite sensibly. In the second place, as St Paul points out, Christ never meant that we were to remain children in *intelligence*: on the contrary. He told us to be not only 'as harmless as doves', but also 'as wise as serpents'. He wants a child's heart, but a grown-up's head. He wants us to be simple, single-minded, affectionate, and teachable, as good children are; but He also wants every bit of intelligence we have to be alert at its job, and in first-class fighting trim. The fact that you are giving money to a charity does not mean that you need not try to find out whether that charity is a fraud or not. The fact that what you are thinking about is God Himself (for example, when you are praying) does not mean that you can be content with the same babyish ideas which you had when you were a five-year-old. It is, of course, quite true that God will not love you any the less, or have less use for you, if you happen to have been born with a very second-rate brain. He has room for people with very little sense, but He wants every one to use what sense they have. The proper motto is not 'Be good, sweet maid and let who can be clever,' but 'Be good, sweet maid, and don't forget that this involves being as clever as you can.' God is no fonder of intellectual slackers than of any other slackers. If you are thinking of becoming a Christian, I warn you, you are embarking on something which is going to take the whole of you, brains and all. But, fortunately, it works the other way round. Anyone who is honestly trying to be a Christian will soon find his intelligence being sharpened: one of the reasons why it needs no special education to be a Christian is that Christianity is an education itself. That is why an uneducated believer like Bunyan was able to write a book that has astonished the whole world.

Temperance is, unfortunately, one of those words that has changed its meaning. It now usually means teetotalism. But in the days when the second Cardinal virtue was christened 'Temperance', it meant nothing of the sort. Temperance referred not specially to drink, but to all pleasures; and it meant not abstaining, but going the right length and no further. It is a mistake to think that Christians ought all to be teetotallers; Mohammedanism, not Christianity, is the teetotal religion. Of course it may be the duty of a particular Christian, or of any Christian, at a particular time, to abstain from strong drink, either because he is the sort of man who cannot drink at all without drinking too much, or because he is with people who are inclined to drunkenness and must not encourage them by drinking himself. But the whole point is that he is abstaining, for a good reason, from something which he does not condemn and which he likes to see other people enjoying. One of the marks of a certain type of bad man is that he cannot give up a thing himself without wanting everyone else to give it up. That is not the Christian way. An individual Christian may see fit to give up all sorts of things for special reasons – marriage, or meat, or beer, or the cinema; but the moment he starts saying the things are bad in themselves, or looking down his nose at other people who do use them, he has taken the wrong turning.

One great piece of mischief has been done by the modern restriction of the word Temperance to the question of drink. It helps people to forget that you can be just as intemperate about lots of other things. A man who makes his golf or his motor-bicycle the centre of his life, or a woman who devotes all her thoughts to clothes or bridge or her dog, is being just as 'intemperate' as someone who gets drunk every evening. Of course, it does not show on the outside so easily: bridge-mania or golf-mania do not make you fall down in the middle of the road. But God is not deceived by externals.

Justice means much more than the sort of thing that goes on in law courts. It is the old name for everything we should now call 'fairness'; it includes honesty, give and take, truthfulness, keeping promises, and all that side of life. And Fortitude includes both kinds of courage – the kind that faces danger as well as the kind that 'sticks it' under pain. 'Guts' is perhaps the nearest modern English. You will notice, of course, that you cannot practise any of the other virtues very long without bringing this one into play.

There is one further point about the virtues that ought to be noticed. There is a difference between doing some particular just or temperate action and being a just or temperate man. Someone who is not a good tennis player may now and then make a good shot. What you mean by a good player is a man whose eye and muscles and nerves have been so trained by making innumerable good shots that they can now be relied on. They have a certain tone or quality which is there even when he is not playing, just as a mathematician's mind has a certain habit and outlook which is there even when he is not doing mathematics. In the same way a man who perseveres in doing just actions gets in the end a certain quality of character. Now it is that quality rather than the particular actions which we mean when we talk of a 'virtue'.

This distinction is important for the following reason. If we thought only of the particular actions we might encourage three wrong ideas.

(1) We might think that, provided you did the right thing, it did not matter how or why you did it – whether you did it willingly or unwillingly, sulkily or cheerfully, through fear of public opinion or for its own sake. But the truth is that right actions done for the wrong reason do not help to build the internal quality or character called a 'virtue', and it is this quality or character that really matters. (If the bad tennis player hits very hard, not because he sees that a very hard stroke is required, but because he has lost his temper, his stroke might possibly, by luck, help him to win that particular game; but it will not be helping him to become a reliable player.)

(2) We might think that God wanted simply obedience to a set of rules: whereas He really wants people of a particular sort.

(3) We might think that the 'virtues' were necessary only for this present life – that in the other world we could stop being just because there is nothing to quarrel about and stop being brave because there is no danger. Now it is quite true that there will probably be no occasion for just or courageous acts in the next world, but there will be every occasion for being the sort of people that we can become only as the result of doing such acts here. The point is not that God will refuse you admission to His eternal world if you

have not got certain qualities of character: the point is that if people have not got at least the beginnings of those qualities inside them, then no possible external conditions could make a 'Heaven' for them – that is, could make them happy with the deep, strong, unshakable kind of happiness God intends for us.

3

SOCIAL MORALITY

The first thing to get clear about Christian morality between man and man is that in this department Christ did not come to preach any brand new morality. The Golden Rule of the New Testament (Do as you would be done by) is a summing up of what every one, at bottom, had always known to be right. Really great moral teachers never do introduce new moralities: it is quacks and cranks who do that. As Dr Johnson said, 'People need to be reminded more often than they need to be instructed.' The real job of every moral teacher is to keep on bringing us back, time after time, to the old simple principles which we are all so anxious not to see; like bringing a horse back and back to the fence it has refused to jump or bringing a child back and back to the bit in its lesson that it wants to shirk.

The second thing to get clear is that Christianity has not, and does not profess to have, a detailed political programme for applying 'Do as you would be done by' to a particular society at a particular moment. It could not have. It is meant for all men at all times and the particular programme which suited one place or time would not suit another. And, anyhow, that is not how Christianity works. When it tells you to feed the hungry it does not give you lessons in cookery. When it tells you to read the Scriptures it does not give you lessons in Hebrew and Greek, or even in English grammar. It was never intended to replace or supersede the ordinary human arts and sciences: it is rather a director which will set them all to the right jobs, and a source of energy which will give them all new life, if only they will put themselves at its disposal.

People say, 'The Church ought to give us a lead.' That is true if they mean it in the right way, but false if they mean it in the wrong way. By the Church they ought to mean the whole body of practising Christians. And when they say that the Church should give us a lead, they ought to mean that some Christians – those who happen to have the right talents – should be economists and statesmen, and that all economists and statesmen should be Christians, and that their whole efforts in politics and economics should be directed to putting 'Do as you would be done by' into action. If that happened, and if we others were really ready to take it, then we should find the Christian solution for our own social problems pretty quickly. But, of course, when they ask for a lead from the Church most people mean they want the clergy to put out a political programme. That is silly. The clergy are those particular people within the whole Church who have been specially trained and set aside to look after what concerns us as creatures who are going to live for ever: and we are asking them to do a quite different job for which they have not been trained. The job is really on us, on the laymen. The application of Christian principles, say, to trade unionism or education, must come from Christian trade unionists and Christian schoolmasters: just as Christian literature comes from Christian novelists and dramatists – not from the bench of bishops getting together and trying to write plays and novels in their spare time.

All the same, the New Testament, without going into details, gives us a pretty clear hint of what a fully Christian society would be like. Perhaps it gives us more than we can take. It tells us that there are to be no passengers or parasites: if man does not work, he ought not to eat. Every one is to work with his own hands, and what is more, every one's work is to produce something good: there will be no manufacture of silly luxuries and then of sillier advertisements to persuade us to buy them. And there is to be no 'swank' or 'side', no putting on airs. To that extent a Christian society would be what we now call Leftist. On the other hand, it is always insisting on obedience – obedience (and outward marks of respect) from all of us to properly appointed magistrates, from children to parents, and (I am afraid this is going to be very unpopular) from wives to husbands. Thirdly, it is to be a cheerful society: full of singing and rejoicing, and regarding worry or anxiety as wrong. Courtesy is one of the Christian virtues; and the New Testament hates what it calls 'busybodies'.

If there were such a society in existence and you or I visited it, I think we should come away with a curious impression. We should feel that its economic life was very socialistic and, in that sense, 'advanced', but that its family life and its code of manners were rather old fashioned – perhaps even ceremonious and aristocratic. Each of us would like some bits of it, but I am afraid very few of us would like the whole thing. That is just what one would expect if Christianity is the total plan for the human machine. We have all departed from that total plan in different ways, and each of us wants to make out that his own modification of the original plan is the plan itself. You will find this again and again about anything that is really Christian: every one is attracted by bits of it and wants to pick out those bits and leave the rest. That is why we do not get much further: and that is why people who are fighting for quite opposite things can both say they are fighting for Christianity.

Now another point. There is one bit of advice given to us by the ancient heathen Greeks, and by the Jews in the Old Testament, and by the great Christian teachers of the Middle Ages, which the modern economic system has completely disobeyed. All these people told us not to lend money at interest; and lending money at interest – what we call investment — is the basis of our whole system. Now it may not absolutely follow that we are wrong. Some people say that when Moses and Aristotle and the Christians agreed in forbidding interest (or 'usury' as they called it), they could not foresee the joint stock company, and were only thinking of the private money-lender, and that, therefore, we need not bother about what they said. That is a question I cannot decide on. I am not an economist and I simply do not know whether the investment system is responsible for the state we are in or not. This is where we want the Christian economist. But I should not have been honest if I had not told you that three great civilisations had agreed (or so it seems at first sight) in condemning the very thing on which we have based our whole life.

One more point and I am done. In the passage where the New Testament says that every one must work, it gives as a reason 'in order that he may have something to give to those in need'. Charity – giving to the poor – is an essential part of Christian morality: in the frightening parable of the sheep and the goats it seems to be the point on which everything turns. Some people nowadays say that charity ought to be unnecessary and that instead of giving to the poor we ought to be producing a society in which there were no poor to give to. They may be quite right in saying that we ought to produce this kind of society. But if anyone thinks that, as a consequence, you can stop giving in the meantime, then he has parted company with all Christian morality. I do not believe one can settle how much we ought to give. I am afraid the only safe rule is to give more than we can spare. In other words, if our expenditure on comforts, luxuries, amusements, etc., is up to the standard common among those with the same income as our own, we are probably giving away too little. If our charities do not at all pinch or hamper us, I should say they are too small. There ought to be things we should like to do and cannot do because our charities expenditure excludes them. I am speaking now of 'charities' in the common way. Particular cases of distress among your own relatives, friends, neighbours or employees, which God, as it were, forces upon your notice, may demand much more: even to the crippling and endangering of your own position. For many of us the great obstacle to charity lies not in our luxurious living or desire for more money, but in our fear – fear of insecurity. This must often be recognised as a temptation. Sometimes our pride also hinders our charity; we are tempted to spend more than we ought on the showy forms of generosity (tipping, hospitality) and less than we ought on those who really need our help.

And now, before I end, I am going to venture on a guess as to how this section has affected any who have read it. My guess is that there are some Leftist people among them who are very angry that it has not gone further in that direction, and some people of an opposite sort who are angry because they think it has gone much too far. If so, that brings us right up against the real snag in all this drawing up of blueprints for a Christian society. Most of us are not really approaching the subject in order to find out what Christianity says: we are approaching it in the hope of finding support from Christianity for the views of our own party. We are looking for an ally where we are offered either a Master or – a Judge. I am just the same. There are bits in this section that I wanted to leave out. And that is why nothing whatever is going to come of such talks unless we go a much longer way round. A Christian society is not going to arrive until most of us really want it: and we are not going to want it until we become fully Christian. I may repeat 'Do as you would be done by' till I am black in the face, but I cannot really carry it out till I love my neighbour as myself: and I cannot learn to love my neighbour as myself till I learn to love God: and I cannot learn to love God except by learning to obey Him. And so, as I warned you, we are driven on to something more inward – driven on from social matters to religious matters. For the longest way round is the shortest way home.

4

MORALITY AND

PSYCHOANALYSIS

I have said that we should never get a Christian society unless most of us became Christian individuals. That does not mean, of course, that we can put off doing anything about society until some imaginary date in the far future. It means that we must begin both jobs at once – (1) the job of seeing how 'Do as you would be done by' can be applied in detail to modern society, and (2) the job of becoming the sort of people who really would apply it if we saw how. I now want to begin considering what the Christian idea of a good man is – the Christian specification for the human machine.

Before I come down to details there are two more general points I should like to make. First of all, since Christian morality claims to be a technique for putting the human machine right, I think you would like to know how it is related to another technique which seems to make a similar claim – namely, psychoanalysis.

Now you want to distinguish very clearly between two things: between the actual medical theories and technique of the psychoanalysts, and the general philosophical view of the world which Freud and some others have gone on to add to this. The second thing – the philosophy of Freud – is in direct contradiction to the other great psychologist, Jung. And furthermore, when Freud is talking about how to cure neurotics he is speaking as a specialist on his own subject, but when he goes on to talk general philosophy he is speaking as an amateur. It is therefore quite sensible to attend to him with respect in the one case and not in the other – and that is what I do. I am all the readier to do it because I have found that when he is talking of his own subject and on a subject I do know something about (namely, language) he is very ignorant. But psychoanalysis itself, apart from all the philosophical additions that Freud and others have made to it, is not in the least contradictory to Christianity. Its technique overlaps with Christian morality at some points and it would not be a bad thing if every person knew something about it: but it does not run the same course all the way, for the two techniques are doing rather different things.

When a man makes a moral choice two things are involved. One is the act of choosing. The other is the various feelings, impulses and so on which his psychological outfit presents him with, and which are the raw material of his choice. Now this raw material may be of two kinds. Either it may be what we would call normal: it may consist of the sort of feelings that are common to all men. Or else it may consist of quite unnatural feelings due to things that have gone wrong in his subconscious. Thus fear of things that are really dangerous would be an example of the first kind: an irrational fear of cats or spiders would be an example of the second kind. The desire of a man for a woman would be of the first kind: the perverted desire of a man for a man would be of the second. Now what psychoanalysis undertakes to do is to remove the abnormal feelings, that is, to give the man better raw material for his acts of choice; morality is concerned with the acts of choice themselves.

Put it this way. Imagine three men who go to a war. One has the ordinary natural fear of danger that any man has and he subdues it by moral effort and becomes a brave man. Let us suppose that the other two have, as a result of things in their subconscious, exaggerated, irrational fears, which no amount of moral effort can do anything about. Now suppose that a psycho-analyst comes along and cures these two: that is, he puts them both back in the position of the first man. Well it is just then that the psychoanalytical problem is over and the moral problem begins. Because, now that they are cured, these two men might take quite different lines. The first might say, 'Thank goodness I've got rid of all those doo-dahs. Now at last I can do what I always wanted to do – my duty to my country.' But the other might say, 'Well, I'm very glad that I now feel moderately cool under fire, but, of course, that doesn't alter the fact that I'm still jolly well determined to look after Number One and let the other chap do the dangerous job whenever I can. Indeed one of the good things about feeling less frightened is that I can now look after myself much more efficiently and can be much cleverer at hiding the fact from the others.' Now this difference is a purely moral one and psychoanalysis cannot do anything about it. However much you improve the man's raw material, you have still got something else: the real, free choice of the man, on the material presented to him, either to put his own advantage first or to put it last. And this free choice is the only thing that morality is concerned with.

The bad psychological material is not a sin but a disease. It does not need to be repented of, but to be cured. And by the way, that is very important. Human beings judge one another by their external actions. God judges them by their moral choices. When a neurotic who has a pathological horror of cats forces himself to pick up a cat for some good reason, it is quite possible that in God's eyes he has shown more courage than a healthy man may have shown in winning the V.C. When a man who has been perverted from his youth and taught that cruelty is the right thing, does some tiny little kindness, or refrains from some cruelty he might have committed, and thereby, perhaps, risks being sneered at by his companions, he may, in God's eyes, be doing more than you and I would do if we gave up life itself for a friend.

It is as well to put this the other way round. Some of us who seem quite nice people may, in fact, have made so little use of a good heredity and a good upbringing that we are really worse than those whom we regard as fiends. Can we be quite certain how we should have behaved if we had been saddled with the psychological outfit, and then with the bad upbringing, and then with the power, say, of Himmler? That is why Christians are told not to judge. We see only the results which a man's choices make out of his raw material. But God does not judge him on the raw material at all, but on what he has done with it. Most of the man's psychological makeup is probably due to his body: when his body dies all that will fall off him, and the real central man, the thing that chose, that made the best or the worst out of this material, will stand naked. All sorts of nice things which we thought our own, but which were really due to a good digestion, will fall off some of us: all sorts of nasty things which were due to complexes or bad health will fall off others. We shall then, for the first time, see every one as he really was. There will be surprises.

And that leads on to my second point. People often think of Christian morality as a kind of bargain in which God says, 'If you keep a lot of rules I'll reward you, and if you don't I'll do the other thing.' I do not think that is the best way of looking at it. I would much rather say that every time you make a choice you are turning the central part of you, the part of you that chooses, into something a little different from what it was before. And taking your life as a whole, with all your innumerable choices, all your life long you are slowly turning this central thing either into a heavenly creature or into a hellish creature: either into a creature that is in harmony with God, and with other creatures, and with itself, or else into one that is in a state of war and hatred with God, and with its fellow-creatures, and with itself. To be the one kind of creature is heaven: that is, it is joy and peace and knowledge and power. To be the other means madness, horror, idiocy, rage, impotence, and eternal loneliness. Each of us at each moment is progressing to the one state or the other.

That explains what always used to puzzle me about Christian writers; they seem to be so very strict at one moment and so very free and easy at another. They talk about mere sins of thought as if they were immensely important: and then they talk about the most frightful murders and treacheries as if you had only got to repent and all would be forgiven. But I have come to see that they are right. What they are always thinking of is the mark which the action leaves on that tiny central self which no one sees in this life but which each of us will have to endure – or enjoy – for ever. One man may be so placed that his anger sheds the blood of thousands, and another so placed that however angry he gets he will only be laughed at. But the little mark on the soul may be much the same in both. Each has done something to himself which, unless he repents, will make it harder for him to keep out of the rage next time he is tempted, and will make the rage worse when he does fall into it. Each of them, if he seriously turns to God, can have that twist in the central man straightened out again: each is, in the long run, doomed if he will not. The bigness or smallness of the thing, seen from the outside, is not what really matters.

One last point. Remember that, as I said, the right direction leads not only to peace but to knowledge. When a man is getting better he understands more and more clearly the evil that is still left in him. When a man is getting worse he understands his own badness less and less. A moderately bad man knows he is not very good: a thoroughly bad man thinks he is all right. This is common sense, really. You understand sleep when you are awake, not while you are sleeping. You can see mistakes in arithmetic when your mind is working properly: while you are making them you cannot see them. You can understand the nature of drunkenness when you are sober, not when you are drunk. Good people know about both good and evil: bad people do not know about either.

SEXUAL MORALITY

We must now consider Christian morality as regards sex, what Christians call the virtue of chastity. The Christian rule of chastity must not be confused with the social rule of 'modesty' (in one sense of that word); i.e. propriety, or decency. The social rule of propriety lays down how much of the human body should be displayed and what subjects can be referred to, and in what words, according to the customs of a given social circle. Thus, while the rule of chastity is the same for all Christians at all times, the rule of propriety changes. A girl in the Pacific islands wearing hardly any clothes and a Victorian lady completely covered in clothes might both be equally 'modest', proper, or decent, according to the standards of their own societies: and both, for all we could tell by their dress, might be equally chaste (or equally unchaste). Some of the language which chaste women used in Shakespeare's time would have been used in the nineteenth century only by a woman completely abandoned. When people break the rule of propriety current in their own time and place, if they do so in order to excite lust in themselves or others, then they are offending against chastity. But if they break it through ignorance or carelessness they are guilty only of bad manners. When, as often happens, they break it defiantly in order to shock or embarrass others, they are not necessarily being unchaste, but they are being uncharitable: for it is uncharitable to take pleasure in making other people uncomfortable. I do not think that a very strict or fussy standard of propriety is any proof of chastity or any help to it, and I therefore regard the great relaxation and simplifying of the rule which has taken place in my own lifetime as a good thing. At its present stage, however, it has this inconvenience, that people of different ages and different types do not all acknowledge the same standard, and we hardly know where we are. While this confusion lasts I think that old, or old-fashioned, people should be very careful not to assume that young or 'emancipated' people are corrupt whenever they are (by the old standard) improper; and, in return, that young people should not call their elders prudes or puritans because they do not easily adopt the new standard. A real desire to believe all the good you can of others and to make others as comfortable as you can will solve most of the problems.

Chastity is the most unpopular of the Christian virtues. There is no getting away from it; the Christian rule is, 'Either marriage, with complete faithfulness to your partner, or else total abstinence.' Now this is so difficult and so contrary to our instincts, that obviously either Christianity is wrong or our sexual instinct, as it now is, has gone wrong. One or the other. Of course, being a Christian, I think it is the instinct which has gone wrong.

But I have other reasons for thinking so. The biological purpose of sex is children, just as the biological purpose of eating is to repair the body. Now if we eat whenever we feel inclined and just as much as we want, it is quite true most of us will eat too much: but not terrifically too much. One man may eat enough for two, but he does not eat enough for ten. The appetite goes a little beyond its biological purpose, but not enormously. But if a healthy young man indulged his sexual appetite whenever he felt inclined, and if each act produced a baby, then in ten years he might easily populate a small village. This appetite is in ludicrous and preposterous excess of its function.

Or take it another way. You can get a large audience together for a strip-tease act – that is, to watch a girl undress on the stage. Now suppose you come to a country where you could fill a theatre by simply bringing a covered plate on to the stage and then slowly lifting the cover so as to let every one see, just before the lights went out, that it contained a mutton chop or a bit of bacon, would you not think that in that country something had gone wrong with the appetite for food? And would not anyone who had grown up in a different world think there was something equally queer about the state of the sex instinct among us?

One critic said that if he found a country in which such strip-tease acts with food were popular, he would conclude that the people of that country were starving. He meant, of course, to imply that such things as the strip-tease act resulted not from sexual corruption but from sexual starvation. I agree with him that if, in some strange land, we found that similar acts with mutton chops were popular, one of the possible explanations which would occur to me would be famine. But the next step would be to test our hypothesis by finding out whether, in fact, much or little food was being consumed in that country. If the evidence showed that a good deal was being eaten, then of course we should have to abandon the hypothesis of starvation and try to think of another one. In the same way, before accepting sexual starvation as the cause of the strip-tease, we should have to look for evidence that there is in fact more sexual abstinence in our age than in those ages when things like the strip-tease were unknown. But surely there is no such evidence. Contraceptives have made sexual indulgence far less costly within marriage and far safer outside it than ever before, and public opinion is less hostile to illicit unions and even to perversion than it has been since Pagan times. Nor is the hypothesis of 'starvation' the only one we can imagine. Everyone knows that the sexual appetite, like our other appetites, grows by indulgence. Starving men may think much about food, but so do gluttons; the gorged, as well as the famished, like titillations.

Here is a third point. You find very few people who want to eat things that really are not food or to do other things with food instead of eating it. In other words, perversions of the food appetite are rare. But perversions of the sex instinct are numerous, hard to cure, and frightful. I am sorry to have to go into all these details but I must. The reason why I must is that you and I, for the last twenty years, have been fed all day long on good solid lies about sex. We have been told, till one is sick of hearing it, that sexual desire is in the same state as any of our other natural desires and that if only we abandon the silly old Victorian idea of hushing it up, everything in the garden will be lovely. It is not true. The moment you look at the facts, and away from the propaganda, you see that it is not.

They tell you sex has become a mess because it was hushed up. But for the last twenty years it has not been. It has been chattered about all day long. Yet it is still in a mess. If hushing up had been the cause of the trouble, ventilation would have set it right. But it has not. I think it is the other way round. I think the human race originally hushed it up because it had become such a mess. Modern people are always saying, 'Sex is nothing to be ashamed of.' They may mean two things. They may mean 'There is nothing to be ashamed of in the fact that the human race reproduces itself in a certain way, nor in the fact that it gives pleasure.' If they mean that, they are right. Christianity says the same. It is not the thing, nor the pleasure, that is the trouble. The old Christian teachers said that if man had never fallen, sexual pleasure, instead of being less than it is now, would actually have been greater. I know some muddle-headed Christians have talked as if Christianity thought that sex, or the body, or pleasure, were bad in themselves. But they were wrong. Christianity is almost the only one of the great religions which thoroughly approves of the body – which believes that matter is good, that God Himself once took on a human body, that some kind of body is going to be given to us even in Heaven and is going to be an essential part of our happiness, or beauty and our energy. Christianity has glorified marriage more than any other religion: and nearly all the greatest love poetry in the world has been produced by Christians. If anyone says that sex, in itself, is bad, Christianity contradicts him at once. But, of course, when people say, 'Sex is nothing to be ashamed of,' they may mean 'the state into which the sexual instinct has now got is nothing to be ashamed of'.

If they mean that, I think they are wrong. I think it is everything to be ashamed of. There is nothing to be ashamed of in enjoying your food: there would be everything to be ashamed of if half the world made food the main interest of their lives and spent their time looking at pictures of food and dribbling and smacking their lips. I do not say you and I are individually responsible for the present situation. Our ancestors have handed over to us organisms which are warped in this respect: and we grow up surrounded by propaganda in favour of unchastity. There are people who want to keep our sex instinct inflamed in order to make money out of us. Because, of course, a man with an obsession is a man who has very little sales-resistance. God knows our situation; He will not judge us as if we had no difficulties to overcome. What matters is the sincerity and perseverance of our will to overcome them.

Before we can be cured we must want to be cured. Those who really wish for help will get it; but for many modern people even the wish is difficult. It is easy to think that we want something when we do not really want it. A famous Christian long ago told us that when he was a young man he prayed constantly for chastity; but years later he realised that while his lips had been saying, 'Oh Lord, make me chaste,' his heart had been secretly adding, 'But please don't do it just yet.' This may happen in prayers for other virtues too; but there are three reasons why it is now specially difficult for us to desire – let alone to achieve – complete chastity.

In the first place our warped natures, the devils who tempt us, and all the contemporary propaganda for lust, combine to make us feel that the desires we are resisting are so 'natural', so 'healthy', and so reasonable, that it is almost perverse and abnormal to resist them. Poster after poster, film after film, novel after novel, associate the idea of sexual indulgence with the ideas of health, normality, youth, frankness, and good humour. Now this association is a lie. Like all powerful lies, it is based on a truth – the truth, acknowledged above, that sex in itself (apart from the excesses and obsessions that have grown round it) is 'normal' and 'healthy', and all the rest of it. The lie consists in the suggestion that any sexual act to which you are tempted at the moment is also healthy and normal. Now this, on any conceivable view, and quite apart from Christianity, must be nonsense. Surrender to all our desires obviously leads to impotence, disease, jealousies, lies, concealment, and everything that is the reverse of health, good humour, and frankness. For any happiness, even in this world, quite a lot of restraint is going to be necessary; so the claim made by every desire, when it is strong, to be healthy and reasonable, counts for nothing. Every sane and civilised man must have some set of principles by which he chooses to reject some of his desires and to permit others. One man does this on Christian principles, another on hygienic principles, another on sociological principles. The real conflict is not between Christianity and 'nature', but between Christian principles and other principles in the control of 'nature'. For 'nature' (in the sense of natural desire) will have to be controlled anyway, unless you are going to ruin your whole life. The Christian principles are, admittedly, stricter than the others; but then we think you will get help towards obeying them which you will not get towards obeying the others.

In the second place, many people are deterred from seriously attempting Christian chastity because they think (before trying) that it is impossible. But when a thing has to be attempted, one must never think about possibility or impossibility. Faced with an optional question in an examination paper, one considers whether one can do it or not: faced with a compulsory question, one must do the best one can. You may get some marks for a very imperfect answer: you will certainly get none for leaving the question alone. Not only in examinations but in war, in mountain climbing, in learning to skate, or swim, or ride a bicycle, even in fastening a stiff collar with cold fingers, people quite often do what seemed impossible before they did it. It is wonderful what you can do when you have to.

We may, indeed, be sure that perfect chastity – like perfect charity – will not be attained by any merely human efforts. You must ask for God's help. Even when you have done so, it may seem to you for a long time that no help, or less help than you need, is being given. Never mind. After each failure, ask forgiveness, pick yourself up, and try again. Very often what God first helps us towards is not the virtue itself but just this power of always trying again. For however important chastity (or courage, or truthfulness, or any other virtue) may be, this process trains us in habits of the soul which are more important still. It cures our illusions about ourselves and teaches us to depend on God. We learn, on the one hand, that we cannot trust ourselves even in our best moments, and, on the other, that we need not despair even in our worst, for our failures are forgiven. The only fatal thing is to sit down content with anything less than perfection.

Thirdly, people often misunderstand what psychology teaches about 'repressions'. It teaches us that 'repressed' sex is dangerous. But 'repressed' is here a technical term: it does not mean 'suppressed' in the sense of 'denied' or 'resisted'. A repressed desire or thought is one which has been thrust into the subconscious (usually at a very early age) and can now come before the mind only in a disguised and unrecognisable form. Repressed sexuality does not appear to the patient to be sexuality at all. When an adolescent or an adult is engaged in resisting a conscious desire, he is not dealing with a repression nor is he in the least danger of creating a repression. On the contrary, those who are seriously attempting chastity are more conscious, and soon know a great deal more about their own sexuality than anyone else. They come to know their desires as Wellington knew Napoleon, or as

Sherlock Holmes knew Moriarty; as a rat-catcher knows rats or a plumber knows about leaky pipes. Virtue – even attempted virtue – brings light; indulgence brings fog.

Finally, though I have had to speak at some length about sex, I want to make it as clear as I possibly can that the centre of Christian morality is not here. If anyone thinks that Christians regard unchastity as the supreme vice, he is quite wrong. The sins of the flesh are bad, but they are the least bad of all sins. All the worst pleasures are purely spiritual: the pleasure of putting other people in the wrong, of bossing and patronising and spoiling sport, and back-biting, the pleasures of power, of hatred. For there are two things inside me, competing with the human self which I must try to become. They are the Animal self, and the Diabolical self. The Diabolical self is the worse of the two. That is why a cold, self-righteous prig who goes regularly to church may be far nearer to hell than a prostitute. But, of course, it is better to be neither.

6

CHRISTIAN MARRIAGE

The last chapter was mainly negative. I discussed what was wrong with the sexual impulse in man, but said very little about its right working – in other words, about Christian marriage. There are two reasons why I do not particularly want to deal with marriage. The first is that the Christian doctrines on this subject are extremely unpopular. The second is that I have never been married myself, and, therefore, can speak only at second hand. But in spite of that, I feel I can hardly leave the subject out in an account of Christian morals.

The Christian idea of marriage is based on Christ's words that a man and wife are to be regarded as a single organism – for that is what the words 'one flesh' would be in modern English. And the Christians believe that when He said this He was not expressing a sentiment but stating a fact – just as one is stating a fact when one says that a lock and its key are one mechanism, or that a violin and a bow are one musical instrument. The inventor of the human machine was telling us that its two halves, the male and the fe-male, were made to be combined together in pairs, not simply on the sexual level, but totally combined. The monstrosity of sexual intercourse outside marriage is that those who indulge in it are trying to isolate one kind of union (the sexual) from all the other kinds of union which were intended to go along with it and make up the total union. The Christian attitude does not mean that there is anything wrong about sexual pleasure, any more than about the pleasure of eating. It means that you must not isolate that pleasure and try to get it by itself, any more than you ought to try to get the pleasures of taste without swallowing and digesting, by chewing things and spitting them out again.

As a consequence, Christianity teaches that marriage is for life. There is, of course, a difference here between different Churches: some do not admit divorce at all; some allow it reluctantly in very special cases. It is a great pity that Christians should disagree about such a question; but for an ordinary layman the thing to notice is that the Churches all agree with one another about marriage a great deal more than any of them agrees with the outside world. I mean, they all regard divorce as something like cutting up a living body, as a kind of surgical operation. Some of them think the operation so violent that it cannot be done at all; others admit it as a desperate remedy in extreme cases. They are all agreed that it is more like having both your legs cut off than it is like dissolving a business partnership or even deserting a regiment. What they all disagree with is the modern view that it is a simple readjustment of partners, to be made whenever people feel they are no longer in love with one another, or when either of them falls in love with someone else.

Before we consider this modern view in its relation to chastity, we must not forget to consider it in relation to another virtue, namely justice. Justice, as I said before, includes the keeping of promises. Now everyone who has been married in a church has made a public, solemn promise to stick to his (or her) partner till death. The duty of keeping that promise has no special connection with sexual morality: it is in the same position as any other promise. If, as modern people are always telling us, the sexual impulse is just like all our other impulses, then it ought to be treated like all our other impulses; and as their indulgence is controlled by our promises, so should its be. If, as I think, it is not like all our other impulses, but is morbidly inflamed, then we should be specially careful not to let it lead us into dishonesty.

To this someone may reply that he regarded the promise made in church as a mere formality and never intended to keep it. Whom, then, was he trying to deceive when he made it? God? That was really very unwise. Himself? That was not very much wiser. The bride, or bridegroom, or the 'in-laws'? That was treacherous. More often, I think, the couple (or one of them) hoped to deceive the public. They wanted the respectability that is attached to marriage without intending to pay the price: that is, they were impostors, they cheated. If they are still contented cheats, I have nothing to say to them: who would urge the high and hard duty of chastity on people who have not yet wished to be merely honest? If they have now come to their senses and want to be honest, their promise, already made, constrains them. And this, you will see, comes under the heading of justice, not that of chastity. If people do not believe in permanent marriage, it is perhaps better that they should live together unmarried than that they should make vows they do not mean to keep. It is true that by living together without marriage they will be guilty (in Christian eyes) of fornication. But one fault is not mended by adding another: unchastity is not improved by adding perjury.

The idea that 'being in love' is the only reason for remaining married really leaves no room for marriage as a contract or promise at all. If love is the whole thing, then the promise can add nothing; and if it adds nothing, then it should not be made. The curious thing is that lovers themselves, while they remain really in love, know this better than those who talk about love. As Chesterton pointed out, those who are in love have a natural inclination to bind themselves by promises. Love songs all over the world are full of vows of eternal constancy. The Christian law is not forcing upon the passion of love something which is foreign to that passion's own nature: it is demanding that lovers should take seriously something which their passion of itself impels them to do.

And, of course, the promise, made when I am in love and because I am in love, to be true to the beloved as long as I live, commits me to being true even if I cease to be in love. A promise must be about things that I can do, about actions: no one can promise to go on feeling in a certain way. He might as well promise never to have a headache or always to feel hungry. But what, it may be asked, is the use of keeping two people together if they are no longer in love? There are several sound, social reasons; to provide a home for their children, to protect the woman (who has probably sacrificed or damaged her own career by getting married) from being dropped whenever the man is tired of her. But there is also another reason of which I am very sure, though I find it a little hard to explain.

It is hard because so many people cannot be brought to realise that when B is better than C, A may be even better than B. They like thinking in terms of good and bad, not of good, better, and best, or bad, worse and worst. They want to know whether you think patriotism a good thing: if you reply that it is, of course, far better than individual selfishness, but that it is inferior to universal charity and should always give way to universal charity when the two conflict, they think you are being evasive. They ask what you think of duelling. If you reply that it is far better to forgive a man than to fight a duel with him, but that even a duel might be better than a lifelong enmity which expresses itself in secret efforts to 'do the man down', they go away complaining that you would not give them a straight answer. I hope no one will make this mistake about what I am now going to say.

What we call 'being in love' is a glorious state, and, in several ways, good for us. It helps to make us generous and courageous, it opens our eyes not only to the beauty of the beloved but to all beauty, and it subordinates (especially at first) our merely animal sexuality; in that sense, love is the great conqueror of lust. No one in his senses would deny that being in love is far better than either common sensuality or cold self-centredness. But, as I said before, 'the most dangerous thing you can do is to take any one impulse of our own nature and set it up as the thing you ought to follow at all costs'. Being in love is a good thing, but it is not the best thing. There are many things below it, but there are also things above it. You cannot make it the basis of a whole life. It is a noble feeling, but it is still a feeling. Now no feeling can be relied on to last in its full intensity, or even to last at all.

Knowledge can last, principles can last, habits can last; but feelings come and go. And in fact, whatever people say, the state called 'being in love' usually does not last. If the old fairy-tale ending 'They lived happily ever after' is taken to mean 'They felt for the next fifty years exactly as they felt the day before they were married', then it says what probably never was nor ever would be true, and would be highly undesirable if it were. Who could bear to live in that excitement for even five years? What would become of your work, your appetite, your sleep, your friendships? But, of course, ceasing to be 'in love' need not mean ceasing to love. Love in this second sense – love as distinct from 'being in love' – is not merely a feeling. It is a deep unity, maintained by the will and deliberately strengthened by habit; reinforced by (in Christian marriages) the grace which both partners ask, and receive, from God. They can have this love for each other even at those moments when they do not like each other; as you love yourself even when you do not like yourself. They can retain this love even when each would easily, if they allowed themselves, be 'in love' with someone else. 'Being in love' first moved them to promise fidelity: this quieter love enables them to keep the promise. It is on this love that the engine of marriage is run: being in love was the explosion that started it.

If you disagree with me, of course, you will say, 'He knows nothing about it, he is not married.' You may quite possibly be right. But before you say that, make quite sure that you are judging me by what you really know from your own experience and from watching the lives of your friends, and not by ideas you have derived from novels and films. This is not so easy to do as people think. Our experience is coloured through and through by books and plays and the cinema, and it takes patience and skill to disentangle the things we have really learned from life for ourselves.

People get from books the idea that if you have married the right person you may expect to go on 'being in love' for ever. As a result, when they find they are not, they think this proves they have made a mistake and are entitled to a change – not realising that, when they have changed, the glamour will presently go out of the new love just as it went out of the old one. In this department of life, as in every other, thrills come at the beginning and do not last. The sort of thrill a boy has at the first idea of flying will not go on when he has joined the R.A.F. and is really learning to fly. The thrill you feel on first seeing some delightful place dies away when you really go to live there. Does this mean it would be better not to learn to fly and not to live in the beautiful place? By no means. In both cases, if you go through with it, the dying away of the first thrill will be compensated for by a quieter and more lasting kind of interest. What is more (and I can hardly find words to tell you how important I think this), it is just the people who are ready to submit to the loss of the thrill and settle down to the sober interest, who are then most likely to meet new thrills in some quite different direction. The man who has learned to fly and become a good pilot will suddenly discover music; the man who has settled down to live in the beauty spot will discover gardening.

This is, I think, one little part of what Christ meant by saying that a thing will not really live unless it first dies. It is simply no good trying to keep any thrill: that is the very worst thing you can do. Let the thrill go – let it die away – go on through that period of death into the quieter inter- est and happiness that follow – and you will find you are living in a world of new thrills all the time. But if you decide to make thrills your regular diet and try to prolong them artificially, they will all get weaker and weaker, and fewer and fewer, and you will be a bored, disillusioned old man for the rest of your life. It is because so few people understand this that you find many middle-aged men and women maundering about their lost youth, at the very age when new horizons ought to be appearing and new doors opening all round them. It is much better fun to learn to swim than to go on endlessly (and hopelessly) trying to get back the feeling you had when you first went paddling as a small boy.

Another notion we get from novels and plays is that 'falling in love' is something quite irresistible; something that just happens to one, like measles. And because they believe this, some married people throw up the sponge and give in when they find themselves attracted by a new acquain- tance. But I am inclined to think that these irresistible passions are much rarer in real life than in books, at any rate when one is grown up. When we meet someone beautiful and clever and sympathetic, of course we ought, in one sense, to admire and love these good qualities. But is it not very largely in our own choice whether this love shall, or shall not, turn into what we call 'being in love'? No doubt, if our minds are full of novels and plays and sentimental songs, and our bodies full of alcohol, we shall turn any love we feel into that kind of love: just as if you have a rut in your path all the rainwater will run into that rut, and if you wear blue spectacles everything you see will turn blue. But that will be our own fault.

Before leaving the question of divorce, I should like to distinguish two things which are very often confused. The Christian conception of marriage is one: the other is the quite different question – how far Christians, if they are voters or Members of Parliament, ought to try to force their views of marriage on the rest of the community by embodying them in the divorce laws. A great many people seem to think that if you are a Christian yourself you should try to make divorce difficult for every one. I do not think that. At least I know I should be very angry if the Mohammedans tried to prevent the rest of us from drinking wine. My own view is that the Churches should frankly recognise that the majority of the British people are not Christians and, therefore, cannot be expected to live Christian lives. There ought to be two distinct kinds of marriage: one governed by the State with rules enforced on all citizens, the other governed by the Church with rules enforced by her on her own members. The distinction ought to be quite sharp, so that a man knows which couples are married in a Christian sense and which are not.

So much for the Christian doctrine about the permanence of marriage. Something else, even more unpopular, remains to be dealt with. Christian wives promise to obey their husbands. In Christian marriage the man is said to be the 'head'. Two questions obviously arise here. (1) Why should there be a head at all – why not equality? (2) Why should it be the man?

(1) The need for some head follows from the idea that marriage is permanent. Of course, as long as the husband and wife are agreed, no question of a head need arise; and we may hope that this will be the normal state of affairs in a Christian marriage. But when there is a real disagreement, what is to happen? Talk it over, of course; but I am assuming they have done that and still failed to reach agreement. What do they do next? They cannot decide by a majority vote, for in a council of two there can be no majority. Surely, only one or other of two things can happen: either they must separate and go their own ways or else one or other of them must have a casting vote. If marriage is permanent, one or other party must, in the last resort, have the power of deciding the family policy. You cannot have a permanent association without a constitution.

(2) If there must be a head, why the man? Well, firstly is there any very serious wish that it should be the woman? As I have said, I am not married myself, but as far as I can see, even a woman who wants to be the head of her own house does not usually admire the same state of things when she finds it going on next door. She is much more likely to say 'Poor Mr X! Why he allows that appalling woman to boss him about the way she does is more than I can imagine.' I do not think she is even very flattered if anyone mentions the fact of her own 'headship'. There must be something unnatural about the rule of wives over husbands, because the wives themselves are half ashamed of it and despise the husbands whom they rule. But there is also another reason; and here I speak quite frankly as a bachelor, because it is a reason you can see from outside even better than from inside. The relations of the family to the outer world – what might be called its foreign policy – must depend, in the last resort, upon the man, because he always ought to be, and usually is, much more just to the outsiders. A woman is primarily fighting for her own children and husband against the rest of the world. Naturally, almost, in a sense, rightly, their claims override, for her, all other claims. She is the special trustee of their interests. The function of the husband is to see that this natural preference of hers is not given its head. He has

the last word in order to protect other people from the intense family patriotism of the wife. If anyone doubts this, let me ask a simple question. If your dog has bitten the child next door, or if your child has hurt the dog next door, which would you sooner have to deal with, the master of that house or the mistress? Or, if you are a married woman, let me ask you this question. Much as you admire your husband, would you not say that his chief failing is his tendency not to stick up for his rights and yours against the neighbours as vigorously as you would like? A bit of an Appeaser?

7

FORGIVENESS

I said in a previous chapter that chastity was the most unpopular of the
Christian virtues. But I am not sure I was right. I believe there is one even
more unpopular. It is laid down in the Christian rule, 'Thou shalt love thy
neighbour as thyself.' Because in Christian morals 'thy neighbour' includes
'thy enemy', and so we come up against this terrible duty of forgiving our
enemies.

Every one says forgiveness is a lovely idea, until they have something to
forgive, as we had during the war. And then, to mention the subject at all is
to be greeted with howls of anger. It is not that people think this too high
and difficult a virtue: it is that they think it hateful and contemptible. 'That
sort of talk makes them sick,' they say. And half of you already want to ask
me, 'I wonder how you'd feel about forgiving the Gestapo if you were a
Pole or a Jew?'

So do I. I wonder very much. Just as when Christianity tells me that
I must not deny my religion even to save myself from death by torture, I
wonder very much what I should do when it came to the point. I am not trying to tell you in this book what I could do – I can do precious little – I am
telling you what Christianity is. I did not invent it. And there, right in the
middle of it, I find 'Forgive us our sins as we forgive those that sin against
us.' There is no slightest suggestion that we are offered forgiveness on any
other terms. It is made perfectly clear that if we do not forgive we shall not
be forgiven. There are no two ways about it. What are we to do?

It is going to be hard enough, anyway, but I think there are two things we
can do to make it easier. When you start mathematics you do not begin with
the calculus; you begin with simple addition. In the same way, if we really
want (but all depends on really wanting) to learn how to forgive, perhaps we
had better start with something easier than the Gestapo. One might start
with forgiving one's husband or wife, or parents or children, or the nearest
N.C.O., for something they have done or said in the last week. That will
probably keep us busy for the moment. And secondly, we might try to

understand exactly what loving your neighbour as yourself means. I have to love him as I love myself. Well, how exactly do I love myself?

Now that I come to think of it, I have not exactly got a feeling of fondness or affection for myself, and I do not even always enjoy my own society. So apparently 'Love your neighbour' does not mean 'feel fond of him' or 'find him attractive'. I ought to have seen that before, because, of course, you cannot feel fond of a person by trying. Do I think well of myself, think myself a nice chap? Well, I am afraid I sometimes do (and those are, no doubt, my worst moments) but that is not why I love myself. In fact it is the other way round: my self-love makes me think myself nice, but thinking myself nice is not why I love myself. So loving my enemies does not apparently mean thinking them nice either. That is an enormous relief. For a good many people imagine that forgiving your enemies means making out that they are really not such bad fellows after all, when it is quite plain that they are. Go a step further. In my most clear-sighted moments not only do I not think myself a nice man, but I know that I am a very nasty one. I can look at some of the things I have done with horror and loathing. So apparently I am allowed to loathe and hate some of the things my enemies do. Now that I come to think of it, I remember Christian teachers telling me long ago that I must hate a bad man's actions, but not hate the bad man: or, as they would say, hate the sin but not the sinner.

For a long time I used to think this a silly, straw-splitting distinction: how could you hate what a man did and not hate the man? But years later it occurred to me that there was one man to whom I had been doing this all my life – namely myself. However much I might dislike my own cowardice or conceit or greed, I went on loving myself. There had never been the slightest difficulty about it. In fact the very reason why I hated the things was that I loved the man. Just because I loved myself, I was sorry to find that I was the sort of man who did those things. Consequently, Christianity does not want us to reduce by one atom the hatred we feel for cruelty and treachery. We ought to hate them. Not one word of what we have said about them needs to be unsaid. But it does want us to hate them in the same way in which we hate things in ourselves: being sorry that the man should have done such things, and hoping, if it is anyway possible, that somehow, sometime, somewhere he can be cured and made human again.

The real test is this. Suppose one reads a story of filthy atrocities in the paper. Then suppose that something turns up suggesting that the story might not be quite true, or not quite so bad as it was made out. Is one's first feeling, 'Thank God, even they aren't quite so bad as that,' or is it a feeling of disappointment, and even a determination to cling to the first story for the sheer pleasure of thinking your enemies as bad as possible? If it is the second then it is, I am afraid, the first step in a process which, if followed to the end, will make us into devils. You see, one is beginning to wish that black was a little blacker. If we give that wish its head, later on we shall wish to see grey as black, and then to see white itself as black. Finally, we shall insist on seeing everything – God and our friends and ourselves included – as bad, and not be able to stop doing it: we shall be fixed for ever in a universe of pure hatred.

Now a step further. Does loving your enemy mean not punishing him? No, for loving myself does not mean that I ought not to subject myself to punishment – even to death. If you had committed a murder, the right Christian thing to do would be to give yourself up to the police and be hanged. It is, therefore, in my opinion, perfectly right for a Christian judge to sentence a man to death or a Christian soldier to kill an enemy. I always have thought so, ever since I became a Christian, and long before the war, and I still think so now that we are at peace. It is no good quoting 'Thou shalt not kill.' There are two Greek words: the ordinary word to *kill* and the word to *murder*. And when Christ quotes that commandment He uses the *murder* one in all three accounts. Matthew, Mark, and Luke. And I am told there is the same distinction in Hebrew. All killing is not murder any more than all sexual intercourse is adultery. When soldiers came to St John the Baptist asking what to do, he never remotely suggested that they ought to leave the army: nor did Christ when He met a Roman sergeant-major – what they called a centurion. The idea of the knight – the Christian in arms for the defence of a good cause – is one of the great Christian ideas. War is a dreadful thing, and I can respect an honest pacifist, thought I think he is entirely mistaken. What I cannot understand is this sort of semi-pacifism you get nowadays which gives people the idea that though you have to fight, you ought to do it with a long face and as if you were ashamed of it. It is that feeling that robs lots of magnificent young Christians in the Services of something they have a right to, something which is the natural accompaniment of courage – a kind of gaiety and wholeheartedness.

I have often thought to myself how it would have been if, when I served in the first world war, I and some young German had killed each other simultaneously and found ourselves together a moment after death. I cannot imagine that either of us would have felt any resentment or even any embarrassment. I think we might have laughed over it.

I imagine somebody will say, 'Well, if one is allowed to condemn the enemy's acts, and punish him, and kill him, what difference is left between Christian morality and the ordinary view?' All the difference in the world. Remember, we Christians think man lives for ever. Therefore, what really matters is those little marks or twists on the central, inside part of the soul which are going to turn it, in the long run, into a heavenly or a hellish creature. We may kill if necessary, but we must not hate and enjoy hating.

We may punish if necessary, but we must not enjoy it. In other words, something inside us, the feeling of resentment, the feeling that wants to get one's own back, must be simply killed. I do not mean that anyone can decide this moment that he will never feel it any more. That is not how things happen. I mean that every time it bobs its head up, day after day, year after year, all our lives long, we must hit it on the head. It is hard work, but the attempt is not impossible. Even while we kill and punish we must try to feel about the enemy as we feel about ourselves – to wish that he were not bad, to hope that he may, in this world or another, be cured: in fact, to wish his good. That is what is meant in the Bible by loving him: wishing his good, not feeling fond of him nor saying he is nice when he is not.

I admit that this means loving people who have nothing lovable about them. But then, has oneself anything lovable about it? You love it simply because it is yourself. God intends us to love all selves in the same way and for the same reason: but He has given us the sum ready worked out in our own case to show us how it works. We have then to go on and apply the rule to all the other selves. Perhaps it makes it easier if we remember that that is how He loves us. Not for any nice, attractive qualities we think we have, but just because we are the things called selves. For really there is nothing else in us to love: creatures like us who actually find hatred such a pleasure that to give it up is like giving up beer or tobacco...

8

THE GREAT SIN

I now come to that part of Christian morals where they differ most sharply from all other morals. There is one vice of which no man in the world is free; which every one in the world loathes when he sees it in someone else; and of which hardly any people, except Christians, ever imagine that they are guilty themselves. I have heard people admit that they are bad-tempered, or that they cannot keep their heads about girls or drink, or even that they are cowards. I do not think I have ever heard anyone who was not a Christian accuse himself of this vice. And at the same time I have very seldom met anyone, who was not a Christian, who showed the slightest mercy to it in others. There is no fault which makes a man more unpopular, and no fault which we are more unconscious of in ourselves. And the more we have it ourselves, the more we dislike it in others.

The vice I am talking of is Pride or Self-Conceit: and the virtue opposite to it, in Christian morals, is called Humility. You may remember, when I was talking about sexual morality, I warned you that the centre of Christian morals did not lie there. Well, now, we have come to the centre. According to Christian teachers, the essential vice, the utmost evil, is Pride. Unchastity, anger, greed, drunkenness, and all that, are mere fleabites in comparison: it was through Pride that the devil became the devil: Pride leads to every other vice: it is the complete anti-God state of mind.

Does this seem to you exaggerated? If so, think it over. I pointed out a moment ago that the more pride one had, the more one disliked pride in others. In fact, if you want to find out how proud you are the easiest way is to ask yourself, 'How much do I dislike it when other people snub me, or refuse to take any notice of me, or shove their oar in, or patronise me, or show off?' The point is that each person's pride is in competition with every one else's pride. It is because I wanted to be the big noise at the party that I am so annoyed at someone else being the big noise. Two of a trade never agree. Now what you want to get clear is that Pride is *essentially* competitive – is competitive by its very nature – while the other vices are competitive only, so to speak, by accident. Pride gets no pleasure out of having something, only out of having more of it than the next man. We say that people are proud of being rich, or clever, or good-looking, but they are not. They are proud of being richer, or cleverer, or better-looking than others. If everyone else became equally rich, or clever, or good-looking there would be nothing to be proud about. It is the comparison that makes you proud: the pleasure of being above the rest. Once the element of competition has gone, pride has gone. That is why I say that Pride is essentially competitive in a way the other vices are not. The sexual impulse may drive two men into competition if they both want the same girl. But that is only by accident; they might just as likely have wanted two different girls. But a proud man will take your girl from you, not because he wants her, but just to prove to himself that he is a better man than you. Greed may drive men into competition if there is not enough to go round; but the proud man, even when he has got more than he can possibly want, will try to get still more just to assert his power. Nearly all those evils in the world which people put down to greed or selfishness are really far more the result of Pride.

Take it with money. Greed will certainly make a man want money, for the sake of a better house, better holidays, better things to eat and drink. But only up to a point. What is it that makes a man with £10,000 a year anxious to get £20,000 a year? It is not the greed for more pleasure. £10,000 will give all the luxuries that any man can really enjoy. It is Pride – the wish to be richer than some other rich man, and (still more) the wish for power. For, of course, power is what Pride really enjoys: there is nothing makes a man feel so superior to others as being able to move them about like toy soldiers. What makes a pretty girl spread misery wherever she goes by collecting admirers? Certainly not her sexual instinct: that kind of girl is quite often sexually frigid. It is Pride. What is it that makes a political leader or a whole nation go on and on, demanding more and more? Pride again. Pride is competitive by its very nature: that is why it goes on and on. If I am a proud man, then, as long as there is one man in the whole world more powerful, or richer, or cleverer than I, he is my rival and my enemy.

The Christians are right: it is Pride which has been the chief cause of misery in every nation and every family since the world began. Other vices may sometimes bring people together: you may find good fellowship and jokes and friendliness among drunken people or unchaste people. But pride always means enmity – it *is* enmity. And not only enmity between man and man, but enmity to God.

In God you come up against something which is in every respect immeasurably superior to yourself. Unless you know God as that – and, therefore, know yourself as nothing in comparison – you do not know God at all. As long as you are proud you cannot know God. A proud man is always looking down on things and people: and, of course, as long as you are look-ing down, you cannot see something that is above you.

That raises a terrible question. How is it that people who are quite obviously eaten up with Pride can say they believe in God and appear to themselves very religious? I am afraid it means they are worshipping an imaginary God. They theoretically admit themselves to be nothing in the presence of this phantom God, but are really all the time imagining how He approves of them and thinks them far better than ordinary people: that is, they pay a pennyworth of imaginary humility to Him and get out of it a pound's worth of Pride towards their fellow-men. I suppose it was of those people Christ was thinking when He said that some would preach about Him and cast out devils in His name, only to be told at the end of the world that He had never known them. And any of us may at any moment be in this death-trap. Luckily, we have a test. Whenever we find that our religious life is making us feel that we are good – above all, that we are better than some-one else – I think we may be sure that we are being acted on, not by God, but by the devil. The real test of being in the presence of God is, that you either forget about yourself altogether or see yourself as a small, dirty object. It is better to forget about yourself altogether.

It is a terrible thing that the worst of all the vices can smuggle itself into the very centre of our religious life. But you can see why. The other, and less bad, vices come from the devil working on us through our animal nature. But this does not come through our animal nature at all. It comes direct from Hell. It is purely spiritual: consequently it is far more subtle and deadly. For the same reason, Pride can often be used to beat down the sim-pler vices. Teachers, in fact, often appeal to a boy's Pride, or, as they call it, his self-respect, to make him behave decently: many a man has overcome cowardice, or lust, or ill-temper, by learning to think that they are beneath his dignity – that is, by Pride. The devil laughs. He is perfectly content to see you becoming chaste and brave and self-controlled provided, all the time, he is setting up in you the Dictatorship of Pride – just as he would be quite con-tent to see your chilblains cured if he was allowed, in return, to give you cancer. For Pride is spiritual cancer: it eats up the very possibility of love, or contentment, or even common sense.

Before leaving this subject I must guard against some possible misunder-standings:

(1) Pleasure in being praised is not Pride. The child who is patted on the back for doing a lesson well, the woman whose beauty is praised by her lover, the saved soul to whom Christ says 'Well done,' are pleased and ought to be. For here the pleasure lies not in what you are but in the fact that you have pleased someone you wanted (and rightly wanted) to please. The trou-ble begins when you pass from thinking, 'I have pleased him; all is well,' to

thinking, 'What a fine person I must be to have done it.' The more you delight in yourself and the less you delight in the praise, the worse you are becoming. When you delight wholly in yourself and do not care about the praise at all, you have reached the bottom. That is why vanity, though it is the sort of Pride which shows most on the surface, is really the least bad and most pardonable sort. The vain person wants praise, applause, admiration, too much and is always angling for it. It is a fault, but a child-like and even (in an odd way) a humble fault. It shows that you are not yet completely contented with your own admiration. You value other people enough to want them to look at you. You are, in fact, still human. The real black, diabolical Pride, comes when you look down on others so much that you do not care what they think of you. Of course, it is very right, and often our duty, not to care what people think of us, if we do so for the right reason; namely, because we care so incomparably more what God thinks. But the Proud man has a different reason for not caring. He says 'Why should I care for the applause of that rabble as if their opinion were worth anything? And even if their opinions were of value, am I the sort of man to blush with pleasure at a compliment like some chit of a girl at her first dance? No, I am an integrated, adult personality. All I have done has been done to satisfy my own ideals – or my artistic conscience – or the traditions of my family – or, in a word, because I'm That Kind of Chap. If the mob like it, let them. They're nothing to me.' In this way real thorough-going pride may act as a check on vanity; for, as I said a moment ago, the devil loves 'curing' a small fault by giving you a great one. We must try not to be vain, but we must never call in our Pride to cure our vanity.

(2) We say in English that a man is 'proud' of his son, or his father, or his school, or regiment, and it may be asked whether 'pride' in this sense is a sin. I think it depends on what, exactly, we mean by 'proud of'. Very often, in such sentences, the phrase 'is proud of' means 'has a warm-hearted admiration for'. Such an admiration is, of course, very far from being a sin. But it might, perhaps, mean that the person in question gives himself airs on the ground of his distinguished father, or because he belongs to a famous regiment. This would, clearly, be a fault; but even then, it would be better than being proud simply of himself. To love and admire anything outside yourself is to take one step away from utter spiritual ruin; though we shall not be well so long as we love and admire anything more than we love and admire God.

(3) We must not think Pride is something God forbids because He is offended at it, or that Humility is something He demands as due to His own dignity – as if God Himself was proud. He is not in the least worried about His dignity. The point is, He wants you to know Him: wants to give you Himself. And He and you are two things of such a kind that if you really get

into any kind of touch with Him you will, in fact, be humble – delightedly humble, feeling the infinite relief of having for once got rid of all the silly nonsense about your own dignity which has made you restless and unhappy all your life. He is trying to make you humble in order to make this moment possible: trying to take off a lot of silly, ugly, fancy-dress in which we have all got ourselves up and are strutting about like the little idiots we are. I wish I had got a bit further with humility myself: if I had, I could probably tell you more about the relief, the comfort, of taking the fancy-dress off – getting rid of the false self, with all its 'Look at me' and 'Aren't I a good boy?' and all its posing and posturing. To get even near it, even for a moment, is like a drink of cold water to a man in a desert.

(4) Do not imagine that if you meet a really humble man he will be what most people call 'humble' nowadays: he will not be a sort of greasy, smarmy person, who is always telling you that, of course, he is nobody. Probably all you will think about him is that he seemed a cheerful, intelligent chap who took a real interest in what *you* said to *him*. If you do dislike him it will be because you feel a little envious of anyone who seems to enjoy life so easily. He will not be thinking about humility: he will not be thinking about himself at all.

If anyone would like to acquire humility, I can, I think, tell him the first step. The first step is to realise that one is proud. And a biggish step, too. At least, nothing whatever can be done before it. If you think you are not conceited, it means you are very conceited indeed.

9

CHARITY

I said in an earlier chapter that there were four 'Cardinal' virtues and three 'Theological' virtues. The three Theological ones are Faith, Hope, and Charity. Faith is going to be dealt with in the last two chapters. Charity was partly dealt with in Chapter 7, but there I concentrated on that part of Charity which is called Forgiveness. I now want to add a little more.

First, as to the meaning of the word. 'Charity' now means simply what used to be called 'alms' – that is, giving to the poor. Originally it had a much wider meaning. (You can see how it got the modern sense. If a man has 'charity', giving to the poor is one of the most obvious things he does, and so people came to talk as if that were the whole of charity. In the same way, 'rhyme' is the most obvious thing about poetry, and so people come to mean by 'poetry' simply rhyme and nothing more.) Charity means 'Love, in the Christian sense'. But love, in the Christian sense, does not mean an emotion. It is a state not of the feelings but of the will; that state of the will which we have naturally about ourselves, and must learn to have about other people.

I pointed out in the chapter on Forgiveness that our love for ourselves does not mean that we *like* ourselves. It means that we wish our own good. In the same way Christian Love (or Charity) for our neighbours is quite a different thing from liking or affection. We 'like' or are 'fond of' some people, and not of others. It is important to understand that this natural 'liking' is neither a sin nor a virtue, any more than your likes and dislikes in food are a sin or a virtue. It is just a fact. But, of course, what we do about it is either sinful or virtuous.

Natural liking or affection for people makes it easier to be 'charitable' towards them. It is, therefore, normally a duty to encourage our affections – to 'like' people as much as we can (just as it is often our duty to encourage our liking for exercise or wholesome food) – not because this liking is itself the virtue of charity, but because it is a help to it. On the other hand, it is also necessary to keep a very sharp look-out for fear our liking for some one person makes us uncharitable, or even unfair, to someone else. There are even cases where our liking conflicts with our charity towards the person we like. For example, a doting mother may be tempted by natural affection to 'spoil' her child; that is, to gratify her own affectionate impulses at the expense of the child's real happiness later on.

But though natural likings should normally be encouraged, it would be quite wrong to think that the way to become charitable is to sit trying to manufacture affectionate feelings. Some people are 'cold' by temperament; that may be a misfortune for them, but it is no more a sin than having a bad digestion is a sin; and it does not cut them out from the chance, or excuse them from the duty, of learning charity. The rule for all of us is perfectly simple. Do not waste time bothering whether you 'love' your neighbour; act as if you did. As soon as we do this we find one of the great secrets. When you are behaving as if you loved someone, you will presently come to love him. If you injure someone you dislike, you will find yourself disliking him more. If you do him a good turn, you will find yourself disliking him less. There is, indeed, one exception. If you do him a good turn, not to please God and obey the law of charity, but to show him what a fine forgiving chap you are, and to put him in your debt, and then sit down to wait for his 'grat-itude', you will probably be disappointed. (People are not fools: they have a very quick eye for anything like showing off, or patronage.) But whenever we do good to another self, just because it is a self, made (like us) by God, and desiring its own happiness as we desire ours, we shall have learned to love it a little more or, at least, to dislike it less.

Consequently, though Christian charity sounds a very cold thing to people whose heads are full of sentimentality, and though it is quite distinct from affection, yet it leads to affection. The difference between a Christian and a worldly man is not that the worldly man has only affections or 'likings' and the Christian has only 'charity'. The worldly man treats certain people kindly because he 'likes' them: the Christian, trying to treat every one kindly, finds himself liking more and more people as he goes on – including people he could not even have imagined himself liking at the beginning.

This same spiritual law works terribly in the opposite direction. The Germans, perhaps, at first ill-treated the Jews because they hated them: afterwards they hated them much more because they had ill-treated them. The more cruel you are, the more you will hate; and the more you hate, the more cruel you will become – and so on in a vicious circle for ever.

Good and evil both increase at compound interest. That is why the little decisions you and I make every day are of such infinite importance. The smallest good act today is the capture of a strategic point from which, a few months later, you may be able to go on to victories you never dreamed of. An apparently trivial indulgence in lust or anger today is the loss of a ridge or railway line or bridgehead from which the enemy may launch an attack otherwise impossible.

Some writers use the word charity to describe not only Christian love between human beings, but also God's love for man and man's love for God. About the second of these two, people are often worried. They are told they ought to love God. They cannot find any such feeling in themselves. What are they to do? The answer is the same as before. Act as if you did. Do not sit trying to manufacture feelings. Ask yourself, 'If I were sure that I loved God, what would I do?' When you have found the answer, go and do it.

On the whole, God's love for us is a much safer subject to think about than our love for Him. Nobody can always have devout feelings: and even if we could, feelings are not what God principally cares about. Christian Love, either towards God or towards man, is an affair of the will. If we are trying to do His will we are obeying the commandment, 'Thou shalt love the Lord thy God.' He will give us feelings of love if He pleases. We cannot create them for ourselves, and we must not demand them as a right. But the great thing to remember is that, though our feelings come and go, His love for us does not. It is not wearied by our sins, or our indifference; and, therefore, it is quite relentless in its determination that we shall be cured of those sins, at whatever cost to us, at whatever cost to Him.

10

HOPE

Hope is one of the Theological virtues. This means that a continual looking forward to the eternal world is not (as some modern people think) a form of escapism or wishful thinking, but one of the things a Christian is meant to do. It does not mean that we are to leave the present world as it is. If you read history you will find that the Christians who did most for the present world were just those who thought most of the next. The Apostles themselves, who set on foot the conversion of the Roman Empire, the great men who built up the Middle Ages, the English Evangelicals who abolished the Slave Trade, all left their mark on Earth, precisely because their minds were occupied with Heaven. It is since Christians have largely ceased to think of the other world that they have become so ineffective in this. Aim at Heaven and you will get earth 'thrown in': aim at earth and you will get neither. It seems a strange rule, but something like it can be seen at work in other matters. Health is a great blessing, but the moment you make health one of your main, direct objects you start becoming a crank and imagining there is something wrong with you. You are only likely to get health provided you want other things more – food, games, work, fun, open air. In the same way, we shall never save civilisation as long as civilisation is our main object. We must learn to want something else even more.

Most of us find it very difficult to want 'Heaven' at all – except in so far as 'Heaven' means meeting again our friends who have died. One reason for this difficulty is that we have not been trained: our whole education tends to fix our minds on this world. Another reason is that when the real want for Heaven is present in us, we do not recognise it. Most people, if they had really learned to look into their own hearts, would know that they do want, and want acutely, something that cannot be had in this world. There are all sorts of things in this world that offer to give it to you, but they never quite keep their promise. The longings which arise in us when we first fall in love, or first think of some foreign country, or first take up some subject that excites us, are longings which no marriage, no travel, no learning, can really satisfy. I am not now speaking of what would be ordinarily called unsuccessful marriages, or holidays, or learned careers. I am speaking of the best possible ones. There was something we grasped at, in that first moment of longing, which just fades away in the reality. I think everyone knows what I mean. The wife may be a good wife, and the hotels and scenery may have been excellent, and chemistry may be a very interesting job: but something has evaded us. Now there are two wrong ways of dealing with this fact, and one right one.

(1) The Fool's Way – He puts the blame on the things themselves. He goes on all his life thinking that if only he tried another woman, or went for a more expensive holiday, or whatever it is, then, this time, he really would catch the mysterious something we are all after. Most of the bored, discontented, rich people in the world are of this type. They spend their whole lives trotting from woman to woman (through the divorce courts), from continent to continent, from hobby to hobby, always thinking that the latest is 'the Real Thing' at last, and always disappointed.

(2) The Way of the Disillusioned 'Sensible Man' – He soon decides that the whole thing was moonshine. 'Of course,' he says, 'one feels like that when one's young. But by the time you get to my age you've given up chasing the rainbow's end.' And so he settles down and learns not to expect too much and represses the part of himself which used, as he would say, 'to cry for the moon'. This is, of course, a much better way than the first, and makes a man much happier, and less of a nuisance to society. It tends to make him a prig (he is apt to be rather superior towards what he calls 'adolescents'), but, on the whole, he rubs along fairly comfortably. It would be the best line we could take if man did not live for ever. But supposing infinite happiness really is there, waiting for us? Supposing one really can reach the rainbow's end? In that case it would be a pity to find out too late (a moment after death) that by our supposed 'common sense' we had stifled in ourselves the faculty of enjoying it.

(3) The Christian Way – The Christian says, 'Creatures are not born with desires unless satisfaction for those desires exists. A baby feels hunger: well, there is such a thing as food. A duckling wants to swim: well, there is such a thing as water. Men feel sexual desire: well, there is such a thing as sex. If I find in myself a desire which no experience in this world can satisfy, the most probable explanation is that I was made for another world. If none of my earthly pleasures satisfy it, that does not prove that the universe is a fraud. Probably earthly pleasures were never meant to satisfy it, but only to arouse it, to suggest the real thing. If that is so, I must take care, on the one hand, never to despise, or be unthankful for, these earthly blessings, and on the other, never to mistake them for the something else of which they

are only a kind of copy, or echo, or mirage. I must keep alive in myself the desire for my true country, which I shall not find till after death; I must never let it get snowed under or turned aside; I must make it the main object of life to press on to that other country and to help others to do the same.'

There is no need to be worried by facetious people who try to make the Christian hope of 'Heaven' ridiculous by saying they do not want 'to spend eternity playing harps'. The answer to such people is that if they cannot understand books written for grown-ups, they should not talk about them. All the scriptural imagery (harps, crowns, gold, etc.) is, of course, a merely symbolical attempt to express the inexpressible. Musical instruments are mentioned because for many people (not all) music is the thing known in the present life which most strongly suggests ecstasy and infinity. Crowns are mentioned to suggest the fact that those who are united with God in eternity share His splendour and power and joy. Gold is mentioned to suggest the timelessness of Heaven (gold does not rust) and the preciousness of it. People who take these symbols literally might as well think that when Christ told us to be like doves, He meant that we were to lay eggs.

11

FAITH

I must talk in this chapter about what the Christians call Faith. Roughly speaking, the word Faith seems to be used by Christians in two senses or on two levels, and I will take them in turn. In the first sense it means simply Belief – accepting or regarding as true the doctrines of Christianity. That is fairly simple. But what does puzzle people – at least it used to puzzle me – is the fact that Christians regard faith in this sense as a virtue. I used to ask how on earth it can be a virtue – what is there moral or immoral about believing or not believing a set of statements? Obviously, I used to say, a sane man accepts or rejects any statement, not because he wants to or does not want to, but because the evidence seems to him good or bad. If he were mistaken about the goodness or badness of the evidence that would not mean he was a bad man, but only that he was not very clever. And if he thought the evidence bad but tried to force himself to believe in spite of it, that would be merely stupid.

Well, I think I still take that view. But what I did not see then – and a good many people do not see still – was this. I was assuming that if the human mind once accepts a thing as true it will automatically go on regarding it as true, until some real reason for reconsidering it turns up. In fact, I was assuming that the human mind is completely ruled by reason. But that is not so. For example, my reason is perfectly convinced by good evidence that anaesthetics do not smother me and that properly trained surgeons do not start operating until I am unconscious. But that does not alter the fact that when they have me down on the table and clap their horrible mask over my face, a mere childish panic begins inside me. I start thinking I am going to choke, and I am afraid they will start cutting me up before I am properly under. In other words, I lose my faith in anaesthetics. It is not reason that is taking away my faith: on the contrary, my faith is based on reason. It is my imagination and emotions. The battle is between faith and reason on one side and emotion and imagination on the other.

When you think of it you will see lots of instances of this. A man knows, on perfectly good evidence, that a pretty girl of his acquaintance is a liar and cannot keep a secret and ought not to be trusted: but when he finds himself with her his mind loses its faith in that bit of knowledge and he starts thinking, 'Perhaps she'll be different this time,' and once more makes a fool of himself and tells her something he ought not to have told her. His senses and emotions have destroyed his faith in what he really knows to be true. Or take a boy learning to swim. His reason knows perfectly well that an unsupported human body will not necessarily sink in water: he has seen dozens of people float and swim. But the whole question is whether he will be able to go on believing this when the instructor takes away his hand and leaves him unsupported in the water – or whether he will suddenly cease to believe it and get in a fright and go down.

Now just the same thing happens about Christianity. I am not asking anyone to accept Christianity if his best reasoning tells him that the weight of the evidence is against it. That is not the point at which Faith comes in. But supposing a man's reason once decides that the weight of the evidence is for it. I can tell that man what is going to happen to him in the next few weeks. There will come a moment when there is bad news, or he is in trouble, or is living among a lot of other people who do not believe it, and all at once his emotions will rise up and carry out a sort of blitz on his belief. Or else there will come a moment when he wants a woman, or wants to tell a lie, or feels very pleased with himself, or sees a chance of making a little money in some way that is not perfectly fair: some moment, in fact, at which it would be very convenient if Christianity were not true. And once again his wishes and desires will carry out a blitz. I am not talking of moments at which any real new reasons against Christianity turn up. Those have to be faced and that is a different matter. I am talking about moments when a mere mood rises up against it.

Now Faith, in the sense in which I am here using the word, is the art of holding on to things your reason has once accepted, in spite of your changing moods. For moods will change, whatever view your reason takes. I know that by experience. Now that I am a Christian I do have moods in which the whole thing looks very improbable: but when I was an atheist I had moods in which Christianity looked terribly probable. This rebellion of your moods against your real self is going to come anyway. That is why Faith is such a necessary virtue: unless you teach your moods 'where they get off', you can never be either a sound Christian or even a sound atheist, but just a creature dithering to and fro, with its beliefs really dependent on the weather and the state of its digestion. Consequently one must train the habit of Faith.

The first step is to recognise the fact that your moods change. The next is to make sure that, if you have once accepted Christianity, then some of its main doctrines shall be deliberately held before your mind for some time every day. That is why daily prayers and religious readings and churchgoing are necessary parts of the Christian life. We have to be continually reminded of what we believe. Neither this belief nor any other will automatically remain alive in the mind. It must be fed. And as a matter of fact, if you examined a hundred people who had lost their faith in Christianity, I wonder how many of them would turn out to have been reasoned out of it by honest argument? Do not most people simply drift away?

Now I must turn to Faith in the second or higher sense: and this is the most difficult thing I have tackled yet. I want to approach it by going back to the subject of Humility. You may remember I said that the first step towards humility was to realise that one is proud. I want to add now that the next step is to make some serious attempt to practise the Christian virtues. A week is not enough. Things often go swimmingly for the first week. Try six weeks. By that time, having, as far as one can see, fallen back completely or even fallen lower than the point one began from, one will have discovered some truths about oneself. No man knows how bad he is till he has tried very hard to be good. A silly idea is current that good people do not know what temptation means. This is an obvious lie. Only those who try to resist temptation know how strong it is. After all, you find out the strength of the German army by fighting against it, not by giving in. You find out the strength of a wind by trying to talk against it, not by lying down. A man who gives in to temptation after five minutes simply does not know what it would have been like an hour later. That is why bad people, in one sense, know very little about badness. They have lived a sheltered life by always giving in. We never find out the strength of the evil impulse inside us until we try to fight it: and Christ, because He was the only man who never yielded to temptation, is also the only man who knows to the full what temptation means – the only complete realist. Very well, then. The main thing we learn from a serious attempt to practise the Christian virtues is that we fail. If there was any idea that God had set us a sort of exam. and that we might get good marks by deserving them, that has to be wiped out. If there was any idea of a sort of bargain – any idea that we could perform our side of the contract and thus put God in our debt so that it was up to Him, in mere justice, to perform His side – that has to be wiped out.

I think every one who has some vague belief in God, until he becomes a Christian, has the idea of an exam. or of a bargain in his mind. The first result of real Christianity is to blow that idea into bits. When they find it blown into bits, some people think this means that Christianity is a failure and give up. They seem to imagine that God is very simple-minded. In fact, of course, He knows all about this. One of the very things Christianity was designed to do was to blow this idea to bits. God has been waiting for the moment at which you discover that there is no question of earning a pass mark in this exam. or putting Him in your debt.

Then comes another discovery. Every faculty you have, your power of thinking or of moving your limbs from moment to moment, is given you by God. If you devoted every moment of your whole life exclusively to His service you could not give Him anything that was not in a sense His own already. So that when we talk of a man doing anything for God or giving anything to God, I will tell you what it is really like. It is like a small child going to its father and saying, 'Daddy, give me sixpence to buy you a birthday present.' Of course, the father does, and he is pleased with the child's present. It is all very nice and proper, but only an idiot would think that the father is sixpence to the good on the transaction. When a man has made these two discoveries God can really get to work. It is after this that real life begins. The man is awake now. We can now go on to talk of Faith in the second sense.

12

FAITH

I want to start by saying something that I would like every one to notice carefully. It is this. If this chapter means nothing to you, if it seems to be trying to answer questions you never asked, drop it at once. Do not bother about it at all. There are certain things in Christianity that can be understood from the outside, before you have become a Christian. But there are a great many things that cannot be understood until after you have gone a certain distance along the Christian road. These things are purely practical, though they do not look as if they were. They are directions for dealing with particular cross-roads and obstacles on the journey and they do not make sense until a man has reached those places. Whenever you find any statement in Christian writings which you can make nothing of, do not worry. Leave it alone. There will come a day, perhaps years later, when you suddenly see what it meant. If one could understand it now, it would only do one harm.

Of course, all this tells against me as much as anyone else. The thing I am going to try to explain in this chapter may be ahead of me. I may be thinking I have got there when I have not. I can only ask instructed Christians to watch very carefully, and tell me when I go wrong; and others to take what I say with a grain of salt – as something offered, because it may be a help, not because I am certain that I am right.

I am trying to talk about Faith in the second sense, the higher sense. I said just now that the question of Faith in this sense arises after a man has tried his level best to practise the Christian virtues, and found that he fails, and seen that even if he could he would only be giving back to God what was already God's own. In other words, he discovers his bankruptcy. Now, once again, what God cares about is not exactly our actions. What he cares about is that we should be creatures of a certain kind or quality – the kind of creatures He intended us to be – creatures related to Himself in a certain way. I do not add 'and related to one another in a certain way', because that is included: if you are right with Him you will inevitably be right with all your fellow-creatures, just as if all the spokes of a wheel are fitted rightly into the hub and the rim they are bound to be in the right positions to one another. And as long as a man is thinking of God as an examiner who has set him a sort of paper to do, or as the opposite party in a sort of bargain – as long as he is thinking of claims and counter-claims between himself and God – he is not yet in the right relation to Him. He is misunderstanding what he is and what God is. And he cannot get into the right relation until he has discovered the fact of our bankruptcy.

When I say 'discovered', I mean really discovered: not simply said it parrot-fashion. Of course, any child, if given a certain kind of religious education, will soon learn to say that we have nothing to offer to God that is not already His own and that we find ourselves failing to offer even that without keeping something back. But I am talking of really discovering this: really finding out by experience that it is true.

Now we cannot, in that sense, discover our failure to keep God's law except by trying our very hardest (and then failing). Unless we really try, whatever we say there will always be at the back of our minds the idea that if we try harder next time we shall succeed in being completely good. Thus, in one sense, the road back to God is a road of moral effort, of trying harder and harder. But in another sense it is not trying that is ever going to bring us home. All this trying leads up to the vital moment at which you turn to God and say, 'You must do this. I can't.' Do not, I implore you, start asking yourselves, 'Have I reached that moment?' Do not sit down and start watching your own mind to see if it is coming along. That puts a man quite on the wrong track. When the most important things in our life happen we quite often do not know, at the moment, what is going on. A man does not always say to himself, 'Hullo! I'm growing up.' It is often only when he looks back that he realises what has happened and recognises it as what people call 'growing up'. You can see it even in simple matters. A man who starts anxiously watching to see whether he is going to sleep is very likely to remain wide awake. As well, the thing I am talking of now may not happen to every one in a sudden flash – as it did to St Paul or Bunyan: it may be so gradual that no one could ever point to a particular hour or even a particular year. And what matters is the nature of the change in itself, not how we feel while it is happening. It is the change from being confident about our own efforts to the state in which we despair of doing anything for ourselves and leave it to God.

I know the words 'leave it to God' can be misunderstood, but they must stay for the moment. The sense in which a Christian leaves it to God is that he puts all his trust in Christ: trusts that Christ will somehow share with him the perfect human obedience which He carried out from His birth to His crucifixion: that Christ will make the man more like Himself and, in a sense, make good his deficiencies. In Christian language, He will share His 'sonship' with us, will make us, like Himself, 'Sons of God': in Book IV I shall attempt to analyse the meaning of those words a little further. If you like to put it that way, Christ offers something for nothing: He even offers everything for nothing. In a sense, the whole Christian life consists in accepting that very remarkable offer. But the difficulty is to reach the point of recognising that all we have done and can do is nothing. What we should have liked would be for God to count our good points and ignore our bad ones. Again, in a sense, you may say that no temptation is ever overcome until we stop trying to overcome it – throw up the sponge. But then you could not 'stop trying' in the right way and for the right reason until you had tried your very hardest. And, in yet another sense, handing everything over to Christ does not, of course, mean that you stop trying. To trust Him means, of course, trying to do all that He says. There would be no sense in saying you trusted a person if you would not take his advice. Thus if you have really handed yourself over to Him, it must follow that you are trying to obey Him. But trying in a new way, a less worried way. Not doing these things in order to be saved, but because He has begun to save you already. Not hoping to get to Heaven as a reward for your actions, but inevitably wanting to act in a certain way because a first faint gleam of Heaven is already inside you.

Christians have often disputed as to whether what leads the Christian home is good actions, or Faith in Christ. I have no right really to speak on such a difficult question, but it does seem to me like asking which blade in a pair of scissors is most necessary. A serious moral effort is the only thing that will bring you to the point where you throw up the sponge. Faith in Christ is the only thing to save you from despair at that point: and out of that Faith in Him good actions must inevitably come. There are two parodies of the truth which different sets of Christians have, in the past, been accused by other Christians of believing: perhaps they may make the truth clearer. One set were accused of saying, 'Good actions are all that matters. The best good action is charity. The best kind of charity is giving money. The best thing to give money to is the Church. So hand us over £10,000 and we will see you through.' The answer to that nonsense, of course, would be that good actions done for that motive, done with the idea that Heaven can be bought, would not be good actions at all, but only commercial speculations. The other set were accused of saying, 'Faith is all that matters. Consequently, if you have faith, it doesn't matter what you do. Sin away, my lad, and have a good time and Christ will see that it makes no difference in the end.' The answer to that nonsense is that, if what you call your 'faith' in Christ does not involve taking the slightest notice of what He says, then it is not Faith at all – not faith or trust in Him, but only intellectual acceptance of some theory about Him.

The Bible really seems to clinch the matter when it puts the two things together into one amazing sentence. The first half is, 'Work out your own salvation with fear and trembling' – which looks as if everything depended on us and our good actions: but the second half goes on, 'For it is God who worketh in you' – which looks as if God did everything and we nothing. I am afraid that is the sort of thing we come up against in Christianity. I am puzzled, but I am not surprised. You see, we are now trying to understand, and to separate into water-tight compartments, what exactly God does and what man does when God and man are working together. And, of course, we begin by thinking it is like two men working together, so that you could say, 'He did this bit and I did that.' But this way of thinking breaks down. God is not like that. He is inside you as well as outside: even if we could understand who did what, I do not think human language could properly express it. In the attempt to express it different Churches say different things. But you will find that even those who insist most strongly on the importance of good actions tell you you need Faith; and even those who insist most strongly on Faith tell you to do good actions. At any rate that is as far as I can go.

I think all Christians would agree with me if I said that though Christianity seems at the first to be all about morality, all about duties and rules and guilt and virtue, yet it leads you on, out of all that, into something beyond. One has a glimpse of a country where they do not talk of those things, except perhaps as a joke. Every one there is filled full with what we should call goodness as a mirror is filled with light. But they do not call it goodness. They do not call it anything. They are not thinking of it. They are too busy looking at the source from which it comes. But this is near the stage where the road passes over the rim of our world. No one's eyes can see very far beyond that: lots of people's eyes can see further than mine.

BOOK 4

BEYOND PERSONALITY:

OR

FIRST STEPS IN THE
DOCTRINE OF THE TRINITY

MAKING AND BEGETTING

Everyone has warned me not to tell you what I am going to tell you in this last book. They all say 'the ordinary reader does not want Theology; give him plain practical religion'. I have rejected their advice. I do not think the ordinary reader is such a fool. Theology means 'the science of God', and I think any man who wants to think about God at all would like to have the clearest and most accurate ideas about Him which are available. You are not children: why should you be treated like children?

In a way I quite understand why some people are put off by Theology. I remember once when I had been giving a talk to the R.A.F., an old, hard-bitten officer got up and said, 'I've no use for all that stuff. But, mind you, I'm a religious man too. I know there's a God. I've felt Him: out alone in the desert at night: the tremendous mystery. And that's just why I don't believe all your neat little dogmas and formulas about Him. To anyone who's met the real thing they all seem so petty and pedantic and unreal!'

Now in a sense I quite agreed with that man. I think he had probably had a real experience of God in the desert. And when he turned from that experience to the Christian creeds, I think he really was turning from something real to something less real. In the same way, if a man has once looked at the Atlantic from the beach, and then goes and looks at a map of the Atlantic, he also will be turning from something real to something less real: turning from real waves to a bit of coloured paper. But here comes the point. The map is admittedly only coloured paper, but there are two things you have to remember about it. In the first place, it is based on what hundreds and thousands of people have found out by sailing the real Atlantic. In that way it has behind it masses of experience just as real as the one you could have from the beach; only, while yours would be a single glimpse, the map fits all those different experiences together. In the second place, if you want to go anywhere, the map is absolutely necessary. As long as you are content with walks on the beach, your own glimpses are far more fun than looking at a map. But the map is going to be more use than walks on the beach if you want to get to America.

Now, Theology is like the map. Merely learning and thinking about the Christian doctrines, if you stop there, is less real and less exciting than the sort of thing my friend got in the desert. Doctrines are not God: they are only a kind of map. But that map is based on the experience of hundreds of people who really were in touch with God – experiences compared with which any thrills or pious feelings you and I are likely to get on our own are very elementary and very confused. And secondly, if you want to get any further, you must use the map. You see, what happened to that man in the desert may have been real, and was certainly exciting, but nothing comes of it. It leads nowhere. There is nothing to do about it. In fact, that is just why a vague religion – all about feeling God in nature, and so on – is so attractive. It is all thrills and no work: like watching the waves from the beach. But you will not get to Newfoundland by studying the Atlantic that way, and you will not get eternal life by simply feeling the presence of God in flowers or music. Neither will you get anywhere by looking at maps without going to sea. Nor will you be very safe if you go to sea without a map.

In other words, Theology is practical: especially now. In the old days, when there was less education and discussion, perhaps it was possible to get on with a very few simple ideas about God. But it is not so now. Everyone reads, everyone hears things discussed. Consequently, if you do not listen to Theology, that will not mean that you have no ideas about God. It will mean that you have a lot of wrong ones – bad, muddled, out-of-date ideas. For a great many of the ideas about God which are trotted out as novelties today are simply the ones which real Theologians tried centuries ago and rejected. To believe in the popular religion of modern England is retrogression – like believing the earth is flat.

For when you get down to it, is not the popular idea of Christianity simply this: that Jesus Christ was a great moral teacher and that if only we took His advice we might be able to establish a better social order and avoid another war? Now, mind you, that is quite true. But it tells you much less than the whole truth about Christianity and it has no practical importance at all.

It is quite true that if we took Christ's advice we should soon be living in a happier world. You need not even go as far as Christ. If we did all that Plato or Aristotle or Confucius told us, we should get on a great deal better than we do. And so what? We never have followed the advice of the great teachers. Why are we likely to begin now? Why are we more likely to follow Christ than any of the others? Because He is the best moral teacher? But that makes it even less likely that we shall follow Him. If we cannot take the elementary lessons, is it likely we are going to take the most advanced one? If Christianity only means one more bit of good advice, then Christianity is of no importance. There has been no lack of good advice for the last four thousand years. A bit more makes no difference.

But as soon as you look at any real Christian writings, you find that they are talking about something quite different from this popular religion. They say that Christ is the Son of God (whatever that means). They say that those who give Him their confidence can also become Sons of God (whatever that means). They say that His death saved us from our sins (whatever that means).

There is no good complaining that these statements are difficult. Christianity claims to be telling us about another world, about something behind the world we can touch and hear and see. You may think the claim false, but if it were true, what it tells us would be bound to be difficult – at least as difficult as modern Physics, and for the same reason.

Now the point in Christianity which gives us the greatest shock is the statement that by attaching ourselves to Christ, we can 'become Sons of God'. One asks 'Aren't we Sons of God already? Surely the fatherhood of God is one of the main Christian ideas?' Well, in a certain sense, no doubt we are sons of God already. I mean, God has brought us into existence and loves us and looks after us, and in that way is like a father. But when the Bible talks of our 'becoming' Sons of God, obviously it must mean something different. And that brings us up against the very centre of Theology.

One of the creeds says that Christ is the Son of God 'begotten, not created'; and it adds 'begotten by his Father before all worlds'. Will you please get it quite clear that this has nothing to do with the fact that when Christ was born on earth as a man, that man was the son of a virgin? We are not now thinking about the Virgin Birth. We are thinking about something that happened before Nature was created at all, before time began. 'Before all worlds' Christ is begotten, not created. What does it mean?

We don't use the words *begetting* or *begotten* much in modern English, but everyone still knows what they mean. To beget is to become the father of: to create is to make. And the difference is this. When you beget, you beget something of the same kind as yourself. A man begets human babies, a beaver begets little beavers and a bird begets eggs which turn into little birds. But when you make, you make something of a different kind from yourself. A bird makes a nest, a beaver builds a dam, a man makes a wireless set – or he may make something more like himself than a wireless set: say, a statue. If he is a clever enough carver he may make a statue which is very like a man indeed. But, of course, it is not a real man; it only looks like one. It cannot breathe or think. It is not alive.

Now that is the first thing to get clear. What God begets is God; just as what man begets is man. What God creates is not God; just as what man makes is not man. That is why men are not Sons of God in the sense that Christ is. They may be like God in certain ways, but they are not things of the same kind. They are more like statues or pictures of God.

A statue has the shape of a man but is not alive. In the same way, man has (in a sense I am going to explain) the 'shape' or likeness of God, but he has not got the kind of life God has. Let us take the first point (man's resemblance to God) first. Everything God has made has some likeness to Himself. Space is like Him in its hugeness: not that the greatness of space is the same kind of greatness as God's, but it is a sort of symbol of it, or a translation of it into non-spiritual terms. Matter is like God in having energy: though, again, of course, physical energy is a different kind of thing from the power of God. The vegetable world is like Him because it is alive, and He is the 'living God'. But life, in this biological sense, is not the same as the life there is in God: it is only a kind of symbol or shadow of it. When we come on to the animals, we find other kinds of resemblance in addition to biological life. The intense activity and fertility of the insects, for example, is a first dim resemblance to the unceasing activity and the creativeness of God. In the higher mammals we get the beginnings of instinctive affection. That is not the same thing as the love that exists in God: but it is like it – rather in the way that a picture drawn on a flat piece of paper can nevertheless be 'like' a landscape. When we come to man, the highest of the animals, we get the completest resemblance to God which we know of. (There may be creatures in other worlds who are more like God than man is, but we do not know about them.) Man not only lives, but loves and reasons: biological life reaches its highest known level in him.

But what man, in his natural condition, has not got, is Spiritual life – the higher and different sort of life that exists in God. We use the same word *life* for both: but if you thought that both must therefore be the same sort of thing, that would be like thinking that the 'greatness' of space and the 'greatness' of God were the same sort of greatness. In reality, the difference between Biological life and Spiritual life is so important that I am going to give them two distinct names. The Biological sort which comes to us through Nature, and which (like everything else in Nature) is always tending to run down and decay so that it can only be kept up by incessant subsidies from Nature in the form of air, water, food, etc., is *Bios*. The Spiritual life which is in God from all eternity, and which made the whole natural universe, is *Zoe*. *Bios* has, to be sure, a certain shadowy or symbolic resemblance to *Zoe*: but only the sort of resemblance there is between a photo and a place, or a statue and a man. A man who changed from having *Bios* to having *Zoe* would have gone through as big a change as a statue which changed from being a carved stone to being a real man.

And that is precisely what Christianity is about. This world is a great sculptor's shop. We are the statues and there is a rumour going round the shop that some of us are some day going to come to life.

2

THE THREE-PERSONAL GOD

The last chapter was about the difference between begetting and making. A man begets a child, but he only makes a statue. God begets Christ but He only makes men. But by saying that, I have illustrated only one point about God, namely, that what God the Father begets is God, something of the same kind as Himself. In that way it is like a human father begetting a human son. But not quite like it. So I must try to explain a little more.

A good many people nowadays say, 'I believe in a God, but not in a personal God.' They feel that the mysterious something which is behind all other things must be more than a person. Now the Christians quite agree. But the Christians are the only people who offer any idea of what a being that is beyond personality could be like. All the other people, though they say that God is beyond personality, really think of Him as something impersonal: that is, as something less than personal. If you are looking for something super-personal, something more than a person, then it is not a question of choosing between the Christian idea and the other ideas. The Christian idea is the only one on the market.

Again, some people think that after this life, or perhaps after several lives, human souls will be 'absorbed' into God. But when they try to explain what they mean, they seem to be thinking of our being absorbed into God as one material thing is absorbed into another. They say it is like a drop of water slipping into the sea. But of course that is the end of the drop. If that is what happens to us, then being absorbed is the same as ceasing to exist. It is only the Christians who have any idea of how human souls can be taken into the life of God and yet remain themselves – in fact, be very much more themselves than they were before.

I warned you that Theology is practical. The whole purpose for which we exist is to be thus taken into the life of God. Wrong ideas about what that life is will make it harder. And now, for a few minutes, I must ask you to follow rather carefully.

You know that in space you can move in three ways – to left or right, backwards or forwards, up or down. Every direction is either one of these three or a compromise between them. They are called the three Dimensions. Now notice this. If you are using only one dimension, you could draw only a straight line. If you are using two, you could draw a figure: say, a square. And a square is made up of four straight lines. Now a step further. If you have three dimensions, you can then build what we call a solid body: say, a cube – a thing like a dice or a lump of sugar. And a cube is made up of six squares.

Do you see the point? A world of one dimension would be a straight line. In a two-dimensional world, you still get straight lines, but many lines make one figure. In a three-dimensional world, you still get figures but many figures make one solid body. In other words, as you advance to more real and more complicated levels, you do not leave behind you the things you found on the simpler levels: you still have them, but combined in new ways – in ways you could not imagine if you knew only the simpler levels.

Now the Christian account of God involves just the same principle. The human level is a simple and rather empty level. On the human level one person is one being, and any two persons are two separate beings – just as, in two dimensions (say on a flat sheet of paper) one square is one figure, and any two squares are two separate figures. On the Divine level you still find personalities; but up there you find them combined in new ways which we, who do not live on that level, cannot imagine. In God's dimension, so to speak, you find a being who is three Persons while remaining one Being, just as a cube is six squares while remaining one cube. Of course we cannot fully conceive a Being like that: just as, if we were so made that we perceived only two dimensions in space we could never properly imagine a cube. But we can get a sort of faint notion of it. And when we do, we are then, for the first time in our lives, getting some positive idea, however faint, of something super-personal – something more than a person. It is something we could never have guessed, and yet, once we have been told, one almost feels one ought to have been able to guess it because it fits in so well with all the things we know already.

You may ask, 'if we cannot imagine a three-personal Being, what is the good of talking about Him?' Well, there isn't any good talking about Him. The thing that matters is being actually drawn into that three-personal life, and that may begin any time – tonight, if you like.

What I mean is this. An ordinary simple Christian kneels down to say his prayers. He is trying to get into touch with God. But if he is a Christian he knows that what is prompting him to pray is also God: God, so to speak, inside him. But he also knows that all his real knowledge of God comes through Christ, the Man who was God – that Christ is standing beside him, helping him to pray, praying for him. You see what is happening. God is the thing to which he is praying – the goal he is trying to reach. God is also the thing inside him which is pushing him on – the motive power. God is also the road or bridge along which he is being pushed to that goal. So that the whole threefold life of the three-personal Being is actually going on in that ordinary little bedroom where an ordinary man is saying his prayers. The man is being caught up into the higher kinds of life – what I called *Zoe* or spiritual life: he is being pulled into God, by God, while still remaining himself.

And that is how Theology started. People already knew about God in a vague way. Then came a man who claimed to be God; and yet He was not the sort of man you could dismiss as a lunatic. He made them believe Him. They met Him again after they had seen Him killed. And then, after they had been formed into a little society or community, they found God somehow inside them as well: directing them, making them able to do things they could not do before. And when they worked it all out they found they had arrived at the Christian definition of the three-personal God.

This definition is not something we have made up; Theology is, in a sense, an experimental science. It is simple religions that are the made-up ones. When I say it is an experimental science 'in a sense', I mean that it is like the other experimental sciences in some ways, but not in all. If you are a geologist studying rocks, you have to go and find the rocks. They will not come to you, and if you go to them they cannot run away. The initiative lies all on your side. They cannot either help or hinder. But suppose you are a zoologist and want to take photos of wild animals in their native haunts. That is a bit different from studying rocks. The wild animals will not come to you: but they can run away from you. Unless you keep very quiet, they will. There is beginning to be a tiny little trace of initiative on their side.

Now a stage higher; suppose you want to get to know a human person. If he is determined not to let you, you will not get to know him. You have to win his confidence. In this case the initiative is equally divided – it takes two to make a friendship.

When you come to knowing God, the initiative lies on His side. If He does not show Himself, nothing you can do will enable you to find Him. And, in fact, He shows much more of Himself to some people than to others – not because He has favourites, but because it is impossible for Him to show Himself to a man whose whole mind and character are in the wrong condition. Just as sunlight, though it has no favourites, cannot be reflected in a dusty mirror as clearly as in a clean one.

You can put this another way by saying that while in other sciences the instruments you use are things external to yourself (things like microscopes and telescopes), the instrument through which you see God is your whole self. And if a man's self is not kept clean and bright, his glimpse of God will be blurred – like the Moon seen through a dirty telescope. That is why horrible nations have horrible religions: they have been looking at God through a dirty lens.

God can show Himself as He really is only to real men. And that means not simply to men who are individually good, but to men who are united together in a body, loving one another, helping one another, showing Him to one another. For that is what God meant humanity to be like; like players in one band, or organs in one body.

Consequently, the one really adequate instrument for learning about God is the whole Christian community, waiting for Him together. Christian brotherhood is, so to speak, the technical equipment for this science – the laboratory outfit. That is why all these people who turn up every few years with some patent simplified religion of their own as a substitute for the Christian tradition are really wasting time. Like a man who has no instrument but an old pair of field glasses setting out to put all the real astronomers right. He may be a clever chap – he may be cleverer than some of the real astronomers, but he is not giving himself a chance. And two years later everyone has forgotten all about him, but the real science is still going on.

If Christianity was something we were making up, of course we could make it easier. But it is not. We cannot compete, in simplicity, with people who are inventing religions. How could we? We are dealing with Fact. Of course anyone can be simple if he has no facts to bother about.

3

TIME AND BEYOND TIME

It is a very silly idea that in reading a book you must never 'skip'. All sensible people skip freely when they come to a chapter which they find is going to be no use to them. In this chapter I am going to talk about something which may be helpful to some readers, but which may seem to others merely an unnecessary complication. If you are one of the second sort of readers, then I advise you not to bother about this chapter at all but to turn on to the next.

In the last chapter I had to touch on the subject of prayer, and while that is still fresh in your mind and my own, I should like to deal with a difficulty that some people find about the whole idea of prayer. A man put it to me by saying 'I can believe in God all right, but what I cannot swallow is the idea of Him attending to several hundred million human beings who are all addressing Him at the same moment.' And I have found that quite a lot of people feel this.

Now, the first thing to notice is that the whole sting of it comes in the words *at the same moment*. Most of us can imagine God attending to any number of applicants if only they came one by one and He had an endless time to do it in. So what is really at the back of this difficulty is the idea of God having to fit too many things into one moment of time.

Well that is of course what happens to us. Our life comes to us moment by moment. One moment disappears before the next comes along: and there is room for very little in each. That is what Time is like. And of course you and I tend to take it for granted that this Time series – this arrangement of past, present and future – is not simply the way life comes to us but the way all things really exist. We tend to assume that the whole universe and God Himself are always moving on from past to future just as we do. But many learned men do not agree with that. It was the Theologians who first started the idea that some things are not in Time at all: later the Philosophers took it over: and now some of the scientists are doing the same.

Almost certainly God is not in Time. His life does not consist of moments following one another. If a million people are praying to Him at ten-thirty tonight, He need not listen to them all in that one little snippet which we call ten-thirty. Ten-thirty – and every other moment from the beginning of the world – is always the Present for Him. If you like to put it that way, He has all eternity in which to listen to the split second of prayer put up by a pilot as his plane crashes in flames.

That is difficult, I know. Let me try to give something, not the same, but a bit like it. Suppose I am writing a novel. I write 'Mary laid down her work; next moment came a knock at the door!' For Mary who has to live in the imaginary time of my story there is no interval between putting down the work and hearing the knock. But I, who am Mary's maker, do not live in that imaginary time at all. Between writing the first half of that sentence and the second, I might sit down for three hours and think steadily about Mary. I could think about Mary as if she were the only character in the book and for as long as I pleased, and the hours I spent in doing so would not appear in Mary's time (the time inside the story) at all.

This is not a perfect illustration, of course. But it may give just a glimpse of what I believe to be the truth. God is not hurried along in the Time-stream of this universe any more than an author is hurried along in the imaginary time of his own novel. He has infinite attention to spare for each one of us. He does not have to deal with us in the mass. You are as much alone with Him as if you were the only being He had ever created. When Christ died, He died for you individually just as much as if you had been the only man in the world.

The way in which my illustration breaks down is this. In it the author gets out of one Time-series (that of the novel) only by going into another Time-series (the real one). But God, I believe, does not live in a Time-series at all. His life is not dribbled out moment by moment like ours: with Him it is, so to speak, still 1920 and already 1960. For His life is Himself.

If you picture Time as a straight line along which we have to travel, then you must picture God as the whole page on which the line is drawn. We come to the parts of the line one by one: we have to leave A behind before we get to B, and cannot reach C until we leave B behind. God, from above or outside or all round, contains the whole line, and sees it all.

The idea is worth trying to grasp because it removes some apparent difficulties in Christianity. Before I became a Christian one of my objections was as follows. The Christians said that the eternal God who is every-where and keeps the whole universe going, once became a human being. Well, then, said I, how did the whole universe keep going while He was a baby, or while He was asleep? How could He at the same time be God who knows everything and also a man asking his disciples 'Who touched me?'

You will notice that the sting lay in the *time* words: '*While* He was a baby' – How could He *at the same time?*' In other words I was assuming that Christ's life as God was in time, and that His life as the man Jesus in Palestine was a shorter period taken out of that time – just as my service in the army was a shorter period taken out of my total life. And that is how most of us perhaps tend to think about it. We picture God living through a period when His human life was still in the future: then coming to a period when it was present: then going on to a period when He could look back on it as something in the past. But probably these ideas correspond to nothing in the actual facts. You cannot fit Christ's earthly life in Palestine into any time-relations with His life as God beyond all space and time. It is really, I suggest, a timeless truth about God that human nature, and the human experience of weakness and sleep and ignorance, are somehow included in His whole divine life. This human life in God is from our point of view a particular period in the history of our world (from the year A.D. one till the Crucifixion). We therefore imagine it is also a period in the history of God's own existence. But God has no history. He is too completely and utterly real to have one. For, of course, to have a history means losing part of your reality (because it has already slipped away into the past) and not yet having another part (because it is still in the future): in fact having nothing but the tiny little present, which has gone before you can speak about it. God forbid we should think God was like that. Even we may hope not to be always rationed in that way.

Another difficulty we get if we believe God to be in time is this. Everyone who believes in God at all believes that He knows what you and I are going to do tomorrow. But if He knows I am going to do so-and-so, how can I be free to do otherwise? Well, here once again, the difficulty comes from thinking that God is progressing along the Time-line like us: the only difference being that He can see ahead and we cannot. Well, if that were true, if God *foresaw* our acts, it would be very hard to understand how we could be free not to do them. But suppose God is outside and above the Time-line. In that case, what we call 'tomorrow' is visible to Him in just the same way as what we call 'today'. All the days are 'Now' for Him. He does not remember you doing things yesterday; He simply sees you doing them, because, though you have lost yesterday, He has not. He does not 'foresee' you doing things tomorrow; He simply sees you doing them: because, though tomorrow is not yet there for you, it is for Him. You never supposed that your actions at this moment were any less free because God knows what you are doing. Well, He knows your tomorrow's actions in just the same way – because He is already in tomorrow and can simply watch you. In a sense, He does not know your action till you have done it: but then the moment at which you have done it is already 'Now' for Him.

This idea has helped me a good deal. If it does not help you, leave it alone. It is a 'Christian idea' in the sense that great and wise Christians have held it and there is nothing in it contrary to Christianity. But it is not in the Bible or any of the creeds. You can be a perfectly good Christian without accepting it, or indeed without thinking of the matter at all.

4

GOOD INFECTION

I begin this chapter by asking you to get a certain picture clear in your minds. Imagine two books lying on a table one on top of the other. Obviously the bottom book is keeping the other one up – supporting it. It is because of the underneath book that the top one is resting, say, two inches from the surface of the table instead of touching the table. Let us call the underneath book A and the top one B. The position of A is causing the position of B. That is clear? Now let us imagine – it could not really happen, of course, but it will do for an illustration – let us imagine that both books have been in that position for ever and ever. In that case B's position would always have been resulting from A's position. But all the same, A's position would not have existed before B's position. In other words the result does not come *after* the cause. Of course, results usually do: you eat the cucumber first and have the indigestion afterwards. But it is not so with all causes and results. You will see in a moment why I think this important.

I said a few pages back that God is a Being which contains three Persons while remaining one Being, just as a cube contains six squares while remaining one body. But as soon as I begin trying to explain how these Persons are connected I have to use words which make it sound as if one of them was there before the others. The First Person is called the Father and the Second the Son. We say that the First begets or produces the second; we call it *begetting*, not *making*, because what He produces is of the same kind as Himself. In that way the word Father is the only word to use. But unfortunately it suggests that He is there first – just as a human father exists before his son. But that is not so. There is no before and after about it. And that is why I think it important to make clear how one thing can be the source, or cause, or origin, of another without being there before it. The Son exists because the Father exists: but there never was a time before the Father produced the Son.

Perhaps the best way to think of it is this. I asked you just now to imagine those two books, and probably most of you did. That is, you made an act of imagination and as a result you had a mental picture. Quite obviously your act of imagining was the cause and the mental picture the result. But that does not mean that you first did the imagining and then got the picture. The moment you did it, the picture was there. Your will was keeping the picture before you all the time. Yet that act of will and the picture began at exactly the same moment and ended at the same moment. If there were a Being who had always existed and had always been imagining one thing, his act would always have been producing a mental picture; but the picture would be just as eternal as the act.

In the same way we must think of the Son always, so to speak, streaming forth from the Father, like light from a lamp, or heat from a fire, or thoughts from a mind. He is the self-expression of the Father – what the Father has to say. And there never was a time when He was not saying it. But have you noticed what is happening? All these pictures of light or heat are making it sound as if the Father and Son were two things instead of two Persons. So that after all, the New Testament picture of a Father and a Son turns out to be much more accurate than anything we try to substitute for it. That is what always happens when you go away from the words of the Bible. It is quite right to go away from them for a moment in order to make some special point clear. But you must always go back. Naturally God knows how to describe Himself much better than we know how to describe Him. He knows that Father and Son is more like the relation between the First and Second Persons than anything else we can think of. Much the most important thing to know is that it is a relation of love. The Father delights in His Son; the Son looks up to His Father.

Before going on, notice the practical importance of this. All sorts of people are fond of repeating the Christian statement that 'God is love'. But they seem not to notice that the words 'God is love' have no real meaning unless God contains at least two Persons. Love is something that one person has for another person. If God was a single person, then before the world was made, He was not love. Of course, what these people mean when they say that God is love is often something quite different: they really mean 'Love is God'. They really mean that our feelings of love, however and wherever they arise, and whatever results they produce, are to be treated with great respect. Perhaps they are: but that is something quite different from what Christians mean by the statement 'God is love'. They believe that the living, dynamic activity of love has been going on in God forever and has created everything else.

And that, by the way, is perhaps the most important difference between Christianity and all other religions: that in Christianity God is not a static thing – not even a person – but a dynamic, pulsating activity, a life, almost a kind of drama. Almost, if you will not think me irreverent, a kind of dance. The union between the Father and the Son is such a live concrete thing that this union itself is also a Person. I know this is almost inconceivable, but look at it thus. You know that among human beings, when they get together in a family, or a club, or a trade union, people talk about the 'spirit' of that family, or club, or trade union. They talk about its 'spirit' because the individual members, when they are together, do really develop particular ways of talking and behaving which they would not have if they were apart.* It is as if a sort of communal personality came into existence. Of course, it is not a real person: it is only rather like a person. But that is just one of the differences between God and us. What grows out of the joint life of the Father and Son is a real Person, is in fact the Third of the three Persons who are God.

This third Person is called, in technical language, the Holy Ghost or the 'spirit' of God. Do not be worried or surprised if you find it (or Him) rather vaguer or more shadowy in your mind than the other two. I think there is a reason why that must be so. In the Christian life you are not usually looking *at* Him. He is always acting through you. If you think of the Father as something 'out there', in front of you, and of the Son as someone standing at your side, helping you to pray, trying to turn you into another son, then you have to think of the third Person as something inside you, or behind you. Perhaps some people might find it easier to begin with the third Person and work backwards. God is love, and that love works through men – especially through the whole community of Christians. But this spirit of love is, from all eternity, a love going on between the Father and the Son.

And now, what does it all matter? It matters more than anything else in the world. The whole dance, or drama, or pattern of this three-Personal life is to be played out in each one of us: or (putting it the other way round) each one of us has got to enter that pattern, take his place in that dance. There is no other way to the happiness for which we were made. Good things as well as bad, you know, are caught by a kind of infection. If you want to get warm you must stand near the fire: if you want to be wet you must get into the water. If you want joy, power, peace, eternal life, you must get close to, or even into, the thing that has them. They are not a sort of prize which God could, if He chose, just hand out to anyone. They are a great fountain of energy and beauty spurting up at the very centre of reality. If you are close to it, the spray will wet you: if you are not, you will remain dry. Once a man is united to God, how could he not live forever? Once a man is separated from God, what can he do but wither and die?

But how is he to be united to God? How is it possible for us to be taken into the three-Personal life?

---

* This corporate behaviour may, of course, be either better or worse than their individual behaviour.

You remember what I said in Chapter II about *begetting* and *making*. We are not begotten by God, we are only made by Him: in our natural state we are not sons of God, only (so to speak) statues. We have not got *Zoe* or spiritual life: only *Bios* or biological life which is presently going to run down and die. Now the whole offer which Christianity makes is this: that we can, if we let God have His way, come to share in the life of Christ. If we do, we shall then be sharing a life which was begotten, not made, which always has existed and always will exist. Christ is the Son of God. If we share in this kind of life we also shall be sons of God. We shall love the Father as He does and the Holy Ghost will arise in us. He came to this world and became a man in order to spread to other men the kind of life He has – by what I call 'good infection'. Every Christian is to become a little Christ. The whole purpose of becoming a Christian is simply nothing else.

5

THE OBSTINATE TOY

SOLDIERS

The Son of God became a man to enable men to become sons of God. We do not know – anyway, I do not know – how things would have worked if the human race had never rebelled against God and joined the enemy. Perhaps every man would have been 'in Christ', would have shared the life of the Son of God, from the moment he was born. Perhaps the *Bios* or natural life would have been drawn up into the *Zoe*, the uncreated life, at once and as a matter of course. But that is guesswork. You and I are concerned with the way things work now.

And the present state of things is this. The two kinds of life are now not only different (they would always have been that) but actually opposed. The natural life in each of us is something self-centred, something that wants to be petted and admired, to take advantage of other lives, to exploit the whole universe. And especially it wants to be left to itself: to keep well away from anything better or stronger or higher than it, anything that might make it feel small. It is afraid of the light and air of the spiritual world, just as people who have been brought up to be dirty are afraid of a bath. And in a sense it is quite right. It knows that if the spiritual life gets hold of it, all its self-centredness and self-will are going to be killed and it is ready to fight tooth and nail to avoid that.

Did you ever think, when you were a child, what fun it would be if your toys could come to life? Well suppose you could really have brought them to life. Imagine turning a tin soldier into a real little man. It would involve turning the tin into flesh. And suppose the tin soldier did not like it. He is not interested in flesh: all he sees is that the tin is being spoilt. He thinks you are killing him. He will do everything he can to prevent you. He will not be made into a man if he can help it.

What you would have done about that tin soldier I do not know. But what God did about us was this. The Second Person in God, the Son, became human Himself: was born into the world as an actual man – a real man of a particular height, with hair of a particular colour, speaking

435

a particular language, weighing so many stone. The Eternal Being, who knows everything and who created the whole universe, became not only a man but (before that) a baby, and before that a *foetus* inside a Woman's body. If you want to get the hang of it, think how you would like to become a slug or a crab.

The result of this was that you now had one man who really was what all men were intended to be: one man in whom the created life, derived from His Mother, allowed itself to be completely and perfectly turned into the begotten life. The natural human creature in Him was taken up fully into the divine Son. Thus in one instance humanity had, so to speak, arrived: had passed into the life of Christ. And because the whole difficulty for us is that the natural life has to be, in a sense, 'killed', He chose an earthly career which involved the killing of His human desires at every turn – poverty, misunderstanding from His own family, betrayal by one of His intimate friends, being jeered at and manhandled by the Police, and execution by torture. And then, after being thus killed – killed every day in a sense – the human creature in Him, because it was united to the divine Son, came to life again. The Man in Christ rose again: not only the God. That is the whole point. For the first time we saw a real man. One tin soldier – real tin, just like the rest – had come fully and splendidly alive.

And here, of course, we come to the point where my illustration about the tin soldier breaks down. In the case of real toy soldiers or statues, if one came to life, it would obviously make no difference to the rest. They are all separate. But human beings are not. They look separate because you see them walking about separately. But then, we are so made that we can see only the present moment. If we could see the past, then of course it would look different. For there was a time when every man was part of his mother, and (earlier still) part of his father as well: and when they were part of his grandparents. If you could see humanity spread out in time, as God sees it, it would not look like a lot of separate things dotted about. It would look like one single growing thing – rather like a very complicated tree. Every individual would appear connected with every other. And not only that. Individuals are not really separate from God any more than from one another. Every man, woman, and child all over the world is feeling and breathing at this moment only because God, so to speak, is 'keeping him going'.

Consequently, when Christ becomes man it is not really as if you could become one particular tin soldier. It is as if something which is always affecting the whole human mass begins, at one point, to affect the whole human mass in a new way. From that point the effect spreads through all mankind. It makes a difference to people who lived before Christ as well as to people who lived after Him. It makes a difference to people who have never heard of Him. It is like dropping into a glass of water one drop of something which gives a new taste or a new colour to the whole lot. But, of course, none of these illustrations really works perfectly. In the long run God is no one but Himself and what He does is like nothing else. You could hardly expect it to be.

What, then, is the difference which He has made to the whole human mass? It is just this; that the business of becoming a son of God, of being turned from a created thing into a begotten thing, of passing over from the temporary biological life into timeless 'spiritual' life, has been done for us. Humanity is already 'saved' in principle. We individuals have to appropriate that salvation. But the really tough work – the bit we could not have done for ourselves – has been done for us. We have not got to try to climb up into spiritual life by our own efforts; it has already come down into the human race. If we will only lay ourselves open to the one Man in whom it was fully present, and who, in spite of being God, is also a real man, He will do it in us and for us. Remember what I said about 'good infection'. One of our own race has this new life: if we get close to Him we shall catch it from Him.

Of course, you can express this in all sorts of different ways. You can say that Christ died for our sins. You may say that the Father has forgiven us because Christ has done for us what we ought to have done. You may say that we are washed in the blood of the Lamb. You may say that Christ has defeated death. They are all true. If any of them do not appeal to you, leave it alone and get on with the formula that does. And, whatever you do, do not start quarrelling with other people because they use a different formula from yours.

6

TWO NOTES

In order to avoid misunderstanding I here add notes on two points arising out of the last chapter.

(1) One sensible critic wrote asking me why, if God wanted sons instead of 'toy soldiers', He did not *beget* many sons at the outset instead of first *making* toy soldiers and then bringing them to life by such a difficult and painful process. One part of the answer to this question is fairly easy: the other part is probably beyond all human knowledge. The easy part is this. The process of being turned from a creature into a son would not have been difficult or painful if the human race had not turned away from God centuries ago. They were able to do this because He gave them free will: He gave them free will because a world of mere automata could never love and therefore never know infinite happiness. The difficult part is this. All Christians are agreed that there is, in the full and original sense, only one 'Son of God'. If we insist on asking 'But could there have been many?' we find ourselves in very deep water. Have the words 'Could have been' any sense at all when applied to God? You can say that one particular finite thing 'could have been' different from what it is, because it would have been different if something else had been different, and the something else would have been different if some third thing had been different, and so on. (The letters on this page would have been red if the printer had used red ink, and he would have used red ink if he had been instructed to, and so on.) But when you are talking about God – i.e. about the rock bottom, irreducible Fact on which all other facts depend – it is nonsensical to ask if it could have been otherwise. It is what it is, and there is an end of the matter. But quite apart from this, I find a difficulty about the very idea of the Father begetting many sons from all eternity. In order to be many they would have to be somehow different from one another. Two pennies have the same shape. How are they two? By occupying different places and containing different atoms. In other words, to think of them as different, we have had to bring in space and matter; in fact we have had to bring in 'Nature' or the

438

created universe. I can understand the distinction between the Father and the Son without bringing in space or matter, because the one begets and the other is begotten. The Father's relation to the Son is not the same as the Son's relation to the Father. But if there were several sons they would all be related to one another and to the Father in the same way. How would they differ from one another? One does not notice the difficulty at first, of course. One thinks one can form the idea of several 'sons'. But when I think closely, I find that the idea seemed possible only because I was vaguely imagining them as human forms standing about together in some kind of space. In other words, though I pretended to be thinking about something that exists before any universe was made, I was really smuggling in the picture of a universe and putting that something *inside* it. When I stop doing that and still try to think of the Father begetting many sons 'before all worlds' I find I am not really thinking of anything. The idea fades away into mere words. (Was Nature – space and time and matter – created precisely in order to make many-ness possible? Is there perhaps no other way of getting many eternal spirits except by first making many natural creatures, in a universe, and then spiritualising them? But of course all this is guesswork.)

(2) The idea that the whole human race is, in a sense, one thing – one huge organism, like a tree – must not be confused with the idea that individual differences do not matter or that real people, Tom and Nobby and Kate, are somehow less important than collective things like classes, races, and so forth. Indeed the two ideas are opposites. Things which are parts of a single organism may be very different from one another: things which are not, may be very alike. Six pennies are quite separate and very alike: my nose and my lungs are very different but they are only alive at all because they are parts of my body and share its common life. Christianity thinks of human individuals not as mere members of a group or items in a list, but as organs in a body – different from one another and each contributing what no other could. When you find yourself wanting to turn your children, or pupils, or even your neighbours, into people exactly like yourself, remember that God probably never meant them to be that. You and they are different organs, intended to do different things. On the other hand, when you are tempted not to bother about someone else's troubles because they are 'no business of yours', remember that though he is different from you he is part of the same organism as you. If you forget that he belongs to the same organism as yourself you will become an Individualist. If you forget that he is a different organ from you, if you want to suppress differences and make people all alike, you will become a Totalitarian. But a Christian must not be either a Totalitarian or an Individualist.

I feel a strong desire to tell you – and I expect you feel a strong desire to tell me – which of these two errors is the worse. That is the devil getting at us. He always sends errors into the world in pairs – pairs of opposites. And he always encourages us to spend a lot of time thinking which is the worse. You see why, of course? He relies on your extra dislike of the one error to draw you gradually into the opposite one. But do not let us be fooled. We have to keep our eyes on the goal and go straight through between both errors. We have no other concern than that with either of them.

7

LET'S PRETEND

May I once again start by putting two pictures, or two stories rather, into your minds? One is the story you have all read called *Beauty and the Beast*. The girl, you remember, had to marry a monster for some reason. And she did. She kissed it as if it were a man. And then, much to her relief, it really turned into a man and all went well. The other story is about someone who had to wear a mask; a mask which made him look much nicer than he really was. He had to wear it for years. And when he took it off he found his own face had grown to fit it. He was now really beautiful. What had begun as disguise had become a reality. I think both these stories may (in a fanciful way, of course) help to illustrate what I have to say in this chapter. Up till now, I have been trying to describe facts – what God is and what He has done. Now I want to talk about practice – what do we do next? What difference does all this theology make? It can start making a difference tonight. If you are interested enough to have read thus far you are probably interested enough to make a shot at saying your prayers: and, whatever else you say, you will probably say the Lord's Prayer.

Its very first words are *Our Father*. Do you now see what those words mean? They mean quite frankly, that you are putting yourself in the place of a son of God. To put it bluntly, you are *dressing up as Christ*. If you like, you are pretending. Because, of course, the moment you realise what the words mean, you realise that you are not a son of God. You are not a being like The Son of God, whose will and interests are at one with those of the Father: you are a bundle of self-centred fears, hopes, greeds, jealousies, and self-conceit, all doomed to death. So that, in a way, this dressing up as Christ is a piece of outrageous cheek. But the odd thing is that He has ordered us to do it.

Why? What is the good of pretending to be what you are not? Well, even on the human level, you know, there are two kinds of pretending. There is a bad kind, where the pretence is there instead of the real thing; as when a man pretends he is going to help you instead of really helping you. But there is also a good kind, where the pretence leads up to the real thing. When you are not feeling particularly friendly but know you ought to be, the best thing you can do, very often, is to put on a friendly manner and behave as if you were a nicer person than you actually are. And in a few minutes, as we have all noticed, you will be really feeling friendlier than you were. Very often the only way to get a quality in reality is to start behaving as if you had it already. That is why children's games are so important. They are always pretending to be grown-ups – playing soldiers, playing shop. But all the time, they are hardening their muscles and sharpening their wits so that the pretence of being grown-up helps them to grow up in earnest.

Now, the moment you realise 'Here I am, dressing up as Christ,' it is extremely likely that you will see at once some way in which at that very moment the pretence could be made less of a pretence and more of a reality. You will find several things going on in your mind which would not be going on there if you were really a son of God. Well, stop them. Or you may realise that, instead of saying your prayers, you ought to be downstairs writing a letter, or helping your wife to wash-up. Well, go and do it.

You see what is happening. The Christ Himself, the Son of God who is man (just like you) and God (just like His Father) is actually at your side and is already at that moment beginning to turn your pretence into a reality. This is not merely a fancy way of saying that your conscience is telling you what to do. If you simply ask your conscience, you get one result; if you remember that you are dressing up as Christ, you get a different one. There are lots of things which your conscience might not call definitely wrong (specially things in your mind) but which you will see at once you cannot go on doing if you are seriously trying to be like Christ. For you are no longer thinking simply about right and wrong; you are trying to catch the good infection from a Person. It is more like painting a portrait than like obeying a set of rules. And the odd thing is that while in one way it is much harder than keeping rules, in another way it is far easier.

The real Son of God is at your side. He is beginning to turn you into the same kind of thing as Himself. He is beginning, so to speak, to 'inject' His kind of life and thought, His *Zoe*, into you; beginning to turn the tin soldier into a live man. The part of you that does not like it is the part that is still tin.

Some of you may feel that this is very unlike your own experience. You may say 'I've never had the sense of being helped by an invisible Christ, but I often have been helped by other human beings.' That is rather like the woman in the first war who said that if there were a bread shortage it would not bother her house because they always ate toast. If there is no bread there will be no toast. If there were no help from Christ, there would be no help from other human beings. He works on us in all sorts of ways: not only through what we think our 'religious life'. He works through Nature, through our own bodies, through books, sometimes through experiences which seem (at the time) *anti*-Christian. When a young man who has been going to church in a routine way honestly realises that he does not believe in Christianity and stops going – provided he does it for honesty's sake and not just to annoy his parents – the spirit of Christ is probably nearer to him then than it ever was before. But above all, He works on us through each other.

Men are mirrors, or 'carriers' of Christ to other men. Sometimes unconscious carriers. This 'good infection' can be carried by those who have not got it themselves. People who were not Christians themselves helped me to Christianity. But usually it is those who know Him that bring Him to others. That is why the Church, the whole body of Christians showing Him to one another, is so important. You might say that when two Christians are following Christ together there is not twice as much Christianity as when they are apart, but sixteen times as much.

But do not forget this. At first it is natural for a baby to take its mother's milk without knowing its mother. It is equally natural for us to see the man who helps us without seeing Christ behind him. But we must not remain babies. We must go on to recognise the real Giver. It is madness not to. Because, if we do not, we shall be relying on human beings. And that is going to let us down. The best of them will make mistakes; all of them will die. We must be thankful to all the people who have helped us, we must honour them and love them. But never, never pin your whole faith on any human being: not if he is the best and wisest in the whole world. There are lots of nice things you can do with sand: but do not try building a house on it.

And now we begin to see what it is that the New Testament is always talking about. It talks about Christians 'being born again'; it talks about them 'putting on Christ'; about Christ 'being formed in us'; about our coming to 'have the mind of Christ'.

Put right out of your head the idea that these are only fancy ways of saying that Christians are to read what Christ said and try to carry it out – as a man may read what Plato or Marx said and try to carry it out. They mean something much more than that. They mean that a real Person, Christ, here and now, in that very room where you are saying your prayers, is doing things to you. It is not a question of a good man who died two thousand years ago. It is a living Man, still as much a man as you, and still as much God as He was when He created the world, really coming and interfering with your very self; killing the old natural self in you and replacing it with the kind of self He has. At first, only for moments. Then for longer periods. Finally, if all goes well, turning you permanently into a different sort of thing; into a new little Christ, a being which, in its own small way, has the same kind of life as God; which shares in His power, joy, knowledge and eternity. And soon we make two other discoveries.

(1) We begin to notice, besides our particular sinful acts, our sinfulness; begin to be alarmed not only about what we do, but about what we are. This may sound rather difficult, so I will try to make it clear from my own case. When I come to my evening prayers and try to reckon up the sins of the day, nine times out of ten the most obvious one is some sin against charity; I have sulked or snapped or sneered or snubbed or stormed. And the excuse that immediately springs to my mind is that the provocation was so sudden and unexpected; I was caught off my guard, I had not time to collect myself. Now that may be an extenuating circumstance as regards those particular acts: they would obviously be worse if they had been deliberate and premeditated. On the other hand, surely what a man does when he is taken off his guard is the best evidence for what sort of a man he is? Surely what pops out before the man has time to put on a disguise is the truth? If there are rats in a cellar you are most likely to see them if you go in very suddenly. But the suddenness does not create the rats: it only prevents them from hiding. In the same way the suddenness of the provocation does not make me an ill-tempered man; it only shows me what an ill-tempered man I am. The rats are always there in the cellar, but if you go in shouting and noisily they will have taken cover before you switch on the light. Apparently the rats of resentment and vindictiveness are always there in the cellar of my soul. Now that cellar is out of reach of my conscious will. I can to some extent control my acts: I have no direct control over my temperament. And if (as I said before) what we are matters even more than what we do – if, indeed, what we do matters chiefly as evidence of what we are – then it follows that the change which I most need to undergo is a change that my own direct, voluntary efforts cannot bring about. And this applies to my good actions too. How many of them were done for the right motive? How many for fear of public opinion, or a desire to show off? How many from a sort of obstinacy or sense of superiority which, in different circumstances, might equally have led to some very bad act? But I cannot, by direct moral effort, give myself new motives. After the first few steps in the Christian life we realise that everything which really needs to be done in our souls can be done only by God. And that brings us to something which has been very misleading in my language up to now.

(2) I have been talking as if it were we who did everything. In reality, of course, it is God who does everything. We, at most, allow it to be done to us. In a sense you might even say it is God who does the pretending. The Three-Personal God, so to speak, sees before Him in fact a self-centred, greedy, grumbling, rebellious human animal. But He says 'Let us pretend that this is not a mere creature, but our Son. It is like Christ in so far as it is a Man, for He became Man. Let us pretend that it is also like Him in Spirit. Let us treat it as if it were what in fact it is not. Let us pretend in order to make the

pretence into a reality.' God looks at you as if you were a little Christ: Christ stands beside you to turn you into one. I daresay this idea of a divine make-believe sounds rather strange at first. But, is it so strange really? Is not that how the higher thing always raises the lower? A mother teaches her baby to talk by talking to it as if it understood long before it really does. We treat our dogs as if they were 'almost human': that is why they really become 'almost human' in the end.

IS CHRISTIANITY
HARD OR EASY?

In the previous chapter we were considering the Christian idea of 'putting on Christ', or first 'dressing up' as a son of God in order that you may finally become a real son. What I want to make clear is that this is not one among many jobs a Christian has to do; and it is not a sort of special exercise for the top class. It is the whole of Christianity. Christianity offers nothing else at all. And I should like to point out how it differs from ordinary ideas of 'morality' and 'being good'.

The ordinary idea which we all have before we become Christians is this. We take as starting point our ordinary self with its various desires and interests. We then admit that something else – call it 'morality' or 'decent behaviour', or 'the good of society' – has claims on this self: claims which interfere with its own desires. What we mean by 'being good' is giving in to those claims. Some of the things the ordinary self wanted to do turn out to be what we call 'wrong': well, we must give them up. Other things, which the self did not want to do, turn out to be what we call 'right': well, we shall have to do them. But we are hoping all the time that when all the demands have been met, the poor natural self will still have some chance, and some time, to get on with its own life and do what it likes. In fact, we are very like an honest man paying his taxes. He pays them all right, but he does hope that there will be enough left over for him to live on. Because we are still taking our natural self as the starting point.

As long as we are thinking that way, one or other of two results is likely to follow. Either we give up trying to be good, or else we become very unhappy indeed. For, make no mistake: if you are really going to try to meet all the demands made on the natural self, it will not have enough left over to live on. The more you obey your conscience, the more your conscience will demand of you. And your natural self, which is thus being starved and hampered and worried at every turn, will get angrier and angrier. In the end, you will either give up trying to be good, or else become one of those people who, as they say, 'live for others' but always in a discontented, grumbling way – always wondering why the others do not notice it more and always making a martyr of yourself. And once you have become that you will be a far greater pest to anyone who has to live with you than you would have been if you had remained frankly selfish.

The Christian way is different: harder, and easier. Christ says 'Give me All. I don't want so much of your time and so much of your money and so much of your work: I want You. I have not come to torment your natural self, but to kill it. No half-measures are any good. I don't want to cut off a branch here and a branch there, I want to have the whole tree down. I don't want to drill the tooth, or crown it, or stop it, but to have it out. Hand over the whole natural self, all the desires which you think innocent as well as the ones you think wicked – the whole outfit. I will give you a new self instead. In fact, I will give you Myself: my own will shall become yours.'

Both harder and easier than what we are all trying to do. You have noticed, I expect, that Christ Himself sometimes describes the Christian way as very hard, sometimes as very easy. He says, 'Take up your Cross' – in other words, it is like going to be beaten to death in a concentration camp. Next minute he says, 'My yoke is easy and my burden light.' He means both. And one can just see why both are true.

Teachers will tell you that the laziest boy in the class is the one who works hardest in the end. They mean this. If you give two boys, say, a proposition in geometry to do, the one who is prepared to take trouble will try to understand it. The lazy boy will try to learn it by heart because, for the moment, that needs less effort. But six months later, when they are preparing for an exam, that lazy boy is doing hours and hours of miserable drudgery over things the other boy understands, and positively enjoys, in a few minutes. Laziness means more work in the long run. Or look at it this way. In a battle, or in mountain climbing, there is often one thing which it takes a lot of pluck to do; but it is also, in the long run, the safest thing to do. If you funk it, you will find yourself, hours later, in far worse danger. The cowardly thing is also the most dangerous thing.

It is like that here. The terrible thing, the almost impossible thing, is to hand over your whole self – all your wishes and precautions – to Christ. But it is far easier than what we are all trying to do instead. For what we are trying to do is to remain what we call 'ourselves', to keep personal happiness as our great aim in life, and yet at the same time be 'good'. We are all trying to let our mind and heart go their own way – centred on money or pleasure or ambition – and hoping, in spite of this, to behave honestly and chastely and humbly. And that is exactly what Christ warned us you could not do. As He said, a thistle cannot produce figs. If I am a field that contains nothing but grass-seed, I cannot produce wheat. Cutting the grass may keep it short: but I shall still produce grass and no wheat. If I want to produce wheat, the change must go deeper than the surface. I must be ploughed up and re-sown.

That is why the real problem of the Christian life comes where people do not usually look for it. It comes the very moment you wake up each morning. All your wishes and hopes for the day rush at you like wild animals. And the first job each morning consists simply in shoving them all back; in listening to that other voice, taking that other point of view, letting that other larger, stronger, quieter life come flowing in. And so on, all day. Standing back from all your natural fussings and frettings; coming in out of the wind.

We can only do it for moments at first. But from those moments the new sort of life will be spreading through our system: because now we are letting Him work at the right part of us. It is the difference between paint, which is merely laid on the surface, and a dye or stain which soaks right through. He never talked vague, idealistic gas. When he said, 'Be perfect,' He meant it. He meant that we must go in for the full treatment. It is hard; but the sort of compromise we are all hankering after is harder – in fact, it is impossible. It may be hard for an egg to turn into a bird: it would be a jolly sight harder for it to learn to fly while remaining an egg. We are like eggs at present. And you cannot go on indefinitely being just an ordinary, decent egg. We must be hatched or go bad.

May I come back to what I said before? This is the whole of Christianity. There is nothing else. It is so easy to get muddled about that. It is easy to think that the Church has a lot of different objects – education, building, missions, holding services. Just as it is easy to think the State has a lot of different objects – military, political, economic, and what not. But in a way things are much simpler than that. The State exists simply to promote and to protect the ordinary happiness of human beings in this life. A husband and wife chatting over a fire, a couple of friends having a game of darts in a pub, a man reading a book in his own room or digging in his own garden – that is what the State is there for. And unless they are helping to increase and prolong and protect such moments, all the laws, parliaments, armies, courts, police, economics, etc., are simply a waste of time. In the same way the Church exists for nothing else but to draw men into Christ, to make them little Christs. If they are not doing that, all the cathedrals, clergy, missions, sermons, even the Bible itself, are simply a waste of time. God became Man for no other purpose. It is even doubtful, you know, whether the whole universe was created for any other purpose. It says in the Bible that the whole universe was made for Christ and that everything is to be gathered together in Him. I do not suppose any of us can understand how this will happen as regards the whole universe. We do not know what (if anything) lives in the parts of it that are millions of miles away from this Earth. Even on this Earth we do not know how it applies to things other than men. After all, that is what you would expect. We have been shown the plan only in so far as it concerns ourselves.

I sometimes like to imagine that I can just see how it might apply to other things. I think I can see how the higher animals are in a sense drawn into Man when he loves them and makes them (as he does) much more nearly human than they would otherwise be. I can even see a sense in which the dead things and plants are drawn into Man as he studies them and uses and appreciates them. And if there were intelligent creatures in other worlds they might do the same with their worlds. It might be that when intelligent creatures entered into Christ they would, in that way, bring all the other things in along with them. But I do not know: it is only a guess.

What we have been told is how we men can be drawn into Christ – can become part of that wonderful present which the young Prince of the universe wants to offer to His Father – that present which is Himself and therefore us in Him. It is the only thing we were made for. And there are strange, exciting hints in the Bible that when we are drawn in, a great many other things in Nature will begin to come right. The bad dream will be over: it will be morning.

9

COUNTING THE COST

I find a good many people have been bothered by what I said in the previous chapter about Our Lord's words, 'Be ye perfect'. Some people seem to think this means 'Unless you are perfect, I will not help you'; and as we cannot be perfect, then, if He meant that, our position is hopeless. But I do not think He did mean that. I think He meant 'The only help I will give is help to become perfect. You may want something less: but I will give you nothing less.'

Let me explain. When I was a child I often had toothache, and I knew that if I went to my mother she would give me something which would deaden the pain for that night and let me get to sleep. But I did not go to my mother – at least, not till the pain became very bad. And the reason I did not go was this. I did not doubt she would give me the aspirin; but I knew she would also do something else. I knew she would take me to the dentist next morning. I could not get what I wanted out of her without getting something more, which I did not want. I wanted immediate relief from pain: but I could not get it without having my teeth set permanently right. And I knew those dentists: I knew they started fiddling about with all sorts of other teeth which had not yet begun to ache. They would not let sleeping dogs lie, if you gave them an inch they took an ell.

Now, if I may put it that way, Our Lord is like the dentists. If you give Him an inch, He will take an ell. Dozens of people go to Him to be cured of some one particular sin which they are ashamed of (like masturbation or physical cowardice) or which is obviously spoiling daily life (like bad temper or drunkenness). Well, He will cure it all right: but He will not stop there. That may be all you asked; but if once you call Him in, He will give you the full treatment.

That is why He warned people to 'count the cost' before becoming Christians. 'Make no mistake,' He says, 'if you let me, I will make you perfect. The moment you put yourself in My hands, that is what you are in for. Nothing less, or other, than that. You have free will, and if you choose, you can push Me away. But if you do not push Me away, understand that I am going to see this job through. Whatever suffering it may cost you in your earthly life, whatever inconceivable purification it may cost you after death, whatever it costs Me, I will never rest, nor let you rest, until you are literally perfect – until my Father can say without reservation that He is well pleased with you, as He said He was well pleased with me. This I can do and will do. But I will not do anything less.'

And yet – this is the other and equally important side of it – this Helper who will, in the long run, be satisfied with nothing less than absolute perfection, will also be delighted with the first feeble, stumbling effort you make tomorrow to do the simplest duty. As a great Christian writer (George MacDonald) pointed out, every father is pleased at the baby's first attempt to walk: no father would be satisfied with anything less than a firm, free, manly walk in a grown-up son. In the same way, he said, 'God is easy to please, but hard to satisfy.'

The practical upshot is this. On the one hand, God's demand for perfection need not discourage you in the least in your present attempts to be good, or even in your present failures. Each time you fall He will pick you up again. And He knows perfectly well that your own efforts are never going to bring you anywhere near perfection. On the other hand, you must realise from the outset that the goal towards which He is beginning to guide you is absolute perfection; and no power in the whole universe, except you yourself, can prevent Him from taking you to that goal. That is what you are in for. And it is very important to realise that. If we do not, then we are very likely to start pulling back and resisting Him after a certain point. I think that many of us, when Christ has enabled us to overcome one or two sins that were an obvious nuisance, are inclined to feel (though we do not put it into words) that we are now good enough. He has done all we wanted Him to do, and we should be obliged if He would now leave us alone. As we say 'I never expected to be a saint, I only wanted to be a decent ordinary chap.' And we imagine when we say this that we are being humble.

But this is the fatal mistake. Of course we never wanted, and never asked, to be made into the sort of creatures He is going to make us into. But the question is not what we intended ourselves to be, but what He intended us to be when He made us. He is the inventor, we are only the machine. He is the painter, we are only the picture. How should we know what He means us to be like? You see, He has already made us something very different from what we were. Long ago, before we were born, when we were inside our mothers' bodies, we passed through various stages. We were once rather like vegetables, and once rather like fish: it was only at a later stage that we became like human babies. And if we had been conscious at those earlier stages, I daresay we should have been quite contented to stay as vegetables or fish – should not have wanted to be made into babies. But all the time He knew His plan for us and was determined to carry it out. Something the same is now happening at a higher level. We may be content to remain what we call 'ordinary people': but He is determined to carry out a quite different plan. To shrink back from that plan is not humility: it is laziness and cowardice. To submit to it is not conceit or megalomania; it is obedience.

Here is another way of putting the two sides of the truth. On the one hand we must never imagine that our own unaided efforts can be relied on to carry us even through the next twenty-four hours as 'decent' people. If He does not support us, not one of us is safe from some gross sin. On the other hand, no possible degree of holiness or heroism which has ever been recorded of the greatest saints is beyond what He is determined to produce in every one of us in the end. The job will not be completed in this life; but He means to get us as far as possible before death.

That is why we must not be surprised if we are in for a rough time. When a man turns to Christ and seems to be getting on pretty well (in the sense that some of his bad habits are now corrected) he often feels that it would now be natural if things went fairly smoothly. When troubles come along – illnesses, money troubles, new kinds of temptation – he is disappointed. These things, he feels, might have been necessary to rouse him and make him repent in his bad old days; but why now? Because God is forcing him on, or up, to a higher level: putting him into situations where he will have to be very much braver, or more patient, or more loving, than he ever dreamed of being before. It seems to us all unnecessary: but that is because we have not yet had the slightest notion of the tremendous thing He means to make of us.

I find I must borrow yet another parable from George MacDonald. Imagine yourself as a living house. God comes in to rebuild that house. At first, perhaps, you can understand what He is doing. He is getting the drains right and stopping the leaks in the roof and so on: you knew that those jobs needed doing and so you are not surprised. But presently he starts knocking the house about in a way that hurts abominably and does not seem to make sense. What on earth is He up to? The explanation is that He is building quite a different house from the one you thought of – throwing out a new wing here, putting on an extra floor there, running up towers, making courtyards. You thought you were going to be made into a decent little cottage: but He is building a palace. He intends to come and live in it Himself.

The command *Be ye perfect* is not idealistic gas. Nor is it a command to do the impossible. He is going to make us into creatures that can obey that command. He said (in the Bible) that we were 'gods' and He is going to make good His words. If we let Him – for we can prevent Him, if we choose – He will make the feeblest and filthiest of us into a god or goddess, a dazzling, radiant, immortal creature, pulsating all through with such energy and joy and wisdom and love as we cannot now imagine, a bright stainless mirror which reflects back to God perfectly (though, of course, on a smaller scale) His own boundless power and delight and goodness. The process will be long and in parts very painful, but that is what we are in for. Nothing less. He meant what He said.

NICE PEOPLE OR

NEW MEN

He meant what He said. Those who put themselves in His hands will become perfect, as He is perfect – perfect in love, wisdom, joy, beauty, and immortality. The change will not be completed in this life, for death is an important part of the treatment. How far the change will have gone before death in any particular Christian is uncertain.

I think this is the right moment to consider a question which is often asked: If Christianity is true why are not all Christians obviously nicer than all non-Christians? What lies behind that question is partly something very reasonable and partly something that is not reasonable at all. The reasonable part is this. If conversion to Christianity makes no improvement in a man's outward actions – if he continues to be just as snobbish or spiteful or envious or ambitious as he was before – then I think we must suspect that his 'conversion' was largely imaginary; and after one's original conversion, every time one thinks one has made an advance, that is the test to apply. Fine feelings, new insights, greater interest in 'religion' mean nothing unless they make our actual behaviour better; just as in an illness 'feeling better' is not much good if the thermometer shows that your temperature is still going up. In that sense the outer world is quite right to judge Christianity by its results. Christ told us to judge by results. A tree is known by its fruit; or, as we say, the proof of the pudding is in the eating. When we Christians behave badly, or fail to behave well, we are making Christianity unbelievable to the outside world. The war-time posters told us that Careless Talk costs Lives. It is equally true that Careless Lives cost Talk. Our careless lives set the outer world talking; and we give them grounds for talking in a way that throws doubt on the truth of Christianity itself.

But there is another way of demanding results in which the outer world may be quite illogical. They may demand not merely that each man's life should improve if he becomes a Christian: they may also demand before they believe in Christianity that they should see the whole world neatly divided into two camps – Christian and non-Christian – and that all the people in the first camp at any given moment should be obviously nicer than all the people in the second. This is unreasonable on several grounds.

(1) In the first place the situation in the actual world is much more complicated than that. The world does not consist of 100 per cent. Christians and 100 per cent. non-Christians. There are people (a great many of them) who are slowly ceasing to be Christians but who still call themselves by that name: some of them are clergymen. There are other people who are slowly becoming Christians though they do not yet call themselves so. There are people who do not accept the full Christian doctrine about Christ but who are so strongly attracted by Him that they are His in a much deeper sense than they themselves understand. There are people in other religions who are being led by God's secret influence to concentrate on those parts of their religion which are in agreement with Christianity, and who thus belong to Christ without knowing it. For example, a Buddhist of good will may be led to concentrate more and more on the Buddhist teaching about mercy and to leave in the background (though he might still say he believed) the Buddhist teaching on certain other points. Many of the good Pagans long before Christ's birth may have been in this position. And always, of course, there are a great many people who are just confused in mind and have a lot of inconsistent beliefs all jumbled up together. Consequently, it is not much use trying to make judgments about Christians and non-Christians in the mass. It is some use comparing cats and dogs, or even men and women, in the mass, because there one knows definitely which is which. Also, an animal does not turn (either slowly or suddenly) from a dog into a cat. But when we are comparing Christians in general with non-Christians in general, we are usually not thinking about real people whom we know at all, but only about two vague ideas which we have got from novels and newspapers. If you want to compare the bad Christian and the good Atheist, you must think about two real specimens whom you have actually met. Unless we come down to brass tacks in that way, we shall only be wasting time.

(2) Suppose we have come down to brass tacks and are now talking not about an imaginary Christian and an imaginary non-Christian, but about two real people in our own neighbourhood. Even then we must be careful to ask the right question. If Christianity is true then it ought to follow (a) That any Christian will be nicer than the same person would be if he were not a Christian. (b) That any man who becomes a Christian will be nicer than he was before. Just in the same way, if the advertisements of Whitesmile's toothpaste are true it ought to follow (a) That anyone who uses it will have better teeth than the same person would have if he did not use it. (b) That if anyone begins to use it his teeth will improve. But to point out that I, who use Whitesmile's (and also have inherited bad teeth from both my parents) have not got as fine a set as some healthy young negro who never used any

toothpaste at all, does not, by itself, prove that the advertisements are untrue: Christian Miss Bates may have an unkinder tongue than unbelieving Dick Firkin. That, by itself, does not tell us whether Christianity works. The question is what Miss Bates's tongue would be like if she were not a Christian and what Dick's would be like if he became one. Miss Bates and Dick, as a result of natural causes and early upbringing, have certain temperaments: Christianity professes to put both temperaments under new management if they will allow it to do so. What you have a right to ask is whether that management, if allowed to take over, improves the concern. Everyone knows that what is being managed in Dick Firkin's case is much 'nicer' than what is being managed in Miss Bates's. That is not the point. To judge the management of a factory, you must consider not only the output but the plant. Considering the plant at Factory A it may be a wonder that it turns out anything at all; considering the first-class outfit at Factory B its output, though high, may be a great deal lower than it ought to be. No doubt the good manager at Factory A is going to put in new machinery as soon as he can, but that takes time. In the meantime low output does not prove that he is a failure.

(3) And now, let us go a little deeper. The manager is going to put in new machinery: before Christ has finished with Miss Bates, she is going to be very 'nice' indeed. But if we left it at that, it would sound as though Christ's only aim was to pull Miss Bates up to the same level on which Dick had been all along. We have been talking, in fact, as if Dick were all right; as if Christianity was something nasty people needed and nice ones could afford to do without; and as if niceness was all that God demanded. But this would be a fatal mistake. The truth is that in God's eyes Dick Firkin needs 'saving' every bit as much as Miss Bates. In one sense (I will explain what sense in a moment) niceness hardly comes into the question.

You cannot expect God to look at Dick's placid temper and friendly disposition exactly as we do. They result from natural causes which God Himself creates. Being merely temperamental, they will all disappear if Dick's digestion alters. The niceness, in fact, is God's gift to Dick, not Dick's gift to God. In the same way, God has allowed natural causes, working in a world spoiled by centuries of sin to produce in Miss Bates the narrow mind and jangled nerves which account for most of her nastiness. He intends, in His own good time, to set that part of her right. But that is not, for God, the critical part of the business. It presents no difficulties. It is not what He is anxious about. What He is watching and waiting and working for is something that is not easy even for God, because, from the nature of the case, even He cannot produce it by a mere act of power. He is waiting and watching for it both in Miss Bates and in Dick Firkin. It is something they can freely give Him or freely refuse to Him. Will they, or will they not, turn to

Him and thus fulfil the only purpose for which they were created? Their free will is trembling inside them like the needle of a compass. But this is a needle that can choose. It *can* point to its true North; but it need not. Will the needle swing round, and settle, and point to God?

He can help it to do so. He cannot force it. He cannot, so to speak, put out His own hand and pull it into the right position, for then it would not be free will any more. Will it point North? That is the question on which all hangs. Will Miss Bates and Dick offer their natures to God? The question whether the natures they offer or withhold are, at that moment, nice or nasty ones, is of secondary importance. God can see to that part of the problem.

Do not misunderstand me. Of course God regards a nasty nature as a bad and deplorable thing. And, of course, He regards a nice nature as a good thing – good like bread, or sunshine, or water. But these are the good things which He gives and we receive. He created Dick's sound nerves and good digestion, and there is plenty more where they came from. It costs God nothing, so far as we know, to create nice things: but to convert rebellious wills cost His crucifixion. And because they are wills they can – in nice people just as much as in nasty ones – refuse His request. And then, because that niceness in Dick was merely part of nature, it will all go to pieces in the end. Nature herself will all pass away. Natural causes come together in Dick to make a pleasant psychological pattern, just as they come together in a sunset to make a pleasant pattern of colours. Presently (for that is how nature works) they will fall apart again and the pattern in both cases will disappear. Dick has had the chance to turn (or rather, to allow God to turn) that momentary pattern into the beauty of an eternal spirit: and he has not taken it.

There is a paradox here. As long as Dick does not turn to God, he thinks his niceness is his own, and just as long as he thinks that, it is not his own. It is when Dick realises that his niceness is not his own but a gift from God, and when he offers it back to God – it is just then that it begins to be really his own. For now Dick is beginning to take a share in his own creation. The only things we can keep are the things we freely give to God. What we try to keep for ourselves is just what we are sure to lose.

We must, therefore, not be surprised if we find among the Christians some people who are still nasty. There is even, when you come to think it over, a reason why nasty people might be expected to turn to Christ in greater numbers than nice ones. That was what people objected to about Christ during His life on earth: He seemed to attract 'such awful people'. That is what people still object to and always will. Do you not see why? Christ said 'Blessed are the poor' and 'How hard it is for the rich to enter the Kingdom,' and no doubt He primarily meant the economically rich and economically poor. But do not His words also apply to another kind of riches and poverty? One of the dangers of having a lot of money is that you may be quite satisfied with the kinds of happiness money can give and so fail to realise your need for God. If everything seems to come simply by signing cheques, you may forget that you are at every moment totally dependent on God. Now quite plainly, natural gifts carry with them a similar danger. If you have sound nerves and intelligence and health and popularity and a good upbringing, you are likely to be quite satisfied with your character as it is. 'Why drag God into it?' you may ask. A certain level of good conduct comes fairly easily to you. You are not one of those wretched creatures who are always being tripped up by sex, or dipsomania, or nervousness, or bad temper. Everyone says you are a nice chap and (between ourselves) you agree with them. You are quite likely to believe that all this niceness is your own doing: and you may easily not feel the need for any better kind of goodness. Often people who have all these natural kinds of goodness cannot be brought to recognise their need for Christ at all until, one day, the natural goodness lets them down and their self-satisfaction is shattered. In other words, it is hard for those who are 'rich' in this sense to enter the Kingdom.

It is very different for the nasty people – the little, low, timid, warped, thin-blooded, lonely people, or the passionate, sensual, unbalanced people. If they make any attempt at goodness at all, they learn, in double quick time, that they need help. It is Christ or nothing for them. It is taking up the cross and following – or else despair. They are the lost sheep; He came specially to find them. They are (in one very real and terrible sense) the 'poor': He blessed them. They are the 'awful set' He goes about with – and of course the Pharisees say still, as they said from the first, 'If there were anything in Christianity those people would not be Christians.'

There is either a warning or an encouragement here for every one of us. If you are a nice person – if virtue comes easily to you – beware! Much is expected from those to whom much is given. If you mistake for your own merits what are really God's gifts to you through nature, and if you are contented with simply being nice, you are still a rebel: and all those gifts will only make your fall more terrible, your corruption more complicated, your bad example more disastrous. The Devil was an archangel once; his natural gifts were as far above yours as yours are above those of a chimpanzee.

But if you are a poor creature – poisoned by a wretched upbringing in some house full of vulgar jealousies and senseless quarrels – saddled, by no choice of your own, with some loathsome sexual perversion – nagged day in and day out by an inferiority complex that makes you snap at your best friends – do not despair. He knows all about it. You are one of the poor whom He blessed. He knows what a wretched machine you are trying to drive. Keep on. Do what you can. One day (perhaps in another world, but perhaps far sooner than that) He will fling it on the scrap-heap and give you a new one. And then you may astonish us all – not least yourself: for you have learned your driving in a hard school. (Some of the last will be first and some of the first will be last).

'Niceness' – wholesome, integrated personality – is an excellent thing. We must try by every medical, educational, economic, and political means in our power to produce a world where as many people as possible grow up 'nice'; just as we must try to produce a world where all have plenty to eat. But we must not suppose that even if we succeeded in making everyone nice we should have saved their souls. A world of nice people, content in their own niceness, looking no further, turned away from God, would be just as desperately in need of salvation as a miserable world – and might even be more difficult to save.

For mere improvement is not redemption, though redemption always improves people even here and now and will, in the end, improve them to a degree we cannot yet imagine. God became man to turn creatures into sons: not simply to produce better men of the old kind but to produce a new kind of man. It is not like teaching a horse to jump better and better but like turning a horse into a winged creature. Of course, once it has got its wings, it will soar over fences which could never have been jumped and thus beat the natural horse at its own game. But there may be a period, while the wings are just beginning to grow, when it cannot do so: and at that stage the lumps on the shoulders – no one could tell by looking at them that they are going to be wings – may even give it an awkward appearance.

But perhaps we have already spent too long on this question. If what you want is an argument against Christianity (and I well remember how eagerly I looked for such arguments when I began to be afraid it was true) you can easily find some stupid and unsatisfactory Christian and say, 'So there's your boasted new man! Give me the old kind.' But if once you have begun to see that Christianity is on other grounds probable, you will know in your heart that this is only evading the issue. What can you ever really know of other people's souls – of their temptations, their opportunities, their struggles? One soul in the whole creation you do know: and it is the only one whose fate is placed in your hands. If there is a God, you are, in a sense, alone with Him. You cannot put Him off with speculations about your next door neighbours or memories of what you have read in books. What will all that chatter and hearsay count (will you even be able to remember it?) when the anaesthetic fog which we call 'nature' or 'the real world' fades away and the Presence in which you have always stood becomes palpable, immediate, and unavoidable?

11

THE NEW MEN

In the last chapter I compared Christ's work of making New Men to the process of turning a horse into a winged creature. I used that extreme example in order to emphasise the point that it is not mere improvement but Transformation. The nearest parallel to it in the world of nature is to be found in the remarkable transformations we can make in insects by applying certain rays to them. Some people think this is how Evolution worked. The alterations in creatures on which it all depends may have been produced by rays coming from outer space. (Of course once the alterations are there, what they call 'Natural Selection' gets to work on them: i.e. the useful alterations survive and the other ones get weeded out.)

Perhaps a modern man can understand the Christian idea best if he takes it in connection with Evolution. Everyone now knows about Evolution (though, of course, some educated people disbelieve it): everyone has been told that man has evolved from lower types of life. Consequently, people often wonder 'What is the next step? When is the thing beyond man going to appear?' Imaginative writers try sometimes to picture this next step – the 'Superman' as they call him; but they usually only succeed in picturing someone a good deal nastier than man as we know him and then try to make up for that by sticking on extra legs or arms. But supposing the next step was to be something even more different from the earlier steps than they ever dreamed of? And is it not very likely it would be? Thousands of centuries ago huge, very heavily armoured creatures were evolved. If anyone had at that time been watching the course of Evolution he would probably have expected that it was going to go on to heavier and heavier armour. But he would have been wrong. The future had a card up its sleeve which nothing at that time would have led him to expect. It was going to spring on him little, naked, unarmoured animals which had better brains: and with those brains they were going to master the whole planet. They were not merely going to have more power than the prehistoric monsters, they were going to have a new kind of power. The next step was not only going to be different, but different with a new kind of difference. The stream of Evolution was not going to flow on in the direction in which he saw it flowing: it was in fact going to take a sharp bend.

Now it seems to me that most of the popular guesses at the Next Step are making just the same sort of mistake. People see (or at any rate they think they see) men developing great brains and getting greater mastery over nature. And because they think the stream is flowing in that direction, they imagine it will go on flowing in that direction. But I cannot help thinking that the Next Step will be really new; it will go off in a direction you could never have dreamed of. It would hardly be worth calling a New Step unless it did. I should expect not merely difference but a new kind of difference. I should expect not merely change but a new method of producing the change. Or, to make an Irish bull, I should expect the next stage in Evolution not to be a stage in Evolution at all: should expect that Evolution itself as a method of producing change will be superseded. And finally, I should not be surprised if, when the thing happened, very few people noticed that it was happening.

Now, if you care to talk in these terms, the Christian view is precisely that the Next Step has already appeared. And it is really new. It is not a change from brainy men to brainier men: it is a change that goes off in a totally different direction – a change from being creatures of God to being sons of God. The first instance appeared in Palestine two thousand years ago. In a sense, the change is not 'Evolution' at all, because it is not something arising out of the natural process of events but something coming into nature from outside. But that is what I should expect. We arrived at our idea of 'Evolution' from studying the past. If there are real novelties in store then of course our idea, based on the past, will not really cover them. And in fact this New Step differs from all previous ones not only in coming from outside nature but in several other ways as well.

(1) It is not carried on by sexual reproduction. Need we be surprised at that? There was a time before sex had appeared; development used to go on by different methods. Consequently, we might have expected that there would come a time when sex disappeared, or else (which is what is actually happening) a time when sex, though it continued to exist, ceased to be the main channel of a development.

(2) At the earlier stages living organisms have had either no choice or very little choice about taking the new step. Progress was, in the main, something that happened to them, not something that they did. But the new step, the step from being creatures to being sons, is voluntary. At least, voluntary in one sense. It is not voluntary in the sense that we, of ourselves, could have chosen to take it or could even have imagined it; but it is voluntary in the sense that when it is offered to us, we can refuse it. We can, if we

please, shrink back; we can dig in our heels and let the new Humanity go on without us.

(3) I have called Christ the 'first instance' of the new man. But of course He is something much more than that. He is not merely a new man, one specimen of the species, but *the* new man. He is the origin and centre and life of all the new men. He came into the created universe, of His own will, bringing with Him the *Zoe*, the new life. (I mean new to us, of course: in its own place *Zoe* has existed for ever and ever.) And He transmits it not by heredity but by what I have called 'good infection'. Everyone who gets it gets it by personal contact with Him. Other men become 'new' by being 'in Him'.

(4) This step is taken at a different speed from the previous ones. Compared with the development of man on this planet, the diffusion of Christianity over the human race seems to go like a flash of lightning – for two thousand years is almost nothing in the history of the universe. (Never forget that we are all still 'the early Christians'. The present wicked and wasteful divisions between us are, let us hope, a disease of infancy: we are still teething. The outer world, no doubt, thinks just the opposite. It thinks we are dying of old age. But it has thought that very often before. Again and again it has thought Christianity was dying, dying by persecutions from without and corruptions from within, by the rise of Mohammedanism, the rise of the physical sciences, the rise of great anti-Christian revolutionary movements. But every time the world has been disappointed. Its first disappointment was over the crucifixion. The Man came to life again. In a sense – and I quite realise how frightfully unfair it must seem to them – that has been happening ever since. They keep on killing the thing that He started: and each time, just as they are patting down the earth on its grave, they suddenly hear that it is still alive and has even broken out in some new place. No wonder they hate us.)

(5) The stakes are higher. By falling back at the earlier steps a creature lost, at the worst, its few years of life on this earth: very often it did not lose even that. By falling back at this step we lose a prize which is (in the strictest sense of the word) infinite. For now the critical moment has arrived. Century by century God has guided nature up to the point of producing creatures which can (if they will) be taken right out of nature, turned into 'gods'. Will they allow themselves to be taken? In a way, it is like the crisis of birth. Until we rise and follow Christ we are still parts of Nature, still in the womb of our great mother. Her pregnancy has been long and painful and anxious, but it has reached its climax. The great moment has come. Everything is ready. The Doctor has arrived. Will the birth 'go off all right'? But of course it differs from an ordinary birth in one important respect. In an ordinary birth the baby has not much choice: here it has. I wonder what an ordinary baby would do if it had the choice. It might prefer to stay in the

dark and warmth and safety of the womb. For of course it would think the womb meant safety. That would be just where it was wrong; for if it stays there it will die.

On this view the thing has happened: the new step has been taken and is being taken. Already the new men are dotted here and there all over the earth. Some, as I have admitted, are still hardly recognisable: but others can be recognised. Every now and then one meets them. Their very voices and faces are different from ours: stronger, quieter, happier, more radiant. They begin where most of us leave off. They are, I say, recognisable; but you must know what to look for. They will not be very like the idea of 'religious people' which you have formed from your general reading. They do not draw attention to themselves. You tend to think that you are being kind to them when they are really being kind to you. They love you more than other men do, but they need you less. (We must get over wanting to be needed: in some goodish people, specially women, that is the hardest of all temptations to resist.) They will usually seem to have a lot of time: you will wonder where it comes from. When you have recognised one of them, you will recognise the next one much more easily. And I strongly suspect (but how should I know?) that they recognise one another immediately and infallibly, across every barrier of colour, sex, class, age, and even of creeds. In that way, to become holy is rather like joining a secret society. To put it at the very lowest, it must be great *fun*.

But you must not imagine that the new men are, in the ordinary sense, all alike. A good deal of what I have been saying in this last book might make you suppose that that was bound to be so. To become new men means losing what we now call 'ourselves'. Out of our selves, into Christ, we must go. His will is to become ours and we are to think His thoughts, to 'have the mind of Christ' as the Bible says. And if Christ is one, and if He is thus to be 'in' us all, shall we not be exactly the same? It certainly sounds like it; but in fact it is not so.

It is difficult here to get a good illustration; because, of course, no other two things are related to each other just as the Creator is related to one of His creatures. But I will try two very imperfect illustrations which may give a hint of the truth. Imagine a lot of people who have always lived in the dark. You come and try to describe to them what light is like. You might tell them that if they come into the light that same light would fall on them all and they would all reflect it and thus become what we call visible. Is it not quite possible that they would imagine that, since they were all receiving the same light, and all reacting to it in the same way (i.e. all reflecting it), they would all look alike? Whereas you and I know that the light will in fact bring out, or show up, how different they are. Or again, suppose a person who knew nothing about salt. You give him a pinch to taste and he experiences a particular strong, sharp taste. You then tell him that in your country people use salt in all their cookery. Might he not reply 'In that case I suppose all your dishes taste exactly the same: because the taste of that stuff you have just given me is so strong that it will kill the taste of everything else.' But you and I know that the real effect of salt is exactly the opposite. So far from killing the taste of the egg and the tripe and the cabbage, it actually brings it out. They do not show their real taste till you have added the salt. (Of course, as I warned you, this is not really a very good illustration, because you can, after all, kill the other tastes by putting in too much salt, whereas you cannot kill the taste of a human personality by putting in too much Christ. I am doing the best I can.)

It is something like that with Christ and us. The more we get what we now call 'ourselves' out of the way and let Him take us over, the more truly ourselves we become. There is so much of Him that millions and millions of 'little Christs', all different, will still be too few to express Him fully. He made them all. He invented – as an author invents characters in a novel – all the different men that you and I were intended to be. In that sense our real selves are all waiting for us in Him. It is no good trying to 'be myself' without Him. The more I resist Him and try to live on my own, the more I become dominated by my own heredity and upbringing and surroundings and natural desires. In fact what I so proudly call 'Myself' becomes merely the meeting place for trains of events which I never started and which I cannot stop. What I call 'My wishes' become merely the desires thrown up by my physical organism or pumped into me by other men's thoughts or even suggested to me by devils. Eggs and alcohol and a good night's sleep will be the real origins of what I flatter myself by regarding as my own highly personal and discriminating decision to make love to the girl opposite to me in the railway carriage. Propaganda will be the real origin of what I regard as my own personal political ideas. I am not, in my natural state, nearly so much of a person as I like to believe: most of what I call 'me' can be very easily explained. It is when I turn to Christ, when I give myself up to His Personality, that I first begin to have a real personality of my own.

At the beginning I said there were Personalities in God. I will go further now. There are no real personalities anywhere else. Until you have given up your self to Him you will not have a real self. Sameness is to be found most among the most 'natural' men, not among those who surrender to Christ. How monotonously alike all the great tyrants and conquerors have been: how gloriously different are the saints.

But there must be a real giving up of the self. You must throw it away 'blindly' to so speak. Christ will indeed give you a real personality: but you must not go to Him for the sake of that. As long as your own personality is what you are bothering about you are not going to Him at all. The very first step is to try to forget about the self altogether. Your real, new self (which is

Christ's and also yours, and yours just because it is His) will not come as long as you are looking for it. It will come when you are looking for Him. Does that sound strange? The same principle holds, you know, for more everyday matters. Even in social life, you will never make a good impression on other people until you stop thinking about what sort of impression you are making. Even in literature and art, no man who bothers about originality will ever be original: whereas if you simply try to tell the truth (without caring twopence how often it has been told before) you will, nine times out of ten, become original without ever having noticed it. The principle runs through all life from top to bottom. Give up yourself, and you will find your real self. Lose your life and you will save it. Submit to death, death of your ambitions and favourite wishes every day and death of your whole body in the end: submit with every fibre of your being, and you will find eternal life. Keep back nothing. Nothing that you have not given away will be really yours. Nothing in you that has not died will ever be raised from the dead. Look for yourself, and you will find in the long run only hatred, loneliness, despair, rage, ruin, and decay. But look for Christ and you will find Him, and with Him everything else thrown in.

THE END

THE PROBLEM
OF PAIN

To
The Inklings

Contents

The Son of God suffered unto the death, not that men might not suffer, but that their sufferings might be like His.

GEORGE MACDONALD,
Unspoken Sermons, First Series

PREFACE

When Mr Ashley Sampson suggested to me the writing of this book, I asked leave to be allowed to write it anonymously, since, if I were to say what I really thought about pain, I should be forced to make statements of such apparent fortitude that they would become ridiculous if anyone knew who made them. Anonymity was rejected as inconsistent with the series; but Mr Sampson pointed out that I could write a preface explaining that I did not live up to my own principles! This exhilarating programme I am now carrying out. Let me confess at once, in the words of good Walter Hilton, that throughout this book 'I feel myself so far from true feeling of that I speak, that I can naught else but cry mercy and desire after it as I may'.[1] Yet for that very reason there is one criticism which cannot be brought against me. No one can say 'He jests at scars who never felt a wound', for I have never for one moment been in a state of mind to which even the imagination of serious pain was less than intolerable. If any man is safe from the danger of underestimating this adversary, I am that man. I must add, too, that the only purpose of the book is to solve the intellectual problem raised by suffering; for the far higher task of teaching fortitude and patience I was never fool enough to suppose myself qualified, nor have I anything to offer my readers except my conviction that when pain is to be borne, a little courage helps more than much knowledge, a little human sympathy more than much courage, and the least tincture of the love of God more than all.

If any real theologian reads these pages he will very easily see that they are the work of a layman and an amateur. Except in the last two chapters, parts of which are admittedly speculative, I have believed myself to be restating ancient and orthodox doctrines. If any parts of the book are 'original', in the sense of being novel or unorthodox, they are so against my will and as a

[1] *Scale of Perfection*, I, xvi.

471

result of my ignorance. I write, of course, as a layman of the Church of England: but I have tried to assume nothing that is not professed by all baptised and communicating Christians.

As this is not a work of erudition I have taken little pains to trace ideas or quotations to their sources when they were not easily recoverable. Any theologian will see easily enough what, and how little, I have read.

C. S. Lewis
Magdalen College, Oxford, 1940

INTRODUCTORY

*I wonder at the hardihood with which such
persons undertake to talk about God. In a
treatise addressed to infidels they begin with
a chapter proving the existence of God from
the works of Nature ... this only gives their
readers grounds for thinking that the proofs
of our religion are very weak. ... It is a
remarkable fact that no canonical writer has
ever used Nature to prove God.*

PASCAL, *Pensées*, IV, 242, 243

Not many years ago when I was an atheist, if anyone had asked me, 'Why do you not believe in God?' my reply would have run something like this: 'Look at the universe we live in. By far the greatest part of it consists of empty space, completely dark and unimaginably cold. The bodies which move in this space are so few and so small in comparison with the space itself that even if every one of them were known to be crowded as full as it could hold with perfectly happy creatures, it would still be difficult to believe that life and happiness were more than a by-product to the power that made the universe. As it is, however, the scientists think it likely that very few of the suns of space – perhaps none of them except our own - have any planets; and in our own system it is improbable that any planet except the Earth sustains life. And Earth herself existed without life for millions of years and may exist for millions more when life has left her. And what is it like while it lasts? It is so arranged that all the forms of it can live only by preying upon one another. In the lower forms this process entails only death, but in the higher there appears a new quality called consciousness which enables it to be attended with pain. The creatures cause pain by being born, and live by inflicting pain, and in pain they mostly die. In the most complex of all the creatures, Man, yet another quality appears, which we call reason, whereby he is enabled to foresee his own pain which henceforth is preceded with acute mental suffering, and to foresee his own death while keenly desiring permanence. It also enables men by a hundred ingenious contrivances to inflict a great deal more pain than they otherwise could have done on one another and on the irrational creatures. This power they have exploited to the full. Their history is largely a record of crime, war, disease, and terror, with just sufficient happiness interposed to give them, while it lasts, an agonised apprehension of losing it, and, when it is lost, the poignant misery of remembering. Every now and then they improve their condition a little and what we call a civilisation appears. But all civilisations pass away and, even while they remain, inflict peculiar sufferings of their own proba- bly sufficient to outweigh what alleviations they may have brought to the normal pains of man. That our own civilisation has done so, no one will dis- pute; that it will pass away like all its predecessors is surely probable. Even if it should not, what then? The race is doomed. Every race that comes into being in any part of the universe is doomed; for the universe, they tell us, is running down, and will sometime be a uniform infinity of homogeneous matter at a low temperature. All stories will come to nothing: all life will turn out in the end to have been a transitory and senseless contortion upon the idiotic face of infinite matter. If you ask me to believe that this is the work of a benevolent and omnipotent spirit, I reply that all the evidence points in the opposite direction. Either there is no spirit behind the universe, or else a spirit indifferent to good and evil, or else an evil spirit.

There was one question which I never dreamed of raising. I never noticed that the very strength and facility of the pessimists' case at once poses us a problem. If the universe is so bad, or even half so bad, how on earth did human beings ever come to attribute it to the activity of a wise and good Creator? Men are fools, perhaps; but hardly so foolish as that. The direct inference from black to white, from evil flower to virtuous root, from sense- less work to a workman infinitely wise, staggers belief. The spectacle of the universe as revealed by experience can never have been the ground of reli- gion: it must always have been something in spite of which religion, acquired from a different source, was held.

It would be an error to reply that our ancestors were ignorant and there- fore entertained pleasing illusions about nature which the progress of sci- ence has since dispelled. For centuries, during which all men believed, the nightmare size and emptiness of the universe was already known. You will read in some books that the men of the Middle Ages thought the Earth flat and the stars near, but that is a lie. Ptolemy had told them that the Earth was a mathematical point without size in relation to the distance of the fixed stars – a distance which one medieval popular text estimates as a hundred and seventeen million miles. And in times yet earlier, even from the begin- nings, men must have got the same sense of hostile immensity from a more obvious source. To prehistoric man the neighbouring forest must have been infinite enough, and the utterly alien and infest which we have to fetch from the thought of cosmic rays and cooling suns, came snuffing and howling nightly to his very doors. Certainly at all periods the pain and waste of human life was equally obvious. Our own religion begins among the Jews, a people squeezed between great warlike empires, continually defeated and led captive, familiar as Poland or Armenia with the tragic story of the conquered. It is mere nonsense to put pain among the discoveries of science. Lay down this book and reflect for five minutes on the fact that all the great religions were first preached, and long practised, in a world without chloroform.

At all times, then, an inference from the course of events in this world to the goodness and wisdom of the Creator would have been equally preposterous; and it was never made.[1] Religion has a different origin. In what follows it must be understood that I am not *primarily* arguing the truth of Christianity but describing its origin – a task, in my view, necessary if we are to put the problem of pain in its right setting.

In all developed religion we find three strands or elements, and in Christianity one more. The first of these is what Professor Otto calls the experience of the *Numinous*. Those who have not met this term may be introduced to it by the following device. Suppose you were told there was a tiger in the next room: you would know that you were in danger and would probably feel fear. But if you were told 'There is a ghost in the next room', and believed it, you would feel, indeed, what is often called fear, but of a different kind. It would not be based on the knowledge of danger, for no one is primarily afraid of what a ghost may do to him, but of the mere fact that it is a ghost. It is 'uncanny' rather than dangerous, and the special kind of fear it excites may be called Dread. With the Uncanny one has reached the fringes of the Numinous. Now suppose that you were told simply 'There is a mighty spirit in the room', and believed it. Your feelings would then be even less like the mere fear of danger: but the disturbance would be profound. You would feel wonder and a certain shrinking – a sense of inadequacy to cope with such a visitant and of prostration before it – an emotion which might be expressed in Shakespeare's words 'Under it my genius is rebuked'. This feeling may be described as awe, and the object which excites it as the *Numinous*.

Now nothing is more certain than that man, from a very early period, began to believe that the universe was haunted by spirits. Professor Otto perhaps assumes too easily that from the very first such spirits were regarded with numinous awe. This is impossible to prove for the very good reason that utterances expressing awe of the Numinous and utterances expressing mere fear of danger may use identical language – as we can still say that we are 'afraid' of a ghost or 'afraid' of a rise in prices. It is therefore theoretically possible that there was a time when men regarded these spirits

---

[1] I.e., never made at the beginnings of a religion. *After* belief in God has been accepted, 'theodicies' explaining, or explaining away, the miseries of life, will naturally appear often enough.

simply as dangerous and felt towards them just as they felt towards tigers. What is certain is that now, at any rate, the numinous experience exists and that if we start from ourselves we can trace it a long way back.

A modern example may be found (if we are not too proud to seek it there) in *The Wind in the Willows* where Rat and Mole approach Pan on the island.

'"Rat," he found breath to whisper, shaking, "Are you afraid?" "Afraid?" murmured the Rat, his eyes shining with unutterable love. "Afraid? of Him? O, never, never. And yet – and yet – O Mole, I am afraid."'

Going back about a century we find copious examples in Wordsworth – perhaps the finest being that passage in the first book of the *Prelude* where he describes his experience while rowing on the lake in the stolen boat. Going back further we get a very pure and strong example in Malory,[1] when Galahad 'began to tremble right hard when the deadly (= mortal) flesh began to behold the spiritual things'. At the beginning of our era it finds expression in the Apocalypse where the writer fell at the feet of the risen Christ 'as one dead'. In Pagan literature we find Ovid's picture of the dark grove on the Aventine of which you would say at a glance *numen inest*[2] – the place is haunted, or there is a Presence here; and Virgil gives us the palace of Latinus 'awful (*horrendum*) with woods and sanctity (*religione*) of elder days'.[3] A Greek fragment attributed, but improbably, to Aeschylus, tells us of earth, sea, and mountain shaking beneath the 'dread eye of their Master'.[4] And far further back Ezekiel tells us of the 'rings' in his Theophany that 'they were so high that they were dreadful':[5] and Jacob, rising from sleep, says 'How dreadful is this place!'[6]

We do not know how far back in human history this feeling goes. The earliest men almost certainly believed in things which would excite the feeling in us if *we* believed in them, and it seems therefore probable that numinous awe is as old as humanity itself. But our main concern is not with its dates. The important thing is that somehow or other it has come into existence, and is widespread, and does not disappear from the mind with the growth of knowledge and civilisation.

Now this awe is not the result of an inference from the visible universe. There is no possibility of arguing from mere danger to the uncanny, still less to the fully Numinous. You may say that it seems to you very natural that early man, being surrounded by real dangers, and therefore frightened, should invent the un-canny and the Numinous. In a sense it is, but let us

[1] XVII, xxii.
[2] *Fasti*, III, 296.
[3] *Aen.* VII, 172.
[4] Fragm. 464. Sidgwick's edition.
[5] Ezekiel 1:18.
[6] Genesis 28:17.

understand what we mean. You feel it to be natural because, sharing human nature with your remote ancestors, you can imagine yourself reacting to perilous solitudes in the same way; and this reaction is indeed 'natural' in the sense of being in accord with human nature. But it is not in the least 'natural' in the sense that the idea of the uncanny or the Numinous is already contained in the idea of the dangerous, or that any perception of danger or any dislike of the wounds and death which it may entail could give the slightest conception of ghostly dread or numinous awe to an intelligence which did not already understand them. When man passes from physical fear to dread and awe, he makes a sheer jump, and apprehends something which could never be *given*, as danger is, by the physical facts and logical deductions from them. Most attempts to explain the Numinous presuppose the thing to be explained – as when anthropologists derive it from fear of the dead, without explaining why dead men (assuredly the least dangerous kind of men) should have attracted this peculiar feeling. Against all such attempts we must insist that dread and awe are in a different dimension from fear. They are in the nature of an interpretation man gives to the universe, or an impression he gets from it; and just as no enumeration of the physical qualities of a beautiful object could ever include its beauty, or give the faintest hint of what we mean by beauty to a creature without aesthetic experience, so no factual description of any human environment could include the uncanny and the Numinous or even hint at them. There seem, in fact, to be only two views we can hold about awe. Either it is a mere twist in the human mind, corresponding to nothing objective and serving no biological function, yet showing no tendency to disappear from that mind at its fullest development in poet, philosopher, or saint: or else it is a direct experience of the really supernatural, to which the name Revelation might properly be given.

The Numinous is not the same as the morally good, and a man overwhelmed with awe is likely, if left to himself, to think the numinous object 'beyond good and evil'. This brings us to the second strand or element in religion. All the human beings that history has heard of acknowledge some kind of morality; that is, they feel towards certain proposed actions the experiences expressed by the words 'I ought' or 'I ought not'. These experiences resemble awe in one respect, namely that they cannot be logically deduced from the environment and physical experiences of the man who undergoes them. You can shuffle 'I want' and 'I am forced' and 'I shall be well advised' and 'I dare not' as long as you please without getting out of them the slightest hint of 'ought' and 'ought not'. And, once again, attempts to resolve the moral experience into something else always presuppose the very thing they are trying to explain – as when a famous psychoanalyst deduces it from prehistoric parricide. If the parricide produced a sense of guilt, that was because men felt that they ought not to have committed it: if they did not so feel, it could produce no sense of guilt Morality, like numinous awe, is a jump; in it, man goes beyond anything that can be 'given' in the facts of experience. And it has one characteristic too remarkable to be ignored. The moralities accepted among men may differ – though not, at bottom, so widely as is often claimed – but they all agree in prescribing a behaviour which their adherents fail to practise. All men alike stand condemned, not by alien codes of ethics, but by their own, and all men therefore are conscious of guilt. The second element in religion is the consciousness not merely of a moral law, but of a moral law at once approved and disobeyed. This consciousness is neither a logical, nor an illogical, inference from the facts of experience; if we did not bring it to our experience we could not find it there. It is either inexplicable illusion, or else revelation.

The moral experience and the numinous experience are so far from being the same that they may exist for quite long periods without establishing a mutual contact. In many forms of Paganism the worship of the gods and the ethical discussions of the philosophers have very little to do with each other. The third stage in religious development arises when men identify them – when the Numinous Power to which they feel awe is made the guardian of the morality to which they feel obligation. Once again, this may seem to you very 'natural'. What can be more natural than for a savage haunted at once by awe and by guilt to think that the power which awes him is also the authority which condemns his guilt? And it is, indeed, natural to humanity. But it is not in the least obvious. The actual behaviour of that universe which the Numinous haunts bears no resemblance to the behaviour which morality demands of us. The one seems wasteful, ruthless, and unjust; the other enjoins upon us the opposite qualities. Nor can the identification of the two be explained as a wish-fulfilment, for it fulfils no one's wishes. We desire nothing less than to see that Law whose naked authority is already unsupportable armed with the incalculable claims of the Numinous. Of all the jumps that humanity takes in its religious history this is certainly the most surprising. It is not unnatural that many sections of the human race refused it; non-moral religion, and non-religious morality, existed and still exist. Perhaps only a single people, as a people, took the new step with perfect decision – I mean the Jews: but great individuals in all times and places have taken it also, and only those who take it are safe from the obscenities and barbarities of the unmoralised worship or the cold, sad self-righteousness of sheer moralism. Judged by its fruits, this step is a step towards increased health. And though logic does not compel us to take it, it is very hard to resist – even on Paganism and Pantheism morality is always breaking in, and even Stoicism finds itself willy-nilly bowing the knee to God. Once more, it may be madness – a madness congenital to man and oddly fortunate in its results – or it may be revelation. And if revelation, then it is most really and truly in Abraham that all people shall be blessed, for it was the Jews who fully and unambiguously identified the awful Presence haunting black mountain-tops and thunderclouds with 'the *righteous* Lord' who 'loveth righteousness'.[1]

The fourth strand or element is a historical event. There was a man born among these Jews who claimed to be, or to be the son of, or to be 'one with', the Something which is at once the awful haunter of nature and the giver of the moral law. The claim is so shocking – a paradox, and even a horror, which we may easily be lulled into taking too lightly – that only two views of this man are possible. Either he was a raving lunatic of an unusually abominable type, or else He was, and is, precisely what He said. There is no middle way. If the records make the first hypothesis unacceptable, you must submit to the second. And if you do that, all else that is claimed by Christians becomes credible – that this Man, having been killed, was yet alive, and that His death, in some manner incomprehensible to human thought, has effected a real change in our relations to the 'awful' and 'righteous' Lord, and a change in our favour.

To ask whether the universe as we see it looks more like the work of a wise and good Creator or the work of chance, indifference, or malevolence, is to omit from the outset all the relevant factors in the religious problem. Christianity is not the conclusion of a philosophical debate on the origins of the universe: it is a catastrophic historical event following on the long spiritual preparation of humanity which I have described. It is not a system into which we have to fit the awkward fact of pain: it is itself one of the awkward facts which have to be fitted into any system we make. In a sense, it creates, rather than solves, the problem of pain, for pain would be no problem unless, side by side with our daily experience of this painful world, we had received what we think a good assurance that ultimate reality is righteous and loving.

Why this assurance seems to me good, I have more or less indicated. It does not amount to logical compulsion. At every stage of religious development man may rebel, if not without violence to his own nature, yet without absurdity. He can close his spiritual eyes against the Numinous, if he is prepared to part company with half the great poets and prophets of his race, with his own childhood, with the richness and depth of uninhibited experience. He can regard the moral law as an illusion, and so cut himself off from the common ground of humanity. He can refuse to identify the Numinous with the righteous, and remain a barbarian, worshipping sexuality, or the dead, or the lifeforce, or the future. But the cost is heavy. And when we come to the last step of all, the historical Incarnation, the assurance is strongest of all. The story is strangely like many myths which have haunted

[1] Psalm 11:8.

479

religion from the first, and yet it is not like them. It is not transparent to the reason: we could not have invented it ourselves. It has not the suspicious *a priori* lucidity of Pantheism or of Newtonian physics. It has the seemingly arbitrary and idiosyncratic character which modern science is slowly teaching us to put up with in this wilful universe, where energy is made up in little parcels of a quantity no one could predict, where speed is not unlimited, where irreversible entropy gives time a real direction and the cosmos, no longer static or cyclic, moves like a drama from a real beginning to a real end. If any message from the core of reality ever were to reach us, we should expect to find in it just that unexpectedness, that wilful, dramatic anfractuosity which we find in the Christian faith. It has the master touch – the rough, male taste of reality, not made by us, or, indeed, for us, but hitting us in the face.

If, on such grounds, or on better ones, we follow the course on which humanity has been led, and become Christians, we then have the 'problem' of pain.

2

DIVINE OMNIPOTENCE

*Nothing which implies contradiction falls
under the omnipotence of God.*
THOMAS AQUINAS, *Summ. Theol.*, Iᵃ Q XXV, Art 4

'I f God were good, He would wish to make His creatures perfectly
happy, and if God were almighty He would be able to do what
He wished. But the creatures are not happy. Therefore God lacks either
goodness, or power, or both.' This is the problem of pain, in its simplest
form. The possibility of answering it depends on showing that the terms
'good' and 'almighty', and perhaps also the term 'happy', are equivocal: for
it must be admitted from the outset that if the popular meanings attached to
these words are the best, or the only possible, meanings, then the argument
is unanswerable. In this chapter I shall make some comments on the idea of
Omnipotence, and, in the following, some on the idea of Goodness.

Omnipotence means 'power to do all, or everything'.[1] And we are told in
Scripture that 'with God all things are possible'. It is common enough, in
argument with an unbeliever, to be told that God, if He existed and were
good, would do this or that; and then, if we point out that the proposed action
is impossible, to be met with the retort 'But I thought God was supposed to
be able to do anything'. This raises the whole question of impossibility.

In ordinary usage the word *impossible* generally implies a suppressed
clause beginning with the word *unless*. Thus it is impossible for me to see the
street from where I sit writing at this moment; that is, it is impossible to see
the street *unless* I go up to the top floor where I shall be high enough to
overlook the intervening building. If I had broken my leg I should say 'But
it is impossible to go up to the top floor' – meaning, however, that it is
impossible *unless* some friends turn up who will carry me. Now let us
advance to a different plane of impossibility, by saying 'It is, at any rate,
impossible to see the street *so long as* I remain where I am and the intervening building remains where it is.' Someone might add 'unless the nature of
space, or of vision, were different from what it is'. I do not know what the

---

[1] The original meaning in Latin may have been 'power *over* or *in* all'. I give what I take to be the
current sense.

best philosophers and scientists would say to this, but I should have to reply 'I don't know whether space and vision *could possibly* have been of such a nature as you suggest.' Now it is clear that the words *could possibly* here refer to some absolute kind of possibility or impossibility which is different from the relative possibilities and impossibilities we have been considering. I cannot say whether seeing round corners is, in this new sense, possible or not, because I do not know whether it is self-contradictory or not. But I know very well that if it is self-contradictory it is absolutely impossible. The absolutely impossible may also be called the intrinsically impossible because it carries its impossibility within itself, instead of borrowing it from other impossibilities which in their turn depend upon others. It has no *unless* clause attached to it. It is impossible under all conditions and in all worlds and for all agents.

'All agents' here includes God Himself. His Omnipotence means power to do all that is intrinsically possible, not to do the intrinsically impossible. You may attribute miracles to Him, but not nonsense. This is no limit to His power. If you choose to say 'God can give a creature free will and at the same time withhold free will from it,' you have not succeeded in saying *anything* about God: meaningless combinations of words do not suddenly acquire meaning simply because we prefix to them the two other words 'God can'. It remains true that all *things* are possible with God: the intrinsic impossibilities are not things but nonentities. It is no more possible for God than for the weakest of His creatures to carry out both of two mutually exclusive alternatives; not because His power meets an obstacle, but because nonsense remains nonsense even when we talk it about God.

It should, however, be remembered that human reasoners often make mistakes, either by arguing from false data or by inadvertence in the argument itself. We may thus come to think things possible which are really impossible, and *vice versa*.[1] We ought, therefore, to use great caution in defining those intrinsic impossibilities which even Omnipotence cannot perform. What follows is to be regarded less as an assertion of what they are than a sample of what they might be like.

The inexorable 'laws of Nature' which operate in defiance of human suffering or desert, which are not turned aside by prayer, seem, at first sight, to furnish a strong argument against the goodness and power of God. I am going to submit that not even Omnipotence could create a society of free souls without at the same time creating a relatively independent and 'inexorable' Nature.

---

[1] E.g., every good conjuring trick does something which to the audience, with their data and their power of reasoning, seems self-contradictory.

There is no reason to suppose that self-consciousness, the recognition of a creature by itself as a 'self', can exist except in contrast with an 'other', a something which is not the self. It is against an environment and preferably a social environment, an environment of other selves, that the awareness of Myself stands out. This would raise a difficulty about the consciousness of God if we were mere theists: being Christians, we learn from the doctrine of the Blessed Trinity that something analogous to 'society' exists within the Divine being from all eternity – that God is Love, not merely in the sense of being the Platonic form of love, but because, within Him, the concrete reciprocities of love exist before all worlds and are thence derived to the creatures.

Again, the freedom of a creature must mean freedom to choose: and choice implies the existence of things to choose between. A creature with no environment would have no choices to make: so that freedom, like self-consciousness (if they are not, indeed, the same thing), again demands the presence to the self of something other than the self.

The minimum condition of self-consciousness and freedom, then, would be that the creature should apprehend God and, therefore, itself as distinct from God. It is possible that such creatures exist, aware of God and themselves, but of no fellow-creatures. If so, their freedom is simply that of making a single naked choice – of loving God more than the self or the self more than God. But a life so reduced to essentials is not imaginable to us. As soon as we attempt to introduce the mutual knowledge of fellow-creatures we run up against the necessity of 'Nature'.

People often talk as if nothing were easier than for two naked minds to 'meet' or become aware of each other. But I see no possibility of their doing so except in a common medium which forms their 'external world' or environment. Even our vague attempt to imagine such a meeting between disembodied spirits usually slips in surreptitiously the idea of, at least, a common space and common time, to give the *co-* in *co-existence* a meaning: and space and time are already an environment. But more than this is required. If your thoughts and passions were directly present to me, like my own, without any mark of externality or otherness, how should I distinguish them from mine? And what thoughts or passions could we begin to have without objects to think and feel about? Nay, could I even begin to have the conception of 'external' and 'other' unless I had experience of an 'external world'? You may reply, as a Christian, that God (and Satan) do, in fact, affect my consciousness in this direct way without signs of 'externality'. Yes: and the result is that most people remain ignorant of the existence of both. We may therefore suppose that if human souls affected one another directly and immaterially, it would be a rare triumph of faith and insight for any one of them to believe in the existence of the others. It would be harder for me to know my neighbour under such conditions than it now is for me to know

God: for in recognising the impact of God upon me I am now helped by things that reach me through the external world, such as the tradition of the Church, Holy Scripture, and the conversation of religious friends. What we need for human society is exactly what we have – a neutral something, neither you nor I, which we can both manipulate so as to make signs to each other. I can talk to you because we can both set up sound-waves in the common air between us. Matter, which keeps souls apart, also brings them together. It enables each of us to have an 'outside' as well as an 'inside', so that what are acts of will and thought for you are noises and glances for me; you are enabled not only to *be*, but to *appear*: and hence I have the pleasure of making your acquaintance.

Society, then, implies a common field or 'world' in which its members meet. If there is an angelic society, as Christians have usually believed, then the angels also must have such a world or field; something which is to them as 'matter' (in the modern, not the scholastic, sense) is to us.

But if matter is to serve as a neutral field it must have a fixed nature of its own. If a 'world' or material system had only a single inhabitant it might conform at every moment to his wishes – 'trees for his sake would crowd into a shade'. But if you were introduced into a world which thus varied at my every whim, you would be quite unable to act in it and would thus lose the exercise of your free will. Nor is it clear that you could make your presence known to me – all the matter by which you attempted to make signs to me being already in my control and therefore not capable of being manipulated by you.

Again, if matter has a fixed nature and obeys constant laws, not all states of matter will be equally agreeable to the wishes of a given soul, nor all equally beneficial for that particular aggregate of matter which he calls his body. If fire comforts that body at a certain distance, it will destroy it when the distance is reduced. Hence, even in a perfect world, the necessity for those danger signals which the pain-fibres in our nerves are apparently designed to transmit. Does this mean an inevitable element of evil (in the form of pain) in any possible world? I think not: for while it may be true that the least sin is an incalculable evil, the evil of pain depends on degree, and pains below a certain intensity are not feared or resented at all. No one minds the process 'warm – beautifully hot – too hot – it stings' which warns him to withdraw his hand from exposure to the fire: and, if I may trust my own feeling, a slight aching in the legs as we climb into bed after a good day's walking is, in fact, pleasurable.

Yet again, if the fixed nature of matter prevents it from being always, and in all its dispositions, equally agreeable even to a single soul, much less is it possible for the matter of the universe at any moment to be distributed so that it is equally convenient and pleasurable to each member of a society. If a

man travelling in one direction is having a journey down hill, a man going in
the opposite direction must be going up hill. If even a pebble lies where I
want it to lie, it cannot, except by a coincidence, be where you want it to lie.
And this is very far from being an evil: on the contrary, it furnishes occasion
for all those acts of courtesy, respect, and unselfishness by which love and
good humour and modesty express themselves. But it certainly leaves the
way open to a great evil, that of competition and hostility. And if souls are
free, they cannot be prevented from dealing with the problem by competition instead of courtesy. And once they have advanced to actual hostility,
they can then exploit the fixed nature of matter to hurt one another. The
permanent nature of wood which enables us to use it as a beam also enables
us to use it for hitting our neighbour on the head. The permanent nature of
matter in general means that when human beings fight, the victory ordinarily goes to those who have superior weapons, skill, and numbers, even if
their cause is unjust.

We can, perhaps, conceive of a world in which God corrected the results
of this abuse of free will by His creatures at every moment: so that a
wooden beam became soft as grass when it was used as a weapon, and the
air refused to obey me if I attempted to set up in it the sound-waves that
carry lies or insults. But such a world would be one in which wrong actions
were impossible, and in which, therefore, freedom of the will would be
void; nay, if the principle were carried out to its logical conclusion, evil
thoughts would be impossible, for the cerebral matter which we use in
thinking would refuse its task when we attempted to frame them. All matter in the neighbourhood of a wicked man would be liable to undergo
unpredictable alterations. That God can and does, on occasions, modify the
behaviour of matter and produce what we call miracles, is part of Christian
faith; but the very conception of a common, and therefore stable, world,
demands that these occasions should be extremely rare. In a game of chess
you can make certain arbitrary concessions to your opponent, which stand
to the ordinary rules of the game as miracles stand to the laws of nature.
You can deprive yourself of a castle, or allow the other man sometimes to
take back a move made inadvertently. But if you conceded everything that
at any moment happened to suit him – if all his moves were revocable and if
all your pieces disappeared whenever their position on the board was not to
his liking – then you could not have a game at all. So it is with the life of
souls in a world: fixed laws, consequences unfolding by causal necessity,
the whole natural order, are at once limits within which their common life
is confined and also the sole condition under which any such life is possible. Try to exclude the possibility of suffering which the order of nature
and the existence of free wills involve, and you find that you have excluded
life itself.

As I said before, this account of the intrinsic necessities of a world is meant merely as a specimen of what they might be. What they really are, only Omniscience has the data and the wisdom to see: but they are not likely to be *less* complicated than I have suggested. Needless to say, 'complicated' here refers solely to the human understanding of them; we are not to think of God arguing, as we do, from an end (co-existence of free spirits) to the conditions involved in it, but rather of a single, utterly self-consistent act of creation which to us appears, at first sight, as the creation of many independent things, and then, as the creation of things mutually necessary. Even we can rise a little beyond the conception of mutual necessities as I have outlined it – can reduce matter as that which separates souls and matter as that which brings them together under the single concept of Plurality, whereof 'separation' and 'togetherness' are only two aspects. With every advance in our thought the unity of the creative act, and the impossibility of tinkering with the creation as though this or that element of it could have been removed, will become more apparent. Perhaps this is not the 'best of all possible' universes, but the only possible one. Possible worlds can mean only 'worlds that God could have made, but didn't'. The idea of that which God 'could have' done involves a too anthropomorphic conception of God's freedom. Whatever human freedom means, Divine freedom cannot mean indeterminacy between alternatives and choice of one of them. Perfect goodness can never debate about the end to be attained, and perfect wisdom cannot debate about the means most suited to achieve it. The freedom of God consists in the fact that no cause other than Himself produces His acts and no external obstacle impedes them – that His own goodness is the root from which they all grow and His own omnipotence the air in which they all flower.

And that brings us to our next subject – the Divine goodness. Nothing so far has been said of this, and no answer attempted to the objection that if the universe must, from the outset, admit the possibility of suffering, then absolute goodness would have left the universe uncreated. And I must warn the reader that I shall not attempt to prove that to create was better than not to create: I am aware of no human scales in which such a portentous question can be weighed. Some comparison between one state of being and another can be made, but the attempt to compare being and not being ends in mere words. 'It would be better for me not to exist' – in what sense 'for me'? How should I, if I did not exist, profit by not existing? Our design is a less formidable one: it is only to discover how, perceiving a suffering world, and being assured, on quite different grounds, that God is good, we are to conceive that goodness and that suffering without contradiction.

3

DIVINE GOODNESS

Love can forbear, and Love can forgive ...
but Love can never be reconciled to an
unlovely object. ... He can never therefore
be reconciled to your sin, because sin itself is
incapable of being altered; but He may
be reconciled to your person, because
that may be restored.
TRAHERNE, *Centuries of Meditation*, II, 30

Any consideration of the goodness of God at once threatens us with the following dilemma.

On the one hand, if God is wiser than we His judgement must differ from ours on many things, and not least on good and evil. What seems to us good may therefore not be good in His eyes, and what seems to us evil may not be evil.

On the other hand, if God's moral judgement differs from ours so that our 'black' may be His 'white', we can mean nothing by calling Him good; for to say 'God is good', while asserting that His goodness is wholly other than ours, is really only to say 'God is we know not what'. And an utterly unknown quality in God cannot give us moral grounds for loving or obeying Him. If He is not (in our sense) 'good' we shall obey, if at all, only through fear – and should be equally ready to obey an omnipotent Fiend. The doctrine of Total Depravity – when the consequence is drawn that, since we are totally depraved, our idea of good is worth simply nothing – may thus turn Christianity into a form of devil-worship.

The escape from this dilemma depends on observing what happens, in human relations, when the man of inferior moral standards enters the society of those who are better and wiser than he and gradually learns to accept *their* standards – a process which, as it happens, I can describe fairly accurately, since I have undergone it. When I came first to the University I was as nearly without a moral conscience as a boy could be. Some faint distaste for cruelty and for meanness about money was my utmost reach – of chastity, truthfulness, and self-sacrifice I thought as a baboon thinks of classical music. By the mercy of God I fell among a set of young men (none of them, by the way, Christians) who were sufficiently close to me in intellect and imagination to secure immediate intimacy, but who knew, and tried to obey, the moral law. Thus their judgement of good and evil was very different from mine. Now what happens in such a case is not in the least like being asked to treat as 'white' what was hitherto called black. The new moral judgements never enter the mind as mere reversals (though they do reverse them) of previous judgements but 'as lords that are certainly expected'. You can have no doubt in which direction you are moving: they are more like good than the little shreds of good you already had, but are, in a sense, continuous with them. But the great test is that the recognition of the new standards is accompanied with the sense of shame and guilt: one is conscious of having blundered into society that one is unfit for. It is in the light of such experiences that we must consider the goodness of God. Beyond all doubt, His idea of 'goodness' differs from ours; but you need have no fear that, as you approach it, you will be asked simply to reverse your moral standards. When the relevant difference between the Divine ethics and your own appears to you, you will not, in fact, be in any doubt that the change demanded of you is in the direction you already call 'better'. The Divine 'goodness' differs from ours, but it is not sheerly different: it differs from ours not as white from black but as a perfect circle from a child's first attempt to draw a wheel. But when the child has learned to draw, it will know that the circle it then makes is what it was trying to make from the very beginning.

This doctrine is presupposed in Scripture. Christ calls men to repent – a call which would be meaningless if God's standards were sheerly different from that which they already knew and failed to practise. He appeals to our existing moral judgement – 'Why even of yourselves judge ye not what is right?'[1] God in the Old Testament expostulates with men on the basis of their own conceptions of gratitude, fidelity, and fair play: and puts Himself, as it were, at the bar before His own creatures – 'What iniquity have your fathers found in me, that they are gone far from me?'[2]

After these preliminaries it will, I hope, be safe to suggest that some conceptions of the Divine goodness which tend to dominate our thought, though seldom expressed in so many words, are open to criticism.

By the goodness of God we mean nowadays almost exclusively His lovingness; and in this we may be right. And by Love, in this context, most of us mean kindness – the desire to see others than the self happy; not happy in this way or in that, but just happy. What would really satisfy us would be a God who said of anything we happened to like doing, 'What does it matter so long as they are contented?' We want, in fact, not so much a Father in

[1] Luke 12:57.
[2] Jeremiah 2:5.

Heaven as a grandfather in heaven – a senile benevolence who, as they say, 'liked to see young people enjoying themselves' and whose plan for the universe was simply that it might be truly said at the end of each day, 'a good time was had by all'. Not many people, I admit, would formulate a theology in precisely those terms: but a conception not very different lurks at the back of many minds. I do not claim to be an exception: I should very much like to live in a universe which was governed on such lines. But since it is abundantly clear that I don't, and since I have reason to believe, nevertheless, that God is Love, I conclude that my conception of love needs correction.

I might, indeed, have learned, even from the poets, that Love is something more stern and splendid than mere kindness: that even the love between the sexes is, as in Dante, 'a lord of terrible aspect'. There is kindness in Love: but Love and kindness are not coterminous, and when kindness (in the sense given above) is separated from the other elements of Love, it involves a certain fundamental indifference to its object, and even something like contempt of it. Kindness consents very readily to the removal of its object – we have all met people whose kindness to animals is constantly leading them to kill animals lest they should suffer. Kindness, merely as such, cares not whether its object becomes good or bad, provided only that it escapes suffering. As Scripture points out, it is bastards who are spoiled: the legitimate sons, who are to carry on the family tradition, are punished.[1] It is for people whom we care nothing about that we demand happiness on any terms: with our friends, our lovers, our children, we are exacting and would rather see them suffer much than be happy in contemptible and estranging modes. If God is Love, He is, by definition, something more than mere kindness. And it appears, from all the records, that though He has often rebuked us and condemned us, He has never regarded us with contempt. He has paid us the intolerable compliment of loving us, in the deepest, most tragic, most inexorable sense.

The relation between Creator and creature is, of course, unique, and cannot be paralleled by any relations between one creature and another. God is both further from us, and nearer to us, than any other being. He is further from us because the sheer difference between that which has Its principle of being in Itself and that to which being is communicated, is one compared with which the difference between an archangel and a worm is quite insignificant. He makes, we are made: He is original, we derivative. But at the same time, and for the same reason, the intimacy between God and even the meanest creature is closer than any that creatures can attain with one another. Our life is, at every moment, supplied by Him: our tiny, miraculous power of free will only operates on bodies which His continual energy keeps in existence – our very

[1] Hebrews 12:8.

power to think is His power communicated to us. Such a unique relation can be apprehended only by analogies: from the various types of love known among creatures we reach an inadequate, but useful, conception of God's love for man.

The lowest type, and one which is 'love' at all only by an extension of the word, is that which an artist feels for an artefact. God's relation to man is pictured thus in Jeremiah's vision of the potter and the clay,[1] or when St Peter speaks of the whole Church as a building on which God is at work, and of the individual members as stones.[2] The limitation of such an analogy is, of course, that in the symbol the patient is not sentient, and that certain questions of justice and mercy which arise when the 'stones' are really 'living' therefore remain unrepresented. But it is an important analogy so far as it goes. We are, not metaphorically but in very truth, a Divine work of art, something that God is making, and therefore something with which He will not be satisfied until it has a certain character. Here again we come up against what I have called the 'intolerable compliment'. Over a sketch made idly to amuse a child, an artist may not take much trouble: he may be content to let it go even though it is not exactly as he meant it to be. But over the great picture of his life – the work which he loves, though in a different fashion, as intensely as a man loves a woman or a mother a child – he will take endless trouble – and would, doubtless, thereby *give* endless trouble to the picture if it were sentient. One can imagine a sentient picture, after being rubbed and scraped and recommenced for the tenth time, wishing that it were only a thumbnail sketch whose making was over in a minute. In the same way, it is natural for us to wish that God had designed for us a less glorious and less arduous destiny; but then we are wishing not for more love but for less.

Another type is the love of a man for a beast – a relation constantly used in Scripture to symbolise the relation between God and men; 'we are his people and the sheep of his pasture'. This is in some ways a better analogy than the preceding, because the inferior party is sentient, and yet unmistakably inferior: but it is less good in so far as man has not made the beast and does not fully understand it. Its great merit lies in the fact that the association of (say) man and dog is primarily for the man's sake: he tames the dog primarily that he may love it, not that it may love him, and that it may serve him, not that he may serve it. Yet at the same time, the dog's interests are not sacrificed to the man's. The one end (that he may love it) cannot be fully attained unless it also, in its fashion, loves him, nor can it serve him unless

[1] Jeremiah 18.
[2] 1 Peter 2:5.

he, in a different fashion, serves it. Now just because the dog is by human standards one of the 'best' of irrational creatures, and a proper object for a man to love – of course, with that degree and kind of love which is proper to such an object, and not with silly anthropomorphic exaggerations – man interferes with the dog and makes it more lovable than it was in mere nature. In its state of nature it has a smell, and habits, which frustrate man's love: he washes it, house-trains it, teaches it not to steal, and is so enabled to love it completely. To the puppy the whole proceeding would seem, if it were a theologian, to cast grave doubts on the 'goodness' of man: but the full-grown and full-trained dog, larger, healthier, and longer-lived than the wild dog, and admitted, as it were by Grace, to a whole world of affections, loyalties, interests, and comforts entirely beyond its animal destiny, would have no such doubts. It will be noted that the man (I am speaking throughout of the good man) takes all these pains with the dog, and gives all these pains to the dog, only because it is an animal high in the scale – because it is so nearly lovable that it is worth his while to make it fully lovable. He does not house-train the earwig or give baths to centipedes. We may wish, indeed, that we were of so little account to God that He left us alone to follow our natural impulses – that He would give over trying to train us into something so unlike our natural selves: but once again, we are asking not for more love, but for less.

A nobler analogy, sanctioned by the constant tenor of Our Lord's teaching, is that between God's love for man and a father's love for a son. Whenever this is used, however (that is, whenever we pray the Lord's Prayer), it must be remembered that the Saviour used it in a time and place where paternal authority stood much higher than it does in modern England. A father half apologetic for having brought his son into the world, afraid to restrain him lest he should create inhibitions or even to instruct him lest he should interfere with his independence of mind, is a most misleading symbol of the Divine Fatherhood. I am not here discussing whether the authority of fathers, in its ancient extent, was a good thing or a bad thing: I am only explaining what conception of Fatherhood would have meant to Our Lord's first hearers, and indeed to their successors for many centuries. And it will become even plainer if we consider how Our Lord (though, in our belief, one with His Father and co-eternal with Him as no earthly son is with an earthly father) regards His own Sonship, surrendering His will wholly to the paternal will and not even allowing Himself to be called 'good' because Good is the name of the Father. Love between father and son, in this symbol, means essentially authoritative love on the one side, and obedient love on the other. The father uses his authority to make the son into the sort of human being he, rightly, and in his superior wisdom, wants him to be. Even in our own days, though a man might say it, he could mean nothing by saying, 'I love my son but don't care how great a blackguard he is provided he has a good time.'

Finally we come to an analogy full of danger, and of much more limited application, which happens, nevertheless, to be the most useful for our special purpose at the moment – I mean, the analogy between God's love for man and a man's love for a woman. It is freely used in Scripture. Israel is a false wife, but her heavenly Husband cannot forget the happier days; 'I remember thee, the kindness of thy youth, the love of thy espousals, when thou wentest after Me in the wilderness.'[1] Israel is the pauper bride, the waif whom her Lover found abandoned by the wayside, and clothed and adorned and made lovely and yet she betrayed Him.[2] 'Adulteresses' St James calls us, because we turn aside to the 'friendship of the world', while God 'jealously longs for the spirit He has implanted in us'.[3] The Church is the Lord's bride whom He so loves that in her no spot or wrinkle is endurable.[4] For the truth which this analogy serves to emphasise is that Love, in its own nature, demands the perfecting of the beloved; that the mere 'kindness' which tolerates anything except suffering in its object is, in that respect, at the opposite pole from Love. When we fall in love with a woman, do we cease to care whether she is clean or dirty, fair or foul? Do we not rather then first begin to care? Does any woman regard it as a sign of love in a man that he neither knows nor cares how she is looking? Love may, indeed, love the beloved when her beauty is lost: but not because it is lost. Love may forgive all infirmities and love still in spite of them: but Love cannot cease to will their removal. Love is more sensitive than hatred itself to every blemish in the beloved; his 'feeling is more soft and sensible than are the tender horns of cockled snails'. Of all powers he forgives most, but he condones least: he is pleased with little, but demands all.

When Christianity says that God loves man, it means that God *loves* man: not that He has some 'disinterested', because really indifferent, concern for our welfare, but that, in awful and surprising truth, we are the objects of His love. You asked for a loving God: you have one. The great spirit you so lightly invoked, the 'lord of terrible aspect', is present: not a senile benevolence that drowsily wishes you to be happy in your own way, not the cold philanthropy of a conscientious magistrate, nor the care of a host who feels responsible for the comfort of his guests, but the consuming fire Himself, the Love that made the worlds, persistent as the artist's love for his work and despotic as a man's love for a dog, provident and venerable as a father's love

[1] Jeremiah 2:2.
[2] Ezekiel 16:6–15.
[3] James 4:4, 5. Authorised Version mistranslates.
[4] Ephesians 5:27.

for a child, jealous, inexorable, exacting as love between the sexes. How this should be, I do not know: it passes reason to explain why any creatures, not to say creatures such as we, should have a value so prodigious in their Creator's eyes. It is certainly a burden of glory not only beyond our deserts but also, except in rare moments of grace, beyond our desiring; we are inclined, like the maidens in the old play, to deprecate the love of Zeus.[1] But the fact seems unquestionable. The Impassible speaks as if it suffered passion, and that which contains in Itself the cause of its own and all other bliss talks as though it could be in want and yearning. 'Is Ephraim my dear son? is he a pleasant child? for since I spake against him I do earnestly remember him still: therefore my bowels are troubled for him.'[2] 'How shall I give thee up, Ephraim? How shall I abandon thee, Israel? Mine heart is turned within me.'[3] 'Oh Jerusalem, how often would I have gathered thy children together, even as a hen gathereth her chickens under her wings, and ye would not.'[4]

The problem of reconciling human suffering with the existence of a God who loves, is only insoluble so long as we attach a trivial meaning to the word 'love', and look on things as if man were the centre of them. Man is not the centre. God does not exist for the sake of man. Man does not exist for his own sake. 'Thou hast created all things, and for thy pleasure they are and were created.'[5] We were made not primarily that we may love God (though we were made for that too) but that God may love us, that we may become objects in which the Divine love may rest 'well pleased'. To ask that God's love should be content with us as we are is to ask that God should cease to be God: because He is what He is, His love must, in the nature of things, be impeded and repelled, by certain stains in our present character, and because He already loves us He must labour to make us lovable. We cannot even wish, in our better moments, that He could reconcile Himself to our present impurities – no more than the beggar maid could wish that King Cophetua should be content with her rags and dirt, or a dog, once having learned to love man, could wish that man were such as to tolerate in his house the snapping, verminous, polluting creature of the wild pack. What we would here and now call our 'happiness' is not the end God chiefly has in view: but when we are such as He can love without impediment, we shall in fact be happy.

I plainly foresee that the course of my argument may provoke a protest. I had promised that in coming to understand the Divine goodness we should not be asked to accept a mere reversal of our own ethics. But it may be

---

[1] *Prometheus Vinctus*, 887–900.
[2] Jeremiah 31:20.
[3] Hosea 11:8.
[4] Matthew 23:37.
[5] Revelation 4:11.

objected that a reversal is precisely what we have been asked to accept. The kind of love which I attribute to God, it may be said, is just the kind which in human beings we describe as 'selfish' or 'possessive', and contrast unfavourably with another kind which seeks first the happiness of the beloved and not the contentment of the lover. I am not sure that this is quite how I feel even about human love. I do not think I should value much the love of a friend who cared only for my happiness and did not object to my becoming dishonest. Nevertheless, the protest is welcome, and the answer to it will put the subject in a new light, and correct what has been one-sided in our discussion.

The truth is that this antithesis between egoistic and altruistic love cannot be unambiguously applied to the love of God for His creatures. Clashes of interest, and therefore opportunities either of selfishness or unselfishness, occur only between beings inhabiting a common world: God can no more be in competition with a creature than Shakespeare can be in competition with Viola. When God becomes a Man and lives as a creature among His own creatures in Palestine, then indeed His life is one of supreme self-sacrifice and leads to Calvary. A modern pantheistic philosopher has said, 'When the Absolute falls into the sea it becomes a fish'; in the same way, we Christians can point to the Incarnation and say that when God empties Himself of His glory and submits to those conditions under which alone egoism and altruism have a clear meaning, He is seen to be wholly altruistic. But God in His transcendence – God as the unconditioned ground of all conditions – cannot easily be thought of in the same way. We call human love selfish when it satisfies its own needs at the expense of the object's needs – as when a father keeps at home, because he cannot bear to relinquish their society, children who ought, in their own interests, to be put out into the world. The situation implies a need or passion on the part of the lover, an incompatible need on the part of the beloved, and the lover's disregard or culpable ignorance of the beloved's need. None of these conditions is present in the relation of God to man. God has no needs. Human love, as Plato teaches us, is the child of Poverty – of a want or lack; it is caused by a real or supposed good in its beloved which the lover needs and desires. But God's love, far from being caused by goodness in the object, causes all the goodness which the object has, loving it first into existence and then into real, though derivative, lovability. God is Goodness. He can give good, but cannot need or get it. In that sense all His love is, as it were, bottomlessly selfless by very definition; it has everything to give and nothing to receive. Hence, if God sometimes speaks as though the Impassible could suffer passion and eternal fullness could be in want, and in want of those beings on whom it bestows all from their bare existence upwards, this can mean only, if it means anything intelligible by us, that God of mere miracle has made

Himself able so to hunger and created in Himself that which we can satisfy. If He requires us, the requirement is of His own choosing. If the immutable heart can be grieved by the puppets of its own making, it is Divine Omnipotence, no other, that has so subjected it, freely, and in a humility that passes understanding. If the world exists not chiefly that we may love God but that God may love us, yet that very fact, on a deeper level, is so for our sakes. If He who in Himself can lack nothing chooses to need us, it is because we need to be needed. Before and behind all the relations of God to man, as we now learn them from Christianity, yawns the abyss of a Divine act of pure giving – the election of man, from nonentity, to be the beloved of God, and therefore (in some sense) the needed and desired of God, who but for that act needs and desires nothing, since He eternally has, and is, all goodness. And that act is for our sakes. It is good for us to know love; and best for us to know the love of the best object, God. But to know it as a love in which we were primarily the wooers and God the wooed, in which we sought and He was found, in which His conformity to our needs, not ours to His, came first, would be to know it in a form false to the very nature of things. For we are only creatures: our role must always be that of patient to agent, female to male, mirror to light, echo to voice. Our highest activity must be response, not initiative. To experience the love of God in a true, and not an illusory form, is therefore to experience it as our surrender to His demand, our conformity to His desire: to experience it in the opposite way is, as it were, a solecism against the grammar of being. I do not deny, of course, that on a certain level we may rightly speak of the soul's search for God, and of God as receptive of the soul's love: but in the long run the soul's search for God can only be a mode, or appearance (*Erscheinung*) of His search for her, since all comes from Him, since the very possibility of our loving is His gift to us, and since our freedom is only a freedom of better or worse response. Hence I think that nothing marks off Pagan theism from Christianity so sharply as Aristotle's doctrine that God moves the universe, Himself unmoving, as the Beloved moves a lover.[1] But for Christendom 'Herein is love, not that we loved God but that He loved us'.[2]

The first condition, then, of what is called a selfish love among men is lacking with God. He has no natural necessities, no passion, to compete with His wish for the beloved's welfare: or if there is in Him something which we have to imagine after the analogy of a passion, a want, it is there by His own will and for our sakes. And the second condition is lacking too. The real interests of a child may differ from that which his father's affection

[1] *Met.*, XII, 7.
[2] I John 4:10.

instinctively demands, because the child is a separate being from the father with a nature which has its own needs and does not exist solely for the father nor find its whole perfection in being loved by him, and which the father does not fully understand. But creatures are not thus separate from their Creator, nor can He misunderstand them. The place for which He designs them in His scheme of things is the place they are made for. When they reach it their nature is fulfilled and their happiness attained: a broken bone in the universe has been set, the anguish is over. When we want to be something other than the thing God wants us to be, we must be wanting what, in fact, will not make us happy. Those Divine demands which sound to our natural ears most like those of a despot and least like those of a lover, in fact marshal us where we should want to go if we knew what we wanted. He demands our worship, our obedience, our prostration. Do we suppose that they can do Him any good, or fear, like the chorus in Milton, that human irreverence can bring about 'His glory's diminution'? A man can no more diminish God's glory by refusing to worship Him than a lunatic can put out the sun by scribbling the word 'darkness' on the walls of his cell. But God wills our good, and our good is to love Him (with that responsive love proper to creatures) and to love Him we must know Him: and if we know Him, we shall in fact fall on our faces. If we do not, that only shows that what we are trying to love is not yet God – though it may be the nearest approximation to God which our thought and fantasy can attain. Yet the call is not only to prostration and awe; it is to a reflection of the Divine life, a creaturely participation in the Divine attributes which is far beyond our present desires. We are bidden to 'put on Christ', to become like God. That is, whether we like it or not, God intends to give us what we need, not what we now think we want. Once more, we are embarrassed by the intolerable compliment, by too much love, not too little.

Yet perhaps even this view falls short of the truth. It is not simply that God has arbitrarily made us such that He is our only good. Rather God is the only good of all creatures: and by necessity, each must find its good in that kind and degree of the fruition of God which is proper to its nature. The kind and degree may vary with the creature's nature: but that there ever could be any other good, is an atheistic dream. George Macdonald, in a passage I cannot now find, represents God as saying to men, 'You must be strong with my strength and blessed with my blessedness, *for I have no other to give you.*' That is the conclusion of the whole matter. God gives what He has, not what He has not: He gives the happiness that there is, not the happiness that is not. To be God – to be like God and to share His goodness in creaturely response – to be miserable – these are the only three alternatives. If we will not learn to eat the only food that the universe grows – the only food that any possible universe ever can grow – then we must starve eternally.

4

HUMAN WICKEDNESS

You can have no greater sign of
confirmed pride than when you
think you are humble enough.
LAW, *Serious Call*, cap. XVI

The examples given in the last chapter went to show that love may cause pain to its object, but only on the supposition that that object needs alteration to become fully lovable. Now why do we men need so much alteration? The Christian answer – that we have used our free will to become very bad – is so well known that it hardly needs to be stated. But to bring this doctrine into real life in the minds of modern men, and even of modern Christians, is very hard. When the apostles preached, they could assume even in their Pagan hearers a real consciousness of deserving the Divine anger. The Pagan mysteries existed to allay this consciousness, and the Epicurean philosophy claimed to deliver men from the fear of eternal punishment. It was against this background that the Gospel appeared as good news. It brought news of possible healing to men who knew that they were mortally ill. But all this has changed. Christianity now has to preach the diagnosis – in itself very bad news – before it can win a hearing for the cure.

There are two principal causes. One is the fact that for about a hundred years we have so concentrated on one of the virtues – 'kindness' or mercy – that most of us do not feel anything except kindness to be really good or anything but cruelty to be really bad. Such lopsided ethical developments are not uncommon, and other ages too have had their pet virtues and curious insensibilities. And if one virtue must be cultivated at the expense of all the rest, none has a higher claim than mercy – for every Christian must reject with detestation that covert propaganda for cruelty which tries to drive mercy out of the world by calling it names such as 'Humanitarianism' and 'Sentimentality'. The real trouble is that 'kindness' is a quality fatally easy to attribute to ourselves on quite inadequate grounds. Everyone *feels* benevolent if nothing happens to be annoying him at the moment. Thus a man easily comes to console himself for all his other vices by a conviction that 'his heart's in the right place' and 'he wouldn't hurt a fly', though in fact he has never made the slightest sacrifice for a fellow creature. We think we are kind when we are only happy: it is not so easy, on the same grounds, to imagine oneself temperate, chaste, or humble.

The second cause is the effect of Psychoanalysis on the public mind, and, in particular, the doctrine of repressions and inhibitions. Whatever these doctrines really mean, the impression they have actually left on most people is that the sense of Shame is a dangerous and mischievous thing. We have laboured to overcome that sense of shrinking, that desire to conceal, which either Nature herself or the tradition of almost all mankind has attached to cowardice, unchastity, falsehood, and envy. We are told to 'get things out into the open', not for the sake of self-humiliation, but on the grounds that these 'things' are very natural and we need not be ashamed of them. But unless Christianity is wholly false, the perception of ourselves which we have in moments of shame must be the only true one; and even Pagan society has usually recognised 'shamelessness' as the nadir of the soul. In trying to extirpate shame we have broken down one of the ramparts of the human spirit, madly exulting in the work as the Trojans exulted when they broke their walls and pulled the Horse into Troy. I do not know that there is anything to be done but to set about the rebuilding as soon as we can. It is mad work to remove hypocrisy by removing the *temptation* to hypocrisy: the 'frankness' of people sunk below shame is a very cheap frankness.

A recovery of the old sense of sin is essential to Christianity. Christ takes it for granted that men are bad. Until we really feel this assumption of His to be true, though we are part of the world He came to save, we are not part of the audience to whom His words are addressed. We lack the first condition for understanding what He is talking about. And when men attempt to be Christians without this preliminary consciousness of sin, the result is almost bound to be a certain resentment against God as to one always inexplicably angry. Most of us have at times felt a secret sympathy with the dying farmer who replied to the Vicar's dissertation on repentance by asking 'What harm have I ever done *Him*?' There is the real rub. The worst we have done to God is to leave Him alone – why can't He return the compliment? Why not live and let live? What call has He, of all beings, to be 'angry'? It's easy for Him to be good!

Now at the moment when a man feels real guilt – moments too rare in our lives – all these blasphemies vanish away. Much, we may feel, can be excused to human infirmities: but not *this* – this incredibly mean and ugly action which none of our friends would have done, which even such a thorough-going little rotter as X would have been ashamed of, which we would not for the world allow to be published. At such a moment we really do know that our character, as revealed in this action, is, and ought to be, hateful to all good men, and, if there are powers above man, to them. A God who did not regard this with unappeasable distaste would not be a good being.

We cannot even wish for such a God – it is like wishing that every nose in the universe were abolished, that smell of hay or roses or the sea should never again delight any creature, because our own breath happens to stink.

When we merely *say* that we are bad, the 'wrath' of God seems a barbarous doctrine; as soon as we *perceive* our badness, it appears inevitable, a mere corollary from God's goodness. To keep ever before us the insight derived from such a moment as I have been describing, to learn to detect the same real inexcusable corruption under more and more of its complex disguises, is therefore indispensable to a real understanding of the Christian faith. This is not, of course, a new doctrine. I am attempting nothing very splendid in this chapter. I am merely trying to get my reader (and, still more, myself) over a *pons asinorum* – to take the first step out of fools' paradise and utter illusion. But the illusion has grown, in modern times, so strong, that I must add a few considerations tending to make the reality less incredible.

1. We are deceived by looking on the outside of things. We suppose ourselves to be roughly not much worse than Y, whom all acknowledge for a decent sort of person, and certainly (though we should not claim it out loud) better than the abominable X. Even on the superficial level we are probably deceived about this. Don't be too sure that your friends think you as good as Y. The very fact that you selected him for the comparison is suspicious: he is probably head and shoulders above you and your circle. But let us suppose that Y and yourself both appear 'not bad'. How far Y's appearance is deceptive, is between Y and God. His may not be deceptive: you know that yours is. Does this seem to you a mere trick, because I could say the same to Y and so to every man in turn? But that is just the point. Every man, not very holy or very arrogant, has to 'live up to' the outward appearance of other men: he knows there is that within him which falls far below even his most careless public behaviour, even his loosest talk. In an instant of time – while your friend hesitates for a word – what things pass through your mind? We have never told the whole truth. We may confess ugly *facts* – the meanest cowardice or the shabbiest and most prosaic impurity – but the *tone* is false. The very act of confessing – an infinitesimally hypocritical glance – a dash of humour – all this contrives to dissociate the facts from your very self. No one could guess how familiar and, in a sense, congenial to your soul these things were, how much of a piece with all the rest: down there, in the dreaming inner warmth, they struck no such discordant note, were not nearly so odd and detachable from the rest of you, as they seem when they are turned into words. We imply, and often believe, that habitual vices are exceptional single acts, and make the opposite mistake about our virtues – like the bad tennis player who calls his normal form his 'bad days' and mistakes his rare successes for his normal. I do not think it is our fault that we cannot tell the real truth about ourselves; the persistent, life-long, inner murmur of spite,

jealousy, prurience, greed and self-complacence, simply will not go into words. But the important thing is that we should not mistake our inevitably limited utterances for a full account of the worst that is inside.

2. A reaction – in itself wholesome – is now going on against purely private or domestic conceptions of morality, a reawakening of the *social* conscience. We feel ourselves to be involved in an iniquitous social system and to share a corporate guilt. This is very true: but the enemy can exploit even truths to our deception. Beware lest you are making use of the idea of corporate guilt to distract your attention from those humdrum, old-fashioned guilts of your own which have nothing to do with 'the system' and which can be dealt with without waiting for the millennium. For corporate guilt perhaps cannot be, and certainly is not, felt with the same force as personal guilt. For most of us, as we now are, this conception is a mere excuse for evading the real issue. When we have really learned to know our individual corruption, then indeed we can go on to think of the corporate guilt and can hardly think of it too much. But we must learn to walk before we run.

3. We have a strange illusion that mere time cancels sin. I have heard others, and I have heard myself, recounting cruelties and falsehoods committed in boyhood as if they were no concern of the present speaker's, and even with laughter. But mere time does nothing either to the fact or to the guilt of a sin. The guilt is washed out not by time but by repentance and the blood of Christ: if we have repented these early sins we should remember the price of our forgiveness and be humble. As for the fact of a sin, is it probable that anything cancels it? All times are eternally present to God. Is it not at least possible that along some one line of His multi-dimensional eternity He sees you forever in the nursery pulling the wings off a fly, forever toadying, lying, and lusting as a schoolboy, forever in that moment of cowardice or insolence as a subaltern? It may be that salvation consists not in the cancelling of these eternal moments but in the perfected humanity that bears the shame forever, rejoicing in the occasion which it furnished to God's compassion and glad that it should be common knowledge to the universe. Perhaps in that eternal moment St Peter – he will forgive me if I am wrong – forever denies his Master. If so, it would indeed be true that the joys of Heaven are for most of us, in our present condition, 'an acquired taste' – and certain ways of life may render the taste impossible of acquisition. Perhaps the lost are those who dare not go to such a *public* place. Of course I do not know that this is true; but I think the possibility is worth keeping in mind.

4. We must guard against the feeling that there is 'safety in numbers'. It is natural to feel that if *all* men are as bad as the Christians say, then badness must be very excusable. If all the boys plough in the examination, surely the papers must have been too hard? And so the masters at that school feel till

they learn that there are other schools where ninety per cent of the boys passed on the same papers. Then they begin to suspect that the fault did not lie with the examiners. Again, many of us have had the experience of living in some local pocket of human society – some particular school, college, regiment or profession where the tone was bad. And inside that pocket certain actions were regarded as merely normal ('Everyone does it') and certain others as impracticably virtuous and Quixotic. But when we emerged from that bad society we made the horrible discovery that in the outer world our 'normal' was the kind of thing that no decent person ever dreamed of doing, and our 'Quixotic' was taken for granted as the minimum standard of decency. What had seemed to us morbid and fantastic scruples so long as we were in the 'pocket' now turned out to be the only moments of sanity we there enjoyed. It is wise to face the possibility that the whole human race (being a small thing in the universe) is, in fact, just such a local pocket of evil – an isolated bad school or regiment inside which minimum decency passes for heroic virtue and utter corruption for pardonable imperfection. But is there any evidence – except Christian doctrine itself – that this is so? I am afraid there is. In the first place, there are those odd people among us who do not accept the local standard, who demonstrate the alarming truth that a quite different behaviour is, in fact, possible. Worse still, there is the fact that these people, even when separated widely in space and time, have a suspicious knack of agreeing with one another in the main – almost as if they were in touch with some larger public opinion outside the pocket. What is common to Zarathustra, Jeremiah, Socrates, Gautama, Christ[1] and Marcus Aurelius, is something pretty substantial. Thirdly, we find in ourselves even now a theoretical approval of this behaviour which no one practises. Even inside the pocket we do not say that justice, mercy, fortitude, and temperance are of no value, but only that the local custom is as just, brave, temperate and merciful as can reasonably be expected. It begins to look as if the neglected school rules even inside this bad school were connected with some larger world – and that when the term ends we might find ourselves facing the public opinion of that larger world. But the worst of all is this: we cannot help seeing that only the degree of virtue which we now regard as impracticable can possibly save our race from disaster even on this planet. The standard which seems to have come into the 'pocket' from outside, turns out to be terribly relevant to conditions inside the pocket – so relevant that a consistent practice of virtue by the human race even for ten years would fill the earth from pole to pole with peace, plenty, health, merriment, and

---

[1] I mention the Incarnate God among human teachers to emphasise the fact that the *principal* difference between Him and them lies not in ethical teaching (which is here my concern) but in Person and Office.

heartsease, and that nothing else will. It may be the custom, down here, to treat the regimental rules as a dead letter or a counsel of perfection: but even now, everyone who stops to think can see that when we meet the enemy this neglect is going to cost every man of us his life. It is then that we shall envy the 'morbid' person, the 'pedant' or 'enthusiast' who really *has* taught his company to shoot and dig in and spare their water bottles.

5. The larger society to which I here contrast the human 'pocket' may not exist according to some people, and at any rate we have no experience of it. We do not meet angels, or unfallen races. But we can get some inkling of the truth even inside our own race. Different ages and cultures can be regarded as 'pockets' in relation to one another. I said, a few pages back, that different ages excelled in different virtues. If, then, you are ever tempted to think that we modern Western Europeans cannot really be so very bad because we are, comparatively speaking, humane – if, in other words, you think God might be content with us on that ground – ask yourself whether you think God ought to have been content with the cruelty of cruel ages because they excelled in courage or chastity. You will see at once that this is an impossibility. From considering how the cruelty of our ancestors looks to us, you may get some inkling how our softness, worldliness, and timidity would have looked to them, and hence how both must look to God.

6. Perhaps my harping on the word 'kindness' has already aroused a protest in some readers' minds. Are we not really an increasingly cruel age? Perhaps we are: but I think we have become so in the attempt to reduce all virtues to kindness. For Plato rightly taught that virtue is one. You cannot be kind unless you have all the other virtues. If, being cowardly, conceited and slothful, you have never yet done a fellow creature great mischief, that is only because your neighbour's welfare has not yet happened to conflict with your safety, self-approval, or ease. Every vice leads to cruelty. Even a good emotion, pity, if not controlled by charity and justice, leads through anger to cruelty. Most atrocities are stimulated by accounts of the enemy's atrocities; and pity for the oppressed classes, when separated from the moral law as a whole, leads by a very natural process to the unremitting brutalities of a reign of terror.

7. Some modern theologians have, quite rightly, protested against an excessively moralistic interpretation of Christianity. The Holiness of God is something more and other than moral perfection: His claim upon us is something more and other than the claim of moral duty. I do not deny it: but this conception, like that of corporate guilt, is very easily used as an evasion of the real issue. God may be more than moral goodness: He is not less. The road to the promised land runs past Sinai. The moral law may exist to be transcended: but there is no transcending it for those who have not first

admitted its claims upon them, and then tried with all their strength to meet that claim, and fairly and squarely faced the fact of their failure.

8. 'Let no man say when he is tempted, I am tempted of God.'[1] Many schools of thought encourage us to shift the responsibility for our behaviour from our own shoulders to some inherent necessity in the nature of human life, and thus, indirectly, to the Creator. Popular forms of this view are the evolutionary doctrine that what we call badness is an unavoidable legacy from our animal ancestors, or the idealistic doctrine that it is merely a result of our being finite. Now Christianity, if I have understood the Pauline epistles, does admit that perfect obedience to the moral law, which we find written in our hearts and perceive to be necessary even on the biological level, is not in fact possible to men. This would raise a real difficulty about our responsibility if perfect obedience had any practical relation at all to the lives of most of us. Some degree of obedience which you and I have failed to attain in the last twenty-four hours is certainly possible. The ultimate problem must not be used as one more means of evasion. Most of us are less urgently concerned with the Pauline question than with William Law's simple statement: 'If you will here stop and ask yourselves why you are not as pious as the primitive Christians were, your own heart will tell you, that it is neither through ignorance nor inability, but purely because you never thoroughly intended it.'[2]

This chapter will have been misunderstood if anyone describes it as a reinstatement of the doctrine of Total Depravity. I disbelieve that doctrine, partly on the logical ground that if our depravity were total we should not know ourselves to be depraved, and partly because experience shows us much goodness in human nature. Nor am I recommending universal gloom. The emotion of shame has been valued not as an emotion but because of the insight to which it leads. I think that insight should be permanent in each man's mind: but whether the painful emotions that attend it should also be encouraged, is a technical problem of spiritual direction on which, as a layman, I have little call to speak. My own idea, for what it is worth, is that all sadness which is not either arising from the repentance of a concrete sin and hastening towards concrete amendment or restitution, or else arising from pity and hastening to active assistance, is simply bad; and I think we all sin by needlessly disobeying the apostolic injunction to 'rejoice' as much as by anything else. Humility, after the first shock, is a cheerful virtue: it is the high-minded unbeliever, desperately trying in the teeth of repeated disillusions to retain his 'faith in human nature', who is really sad. I have been aiming at an intellectual, not an emotional, effect: I have been trying to

[1] James 1:13.
[2] *Serious Call*, cap 2.

make the reader believe that we actually are, at present, creatures whose character must be, in some respects, a horror to God, as it is, when we really see it, a horror to ourselves. This I believe to be a fact: and I notice that the holier a man is, the more fully he is aware of that fact. Perhaps you have imagined that this humility in the saints is a pious illusion at which God smiles. That is a most dangerous error. It is theoretically dangerous, because it makes you identify a virtue (i.e., a perfection) with an illusion (i.e., an imperfection), which must be nonsense. It is practically dangerous because it encourages a man to mistake his first insights into his own corruption for the first beginnings of a halo round his own silly head. No; depend upon it, when the saints say that they – even they – are vile, they are recording truth with scientific accuracy.

How did this state of affairs come about? In the next chapter I shall give as much as I can understand of the Christian answer to that question.

5

THE FALL OF MAN

To obey is the proper office of a rational soul.
Montaigne II, xii

The Christian answer to the question proposed in the last chapter is contained in the doctrine of the Fall. According to that doctrine, man is now a horror to God and to himself and a creature ill-adapted to the universe not because God made him so but because he has made himself so by the abuse of his free will. To my mind this is the sole function of the doctrine. It exists to guard against two sub-Christian theories of the origin of evil – Monism, according to which God Himself, being 'above good and evil', produces impartially the effects to which we give those two names, and Dualism, according to which God produces good, while some equal and independent Power produces evil. Against both these views Christianity asserts that God is good; that He made all things good and for the sake of their goodness; that one of the good things He made, namely, the free will of rational creatures, by its very nature included the possibility of evil; and that creatures, availing themselves of this possibility, have become evil. Now this function – which is the only one I allow to the doctrine of the Fall – must be distinguished from two other functions which it is sometimes, perhaps, represented as performing, but which I reject. In the first place, I do not think the doctrine answers the question 'Was it better for God to create than not to create?' That is a question I have already declined. Since I believe God to be good, I am sure that, if the question has a meaning, the answer must be Yes. But I doubt whether the question has any meaning: and even if it has, I am sure that the answer cannot be attained by the sort of value-judgement which men can significantly make. In the second place, I do not think the doctrine of the Fall can be used to show that it is 'just', in terms of retributive justice, to punish individuals for the faults of their remote ancestors. Some forms of doctrine seem to involve this; but I question whether any of them, as understood by its exponents, really meant it. The Fathers may sometimes say that we are punished for Adam's sin: but they much more often say that *we* sinned 'in Adam'. It may be impossible to find out what they meant by this, or we may decide that what they meant was erroneous.

But I do not think we can dismiss their way of talking as a mere 'idiom'. Wisely, or foolishly, they believed that we were *really* – and not simply by legal fiction – involved in Adam's action. The attempt to formulate this belief by saying that we were 'in' Adam in a physical sense – Adam being the first vehicle of the 'immortal germ plasm' – may be unacceptable: but it is, of course, a further question whether the belief itself is merely a confusion or a real insight into spiritual realities beyond our normal grasp. At the moment, however, this question does not arise; for, as I have said, I have no intention of arguing that the descent to modern man of inabilities contracted by his remote ancestors is a specimen of retributive justice. For me it is rather a specimen of those things necessarily involved in the creation of a stable world which we considered in Chapter 2. It would, no doubt, have been possible for God to remove by miracle the results of the first sin ever committed by a human being; but this would not have been much good unless He was prepared to remove the results of the second sin, and of the third, and so on forever. If the miracles ceased, then sooner or later we might have reached our present lamentable situation: if they did not, then a world thus continually underpropped and corrected by Divine interference, would have been a world in which nothing important ever depended on human choice, and in which choice itself would soon cease from the certainty that one of the apparent alternatives before you would lead to no results and was therefore not really an alternative. As we saw, the chess player's freedom to play chess depends on the rigidity of the squares and the moves.

Having isolated what I conceive to be the true import of the doctrine that Man is fallen, let us now consider the doctrine in itself. The story in Genesis is a story (full of the deepest suggestion) about a magic apple of knowledge; but in the developed doctrine the inherent magic of the apple has quite dropped out of sight, and the story is simply one of disobedience. I have the deepest respect even for Pagan myths, still more for myths in Holy Scripture. I therefore do not doubt that the version which emphasises the magic apple, and brings together the trees of life and knowledge, contains a deeper and subtler truth than the version which makes the apple simply and solely a pledge of obedience. But I assume that the Holy Spirit would not have allowed the latter to grow up in the Church and win the assent of great doctors unless it also was true and useful as far as it went. It is this version which I am going to discuss, because, though I suspect the primitive version to be far more profound, I know that I, at any rate, cannot penetrate its profundities. I am to give my readers not the best absolutely but the best I have.

In the developed doctrine, then, it is claimed that Man, as God made him, was completely good and completely happy, but that he disobeyed God and became what we now see. Many people think that this proposition has been proved false by modern science. 'We now know,' it is said, 'that so far from having fallen out of a primeval state of virtue and happiness, men have slowly risen from brutality and savagery.' There seems to me to be a complete confusion here. *Brute* and *savage* both belong to that unfortunate class of words which are sometimes used rhetorically, as terms of reproach, and sometimes scientifically, as terms of description; and the pseudo-scientific argument against the Fall depends on a confusion between the usages. If by saying that man rose from brutality you mean simply that man is physically descended from animals, I have no objection. But it does not follow that the further back you go the more *brutal* – in the sense or wicked or wretched – you will find man to be. No animal has moral virtue: but it is not true that all animal behaviour is of the kind one should call 'wicked' if it were practised by men. On the contrary, not all animals treat other creatures of their own species as badly as men treat men. Not all are as gluttonous or lecherous as we, and no animal is ambitious. Similarly if you say that the first men were 'savages', meaning by this that their artefacts were few and clumsy like those of modern 'savages', you may well be right; but if you mean that they were 'savage' in the sense of being lewd, ferocious, cruel, and treacherous, you will be going beyond your evidence, and that for two reasons. In the first place, modern anthropologists and missionaries are less inclined than their fathers to endorse your unfavourable picture even of the modern savage. In the second place you cannot argue from the artefacts of the earliest men that they were in all respects like the contemporary people who make similar artefacts. We must be on our guard here against an illusion which the study of prehistoric man seems naturally to beget. Prehistoric man, because he is prehistoric, is known to us only by the material things he made – or rather by a chance selection from among the more durable things he made. It is not the fault of archaeologists that they have no better evidence: but this penury constitutes a continual temptation to infer more than we have any right to infer, to assume that the community which made the superior artefacts was superior in all respects. Everyone can see that the assumption is false; it would lead to the conclusion that the leisured classes of our own time were in all respects superior to those of the Victorian age. Clearly the prehistoric men who made the worst pottery might have made the best poetry and we should never know it. And the assumption becomes even more absurd when we are comparing prehistoric men with modern savages. The equal crudity of artefacts here tells you nothing about the intelligence or virtue of the makers. What is learned by trial and error must begin by being crude, whatever the character of the beginner. The very same pot which would prove its maker a genius if it were the first pot ever made in the world, would prove its maker a dunce if it came after millenniums of pot-making. The whole modern estimate of primitive man is based upon that idolatry of artefacts which is a great corporate sin of our own civilisation. We forget that our prehistoric ancestors made all the useful discoveries, except that of chloroform, which have ever been made. To them we owe language, the family, clothing, the use of fire, the domestication of animals, the wheel, the ship, poetry and agriculture.

Science, then, has nothing to say for or against the doctrine of the Fall. A more philosophical difficulty has been raised by the modern theologian to whom all students of the subject are most indebted.[1] This writer points out that the idea of sin presupposes a law to sin against: and since it would take centuries for the 'herd-instinct' to crystallise into custom and for custom to harden into law, the first man – if there ever was a being who could be so described – could not commit the first sin. This argument assumes that virtue and the herd-instinct commonly coincide, and that the 'first sin' was essentially a *social* sin. But the traditional doctrine points to a sin against God, an act of disobedience, not a sin against the neighbour. And certainly, if we are to hold the doctrine of the Fall in any real sense, we must look for the great sin on a deeper and more timeless level than that of social morality.

This sin has been described by Saint Augustine as the result of Pride, of the movement whereby a creature (that is, an essentially dependent being whose principle of existence lies not in itself but in another) tries to set up on its own, to exist for itself.[2] Such a sin requires no complex social conditions, no extended experience, no great intellectual development. From the moment a creature becomes aware of God as God and of itself as self, the terrible alternative of choosing God or self for the centre is opened to it. This sin is committed daily by young children and ignorant peasants as well as by sophisticated persons, by solitaries no less than by those who live in society: it is the fall in every individual life, and in each day of each individual life, the basic sin behind all particular sins: at this very moment you and I are either committing it, or about to commit it, or repenting it. We try, when we wake, to lay the new day at God's feet; before we have finished shaving, it becomes *our* day and God's share in it is felt as a tribute which we must pay out of 'our own' pocket, a deduction from the time which ought, we feel, to be 'our own'. A man starts a new job with a sense of vocation and, perhaps, for the first week still keeps the discharge of the vocation as his end, taking the pleasures and pains from God's hand, as they come, as 'accidents'. But in the second week he is beginning to 'know the ropes': by the third, he has quarried out of the total job his own plan for himself within that job, and when he can pursue this he feels that he is getting no more than his rights, and, when he cannot, that he is being interfered with. A lover, in obedience to a quite uncalculating impulse, which may be full of good will

[1] N. P. Williams, *The Ideas of the Fall and of Original Sin*, p. 516.
[2] *De Civitate Dei*, XIV, xiii.

as well as of desire and need not be forgetful of God, embraces his beloved, and then, quite innocently, experiences a thrill of sexual pleasure; but the second embrace may have that pleasure in view, may be a means to an end, may be the first downward step towards the state of regarding a fellow creature as a thing, as a machine to be used for his pleasure. Thus the bloom of innocence, the element of obedience and the readiness to take what comes is rubbed off every activity. Thoughts undertaken for God's sake – like that on which we are engaged at the moment – are continued as if they were an end in themselves, and then as if our pleasure in thinking were the end, and finally as if our pride or celebrity were the end. Thus all day long, and all the days of our life, we are sliding, slipping, falling away – as if God were, to our present consciousness, a smooth inclined plane on which there is no resting. And indeed we are now of such a nature that we must slip off, and the sin, because it is unavoidable, may be venial. But God cannot have made us so. The gravitation away from God, 'the journey homeward to habitual self', must, we think, be a product of the Fall. What exactly happened when Man fell, we do not know; but if it is legitimate to guess, I offer the following picture – a 'myth' in the Socratic sense,[1] a not unlikely tale.

For long centuries God perfected the animal form which was to become the vehicle of humanity and the image of Himself. He gave it hands whose thumb could be applied to each of the fingers, and jaws and teeth and throat capable of articulation, and a brain sufficiently complex to execute all the material motions whereby rational thought is incarnated. The creature may have existed for ages in this state before it became man: it may even have been clever enough to make things which a modern archaeologist would accept as proof of its humanity. But it was only an animal because all its physical and psychical processes were directed to purely material and natural ends. Then, in the fullness of time, God caused to descend upon this organism, both on its psychology and physiology, a new kind of consciousness which could say 'I' and 'me', which could look upon itself as an object, which knew God, which could make judgements of truth, beauty, and goodness, and which was so far above time that it could perceive time flowing past. This new consciousness ruled and illuminated the whole organism, flooding every part of it with light, and was not, like ours, limited to a selection of the movements going on in one part of the organism, namely the brain. Man was then all consciousness. The modern Yogi claims – whether falsely or truly – to have under control those functions which to us are almost part of the external world, such as digestion and circulation. This power the first man had in eminence. His organic processes obeyed the law of his own will, not the law of nature. His organs

[1] I.e., an account of what *may have been* the historical fact. Not to be confused with 'myth' in Dr Niebuhr's sense (i.e., a symbolical representation of non-historical truth).

sent up appetites to the judgement seat of will not because they had to, but because he chose. Sleep meant to him not the stupor which we undergo, but willed and conscious repose – he remained awake to enjoy the pleasure and duty of sleep. Since the processes of decay and repair in his tissues were similarly conscious and obedient, it may not be fanciful to suppose that the length of his life was largely at his own discretion. Wholly commanding himself, he commanded all lower lives with which he came into contact. Even now we meet rare individuals who have a mysterious power of taming beasts. This power the Paradisal man enjoyed in eminence. The old picture of the brutes sporting before Adam and fawning upon him may not be wholly symbolical. Even now more animals than you might expect are ready to adore man if they are given a reasonable opportunity: for man was made to be the priest and even, in one sense, the Christ, of the animals – the mediator through whom they apprehend so much of the Divine splendour as their irrational nature allows. And God was to such a man no slippery, inclined plane. The new consciousness had been made to repose on its Creator, and repose it did. However rich and varied man's experience of his fellows (or fellow) in charity and friendship and sexual love, or of the beasts, or of the surrounding world then first recognised as beautiful and awful, God came first in his love and in his thought, and that without painful effort. In perfect cyclic movement, being, power and joy descended from God to man in the form of gift and returned from man to God in the form of obedient love and ecstatic adoration: and in this sense, though not in all, man was then truly the son of God, the prototype of Christ, perfectly enacting in joy and ease of all the faculties and all the senses that filial self-surrender which Our Lord enacted in the agonies of the crucifixion.

Judged by his artefacts, or perhaps even by his language, this blessed creature was, no doubt, a savage. All that experience and practice can teach he had still to learn: if he chipped flints, he doubtless chipped them clumsily enough. He may have been utterly incapable of expressing in conceptual form his Paradisal experience. All that is quite irrelevant. From our own childhood we remember that before our elders thought us capable of 'understanding' anything, we already had spiritual experience as pure and as momentous as any we have undergone since, though not, of course, as rich in factual context. From Christianity itself we learn that there is a level – in the long run the only level of importance – on which the learned and the adult have no advantage at all over the simple and the child. I do not doubt that if the Paradisal man could now appear among us, we should regard him as an utter savage, a creature to be exploited or, at best, patronised. Only one or two, and those the holiest among us, would glance a second time at the naked, shaggy-bearded, slow-spoken creature: but they, after a few minutes, would fall at his feet.

We do not know how many of these creatures God made, nor how long they continued in the Paradisal state. But sooner or later they fell. Someone or something whispered that they could become as gods – that they could cease directing their lives to their Creator and taking all their delights as uncovenanted mercies, as 'accidents' (in the logical sense) which arose in the course of a life directed not to those delights but to the adoration of God. As a young man wants a regular allowance from his father which he can count on as his own, within which he makes his own plans (and rightly, for his father is after all a fellow creature), so they desired to be on their own, to take care for their own future, to plan for pleasure and for security, to have a *meum* from which, no doubt, they would pay some reasonable tribute to God in the way of time, attention, and love, but which, nevertheless, was theirs not His. They wanted, as we say, to 'call their souls their own'. But that means to live a lie, for our souls are not, in fact, our own. They wanted some corner in the universe of which they could say to God, 'This is our business, not yours.' But there is no such corner. They wanted to be nouns, but they were, and eternally must be, mere adjectives. We have no idea in what particular act, or series of acts, the self-contradictory, impossible wish found expression. For all I can see, it might have concerned the literal eating of a fruit, but the question is of no consequence.

This act of self-will on the part of the creature, which constitutes an utter falseness to its true creaturely position, is the only sin that can be conceived as the Fall. For the difficulty about the first sin is that it must be very heinous, or its consequences would not be so terrible, and yet it must be something which a being free from the temptations of fallen man could conceivably have committed. The turning from God to self fulfils both conditions. It is a sin possible even to Paradisal man, because the mere existence of a self – the mere fact that we call it 'me' – includes, from the first, the danger of self-idolatry. Since I am I, I must make an act of self-surrender, however small or however easy, in living to God rather than to myself. This is, if you like, the 'weak spot' in the very nature of creation, the risk which God apparently thinks worth taking. But the sin was very heinous, because the self which Paradisal man had to surrender contained no natural recalcitrancy to being surrendered. His *data*, so to speak, were a psycho-physical organism wholly subject to the will and a will wholly disposed, though not compelled, to turn to God. The self-surrender which he practised before the Fall meant no struggle but only the delicious overcoming of an infinitesimal self-adherence which delighted to be overcome – of which we see a dim analogy in the rapturous mutual self-surrenders of lovers even now. He had, therefore, no *temptation* (in our sense) to choose the self – no passion or inclination obstinately inclining that way – nothing but the bare fact that the self was *him*self.

Up to that moment the human spirit had been in full control of the human organism. It doubtless expected that it would retain this control when it had ceased to obey God. But its authority over the organism was a delegated authority which it lost when it ceased to be God's delegate. Having cut itself off, as far as it could, from the source of its being, it had cut itself off from the source of power. For when we say of created things that A rules B this must mean that God rules B through A. I doubt whether it would have been intrinsically possible for God to continue to rule the organism *through* the human spirit when the human spirit was in revolt against Him. At any rate He did not. He began to rule the organism in a more external way, not by the laws of spirit, but by those of nature.[1] Thus the organs, no longer governed by man's will, fell under the control of ordinary biochemical laws and suffered whatever the inter-workings of those laws might bring about in the way of pain, senility and death. And desires began to come up into the mind of man, not as his reason chose, but just as the biochemical and environmental facts happened to cause them. And the mind itself fell under the psychological laws of association and the like which God had made to rule the psychology of the higher anthropoids. And the will, caught in the tidal wave of mere nature, had no resource but to force back some of the new thoughts and desires by main strength, and these uneasy rebels became the subconscious as we now know it. The process was not, I conceive, comparable to mere deterioration as it may now occur in a human individual; it was a loss of status as a *species*. What man lost by the Fall was his original specific nature. 'Dust thou art, and unto dust shalt thou return.' The total organism which had been taken up into his spiritual life was allowed to fall back into the merely natural condition from which, at his making, it had been raised – just as, far earlier in the story of creation, God had raised vegetable life to become the vehicle of animality, and chemical process to be the vehicle of vegetation, and physical process to be the vehicle of chemical. Thus human spirit from being the master of human nature became a mere lodger in its own house, or even a prisoner; rational consciousness became what it now is – a fitful spotlight resting on a small part of the cerebral motions. But this limitation of the spirit's powers was a lesser evil than the corruption of the spirit itself. It had turned from God and become its own idol, so that though it could still turn back to God,[2] it could do so only

---

[1] This is a development of Hooker's conception of Law. To disobey your *proper* law (i.e., the law God makes for a being such as you) means to find yourself obeying one of God's lower laws: e.g., if, when walking on a slippery pavement, you neglect the law of Prudence, you suddenly find yourself obeying the law of gravitation.

[2] Theologians will note that I am not here intending to make any contribution to the Pelagian-Augustinian controversy. I mean only that such return to God was not, even now, an impossibility. Where the initiative lies in any instance of such return is a question on which I am saying nothing.

by painful effort, and its inclination was self-ward. Hence pride and ambition, the desire to be lovely in its own eyes and to depress and humiliate all rivals, envy, and restless search for more, and still more, security, were now the attitudes that came easiest to it. It was not only a weak king over its own nature, but a bad one: it sent down into the psycho-physical organism desires far worse than the organism sent up into it. This condition was transmitted by heredity to all later generations, for it was not simply what biologists call an acquired variation; it was the emergence of a new kind of man – a new species, never made by God, had sinned itself into existence. The change which man had undergone was not parallel to the development of a new habit; it was a radical alteration of his constitution, a disturbance of the relation between his component parts, and an internal perversion of one of them.

God might have arrested this process by miracle: but this – to speak in somewhat irreverent metaphor – would have been to decline the problem which God had set Himself when He created the world, the problem of expressing His goodness through the total drama of a world containing free agents, in spite of, and by means of, their rebellion against Him. The symbol of a drama, a symphony, or a dance, is here useful to correct a certain absurdity which may arise if we talk too much of God planning and creating the world process for good and of that good being frustrated by the free will of the creatures. This may raise the ridiculous idea that the Fall took God by surprise and upset His plan, or else – more ridiculously still – that God planned the whole thing for conditions which, He well knew, were never going to be realised. In fact, of course, God saw the crucifixion in the act of creating the first nebula. The world is a dance in which good, descending from God, is disturbed by evil arising from the creatures, and the resulting conflict is resolved by God's own assumption of the suffering nature which evil produces. The doctrine of the free Fall asserts that the evil which thus makes the fuel or raw material for the second and more complex kind of good is not God's contribution but man's. This does not mean that if man had remained innocent God could not then have contrived an equally splendid symphonic whole – supposing that we insist on asking such questions. But it must always be remembered that when we talk of what might have happened, of contingencies outside the whole actuality, we do not really know what we are talking about. There are no times or places outside the existing universe in which all this 'could happen' or 'could have happened'. I think the most significant way of stating the real freedom of man is to say that if there are other rational species than man, existing in some other part of the actual universe, then it is not necessary to suppose that they also have fallen.

Our present condition, then, is explained by the fact that we are members of a spoiled species. I do not mean that our sufferings are a punishment for being what we cannot now help being nor that we are morally responsible for the rebellion of a remote ancestor. If, none the less, I call our present condition one of original Sin, and not merely one of original misfortune, that is because our actual religious experience does not allow us to regard it in any other way. Theoretically, I suppose, we might say 'Yes: we behave like vermin, but then that is because we *are* vermin. And that, at any rate, is not our fault.' But the fact that we are vermin, so far from being felt as an excuse, is a greater shame and grief to us than any of the particular acts which it leads us to commit. The situation is not nearly so hard to understand as some people make out. It arises among human beings whenever a very badly brought up boy is introduced into a decent family. They rightly remind themselves that it is 'not his own fault' that he is a bully, a coward, a tale-bearer and a liar. But none the less, however it came there, his present character is detestable. They not only hate it, but ought to hate it. They cannot love him for what he is, they can only try to turn him into what he is not. In the meantime, though the boy is most unfortunate in having been so brought up, you cannot quite call his character a 'misfortune' as if he were one thing and his character another. It is he – he himself – who bullies and sneaks and likes doing it. And if he begins to mend he will inevitably feel shame and guilt at what he is just beginning to cease to be.

With this I have said all that can be said on the level at which alone I feel able to treat the subject of the Fall. But I warn my readers once more that this level is a shallow one. We have said nothing about the trees of life and of knowledge which doubtless conceal some great mystery: and we have said nothing about the Pauline statement that 'as in Adam all die, so in Christ shall all be made alive'.[1] It is this passage which lies behind the Patristic doctrine of our physical presence in Adam's loins and Anselm's doctrine of our inclusion, by legal fiction, in the suffering Christ. These theories may have done good in their day but they do no good to me, and I am not going to invent others. We have recently been told by the scientists that we have no right to expect that the real universe should be picturable, and that if we make mental pictures to illustrate quantum physics we are moving further away from reality, not nearer to it.[2] We have clearly even less right to demand that the highest spiritual realities should be picturable, or even explicable in terms of our abstract thought. I observe that the difficulty of the Pauline formula turns on the word *in*, and that this word, again and again in the New Testament, is used in senses we cannot fully understand. That we can die 'in' Adam and live 'in' Christ seems to me to imply that man, as he really is, differs a good deal from man as our categories of

[1] 1 Corinthians 15:22.
[2] Sir James Jeans' *The Mysterious Universe*, cap. 5.

thought and our three-dimensional imaginations represent him; that the separateness – modified only by causal relations – which we discern between individuals, is balanced, in absolute reality, by some kind of 'inter-inanimation' of which we have no conception at all. It may be that the acts and sufferings of great archetypal individuals such as Adam and Christ are ours, not by legal fiction, metaphor, or causality, but in some much deeper fashion. There is no question, of course, of individuals melting down into a kind of spiritual continuum such as Pantheistic systems believe in; that is excluded by the whole tenor of our faith. But there may be a tension between individuality and some other principle. We believe that the Holy Spirit can be really present and operative in the human spirit, but we do not, like Pantheists, take this to mean that we are 'parts' or 'modifications' or 'appearances' of God. We may have to suppose, in the long run, that something of the same kind is true, in its appropriate degree, even of created spirits, that each, though distinct, is really present in all, or in some, others – just as we may have to admit 'action at a distance' into our conception of matter. Everyone will have noticed how the Old Testament seems at times to ignore our conception of the individual. When God promises Jacob that 'He will go down with him into Egypt and will also surely bring him up again',[1] this is fulfilled either by the burial of Jacob's body in Palestine or by the exodus of Jacob's descendants from Egypt. It is quite right to connect this notion with the social structure of early communities in which the individual is constantly overlooked in favour of the tribe or family: but we ought to express this connection by two propositions of equal importance – firstly that their social experience blinded the ancients to some truths which we perceive, and secondly that it made them sensible of some truths to which we are blind. Legal fiction, adoption, and transference or imputation of merit and guilt, could never have played the part they did play in theology if they had always been felt to be so artificial as we now feel them to be.

I have thought it right to allow this one glance at what is for me an impenetrable curtain, but, as I have said, it makes no part of my present argument. Clearly it would be futile to attempt to solve the problem of pain by producing another problem. The thesis of this chapter is simply that man, as a species, spoiled himself, and that good, to us in our present state, must therefore mean primarily remedial or corrective good. What part pain actually plays in such remedy or correction, is now to be considered.

[1] Genesis 46:4.

6

HUMAN PAIN

Since the life of Christ is every way most
bitter to nature and the Self and the Me (for
in the true life of Christ, the Self and the Me
and nature must be forsaken and lost and die
altogether), therefore in each of us, nature
hath a horror of it.
Theologia Germanica, xx

I have tried to show in a previous chapter that the possibility of pain is
inherent in the very existence of a world where souls can meet. When souls
become wicked they will certainly use this possibility to hurt one another;
and this, perhaps, accounts for four-fifths of the sufferings of men. It is men,
not God, who have produced racks, whips, prisons, slavery, guns, bayonets,
and bombs; it is by human avarice or human stupidity, not by the churlish-
ness of nature, that we have poverty and overwork. But there remains, none
the less, much suffering which cannot thus be traced to ourselves. Even if all
suffering were man-made, we should like to know the reason for the enormous permission to torture their fellows which God gives to the worst of
men.[1] To say, as was said in the last chapter, that good, for such creatures as
we now are, means primarily corrective or remedial good, is an incomplete
answer. Not all medicine tastes nasty: or if it did, that is itself one of the
unpleasant facts for which we should like to know the reason.

Before proceeding I must pick up a point made in Chapter 2.
I there said that pain, below a certain level of intensity, was not resented and
might even be rather liked. Perhaps you then wanted to reply 'In that case
I should not call it Pain,' and you may have been right. But the truth is
that the word Pain has two senses which must now be distinguished. A. A
particular kind of sensation, probably conveyed by specialised nerve fibres,
and recognisable by the patient as that kind of sensation whether he dislikes

---

[1] Or perhaps it would be safer to say 'of creatures'. I by no means reject the view that the 'efficient
cause' of disease, or some disease, may be a created being other than man (see Chapter 9). In
Scripture Satan is specially associated with disease in Job, in Luke 13:16, 1 Corinthians 5:5, and
(probably) in 1 Timothy 1:20. It is, at the present stage of the argument, indifferent whether all the
created wills to which God allows a power of tormenting other creatures are human or not.

it or not (e.g., the faint ache in my limbs would be recognised as an ache even if I didn't object to it). **B.** Any experience, whether physical or mental, which the patient dislikes. It will be noticed that all Pains in sense A become Pains in sense B if they are raised above a certain very low level of intensity, but that Pains in the B sense need not be Pains in the A sense. Pain in the B sense, in fact, is synonymous with 'suffering', 'anguish', 'tribulation', 'adversity', or 'trouble', and it is about it that the problem of pain arises. For the rest of this book Pain will be used in the B sense and will include all types of suffering: with the A sense we have no further concern.

Now the proper good of a creature is to surrender itself to its Creator – to enact intellectually, volitionally, and emotionally, that relationship which is given in the mere fact of its being a creature. When it does so, it is good and happy. Lest we should think this a hardship, this kind of good begins on a level far above the creatures, for God Himself, as Son, from all eternity renders back to God as Father by filial obedience the being which the Father by paternal love eternally generates in the Son. This is the pattern which man was made to imitate – which Paradisal man did imitate – and wherever the will conferred by the Creator is thus perfectly offered back in delighted and delighting obedience by the creature, there, most undoubtedly, is Heaven, and there the Holy Ghost proceeds. In the world as we now know it, the problem is how to recover this self-surrender. We are not merely imperfect creatures who must be improved: we are, as Newman said, rebels who must lay down our arms. The first answer, then, to the question why our cure should be painful, is that to render back the will which we have so long claimed for our own, is in itself, wherever and however it is done, a grievous pain. Even in Paradise I have supposed a minimal self-adherence to be overcome, though the overcoming, and the yielding, would there be rapturous. But to surrender a self-will inflamed and swollen with years of usurpation is a kind of death. We all remember this self-will as it was in childhood: the bitter, prolonged rage at every thwarting, the burst of passionate tears, the black, Satanic wish to kill or die rather than to give in. Hence the older type of nurse or parent was quite right in thinking that the first step in education is 'to break the child's will'. Their methods were often wrong: but not to see the necessity is, I think, to cut oneself off from all understanding of spiritual laws. And if, now that we are grown up, we do not howl and stamp quite so much, that is partly because our elders began the process of breaking or killing our self-will in the nursery, and partly because the same passions now take more subtle forms and have grown clever at avoiding death by various 'compensations'. Hence the necessity to die daily: however often we think we have broken the rebellious self we shall still find it alive. That this process cannot be without pain is sufficiently witnessed by the very history of the word 'Mortification'.

But this intrinsic pain, or death, in mortifying the usurped self, is not the whole story. Paradoxically, mortification, though itself a pain, is made easier by the presence of pain in its context. This happens, I think, principally in three ways.

The human spirit will not even begin to try to surrender self-will as long as all seems to be well with it. Now error and sin both have this property, that the deeper they are the less their victim suspects their existence; they are masked evil. Pain is unmasked, unmistakable evil; every man knows that something is wrong when he is being hurt. The Masochist is no real exception. Sadism and Masochism respectively isolate, and then exaggerate, a 'moment' or 'aspect' in normal sexual passion. Sadism[1] exaggerates the aspect of capture and domination to a point at which only ill-treatment of the beloved will satisfy the pervert – as though he said, 'I am so much master that I even torment you.' Masochism exaggerates the complementary and opposite aspect, and says 'I am so enthralled that I welcome even pain at your hands.' Unless the pain were felt as evil – as an outrage underlining the complete mastery of the other party – it would cease, for the Masochist, to be an erotic stimulus. And pain is not only immediately recognisable evil, but evil impossible to ignore. We can rest contentedly in our sins and in our stupidities; and anyone who has watched gluttons shovelling down the most exquisite foods as if they did not know what they were eating, will admit that we can ignore even pleasure. But pain insists upon being attended to. God whispers to us in our pleasures, speaks in our conscience, but shouts in our pain: it is His megaphone to rouse a deaf world. A bad man, happy, is a man without the least inkling that his actions do not 'answer', that they are not in accord with the laws of the universe.

A perception of this truth lies at the back of the universal human feeling that bad men ought to suffer. It is no use turning up our noses at this feeling, as if it were wholly base. On its mildest level it appeals to everyone's sense of justice. Once when my brother and I, as very small boys, were drawing pictures at the same table, I jerked his elbow and caused him to make an irrelevant line across the middle of his work; the matter was amicably settled by my allowing him to draw a line of equal length across mine. That is, I was 'put in his place', made to see my negligence from the other end. On a sterner level the same idea appears as 'retributive punishment', or 'giving a man what he deserves'. Some enlightened people would like to banish all conceptions of retribution or desert from their theory of punishment and place its value wholly in the deterrence of others or the reform of the criminal himself. They do not see that by so doing they render all punishment

[1] The modern tendency to mean by 'sadistic cruelty' simply 'great cruelty', or cruelty specially condemned by the writer, is not useful.

unjust. What can be more immoral than to inflict suffering on me for the sake of deterring others if I do not *deserve* it? And if I do deserve it, you are admitting the claims of 'retribution'. And what can be more outrageous than to catch me and submit me to a disagreeable process of moral improvement without my consent, unless (once more) I *deserve* it? On yet a third level we get vindictive passion – the thirst for revenge. This, of course, is evil and expressly forbidden to Christians. But it has perhaps appeared already from our discussion of Sadism and Masochism that the ugliest things in human nature are perversions of good or innocent things. The good thing of which vindictive passion is the perversion comes out with startling clarity in Hobbes's definition of Revengefulness; 'desire by doing hurt to another to make him condemn some fact of his own'.[1] Revenge loses sight of the end in the means, but its end is not wholly bad – it wants the evil of the bad man to be to him what it is to everyone else. This is proved by the fact that the avenger wants the guilty party not merely to suffer, but to suffer at his hands, and to know it, and to know why. Hence the impulse to taunt the guilty man with his crime at the moment of taking vengeance: hence, too, such natural expressions as 'I wonder how he'd like it if the same thing were done to him' or 'I'll teach him'. For the same reason when we are going to abuse a man in words we say we are going to 'let him know what we think of him'.

When our ancestors referred to pains and sorrows as God's 'vengeance' upon sin they were not necessarily attributing evil passions to God; they may have been recognising the good element in the idea of retribution. Until the evil man finds evil unmistakably present in his existence, in the form of pain, he is enclosed in illusion. Once pain has roused him, he knows that he is in some way or other 'up against' the real universe: he either rebels (with the possibility of a clearer issue and deeper repentance at some later stage) or else makes some attempt at an adjustment, which, if pursued, will lead him to religion. It is true that neither effect is so certain now as it was in ages when the existence of God (or even of the gods) was more widely known, but even in our own days we see it operating. Even atheists rebel and express, like Hardy and Housman, their rage against God although (or because) He does not, in their view, exist: and other atheists, like Mr Huxley, are driven by suffering to raise the whole problem of existence and to find some way of coming to terms with it which, if not Christian, is almost infinitely superior to fatuous contentment with a profane life. No doubt Pain as God's megaphone is a terrible instrument; it may lead to final and unrepented rebellion. But it gives the only opportunity the bad man can have for amendment. It removes the veil; it plants the flag of truth within the fortress of a rebel soul.

[1] *Leviathan*, Pt. I, cap. 6.

If the first and lowest operation of pain shatters the illusion that all is well, the second shatters the illusion that what we have, whether good or bad in itself, is our own and enough for us. Everyone has noticed how hard it is to turn our thoughts to God when everything is going well with us. We 'have all we want' is a terrible saying when 'all' does not include God. We find God an interruption. As St Augustine says somewhere, 'God wants to give us something, but cannot, because our hands are full – there's nowhere for Him to put it.' Or as a friend of mine said, 'We regard God as an airman regards his parachute; it's there for emergencies but he hopes he'll never have to use it.' Now God, who has made us, knows what we are and that our happiness lies in Him. Yet we will not seek it in Him as long as He leaves us any other resort where it can even plausibly be looked for. While what we call 'our own life' remains agreeable we will not surrender it to Him. What then can God do in our interests but make 'our own life' less agreeable to us, and take away the plausible source of false happiness? It is just here, where God's providence seems at first to be most cruel, that the Divine humility, the stooping down of the Highest, most deserves praise. We are perplexed to see misfortune falling upon decent, inoffensive, worthy people – on capable, hard-working mothers of families or diligent, thrifty little tradespeople, on those who have worked so hard, and so honestly, for their modest stock of happiness and now seem to be entering on the enjoyment of it with the fullest right. How can I say with sufficient tenderness what here needs to be said? It does not matter that I know I must become, in the eyes of every hostile reader, as it were, personally responsible for all the sufferings I try to explain – just as, to this day, everyone talks as if St Augustine *wanted* unbaptised infants to go to Hell. But it matters enormously if I alienate anyone from the truth. Let me implore the reader to try to believe, if only for the moment, that God, who made these deserving people, may really be right when He thinks that their modest prosperity and the happiness of their children are not enough to make them blessed: that all this must fall from them in the end, and that if they have not learned to know Him they will be wretched. And therefore He troubles them, warning them in advance of an insufficiency that one day they will have to discover. The life to themselves and their families stands between them and the recognition of their need; He makes that life less sweet to them. I call this a Divine humility because it is a poor thing to strike our colours to God when the ship is going down under us; a poor thing to come to Him as a last resort, to offer up 'our own' when it is no longer worth keeping. If God were proud He would hardly have us on such terms: but He is not proud, He stoops to conquer, He will have us even though we have shown that we prefer everything else to Him, and come to Him because there is 'nothing better' now to be had. The same humility is shown by all those Divine appeals to our fears which trouble high-minded readers of Scripture. It is hardly complimentary to God that we should choose Him as an alternative to Hell: yet even this He accepts. The creature's illusion of self-sufficiency must, for the creature's sake, be shattered; and by trouble or fear of trouble on earth, by crude fear of the eternal flames, God shatters it 'unmindful of His glory's diminution'. Those who would like the God of Scripture to be more purely ethical, do not know what they ask. If God were a Kantian, who would not have us till we came to Him from the purest and best motives, who could be saved? And this illusion of self-sufficiency may be at its strongest in some very honest, kindly, and temperate people, and on such people, therefore, misfortune must fall.

The dangers of apparent self-sufficiency explain why Our Lord regards the vices of the feckless and dissipated so much more leniently than the vices that lead to worldly success. Prostitutes are in no danger of finding their present life so satisfactory that they cannot turn to God: the proud, the avaricious, the self-righteous, are in that danger.

The third operation of suffering is a little harder to grasp. Everyone will admit that choice is essentially conscious; to choose involves knowing that you choose. Now Paradisal man always chose to follow God's will. In following it he also gratified his own desire, both because all the actions demanded of him were, in fact, agreeable to his blameless inclination, and also because the service of God was itself his keenest pleasure, without which as their razor edge all joys would have been insipid to him. The question 'Am I doing this for God's sake or only because I happen to like it?' did not then arise, since doing things for God's sake was what he chiefly 'happened to like'. His Godward will rode his happiness like a well-managed horse, whereas our will, when we are happy, is carried away in the happiness as in a ship racing down a swift stream. Pleasure was then an acceptable offering to God because offering was a pleasure. But we inherit a whole system of desires which do not necessarily contradict God's will but which, after centuries of usurped autonomy, steadfastly ignore it. If the thing we like doing is, in fact, the thing God wants us to do, yet that is not our reason for doing it; it remains a mere happy coincidence. We cannot therefore know that we are acting at all, or primarily, for God's sake, unless the material of the action is contrary to our inclinations, or (in other words) painful, and what we cannot know that we are choosing, we cannot choose. The full acting out of the self's surrender to God therefore demands pain: this action, to be perfect, must be done from the pure will to obey, in the absence, or in the teeth, of inclination. How impossible it is to enact the surrender of the self by doing what we like, I know very well from my own experience at the moment. When I undertook to write this book I hoped that the will to obey what might be a 'leading' had at least some place in my motives. But now that I am thoroughly immersed in it, it has become a temptation rather than a duty. I may still hope that the writing of the book is, in fact, in conformity with God's will: but to contend that I am learning to surrender myself by doing what is so attractive to me would be ridiculous.

Here we tread on very difficult ground. Kant thought that no action had moral value unless it were done out of pure reverence for the moral law, that is, without inclination, and he has been accused of a 'morbid frame of mind' which measures the value of an act by its unpleasantness. All popular opinion is, indeed, on Kant's side. The people never admire a man for doing something he likes: the very words 'But he likes it' imply the corollary 'And therefore it has no merit'. Yet against Kant stands the obvious truth, noted by Aristotle, that the more virtuous a man becomes the more he enjoys virtuous actions. What an atheist ought to do about this conflict between the ethics of duty and the ethics of virtue, I do not know: but as a Christian I suggest the following solution.

It has sometimes been asked whether God commands certain things because they are right, or whether certain things are right because God commands them. With Hooker, and against Dr Johnson, I emphatically embrace the first alternative. The second might lead to the abominable conclusion (reached, I think, by Paley) that charity is good only because God arbitrarily commanded it – that He might equally well have commanded us to hate Him and one another and that hatred would then have been right. I believe, on the contrary, that 'they err who think that of the will of God to do this or that there is no reason besides His will'.[1] God's will is determined by His wisdom which always perceives, and His goodness which always embraces, the intrinsically good. But when we have said that God commands things only because they are good, we must add that one of the things intrinsically good is that rational creatures should freely surrender themselves to their Creator in obedience. The content of our obedience – the thing we are commanded to do – will always be something intrinsically good, something we ought to do even if (by an impossible supposition) God had not commanded it. But in addition to the content, the mere obeying is also intrinsically good, for, in obeying, a rational creature consciously enacts its creaturely role, reverses the act by which we fell, treads Adam's dance backward, and returns.

We therefore agree with Aristotle that what is intrinsically right may well be agreeable, and that the better a man is the more he will like it; but we agree with Kant so far as to say that there is one right act – that of self-surrender – which cannot be willed to the height by fallen creatures unless it is unpleasant. And we must add that this one right act includes all other righteousness, and that the supreme cancelling of Adam's fall, the movement

[1] Hooker, *Laws of Eccl. Polity*, I, i, 5.

'full speed astern' by which we retrace our long journey from Paradise, the untying of the old, hard knot, must be when the creature, with no desire to aid it, stripped naked to the bare willing of obedience, embraces what is contrary to its nature, and does that for which only one motive is possible. Such an act may be described as a 'test' of the creature's return to God: hence our fathers said that troubles were 'sent to try us'. A familiar example is Abraham's 'trial' when he was ordered to sacrifice Isaac. With the historicity or the morality of that story I am not now concerned, but with the obvious question 'If God is omniscient He must have known what Abraham would do, without any experiment; why, then, this needless torture?' But as St Augustine points out,[1] whatever God knew, Abraham at any rate did not know that his obedience could endure such a command until the event taught him: and the obedience which he did not know that he would choose, he cannot be said to have chosen. The reality of Abraham's obedience was the act itself; and what God knew in knowing that Abraham 'would obey' was Abraham's actual obedience on that mountain top at that moment. To say that God 'need not have tried the experiment' is to say that because God knows, the thing known by God need not exist.

If pain sometimes shatters the creature's false self-sufficiency, yet in supreme 'Trial' or 'Sacrifice' it teaches him the self-sufficiency which really ought to be his – the 'strength, which, if Heaven gave it, may be called his own': for then, in the absence of all merely natural motives and supports, he acts in that strength, and that alone, which God confers upon him through his subjected will. Human will becomes truly creative and truly our own when it is wholly God's, and this is one of the many senses in which he that loses his soul shall find it. In all other acts our will is fed through nature, that is, through created things other than the self – through the desires which our physical organism and our heredity supply to us. When we act from ourselves alone – that is, from God *in* ourselves – we are collaborators in, or live instruments of, creation: and that is why such an act undoes with 'backward mutters of dissevering power' the uncreative spell which Adam laid upon his species. Hence as suicide is the typical expression of the stoic spirit, and battle of the warrior spirit, martyrdom always remains the supreme enacting and perfection of Christianity. This great action has been initiated for us, done on our behalf, exemplified for our imitation, and inconceivably communicated to all believers, by Christ on Calvary. There the degree of accepted Death reaches the utmost bounds of the imaginable and perhaps goes beyond them; not only all natural supports, but the presence of the very Father to whom the sacrifice is made deserts the victim, and surrender to God does not falter though God 'forsakes' it.

[1] *De Civitate Dei*, XVI, xxxii.

The doctrine of death which I describe is not peculiar to Christianity. Nature herself has written it large across the world in the repeated drama of the buried seed and the re-arising corn. From nature, perhaps, the oldest agricultural communities learned it and with animal, or human, sacrifices showed forth for centuries the truth that 'without shedding of blood is no remission';[1] and though at first such conceptions may have concerned only the crops and offspring of the tribe, they came later, in the Mysteries, to concern the spiritual death and resurrection of the individual. The Indian ascetic, mortifying his body on a bed of spikes, preaches the same lesson; the Greek philosopher tells us that the life of wisdom is 'a practice of death'.[2] The sensitive and noble heathen of modern times makes his imagined gods 'die into life'.[3] Mr Huxley expounds 'non-attachment'. We cannot escape the doctrine by ceasing to be Christians. It is an 'eternal gospel' revealed to men wherever men have sought, or endured, the truth: it is the very nerve of redemption, which anatomising wisdom at all times and in all places lays bare; the unescapable knowledge which the Light that lighteneth every man presses down upon the minds of all who seriously question what the universe is 'about'. The peculiarity of the Christian faith is not to teach this doctrine but to render it, in various ways, more tolerable. Christianity teaches us that the terrible task has already in some sense been accomplished for us – that a master's hand is holding ours as we attempt to trace the difficult letters and that our script need only be a 'copy', not an original. Again, where other systems expose our total nature to death (as in Buddhist renunciation) Christianity demands only that we set right a *misdirection* of our nature, and has no quarrel, like Plato, with the body as such, nor with the psychical elements in our make-up. And sacrifice in its supreme realisation is not exacted of all. Confessors as well as martyrs are saved, and some old people whose state of grace we can hardly doubt seem to have got through their seventy years surprisingly easily. The sacrifice of Christ is repeated, or re-echoed, among His followers in very varying degrees, from the cruellest martyrdom down to a self-submission of intention whose outward signs have nothing to distinguish them from the ordinary fruits of temperance and 'sweet reasonableness'. The causes of this distribution I do not know; but from our present point of view it ought to be clear that the real problem is not why some humble, pious, believing people suffer, but why some do *not*. Our Lord Himself, it will be remembered, explained the salvation of those who are fortunate in this world only by referring to the unsearchable omnipotence of God.[4]

[1] Hebrews 9:22.
[2] Plato. *Phaed.*, 81, A (cf. 64, A).
[3] Keats. *Hyperion*, III, 130.
[4] Mark 10:27.

All arguments in justification of suffering provoke bitter resentment against the author. You would like to know how I behave when I am experiencing pain, not writing books about it. You need not guess, for I will tell you; I am a great coward. But what is that to the purpose? When I think of pain – of anxiety that gnaws like fire and loneliness that spreads out like a desert, and the heartbreaking routine of monotonous misery, or again of dull aches that blacken our whole landscape or sudden nauseating pains that knock a man's heart out at one blow, of pains that seem already intolerable and then are suddenly increased, of infuriating scorpion-stinging pains that startle into maniacal movement a man who seemed half dead with his previous tortures – it 'quite o'ercrows my spirit'. If I knew any way of escape I would crawl through sewers to find it. But what is the good of telling you about my feelings? You know them already: they are the same as yours. I am not arguing that pain is not painful. Pain hurts. That is what the word means. I am only trying to show that the old Christian doctrine of being made 'perfect through suffering'[1] is not incredible. To prove it palatable is beyond my design.

In estimating the credibility of the doctrine two principles ought to be observed. In the first place we must remember that the actual moment of present pain is only the centre of what may be called the whole tribulational system which extends itself by fear and pity. Whatever good effects these experiences have are dependent upon the centre; so that even if pain itself was of no spiritual value, yet, if fear and pity were, pain would have to exist in order that there should be something to be feared and pitied. And that fear and pity help us in our return to obedience and charity is not to be doubted. Everyone has experienced the effect of pity in making it easier for us to love the unlovely – that is, to love men not because they are in any way naturally agreeable to us but because they are our brethren. The beneficence of fear most of us have learned during the period of 'crises' that led up to the present war. My own experience is something like this. I am progressing along the path of life in my ordinary contentedly fallen and godless condition, absorbed in a merry meeting with my friends for the morrow or a bit of work that tickles my vanity today, a holiday or a new book, when suddenly a stab of abdominal pain that threatens serious disease, or a headline in the newspapers that threatens us all with destruction, sends this whole pack of cards tumbling down. At first I am overwhelmed, and all my little happinesses look like broken toys. Then, slowly and reluctantly, bit by bit, I try to bring myself into the frame of mind that I should be in at all times. I remind myself that all these toys were never intended to possess my

[1] Hebrews 2:10.

heart, that my true good is in another world and my only real treasure is Christ. And perhaps, by God's grace, I succeed, and for a day or two become a creature consciously dependent on God and drawing its strength from the right sources. But the moment the threat is withdrawn, my whole nature leaps back to the toys: I am even anxious, God forgive me, to banish from my mind the only thing that supported me under the threat because it is now associated with the misery of those few days. Thus the terrible necessity of tribulation is only too clear. God has had me for but forty-eight hours and then only by dint of taking everything else away from me. Let Him but sheathe that sword for a moment and I behave like a puppy when the hated bath is over – I shake myself as dry as I can and race off to reacquire my comfortable dirtiness, if not in the nearest manure heap, at least in the nearest flower bed. And that is why tribulations cannot cease until God either sees us remade or sees that our remaking is now hopeless.

In the second place, when we are considering pain itself – the centre of the whole tribulational system – we must be careful to attend to what we know and not to what we imagine. That is one of the reasons why the whole central part of this book is devoted to human pain, and animal pain is relegated to a special chapter. About human pain we know, about animal pain we only speculate. But even within the human race we must draw our evidence from instances that have come under our own observation. The tendency of this or that novelist or poet may represent suffering as wholly bad in its effects, as producing, and justifying, every kind of malice and brutality in the sufferer. And, of course, pain, like pleasure, can be so received: all that is given to a creature with free will must be two-edged, not by the nature of the giver or of the gift, but by the nature of the recipient.[1] And, again, the evil results of pain can be multiplied if sufferers are persistently taught by the bystanders that such results are the proper and manly results for them to exhibit. Indignation at others' sufferings, though a generous passion, needs to be well managed lest it steal away patience and humanity from those who suffer and plant anger and cynicism in their stead. But I am not convinced that suffering, if spared such officious vicarious indignation, has any natural tendency to produce such evils. I did not find the front-line trenches or the C.C.S. more full than any other place of hatred, selfishness, rebellion, and dishonesty. I have seen great beauty of spirit in some who were great sufferers. I have seen men, for the most part, grow better not worse with advancing years, and I have seen the last illness produce treasures of fortitude and meekness from most unpromising subjects. I see in loved and revered historical figures, such as Johnson and

---

[1] On the two-edged nature of pain, see Appendix.

Cowper, traits which might scarcely have been tolerable if the men had been happier. If the world is indeed a 'vale of soul making' it seems on the whole to be doing its work. Of poverty – the affliction which actually or potentially includes all other afflictions – I would not dare to speak as from myself; and those who reject Christianity will not be moved by Christ's statement that poverty is blessed. But here a rather remarkable fact comes to my aid. Those who would most scornfully repudiate Christianity as a mere 'opiate of the people' have a contempt for the rich, that is, for all mankind *except* the poor. They regard the poor as the only people worth preserving from 'liquidation', and place in them the only hope of the human race. But this is not compatible with a belief that the effects of poverty on those who suffer it are wholly evil; it even implies that they are good. The Marxist thus finds himself in real agreement with the Christian in those two beliefs which Christianity paradoxically demands – that poverty is blessed and yet ought to be removed.

7

HUMAN PAIN, *continued*

> *All things which are as they ought to be are*
> *conformed unto this second law eternal; and*
> *even those things which to this eternal law*
> *are not conformable are notwithstanding in*
> *some sort ordered by the first eternal law.*
>
> HOOKER, *Laws of Eccles. Pol.*, I, iii, 1

In this chapter I advance six propositions necessary to complete our account of human suffering which do not arise out of one another and must therefore be given in an arbitrary order.

1. There is a paradox about tribulation in Christianity. Blessed are the poor, but by 'judgement' (i.e., social justice) and alms we are to remove poverty wherever possible. Blessed are we when persecuted, but we may avoid persecution by flying from city to city, and may pray to be spared it, as Our Lord prayed in Gethsemane. But if suffering is good, ought it not to be pursued rather than avoided? I answer that suffering is not good in itself. What is good in any painful experience is, for the sufferer, his submission to the will of God, and, for the spectators, the compassion aroused and the acts of mercy to which it leads. In the fallen and partially redeemed universe we may distinguish (1) the simple good descending from God, (2) the simple evil produced by rebellious creatures, and (3) the exploitation of that evil by God for His redemptive purpose, which produces (4) the complex good to which accepted suffering and repented sin contribute. Now the fact that God can make complex good out of simple evil does not excuse – though by mercy it may save – those who do the simple evil. And this distinction is central. Offences must come, but woe to those by whom they come; sins *do* cause grace to abound, but we must not make that an excuse for continuing to sin. The crucifixion itself is the best, as well as the worst, of all historical events, but the role of Judas remains simply evil. We may apply this first to the problem of other people's suffering. A merciful man aims at his neighbour's good and so does 'God's will', consciously co-operating with 'the simple good'. A cruel man oppresses his neighbour, and so does simple evil. But in doing such evil, he is used by God, without his own knowledge or consent, to produce the complex good – so that the first man serves God as a son, and the second as a tool. For you will certainly

carry out God's purpose, however you act, but it makes a difference to you whether you serve like Judas or like John. The whole system is, so to speak, calculated for the clash between good men and bad men, and the good fruits of fortitude, patience, pity and forgiveness for which the cruel man is permitted to be cruel, presuppose that the good man ordinarily continues to seek simple good. I say 'ordinarily' because a man is sometimes entitled to hurt (or even, in my opinion, to kill) his fellow, but only where the necessity is urgent and the good to be attained obvious, and usually (though not always) when he who inflicts the pain has a definite authority to do so – a parent's authority derived from nature, a magistrate's or soldier's derived from civil society, or a surgeon's derived, most often, from the patient. To turn this into a general charter for afflicting humanity 'because affliction is good for them' (as Marlowe's lunatic Tamberlaine boasted himself the 'scourge of God') is not indeed to break the Divine scheme but to volunteer for the post of Satan within that scheme. If you do his work, you must be prepared for his wages.

The problem about avoiding our own pain admits a similar solution. Some ascetics have used self-torture. As a layman, I offer no opinion on the prudence of such a regimen; but I insist that, whatever its merits, self-torture is quite a different thing from tribulation sent by God. Everyone knows that fasting is a different experience from missing your dinner by accident or through poverty. Fasting asserts the will against the appetite – the reward being self-mastery and the danger pride: involuntary hunger subjects appetite and will together to the Divine will, furnishing an occasion for submission and exposing us to the danger of rebellion. But the redemptive effect of suffering lies chiefly in its tendency to reduce the rebel will. Ascetic practices, which in themselves strengthen the will, are only useful in so far as they enable the will to put its own house (the passions) in order, as a preparation for offering the whole man to God. They are necessary as a means; as an end, they would be abominable, for in substituting will for appetite and there stopping, they would merely exchange the animal self for the diabolical self. It was, therefore, truly said that 'only God can mortify'. Tribulation does its work in a world where human beings are ordinarily seeking, by lawful means, to avoid their own natural evil and to attain their natural good, and presupposes such a world. In order to submit the will to God, we must have a will and that will must have objects. Christian renunciation does not mean stoic 'Apathy', but a readiness to prefer God to inferior ends which are in themselves lawful. Hence the Perfect Man brought to Gethsemane a will, and a strong will, to escape suffering and death if such escape were compatible with the Father's will, combined with a perfect readiness for obedience if it were not. Some of the saints recommend a 'total renunciation' at the very threshold of our discipleship; but I think this can mean only a total readiness for every particular renunciation[1] that may be demanded, for it would not be possible to live from moment to moment willing nothing but submission to God as such. What would be the *material* for the submission? It would seem self-contradictory to say 'What I will is to subject what I will to God's will,' for the second *what* has no content. Doubtless we all spend too much care in the avoidance of our own pain: but a duly subordinated intention to avoid it, using lawful means, is in accordance with 'nature' – that is, with the whole working system of creaturely life for which the redemptive work of tribulation is calculated.

It would be quite false, therefore, to suppose that the Christian view of suffering is incompatible with the strongest emphasis on our duty to leave the world, even in a temporal sense, 'better' than we found it. In the fullest parabolic picture which He gave of the Judgement, Our Lord seems to reduce all virtue to active beneficence: and though it would be misleading to take that one picture in isolation from the Gospel as a whole, it is sufficient to place beyond doubt the basic principles of the social ethics of Christianity.

2. If tribulation is a necessary element in redemption, we must anticipate that it will never cease till God sees the world to be either redeemed or no further redeemable. A Christian cannot, therefore, believe any of those who promise that if only some reform in our economic, political, or hygienic system were made, a heaven on earth would follow. This might seem to have a discouraging effect on the social worker, but it is not found in practice to discourage him. On the contrary, a strong sense of our common miseries, simply as men, is at least as good a spur to the removal of all the miseries we can, as any of those wild hopes which tempt men to seek their realisation by breaking the moral law and prove such dust and ashes when they are realised. If applied to individual life, the doctrine that an imagined heaven on earth is necessary for vigorous attempts to remove present evil, would at once reveal its absurdity. Hungry men seek food and sick men healing none the less because they know that after the meal or the cure the ordinary ups and downs of life still await them. I am not, of course, discussing whether very drastic changes in our social system are, or are not, desirable; I am only reminding the reader that a particular medicine is not to be mistaken for the elixir of life.

3. Since political issues have here crossed our path, I must make it clear that the Christian doctrine of self-surrender and obedience is a purely theological, and not in the least a political, doctrine. Of forms of government, of civil authority and civil obedience, I have nothing to say. The kind and

---

[1] Cf, Brother Lawrence, *Practice of the Presence of God*, ivth conversation, 25 November 1667. The 'one hearty renunciation' there is 'of everything which we are sensible does not lead us to God'.

degree of obedience which a creature owes to its Creator is unique because the relation between creature and Creator is unique: no inference can be drawn from it to any political proposition whatsoever.

4. The Christian doctrine of suffering explains, I believe, a very curious fact about the world we live in. The settled happiness and security which we all desire, God withholds from us by the very nature of the world: but joy, pleasure, and merriment, He has scattered broadcast. We are never safe, but we have plenty of fun, and some ecstasy. It is not hard to see why. The security we crave would teach us to rest our hearts in this world and oppose an obstacle to our return to God: a few moments of happy love, a landscape, a symphony, a merry meeting with our friends, a bathe or a football match, have no such tendency. Our Father refreshes us on the journey with some pleasant inns, but will not encourage us to mistake them for home.

5. We must never make the problem of pain worse than it is by vague talk about the 'unimaginable sum of human misery'. Suppose that I have a toothache of intensity x: and suppose that you, who are seated beside me, also begin to have a toothache of intensity x. You may, if you choose, say that the total amount of pain in the room is now $2x$. But you must remember that no one is suffering $2x$: search all time and all space and you will not find that composite pain in anyone's consciousness. There is no such thing as a sum of suffering, for no one suffers it. When we have reached the maximum that a single person can suffer, we have, no doubt, reached something very horrible, but we have reached all the suffering there ever can be in the universe. The addition of a million fellow-sufferers adds no more pain.

6. Of all evils, pain only is sterilised or disinfected evil. Intellectual evil, or error, may recur because the cause of the first error (such as fatigue or bad handwriting) continues to operate; but quite apart from that, error in its own right breeds error – if the first step in an argument is wrong, everything that follows will be wrong. Sin may recur because the original temptation continues; but quite apart from that, sin of its very nature breeds sin by strengthening sinful habit and weakening the conscience. Now pain, like the other evils, may of course recur because the cause of the first pain (disease, or an enemy) is still operative: but pain has no tendency, in its own right, to proliferate. When it is over, it is over, and the natural sequel is joy. This distinction may be put the other way round. After an error you need not only to remove the causes (the fatigue or bad writing) but also to correct the error itself: after a sin you must not only, if possible, remove the temptation, you must also go back and repent the sin itself. In each case an 'undoing' is required. Pain requires no such undoing. You may need to heal the disease which caused it, but the pain, once over, is sterile – whereas every uncorrected error and unrepented sin is, in its own right, a fountain of fresh error and fresh sin flowing on to the end of time. Again, when I err, my

error infects every one who believes me. When I sin publicly, every spectator either condones it, thus sharing my guilt, or condemns it with imminent danger to his charity and humility. But suffering naturally produces in the spectators (unless they are unusually depraved) no bad effect, but a good one – pity. Thus that evil which God chiefly uses to produce the 'complex good' is most markedly disinfected, or deprived of that proliferous tendency which is the worst characteristic of evil in general.

8

HELL

What is the world, O soldiers?
It is I:
I, this incessant snow,
This northern sky;
Soldiers, this solitude
Through which we go
Is I.

W. DE LA MARE, *Napoleon*

Richard loves Richard; that is, I am I.

SHAKESPEARE

In an earlier chapter it was admitted that the pain which alone could rouse the bad man to a knowledge that all was not well, might also lead to a final and unrepented rebellion. And it has been admitted throughout that man has free will and that all gifts to him are therefore two edged. From these premises it follows directly that the Divine labour to redeem the world cannot be certain of succeeding as regards every individual soul. Some will not be redeemed. There is no doctrine which I would more willingly remove from Christianity than this, if it lay in my power. But it has the full support of Scripture and, specially, of Our Lord's own words; it has always been held by Christendom; and it has the support of reason. If a game is played, it must be possible to lose it. If the happiness of a creature lies in self-surrender, no one can make that surrender but himself (though many can help him to make it) and he may refuse. I would pay any price to be able to say truthfully 'All will be saved.' But my reason retorts, 'Without their will, or with it?' If I say 'Without their will' I at once perceive a contradiction; how can the supreme voluntary act of self-surrender be involuntary? If I say 'With their will' my reason replies 'How if they *will not* give in?'

The Dominical utterances about Hell, like all Dominical sayings, are addressed to the conscience and the will, not to our intellectual curiosity. When they have roused us into action by convincing us of a terrible possibility, they have done, probably, all they were intended to do; and if all the world were convinced Christians it would be unnecessary to say a word more on the subject. As things are, however, this doctrine is one of the chief

533

grounds on which Christianity is attacked as barbarous, and the goodness of God impugned. We are told that it is a detestable doctrine – and indeed, I too detest it from the bottom of my heart – and are reminded of the tragedies in human life which have come from believing it. Of the other tragedies which come from not believing it we are told less. For these reasons, and these alone, it becomes necessary to discuss the matter.

The problem is not simply that of a God who consigns some of His creatures to final ruin. That would be the problem if we were Mahometans. Christianity, true, as always, to the complexity of the real, presents us with something knottier and more ambiguous – a God so full of mercy that He becomes man and dies by torture to avert that final ruin from His creatures, and who yet, where that heroic remedy fails, seems unwilling, or even unable, to arrest the ruin by an act of mere power. I said glibly a moment ago that I would pay 'any price' to remove this *doctrine*. I lied. I could not pay one-thousandth part of the price that God has already paid to remove the *fact*. And here is the real problem: so much mercy, yet still there is Hell.

I am not going to try to prove the doctrine tolerable. Let us make no mistake; it is *not* tolerable. But I think the doctrine can be shown to be moral, by a critique of the objections ordinarily made, or felt, against it.

First, there is an objection, in many minds, to the idea of retributive pun- ishment as such. This has been partly dealt with in a previous chapter. It was there maintained that all punishment became unjust if the ideas of ill-desert and retribution were removed from it; and a core of righteousness was dis- covered within the vindictive passion itself, in the demand that the evil man must not be left perfectly satisfied with his own evil, that it must be made to appear to him what it rightly appears to others – evil. I said that Pain plants the flag of truth within a rebel fortress. We were then discussing pain which might still lead to repentance. How if it does not – if no further conquest than the planting of the flag ever takes place? Let us try to be honest with ourselves. Picture to yourself a man who has risen to wealth or power by a continued course of treachery and cruelty, by exploiting for purely selfish ends the noble motions of his victims, laughing the while at their simplicity; who, having thus attained success, uses it for the gratification of lust and hatred and finally parts with the last rag of honour among thieves by betray- ing his own accomplices and jeering at their last moments of bewildered disillusionment. Suppose, further, that he does all this, not (as we like to imagine) tormented by remorse or even misgiving, but eating like a school- boy and sleeping like a healthy infant – a jolly, ruddy-cheeked man, without a care in the world, unshakably confident to the very end that he alone has found the answer to the riddle of life, that God and man are fools whom he has got the better of, that his way of life is utterly successful, satisfactory, unassailable. We must be careful at this point. The least indulgence of the passion for revenge is very deadly sin. Christian charity counsels us to make every effort for the conversion of such a man: to prefer his conversion, at the peril of our own lives, perhaps of our own souls, to his punishment; to prefer it infinitely. But that is not the question. Supposing he *will* not be converted, what destiny in the eternal world can you regard as proper for him? Can you really desire that such a man, *remaining what he is* (and he must be able to do that if he has free will) should be confirmed forever in his present happiness – should continue, for all eternity, to be perfectly convinced that the laugh is on his side? And if you cannot regard this as tolerable, is it only your wickedness – only spite – that prevents you from doing so? Or do you find that conflict between Justice and Mercy, which has sometimes seemed to you such an outmoded piece of theology, now actually at work in your own mind, and feeling very much as if it came to you from above, not from below? You are moved not by a desire for the wretched creature's pain as such, but by a truly ethical demand that, soon or late, the right should be asserted, the flag planted in this horribly rebellious soul, even if no fuller and better conquest is to follow. In a sense, it is better for the creature itself, even if it never becomes good, that it should know itself a failure, a mistake. Even mercy can hardly wish to such a man his eternal, contented continuance in such ghastly illusion. Thomas Aquinas said of suffering, as Aristotle had said of shame, that it was a thing not good in itself; but a thing which might have a certain goodness in particular circumstances. That is to say, if evil is present, pain at recognition of the evil, being a kind of knowledge, is relatively good; for the alternative is that the soul should be ignorant of the evil, or ignorant that the evil is contrary to its nature, 'either of which', says the philosopher, 'is *manifestly* bad'.[1] And I think, though we tremble, we agree.

The demand that God should forgive such a man while he remains what he is, is based on a confusion between condoning and forgiving. To condone an evil is simply to ignore it, to treat it as if it were good. But forgiveness needs to be accepted as well as offered if it is to be complete: and a man who admits no guilt can accept no forgiveness.

I have begun with the conception of Hell as a positive retributive punishment inflicted by God because that is the form in which the doctrine is most repellent, and I wished to tackle the strongest objection. But, of course, though Our Lord often speaks of Hell as a sentence inflicted by a tribunal, He also says elsewhere that the judgement consists in the very fact that men prefer darkness to light, and that not He, but His 'word', judges men.[2] We

[1] *Summa Theol.*,I, II^{ae}, Q. xxxix, Art. 1.
[2] John 3:19; 12:48.

are therefore at liberty – since the two conceptions, in the long run, mean the same thing – to think of this bad man's perdition not as a sentence imposed on him but as the mere fact of being what he is. The characteristic of lost souls is 'their rejection of everything that is not simply themselves'.[1] Our imaginary egoist has tried to turn everything he meets into a province or appendage of the self. The taste for the *other*, that is, the very capacity for enjoying good, is quenched in him except in so far as his body still draws him into some rudimentary contact with an outer world. Death removes this last contact. He has his wish – to lie wholly in the self and to make the best of what he finds there. And what he finds there is Hell.

Another objection turns on the apparent disproportion between eternal damnation and transitory sin. And if we think of eternity as a mere prolongation of time, it is disproportionate. But many would reject this idea of eternity. If we think of time as a line – which is a good image, because the parts of time are successive and no two of them can co-exist; i.e., there is no *width* in time, only length – we probably ought to think of eternity as a plane or even a solid. Thus the whole reality of a human being would be represented by a solid figure. That solid would be mainly the work of God, acting through grace and nature, but human free will would have contributed the base-line which we call earthly life: and if you draw your base-line askew, the whole solid will be in the wrong place. The fact that life is short, or, in the symbol, that we contribute only one little line to the whole complex figure, might be regarded as a Divine mercy. For if even the drawing of that little line, left to our free will, is sometimes so badly done as to spoil the whole, how much worse a mess might we have made of the figure if more had been entrusted to us? A simpler form of the same objection consists in saying that death ought not to be final, that there ought to be a second chance.[2] I believe that if a million chances were likely to do good, they would be given. But a master often knows, when boys and parents do not, that it is really useless to send a boy in for a certain examination again. Finality must come some time, and it does not require a very robust faith to believe that omniscience knows when.

A third objection turns on the frightful intensity of the pains of Hell as suggested by medieval art and, indeed, by certain passages in Scripture. Von Hügel here warns us not to confuse the doctrine itself with the *imagery* by which it may be conveyed. Our Lord speaks of Hell under three symbols: first, that of punishment ('everlasting punishment', Matthew 25:46); second, that of destruction ('fear Him who is able to destroy both body and soul in

---

[1] See von Hügel, Essays and Addresses, 1st series, *What do we mean by Heaven and Hell?*
[2] The conception of a 'second chance' must not be confused either with that of Purgatory (for souls already saved) or of Limbo (for souls already lost).

Hell', Matthew 10:28); and thirdly, that of privation, exclusion, or banishment into 'the darkness outside', as in the parables of the man without a wedding garment or of the wise and foolish virgins. The prevalent image of fire is significant because it combines the ideas of torment and destruction. Now it is quite certain that all these expressions are intended to suggest something unspeakably horrible, and any interpretation which does not face that fact is, I am afraid, out of court from the beginning. But it is not necessary to concentrate on the images of torture to the exclusion of those suggesting destruction and privation. What can that be whereof all three images are equally proper symbols? Destruction, we should naturally assume, means the unmaking, or cessation, of the destroyed. And people often talk as if the 'annihilation' of a soul were intrinsically possible. In all our experience, however, the destruction of one thing means the emergence of something else. Burn a log, and you have gases, heat and ash. To *have been* a log means now being those three things. If souls can be destroyed, must there not be a state of *having been* a human soul? And is not that, perhaps, the state which is equally well described as torment, destruction, and privation? You will remember that in the parable, the saved go to a place prepared for *them*, while the damned go to a place never made for men at all.[1] To enter heaven is to become more human than you ever succeeded in being on earth; to enter hell, is to be banished from humanity. What is cast (or casts itself) into hell is not a man: it is 'remains'. To be a complete man means to have the passions obedient to the will and the will offered to God: to *have been* a man – to be an ex-man or 'damned ghost' – would presumably mean to consist of a will utterly centred in its self and passions utterly uncontrolled by the will. It is, of course, impossible to imagine what the consciousness of such a creature – already a loose congeries of mutually antagonistic sins rather than a sinner – would be like. There may be a truth in the saying that 'hell is hell, not from its own point of view, but from the heavenly point of view'. I do not think this belies the severity of Our Lord's words. It is only to the damned that their fate could ever seem less than unendurable. And it must be admitted that as, in these last chapters, we think of eternity, the categories of pain and pleasure, which have engaged us so long, begin to recede, as vaster good and evil loom in sight. Neither pain nor pleasure as such has the last word. Even if it were possible that the experience (if it can be called experience) of the lost contained no pain and much pleasure, still, that black pleasure would be such as to send any soul, not already damned, flying to its prayers in nightmare terror: even if there were pains in heaven, all who understand would desire them.

[1] Matthew 25:34, 41.

A fourth objection is that no charitable man could himself be blessed in heaven while he knew that even one human soul was still in hell; and if so, are we more merciful than God? At the back of this objection lies a mental picture of heaven and hell co-existing in unilinear time as the histories of England and America co-exist: so that at each moment the blessed could say 'The miseries of hell are *now* going on.' But I notice that Our Lord, while stressing the terror of hell with unsparing severity, usually emphasises the idea not of duration but of *finality*. Consignment to the destroying fire is usually treated as the end of the story – not as the beginning of a new story. That the lost soul is eternally fixed in its diabolical attitude we cannot doubt: but whether this eternal fixity implies endless duration – or duration at all – we cannot say. Dr Edwyn Bevan has some interesting speculations on this point.[1] We know much more about heaven than hell, for heaven is the home of humanity and therefore contains all that is implied in a glorified human life: but hell was not made for men. It is in no sense *parallel* to heaven: it is 'the darkness outside', the outer rim where being fades away into nonentity.

Finally, it is objected that the ultimate loss of a single soul means the defeat of omnipotence. And so it does. In creating beings with free will, omnipotence from the outset submits to the possibility of such defeat. What you call defeat, I call miracle: for to make things which are not Itself, and thus to become, in a sense, capable of being resisted by its own handiwork, is the most astonishing and unimaginable of all the feats we attribute to the Deity. I willingly believe that the damned are, in one sense, successful, rebels to the end; that the doors of hell are locked on the *inside*. I do not mean that the ghosts may not *wish* to come out of hell, in the vague fashion wherein an envious man 'wishes' to be happy: but they certainly do not will even the first preliminary stages of that self-abandonment through which alone the soul can reach any good. They enjoy forever the horrible freedom they have demanded, and are therefore self-enslaved: just as the blessed, forever submitting to obedience, become through all eternity more and more free.

In the long run the answer to all those who object to the doctrine of hell, is itself a question: 'What are you asking God to do?' To wipe out their past sins and, at all costs, to give them a fresh start, smoothing every difficulty and offering every miraculous help? But He has done so, on Calvary. To forgive them? They will not be forgiven. To leave them alone? Alas, I am afraid that is what He does.

One caution, and I have done. In order to rouse modern minds to an understanding of the issues, I ventured to introduce in this chapter a picture of the sort of bad man whom we most easily perceive to be truly bad. But when the picture has done that work, the sooner it is forgotten the better. In

---

[1] *Symbolism and Belief*, 101.

all discussions of Hell we should keep steadily before our eyes the possible damnation, not of our enemies nor our friends (since both these disturb the reason) but of ourselves. This chapter is not about your wife or son, nor about Nero or Judas Iscariot; it is about you and me.

9

ANIMAL PAIN

*And whatsoever Adam called every living
creature, that was the name thereof.*

Genesis 2:19

*To find out what is natural, we must study
specimens which retain their nature and not
those which have been corrupted.*

ARISTOTLE, *Politics*, I, v, 5

Thus far of human suffering; but all this time 'a plaint of guiltless hurt doth pierce the sky'. The problem of animal suffering is appalling; not because the animals are so numerous (for, as we have seen, no more pain is felt when a million suffer than when one suffers) but because the Christian explanation of human pain cannot be extended to animal pain. So far as we know beasts are incapable either of sin or virtue: therefore they can neither deserve pain nor be improved by it. At the same time we must never allow the problem of animal suffering to become the centre of the problem of pain; not because it is unimportant – whatever furnishes plausible grounds for questioning the goodness of God is very important indeed – but because it is outside the range of our knowledge. God has given us data which enable us, in some degree, to understand our own suffering: He has given us no such data about beasts. We know neither why they were made nor what they are, and everything we say about them is speculative. From the doctrine that God is good we may confidently deduce that the *appearance* of reckless Divine cruelty in the animal kingdom is an illusion – and the fact that the only suffering we know at first hand (our own) turns out not to be a cruelty will make it easier to believe this. After that, everything is guesswork.

We may begin by ruling out some of the pessimistic bluff put up in the first chapter. The fact that vegetable lives 'prey upon' one another and are in a state of 'ruthless' competition is of no moral importance at all. 'Life' in the biological sense has nothing to do with good and evil until sentience appears. The very words 'prey' and 'ruthless' are mere metaphors. Wordsworth believed that every flower 'enjoyed the air it breathes', but there is no reason to suppose he was right. No doubt, living plants react to injuries differently from inorganic matter; but an anaesthetised human body reacts more differently still and such reactions do not prove sentience. We are, of course, justified in speaking of the death or thwarting of a plant as if it were a tragedy, provided that we know we are using a metaphor. To furnish symbols for spiritual experiences may be one of the functions of the mineral and vegetable worlds. But we must not become the victims of our metaphor. A forest in which half the trees are killing the other half may be a perfectly 'good' forest: for its goodness consists in its utility and beauty and it does not feel.

When we turn to the beasts, three questions arise. There is, first, the question of fact; what do animals suffer? There is, secondly, the question of origin; how did disease and pain enter the animal world? And, thirdly, there is the question of justice; how can animal suffering be reconciled with the justice of God?

1. In the long run the answer to the first question is, We don't know; but some speculations may be worth setting down. We must begin by distinguishing among animals: for if the ape could understand us he would take it very ill to be lumped along with the oyster and the earthworm in a single class of 'animals' and contrasted to men. Clearly in some ways the ape and man are much more like each other than either is like the worm. At the lower end of the animal realm we need not assume anything we could recognise as sentience. Biologists in distinguishing animal from vegetable do not make use of sentience or locomotion or other such characteristics as a layman would naturally fix upon. At some point, however (though where, we cannot say), sentience almost certainly comes in, for the higher animals have nervous systems very like our own. But at this level we must still distinguish sentience from consciousness. If you happen never to have heard of this distinction before, I am afraid you will find it rather startling, but it has great authority and you would be ill-advised to dismiss it out of hand. Suppose that three sensations follow one another – first A, then B, then C. When this happens to you, you have the experience of passing through the process ABC. But note what this implies. It implies that there is something in you which stands sufficiently outside A to notice A passing away, and sufficiently outside B to notice B now beginning and coming to fill the place which A has vacated; and something which recognises itself as the same through the transition from A to B and B to C, so it can say 'I have had the experience ABC'. Now this something is what I call Consciousness or Soul and the process I have just described is one of the proofs that the soul, though experiencing time, is not itself completely 'timeful'. The simplest experience of ABC as a succession demands a soul which is not itself a mere succession of states, but rather a permanent bed along which these different portions of the stream of sensation roll, and which recognises itself as the same beneath them all. Now it is almost certain that the nervous system of one of the higher animals

presents it with successive sensations. It does not follow that it has any 'soul', anything which recognises itself as having had A, and now having B, and now marking how B glides away to make room for C. If it had no such 'soul', what we call the experience ABC would never occur. There would, in philosophic language, be 'a succession of perceptions'; that is, the sensations would, in fact, occur in that order, and God would know that they were so occurring, but the animal would not know. There would not be 'a perception of succession'. This would mean that if you give such a creature two blows with a whip, there are, indeed, two pains: but there is no co-ordinating self which can recognise that 'I have had two pains'. Even in the single pain, there is no self to say 'I am in pain' – for if it could distinguish itself from the sensation – the bed from the stream – sufficiently to say 'I am in pain', it would also be able to connect the two sensations as *its* experience. The correct description would be 'Pain is taking place in this animal'; not, as we commonly say, 'This animal feels pain', for the words 'this' and 'feels' really smuggle in the assumption that it is a 'self' or 'soul' or 'consciousness' standing above the sensations and organising them into an 'experience' as we do. Such sentience without consciousness, I admit, we cannot imagine: not because it never occurs in us, but because, when it does, we describe ourselves as being 'unconscious'. And rightly. The fact that animals react to pain much as we do is, of course, no proof that they are conscious; for we may also so react under chloroform, and even answer questions while asleep.

How far up the scale such unconscious sentience may extend, I will not even guess. It is certainly difficult to suppose that the apes, the elephant, and the higher domestic animals, have not, in some degree, a self or soul which connects experiences and gives rise to rudimentary individuality. But at least a great deal of what appears to be animal suffering need not be suffering in any real sense. It may be we who have invented the 'sufferers' by the 'pathetic fallacy' of reading into the beasts a self for which there is no real evidence.

2. The origin of animal suffering could be traced, by earlier generations, to the Fall of man – the whole world was infected by the uncreating rebellion of Adam. This is now impossible, for we have good reason to believe that animals existed long before men. Carnivorousness, with all that it entails, is older than humanity. Now it is impossible at this point not to remember a certain sacred story which, though never included in the creeds, has been widely believed in the Church and seems to be implied in several Dominical, Pauline, and Johannine utterances – I mean the story that man was not the first creature to rebel against the Creator, but that some older and mightier being long since became apostate and is now the emperor of darkness and (significantly) the Lord of this world. Some people would like to reject all such elements from Our Lord's teaching: and it might be argued

that when He emptied Himself of His glory He also humbled Himself to share, as man, the current superstitions of His time. And I certainly think that Christ, in the flesh, was not omniscient – if only because a human brain could not, presumably, be the vehicle of omniscient consciousness, and to say that Our Lord's thinking was not really conditioned by the size and shape of His brain might be to deny the real incarnation and become a Docetist. Thus, if Our Lord had committed Himself to any scientific or historical statement which we knew to be untrue, this would not disturb my faith in His deity. But the doctrine of Satan's existence and fall is not among the things we know to be untrue: it contradicts not the facts discovered by scientists but the mere, vague 'climate of opinion' that we happen to be living in. Now I take a very low view of 'climates of opinion'. In his own subject every man knows that all discoveries are made and all errors corrected by those who ignore the 'climate of opinion'.

It seems to me, therefore, a reasonable supposition, that some mighty created power had already been at work for ill on the material universe, or the solar system, or, at least, the planet Earth, before ever man came on the scene: and that when man fell, someone had, indeed, tempted him. This hypothesis is not introduced as a general 'explanation of evil': it only gives a wider application to the principle that evil comes from the abuse of free will. If there is such a power, as I myself believe, it may well have corrupted the animal creation before man appeared. The intrinsic evil of the animal world lies in the fact that animals, or some animals, live by destroying each other. That plants do the same I will not admit to be an evil. The Satanic corruption of the beasts would therefore be analogous, in one respect, with the Satanic corruption of man. For one result of man's fall was that his animality fell back from the humanity into which it had been taken up but which could no longer rule it. In the same way, animality may have been encouraged to slip back into behaviour proper to vegetables. It is, of course, true that the immense mortality occasioned by the fact that many beasts live on beasts is balanced, in nature, by an immense birthrate, and it might seem, that if all animals had been herbivorous and healthy, they would mostly starve as a result of their own multiplication. But I take the fecundity and the death rate to be correlative phenomena. There was, perhaps, no necessity for such an excess of the sexual impulse: the Lord of this world thought of it as a response to carnivorousness – a double scheme for securing the maximum amount of torture. If it offends less, you may say that the 'life-force' is corrupted where I say that living creatures were corrupted by an evil angelic being. We mean the same thing: but I find it easier to believe in a myth of gods and demons than in one of hypostatised abstract nouns. And after all, our mythology may be much nearer to literal truth than we suppose. Let us not forget that Our Lord, on one occasion, attributes human disease not to God's wrath, not to nature, but quite explicitly to Satan.[1]

If this hypothesis is worth considering, it is also worth considering whether man, at his first coming into the world, had not already a redemptive function to perform. Man, even now, can do wonders to animals: my cat and dog live together in my house and seem to like it. It may have been one of man's functions to restore peace to the animal world, and if he had not joined the enemy he might have succeeded in doing so to an extent now hardly imaginable.

3. Finally, there is the question of justice. We have seen reason to believe that not all animals suffer as we think they do: but some, at least, look as if they had selves, and what shall be done for these innocents? And we have seen that it is possible to believe that animal pain is not God's handiwork but begun by Satan's malice and perpetuated by man's desertion of his post: still, if God has not caused it, He has permitted it, and, once again, what shall be done for these innocents? I have been warned not even to raise the question of animal immortality, lest I find myself 'in company with all the old maids'.[2] I have no objection to the company. I do not think either virginity or old age contemptible, and some of the shrewdest minds I have met inhabited the bodies of old maids. Nor am I greatly moved by jocular inquiries such as 'Where will you put all the mosquitoes?' – a question to be answered on its own level by pointing out that, if the worst came to the worst, a heaven for mosquitoes and a hell for men could very conveniently be combined. The complete silence of Scripture and Christian tradition on animal immortality is a more serious objection; but it would be fatal only if Christian revelation showed any signs of being intended as a *système de la nature* answering all questions. But it is nothing of the sort: the curtain has been rent at one point, and at one point only, to reveal our immediate practical necessities and not to satisfy our intellectual curiosity. If animals were, in fact, immortal, it is unlikely, from what we discern of God's method in the revelation, that He would have revealed this truth. Even our own immortality is a doctrine that comes late in the history of Judaism. The argument from silence is therefore very weak.

The real difficulty about supposing most animals to be immortal is that immortality has almost no meaning for a creature which is not 'conscious' in the sense explained above. If the life of a newt is merely a succession of sensations, what should we mean by saying that God may recall to life the newt that died today? It would not recognise itself as the same newt; the pleasant sensations of any other newt that lived after its death would be just as much, or just as little, a recompense for its earthly sufferings (if any) as those of its

---

[1] Luke 13:16.
[2] But also with J. Wesley, Sermon LXV. *The Great Deliverance.*

resurrected – I was going to say 'self', but the whole point is that the newt probably has no self. The thing we have to try to say, on this hypothesis, will not even be said. There is, therefore, I take it, no question of immortality for creatures that are merely sentient. Nor do justice and mercy demand that there should be, for such creatures have no painful experience. Their nervous system delivers all the *letters* A, P, N, I, but since they cannot read they never build it up into the word PAIN. And all animals *may* be in that condition.

If, nevertheless, the strong conviction which we have of a real, though doubtless rudimentary, selfhood in the higher animals, and specially in those we tame, is not an illusion, their destiny demands a somewhat deeper consideration. The error we must avoid is that of considering them in themselves. Man is to be understood only in his relation to God. The beasts are to be understood only in their relation to man and, through man, to God. Let us here guard against one of those untransmuted lumps of atheistical thought which often survive in the minds of modern believers. Atheists naturally regard the co-existence of man and the animals as a mere contingent result of interacting biological facts; and the taming of an animal by a man as a purely arbitrary interference of one species with another. The 'real' or 'natural' animal to them is the wild one, and the tame animal is an artificial or unnatural thing. But a Christian must not think so. Man was appointed by God to have dominion over the beasts, and everything a man does to an animal is either a lawful exercise, or a sacrilegious abuse, of an authority by Divine right. The tame animal is therefore, in the deepest sense, the only 'natural' animal – the only one we see occupying the place it was made to occupy, and it is on the tame animal that we must base all our doctrine of beasts. Now it will be seen that, in so far as the tame animal has a real self or personality, it owes this almost entirely to its master. If a good sheepdog seems 'almost human' that is because a good shepherd has made it so. I have already noted the mysterious force of the word 'in'. I do not take all the senses of it in the New Testament to be identical, so that man is *in* Christ and Christ *in* God and the Holy Spirit *in* the Church and also *in* the individual believer in exactly the same sense. They may be senses that rhyme or correspond rather than a single sense. I am now going to suggest – though with great readiness to be set right by real theologians – that there may be a sense, corresponding, though not identical, with these, in which those beasts that attain a real self are *in* their masters. That is to say, you must not think of a beast by itself, and call that a personality and then inquire whether God will raise and bless *that*. You must take the whole context *in* which the beast acquires its selfhood – namely 'The - goodman - and - the - goodwife - ruling - their - children - and - their - beasts - in - the - good - homestead'. That whole context may be regarded as a 'body' in the Pauline (or a closely sub-Pauline) sense; and how much of that 'body' may be raised along with the goodman and the goodwife, who can predict? So much, presumably, as is necessary not only for the glory of God and the beatitude of the human pair, but for that particular glory and that particular beatitude which is eternally coloured by that particular terrestrial experience. And in this way it seems to me possible that certain animals may have an immortality, not in themselves, but in the immortality of their masters. And the difficulty about personal identity in a creature barely personal disappears when the creature is thus kept in its proper context. If you ask, concerning an animal thus raised as a member of the whole Body of the homestead, where its personal identity resides, I answer 'Where its identity always did reside even in the earthly life – in its relation to the Body and, specially, to the master who is the head of that Body.' In other words, the man will know his dog: the dog will know its master and, in knowing him, will *be* itself. To ask that it should, in any other way, *know* itself, is probably to ask for what has no meaning. Animals aren't like that, and don't want to be.

My picture of the good sheepdog in the good homestead does not, of course, cover wild animals nor (a matter even more urgent) ill-treated domestic animals. But it is intended only as an illustration drawn from one privileged instance – which is, also, in my view the only normal and unperverted instance – of the general principles to be observed in framing a theory of animal resurrection. I think Christians may justly hesitate to suppose any beasts immortal, for two reasons. Firstly because they fear, by attributing to beasts a 'soul' in the full sense, to obscure that difference between beast and man which is as sharp in the spiritual dimension as it is hazy and problematical in the biological. And secondly, a future happiness connected with the beast's present life simply as a compensation for suffering – so many millenniums in the happy pastures paid down as 'damages' for so many years of pulling carts – seems a clumsy assertion of Divine goodness. We, because we are fallible, often hurt a child or an animal unintentionally, and then the best we can do is to 'make up for it' by some caress or tit-bit. But it is hardly pious to imagine omniscience acting in that way – as though God trod on the animals' tails in the dark and then did the best He could about it! In such a botched adjustment I cannot recognise the master-touch; whatever the answer is, it must be something better than that. The theory I am suggesting tries to avoid both objections. It makes God the centre of the universe and man the subordinate centre of terrestrial nature: the beasts are not co-ordinate with man, but subordinate to him, and their destiny is through and through related to his. And the derivative immortality suggested for them is not a mere *amende* or compensation: it is part and parcel of the new heaven and new earth, organically related to the whole suffering process of the world's fall and redemption.

Supposing, as I do, that the personality of the tame animals is largely the gift of man – that their mere sentience is reborn to soulhood in us as our mere soulhood is reborn to spirituality in Christ – I naturally suppose that very few animals indeed, in their wild state, attain to a 'self' or ego. But if any do, and if it is agreeable to the goodness of God that they should live again, their immortality would also be related to man – not, this time, to individual masters, but to humanity. That is to say, if in any instance the quasi-spiritual and emotional value which human tradition attributes to a beast (such as the 'innocence' of the lamb or the heraldic royalty of the lion) has a real ground in the beast's nature, and is not merely arbitrary or accidental, then it is in *that* capacity, or principally in that, that the beast may be expected to attend on risen man and make part of his 'train'. Or if the traditional character is quite erroneous, then the beast's heavenly life[1] would be in virtue of the real, but unknown, effect it has actually had on man during his whole history: for if Christian cosmology is in *any* sense (I do not say, in a literal sense) true, then all that exists on our planet is related to man, and even the creatures that were extinct before men existed are then only seen in their true light when they are seen as the unconscious harbingers of man.

When we are speaking of creatures so remote from us as wild beasts, and prehistoric beasts, we hardly know what we are talking about. It may well be that they have no selves and no sufferings. It may even be that each species has a corporate self – that Lionhood, not lions, has shared in the travail of creation and will enter into the restoration of all things. And if we cannot imagine even our own eternal life, much less can we imagine the life the beasts may have as our 'members'. If the earthly lion could read the prophecy of that day when he shall eat hay like an ox, he would regard it as a description not of heaven, but of hell. And if there is nothing in the lion but carnivorous sentience, then he is unconscious and his 'survival' would have no meaning. But if there is a rudimentary Leonine self, to that also God can give a 'body' as it pleases Him – a body no longer living by the destruction of the lamb, yet richly Leonine in the sense that it also expresses whatever energy and splendour and exulting power dwelled within the visible lion on this earth. I think, under correction, that the prophet used an eastern hyperbole when he spoke of the lion and the lamb *lying down* together. That would be rather impertinent of the lamb. To have lions and lambs that so consorted (except on some rare celestial Saturnalia of topsy-turvydom) would be the same as having neither lambs nor lions. I think the lion, when he has ceased to be dangerous, will still be awful: indeed, that we shall then first see that of which the present fangs and claws are a clumsy, and satanically perverted, imitation. There will still be something like the shaking of a golden mane: and often the good Duke will say, 'Let him roar again'.

---

[1] That is, its participation in the heavenly life of men *in* Christ *to* God; to suggest a 'heavenly life' for the beast *as such* is probably nonsense.

10

HEAVEN

It is required
You do awake your faith. Then all stand still;
Or those that think it is unlawful business
I am about, let them depart.

SHAKESPEARE, *Winter's Tale*

Plunged in thy depth of mercy let me die
The death that every soul that lives desires.

COWPER out of *Madame Guion*

'I reckon,' said St Paul, 'that the sufferings of this present time are not
worthy to be compared with the glory that shall be revealed in us.'[1] If
this is so, a book on suffering which says nothing of heaven, is leaving out
almost the whole of one side of the account. Scripture and tradition habitually put the joys of heaven into the scale against the sufferings of earth, and
no solution of the problem of pain which does not do so can be called a
Christian one. We are very shy nowadays of even mentioning heaven. We are
afraid of the jeer about 'pie in the sky', and of being told that we are trying to
'escape' from the duty of making a happy world here and now into dreams of
a happy world elsewhere. But either there is 'pie in the sky' or there is not. If
there is not, then Christianity is false, for this doctrine is woven into its
whole fabric. If there is, then this truth, like any other, must be faced,
whether it is useful at political meetings or no. Again, we are afraid that
heaven is a bribe, and that if we make it our goal we shall no longer be disinterested. It is not so. Heaven offers nothing that a mercenary soul can desire.
It is safe to tell the pure in heart that they shall see God, for only the pure in
heart want to. There are rewards that do not sully motives. A man's love for
a woman is not mercenary because he wants to marry her, nor his love for
poetry mercenary because he wants to read it, nor his love of exercise less
disinterested because he wants to run and leap and walk. Love, by definition,
seeks to enjoy its object.

You may think that there is another reason for our silence about heaven –
namely, that we do not really desire it. But that may be an illusion. What I

[1] Romans 8:18.

am now going to say is merely an opinion of my own without the slightest authority, which I submit to the judgement of better Christians and better scholars than myself. There have been times when I think we do not desire heaven; but more often I find myself wondering whether, in our heart of hearts, we have ever desired anything else. You may have noticed that the books you really love are bound together by a secret thread. You know very well what is the common quality that makes you love them, though you cannot put it into words: but most of your friends do not see it at all, and often wonder why, liking this, you should also like that. Again, you have stood before some landscape, which seems to embody what you have been looking for all your life; and then turned to the friend at your side who appears to be seeing what you saw – but at the first words a gulf yawns between you, and you realise that this landscape means something totally different to him, that he is pursuing an alien vision and cares nothing for the ineffable suggestion by which you are transported. Even in your hobbies, has there not always been some secret attraction which the others are curiously ignorant of – something, not to be identified with, but always on the verge of breaking through, the smell of cut wood in the workshop or the clap-clap of water against the boat's side? Are not all lifelong friendships born at the moment when at last you meet another human being who has some inkling (but faint and uncertain even in the best) of that something which you were born desiring, and which, beneath the flux of other desires and in all the momentary silences between the louder passions, night and day, year by year, from childhood to old age, you are looking for, watching for, listening for? You have never *had* it. All the things that have ever deeply possessed your soul have been but hints of it – tantalising glimpses, promises never quite fulfilled, echoes that died away just as they caught your ear. But if it should really become manifest – if there ever came an echo that did not die away but swelled into the sound itself – you would know it. Beyond all possibility of doubt you would say 'Here at last is the thing I was made for.' We cannot tell each other about it. It is the secret signature of each soul, the incommunicable and unappeasable want, the thing we desired before we met our wives or made our friends or chose our work, and which we shall still desire on our deathbeds, when the mind no longer knows wife or friend or work. While we are, this is. If we lose this, we lose all.[1]

This signature on each soul may be a product of heredity and environment, but that only means that heredity and environment are among the

---

[1] I am not, of course, suggesting that these immortal longings which we have from the Creator because we are men, should be confused with the gifts of the Holy Spirit to those who are in Christ. We must not fancy we are holy because we are human.

instruments whereby God creates a soul. I am considering not how, but why, He makes each soul unique. If He had no use for all these differences, I do not see why He should have created more souls than one. Be sure that the ins and outs of your individuality are no mystery to Him; and one day they will no longer be a mystery to you. The mould in which a key is made would be a strange thing, if you had never seen a key: and the key itself a strange thing if you had never seen a lock. Your soul has a curious shape because it is a hollow made to fit a particular swelling in the infinite con-tours of the Divine substance, or a key to unlock one of the doors in the house with many mansions. For it is not humanity in the abstract that is to be saved, but you – you, the individual reader, John Stubbs or Janet Smith. Blessed and fortunate creature, your eyes shall behold Him and not another's. All that you are, sins apart, is destined, if you will let God have His good way, to utter satisfaction. The Brocken spectre 'looked to every man like his first love', because she was a cheat. But God will look to every soul like its first love because He is its first love. Your place in heaven will seem to be made for you and you alone, because you were made for it – made for it stitch by stitch as a glove is made for a hand.

It is from this point of view that we can understand hell in its aspect of privation. All your life an unattainable ecstasy has hovered just beyond the grasp of your consciousness. The day is coming when you will wake to find, beyond all hope, that you have attained it, or else, that it was within your reach and you have lost it forever.

This may seem a perilously private and subjective notion of the pearl of great price, but it is not. The thing I am speaking of is not an experience. You have experienced only the *want* of it. The thing itself has never actually been embodied in any thought, or image, or emotion. Always it has sum-moned you out of yourself. And if you will not go out of yourself to follow it, if you sit down to brood on the desire and attempt to cherish it, the desire itself will evade you. 'The door into life generally opens behind us' and 'the only wisdom' for one 'haunted with the scent of unseen roses, is work.'[1] This secret fire goes out when you use the bellows: bank it down with what seems unlikely fuel of dogma and ethics, turn your back on it and attend to your duties, and then it will blaze. The world is like a picture with a golden background, and we the figures in that picture. Until you step off the plane of the picture into the large dimensions of death you can-not see the gold. But we have reminders of it. To change our metaphor, the blackout is not quite complete. There are chinks. At times the daily scene looks big with its secret.

[1] George Macdonald, *Alec Forbes*, cap. XXXIII.

Such is my opinion; and it may be erroneous. Perhaps this secret desire also is part of the Old Man and must be crucified before the end. But this opinion has a curious trick of evading denial. The desire – much more the satisfaction – has always refused to be fully present in any experience. Whatever you try to identify with it, turns out to be not it but something else: so that hardly any degree of crucifixion or transformation could go beyond what the desire itself leads us to anticipate. Again, if this opinion is not true, something better is. But 'something better' – not this or that experience, but beyond it – is almost the definition of the thing I am trying to describe.

The thing you long for summons you away from the self. Even the desire for the thing lives only if you abandon it. This is the ultimate law – the seed dies to live, the bread must be cast upon the waters, he that loses his soul will save it. But the life of the seed, the finding of the bread, the recovery of the soul, are as real as the preliminary sacrifice. Hence it is truly said of heaven 'in heaven there is no ownership. If any there took upon him to call anything his own, he would straightway be thrust out into hell and become an evil spirit.'[1] But it is also said 'To him that overcometh I will give a white stone, and in the stone a new name written, which no man knoweth saving he that receiveth it.'[2] What can be more a man's own than this new name which even in eternity remains a secret between God and him? And what shall we take this secrecy to mean? Surely, that each of the redeemed shall forever know and praise some one aspect of the Divine beauty better than any other creature can. Why else were individuals created, but that God, loving all infinitely, should love each differently? And this difference, so far from impairing, floods with meaning the love of all blessed creatures for one another, the communion of the saints. If all experienced God in the same way and returned Him an identical worship, the song of the Church triumphant would have no symphony, it would be like an orchestra in which all the instruments played the same note. Aristotle has told us that a city is a unity of unlikes,[3] and St Paul that a body is a unity of different members.[4] Heaven is a city, and a Body, because the blessed remain eternally different: a society, because each has something to tell all the others – fresh and ever fresh news of the 'My God' whom each finds in Him whom all praise as 'Our God'. For doubtless the continually successful, yet never complete, attempt by each soul to communicate its unique vision to all others (and that by means whereof earthly art and philosophy are but clumsy imitations) is also among the ends for which the individual was created.

[1] *Theologia Germanica*, li.
[2] Revelation 2:17.
[3] *Politics*, ii, 2, 4.
[4] 1 Corinthians 12:12–30.

For union exists only between distincts; and, perhaps, from this point of view, we catch a momentary glimpse of the meaning of all things. Pantheism is a creed not so much false as hopelessly behind the times. Once, before creation, it would have been true to say that everything was God. But God created: He caused things to be other than Himself that, being distinct, they might learn to love Him, and achieve union instead of mere sameness. Thus He also cast His bread upon the waters. Even within the creation we might say that inanimate matter, which has no will, is one with God in a sense in which men are not. But it is not God's purpose that we should go back into that old identity (as, perhaps, some Pagan mystics would have us do) but that we should go on to the maximum distinctness there to be reunited with Him in a higher fashion. Even within the Holy One Himself, it is not sufficient that the Word should *be* God, it must also be *with* God. The Father eternally begets the Son and the Holy Ghost proceeds: deity introduces distinction within itself so that the union of reciprocal loves may transcend mere arithmetical unity or self-identity.

But the eternal distinctness of each soul – the secret which makes of the union between each soul and God a species in itself – will never abrogate the law that forbids ownership in heaven. As to its fellow-creatures, each soul, we suppose, will be eternally engaged in giving away to all the rest that which it receives. And as to God, we must remember that the soul is but a hollow which God fills. Its union with God is, almost by definition, a continual self-abandonment – an opening, an unveiling, a surrender, of itself. A blessed spirit is a mould ever more and more patient of the bright metal poured into it, a body ever more completely uncovered to the meridian blaze of the spiritual sun. We need not suppose that the necessity for something analogous to self-conquest will ever be ended, or that eternal life will not also be eternal dying. It is in this sense that, as there may be pleasures in hell (God shield us from them), there may be something not all unlike pains in heaven (God grant us soon to taste them).

For in self-giving, if anywhere, we touch a rhythm not only of all creation but of all being. For the Eternal Word also gives Himself in sacrifice; and that not only on Calvary. For when He was crucified He 'did that in the wild weather of His outlying provinces which He had done at home in glory and gladness'.[1] From before the foundation of the world He surrenders begotten Deity back to begetting Deity in obedience. And as the Son glorifies the Father, so also the Father glorifies the Son.[2] And, with submission, as becomes a layman, I think it was truly said 'God loveth not Himself as Himself but as Goodness; and if there were aught better than God, He

[1] George Macdonald, *Unspoken Sermons: 3rd Series*, pp. 11, 12.
[2] John 17:1, 4, 5.

would love that and not Himself'.[1] From the highest to the lowest, self exists to be abdicated and, by that abdication, becomes the more truly self, to be thereupon yet the more abdicated, and so forever. This is not a heavenly law which we can escape by remaining earthly, nor an earthly law which we can escape by being saved. What is outside the system of self-giving is not earth, nor nature, nor 'ordinary life', but simply and solely hell. Yet even hell derives from this law such reality as it has. That fierce imprisonment in the self is but the obverse of the self-giving which is absolute reality; the negative shape which the outer darkness takes by surrounding and defining the shape of the real, or which the real imposes on the darkness by having a shape and positive nature of its own.

The golden apple of selfhood, thrown among the false gods, became an apple of discord because they scrambled for it. They did not know the first rule of the holy game, which is that every player must by all means touch the ball and then immediately pass it on. To be found with it in your hands is a fault: to cling to it, death. But when it flies to and fro among the players too swift for eye to follow, and the great master Himself leads the revelry, giving Himself eternally to His creatures in the generation, and back to Himself in the sacrifice, of the Word, then indeed the eternal dance 'makes heaven drowsy with the harmony'. All pains and pleasures we have known on earth are early initiations in the movements of that dance: but the dance itself is strictly incomparable with the sufferings of this present time. As we draw nearer to its uncreated rhythm, pain and pleasure sink almost out of sight. There is joy in the dance, but it does not exist for the sake of joy. It does not even exist for the sake of good, or of love. It is Love Himself, and Good Himself, and therefore happy. It does not exist for us, but we for it. The size and emptiness of the universe which frightened us at the outset of this book, should awe us still, for though they may be no more than a subjective by-product of our three-dimensional imagining, yet they symbolise great truth. As our Earth is to all the stars, so doubtless are we men and our concerns to all creation; as all the stars are to space itself, so are all creatures, all thrones and powers and mightiest of the created gods, to the abyss of the self-existing Being, who is to us Father and Redeemer and indwelling Comforter, but of whom no man nor angel can say nor conceive what He is in and for Himself, or what is the work that he 'maketh from the beginning to the end'. For they are all derived and unsubstantial things. Their vision fails them and they cover their eyes from the intolerable light of utter actuality, which was and is and shall be, which never could have been otherwise, which has no opposite.

[1] *Theol. Germ.*, xxxii.

APPENDIX

(This note on the observed effects of pain has been kindly supplied by R. Havard, MD, from clinical experience.)
Pain is a common and definite event which can easily be recognised: but the observation of character or behaviour is less easy, less complete, and less exact, especially in the transient, if intimate, relation of doctor and patient. In spite of this difficulty certain impressions gradually take form in the course of medical practice which are confirmed as experience grows. A short attack of severe physical pain is overwhelming while it lasts. The sufferer is not usually loud in his complaints. He will beg for relief but does not waste his breath on elaborating his troubles. It is unusual for him to lose self-control and to become wild and irrational. It is rare for the severest physical pain to become in this sense unbearable. When short, severe, physical pain passes it leaves no obvious alteration in behaviour. Long-continued pain has more noticeable effects. It is often accepted with little or no complaint and great strength and resignation are developed. Pride is humbled or, at times, results in a determination to conceal suffering. Women with rheumatoid arthritis show a cheerfulness which is so characteristic that it can be compared to the *spes phthisica* of the consumptive: and is perhaps due more to a slight intoxication of the patient by the infection than to an increased strength of character. Some victims of chronic pain deteriorate. They become querulous and exploit their privileged position as invalids to practise domestic tyranny. But the wonder is that the failures are so few and the heroes so many; there is a challenge in physical pain which most can recognise and answer. On the other hand, a long illness, even without pain, exhausts the mind as well as the body. The invalid gives up the struggle and drifts helplessly and plaintively into a self-pitying despair. Even so, some, in a similar physical state, will preserve their serenity and selflessness to the end. To see it is a rare but moving experience.

Mental pain is less dramatic than physical pain, but it is more common and also more hard to bear. The frequent attempt to conceal mental pain increases the burden: it is easier to say 'My tooth is aching' than to say 'My heart is broken'. Yet if the cause is accepted and faced, the conflict will strengthen and purify the character and in time the pain will usually pass. Sometimes, however, it persists and the effect is devastating; if the cause is not faced or not recognised, it produces the dreary state of the chronic neurotic. But some by heroism overcome even chronic mental pain. They often produce brilliant work and strengthen, harden, and sharpen their characters till they become like tempered steel.

In actual insanity the picture is darker. In the whole realm of medicine there is nothing so terrible to contemplate as a man with chronic melancholia. But most of the insane are not unhappy or, indeed, conscious of their condition. In either case, if they recover, they are surprisingly little changed. Often they remember nothing of their illness.

Pain provides an opportunity for heroism; the opportunity is seized with surprising frequency.

PRAYER:
LETTERS
TO MALCOLM

I

I am all in favour of your idea that we should go back to your old plan of
having a more or less set subject – an *agendum* – for our letters. When we
were last separated the correspondence languished for lack of it. How much
better we did in our undergraduate days with our interminable letters on the
Republic, and classical metres, and what was then the 'new' psychology!
Nothing makes an absent friend so present as a disagreement.

Prayer, which you suggest, is a subject that is a good deal in my mind. I
mean, private prayer. If you were thinking of corporate prayer, I won't play.
There is no subject in the world (always excepting sport) on which I have
less to say than liturgiology. And the almost nothing which I have to say
may as well be disposed of in this letter.

I think our business as laymen is to take what we are given and make the
best of it. And I think we should find this a great deal easier if what we were
given was always and everywhere the same.

To judge from their practice, very few Anglican clergymen take this view.
It looks as if they believed people can be lured to go to church by incessant
brightenings, lightenings, lengthenings, abridgements, simplifications and
complications of the service. And it is probably true that a new, keen vicar
will usually be able to form within his parish a minority who are in favour of
his innovations. The majority, I believe, never are. Those who remain – many
give up churchgoing altogether – merely endure.

Is this simply because the majority are hide-bound? I think not. They have
a good reason for their conservatism. Novelty, simply as such, can have only
an entertainment value. And they don't go to church to be entertained. They
go to *use* the service, or, if you prefer, to *enact* it. Every service is a structure
of acts and words through which we receive a sacrament, or repent, or sup-
plicate, or adore. And it enables us to do these things best – if you like, it
'works' best – when, through long familiarity, we don't have to think about
it. As long as you notice, and have to count, the steps, you are not yet dancing but only learning to dance. A good shoe is a shoe you don't notice. Good

reading becomes possible when you need not consciously think about eyes, or light, or print, or spelling. The perfect church service would be one we were almost unaware of; our attention would have been on God.

But every novelty prevents this. It fixes our attention on the service itself; and thinking about worship is a different thing from worshipping. The important question about the Grail was 'for what does it serve?' ''Tis mad idolatry that makes the service greater than the god.'

A still worse thing may happen. Novelty may fix our attention not even on the service but on the celebrant. You know what I mean. Try as one may to exclude it, the question, 'What on earth is he up to now?' will intrude. It lays one's devotion waste. There is really some excuse for the man who said, 'I wish they'd remember that the charge to Peter was Feed my sheep; not Try experiments on my rats, or even, Teach my performing dogs new tricks.'

Thus my whole liturgiological position really boils down to an entreaty for permanence and uniformity. I can make do with almost any kind of service whatever, if only it will stay put. But if each form is snatched away just when I am beginning to feel at home in it, then I can never make any progress in the art of worship. You give me no chance to acquire the trained habit – *habito dell' arte*.

It may well be that some variations which seem to me merely matters of taste really involve grave doctrinal differences. But surely not all? For if grave doctrinal differences are really as numerous as variations in practice, then we shall have to conclude that no such thing as the Church of England exists. And anyway, the Liturgical Fidget is not a purely Anglican phenomenon; I have heard Roman Catholics complain of it too.

And that brings me back to my starting point. The business of us laymen is simply to endure and make the best of it. Any tendency to a passionate preference for one type of service must be regarded simply as a temptation. Partisan 'Churchmanships' are my *bête noire*. And if we avoid them, may we not possibly perform a very useful function? The shepherds go off, 'every one to his own way' and vanish over diverse points of the horizon. If the sheep huddle patiently together and go on bleating, might they finally recall the shepherds? (Haven't English victories sometimes been won by the rank and file in spite of the generals?)

As to the words of the service – liturgy in the narrower sense – the question is rather different. If you have a vernacular liturgy you must have a changing liturgy; otherwise it will finally be vernacular only in name. The ideal of 'timeless English' is sheer nonsense. No living language can be timeless. You might as well ask for a motionless river.

I think it would have been best, if it were possible, that necessary change should have occurred gradually and (to most people) imperceptibly; here a little and there a little; one obsolete word replaced in a century – like the gradual change of spelling in successive editions of Shakespeare. As things are we must reconcile ourselves, if we can also reconcile government, to a new Book.

If we were – I thank my stars I'm not – in a position to give its authors advice, would you have any advice to give them? Mine could hardly go beyond unhelpful cautions: 'Take care. It is so easy to break eggs without making omelettes.'

Already our liturgy is one of the very few remaining elements of unity in our hideously divided Church. The good to be done by revision needs to be very great and very certain before we throw that away. Can you imagine any new Book which will not be a source of new schism?

Most of those who press for revision seem to wish that it should serve two purposes: that of modernising the language in the interests of intelligibility, and that of doctrinal improvement. Ought the two operations – each painful and each dangerous – to be carried out at the same time? Will the patient survive?

What are the agreed doctrines which are to be embodied in the new Book and how long will agreement on them continue? I ask with trepidation because I read a man the other day who seemed to wish that everything in the old Book which was inconsistent with orthodox Freudianism should be deleted.

For whom are we to cater in revising the language? A country parson I know asked his sexton what he understood by *indifferently* in the phrase 'truly and indifferently administer justice'. The man replied, 'It means making no difference between one chap and another.' 'And what would it mean if it said *impartially*?' asked the parson. 'Don't know. Never heard of it,' said the sexton. Here, you see, we have a change intended to make things easier. But it does so neither for the educated, who understand *indifferently* already, nor for the wholly uneducated, who don't understand *impartially*. It helps only some middle area of the congregation which may not even be a majority. Let us hope the revisers will prepare for their work by a prolonged empirical study of popular speech as it actually is, not as we (*a priori*) assume it to be. How many scholars know (what I discovered by accident) that when uneducated people say *impersonal* they sometimes mean *incorporeal*?

What of expressions which are archaic but not unintelligible? ('Be ye lift up.') I find that people react to archaism most diversely. It antagonises some: makes what is said unreal. To others, not necessarily more learned, it is highly numinous and a real aid to devotion. We can't please both.

I know there must be change. But is this the right moment? Two signs of the right moment occur to me. One would be a unity among us which enabled the Church – not some momentarily triumphant party – to speak through the new work with a united voice. The other would be the manifest presence, somewhere in the Church, of the specifically literary talent needed for composing a good prayer. Prose needs to be not only very good but very good in a very special way, if it is to stand up to reiterated reading aloud. Cranmer may have his defects as a theologian; as a stylist, he can play all the moderns, and many of his predecessors, off the field. I don't see either sign at the moment.

Yet we all want to be tinkering. Even I would gladly see 'Let your light so shine before men' removed from the offertory. It sounds, in that context, so like an exhortation to do our alms that they may be seen by men.

I'd meant to follow up what you say about Rose Macaulay's letters, but that must wait till next week.

2

I can't understand why you say that my view of church services is 'man-centred' and too concentrated with 'mere edification'. How does this follow from anything I said? Actually my ideas about the sacrament would probably be called 'magical' by a good many modern theologians. Surely, the more fully one believes that a strictly supernatural event takes place, the less one can attach any great importance to the dress, gestures, and position of the priest? I agree with you that he is there not only to edify the people but to glorify God. But how can a man glorify God by placing obstacles in the way of the people? Especially if the slightest element of 'clerical one-upmanship' – I owe the phrase to a cleric – underlines some of his eccentricities? How right is that passage in the *Imitation* where the celebrant is told, 'Consult not your own devotion but the edification of your flock.' I've forgotten how the Latin runs.

Now about the Rose Macaulay *Letters*. Like you, I was staggered by this continual search for more and more prayers. If she were merely collecting them as *objets d'art* I could understand it; she was a born collector. But I get the impression that she collected them in order to use them; that her whole prayer-life depended on what we may call 'ready-made' prayers – prayers written by other people.

But though, like you, staggered, I was not, like you, repelled. One reason is that I had – and you hadn't – the luck to meet her. Make no mistake. She was the right sort; one of the most fully civilised people I ever knew. The other reason, as I have so often told you, is that you are a bigot. Broaden your mind, Malcolm, broaden your mind! It takes all sorts to make a world; or a church. This may be even truer of a church. If grace perfects nature it must expand all our natures into the full richness of the diversity which God intended when He made them, and heaven will display far more variety than hell. 'One fold' doesn't mean 'one pool'. Cultivated roses and daffodils are no more alike than wild roses and daffodils. What pleased me most about a Greek Orthodox mass I once attended was that there seemed to be no prescribed behaviour for the congregation. Some stood, some knelt, some sat, some walked; one crawled about the floor like a caterpillar. And the beauty of it was that nobody took the slightest notice of what anyone else was doing. I wish we Anglicans would follow their example. One meets people who are perturbed because someone in the next pew does, or does not, cross himself. They oughtn't even to have seen, let alone censured. 'Who art thou that judgest Another's servant?'

I don't doubt, then, that Rose Macaulay's method was the right one for her. It wouldn't be for me, any more than for you.

All the same, I am not quite such a purist in this matter as I used to be. For many years after my conversion I never used any ready-made forms except the Lord's Prayer. In fact I tried to pray without words at all – not to verbalise the mental acts. Even in praying for others I believe I tended to avoid their names and substituted mental images of them. I still think the prayer without words is the best – if one can really achieve it. But I now see that in trying to make it my daily bread I was counting on a greater mental and spiritual strength than I really have. To pray successfully without words one needs to be 'at the top of one's form'. Otherwise the mental acts become merely imaginative or emotional acts – and a fabricated emotion is a miserable affair. When the golden moments come, when God enables one really to pray without words, who but a fool would reject the gift? But He does not give it – anyway not to me – day in, day out. My mistake was what Pascal, if I remember rightly, calls 'Error of Stoicism': thinking we can do always what we can do sometimes.

And this, you see, makes the choice between ready-made prayers and one's own words rather less important for me than it apparently is for you. For me words are in any case secondary. They are only an anchor. Or, shall I say, they are the movements of a conductor's baton: not the music. They serve to canalise the worship or penitence or petition which might without them – such are our minds – spread into wide and shallow puddles. It does not matter very much who first put them together. If they are our own words they will soon, by unavoidable repetition, harden into a formula. If they are someone else's, we shall continually pour into them our own meaning.

At present – for one's practice changes and, I think, ought to change – I find it best to make 'my own words' the staple but introduce a modicum of the ready-made.

Writing to you, I need not stress the importance of the home-made staple. As Solomon said at the dedication of the temple, each man who prays knows 'the plague of his own heart'. Also, the comforts of his own heart. No other creature is identical with me; no other situation identical with mine. Indeed, I myself and my situation are in continual change. A ready-made form can't serve for my intercourse with God any more than it could serve for my intercourse with you.

This is obvious. Perhaps I shan't find it so easy to persuade you that the ready-made modicum has also its use: for me, I mean – I'm not suggesting rules for anyone else in the whole world.

First, it keeps me in touch with 'sound doctrine'. Left to oneself, one could easily slide away from 'the faith once given' into a phantom called 'my religion'.

Secondly, it reminds me 'what things I ought to ask' (perhaps especially when I am praying for other people). The crisis of the present moment, like the nearest telegraph-post, will always loom largest. Isn't there a danger that our great, permanent, objective necessities – often more important – may get crowded out? By the way, that's another thing to be avoided in a revised Prayer Book. 'Contemporary problems' may claim an undue share. And the more 'up to date' the Book is, the sooner it will be dated.

Finally, they provide an element of the ceremonial. On your view, that is just what we don't want. On mine, it is part of what we want. I see what you mean when you say that using ready-made prayers would be like 'making love to your own wife out of Petrarch or Donne'. (Incidentally might you not *quote* them – to such a literary wife as Betty?) The parallel won't do.

I fully agree that the relationship between God and a man is more private and intimate than any possible relation between two fellow creatures. Yes, but at the same time there is, in another way, a greater distance between the participants. We are approaching – well I won't say 'the Wholly Other', for I suspect that is meaningless, but the Unimaginably and Insupportably Other. We ought to be – sometimes I hope one is – simultaneously aware of closest proximity and infinite distance. You make things far too snug and confiding. Your erotic analogy needs to be supplemented by 'I fell at His feet as one dead.'

I think the 'low' church *milieu* that I grew up in did tend to be too cosily at ease in Sion. My grandfather, I'm told, used to say that he 'looked forward to having some very interesting conversations with St Paul when he got to heaven.' Two clerical gentlemen talking at ease in a club! It never seemed to cross his mind that an encounter with St Paul might be rather an overwhelming experience even for an Evangelical clergyman of good family. But when Dante saw the great apostles in heaven they affected him like *mountains*. There's lots to be said against devotions to saints; but at least they keep on reminding us that we are very small people compared with them. How much smaller before their Master?

A few formal, ready-made, prayers serve me as a corrective of – well, let's call it 'cheek'. They keep one side of the paradox alive. Of course it is only one side. It would be better not to be reverent at all than to have a reverence which denied the proximity.

Oh for Mercy's sake. Not you too! Why, just because I raise an objection to your parallel between prayer and a man making love to his own wife, must you trot out all the rigmarole about the 'holiness' of sex and start lecturing me as if I were a Manichaean? I know that in most circles nowadays one need only mention sex to set everyone in the room emitting this gas. But, I did hope, not you. Didn't I make it plain that I objected to your image solely on the ground of its nonchalance, or presumption?

I'm not saying anything against (or for) 'sex'. Sex in itself cannot be moral or immoral any more than gravitation or nutrition. The sexual behaviour of human beings can. And like their economic, or political, or agricultural, or parental, or filial behaviour, it is sometimes good and sometimes bad. And the sexual act, when lawful – which means chiefly when consistent with good faith and charity – can, like all other merely natural acts ('whether we eat or drink, etc.', as the apostle says), be done to the glory of God, and will then be holy. And like other natural acts it is sometimes so done, and sometimes not. This may be what the poor Bishop of Woolwich was trying to say. Anyway, what more is there to be said? And can we now get this red herring out of the way? I'd be glad if we could; for the moderns have achieved the feat, which I should have thought impossible, of making the whole subject a bore. Poor Aphrodite! They have sandpapered most of the Homeric laughter off her face.

Apparently I have been myself guilty of introducing another red herring by mentioning devotions to saints. I didn't in the least want to go off into a discussion on that subject. There is clearly a theological defence for it; if you can ask for the prayers of the living, why should you not ask for the prayers of the dead? There is clearly also a great danger. In some popular practice we see it leading off into an infinitely silly picture of heaven as an earthly court where applicants will be wise to pull the right wires, discover the best 'channels', and attach themselves to the most influential pressure groups. But I have nothing to do with all this. I am not thinking of adopting the practice myself; and who am I to judge the practices of others? I only hope there'll be no scheme for canonisations in the Church of England. Can you imagine a better hot-bed for yet more divisions between us?

The consoling thing is that while Christendom is divided about the rationality, and even the lawfulness, of praying *to* the saints, we are all agreed about praying *with* them. 'With angels and archangels and all the company of heaven.' Will you believe it? It is only quite recently I made that quotation a part of my private prayers – I festoon it round 'hallowed be Thy name'. This, by the way, illustrates what I was saying last week about the uses of ready-made forms. They remind one. And I have found this quotation a great enrichment. One always accepted this *with* theoretically. But it is quite different when one brings it into consciousness at an appropriate moment and wills the association of one's own little twitter with the voice of the great saints and (we hope) of our own dear dead. They may drown some of the uglier qualities and set off any tiny value it has.

You may say that the distinction between the communion of the saints as I find it in that act and full-fledged prayers to saints is not, after all, very great. All the better if so. I sometimes have a bright dream of reunion engulfing us unawares, like a great wave from behind our backs, perhaps at the very moment when our official representatives are still pronouncing it impossible. Discussions usually separate us; actions sometimes unite us.

When I spoke of prayer without words I don't think I meant anything so exalted as what mystics call the 'prayer of silence'. And when I spoke of being 'at the top of one's form' I didn't mean it purely in a spiritual sense. The condition of the body comes in; for I suppose a man may be in a state of grace and yet very sleepy.

And, talking of sleepiness, I entirely agree with you that no one in his senses, if he has any power of ordering his own day, would reserve his chief prayers for bedtime – obviously the worst possible hour for any action which needs concentration. The trouble is that thousands of unfortunate people can hardly find any other. Even for us, who are the lucky ones, it is not always easy. My own plan, when hard pressed, is to seize any time, and place, however unsuitable, in preference to the last waking moment. On a day of travelling – with, perhaps, some ghastly meeting at the end of it – I'd rather pray sitting in a crowded train than put it off till midnight when one reaches a hotel bedroom with aching head and dry throat and one's mind partly in a stupor and partly in a whirl. On other, and slightly less crowded, days a bench in a park, or a back street where one can pace up and down, will do.

A man to whom I was explaining this said, 'But why don't you turn into a church?' Partly because, for nine months of the year, it will be freezingly cold but also because I have bad luck with churches. No sooner do I enter one and compose my mind than one or other of two things happens. Either someone starts practising the organ. Or else, with resolute tread, there appears from nowhere a pious woman in elastic-side boots, carrying mop, bucket, and dust-pan, and begins beating hassocks and rolling up carpets and doing things to flower vases. Of course (blessings on her) 'work is prayer', and her enacted *oratio* is probably worth ten times my spoken one. But it doesn't help mine to become worth more.

When one prays in strange places and at strange times one can't kneel, to be sure. I won't say this doesn't matter. The body ought to pray as well as the soul. Body and soul are both the better for it. Bless the body. Mine has led me into many scrapes, but I've led it into far more. If the imagination were obedient the appetites would give us very little trouble. And from how much it has saved me! And but for our body one whole realm of God's glory – all that we receive through the senses – would go unpraised. For the beasts can't appreciate it and the angels are, I suppose, pure intelligences. They *understand* colours and tastes better than our greatest scientists; but have they retinas or palates? I fancy the 'beauties of nature' are a secret God has shared with us alone. That may be one of the reasons why we were made – and why the resurrection of the body is an important doctrine.

But I'm being led into a digression; perhaps because I am still smarting under the charge of being a Manichee! The relevant point is that kneeling does matter, but other things matter even more. A concentrated mind and a sitting body make for better prayer than a kneeling body and a mind half asleep. Sometimes these are the only alternatives. (Since the osteoporosis I can hardly kneel at all in most places, myself.)

A clergyman once said to me that a railway compartment, if one has it to oneself, is an extremely good place to pray in 'because there is just the right amount of distraction'. When I asked him to explain, he said that perfect silence and solitude left one more open to the distractions which come from within, and that a moderate amount of external distraction was easier to cope with. I don't find this so myself, but I can imagine it.

The Jones boy's name is Cyril – though why you find it so important to pray for people by their Christian names I can't imagine. I always assume God knows their surnames as well. I am afraid many people appear in my prayers only as 'that old man at Crewe' or 'the waitress' or even 'that man'. One may have lost, or may never have known, their names and yet remember how badly they need to be prayed for.

No letter next week. I shall be in the thick of exams.

4

Of the two difficulties you mention I think that only one is often a practical problem for believers. The other is in my experience usually
raised by people who are attacking Christianity.

The ideal opening for their attacks – if they know the Bible – is the phrase
in Philippians about 'making your requests known to God'. I mean, the
words making known bring out most clearly the apparent absurdity with
which they charge us. We say that we believe God to be omniscient; yet a
great deal of prayer seems to consist of giving Him information. And indeed
we have been reminded by Our Lord too not to pray as if we forgot the
omniscience – 'for your heavenly Father knows you need all these things.'

This is final against one very silly sort of prayer. I have heard a man offer a
prayer for a sick person which really amounted to a diagnosis followed by
advice as to how God should treat the patient. And I have heard prayers nominally for peace, but really so concerned for various devices which the petitioner believed to be means to peace, that they were open to the same criticism.

But even when that kind of thing is ruled out, the unbeliever's objection
remains. To confess our sins before God is certainly to tell Him what He
knows much better than we. And also, any petition is a kind of telling. If it
does not strictly exclude the belief that God knows our need, it at least
seems to solicit His attention. Some traditional formulae make that implication very clear: 'Hear us, good Lord' – 'O let thine ears consider well the
voice of my complaint.' As if, though God does not need to be informed, He
does need, and even rather frequently, to be reminded. But we cannot really
believe that degrees of attention, and therefore of inattention, and therefore
of something like forgetfulness, exist in the Absolute Mind. I presume that
only God's attention keeps me (or anything else) in existence at all.

What, then, are we really doing? Our whole conception of, so to call it,
the prayer-situation depends on the answer.

We are always completely, and therefore equally, known to God. That is
our destiny whether we like it or not. But though this knowledge never

varies, the quality of our being known can. A school of thought holds that 'freedom is willed necessity'. Never mind if they are right or not. I want this idea only as an analogy. Ordinarily, to be known by God is to be, for this purpose, in the category of things. We are, like earthworms, cabbages, and nebulae, objects of Divine knowledge. But when we (a) become aware of the fact – the present fact, not the generalisation – and (b) assent with all our will to be so known, then we treat ourselves, in relation to God, not as things but as persons. We have unveiled. Not that any veil could have baffled His sight. The change is in us. The passive changes to the active. Instead of merely being known, we show, we tell, we offer ourselves to view.

To put ourselves thus on a personal footing with God could, in itself and without warrant, be nothing but presumption and illusion. But we are taught that it is not; that it is God who gives us that footing. For it is by the Holy Spirit that we cry 'Father'. By unveiling, by confessing our sins and 'making known' our requests, we assume the high rank of persons before Him. And He, descending, becomes a Person to us.

But I should not have said 'becomes'. In Him there is no becoming. He reveals Himself as Person: or reveals that in Him which is Person. For – dare one say it? In a book it would need pages of qualification and insurance – God is in some measure to a man as that man is to God. The door in God that opens is the door he knocks at. (At least, I think so, usually.) The Person in Him – He is more than a person – meets those who can welcome or at least face it. He speaks as 'I' when we truly call Him 'Thou'. (How good Buber is!)

This talk of 'meeting' is, no doubt, anthropomorphic; as if God and I could be face to face, like two fellow-creatures, when in reality He is above me and within me and below me and all about me. That is why it must be balanced by all manner of metaphysical and theological abstractions. But never, here or anywhere else, let us think that while anthropomorphic images are a concession to our weakness, the abstractions are the literal truth. Both are equally concessions; each singly misleading, and the two together mutually corrective. Unless you sit to it very lightly, continually murmuring 'Not thus, not thus, neither is this Thou', the abstraction is fatal. It will make the life of lives inanimate and the love of loves impersonal. The *naïf* image is mischievous chiefly in so far as it holds unbelievers back from conversion. It does believers, even at its crudest, no harm. What soul ever perished for believing that God the Father really has a beard?

Your other question is one which, I think, really gets in pious people's way. It was, you remember, 'How important must a need or desire be before we can properly make it the subject of petition?' *Properly*, I take it, here means either 'Without irreverence' or 'Without silliness', or both.

When I'd thought about it for a bit, it seemed to me that there are really two questions involved.

1. How important must an object be before we can, without sin and folly, allow our desire for it to become a matter of serious concern to us? This, you see, is a question about what old writers call our 'frame'; that is, our 'frame of mind'.

2. Granted the existence of such a serious concern in our minds, can it always be properly laid before God in prayer?

We all know the answer to the first of these in theory. We must aim at what St Augustine (is it?) called 'ordinate loves'. Our deepest concern should be for first things, and our next deepest for second things, and so on down to zero – to total absence of concern for things that are not really good, nor means to good, at all.

Meantime, however, we want to know not how we should pray if we were perfect but how we should pray being as we now are. And if my idea of prayer as 'unveiling' is accepted, we have already answered this. It is no use to ask God with factitious earnestness for A when our whole mind is in reality filled with the desire for B. We must lay before Him what is in us, not what ought to be in us.

Even an intimate human friend is ill used if we talk to him about one thing while our mind is really on another, and even a human friend will soon become aware when we are doing so. You yourself came to see me a few years ago when the great blow had fallen upon me. I tried to talk to you as if nothing were wrong. You saw through it in five minutes. Then I confessed. And you said things which made me ashamed of my attempt at concealment.

It may well be that the desire can be laid before God only as a sin to be repented; but one of the best ways of learning this is to lay it before God. Your problem, however, was not about sinful desires in that sense; rather about desires, intrinsically innocent and sinning, if at all, only by being stronger than the triviality of their object warrants. I have no doubt at all that if they are the subject of our thoughts they must be the subject of our prayers – whether in penitence or in petition or in a little of both: penitence for the excess, yet petition for the thing we desire.

If one forcibly excludes them, don't they wreck all the rest of our prayers? If we lay all the cards on the table, God will help us to moderate the excesses. But the pressure of things we are trying to keep out of our mind is a hopeless distraction. As someone said, 'No noise is so emphatic as one you are trying not to listen to.'

The ordinate frame of mind is one of the blessings we must pray for, not a fancy-dress we must put on when we pray.

And perhaps, as those who do not turn to God in petty trials will have no *habit* or such resort to help them when the great trials come, so those who have not learned to ask Him for childish things will have less readiness to ask Him for great ones. We must not be too high-minded. I fancy we may sometimes be deterred from small prayers by a sense of our own dignity rather than of God's.

5

I don't very much like the job of telling you 'more about my festoonings' – the private overtones I give to certain petitions. I make two conditions: (a) That you will in return tell me some of yours. (b) That you will understand I am not in the least *recommending* mine either to you or to anyone else. There could be many better; and my present festoons will very probably change.

I call them 'festoons', by the way, because they don't (I trust) obliterate the plain, public sense of the petition but are merely hung on it.

What I do about 'hallowed be Thy name' I told a fortnight ago.

Thy kingdom come. That is, may your reign be realised here, as it is realised there. But I tend to take *there* on three levels. First, as in the sinless world beyond the horrors of animal and human life; in the behaviour of stars and trees and water, in sunrise and wind. May there be *here* (in my heart) the beginning of a like beauty. Secondly, as in the best human lives I have known: in all the people who really bear the burdens and ring true, the people we call bricks, and in the quiet, busy, ordered life of really good families and really good religious houses. May that too be 'here'. Finally, of course, in the usual sense: as in heaven, as among the blessed dead.

And *here* can of course be taken not only for 'in my heart', but for 'in this college' – in England – in the world in general. But prayer is not the time for pressing our own favourite social or political panacea. Even Queen Victoria didn't like 'being talked to as if she were a public meeting'.

Thy will be done. My festoons on this have been added gradually. At first I took it exclusively as an act of submission, attempting to do with it what Our Lord did in Gethsemane. I thought of God's will purely as something that would come upon me, something of which I should be the patient. And I also thought of it as a will which would be embodied in pains and disappointments. Not, to be sure, that I suppose God's will for me to consist entirely of disagreeables. But I thought it was only the disagreeables that called for this preliminary submission – the agreeables could look after themselves for the present. When they turned up, one could give thanks.

This interpretation is, I expect, the commonest. And so it must be. And such are the miseries of human life that it must often fill our whole mind. But at other times other meanings can be added. So I added one more.

The peg for it is, I admit, much more obvious in the English version than in the Greek or Latin. No matter: this is where the liberty of festooning comes in. 'Thy will be *done*.' But a great deal of it is to be done by God's creatures; including me. The petition, then, is not merely that I may patiently suffer God's will but also that I may vigorously do it. I must be an agent as well as a patient. I am asking that I may be enabled to do it. In the long run I am asking to be given 'the same mind which was also in Christ'.

Taken this way, I find the words have a more regular daily application. For there isn't always – or we don't always have reason to suspect that there is – some great affliction looming in the near future, but there are always duties to be done; usually, for me, neglected duties to be caught up with. 'Thy will be *done* – by me – now' brings one back to brass tacks.

But more than that, I am at this very moment contemplating a new festoon. Tell me if you think it a vain subtlety. I am beginning to feel that we need a preliminary act of submission not only towards possible future afflictions but also towards possible future blessings. I know it sounds fantastic; but think it over. It seems to me that we often, almost sulkily, reject the good that God offers us because, at that moment, we expected some other good. Do you know what I mean? On every level of our life – in our religious experience, in our gastronomic, erotic, aesthetic and social experience – we are always harking back to some occasion which seemed to us to reach perfection, setting that up as a norm, and depreciating all other occasions by comparison. But these other occasions, I now suspect, are often full of their own new blessings if only we would lay ourselves open to it. God shows us a new facet of the glory, and we refuse to look at it because we're still looking for the old one. And of course we don't get that. You can't, at the twentieth reading, get again the experience of reading *Lycidas* for the first time. But what you do get can be in its own way as good.

This applies especially to the devotional life. Many religious people lament that the first fervours of their conversion have died away. They think – sometimes rightly, but not, I believe always – that their sins account for this. They may even try by pitiful efforts of will to revive what now seem to have been the golden days. But were those fervours – the operative word is *those* – ever intended to last?

It would be rash to say that there is any prayer which God *never* grants. But the strongest candidate is the prayer we might express in the single word *encore*. And how should the Infinite repeat Himself? All space and time are too little for Him to utter Himself in them *once*.

And the joke, or tragedy, of it all is that these golden moments in the past, which are so tormenting if we erect them into a norm, are entirely nourishing, wholesome, and enchanting if we are content to accept them for what they are, for memories. Properly bedded down in a past which we do not miserably try to conjure back, they will send up exquisite growths. Leave the bulbs alone, and the new flowers will come up. Grub them up and hope, by fondling and sniffing, to get last year's blooms, and you will get nothing. 'Unless a seed die...'

I expect we all do much the same with the prayer for our *daily bread*. It means, doesn't it, all we need for the day – 'things requisite and necessary as well for the body as for the soul'. I should hate to make this clause 'purely religious' by thinking of 'spiritual' needs alone. One of its uses, to me, is to remind us daily that what Burnaby calls the *naif* view of prayer is firmly built into Our Lord's teaching.

Forgive us ... as we forgive. Unfortunately there's no need to do any festooning here. To forgive for the moment is not difficult. But to go on forgiving, to forgive the same offence again every time it recurs to the memory – there's the real tussle. My resource is to look for some action of my own which is open to the same charge as the one I'm resenting. If I still smart to remember how A let me down, I must still remember how I let B down. If I find it difficult to forgive those who bullied me at school, let me, at that very moment, remember, and pray for, those I bullied. (Not that we called it *bullying* of course. That is where prayer without words can be so useful. In it there are no names; therefore no aliases.)

I was never worried myself by the words *lead us not into temptation*, but a great many of my correspondents are. The words suggest to them what someone has called 'a fiend-like conception of God', as one who first forbids us certain fruits and then lures us to taste them. But the Greek word (πειρασμός) means 'trial' – 'trying circumstances' – of every sort; a far larger word than English 'temptation'. So that the petition essentially is, 'Make straight our paths. Spare us, where possible, from all crises, whether of temptation or affliction.' By the way, you yourself, though you've doubtless forgotten it, gave me an excellent gloss on it: years ago in the pub at Coton. You said it added a sort of reservation to all our preceding prayers. As if we said, 'In my ignorance I have asked for A, B and C. But don't give me them if you foresee that they would in reality be to me either snares or sorrows.' And you quoted Juvenal, *numinibus vota exaudita malignis*, 'enormous prayers which heaven in vengeance grants'. For we make plenty of such prayers. If God had granted all the silly prayers I've made in my life, where should I be now?

I don't often use *the kingdom, the power and the glory*. When I do, I have an idea of the *kingdom* as sovereignty *de jure*; God, as good, would have a claim on my obedience even if He had no power. The *power* is the sovereignty *de facto* – He is omnipotent. And the *glory* is – well, the glory; the 'beauty so old and new', the 'light from behind the sun'.

6

I can't remember exactly what I said about not making the petition for our daily bread too 'religious', and I'm not quite sure what you mean – nor how ironically – by asking if I've become 'one of Vidler's young men'!

About Vidler. I never heard the programme which created all that scandal, and naturally one wouldn't condemn a dog on newspaper extracts. But I have now read his essay in *Soundings* and I believe I go a good deal further with him than you would. Much of what he quotes from F. D. Maurice and Bonhoeffer seems to me very good; and so, I think, are his own arguments for the Establishment.

At any rate I can well understand how a man who is trying to love God and his neighbour should come to dislike the very word *religion*; a word, by the way, which hardly ever appears in the New Testament. Newman makes my blood run cold when he says in one of the *Parochial and Plain Sermons* that Heaven is like a church because in both, 'one single sovereign subject religion – is brought before us'. He forgets that there is no temple in the new Jerusalem.

He has substituted *religion* for God – as if navigation were substituted for arrival, or battle for victory, or wooing for marriage, or in general the means for the end. But even in this present life, there is danger in the very concept of *religion*. It carries the suggestion that this is one more department of life, an extra department added to the economic, the social, the intellectual, the recreational, and all the rest. But that whose claims are infinite can have no standing as a department. Either it is an illusion or else our whole life falls under it. We have no non-religious activities; only religious and irreligious.

Religion, nevertheless, appears to exist as a department, and, in some ages, to thrive as such. It thrives partly because there exists in many people a 'love of religious observances', which I think Simone Weil is quite right in regarding as a merely natural taste. There exists also – Vidler is rather good on this – the delight in religious (as in any other) organisation. Then all sorts of aesthetic, sentimental, historical, political interests are drawn in. Finally sales of work, the parish magazine, and bell-ringing, and Santa Claus.

None of them bad things. But none of them is necessarily of more spiritual value than the activities we call secular. And they are infinitely dangerous when this is not understood. This department of life, labelled 'sacred', can become an end in itself; an idol that hides both God and my neighbours. ('When the means are autonomous they are deadly.') It may even come about that a man's most genuinely Christian actions fall entirely outside that part of his life which he calls *religious*.

I read in a religious paper, 'Nothing is more important than to teach children to use the sign of the cross.' Nothing? Not compassion, nor veracity, nor justice? *Voila l'ennemi.*

One must, however, walk warily, for the truth that *religion* as a department has really no right to exist can be misunderstood.

Some will conclude that this illegitimate department ought to be abolished. Others will think, coming nearer to the truth, that it ought to cease to be departmental by being extended to the whole of life, but will misinterpret this. They will think it means that more and more of our secular transactions should be 'opened with prayer', that a wearisomely explicit pietism should infest our talk, that there should be no more cakes and ale. A third sort, well aware that God still rules a very small part of their lives, and that 'a departmental religion' is no good, may despair. It would have to be carefully explained to them that to be 'still only a part' is not the same as being a permanent department. In all of us God 'still' holds only a part. D-Day is only a week ago. The bite so far taken out of Normandy shows small on the map of Europe. The resistance is strong, the casualties heavy, and the event uncertain. There is, we have to admit, a line of demarcation between God's part in us and the enemy's region. But it is, we hope, a fighting line; not a frontier fixed by agreement.

But I suspect the real misunderstanding of Vidler's talk lay elsewhere. We have been speaking of *religion* as a pattern of behaviour – which, if contentedly departmental, cannot really be Christian behaviour. But people also, and more often, use *religion* to mean a system of beliefs. When they heard that Vidler wanted a church with 'less religion', they thought he meant that the little – the very little – which liberal theology has still left of the 'faith once given' was to be emptied out. Hence someone asked, 'Is he a Theist?'

Well, he certainly is. He wants – I think he wants very earnestly – to retain some Christian doctrines. But he is prepared to scrap a good deal. 'Traditional doctrines' are to be tested. Many things will have to be 'outgrown' or 'survive chiefly as venerable archaisms or as fairy-stories'. He feels quite happy about this undefined programme of jettison because he trusts in the continued guidance of the Holy Spirit. A noble faith; provided, of course, there is any such being as the Holy Spirit. But I suppose His existence is itself one of the 'traditional doctrines' which, on Vidler's premises, we might any day find we had outgrown. So with the doctrine – Vidler calls it 'the fact' – that man is 'a twofold creature – not only a political creature, but also a spiritual being'. Vidler and you and I (and Plato) think it a fact. Tens of thousands, perhaps millions, think it a fantasy. The neutral description of it is 'a traditional doctrine'. Do you think he means that these two doctrines – and why just these two? – are the hard core of his belief, exempt from the threat of rejection which overhangs all other doctrines? Or would he say that, as the title of the book implies, he is only 'taking soundings' – and if the line is not long enough to reach bottom, soundings can yield only negative information to the navigator?

I was interested in the things you said about *forgive us our trespasses*. Often, to be sure, there is something definite for which to ask forgiveness. This is plain sailing. But, like you, I often find one or other of two less manageable states: either a vague feeling of guilt or a sly, and equally vague, self-approval. What are we to do with these?

Many modern psychologists tell us always to distrust this vague feeling of guilt, as something purely pathological. And if they had stopped at that, I might believe them. But when they go on, as some do, to apply the same treatment to all guilt-feelings whatever, to suggest that one's feeling about a particular unkind act or a particular insincerity is also and equally untrustworthy – I can't help thinking they are talking nonsense. One sees this the moment one looks at other people. I have talked to some who felt guilt when they jolly well ought to have felt it; they have behaved like brutes and know it. I've also met others who felt guilty and weren't guilty by any standard I can apply. And thirdly, I've met people who were guilty and didn't seem to feel guilt. And isn't this what we should expect? People can be *malades imaginaires* who are well and think they are ill; and others, especially consumptives, are ill and think they are well; and thirdly – far the largest class – people are ill and know they are ill. It would be very odd if there were any region in which all mistakes were in one direction.

Some Christians would tell us to go on rummaging and scratching till we find something specific. We may be sure, they say, that there are real sins enough to justify the guilt-feeling or to overthrow the feeling that all is well. I think they are right in saying that if we hunt long enough we shall find, or think we have found, something. But that is just what wakens suspicion. A theory which could never by any experience be falsified can for that reason hardly be verified. And just as, when we are yielding to temptation, we make ourselves believe that what we have always thought a sin will on this occasion, for some strange reason, not be a sin, shan't we persuade ourselves that something we have always (rightly) thought to be innocent was really wrong? We may create scruples. And scruples are always a bad thing – if only because they usually distract us from real duties.

I don't at all know whether I'm right or not, but I have, on the whole, come to the conclusion that one can't directly *do* anything about either feeling. One is not to believe either – indeed, how can one believe a fog? I come back to St John: 'if our heart condemn us, God is greater than our heart.' And equally, if our heart flatter us, God is greater than our heart. I sometimes pray not for self-knowledge in general but for just so much self-knowledge at the moment as I can bear and use at the moment; the little daily dose.

Have we any reason to suppose that total self-knowledge, if it were given us, would be for our good? Children and fools, we are told, should never look at half-done work; and we are not yet, I trust, even half-done. You and I wouldn't, at all stages, think it wise to tell a pupil exactly what we thought of his quality. It is much more important that he should know what to do next.

If one said this in public one would have all the Freudians on one's back. And, mind you, we are greatly indebted to them. They did expose the cowardly evasions of really useful selfknowledge which we had all been practising from the beginning of the world. But there is also a merely morbid and fidgety curiosity about one's self – the slop-over from modern psychology – which surely does no good? The unfinished picture would so like to jump off the easel and have a look at itself! And analysis doesn't cure that. We all know people who have undergone it and seem to have made themselves a lifelong subject of research ever since.

If I am right, the conclusion is that when our conscience won't come down to brass-tacks but will only vaguely accuse or vaguely approve, we must say to it, like Herbert, 'Peace, prattler' – and get on.

7

If you meant in your last letter that we can scrap the whole idea of petitionary prayer – prayer which, as you put it, calls upon God to 'engineer'
particular events in the objective world – and confine ourselves to acts of
penitence and adoration, I disagree with you. It may be true that
Christianity would be, intellectually, a far easier religion if it told us to do
this. And I can understand the people who think it would also be a more
high-minded religion. But remember the psalm: 'Lord, I am not high
minded.' Or better still, remember the New Testament. The most unblush-
ingly petitionary prayers are there recommended to us both by precept and
example. Our Lord in Gethsemane made a petitionary prayer (and did not
get what He asked for).

You'll remind me that He asked with a reservation – 'nevertheless, not my
will but thine'. This makes an enormous difference. But the difference which
it precisely does not make is that of removing the prayer's petitionary character. When poor Bill, on a famous occasion, asked us to advance him £100,
he said, 'If you are sure you can spare it,' and, 'I shall quite understand if
you'd rather not.' This made his request very different from the nagging or
even threatening request which a different sort of man might have made. But
it was still a request.

The servant is not greater, and must not be more high-minded, than the
master. Whatever the theoretical difficulties are, we must continue to make
requests of God. And on this point we can get no help from those who keep
on reminding us that this is the lowest and least essential kind of prayer. They
may be right; but so what? Diamonds are more precious than cairngorms, but
the cairngorms still exist and must be taken into account like anything else.

But don't let us be too easily brow-beaten. Some of the popular objections to petitionary prayer, if they are valid against it, are equally valid
against other things which we all do whether we are Christians or not, and
have done ever since the world began, and shall certainly continue to do. I
don't think the burden of answering these rests especially on us.

There is, for example, the Determinism which, whether under that name or another, seems to be implicit in a scientific view of the world. Determinism does not deny the existence of human behaviour. It rejects as an illusion our spontaneous conviction that our behaviour has its ultimate origin in ourselves. What I call 'my act' is the conduit-pipe through which the torrent of the universal process passes, and was bound to pass, at a particular time and place. The distinction between what we call the 'voluntary' and the 'involuntary' movements of our own bodies is not obliterated, but turns out (on this view) to be not exactly the sort of difference we supposed. What I call the 'involuntary' movements necessarily – and, if we know enough, predictably – result from mechanical causes outside my body or from pathological or organic processes within it. The 'voluntary' ones result from conscious psychological factors which themselves result from unconscious psychological factors dependent on my economic situation, my infantile and prenatal experience, my heredity... and so on back to the beginnings of organic life and beyond. I am a conductor, not a source. I never make an original contribution to the world-process. I move with that process not even as a floating log moves with the river but as a particular pint of the water itself moves.

But even those who believe this will, like anyone else, ask you to hand them the salt. Every form of behaviour, including speech, can go on just the same, and will. If a strict Determinist believed in God (and I think he might) petitionary prayer would be no more irrational in him than in anyone else.

Another argument, put up (but not accepted) by Burnaby in *Soundings*, is this. If man's freedom is to be of any value, if he is to have any power of planning and of adapting means to ends, he must live in a predictable world. But if God alters the course of events in answer to prayer, then the world will be unpredictable. Therefore, if man is to be effectively free, God must be in this respect un-free.

But is it not plain that this predictable world, whether it is necessary to our freedom or no, is not the world we live in? This is a world of bets and insurance policies, of hopes and anxieties, where 'nothing is certain but the unexpected' and prudence lies in 'the masterly administration of the unforeseen'. Nearly all the things people pray about are unpredictable: the result of a battle or an operation, the losing or getting of a job, the reciprocation of a love. We don't pray about eclipses.

But, you will reply, we once did. Every advance of science makes predictable something that was formerly unpredictable. It is only our ignorance that makes petitionary prayer possible. Would it not be rational to assume that all those events we now pray about are in principle just as predictable – though we don't yet know enough to predict them – as things like eclipses? But that is no answer to the point I'm making. I am not now trying to refute

Determinism. I am only arguing that a world where the future is unknown cannot be inconsistent with planned and purposive action since we are actually planning and purposing in such a world now and have been doing so for thousands of years.

Also, between ourselves, I think this objection involves a false idea of what the sciences do. You are here a better judge than I, but I give it for what it may be worth. It is true in one sense that the mark of a genuine science is its power to predict. But does this mean that a perfected science, or a perfected synthesis of all the sciences, would be able to write reliable histories of the future? And would the scientists even want to do so? Doesn't science predict a future event only in so far as, and only because, that event is the instance of some universal law? Everything that makes the event unique – in other words, everything that makes it a concrete historical event – is deliberately ruled out; not only as something which science can't, or can't yet, include, but also as something in which science, as such, has no interest. No one sunrise has ever been exactly like another. Take away from the sunrises that in which they differ and what is left will be identical. Such abstracted identicals are what science predicts. But life as we live it is not reducible to such identities. Every real physical event, much more every human experience, has behind it, in the long run, the whole previous history of the real universe which is not itself an 'instance' of anything – and is therefore always festooned with those particularities which science for her own purposes quite rightly discounts. Doesn't the whole art of contriving a good experiment consist in devising means whereby the irrelevancies – that is, the historical particularities – can be reduced to the minimum?

Later in his essay Burnaby seems to suggest that human wills are the only radically unpredictable factor in history. I'm not happy about this. Partly because I don't see how the gigantic negative which it involves could be proved; partly because I agree with Bradley that unpredictability is not the essence, nor even a symptom, of freedom. (Did you see they've reprinted *Ethical Studies*? The baiting of Arnold, wholly just and in Arnold's own manner, is exquisite.) But suppose it were true. Even then, it would make such a huge rent in the predictability of events that the whole idea of predictability as somehow necessary to human life would be in ruins. Think of the countless human acts, acts of copulation, spread over millennia, that led to the birth of Plato, Attila, or Napoleon. Yet it is on these unpredictables that human history largely depends. Twenty-five years ago you asked Betty to marry you. And now, as a result, we have young George (I hope he's got over his gastric flu?). A thousand years hence he might have a good many descendants, and only modesty could conceal from you the possibility that one of these might have as huge a historical effect as Aristotle – or Hitler!

8

What froth and bubble my last letter must have seemed to you! I had hardly posted it when I got Betty's card with the disquieting news about George – turning my jocular reference to his descendants into a stab (at least I suppose it did) and making our whole discussion on prayer seem to you, as it now does to me, utterly unreal. The distance between the abstract, 'Does God hear petitionary prayers?' and the concrete, 'Will He – can He – grant our prayers for George?' is apparently infinite.

Not of course that I can pretend for a moment to be able to feel it as you do. If I did, you would say to yourself (like the man in *Macbeth*), 'He has no children.' A few years ago when I was in my own trouble you said as much to me. You wrote, 'I know I'm outside. My voice can hardly reach you.' And that was one reason why your letter was more like the real grasp of a real hand than any other I got.

The temptation is to attempt reassurances: to remind you how often a GP's preliminary diagnosis is wrong, that the symptoms are admittedly ambiguous, that threatened men sometimes live to a ripe old age. And it would all in fact be true. But what, in that way, could I say which you are not saying to yourself every hour? And you would know my motive. You'd know how little real scientific candour – or knowledge – lay behind my words. And if, which God forbid, your suspense ended as terribly as mine did, these reassurances would sound like mockeries. So at least I found. The memory of the false hopes was an additional torment. Even now certain remembered moments of fallacious comfort twist my heart more than the remembered moment of despair.

All may yet be well. This is true. Meanwhile you have the waiting – waiting till the X-rays are developed and till the specialist has completed his observations. And while you wait, you still have to go on living – if only one could go underground, hibernate, sleep it out. And then (for me – I believe you are stronger) the horrible by-products of anxiety; the incessant, circular movement of the thoughts, even the Pagan temptation to keep watch for irrational omens. And one prays; but mainly such prayers as are themselves a form of anguish.

Some people feel guilty about their anxieties and regard them as a defect of faith. I don't agree at all. They are afflictions, not sins. Like all afflictions, they are, if we can so take them, our share in the Passion of Christ. For the beginning of the Passion – the first move, so to speak – is in Gethsemane. In Gethsemane a very strange and significant thing seems to have happened.

It is clear from many of His sayings that Our Lord had long foreseen His death. He knew what conduct such as His, in a world such as we have made of this, must inevitably lead to. But it is clear that this knowledge must somehow have been withdrawn from Him before He prayed in Gethsemane. He could not, with whatever reservation about the Father's will, have prayed that the cup might pass and simultaneously known that it would not. That is both a logical and a psychological impossibility. You see what this involves? Lest any trial incident to humanity should be lacking, the torments of hope – of suspense, anxiety – were at the last moment loosed upon Him – the supposed possibility that, after all, He might, He just conceivably might, be spared the supreme horror. There was precedent. Isaac had been spared: he too at the last moment, he also against all apparent probability. It was not quite impossible ... and doubtless He had seen other men crucified ... a sight very unlike most of our religious pictures and images.

But for this last (and erroneous) hope against hope, and the consequent tumult of the soul, the sweat of blood, perhaps He would not have been very Man. To live in a fully predictable world is not to be a man.

At the end, I know, we are told that an angel appeared 'comforting' him. But neither *comforting* in Sixteenth Century English nor ἐννισχύων in Greek means 'consoling'. 'Strengthening' is more the word. May not the strengthening have consisted in the renewed certainty – cold comfort this – that the thing must be endured and therefore could be?

We all try to accept with some sort of submission our afflictions when they actually arrive. But the prayer in Gethsemane shows that the preceding anxiety is equally God's will and equally part of our human destiny. The perfect Man experienced it. And the servant is not greater than the master. We are Christians, not Stoics.

Does not every movement in the Passion write large some common element in the sufferings of our race? First, the prayer of anguish; not granted. Then He turns to His friends. They are asleep – as ours, or we, are so often, or busy, or away, or pre-occupied. Then He faces the Church; the very Church that He brought into existence. It condemns Him. This is also characteristic. In every Church, in every institution, there is something which sooner or later works against the very purpose for which it came into existence. But there seems to be another chance. There is the State; in this case, the Roman state. Its pretensions are far lower than those of the Jewish church, but for that very reason it may be free from local fanaticisms. It claims to be just, on a rough, worldly level. Yes, but only so far as is consistent with political expediency and *raison d'état*. One becomes a counter in a complicated game. But even now all is not lost. There is still an appeal to the People – the poor and simple whom He had blessed, whom He had healed and fed and taught, to whom He himself belongs. But they have become over-night (it is nothing unusual) a murderous rabble shouting for His blood. There is, then, nothing left but God. And to God, God's last words are, 'Why hast thou forsaken me?'

You see how characteristic, how representative it all is. The human situation writ large. These are among the things it means to be a man. Every rope breaks when you seize it. Every door is slammed shut as you reach it. To be like the fox at the end of the run; the earths all staked.

As for the last dereliction of all, how can we either understand or endure it? Is it that God Himself cannot be Man unless God seems to vanish at His greatest need? And if so, why? I sometimes wonder if we have even begun to understand what is involved in the very concept of creation. If God will create, He will make something to be, and yet to be not Himself. To be created is, in some sense, to be ejected or separated. Can it be that the more perfect the creature is, the further this separation must at some point be pushed? It is saints, not common people, who experience the 'dark night'. It is men and angels, not beasts, who rebel. Inanimate matter sleeps in the bosom of the Father. The 'hiddenness' of God perhaps presses most painfully on those who are in another way nearest to Him, and therefore God Himself, made man, will of all men be by God most forsaken? One of the Seventeenth Century divines says: 'By pretending to be visible God could only deceive the world.' Perhaps He does pretend just a little to simple souls who need a full measure of 'sensible consolation'. Not deceiving them, but tempering the wind to the shorn lamb. Of course I'm not saying like Niebühr that evil is inherent in finitude. That would identify the creation with the fall and make God the author of evil. But perhaps there is an anguish, an alienation, a crucifixion involved in the creative act. Yet He who alone can judge judges the far-off consummation to be worth it.

I am, you see, a Job's comforter. Far from lightening the dark valley where you now find yourself, I blacken it. And you know why. Your darkness has brought back my own. But on second thoughts I don't regret what I have written. I think it is only in a shared darkness that you and I can really meet at present; shared with one another and, what matters most, with our Master. We are not on an untrodden path. Rather, on the main road.

Certainly we were talking too lightly and easily about these things a fortnight ago. We were playing with counters. One used to be told as a child:

'Think what you're saying.' Apparently we need also to be told: 'Think what you're thinking.' The stakes have to be raised before we take the game quite seriously. I know this is the opposite of what is often said about the necessity of keeping all emotion out of our intellectual processes – 'You can't think straight unless you are cool.' But then neither can you think deep if you are. I suppose one must try every problem in both states. You remember that the ancient Persians debated everything twice: once when they were drunk and once when they were sober.

I know one of you will let me have news as soon as there is any.

9

Thank God. What a mare's nest! Or, more grimly, what a rehearsal! It is only twenty-four hours since I got Betty's wire, and already the crisis seems curiously far away. Like at sea. Once you have doubled the point and got into smooth water, the point doesn't take long to hide below the horizon.

And now, your letter. I'm not at all surprised at your feeling flattened rather than joyful. That isn't ingratitude. It's only exhaustion. Weren't there moments even during those terrible days when you glided into a sort of apathy – for the same reason? The body (bless it) will not continue indefinitely supplying us with the physical media of emotion.

Surely there's no difficulty about the prayer in Gethsemane on the ground that if the disciples were asleep they couldn't have heard it and therefore couldn't have recorded it? The words they did record would hardly have taken three seconds to utter. He was only 'a stone's throw' away. The silence of night was around them. And we may be sure He prayed aloud. People did everything aloud in those days. You remember how astonished St Augustine was – some centuries later in a far more sophisticated society – to discover that when St Ambrose was reading (to himself) you couldn't hear the words even if you went and stood just beside him? The disciples heard the opening words of the prayer before they went to sleep. They record those opening words as if they were the whole.

There is a rather amusing instance of the same thing in Acts 24. The Jews had got down a professional orator called Tertullos to conduct the prosecution of St Paul. The speech as recorded by St Luke takes eighty-four words in the Greek, if I've counted correctly. Eighty-four words are impossibly short for a Greek advocate on a full-dress occasion. Presumably, then, they are a *précis*? But of those eighty-odd words forty are taken up with preliminary compliments to the bench – stuff, which, in a *précis* on that tiny scale, ought not to have come in at all. It is easy to guess what has happened. St Luke, though an excellent narrator, was no good as a reporter. He starts off by trying to memorise, or to get down, the whole speech *verbatim*. And he succeeds in reproducing a certain amount of the exordium. (The style [is] unmistakable. Only a practising *rhetor* ever talks that way.) But he is soon defeated. The whole of the rest of the speech has to be represented by a ludicrously inadequate abstract. But he doesn't tell us what has happened, and thus seems to attribute to Tertullos a performance which would have spelled professional ruin.

As you say, the problems about prayer which really press upon a man when he is praying for dear life are not the general and philosophical ones; they are those that arise within Christianity itself. At least, this is so for you and me. We have long since agreed that if our prayers are granted at all they are granted from the foundation of the world. God and His acts are not in time. Intercourse between God and man occurs at particular moments for the man, but not for God. If there is – as the very concept of prayer presupposes – an adaptation between the free actions of men in prayer and the course of events, this adaptation is from the beginning inherent in the great single creative act. Our prayers are heard – don't say 'have been heard' or you are putting God into time – not only before we make them but before we are made ourselves.

The real problems are different. Is it our faith that prayers, or some prayers, are real causes? But they are not magical causes: they don't, like spells, act directly on nature. They act, then, on nature through God? This would seem to imply that they act on God. But God, we believe, is impassible. All theology would reject the idea of a transaction in which a creature was the agent and God the patient.

It is quite useless to try to answer this empirically by producing stories – though you and I could tell strange ones – of striking answers to prayer. We shall be told, reasonably enough, that *post hoc* is not *propter hoc*. The thing we prayed for was going to happen anyway. Our action was irrelevant. Even a fellow-creature's action which fulfils our request may not be caused by it; he does what we ask, but perhaps he would equally have done so without our asking. Some cynics will tell us that no woman ever married a man because he proposed to her: she always elicits the proposal because she has determined to marry him.

In these human instances we believe, when we do believe, that our request was the cause, or a cause, of the other party's action, because we have from deep acquaintance a certain impression of that party's character. Certainly not by applying the scientific procedures – control experiments, etc. – for establishing causes. Similarly we believe, when we do believe, that the relation between our prayer and the event is not a mere coincidence only because we have a certain idea of God's character. Only faith vouches for the connection. No empirical proof could establish it. Even a miracle, if one occurred, 'might have been going to happen anyway'.

Again, in the most intimate human instances we really feel that the category of cause and effect will not contain what actually happens. In a real 'proposal' – as distinct from one in an old-fashioned novel – is there any agent-patient relation? Which drop on the window pane moves to join the other?

Now I am going to suggest that strictly causal thinking is even more inadequate when applied to the relation between God and man. I don't mean only when we are thinking of prayer, but whenever we are thinking about what happens at the Frontier, at the mysterious point of junction and separation where absolute being utters derivative being.

One attempt to define causally what happens there has led to the whole puzzle about Grace and free will. You will notice that Scripture just sails over the problem. 'Work out your own salvation in fear and trembling' – pure Pelagianism. But why? 'For it is God who worketh in you' – pure Augustinianism. It is presumably only our presuppositions that make this appear nonsensical. We profanely assume that divine and human action exclude one another like the actions of two fellow-creatures so that 'God did this' and 'I did this' cannot both be true of the same act except in the sense that each contributed a share.

In the end we must admit a two-way traffic at the junction. At first sight no passive verb in the world would seem to be so utterly passive as 'to be created'. Does it not mean 'to *have been* nonentity'? Yet, for us rational creatures, to be created also means 'to be made agents'. We have nothing that we have not received; but part of what we have received is the power of being something more than receptacles. We exercise it, no doubt, briefly by our sins. But they, for my present argument, will do as well as anything else. For God forgives sins. He would not do so if we committed none – 'whereto serves Mercy but to confront the visage of offence?' In that sense the Divine action is consequent upon, conditioned by, elicited by, our behaviour. Does this mean that we can 'act upon' God? I suppose you could put it that way if you wanted. If you do, then we must interpret His 'impassibility' in a way which admits this; for we know that God forgives much better than we know what 'impassible' means. I would rather say that from before all worlds His providential and creative act (for they are all one) takes into account all the situations produced by the acts of His creatures. And if He takes our sins into account, why not our petitions?

10

I see your point. But you must admit that Scripture doesn't take the slight-est pains to guard the doctrine of Divine Impassibility. We are constantly represented as exciting the Divine wrath or pity – even as 'grieving' God. I know this language is analogical. But when we say that, we must not smug-gle in the idea that we can throw the analogy away and, as it were, get in behind it to a purely literal truth. All we can really substitute for the analog-ical expression is some theological abstraction. And the abstraction's value is almost entirely negative. It warns us against drawing absurd consequences from the analogical expression by prosaic extrapolations. By itself, the abstraction 'impassible' can get us nowhere. It might even suggest some-thing far more misleading than the most *naïf* Old Testament picture of a stormily emotional Jehovah. Either something inert, or something which was 'Pure Act' in such a sense that it could take no account of events within the universe it had created.

I suggest two rules for exegetics. (1) Never take the images literally. (2) When the *purport* of the images – what they say to our fear and hope and will and affections – seems to conflict with the theological abstractions, trust the purport of the images every time. For our abstract thinking is itself a tis-sue of analogies: a continual modelling of spiritual reality in legal or chemi-cal or mechanical terms. Are these likely to be more adequate than the sensuous, organic, and personal images of Scripture – light and darkness, river and well, seed and harvest, master and servant, hen and chickens, father and child? The footprints of the Divine are more visible in that rich soil than across rocks or slag-heaps. Hence what they now call 'de-mythologising' Christianity can easily be 're-mythologising' it – and substituting a poorer mythology for a richer.

I agree that my deliberately vague expression about our prayers being 'taken into account' is a retreat from Pascal's magnificent dictum ('God has instituted prayer so as to confer upon His creatures the dignity of being causes'). But Pascal really does suggest a far too explicit agent-and-patient relation, with God as the patient. And I have another ground for preferring my own more modest formula. To think of our prayers as just 'causes' would suggest that the whole importance of petitionary prayer lay in the achievement of the thing asked for. But really, for our spiritual life as a whole, the 'being taken into account', or 'considered', matters more than the being granted. Religious people don't talk about the 'results' of prayer; they talk of its being 'answered' or 'heard'. Someone said 'A suitor wants his suit to be heard as well as granted.' In suits to God, if they are really religious acts at all and not merely attempts at magic, this is even more so. We can bear to be refused but not to be ignored. In other words, our faith can survive many refusals if they really are refusals and not mere disregards. The apparent stone will be bread to us if we believe that a Father's hand put it into ours, in mercy or in justice or even in rebuke. It is hard and bitter; yet it can be chewed and swallowed. But if, having prayed for our heart's desire and got it, we then became convinced that this was a mere accident – that providential designs which had only some quite different end just couldn't help throwing out this satisfaction for us as a by-product – then the apparent bread would become a stone. A pretty stone, perhaps, or even a precious stone. But not edible to the soul.

What we must fight against is Pope's maxim:

the first Almighty Cause
Acts not by partial, but by general laws.

The odd thing is that Pope thought, and all who agree with him think, that this philosophical theology is an advance beyond the religion of the child and the savage (and the New Testament). It seems to them less *naïf* and anthropomorphic. The real difference, however, is that the anthropomorphism is more subtly hidden and of a far more disastrous type.

For the implication is that there exists on the Divine level a distinction with which we are very familiar on our own: that between the plan (or the main plan) and its unintended but unavoidable by-products. Whatever we do, even if it achieves its object, will also scatter round it a spray of consequences which were not its object at all. This is so even in private life. I throw out crumbs for the birds and provide, incidentally, a breakfast for the rats. Much more so in what may be called managerial life. The governing body of the college alters the time of dinner in hall; our object being to let the servants get home earlier. But by doing so we alter the daily pattern of life for every undergraduate. To some the new arrangement will be a convenience, to others the reverse. But we had no special favour for the first lot and no spite against the second. Our arrangement drags these unforeseen and undesired consequences after it. We can't help this.

On Pope's view God has to work in the same way. He has His grand design for the sum of things. Nothing we can say will deflect it. It leaves Him little freedom (or none?) for granting, or even for deliberately refusing, our prayers. The grand design churns out innumerable blessings and curses for individuals. God can't help that. They're all by-products.

I suggest that the distinction between plan and by-product must vanish entirely on the level of omniscience, omnipotence, and perfect goodness. I believe this because even on the human level it diminishes the higher you go. The better a human plan is made, the fewer unconsidered by-products it will have and the more birds it will kill with one stone, the more diverse needs and interests it will meet; the nearer it will come – it can never come very near – to being a plan for each individual. Bad laws make hard cases. But let us go beyond the managerial altogether. Surely a man of genius composing a poem or symphony must be less unlike God than a ruler? But the man of genius has no mere by-products in his work. Every note or word will be more than a means, more than a consequence. Nothing will be present *solely* for the sake of other things. If each note or word were conscious it would say: 'The maker had me myself in view and chose for me, with the whole force of his genius, exactly the context I required.' And it would be right – provided it remembered that every other note or word could say no less.

How should the true Creator work by 'general laws'? 'To generalise is to be an idiot,' said Blake. Perhaps he went too far. But to generalise is to be a finite mind. Generalities are the lenses with which our intellects have to manage. How should God sully the infinite lucidity of this vision with such makeshifts? One might as well think He had to consult books of reference, or that, if He ever considered me individually, He would begin by saying, 'Gabriel, bring me Mr Lewis's file.'

The God of the New Testament who takes into account the death of every sparrow is not more, but far less, anthropomorphic than Pope's.

I will not believe in the Managerial God and his general laws. If there is Providence at all, everything is providential and every providence is a special providence. It is an old and pious saying that Christ died not only for Man but for each man, just as much as if each had been the only man there was. Can I not believe the same of this creative act – which, as spread out in time, we call destiny or history? It is for the sake of each human soul. Each is an end. Perhaps for each beast. Perhaps even each particle of matter – the night sky suggests that the inanimate also has for God some value we cannot imagine. His ways are not (not there, anyway) like ours.

If you ask why I believe all this, I can only reply that we are taught, both by precept and example, to pray, and that prayer would be meaningless in the sort of universe Pope pictured. One of the purposes for which God instituted prayer may have been to bear witness that the course of events is not governed like a state but created like a work of art to which every being makes its contribution and (in prayer) a conscious contribution, and in which every being is both an end and a means. And since I have momentarily considered prayer itself as a means let me hasten to add that it is also an end. The world was made partly that there might be prayer; partly that our prayers for George might be answered. But let's have finished with 'partly'. The great work of art was made for the sake of all it does and is, down to the curve of every wave and the flight of every insect.

I I

I see you won't let me off. And the longer I look at it the less I shall like it.
I must face – or else explicitly decline – the difficulties that really torment
us when we cry for mercy in earnest. I have found no book that helps me
with them all. I have so little confidence in my own power to tackle them
that, if it were possible, I would let sleeping dogs lie. But the dogs are not
sleeping. They are awake and snapping. We both bear the marks of their
teeth. That being so, we had better share our bewilderments. By hiding them
from each other we should not hide them from ourselves.

The New Testament contains embarrassing promises that what we pray
for with faith we shall receive. Mark 11:24 is the most staggering. Whatever
we ask for, believing that we'll get it, we'll get. No question, it seems, of con-
fining it to spiritual gifts; *whatever* we ask for. No question of a merely general faith in God, but a belief that you will get the particular thing you ask.
No question of getting either it or else something that is really far better for
you; you'll get precisely it. And to heap paradox on paradox, the Greek
doesn't even say, 'believing that you *will* get it'. It uses the aorist, ἐλάβετε,
which one is tempted to translate 'believing that you *got* it'. But this final
difficulty I shall ignore. I don't expect Aramaic had anything which we –
brought up on Latin grammar – would recognise as tenses at all.

How is this astonishing promise to be reconciled – (a) With the observed
facts? (b) With the prayer in Gethsemane, and (as a result of that prayer) the
universally accepted view that we should ask everything with a reservation
('if it be Thy will')?

As regards (a), no evasion is possible. Every war, every famine or plague,
almost every death-bed, is the monument to a petition that was not granted.
At this very moment thousands of people in this one island are facing a *fait
accompli*, the very thing against which they have prayed night and day,
pouring out their whole soul in prayer, and, as they thought, with faith.
They have sought and not found. They have knocked and it has not been
opened. 'That which they greatly feared has come upon them.'

But (b), though much less often mentioned, is surely an equal difficulty. How is it possible at one and the same moment to have a perfect faith – an untroubled or unhesitating faith as St James says (1:6) – that you will get what you ask and yet also prepare yourself submissively in advance for a possible refusal? If you envisage a refusal as possible, how can you have simultaneously a perfect confidence that what you ask will not be refused? If you have that confidence, how can you take refusal into account at all?

It is easy to see why so much more is written about worship and contemplation than about 'crudely' or 'naïvely' petitionary prayer. They may be – I think they are – nobler forms of prayer. But they are also a good deal easier to write about.

As regards the first difficulty, I'm not asking why our petitions are so often refused. Anyone can see in general that this must be so. In our ignorance we ask what is not good for us or for others, or not even intrinsically possible. Or again, to grant one man's prayer involves refusing another's. There is much here which it is hard for our will to accept but nothing that is hard for our intellect to understand. The real problem is different; not why refusal is so frequent, but why the opposite result is so lavishly promised.

Shall we then proceed on Vidler's principles and scrap the embarrassing promises as 'venerable archaisms' which have to be 'outgrown'? Surely, even if there were no other objection, that method is too easy. If we are free to delete all inconvenient data we shall certainly have no theological difficulties; but for the same reason no solutions and no progress. The very writers of the 'Tekkies', not to mention the scientists, know better. The troublesome fact, the apparent absurdity which can't be fitted into any synthesis we have yet made, is precisely the one we must not ignore. Ten to one, it's in that covert the fox is lurking. There is always hope if we keep an unsolved problem fairly in view; there's none if we pretend it's not there.

Before going any further, I want to make two purely practical points: 1. These lavish promises are the worst possible place at which to begin Christian instruction in dealing with a child or a Pagan. You remember what happened when the Widow started Huck Finn off with the idea he could get what he wanted by praying for it. He tried the experiment and then, not unnaturally, never gave Christianity a second thought; we had better not talk about the view of prayer embodied in Mark 11:24 as 'naïf' or 'elementary'. If that passage contains a truth, it is a truth for very advanced pupils indeed. I don't think it is 'addressed to our condition' (yours and mine) at all. It is a coping-stone, not a foundation. For most of us the prayer in Gethsemane is the only model. Removing mountains can wait.

2. We must not encourage in ourselves or others any tendency to work up a subjective state which, if we succeeded, we should describe as 'faith', with the idea that this will somehow ensure the granting of our prayer. We have

probably all done this as children. But the state of mind which desperate desire working on a strong imagination can manufacture is not faith in the Christian sense. It is a feat of psychological gymnastics.

It seems to me we must conclude that such promises about prayer with faith refer to a degree or kind of faith which most believers never experience. A far inferior degree is, I hope, acceptable to God. Even the kind that says, 'Help thou my unbelief', may make way for a miracle. Again, the absence of such faith as ensures the granting of the prayer is not even necessarily a sin; for Our Lord had no such assurance when He prayed in Gethsemane.

How or why does such faith occur sometimes, but not always, even in the perfect petitioner? We, or I, can only guess. My own idea is that it occurs only when the one who prays does so as God's fellow-worker, demanding what is needed for the joint work. It is the prophet's, the apostle's, the missionary's, the healer's prayer that is made with this confidence and finds the confidence justified by the event. The difference, we are told, between a servant and a friend is that a servant is not in his master's secrets. For him, 'orders is orders'. He has only his own surmises as to the plans he helps to execute. But the fellow-worker, the companion or (dare we say?) the colleague of God is so united with Him at certain moments that something of the divine fore-knowledge enters his mind. Hence his faith is the 'evidence' – that is, the evidentness, the obviousness – of things not seen.

As the friend is above the servant, the servant is above the suitor, the man praying on his own behalf. It is no sin to be a suitor. Our Lord descends into the humiliation of being a suitor, or praying on His own behalf, in Gethsemane. But when He does so the certitude about His Father's will is apparently withdrawn.

After that it would be no true faith – it would be idle presumption – for us, who are habitually suitors and do not often rise to the level of servants, to imagine that we shall have any assurance which is not an illusion – or correct only by accident – about the events of our prayers. Our struggle is, isn't it? – to achieve and retain faith on a lower level. To believe that, whether He can grant them or not, God will listen to our prayers, will take them into account. Even to go on believing that there is a Listener at all. For as the situation grows more and more desperate, the grisly fears intrude. Are we only talking to ourselves in an empty universe? The silence is often so emphatic. And we have prayed so much already.

What do you think about these things? I have offered only guesses.

12

My experience is the same as yours. I have never met a book on prayer which was much use to people in our position. There are many little books *of* prayers, which may be helpful to those who share Rose Macaulay's approach, but you and I wouldn't know what to do with them. It's not words we lack! And there are books *on* prayer, but they nearly all have a strongly conventual background. Even the *Imitation* is sometimes, to an almost comic degree, 'not addressed to my condition'. The author assumes that you will want to be chatting in the kitchen when you ought to be in your cell. Our temptation is to be in our studies when we ought to be chatting in the kitchen. (Perhaps if our studies were as cold as those cells it would be different.)

You and I are people of the foothills. In the happy days when I was still a walker, I loved the hills, and even mountain walks, but I was no climber. I hadn't the head. So now, I do not attempt the precipices of mysticism. On the other hand, there is, apparently, a level of prayer-life lower even than ours. I don't mean that people who occupy it are spiritually lower than we. They may far excel us. But their praying is of an astonishingly underdeveloped type.

I have only just learned about it – from our Vicar. He assures me that, so far as he has been able to discover, the overwhelming majority of his parishioners mean by 'saying their prayers' repeating whatever little formula they were taught in childhood by their mothers. I wonder how this can come about. It can't be that they are never penitent or thankful – they're dear people, many of them – or have no needs. Is it that there is a sort of watertight bulk-head between their 'religion' and their 'real life', in which case the part of their life which they call 'religious' is really the irreligious part?

But however badly needed a good book on prayer is, I shall never try to write it. Two people on the foothills comparing notes in private are all very well. But in a book one would inevitably seem to be attempting, not discussion, but instruction. And for me to offer the world instruction about prayer would be impudence.

About the higher level – the crags up which the mystics vanish out of my sight – the glaciers and the *aiguilles* – I have only two things to say. One is that I don't think we are all 'called' to that ascent. 'If it were so, He would have told us.'

The second is this. The following position is gaining ground and is extremely plausible. Mystics (it is said) starting from the most diverse religious premises all find the same things. These things have singularly little to do with the professed doctrines of any particular religion – Christianity, Hinduism, Buddhism, Neo-Platonism, etc. Therefore, mysticism is, by empirical evidence, the only real contact Man has ever had with the unseen. The agreement of the explorers proves that they are all in touch with something objective. It is therefore the one true religion. And what we call the 'religions' are either mere delusions or, at best, so many porches through which an entrance into transcendent reality can be effected –

And when he hath the kernel eatn,
Who doth not throw away the shell?

I am doubtful about the premises. Did Plotinus and Lady Julian and St John of the Cross really find 'the same things'? But even admitting some similarity, one thing common to all mysticisms is the temporary shattering of our ordinary spatial and temporal consciousness and of our discursive intellect. The value of this negative experience must depend on the nature of that positive, whatever it is, for which it makes room. But should we not expect that the negative would always *feel* the same? If wine-glasses were conscious, I suppose that *being emptied* would be the same experience for each, even if some were to remain empty and some to be filled with wine and some broken. All who leave the land and put to the sea will 'find the same things' – the land sinking below the horizon, the gulls dropping behind, the salty breeze. Tourists, merchants, sailors, pirates, missionaries – it's all one. But this identical experience vouches for nothing about the utility or unlawfulness or final event of their voyages –

It may be that the gulfs will wash them down,
It may be they will touch the Happy Isles.

I do not at all regard mystical experience as an illusion. I think it shows that there is a way to go, before death, out of what may be called 'this world' – out of the stage set. Out of this; but into what? That's like asking an Englishman, 'Where does the sea lead to?' He will reply, 'To everywhere on earth, including Davy Jones's locker, except England.' The lawfulness, safety, and utility of the mystical voyage depends not at all on its being mystical – that is, on its being a departure – but on the motives, skill, and constancy of the voyager, and on the grace of God. The true religion gives value to its own mysticism; mysticism does not invalidate the religion in which it happens to occur.

I shouldn't be at all disturbed if it could be shown that a diabolical mysticism, or drugs, produced experiences indistinguishable (by introspection) from those of the great Christian mystics. Departures are all alike; it is the landfall that crowns the voyage. The saint, by being a saint, proves that his mysticism (if he was a mystic; not all saints are) led him aright; the fact that he has practised mysticism could never prove his sanctity.

You may wonder that my intense desire to peep behind the scenes has not led me to attempt the mystic way. But would it not be the worst of all possible motives? The saint may win 'a mortal glimpse of death's immortal rose', but it is a by-product. He took ship simply in humble and selfless love.

There can be a desire (like mine) with no carnal element in it at all which is nevertheless, in St Paul's sense, 'flesh' and not 'spirit'. That is, there can be a merely impulsive, headstrong, greedy desire even for spiritual things. It is, like our other appetites, 'cross-fodder'. Yet, being crucified, it can be raised from the dead, and made part of our bliss.

Turning now to quite a different point in your letter. I too had noticed that our prayers for others flow more easily than those we offer on our own behalf. And it would be nice to accept your view that this just shows we are made to live by charity. I'm afraid, however, I detect two much less attractive reasons for the ease of my own intercessory prayers. One is that I am often, I believe, praying for others when I should be doing things for them. It's so much easier to pray for a bore than to go and see him. And the other is like unto it. Suppose I pray that you may be given grace to withstand your besetting sin (a short-list of candidates for this post will be forwarded on demand). Well, all the work has to be done by God and you. If I pray against my own besetting sin there will be work for me. One sometimes fights shy of admitting an act to be a sin for this very reason.

The increasing list of people to be prayed for is, nevertheless, one of the burdens of old age. I have a scruple about crossing anyone off the list. When I say a scruple, I mean precisely a scruple. I don't really think that if one prays for a man at all it is a duty to pray for him all my life. But when it comes to dropping him *now*, this particular day, it somehow goes against the grain. And as the list lengthens, it is hard to make it more than a mere string of names. But here – in some measure – a curious law comes into play. Don't you find that, if you keep your mind fixed upon God, you will automatically think of the person you are praying for; but that there is no tendency for it to work the other way round?

13

I've just found in an old notebook a poem, with no author's name attached, which is rather relevant to something we were talking about a few weeks ago – I mean, the haunting fear that there is no one listening, and that what we call prayer is soliloquy: someone talking to himself. This writer takes the bull by the horns and says in effect: 'Very well, suppose it is,' and gets a surprising result. Here is the poem:

> They tell me, Lord that when I seem
>   To be in speech with you,
> Since but one voice is heard, it's all a dream,
>   One talker aping two.
>
> Sometimes it is, yet not as they
>   Conceive it. Rather, I
> Seek in myself the things I hoped to say,
>   But lo!, my wells are dry.
>
> Then, seeing me empty, you forsake
>   The listener's role and through
> My dumb lips breathe and into utterance wake
>   The thoughts I never knew.
>
> And thus you neither need reply
>   Nor can; thus, while we seem
> Two talkers, thou art One forever, and I
>   No dreamer, but thy dream.

Dream makes it too like Pantheism and was perhaps dragged in for the rhyme. But is he not right in thinking that prayer in its most perfect state is a soliloquy? If the Holy Spirit speaks in the man, then in prayer God speaks to God. But the human petitioner does not therefore become a 'dream'. As you said the other day, God and man cannot exclude one another, as man excludes man, at the point of junction, so to call it, between Creator and creature; the point where the mystery of creation – timeless for God, and incessant in time for us – is actually taking place. 'God did (or said) it' and 'I did (or said) it' can both be true.

You remember the two maxims Owen [Barfield] lays down in *Saving the Appearances*? On the one hand, the man who does not regard God as other than himself cannot be said to have a religion at all. On the other hand, if I think God other than myself in the same way in which my fellow-men, and objects in general, are other than myself, I am beginning to make Him an idol. I am daring to treat His existence as somehow *parallel* to my own. But He is the ground of our being. He is always both within us and over against us. Our reality is so much from His reality as He, moment by moment, projects into us. The deeper the level within ourselves from which our prayer, or any other act, wells up, the more it is His, but not at all the less ours. Rather, most ours when most His. Arnold speaks of us as 'enisled' from one another in 'the sea of life'. But we can't be similarly 'enisled' from God. To be discontinuous from God as I am discontinuous from you would be annihilation.

A question at once arises. Is it still God speaking when a liar or a blasphemer speaks? In one sense, almost Yes. Apart from God he could not speak at all; there are no words not derived from the Word; no acts not derived from Him who is *Actus purus*. And indeed the only way in which I can make real to myself what theology teaches about the heinousness of sin is to remember that every sin is the distortion of an energy breathed into us – an energy which, if not thus distorted, would have blossomed into one of those holy acts whereof 'God did it' and 'I did it' are both true descriptions. We poison the wine as He decants it into us; murder a melody He would play with us as the instrument. We caricature the self-portrait He would paint. Hence all sin, whatever else it is, is sacrilege.

We must, no doubt, distinguish the ontological continuity between Creator and creature which is, so to speak, 'given' by the relation between them, from the union of wills which, under Grace, is reached by a life of sanctity. The ontological continuity is, I take it, unchangeable, and exists between God and a reprobate (or a devil) no less than between God and a saint. 'Whither shall I go then from thy presence? If I go down to hell, thou art there also.'

Where there is prayer at all we may suppose that there is some effort, however feeble, towards the second condition, the union of wills. What God labours to do or say through the man comes back to God with a distortion which at any rate is not total.

Do you object to the apparent 'roundaboutness' – it could easily be made comic – of the whole picture? Why should God speak to Himself through man? I ask, in reply, why should He do anything through His creatures? Why should He achieve, the long way round, through the labours of angels, men (always imperfectly obedient and efficient), and the activity of irrational and inanimate beings, ends which, presumably, the mere *fiat* of omnipotence would achieve with instantaneous perfection?

Creation seems to be delegation through and through. He will do nothing simply of Himself which can be done by creatures. I suppose this is because He is a giver. And He has nothing to give but Himself. And to give Himself is to do His deeds – in a sense, and on varying levels to be Himself – through the things He has made.

In Pantheism God is all. But the whole point of creation surely is that He was not content to be all. He intends to be 'all *in all*'.

One must be careful not to put this in a way which would blur the distinction between the creation of a man and the Incarnation of God. Could one, as a mere model, put it thus? In creation God makes – invents – a person and 'utters' – injects – him into the realm of Nature. In the Incarnation, God the Son takes the body and human soul of Jesus, and, through that, the whole environment of Nature, all the creaturely predicament, into His own being. So that 'He came down from Heaven' can almost be transposed into 'Heaven drew earth up into it', and locality, limitation, sleep, sweat, footsore weariness, frustration, pain, doubt and death, are, from before all worlds, known by God from within. The pure light walks the earth; the darkness, received into the heart of Deity, is there swallowed up. Where, except in uncreated light, can the darkness be drowned?

14

I won't admit without a struggle that when I speak of God 'uttering' or 'inventing' the creatures I am 'watering down the concept of creation'. I am trying to give it, by remote analogies, some sort of content. I know that to create is defined as 'to make out of nothing', *ex nihilo*. But I take that to mean '*not* out of any pre-existing material'. It can't mean that God makes what God has not thought of, or that He gives His creatures any powers or beauties that He Himself does not possess. Why, we think that even human work comes nearest to creation when the maker has 'got it all out of his own head'.

Nor am I suggesting a theory of 'emanations'. The differentia of an 'emanation' – literally an overflowing, a trickling out – would be that it suggests something involuntary. But my words – 'uttering' and 'inventing' – are meant to suggest an act.

This act, as it is for God, must always remain totally inconceivable to man. For we – even our poets and musicians and inventors – never, in the ultimate sense, *make*. We only build. We always have materials to build from. All we can know about the act of creation must be derived from what we can gather about the relation of the creatures to their Creator.

Now the very Pagans knew that any beggar at your door might be a god in disguise: and the parable of the sheep and the goats is Our Lord's comment. What you do, or don't do, to the beggar, you do, or don't do, to Him. Taken at the Pantheist extreme, this could mean that men are only appearances of God – dramatic representations, as it were. Taken at the Legalist extreme, it could mean that God, by a sort of Legal fiction, will 'deem' your kindness to the beggar a kindness done to Himself. Or again, as Our Lord's own words suggest, that since the least of men are His 'brethren', the whole action is, so to speak, 'within the family'. And in what sense brethren? Biologically, because Jesus is Man? Ontologically, because the light lightens them all? Or simply 'loved like brethren'. (It cannot refer only to the regenerate.) I would ask first whether any one of these formulations is 'right' in a sense which makes the others simply wrong? It seems to me improbable. If I ever see more clearly I will speak more surely.

Meanwhile, I stick to Owen's view. All creatures, from the angel to the atom, are other than God; with an otherness to which there is no parallel: incommensurable. The very word 'to be' cannot be applied to Him and to them in exactly the same sense. But also, no creature is other than He in the same way in which it is other than all the rest. He is in it as they can never be in one another. In each of them as the ground and root and continual supply of its reality. And also in good rational creatures as light; in bad ones as fire, as at first the smouldering unease, and later the flaming anguish, of an unwelcome and vainly resisted presence.

Therefore of each creature we can say, 'This also is Thou: neither is this Thou.'

Simple faith leaps to this with astonishing ease. I once talked to a Continental pastor who had seen Hitler, and had, by all human standards, good cause to hate him. 'What did he look like?' I asked. 'Like all men,' he replied, 'that is, like Christ.'

One is always fighting on at least two fronts. When one is among Pantheists one must emphasise the distinctness, and relative independence, of the creatures. Among Deists – or perhaps in Woolwich, if the laity there really think God is to be sought in the sky – one must emphasise the divine presence in my neighbour, my dog, my cabbage-patch.

It is much wiser, I believe, to think of that presence in particular objects than just of 'omnipresence'. The latter gives very *naïf* people (Woolwich again, perhaps?) the idea of something spatially extended, like a gas. It also blurs the distinctions, the truth that God is present in each thing but not necessarily in the same mode; not in a man as in the consecrated bread and wine, nor in a bad man as in a good one, nor in a beast as in a man, nor in a tree as in a beast, nor in inanimate matter as in a tree. I take it there is a paradox here. The higher the creature, the more and also the less God is in it; the more present by grace, and the less present (by a sort of abdication) as mere power. By grace He gives the higher creatures power to will His will ('and wield their little tridents'): the lower ones simply execute it automatically.

It is well to have specifically holy places, and things, and days, for, without these focal points or reminders, the belief that all is holy and 'big with God' will soon dwindle into a mere sentiment. But if these holy places, things, and days cease to remind us, if they obliterate our awareness that all ground is holy and every bush (could we but perceive it) a Burning Bush, then the hallows begin to do harm. Hence both the necessity, and the perennial danger, of 'religion'.

Boehme advises us once an hour 'to fling ourselves beyond every creature'. But in order to find God it is perhaps not always necessary to leave the creatures behind. We may ignore, but we can nowhere evade, the presence of God. The world is crowded with Him. He walks everywhere *incognito*. And the *incognito* is not always hard to penetrate. The real labour is to remember, to attend. In fact, to come awake. Still more, to remain awake.

Oddly enough, what corroborates me in this faith is the fact, otherwise so infinitely deplorable, that the awareness of this presence has so often been unwelcome. I call upon Him in prayer. Often He might reply – I think He does reply – 'But you have been evading me for hours.' For He comes not only to raise up but to cast down; to deny, to rebuke, to interrupt. The prayer 'prevent us in all our doings' is often answered as if the word *prevent* had its modern meaning. The presence which we voluntarily evade is often, and we know it, His presence in wrath.

And out of this evil comes a good. If I never fled from His presence, then I should suspect those moments when I seemed to delight in it of being wish-fulfilment dreams. That, by the way, explains the feebleness of all those watered versions of Christianity which leave out all the darker elements and try to establish a religion of pure consolation. No real belief in the watered versions can last. Bemused and besotted as we are, we still dimly know at heart that nothing which is at all times and in every way agreeable to us can have objective reality. It is of the very nature of the real that it should have sharp corners and rough edges, that it should be resistant, should be itself. Dream-furniture is the only kind on which you never stub your toes or bang your knee. You and I have both known happy marriage. But how different our wives were from the imaginary mistresses of our adolescent dreams! So much less exquisitely adapted to all our wishes; and for that very reason (among others) so incomparably better.

Servile fear is, to be sure, the lowest form of religion. But a god such that there could never be occasion for even servile fear, a *safe* god, a tame god, soon proclaims himself to any sound mind as a fantasy. I have met no people who fully disbelieved in Hell and also had a living and life-giving belief in Heaven.

There is, I know, a belief in both, which is of no religious significance. It makes these spiritual things, or some travesty of them, objects of purely carnal, prudential, self-centred fear and hope. The deeper levels, those things which only immortal spirit can desire or dread, are not concerned at all. Such belief is fortunately very brittle. The old divines exhausted their eloquence especially in arousing such fear: but, as they themselves rather naïvely complain, the effect did not last for more than a few hours after the sermon.

The soul that has once been waked, or stung, or uplifted by the desire of God, will inevitably (I think) awake to the fear of losing Him.

15

I hadn't realised that Betty was the silent third in this dialogue. I ought to have guessed it. Not that her worst enemy ever accused her of being The Silent Woman – remember the night at Mullingar – but that her silences during a prolonged argument between you and me are usually of a very emphatic, audible, and even dialectical character. One knows she is getting her broom ready and will soon sweep up all our breakages. On the present point she is right. I *am* making very heavy weather of what most believers find a very simple matter. What is more natural, and easier, if you believe in God, than to address Him? How could one not?

Yes. But it depends who one is. For those in my position – adult converts from the *intelligentsia* – that simplicity and spontaneity can't always be the starting point. One can't just jump back into one's childhood. If one tries to, the result will only be an archaising revival, like Victorian Gothic – a parody of being born again. We have to work back to the simplicity a long way round.

In actual practice, in my prayers, I often have to use that long way at the very beginning of the prayer.

St François de Sales begins every meditation with the command: *Mettez-vous en la présence de Dieu.* I wonder how many different mental operations have been carried out in intended obedience to that?

What happens to me if I try to take it – as Betty would tell me – 'simply', is the juxtaposition of two 'representations' or ideas or phantoms. One is the bright blur in the mind which stands for God. The other is the ideal I call 'me'. But I can't leave it at that, because I know – and it's useless to pretend I don't know – that they are both phantasmal. The real I has created them both – or, rather, built them up in the vaguest way from all sorts of psychological odds and ends.

Very often, paradoxically, the first step is to banish the 'bright blur' – or, in statelier language, to break the idol. Let's get back to what has at least some degree of resistant reality. Here are the four walls of the room. And here am I. But both terms are merely the façade of impenetrable mysteries.

The walls, they say, are matter. That is, as the physicists will try to tell me, something totally unimaginable, only mathematically describable, existing in a curved space, charged with appalling energies. If I could penetrate far enough into that mystery I should perhaps finally reach what is sheerly real.

And what am I? The façade is what I call consciousness. I am at least conscious of the colour of those walls. I am not, in the same way, or to the same degree, conscious of what I call my thoughts: for if I try to examine what happens when I am thinking, it would, I well know, turn out to be the thinnest possible film on the surface of a vast deep. The psychologists have taught us that. Their real error lies in underestimating the depth and the variety of its contents. Dazzling lightness as well as dark clouds come up. And if all the enchanting visions are, as they rashly claim, mere disguises for sex, where lives the hidden artist who, from such monotonous and claustrophobic material, can make works of such various and liberating art? And depths of time too. All my past; my ancestral past; perhaps my pre-human past.

Here again, if I could dive deeply enough, I might again reach at the bottom that which simply is.

And only now am I ready, in my own fashion, to 'place myself in the presence of God'. Either mystery, if I could follow it far enough, would lead me to the same point – the point where something, in each case unimaginable, leaps forth from God's naked hand. The Indian, looking at the material world, says 'I am that'. I say, 'That and I grow from one root.' *Verbum supernum prodiens*, the Word coming forth from the Father, has made both, and brought them together in this subject-object embrace.

And what, you ask, is the advantage of all this? Well, for me – I am not talking about anyone else – it plants the prayer right in the present reality. For, whatever else is or is not real, this momentary confrontation of subject and object is certainly occurring: always occurring except when I am asleep. Here is the actual meeting of God's activity and man's – not some imaginary meeting that might occur if I were an angel or if God incarnate entered the room. There is here no question of a God 'up there' or 'out there'; rather, the present operation of God 'in here', as the ground of my own being, and God 'in there', as the ground of the matter that surrounds me, and God embracing and uniting both in the daily miracle of finite consciousness.

The two façades – the 'I' as I perceive myself and the room as I perceive it – were obstacles as long as I mistook them for ultimate realities. But the moment I recognised them as façades, as mere surfaces, they became conductors. Do you see? A lie is a delusion only so long as we believe it; but a recognised lie is a reality – a real lie – and as such may be highly instructive. A dream ceases to be a delusion as soon as we wake. But it does not become a nonentity. It is a real dream: and it also may be instructive. A stage set is not a real wood or drawing room: it is a real stage set, and may be a good one. (In fact we should never ask of anything 'Is it real?', for everything is real. The proper question is 'A real *what*?' – e.g. a real snake or a real *delirium tremens*?) The objects around me, and my idea of 'me', will deceive if taken at their face value. But they are momentous if taken as the end-products of divine activities. Thus and not otherwise, the creation of matter and the creation of mind meet one another and the circuit is closed.

Or put it this way. I have called my material surroundings a stage set. A stage set is not a dream nor a nonentity. But if you attack a stage house with a chisel you will not get chips of brick or stone; you'll only get a hole in a piece of canvas and, beyond that, windy darkness. Similarly, if you start investigating the nature of matter, you will not find anything like what imagination has always supposed matter to be. You will get mathematics. From that unimaginable physical reality my senses select a few stimuli. These they translate or symbolise into sensations, which have no likeness at all to the reality of matter. Of these sensations my associative power, very much directed by my practical needs and influenced by social training, makes up little bundles into what I call 'things' (labelled by nouns). Out of these I build myself a neat little box stage, suitably provided with properties such as hills, fields, houses, and the rest. In this I can act.

And you may well say 'act'. For what I call 'myself' (for all practical, everyday purposes) is also a dramatic construction; memories, glimpses in the shaving-glass, and snatches of the very fallible activity called 'introspection', are the principal ingredients. Normally I call this construction 'me', and the stage set 'the real world'.

Now the moment of prayer is for me – or involves for me as its condition – the awareness, the reawakened awareness, that this 'real world' and 'real self' are very far from being rock-bottom realities. I cannot, in the flesh, leave the stage, either to go behind the scenes or to take my seat in the pit; but I can remember that these regions exist. And I also remember that my apparent self – this clown or hero or super – under his grease-paint is a real person with an off-stage life. The dramatic person could not tread the stage unless he concealed a real person: unless the real and unknown I existed, I would not even make mistakes about the imagined me. And in prayer this real I struggles to speak, for once, from his real being, and to address, for once, not the other actors, but – what shall I call Him? The Author, for He invented us all? The Producer, for He controls all? Or the Audience, for He watches, and will judge, the performance?

The attempt is not to escape from space and time and from my creaturely situation as a subject facing objects. It is more modest: to reawake the awareness of that situation. If that can be done, there is no need to go anywhere else. This situation itself, is, at every moment, a possible theophany. Here is the holy ground; the Bush is burning now.

Of course this attempt may be attended with almost every degree of success or failure. The prayer preceding all prayers is, 'May it be the real I who speaks. May it be the real Thou that I speak to.' Infinitely various are the levels from which we pray. Emotional intensity is in itself no proof of spiritual depth. If we pray in terror we shall pray earnestly; it only proves that terror is an earnest emotion. Only God Himself can let the bucket down to the depths in us. And, on the other side, He must constantly work as the iconoclast. Every idea of Him we form, He must in mercy shatter. The most blessed result of prayer would be to rise thinking, 'But I never knew before. I never dreamed...' I suppose it was at such a moment that Thomas Aquinas said of all his own theology: 'It reminds me of straw.'

16

I didn't mean that a 'bright blur' is my only idea of God. I meant that something of that sort tends to be there when I start praying, and would remain if I made no effort to do better. And 'bright blur' is not a very good description. In fact you can't have a good description of anything so vague. If the description became good it would become false.

Betty's recipe – 'use images as the rest of us do' – doesn't help me much. And which does she mean? Images in the outer world, things made of wood or plaster? Or mental images?

As regards the first kind, I am not, as she suggests, suffering from a phobia about 'idolatry'. I don't think people of our type are in danger of that. We shall always be aware that the image is only a bit of matter. But its use, for me, is very limited. I think the mere fact of keeping one's eyes focused on something – almost any object will do – is some help towards concentration. The visual concentration symbolises, and promotes, the mental. That's one of the ways the body teaches the soul. The lines of a well designed church, free from stunts, drawing one's eyes to the altar, have something of the same effect.

But I think that is all an image does for me. If I tried to get more out of it, I think it would get in the way. For one thing, it will have some artistic merits or (more probably) demerits. Both are a distraction. Again, since there can be no plausible images of the Father or the Spirit, it will usually be an image of Our Lord. The continual and exclusive addressing our prayers to Him surely tends to what has been called 'Jesus-worship'? A religion which has its value; but not, in isolation, the religion Jesus taught.

Mental images may have the same defect, but they give rise to another problem as well.

St Ignatius Loyola (I think it was) advised his pupils to begin their meditations with what he called a *compositio loci*. The Nativity or the Marriage at Cana, or whatever the theme might be, was to be visualised in the fullest possible detail. One of his English followers would even have us look up 'what good Authors write of those places' so as to get the topography, 'the height of the hills and the situation of the townes', correct. Now for two different reasons this is not 'addressed to my condition'.

One is that I live in an archaeological age. We can no longer, as St Ignatius could, believingly introduce the clothes, furniture, and utensils of our age into ancient Palestine. I'd know I wasn't getting them right. I'd know that the very sky and sunlight of those latitudes were different from any my northern imagination could supply. I could no doubt pretend to myself a *naïveté* I don't really possess; but that would cast an unreality over the whole exercise.

The second reason is more important. St Ignatius was a great master, and I am sure he knew what his pupils needed. I conclude that they were people whose visual imagination was weak and needed to be stimulated. But the trouble with people like ourselves is the exact reverse. We can say this to one another because, in our mouths, it is not a boast but a confession. We are agreed that the power – indeed, the compulsion – to visualise is not 'Imagination' in the higher sense, not the Imagination which makes a man either a great author or a sensitive reader. Ridden on a *very* tight rein, this visualising power can sometimes serve true Imagination; very often it merely gets in the way.

If I started with a *compositio loci* I should never reach the meditation. The picture would go on elaborating itself indefinitely and becoming every moment of less spiritual relevance.

There is indeed one mental image which does not lure me away into trivial elaborations. I mean the Crucifixion itself; not seen in terms of all the pictures and crucifixes, but as we must suppose it to have been in its raw, historical reality. But even this is of less spiritual value than one might expect. Compunction, compassion, gratitude – all the fruitful emotions – are strangled. Sheer physical horror leaves no room for them. Nightmare. Even so, the image ought to be periodically faced. But no one could live with it. It did not become a frequent motif of Christian art until the generations which had seen real crucifixions were all dead. As for many hymns and sermons on the subject – endlessly harping on blood, as if that were all that mattered – they must be the work either of people so far above me that they can't reach me, or else of people with no imagination at all. (Some might be cut off from me by both these gulfs.)

Yet mental images play an important part in my prayers. I doubt if any act of will or thought or emotion occurs in me without them. But they seem to help me most when they are most fugitive and fragmentary – rising and bursting like bubbles in champagne or wheeling like rooks in a windy sky: contradicting one another (in logic) as the crowded metaphors of a swift poet may do. Fix on any one, and it goes dead. You must do as Blake would do with a joy; kiss it as it flies. And then, in their total effect, they do mediate to me something very important. It is always something qualitative – more like an adjective than a noun. That, for me, gives it the impact of reality. For I think we respect nouns (and what we think they stand for) too much. All my deepest, and certainly all my earliest, experiences seem to be of sheer quality. The terrible and the lovely are older and solider than terrible and lovely things. If a musical phrase could be translated into words at all it would become an adjective. A great lyric is very like a long, utterly adequate, adjective. Plato was not so silly as the Moderns think when he elevated abstract nouns – that is, adjectives disguised as nouns – into the supreme realities – the Forms.

I know very well that in logic God is a 'substance'. Yet my thirst for quality is authorised even here: 'We give thanks to thee for thy great glory.' He *is* this glory. What He is (the quality) is no abstraction from Him. A personal God, to be sure; but so much more than personal. To speak more soberly, our whole distinction between 'things' and 'qualities', 'substances' and 'attitudes', has no application to Him. Perhaps it has much less than we suppose even to the created universe. Perhaps it is only part of the stage set.

The wave of images, thrown off like a spray from the prayer, all momentary, all correcting, refining, 'inter-animating' one another, and giving a kind of spiritual body to the unimaginable, occurs more, I find, in acts of worship than in petitionary prayers. Of which, perhaps, we have written enough. But I don't regret it. They are the right starting point. They raise all the problems. If anyone attempted to practise, or to discuss, the higher forms without going through this turnstile, I should distrust him. 'The higher does not stand without the lower.' An omission or disdain of petitionary prayer can sometimes, I think, spring not from superior sanctity but from a lack of faith and a consequent preference for levels where the question: 'Am I only doing things to myself?' does not jut out in such apparent crudity.

17

It's comical that you, of all people, should ask my views about prayer as worship or adoration. On this subject you yourself taught me nearly all I know. On a walk in the Forest of Dean. Can you have forgotten?

You first taught me the great principle, 'Begin where you are.' I had thought one had to start by summoning up what we believe about the goodness and greatness of God, by thinking about creation and redemption and 'all the blessings of this life'. You turned to the brook and once more splashed your burning face and hands in the little waterfall and said: 'Why not begin with this?'

And it worked. Apparently you have never guessed how much. That cushiony moss, that coldness and sound and dancing light were no doubt very minor blessings compared with 'the means of grace and the hope of glory'. But then they were manifest. So far as they were concerned, sight had replaced faith. They were not the hope of glory, they were an exposition of the glory itself.

Yet you were not – or so it seemed to me – telling me that 'Nature', or 'the beauties of Nature', manifest the glory. No such abstraction as 'Nature' comes into it. I was learning the far more secret doctrine that *pleasures* are shafts of the glory as it strikes our sensibility. As it impinges on our will or our understanding, we give it different names – goodness or truth or the like. But its flash upon our senses and mood is pleasure.

But aren't there bad, unlawful pleasures? Certainly there are. But in calling them 'bad pleasures' I take it we are using a kind of shorthand. We mean 'pleasures snatched by unlawful acts'. It is the stealing of the apple that is bad, not the sweetness. The sweetness is still a beam from the glory. That does not palliate the stealing. It makes it worse. There is sacrilege in the theft. We have abused a holy thing.

I have tried, since that moment, to make every pleasure into a channel of adoration. I don't mean simply by giving thanks for it. One must of course give thanks, but I mean something different. How shall I put it?

We can't – or I can't – hear the song of a bird simply as a sound. Its meaning or message ('That's a bird') comes with it inevitably – just as one can't see a familiar word in print as a merely visual pattern. The reading is as involuntary as the seeing. When the wind roars I don't just hear the roar; I 'hear the wind'. In the same way it is possible to 'read' as well as to 'have' a pleasure. Or not even 'as well as'. The distinction ought to become, and sometimes is, impossible; to receive it and to recognise its divine source are a single experience. This heavenly fruit is instantly redolent of the orchard where it grew. This sweet air whispers of the country from whence it blows. It is a message. We know we are being touched by a finger of that right hand at which there are pleasures for evermore. There need be no question of thanks or praise as a separate event, something done afterwards. To experience the tiny theophany is itself to adore.

Gratitude exclaims, very properly: 'How good of God to give me this.' Adoration says: 'What must be the quality of that Being whose far-off and momentary coruscations are like this!' One's mind runs back up the sunbeam to the sun.

If I could always be what I aim at being, no pleasure would be too ordinary or too usual for such reception; from the first taste of the air when I look out of the window – one's whole cheek becomes a sort of palate – down to one's soft slippers at bedtime.

I don't always achieve it. One obstacle is inattention. Another is the wrong kind of attention. One could, if one practised, hear simply a roar and not the roaring-of-the-wind. In the same way, only far too easily, one can concentrate on the pleasure as an event in one's own nervous system – subjectify it – and ignore the smell of Deity that hangs about it. A third obstacle is greed. Instead of saying: 'This also is Thou', one may say the fatal word *Encore*. There is also conceit: the dangerous reflection that not everyone can find God in a plain slice of bread and butter, or that others would condemn as simply 'grey' the sky in which I am delightedly observing such delicacies of pearl and dove and silver.

You notice that I am drawing no distinction between sensuous and aesthetic pleasures. But why should I? The line is almost impossible to draw and what use would it be if one succeeded in drawing it?

If this is Hedonism, it is also a somewhat arduous discipline. But it is worth some labour: for in so far as it succeeds, almost every day furnishes us with, so to speak, 'bearings' on the Bright Blur. It becomes brighter but less blurry.

William Law remarks that people are merely 'amusing themselves by asking for the patience which a famine or a persecution would call for if, in the meantime, the weather and every other inconvenience sets them grumbling. One must learn to walk before one can run. So here. We – or at least I – shall not be able to adore God on the highest occasions if we have learned no habit of doing so on the lowest. At best, our faith and reason will tell us that He is adorable, but we shall not have *found* Him so, not have 'tasted and seen'. Any patch of sunlight in a wood will show you something about the sun which you could never get from reading books on astronomy. These pure and spontaneous pleasures are 'patches of Godlight' in the woods of our experience.

Of course one wants the books too. One wants a great many things besides this 'adoration in infinitesimals' which I am preaching. And if I were preaching it in public, instead of feeding it back to the very man who taught it me (though he may by now find the lesson nearly unrecognisable?), I should have to pack it in ice, enclose it in barbed-wire reservations, and stick up warning notices in every direction.

Don't imagine I am forgetting that the simplest act of mere obedience is worship of a far more important sort than what I've been describing (to obey is better than sacrifice). Or that God, besides being the Great Creator, is the Tragic Redeemer. Perhaps the Tragic Creator too. For I am not sure that the great canyon of anguish which lies across our lives is *solely* due to some prehistoric catastrophe. Something tragic may, as I think I've said before, be inherent in the very act of creation. So that one sometimes wonders why God thinks the game worth the candle. But then we share, in some degree, the cost of the candle and have not yet seen the 'game'.

There! I've done it again. I know that my tendency to use images like play and dance for the highest things is a stumbling-block to you. You don't, I admit, accuse me of profanity, as you used to – like the night we nearly came to blows at Edinburgh. You now, much more reasonably, call it 'heartless'. You feel it a brutal mockery of every martyr and every slave that a world-process which is so desperately serious to the actors should, at whatever celestial apex, be seen in terms of frivolities. And you add that it comes with a ludicrously ill grace from me who never enjoyed any game and can dance no better than a centipede with wooden legs. But I still think you don't see the real point.

I do *not* think that the life of Heaven bears any analogy to play or dance in respect of frivolity. I do think that while we are in this 'valley of tears', cursed with labour, hemmed round with necessities, tripped up with frustrations, doomed to perpetual plannings, puzzlings, and anxieties, certain qualities that must belong to the celestial condition have no chance to get through, can project no image of themselves, except in activities which, for us here and now, are frivolous. For surely we must suppose the life of the blessed to be an end in itself, indeed The End: to be utterly spontaneous; to be the complete reconciliation of boundless freedom with order – with the most delicately adjusted, supple, intricate, and beautiful order? How can you find any image of this in the 'serious' activities either of our natural or of our (present) spiritual life? – either in our precarious and heart-broken affections or in the Way which is always, in some degree, a *via crucis*: No, Malcolm. It is only in our 'hours-off', only in our moments of permitted festivity, that we find an analogy. Dance and game *are* frivolous, unimportant down here; for 'down here' is not their natural place. Here, they are a moment's rest from the life we were placed here to live. But in this world everything is upside down. That which, if it could be prolonged here, would be a truancy, is likest that which in a better country is the End of ends. Joy is the serious business of Heaven.

18

I plead guilty. When I was writing about pleasures last week I had quite forgotten about the *mala mentis gaudia* – the pleasures of the mind which are intrinsically evil. The pleasure, say, of having a grievance. What a disappointment it is – for one self-revealing moment – to discover that the other party was not really to blame? And how a resentment, while it lasts, draws one back and back to nurse and fondle and encourage it! It behaves just like a lust. But I don't think this leaves my theory (and experience) of ordinary pleasures in ruins. Aren't these intrinsically vicious pleasures, as Plato said, 'mixed'. To use his own image, given the itch, one wants to scratch it. And if you abstain, the temptation is very severe, and if you scratch there is a sort of pleasure in the momentary and deceptive relief. But one didn't want to itch. The scratch is not a pleasure simply, but only by comparison with the context. In the same way, resentment is pleasant only as a relief from, or alternative to, humiliation. I still think that those experiences which are pleasures in their own right can all be regarded as I suggest.

The mere mention of the horrible pleasures – the dainties of Hell – very naturally led you away from the subject of adoration to that of repentance. I'm going to follow you into your digression, for you said something I disagreed with.

I admit of course that penitential prayers – 'acts' of penitence, as I believe they are called – can be on very different levels. At the lowest, what you call 'Pagan penitence', there is simply the attempt to placate a supposedly angry power – 'I'm sorry. I won't do it again. Let me off this time.' At the highest level, you say, the attempt is rather to restore an infinitely valued and vulnerable personal relation which has been shattered by an action of one's own, and if forgiveness, in the 'crude' sense of remission of penalty, comes in, this is valued chiefly as a symptom or seal or even by-product of the reconciliation. I expect you are right about that. I say 'expect' because I can't claim to know much by experience about the highest level either of penitence or of anything else. The ceiling, if there is one, is a long way off.

All the same, there is a difference between us. I can't agree to call your lowest level 'Pagan penitence'. Doesn't your description cover a great deal of Old Testament penitence? Look at the psalms. Doesn't it cover a good deal of Christian penitence – a good deal that is embodied in Christian liturgies? 'Neither take thou vengeance for our sins . . . be not angry with us forever . . . *neque secundum iniquitates nostras retribuas nobis.*'

Here, as nearly always, what we regard as 'crude' and 'low', and what presumably is in fact lowest, spreads far further up the Christian life than we like to admit. And do we find anywhere in Scripture or in the Fathers that explicit and resounding rejection of it which would be so welcome?

I fully grant you that 'wrath' can be attributed to God only by an analogy. The situation of the penitent before God isn't, but is somehow like, that of one appearing before a justly angered sovereign, lover, father, master, or teacher. But what more can we know about it than just this likeness? Trying to get in behind the analogy, you go further and fare worse. You suggest that what is traditionally regarded as our experience of God's anger would be more helpfully regarded as what inevitably happens to us if we behave inappropriately towards a reality of immense power. As you say, 'The live wire doesn't feel angry with us, but if we blunder against it we get a shock.'

My dear Malcolm, what do you suppose you have gained by substituting the image of a live wire for that of angered majesty? You have shut us all up in despair; for the angry can forgive, and electricity can't.

And you give as your reason that 'even by analogy the sort of pardon which arises because a fit of temper is spent cannot worthily be attributed to God nor gratefully accepted by man.' But the belittling words 'fit of temper' are your own choice. Think of the fullest reconciliation between mortals. Is cool disapproval coolly assuaged? Is the culprit let down lightly in a view of 'extenuating circumstances'? Was peace restored by a moral lecture? Was the offence said not to 'matter'? Was it hushed up or passed over? Blake knew better:

I was angry with my friend;
I told my wrath. My wrath did end.
I was angry with my foe;
I hid my wrath. My wrath did grow.

You too know better. Anger – no peevish fit of temper, but just, generous, scalding indignation – passes (not necessarily at once) into embracing, exultant, re-welcoming love. That is how friends and lovers are truly reconciled. Hot wrath, hot love. Such anger is the fluid that love bleeds when you cut it. The *angers*, not the measured remonstrances, of lovers are love's renewal. Wrath and pardon are both, as applied to God, analogies; but they belong together to the same circle of analogy – the circle of life, and love, and deeply personal relationships. All the liberalising and 'civilising' analogies only lead us astray. Turn God's wrath into mere enlightened disapproval, and you also turn His love into mere humanitarianism. The 'consuming fire' and the 'perfect beauty' both vanish. We have, instead, a judicious headmistress or a conscientious magistrate. It comes of being high-minded.

I know that 'the wrath of man worketh not the righteousness of God'. That is not because wrath is wrath but because man is (fallen) man.

But perhaps I've already said too much. All that any imagery can do is to facilitate, or at least not to impede, man's act of penitence and reception of pardon. We cannot see the matter 'from God's side'.

The crude picture of penitence as something like apology or even placation has, for me, the value of making penitence an act. The more high-minded views involve some danger of regarding it simply as a state of feeling. Do you agree that this would be unwholesome?

The question is before my mind at present because I've been reading Alexander Whyte. Morris lent him to me. He was a Presbyterian divine of the last century, whom I'd never heard of. Very well worth reading, and strangely broad-minded – Dante, Pascal, and even Newman, are among his heroes. But I mention him at the moment for a different reason. He brought me violently face to face with a characteristic of Puritanism which I had almost forgotten. For him, one essential symptom of the regenerate life is a permanent, and permanently horrified, perception of one's natural and (it seems) unalterable corruption. The true Christian's nostril is to be continually attentive to the inner cess-pool. I knew that the experience was a regular feature of the old conversion stories. As in *Grace Abounding*: 'But my inward and original corruption ... that I had the guilt of to amazement ... I was more loathsome in mine own eyes than was a toad ... sin and corruption, I said, would as naturally bubble out of my heart, as water would bubble out of a fountain.' Another author, quoted in Haller's *Rise of Puritanism* says that when he looked into his heart, it was 'as if I had in the heat of summer lookt down into the Filth of a Dungeon, where I discerned Millions of crawling living things in the midst of that Sink and liquid Corruption.'

I won't listen to those who describe that vision as merely pathological. I have seen the 'slimy things that crawled with legs' in my own dungeon. I thought the glimpse taught me sense. But Whyte seems to think it should be not a glimpse but a daily, lifelong scrutiny. Can he be right? It sounds so very unlike the New Testament fruits of the spirit – love, joy, peace. And very unlike the Pauline programme; 'forgetting those things which are behind and reaching forth unto those things that are before.' And very unlike St François de Sales' green, dewy chapter on *la douceur* towards one's self. Anyway, what's the use of laying down a programme of permanent emotions? They can be permanent only by being factitious.

What do you think? I know that a spiritual emetic, at the right moment, may be needed. But not a regular diet of emetics! If one survived, one would develop a 'tolerance' of them. This poring over the 'sink' might breed its own perverse pride:

over-just and self-displeased
For self-offence more than for God offended.

Anyway, in solitude, and also in confession, I have found (to my regret) that the degrees of shame and disgust which I actually feel at my own sins do not at all correspond to what my reason tells me about their comparative gravity. Just as the degree to which, in daily life, I feel the emotion of fear has very little to do with my rational judgment of the danger. I'd sooner have really nasty seas when I'm in an open boat than look down in perfect (actual) safety from the edge of a cliff. Similarly, I have confessed ghastly uncharities with less reluctance than small unmentionables – or those sins which happen to be ungentlemanly as well as un-Christian. Our emotional reactions to our own behaviour are of limited ethical significance.

19

Tell Betty that if you hadn't whisked me off on to the subject of repentance, I was just going to say the very thing she blames me for not saying. I was going to say that in adoration, more than in any other kind of prayer, the public or communal act is of the utmost importance. One would lose incomparably more by being prevented from going to church on Easter than on Good Friday. And, even in private, adoration should be communal – 'with angels and archangels and all the company', all the transparent publicity of Heaven. On the other hand, I find that the prayers to which I can most fully attend in church are always those I have most often used in my bedroom.

I deny, with some warmth, the charge of being 'choosy about services'. My whole point was that any form will do me if only I'm given time to get used to it. The idea of allowing myself to be put off by mere inadequacy – an ugly church, a gawky server, a badly turned out celebrant – is horrible. On the contrary, it constantly surprises me how little these things matter, as if

never anything can be amiss
When simpleness and duty tender it.

One of the golden Communions of my life was in a Nissen hut. Sometimes the cockney accent of a choir has a singularly touching quality. A tin mug for a chalice, if there were good reason for it, would not distress me in the least. (I wonder what sort of crockery was used at the Last Supper?)

You ask me why I've never written anything about the Holy Communion. For the very simple reason that I am not good enough at Theology. I have nothing to offer. Hiding any light I think I've got under a bushel is not my besetting sin! I am much more prone to prattle unseasonably. But there is a point at which even I would gladly keep silent. The trouble is that people draw conclusions even from silence. Someone said in print the other day that I seemed to 'admit rather than welcome' the sacraments.

I wouldn't like you and Betty to think the same. But as soon as I try to tell you anything more, I see another reason for silence. It is almost impossible to state the negative effect which certain doctrines have on me – my failure to be nourished by them – without seeming to mount an attack against them. But the very last thing I want to do is to unsettle in the mind of any Christian, whatever his denomination, the concepts – for him traditional – by which he finds it profitable to represent to himself what is happening when he receives the bread and wine. I could wish that no definitions had ever been felt to be necessary; and, still more, that none had been allowed to make divisions between churches.

Some people seem able to discuss different theories of this act as if they understood them all and needed only evidence as to which was best. This light has been withheld from me. I do not know and can't imagine what the disciples understood Our Lord to mean when, His body still unbroken and His blood unshed, He handed them the bread and wine, saying *they* were His body and blood. I can find within the forms of my human understanding no connection between eating a man – and it is as Man that the Lord has flesh – and entering into any spiritual oneness or community or κοινωνία with him. And I find 'substance' (in Aristotle's sense), when stripped of its own accidents and endowed with the accidents of some other substance, an object I cannot think. My effort to do so produces mere nursery-thinking – a picture of something like very rarefied Plasticine. On the other hand, I get on no better with those who tell me that the elements are mere bread and mere wine, used symbolically to remind me of the death of Christ. They are, on the natural level, such a very odd symbol of *that*. But it would be profane to suppose that they are as arbitrary as they seem to me. I well believe there is in reality an appropriateness, even a necessity, in their selection. But it remains, for me, hidden. Again, if they are, if the whole act is, simply memorial, it would seem to follow that its value must be purely psychological, and dependent on the recipient's sensibility at the moment of reception. And I cannot see why *this* particular reminder – a hundred other things may, psychologically, remind me of Christ's death, equally, or perhaps more – should be so uniquely important as all Christendom (and my own heart) unhesitatingly declare.

However, then, it may be for others, for me the something which holds together and 'informs' all the objects, words, and actions of this rite, is unknown and unimaginable. I am not saying to any one in the world: 'Your explanation is wrong.' I am saying: 'Your explanation leaves the mystery for me still a mystery.'

Yet I find no difficulty in believing that the veil between the worlds, nowhere else (for me) so opaque to the intellect, is nowhere else so thin and permeable to divine operation. Here a hand from the hidden country touches not only my soul but my body. Here the prig, the don, the modern, in me have no privilege over the savage or the child. Here is big medicine and strong magic. *Favete linguis.*

When I say 'Magic' I am not thinking of the paltry and pathetic techniques by which fools attempt and quacks pretend to control Nature. I mean rather what is suggested by fairy-tale sentences like: 'This is a magic flower, and if you carry it the seven gates will open to you of their own accord', or: 'This is a magic cave and those who enter it will renew their youth.' I should define magic in this sense as 'objective efficacy which cannot be further analysed'.

Magic, in this sense, will always win a response from a normal imagination because it is in principle so 'true to nature'. Mix these two powders and there will be an explosion. Eat a grain of this and you will die. Admittedly, the 'magical' element in such truths can be got rid of by explanation; that is, by seeing them to be instances or consequences of larger truths. Which larger truths remain 'magical' till they also are, in the same way, explained. In that fashion, the sciences are always pushing further back the realm of mere 'brute fact'. But no scientist, I suppose, believes that the process could ever reach completion. At the very least, there must always remain the utterly 'brute' fact, the completely opaque *datum*, that a universe – or rather *this* universe with its determinate character – exists; as 'magical' as the magic flower in the fairy tale.

Now the value, for me, of the magical element in Christianity is this. It is a permanent witness that the heavenly realm, certainly no less than the natural universe and perhaps very much more, is a realm of objective facts – hard, determinate facts, not to be constructed *a priori*, and not to be dissolved into maxims, ideals, values, and the like. One cannot conceive a more completely 'given', or, if you like, a more 'magical', fact than the existence of God as *causa sui*.

Enlightened people want to get rid of this magical element in favour of what they would call the 'spiritual' element. But the spiritual, conceived as something thus antithetical to 'magical', seems to become merely the psychological or ethical. And neither that by itself, nor the magical by itself, is a religion. I am not going to lay down rules as to the share – quantitatively considered – which the magical should have in anyone's religious life. Individual differences may be permissible. What I insist on is that it can never be reduced to zero. If it is, what remains is only morality, or culture, or philosophy.

What makes some theological works like sawdust to me is the way the authors can go on discussing how far certain positions are adjustable to contemporary thought, or beneficial in relation to social problems, or 'have a future' before them, but never squarely ask what grounds we have for supposing them to be true accounts of any objective reality. As if we were trying to make rather than to learn. Have we no Other to reckon with?

I hope I do not offend God by making my communions in the frame of mind I have been describing. The command, after all, was Take, eat: not Take, understand. Particularly, I hope I need not be tormented by the question 'What is this?' – this wafer, this sip of wine. That has a dreadful effect on me. It invites me to take 'this' out of its holy context and regard it as an object among objects, indeed as part of nature. It is like taking a red coal out of the fire to examine it: it becomes a dead coal. To me, I mean. All this is autobiography, not theology.

20

I really must digress to tell you a bit of good news. Last week, while at prayer, I suddenly discovered – or felt as if I did – that I had forgiven someone I had been trying to forgive for over thirty years. Trying, and praying that I might. When the thing actually happened – sudden as the longed-for cessation of one's neighbour's radio – my feeling was 'But it's so easy. Why didn't you do it ages ago?' So many things are done easily the moment you can do them at all. But till then, sheerly impossible, like learning to swim. There are months during which no efforts will keep you up; then comes the day and hour and minute after which, and ever after, it becomes almost impossible to sink. It also seemed to me that forgiving (that man's cruelty) and being forgiven (my resentment) were the very same thing. 'Forgive and you shall be forgiven' sounds like a bargain. But perhaps it is something much more. By heavenly standards, that is, for pure intelligence, it is perhaps a tautology – forgiving and being forgiven are two names for the same thing. The important thing is that a discord has been resolved, and it is certainly the great Resolver who has done it. Finally, and perhaps best of all, I believed anew what is taught us in the parable of the Unjust Judge. No evil habit is so ingrained nor so long prayed against (as it seemed) in vain, that it cannot, even in dry old age, be whisked away.

I wonder, do the long dead know it when we at last, after countless failures, succeed in forgiving them? It would be a pity if they don't. A pardon given but not received would be frustrated. Which brings me to your question.

Of course I pray for the dead. The action is so spontaneous, so all but inevitable, that only the most compulsive theological case against it would deter me. And I hardly know how the rest of my prayers would survive if those for the dead were forbidden. At our age the majority of those we love best are dead. What sort of intercourse with God could I have if what I love best were unmentionable to Him?

On the traditional Protestant view, all the dead are damned or saved. If they are damned, prayer for them is useless. If they are saved, it is equally useless. God has already done all for them. What more should we ask?

But don't we believe that God has already done and is already doing all that He can for the living? What more should we ask? Yet we are told to ask.

'Yes,' it will be answered, 'but the living are still on the road. Further trials, developments, possibilities of error, await them. But the saved have been made perfect. They have finished the course. To pray for them presupposes that progress and difficulty are still possible. In fact, you are bringing in something like Purgatory.'

Well, I suppose I am. Though even in Heaven some perpetual increase of beatitude, reached by a continually more ecstatic selfsurrender, without the possibility of failure but not perhaps without its own ardours and exertions – for delight also has its severities and steep ascents, as lovers know – might be supposed. But I won't press, or guess, that side for the moment. I believe in Purgatory.

Mind you, the Reformers had good reasons for throwing doubt on 'the Romish doctrine concerning Purgatory' as that Romish doctrine had then become. I don't mean merely the commercial scandal. If you turn from Dante's *Purgatorio* to the Sixteenth Century you will be appalled by the degradation. In Thomas More's *Supplication of Souls* Purgatory is simply temporary Hell. In it the souls are tormented by devils, whose presence is 'more horrible and grievous to us than is the pain itself'. Worse still, Fisher, in his Sermon on Psalm VI, says the tortures are so intense that the spirit who suffers them cannot, for pain, 'remember God as he ought to do'. In fact, the very etymology of the word *purgatory* has dropped out of sight. Its pains do not bring us nearer to God, but make us forget Him. It is a place not of purification but purely of retributive punishment.

The right view returns magnificently in Newman's *Dream*. There, if I remember rightly, the saved soul, at the very foot of the throne, begs to be taken away and cleansed. It cannot bear for a moment longer 'With its darkness to affront that light.' Religion has reclaimed Purgatory.

Our souls *demand* Purgatory, don't they? Would it not break the heart if God said to us, 'It is true, my son, that your breath smells and your rags drip with mud and slime, but we are charitable here and no one will upbraid you with these things, nor draw away from you. Enter into the joy'? Should we not reply, 'With submission, sir, and if there is no objection, I'd *rather* be cleaned first.' 'It may hurt, you know.' – 'Even so, sir.'

I assume that the process of purification will normally involve suffering. Partly from tradition; partly because most real good that has been done me in this life has involved it. But I don't think suffering is the purpose of the purgation. I can well believe that people neither much worse nor much better than I will suffer less than I or more. 'No nonsense about merit.'

The treatment given will be the one required, whether it hurts little or much.

My favourite image on this matter comes from the dentist's chair. I hope that when the tooth of life is drawn and I am 'coming round', a voice will say, 'Rinse your mouth out with this.' *This* will be Purgatory. The rinsing may take longer than I can now imagine. The taste of *this* may be more fiery and astringent than my present sensibility could endure. But More and Fisher shall not persuade me that it will be disgusting and unhallowed.

Your own peculiar difficulty – that the dead are not in time – is another matter.

How do you know they are not? I certainly believe that to be God is to enjoy an infinite present, where nothing has yet passed away and nothing is still to come. Does it follow that we can say the same of saints and angels? Or at any rate exactly the same? The dead might experience a time which was not quite so linear as ours – it might, so to speak, have thickness as well as length. Already in this life we get some thickness whenever we learn to attend to more than one thing at once. One can suppose this increased to any extent, so that though, for them as for us, the present is always becoming the past, yet each present contains unimaginably more than ours.

I *feel* – can you work it out for me and tell me if it is more than a feeling – that to make the life of the blessed dead strictly timeless is inconsistent with the resurrection of the body.

Again, as you and I have agreed, whether we pray on behalf of the living or the dead, the causes which will prevent or exclude the events we pray for are in fact already at work. Indeed they are part of a series which, I suppose, goes back as far as the creation of the universe. The causes which made George's illness a trivial one were already operating while we prayed about it; if it had been what we feared, the causes of that would have been operative. That is why, as I hold, our prayers are granted, or not, in eternity. The task of dovetailing the spiritual and physical histories of the world into each other is accomplished in the total act of creation itself. Our prayers, and other free acts, are known to us only as we come to the moment of doing them. But they are eternally in the score of the great symphony. Not 'predetermined'; the syllable *pre* lets in the notion of eternity as simply an older time. For though we cannot experience our life as an endless present, we are eternal in God's eyes; that is, in our deepest reality. When I say we are 'in time' I don't mean that we are, impossibly, outside the endless present in which He beholds us as He beholds all else. I mean, our creaturely limitation is that our fundamentally timeless reality can be experienced by us only in the mode of succession.

In fact we began by putting the question wrongly. The question is not whether the dead are part of timeless reality. They are; so is a flash of lightning. The question is whether they share the divine perception of time-lessness.

Tell George I should be delighted. *Rendez-vous* in my rooms at 7.15. We do *not* dress for dinner on ordinary nights.

21

Betty is quite right – 'all this about prayer and never a word on the practical problem: its irksomeness.' And she sees fit to add, 'Anyone might think it was a correspondence between two saints!'

That was a barbed shaft and went home. And yet I don't really think we are being hypocritical. Doesn't the mere fact of putting something into words of itself involve an exaggeration? Prose words, I mean. Only poetry can speak low enough to catch the faint murmur of the mind, the 'litel winde, unethe hit might be lesse'. The other day I tried to describe to you a very minimal experience – the tiny wisps of adoration with which (sometimes) I salute my pleasures. But I now see that putting it down in black and white made it sound far bigger than it really is. The truth is, I haven't any language weak enough to depict the weakness of my spiritual life. If I weakened it enough it would cease to be language at all. Like when you try to turn the gas-ring a little lower still, and it merely goes out.

Then again, by talking at this length about prayer at all, we seem to give it a much bigger place in our lives than, I'm afraid, it has. For while we talk about it, all the rest of our experience, which in reality crowds our prayer into the margin or sometimes off the page altogether, is not mentioned. Hence, in the talk, an error of proportion which amounts to, though it was not intended for, a lie.

Well, let's now at any rate come clean. Prayer *is* irksome. An excuse to omit it is never unwelcome. When it is over, this casts a feeling of relief and holiday over the rest of the day. We are reluctant to begin. We are delighted to finish. While we are at prayer, but not while we are reading a novel or solving a crossword puzzle, any trifle is enough to distract us.

And we know that we are not alone in this. The fact that prayers are constantly set as penances tells its own tale.

The odd thing is that this reluctance to pray is not confined to periods of dryness. When yesterday's prayers were full of comfort and exaltation, today's will still be felt as, in some degree, a burden.

Now the disquieting thing is not simply that we skimp and begrudge the duty of prayer. The really disquieting thing is it should have to be numbered among duties at all. For we believe that we were created to 'glorify God and enjoy Him forever'. And if the few, the very few, minutes we now spend on intercourse with God are a burden to us rather than a delight, what then? If I were a Calvinist this symptom would fill me with despair. What can be done *for* – or what should be done *with* – a rose-tree that *dislikes* producing roses? Surely it ought to want to?

Much of our backwardness in prayer is no doubt due to our sins, as every teacher will tell us; to our avoidable immersion in the things of this world, to our neglect of mental discipline. And also to the very worst kind of 'fear of God'. We shrink from too naked a contact, because we are afraid of the divine demands upon us which it might make too audible. As some old writer says, many a Christian prays faintly 'lest God might really hear him, which he, poor man, never intended.' But sins – at any rate, our actual and individual sins – are not perhaps the only cause.

By the very constitution of our minds as they now are – whatever they may have been when God first made man – it is difficult for us to concentrate on anything which is neither sensible (like potatoes) nor abstract (like numbers). What is concrete but immaterial can be kept in view only by painful effort. Some would say, 'Because it does not exist.' But the rest of our experience cannot accept that solution. For we ourselves, and all that we most care about, seem to come in the class 'concrete (that is, individual) and insensible'. If reality consists of nothing but physical objects and abstract concepts, then reality has, in the last resort, nothing to say to us. We are in the wrong universe. Man is a *passion inutile*; and so, good night. And yet, the supposedly real universe has been quarried out of man's sensuous experiences.

The painful effort which prayer involves is no proof that we are doing something we were not created to do.

If we were perfected, prayer would not be a duty, it would be delight. Some day, please God, it will be. The same is true of many other behaviours which now appear as duties. If I loved my neighbour as myself, most of the actions which are now my moral duty would flow out of me as spontaneously as song from a lark or fragrance from a flower. Why is this not so yet? Well, we know, don't we? Aristotle has taught us that delight is the 'bloom' on an unimpeded activity. 'But the very activities for which we were created are, while we live on earth, variously impeded: by evil in ourselves or in others. Not to practise them is to abandon our humanity. To practise them spontaneously and delightfully is not yet possible. This situation creates the category of duty, the whole specifically *moral* realm.

It exists to be transcended. Here is the paradox of Christianity. As practical imperatives for here and now the two great commandments have to be translated 'Behave *as if* you loved God and man.' For no man can love because he is told to. Yet obedience on this practical level is not really obedience at all. And if a man really loved God and man, once again this would hardly be obedience; for if he did, he would be unable to help it. Thus the command really says to us, 'Ye must be born again.' Till then, we have duty, morality, the Law. A schoolmaster, as St Paul says, to bring us to Christ. We must expect no more of it than of a schoolmaster; we must allow it no less. I must say my prayers today whether I feel devout or not; but that is only as I must learn my grammar if I am ever to read the poets.

But the school-days, please God, are numbered. There is no morality in Heaven. The angels never knew (from within) the meaning of the word *ought*, and the blessed dead have long since gladly forgotten it. This is why Dante's Heaven is so right, and Milton's, with its military discipline, so silly. This also explains – to pick up an earlier point – why we have to picture that world in terms which seem almost frivolous. In this world our most momentous actions are impeded. We can picture unimpeded, and therefore delighted, action only by the analogy of our present play and leisure. Thus we get the notion that what is as free as they would have to matter as little.

I said, mind you, that 'most' of the behaviour which is now duty would be spontaneous and delightful if we were, so to speak, good rose-trees. Most, not all. There is, or might be, martyrdom. We are not called upon to like it. Our Master didn't. But the principle holds, that duty is always conditioned by evil. Martyrdom, by the evil in the persecutor; other duties, by lack of love in myself or by the general diffused evil of the world. In the perfect and eternal world the Law will vanish. But the results of having lived faithfully under it will not.

I am therefore not really deeply worried by the fact that prayer is at present a duty, and even an irksome one. This is humiliating. It is frustrating. It is terribly time-wasting – the worse one is praying, the longer one's prayers take. But we are still only at school. Or, like Donne, 'I tune my instrument here at the door.' And even now – how can I weaken the words enough, how speak at all without exaggeration? – we have what seem rich moments. Most frequently, perhaps, in our momentary, only just voluntary, ejaculations; refreshments 'unimplored, unsought, Happy for man so coming'.

But I don't rest much on that; nor would I if it were ten times as much as it is. I have a notion that what seem our worst prayers may really be, in God's eyes, our best. Those, I mean, which are least supported by devotional feeling and contend with the greatest disinclination. For these, perhaps, being nearly all will, come from a deeper level than feeling. In feeling there is so much that is really not ours – so much that comes from weather and health or from the last book read. One thing seems certain. It is no good angling for the rich moments. God sometimes seems to speak to us most intimately when He catches us, as it were, off our guard. Our preparations to receive Him sometimes have the opposite effect. Doesn't Charles Williams say somewhere that 'the altar must often be built in one place in order that the fire from heaven may descend *somewhere else*'?

22

By not belonging to a press-cutting agency I miss most of the bouquets and brickbats which are aimed at me. So I never saw the article you write about. But I have seen others of that kind, and they'll break no bones of mine. Don't, however, misjudge these 'liberal Christians'. They genuinely believe that writers of my sort are doing a great deal of harm.

They themselves find it impossible to accept most of the articles of the 'faith once given to the saints'. They are nevertheless extremely anxious that some vestigial religion which they (not we) can describe as 'Christianity' should continue to exist and make numerous converts. They think these converts will come in only if this religion is sufficiently 'de-mythologised'. The ship must be lightened if she is to keep afloat.

It follows that, to them, the most mischievous people in the world are those who, like myself, proclaim that Christianity essentially involves the supernatural. They are quite sure that belief in the supernatural never will, nor should, be revived, and that if we convince the world that it must choose between accepting the supernatural and abandoning all pretence of Christianity, the world will undoubtedly choose the second alternative. It will thus be we, not the liberals, who have really sold the pass. We shall have re-attached to the name *Christian* a deadly scandal from which, but for us, they might have succeeded in decontaminating it.

If, then, some tone of resentment creeps into their comments on our work, can you blame them? But it would be unpardonable if we allowed ourselves any resentment against them. We do in some measure queer their pitch. But they make no similar contribution to the forces of secularism. It has already a hundred champions who carry far more weight than they. Liberal Christianity can only supply an ineffectual echo to the massive chorus of agreed and admitted unbelief. Don't be deceived by the fact that this echo so often 'hits the headlines'. That is because attacks on Christian doctrine which would pass unnoticed if they were launched (as they are daily launched) by anyone else, become News when the attacker is a clergyman;

just as a very commonplace protest against make-up would be News if it came from a film star.

By the way, did you ever meet, or hear of, anyone who was converted from scepticism to a 'liberal' or 'demythologised' Christianity? I think that when unbelievers come in at all, they come in a good deal further.

Not, of course, that either group is to be judged by its success, as if the question were one of tactics. The liberals are honest men and preach their version of Christianity, as we preach ours, because they believe it to be true. A man who first tried to guess 'what the public wants,' and then preached that as Christianity *because* the public wants it, would be a pretty mixture of fool and knave.

I am enlarging on this because even you, in your last letter, seemed to hint that there was too much of the supernatural in my position; especially in the sense that 'the next world' loomed so large. But how can it loom less than large if it is believed in at all?

You know my history. You know why my withers are quite unwrung by the fear that I was bribed – that I was lured into Christianity by the hope of everlasting life. I believed in God before I believed in Heaven. And even now, even if – let's make an impossible supposition – His voice, unmistakably His, said to me, They have misled you. I can do nothing of that sort for you. My long struggle with the blind forces is nearly over. I die, children. The story is ending' – would that be a moment for changing sides? Would not you and I take the Viking way: 'The Giants and Trolls win. Let us die on the right side, with Father Odin.'

But if it is not so, if that other world is once admitted, how can it, except by sensual or bustling preoccupations, be kept in the background of our minds? How can the 'rest of Christianity' – what is this 'rest'? – be disentangled from it? How can we untwine this idea, if once admitted, from our present experience, in which, even before we believed, so many things at least *looked* like 'bright shoots of everlastingness'?

And yet ... after all, I know. It is a venture. We don't *know* it will be. There is our freedom, our chance for a little generosity, a little sportsmanship.

Isn't it possible that many 'liberals' have a highly illiberal motive for banishing the idea of Heaven? They want the gilt-edged security of a religion so contrived that no possible fact could ever refute it. In such a religion they have the comfortable feeling that, whatever the real universe may be like, they will not have 'been had' or 'backed the wrong horse'. It is close to the spirit of the man who hid his talent in a napkin – 'I know you are a hard man and I'm taking no risks.' But surely the sort of religion they want would consist of nothing but tautologies?

About the resurrection of the body. I agree with you that the old picture of the soul reassuming the corpse – perhaps blown to bits or long since usefully dissipated through nature – is absurd. Nor is it what St Paul's words imply. And I admit that if you ask what I substitute for this, I have only speculations to offer.

The principle behind these speculations is this. We are not, in this doctrine, concerned with matter as such at all: with waves and atoms and all that. What the soul cries out for is the resurrection of the senses. Even in this life matter would be nothing to us if it were not the source of sensations.

Now we already have some feeble and intermittent power of raising dead sensations from their graves. I mean, of course, memory.

You see the way my thought is moving. But don't run away with the idea that when I speak of the resurrection of the body I mean merely that the blessed dead will have excellent memories of their sensuous experiences on earth. I mean it the other way round: that memory as we now know it is a dim foretaste, a mirage even, of a power which the soul, or rather Christ in the soul (he 'went to prepare a place for us') will exercise hereafter. It need no longer be intermittent. Above all, it need no longer be private to the soul in which it occurs. I can now communicate to you the vanished fields of my boyhood – they are building-estates today – only imperfectly by words. Perhaps the day is coming when I can take you for a walk through them.

At present we tend to think of the soul as somehow 'inside' the body. But the glorified body of the resurrection as I conceive it – the sensuous life raised from its death – will be inside the soul. As God is not in space but space is in God.

I have slipped in 'glorified' almost unawares. But this glorification is not only promised, it is already foreshadowed. The dullest of us knows how memory can transfigure; how often some momentary glimpse of beauty in boyhood is

... *a whisper*
Which memory will warehouse as a shout.

Don't talk to me of the 'illusions' of memory. Why should what we see at the moment be more 'real' than what we see from ten years' distance? It is indeed an illusion to believe that the blue hills on the horizon would still look blue if you went to them. But the fact that they are blue five miles away, and the fact that they are green when you are on them, are equally good facts. Traherne's 'orient and immortal wheat' or Wordsworth's landscape 'apparelled in celestial light' may not have been so radiant in the past when it was present as in the remembered past. That is the beginning of the glorification. One day they will be more radiant still. Thus in the sense-bodies of the redeemed the whole New Earth will arise. The same yet not the same as this. It was sown in corruption, it is raised in incorruption.

I dare not omit, though it may be mocked and misunderstood, the extreme example. The strangest discovery of a widower's life is the possibility, sometimes, of recalling with detailed and uninhibited imagination, with tenderness and gratitude, a passage of carnal love, yet with no re-awakening of concupiscence. And when this occurs (it must not be sought) awe comes upon us. It is like seeing Nature itself rising from its grave. What was sown in momentariness is raised in still permanence. What was sown as a becoming rises as being. Sown in subjectivity, it rises in objectivity. The transitory secret of two is now a chord in the ultimate music.

'But this,' you protest, 'is no resurrection of the *body*. You have given the dead a sort of dream world and dream bodies. They are not real.' Surely neither less nor more real than those you have always known: you know better than I that the 'real world' of our present experience (coloured, resonant, soft or hard, cool or warm, all corseted by perspective) has no place in the world described by physics or even physiology. Matter enters our experience only by becoming sensation (when we perceive it) or conception (when we understand it). That is, by becoming soul. That element in the soul which it becomes will, in my view, be raised and glorified; the hills and valleys of Heaven will be to those you now experience not as a copy is to an original, nor as a substitute to the genuine article, but as the flower to the root, or the diamond to the coal. It will be eternally true that they originate with matter; let us therefore bless matter. But in entering our soul as alone it can enter – that is, by being perceived and known – matter has turned into soul (like the Undines who acquired a soul by marriage with a mortal).

I don't say the resurrection of this body will happen at once. It may well be that this part of us sleeps in death and the intellectual soul is sent to Lenten lands where she fasts in naked spirituality – a ghostlike and imperfectly human condition. I don't imply that an angel is a ghost. But naked spirituality is in accordance with his nature: not, I think, with ours. (A two-legged horse is maimed but not a two-legged man.) Yet from that fact my hope is that we shall return and re-assume the wealth we laid down.

Then the new earth and sky, the same yet not the same as these, will rise in us as we have risen in Christ. And once again, after who knows what aeons of the silence and the dark, the birds will sing out and the waters flow, and lights and shadows move across the hills and the faces of our friends laugh upon us with amazed recognition.

Guesses, of course, only guesses. If they are not true, something better will be. For we know that we shall be made like Him, for we shall see Him as He is.

Thank Betty for her note. I'll come by the later train, the 3.40. And tell her not to bother about a bed on the ground floor. I can manage stairs again now, provided I take them 'in bottom'. Till Saturday.

REFLECTIONS ON
THE PSALMS

To
Austin and Katharine Farrer

Contents

INTRODUCTORY

This is not a work of scholarship. I am no Hebraist, no higher critic, no ancient historian, no archaeologist. I write for the unlearned about things in which I am unlearned myself. If an excuse is needed (and perhaps it is) for writing such a book, my excuse would be something like this. It often happens that two schoolboys can solve difficulties in their work for one another better than the master can. When you took the problem to a master, as we all remember, he was very likely to explain what you understood already, to add a great deal of information which you didn't want, and say nothing at all about the thing that was puzzling you. I have watched this from both sides of the net; for when, as a teacher myself, I have tried to answer questions brought me by pupils, I have sometimes, after a minute, seen that expression settle down on their faces which assured me that they were suffering exactly the same frustration which I had suffered from my own teachers. The fellow-pupil can help more than the master because he knows less. The difficulty we want him to explain is one he has recently met. The expert met it so long ago that he has forgotten. He sees the whole subject, by now, in such a different light that he cannot conceive what is really troubling the pupil; he sees a dozen other difficulties which ought to be troubling him but aren't.

In this book, then, I write as one amateur to another, talking about difficulties I have met, or lights I have gained, when reading the Psalms, with the hope that this might at any rate interest, and sometimes even help, other inexpert readers. I am 'comparing notes', not presuming to instruct. It may appear to some that I have used the Psalms merely as pegs on which to hang a series of miscellaneous essays. I do not know that it would have done any harm if I had written the book that way, and I shall have no grievance against anyone who reads it that way. But that is not how it was in fact written. The thoughts it contains are those to which I found myself driven in reading the Psalms; sometimes by my enjoyment of them, sometimes by meeting with what at first I could not enjoy.

The Psalms were written by many poets and at many different dates. Some, I believe, are allowed to go back to the reign of David; I think certain scholars allow that Psalm 18 (of which a slightly different version occurs in 2 Samuel 22) might be by David himself. But many are later than the 'captivity', which we should call the deportation to Babylon. In a scholarly work, chronology would be the first thing to settle: in a book of this sort nothing more need, or can, be said about it.

What must be said, however, is that the Psalms are poems, and poems intended to be sung: not doctrinal treatises, nor even sermons. Those who talk of reading the Bible 'as literature' sometimes mean, I think, reading it without attending to the main thing it is about; like reading Burke with no interest in politics, or reading the *Aeneid* with no interest in Rome. That seems to me to be nonsense. But there is a saner sense in which the Bible, since it is after all literature, cannot properly be read except as literature; and the different parts of it as the different sorts of literature they are. Most emphatically the Psalms must be read as poems; as lyrics, with all the licences and all the formalities, the hyperboles, the emotional rather than logical connections, which are proper to lyric poetry. They must be read as poems if they are to be understood; no less than French must be read as French or English as English. Otherwise we shall miss what is in them and think we see what is not.

Their chief formal characteristic, the most obvious element of pattern, is fortunately one that survives in translation. Most readers will know that I mean what the scholars call 'parallelism'; that is, the practice of saying the same thing twice in different words. A perfect example is 'He that dwelleth in heaven shall laugh them to scorn: the Lord shall have them in derision' (2:4), or again, 'He shall make thy righteousness as clear as the light; and thy just dealing as the noon-day' (37:6). If this is not recognised as pattern, the reader will either find mares' nests (as some of the older preachers did) in his effort to get a different meaning out of each half of the verse or else feel that it is rather silly.

In reality it is a very pure example of what all pattern, and therefore all art, involves. The principle of art has been defined by someone as 'the same in the other'. Thus in a country dance you take three steps and then three steps again. That is the same. But the first three are to the right and the second three to the left. That is the other. In a building there may be a wing on one side and a wing on the other, but both of the same shape. In music the composer may say ABC, and then abc, and then αβγ. Rhyme consists in putting together two syllables that have the same sound except for their initial consonants, which are other. 'Parallelism' is the characteristically Hebrew form of the same in the other, but it occurs in many English poets too: for example, in Marlowe's

Cut is the branch that might have grown full straight
And burned is Apollo's laurel bough,

or in the childishly simple form used by the *Cherry Tree Carol*,

Joseph was an old man and an old man was he.

Of course the Parallelism is often partially concealed on purpose (as the balances between masses in a picture may be something far subtler than complete symmetry). And of course other and more complex patterns may be worked in across it, as in Psalm 119, or in 107 with its refrain. I mention only what is most obvious, the Parallelism itself. It is (according to one's point of view) either a wonderful piece of luck or a wise provision of God's, that poetry which was to be turned into all languages should have as its chief formal characteristic one that does not disappear (as mere metre does) in translation.

If we have any taste for poetry we shall enjoy this feature of the Psalms. Even those Christians who cannot enjoy it will respect it; for Our Lord, soaked in the poetic tradition of His country, delighted to use it. 'For with what judgement ye judge, ye shall be judged; and with what measure ye mete, it shall be measured to you again' (Matthew 7:2). The second half of the verse makes no logical addition; it echoes, with variation, the first, 'Ask, and it shall be given you; seek, and ye shall find; knock and it shall be opened unto you' (7:7). The advice is given in the first phrase, then twice repeated with different images. We may, if we like, see in this an exclusively practical and didactic purpose; by giving to truths which are infinitely worth remembering this rhythmic and incantatory expression, He made them almost impossible to forget. I like to suspect more. It seems to me appropriate, almost inevitable, that when that great Imagination which in the beginning, for Its own delight and for the delight of men and angels and (in their proper mode) of beasts, had invented and formed the whole world of Nature, submitted to express Itself in human speech, that speech should sometimes be poetry. For poetry too is a little incarnation, giving body to what had been before invisible and inaudible.

I think, too, it will do us no harm to remember that, in becoming Man, He bowed His neck beneath the sweet yoke of a heredity and early environment. Humanly speaking, He would have learned this style, if from no one else (but it was all about Him) from His Mother. 'That we should be saved from our enemies and from the hands of all that hate us; to perform the mercy promised to our fathers, and to remember his holy covenant.' Here is the same parallelism. (And incidentally, is this the only aspect in which we can say of His human nature 'He was His Mother's own son'? There is a fierceness, even a touch of Deborah, mixed with the sweetness in the Magnificat to which most painted Madonnas do little justice; matching the frequent severity of His own sayings. I am sure the private life of the holy family was, in many senses, 'mild' and 'gentle', but perhaps hardly in the way some hymn writers have in mind. One may suspect, on proper occasions, a certain astringency; and all in what people at Jerusalem regarded as a rough north-country dialect.)

I have not attempted of course to 'cover the subject' even on my own amateurish level. I have stressed, and omitted, as my own interests led me. I say nothing about the long historical Psalms, partly because they have meant less to me, and partly because they seem to call for little comment. I say the least I can about the history of the Psalms as parts of various 'services'; a wide subject, and not for me. And I begin with those characteristics of the Psalter which are at first most repellent. Other men of my age will know why. Our generation was brought up to eat everything on the plate; and it was the sound principle of nursery gastronomy to polish off the nasty things first and leave the titbits to the end.

I have worked in the main from the translation which Anglicans find in their Prayer Book; that of Coverdale. Even of the old translators he is by no means the most accurate; and of course a sound modern scholar has more Hebrew in his little finger than poor Coverdale had in his whole body. But in beauty, in poetry, he, and St Jerome, the great Latin translator, are beyond all whom I know. I have usually checked, and sometimes corrected, his version from that of Dr Moffatt.

Finally, as will soon be apparent to any reader, this is not what is called an 'apologetic' work. I am nowhere trying to convince unbelievers that Christianity is true. I address those who already believe it, or those who are ready, while reading, to 'suspend their disbelief'. A man can't be always defending the truth; there must be a time to feed on it.

I have written, too, as a member of the Church of England, but I have avoided controversial questions as much as possible. At one point I had to explain how I differed on a certain matter both from Roman Catholics and from Fundamentalists: I hope I shall not for this forfeit the goodwill or the prayers of either. Nor do I much fear it. In my experience the bitterest opposition comes neither from them nor from any other thorough-going believers, and not often from atheists, but from semi-believers of all complexions. There are some enlightened and progressive old gentlemen of this sort whom no courtesy can propitiate and no modesty disarm. But then I dare say I am a much more annoying person than I know. (Shall we, perhaps, in Purgatory, see our own faces and hear our own voices as they really were?)

2

'JUDGEMENT' IN
THE PSALMS

If there is any thought at which a Christian trembles it is the thought of God's 'judgement'. The 'Day' of Judgement is 'that day of wrath, that dreadful day'. We pray for God to deliver us 'in the hour of death and at the day of judgement'. Christian art and literature for centuries have depicted its terrors. This note in Christianity certainly goes back to the teaching of Our Lord Himself; especially to the terrible parable of the Sheep and the Goats. This can leave no conscience untouched, for in it the 'Goats' are condemned entirely for their sins of omission; as if to make us fairly sure that the heaviest charge against each of us turns not upon the things he has done but on those he never did – perhaps never dreamed of doing.

It was therefore with great surprise that I first noticed how the Psalmists talk about the judgements of God. They talk like this: 'O let the nations rejoice and be glad, for thou shalt judge the folk righteously' (67:4), 'Let the field be joyful ... all the trees of the wood shall rejoice before the Lord, for he cometh, for he cometh to judge the earth' (96:12, 13). Judgement is apparently an occasion of universal rejoicing. People ask for it: 'Judge me, O Lord my God, according to thy righteousness' (35:24).

The reason for this soon becomes very plain. The ancient Jews, like ourselves, think of God's judgement in terms of an earthly court of justice. The difference is that the Christian pictures the case to be tried as a criminal case with himself in the dock; the Jew pictures it as a civil case with himself as the plaintiff. The one hopes for acquittal, or rather for pardon; the other hopes for a resounding triumph with heavy damages. Hence he prays 'judge my quarrel', or 'avenge my cause' (35:23). And though, as I said a minute ago, Our Lord in the parable of the Sheep and the Goats painted the characteristically Christian picture, in another place He is very characteristically Jewish. Notice what He means by 'an unjust judge'. By those words most of us would mean someone like Judge Jeffreys or the creatures who sat on the benches of German tribunals during the Nazi *régime*: someone who bullies witnesses and jurymen in order to convict, and then savagely to punish, innocent men. Once again, we are thinking of a criminal trial. We hope we shall never appear in the dock before such a judge. But the Unjust Judge in the parable is quite a different character. There is no danger of appearing in his court against your will: the difficulty is the opposite – to get into it. It is clearly a civil action. The poor woman (Luke 18:1–5) has had her little strip of land – room for a pigsty or a hen-run – taken away from her by a richer and more powerful neighbour (nowadays it would be Town-Planners or some other 'Body'). And she knows she has a perfectly watertight case. If once she could get it into court and have it tried by the laws of the land, she would be bound to get that strip back. But no one will listen to her, she can't get it tried. No wonder she is anxious for 'judgement'.

Behind this lies an age-old and almost world-wide experience which we have been spared. In most places and times it has been very difficult for the 'small man' to get his case heard. The judge (and, doubtless, one or two of his underlings) has to be bribed. If you can't afford to 'oil his palm' your case will never reach court. Our judges do not receive bribes. (We probably take this blessing too much for granted; it will not remain with us automatically.) We need not therefore be surprised if the Psalms, and the Prophets, are full of the longing for judgement, and regard the announcement that 'judgement' is coming as good news. Hundreds and thousands of people who have been stripped of all they possess and who have the right entirely on their side will at last be heard. Of course they are not afraid of judgement. They know their case is unanswerable – if only it could be heard. When God comes to judge, at last it will.

Dozens of passages make the point clear. In Psalm 9 we are told that God will 'minister true judgement' (v. 8), and that is because He 'forgetteth not the complaint of the poor' (v. 12). He 'defendeth the cause' (that is, the 'case') 'of the widows' (68:5). The good king in Psalm 72:2 will 'judge' the people rightly; that is, he will 'defend the poor'. When God 'arises to judgement' he will 'help all the meek upon earth' (76:9), all the timid, helpless people whose wrongs have never been righted yet. When God accuses earthly judges of 'wrong judgement', He follows it up by telling them to see that the poor 'have right' (82:2, 3).

The 'just' judge, then, is primarily he who rights a wrong in a civil case. He would, no doubt, also try a criminal case justly, but that is hardly ever what the Psalmists are thinking of. Christians cry to God for mercy instead of justice; *they* cried to God for justice instead of injustice. The Divine Judge is the defender, the rescuer. Scholars tell me that in the Book of Judges the word we so translate might almost be rendered 'champions'; for though these 'judges' do sometimes perform what we should call judicial functions many of them are much more concerned with rescuing the oppressed Israelites from Philistines and others by force of arms. They are more like

Jack the Giant Killer than like a modern judge in a wig. The knights in romances of chivalry who go about rescuing distressed damsels and widows from giants and other tyrants are acting almost as 'judges' in the old Hebrew sense: so is the modern solicitor (and I have known such) who does unpaid work for poor clients to save them from wrong.

I think there are very good reasons for regarding the Christian picture of God's judgement as far more profound and far safer for our souls than the Jewish. But this does not mean that the Jewish conception must simply be thrown away. I, at least, believe I can still get a good deal of nourishment out of it.

It supplements the Christian picture in one important way. For what alarms us in the Christian picture is the infinite purity of the standard against which our actions will be judged. But then we know that none of us will ever come up to that standard. We are all in the same boat. We must all pin our hopes on the mercy of God and the work of Christ, not on our own goodness. Now the Jewish picture of a civil action sharply reminds us that perhaps we are faulty not only by the Divine standard (that is a matter of course) but also by a very human standard which all reasonable people admit and which we ourselves usually wish to enforce upon others. Almost certainly there are unsatisfied claims, human claims, against each one of us. For who can really believe that in all his dealings with employers and employees, with husband or wife, with parents and children, in quarrels and in collaborations, he has always attained (let alone charity or generosity) mere honesty and fairness? Of course we forget most of the injuries we have done. But the injured parties do not forget even if they forgive. And God does not forget. And even what we can remember is formidable enough. Few of us have always, in full measure, given our pupils or patients or clients (or whatever our particular 'consumers' may be called) what we were being paid for. We have not always done quite our fair share of some tiresome work if we found a colleague or partner who could be beguiled into carrying the heavy end.

Our quarrels provide a very good example of the way in which the Christian and Jewish conceptions differ, while yet both should be kept in mind. As Christians we must of course repent of all the anger, malice, and self-will which allowed the discussion to become, on our side, a quarrel at all. But there is also the question on a far lower level: 'granted the quarrel (we'll go into that later) did you fight fair?' Or did we not quite unknowingly falsify the whole issue? Did we pretend to be angry about one thing when we knew, or could have known, that our anger had a different and much less presentable cause? Did we pretend to be 'hurt' in our sensitive and tender feelings (fine natures like ours are so vulnerable) when envy, ungratified vanity, or thwarted self-will was our real trouble? Such tactics often succeed. The other parties give in. They give in not because they don't know what is really wrong with us but because they have long known it only too well, and that sleeping dog can be roused, that skeleton brought out of its cupboard, only at the cost of imperilling their whole relationship with us. It needs surgery which they know we will never face. And so we win; by cheating. But the unfairness is very deeply felt. Indeed what is commonly called 'sensitiveness' is the most powerful engine of domestic tyranny, sometimes a lifelong tyranny. How we should deal with it in others I am not sure; but we should be merciless to its first appearances in ourselves.

The constant protests in the Psalms against those who oppress 'the poor' might seem at first to have less application to our own society than to most. But perhaps this is superficial; perhaps what changes is not the oppression but only the identity of 'the poor'. It often happens that someone in my acquaintance gets a demand from the Income Tax people which he queries. As a result it sometimes comes back to him reduced by anything up to 50 per cent. One man whom I knew, a solicitor, went round to the office and asked what they had meant by the original demand. The creature behind the counter tittered and said, 'Well, there's never any harm in trying it on.' Now when the cheat is thus attempted against men of the world who know how to look after themselves, no great harm is done. Some time has been wasted, and we all in some measure share the disgrace of belonging to a community where such practices are tolerated, but that is all. When, however, that kind of publican sends a similarly dishonest demand to a poor widow, already half starving on a highly taxable 'unearned' income (actually earned by years of self-denial on her husband's part) which inflation has reduced to almost nothing, a very different result probably follows. She cannot afford legal help; she understands nothing; she is terrified, and pays – cutting down on the meals and the fuel which were already wholly insufficient. The publican who has successfully 'tried it on' with her is precisely 'the ungodly' who 'for his own lust doth persecute the poor' (10:2). To be sure, he does this, not like the ancient publican, for his own immediate rake-off; only to advance himself in the service or to please his masters. This makes a difference. How important that difference is in the eyes of Him who avenges the fatherless and the widow I do not know. The publican may consider the question in the hour of death and will learn the answer at the day of 'judgement'. (But – who knows? – I may be doing the publicans an injustice. Perhaps they regard their work as a sport and observe game laws; and as other sportsmen will not shoot a sitting bird, so they may reserve their illegal demands for those who can defend themselves and hit back, and would never dream of 'trying it on' with the helpless. If so, I can only apologise for my error. If what I have said is unjustified as a rebuke of what they are, it may still be useful as a warning of what they may yet become. Falsehood is habit-forming.)

It will be noticed, however, that I make the Jewish conception of a civil judgement available for my Christian profit by picturing myself as the defendant, not the plaintiff. The writers of the Psalms do not do this. They look forward to 'judgement' because they think they have been wronged and hope to see their wrongs righted. There are, indeed, some passages in which the Psalmists approach to Christian humility and wisely lose their self-confidence. Thus in Psalm 50 (one of the finest) God is the accuser (vv. 6–21); and in 143:2, we have the words which most Christians often repeat – 'Enter not into judgement with Thy servant, for in Thy sight shall no man living be justified.' But these are exceptional. Nearly always the Psalmist is the indignant plaintiff.

He is quite sure, apparently, that his own hands are clean. He never did to others the horrid things that others are doing to him. 'If I have done any such thing' – If I ever behaved like so-and-so, then let so-and-so 'tread my life down upon the earth' (7:3–5). But of course I haven't. It is not as if my enemies are paying me out for any ill turn I ever did them. On the contrary, they have 'rewarded me evil for good'. Even after that, I went on exercising the utmost charity towards them. When they were ill I prayed and fasted on their behalf (35:12–14).

All this of course has its spiritual danger. It leads into that typically Jewish prison of self-righteousness which Our Lord so often terribly rebuked. We shall have to consider that presently. For the moment, however, I think it is important to make a distinction: between the conviction that one is in the right and the conviction that one is 'righteous', is a good man. Since none of us is righteous, the second conviction is always a delusion. But any of us may be, probably all of us at one time or another are, in the right about some particular issue. What is more, the worse man may be in the right against the better man. Their general characters have nothing to do with it. The question whether the disputed pencil belongs to Tommy or Charles is quite distinct from the question which is the nicer little boy, and the parents who allowed the one to influence their decision about the other would be very unfair. (It would be still worse if they said Tommy ought to let Charles have the pencil whether it belonged to him or not, because this would show he had a nice disposition. That may be true, but it is an untimely truth. An exhortation to charity should not come as a rider to a refusal of justice. It is likely to give Tommy a lifelong conviction that charity is a sanctimonious dodge for condoning theft and white-washing favouritism.) We need therefore by no means assume that the Psalmists are deceived or lying when they assert that, as against their particular enemies at some particular moment, they are completely in the right. Their voices while they say so may grate harshly on our ear and suggest to us that they are unamiable people. But that is another matter. And to be wronged does not commonly make people amiable.

But of course the fatal confusion between being in the right and being righteous soon falls upon them. In Psalm 7, from which I have already quoted, we see the transition. In verses 3 to 5 the poet is merely in the right; by verse 8 he is saying 'give sentence with me, O Lord, according to my righteousness and according to the innocency that is in me'. There is also in many of the Psalms a still more fatal confusion – that between the desire for justice and the desire for revenge. These important topics will have to be treated separately. The self-righteous Psalms can be dealt with only at a much later stage; the vindictive Psalms, the cursings, we may turn to at once. It is these that have made the Psalter largely a closed book to many modern church-goers. Vicars, not unnaturally, are afraid to set before their congregations poems so full of that passion to which Our Lord's teaching allows no quarter. Yet there must be some Christian use to be made of them; if, at least, we still believe (as I do) that all Holy Scripture is in some sense – though not all parts of it in the same sense – the word of God. (The sense in which I understand this will be explained later.)

3

THE CURSINGS

In some of the Psalms the spirit of hatred which strikes us in the face is like the heat from a furnace mouth. In others the same spirit ceases to be frightful only by becoming (to a modern mind) almost comic in its naïvety.

Examples of the first can be found all over the Psalter, but perhaps the worst is in Psalm 109. The poet prays that an ungodly man may rule over his enemy and that 'Satan' may stand at his right hand (v. 5). This probably does not mean what a Christian reader naturally supposes. The 'Satan' is an accuser, perhaps an informer. When the enemy is tried, let him be convicted and sentenced, 'and let his prayer be turned into sin' (v. 6). This again means, I think, not his prayers to God, but his supplications to a human judge, which are to make things all the hotter for him (double the sentence because he begged for it to be halved). May his days be few, may his job be given to someone else (v. 7). When he is dead may his orphans be beggars (v. 9). May he look in vain for anyone in the world to pity him (v. 11). Let God always remember against him the sins of his parents (v. 13). Even more devilish in one verse is the otherwise beautiful Psalm 137 where a blessing is pronounced on anyone who will snatch up a Babylonian baby and beat its brains out against the pavement (v. 9). And we get the refinement of malice in 69:23, 'Let their table be made a snare to take themselves withal; and let the things that should have been for their wealth be unto them an occasion of falling.'

The examples which (in me at any rate) can hardly fail to produce a smile may occur most disquietingly in Psalms we love: 143, after proceeding for 11 verses in a strain that brings tears to the eyes, adds in the 12th, almost like an afterthought, 'and of thy goodness slay mine enemies'. Even more naïvely, almost childishly, Psalm 139, in the middle of its hymn of praise throws in (v. 19), 'Wilt thou not slay the wicked, O God?' – as if it were surprising that such a simple remedy for human ills had not occurred to the Almighty. Worst of all in 'The Lord is my shepherd' (Psalm 23), after the green pasture, the waters of comfort, the sure confidence in the valley of the shadow, we suddenly run across (v. 5) 'Thou shalt prepare a table for me *against them that trouble me*' – or, as Dr Moffatt translates it, 'Thou art my host, spreading a feast for me *while my enemies have to look on.*' The poet's enjoyment of his present prosperity would not be complete unless those horrid enemies (who used to look down their noses at him) were watching it all and hating it. This may not be so diabolical as the passages I have quoted above; but the pettiness and vulgarity of it, especially in such surroundings, are hard to endure.

One way of dealing with these terrible or (dare we say?) contemptible Psalms is simply to leave them alone. But unfortunately the bad parts will not 'come away clean'; they may, as we have noticed, be intertwined with the most exquisite things. And if we still believe that all Holy Scripture is 'written for our learning' or that the age-old use of the Psalms in Christian worship was not entirely contrary to the will of God, and if we remember that Our Lord's mind and language were clearly steeped in the Psalter, we shall prefer, if possible, to make some use of them. What use can be made?

Part of the answer to this question cannot be given until we come to consider the subject of allegory. For the moment I can only describe, on the chance that it may help others, the use which I have, undesignedly and gradually, come to make of them myself.

At the outset I felt sure, and I feel sure still, that we must not either try to explain them away or to yield for one moment to the idea that, because it comes in the Bible, all this vindictive hatred must somehow be good and pious. We must face both facts squarely. The hatred is there – festering, gloating, undisguised – and also we should be wicked if we in any way condoned or approved it, or (worse still) used it to justify similar passions in ourselves. Only after these two admissions have been made can we safely proceed.

The first thing that helped me – this is a common experience – came from an angle that did not seem to be religious at all. I found that these maledictions were in one way extremely interesting. For here one saw a feeling we all know only too well. Resentment, expressing itself with perfect freedom, without disguise, without self-consciousness, without shame – as few but children would express it today. I did not of course think that this was because the ancient Hebrews had no conventions or restraints. Ancient and oriental cultures are in many ways more conventional, more ceremonious, and more courteous than our own. But their restraints came in different places. Hatred did not need to be disguised for the sake of social decorum or for fear anyone would accuse you of a neurosis. We therefore see it in its 'wild' or natural condition.

One might have expected that this would immediately, and usefully, have turned my attention to the same thing in my own heart. And that, no doubt, is one very good use we can make of the maledictory Psalms. To be sure, the hates which we fight against in ourselves do not dream of quite such appalling revenges. We live – at least, in some countries we still live – in a milder age. These poets lived in a world of savage punishments, of massacre and violence, of blood sacrifice in all countries and human sacrifice in many. And of course, too, we are far more subtle than they in disguising our ill will from others and from ourselves. 'Well,' we say, 'he'll live to be sorry for it,' as if we were merely, even regretfully, predicting; not noticing, certainly not admitting, that what we predict gives us a certain satisfaction. Still more in the Psalmists' tendency to chew over and over the cud of some injury, to dwell in a kind of self-torture on every circumstance that aggravates it, most of us can recognise something we have met in ourselves. We are, after all, blood-brothers to these ferocious, self-pitying, barbaric men.

That, as I say, is a good use to make of the cursings. In fact, however, something else occurred to me first. It seemed to me that, seeing in them hatred undisguised, I saw also the natural result of injuring a human being. The word *natural* is here important. This result can be obliterated by grace, suppressed by prudence or social convention, and (which is dangerous) wholly disguised by self-deception. But just as the natural result of throwing a lighted match into a pile of shavings is to produce a fire – though damp or the intervention of some more sensible person may prevent it – so the natural result of cheating a man, or 'keeping him down' or neglecting him, is to arouse resentment; that is, to impose upon him the temptation of becoming what the Psalmists were when they wrote the vindictive passages. He may succeed in resisting the temptation; or he may not. If he fails, if he dies spiritually because of his hatred for me, how do I, who provoked that hatred, stand? For in addition to the original injury I have done him a far worse one. I have introduced into his inner life, at best a new temptation, at worst a new besetting sin. If that sin utterly corrupts him, I have in a sense debauched or seduced him. I was the tempter.

There is no use talking as if forgiveness were easy. We all know the old joke, 'You've given up smoking once; I've given it up a dozen times.' In the same way I could say of a certain man, 'Have I forgiven him for what he did that day? I've forgiven him more times than I can count.' For we find that the work of forgiveness has to be done over and over again. We forgive, we mortify our resentment; a week later some chain of thought carries us back to the original offence and we discover the old resentment blazing away as if nothing had been done about it at all. We need to forgive our brother seventy times seven not only for 490 offences but for one offence. Thus the man I am thinking of has introduced a new, and difficult temptation into a soul which had the devil's plenty of them already. And what he has done to me, doubtless I have done to others; I, who am exceptionally blessed in having been allowed a way of life in which, having little power, I have had little opportunity of oppressing and embittering others. Let all of us who have never been school prefects, NCOs, schoolmasters, matrons of hospitals, prison warders, or even magistrates, give hearty thanks for it.

It is monstrously simple-minded to read the cursings in the Psalms with no feeling except one of horror at the uncharity of the poets. They are indeed devilish. But we must also think of those who made them so. Their hatreds are the reaction to something. Such hatreds are the kind of thing that cruelty and injustice, by a sort of natural law, produce. This, among other things, is what wrong-doing means. Take from a man his freedom or his goods and you may have taken his innocence, almost his humanity, as well. Not all the victims go and hang themselves like Mr Pilgrim; they may live and hate.

Then another thought occurred which led me in an unexpected, and at first unwelcome, direction. The reaction of the Psalmists to injury, though profoundly natural, is profoundly wrong. One may try to excuse it on the ground that they were not Christians and knew no better. But there are two reasons why this defence, though it will go some way, will not go very far.

The first is that within Judaism itself the corrective to this natural reaction already existed. 'Thou shalt not hate thy brother in thine heart ... thou shalt not avenge or bear any grudge against the children of thy people, but thou shalt love thy neighbour as thyself,' says Leviticus (19:17, 18). In Exodus we read, 'If thou seest the ass of him that hateth thee lying under his burden ... thou shalt surely help with him,' and 'if thou meet thine enemy's ox or his ass going astray, thou shalt surely bring it back to him' (23:4, 5). 'Rejoice not when thine enemy falleth, and let not thine heart be glad when he stumbleth' (Proverbs 24:17). And I shall never forget my surprise when I first discovered that St Paul's 'If thine enemy hunger, give him bread', etc., is a direct quotation from the same book (Proverbs 25:21). But this is one of the rewards of reading the Old Testament regularly. You keep on discovering more and more what a tissue of quotations from it the New Testament is; how constantly Our Lord repeated, reinforced, continued, refined, and sublimated, the Judaic ethics, how very seldom He introduced a novelty. This indeed was perfectly well known – was almost axiomatic – to millions of unlearned Christians as long as Bible-reading was habitual. Nowadays it seems to be so forgotten that people think they have somehow discredited Our Lord if they can show that some pre-Christian document (or what they take to be pre-Christian) such as the Dead Sea Scrolls has 'anticipated' Him. As if we supposed Him to be a cheapjack, like Nietzsche, inventing a new ethic! Every good teacher, within Judaism as without, has anticipated Him. The whole religious history of the pre-Christian world, on its better side, anticipates Him. It could not be otherwise. The Light which has light-ened every man from the beginning may shine more clearly but cannot change. The Origin cannot suddenly start being, in the popular sense of the word, 'original'.

The second reason is more disquieting. If we are to excuse the poets of the Psalms on the ground that they were not Christians, we ought to be able to point to the same sort of thing, and worse, in Pagan authors. Perhaps if I knew more Pagan literature I should be able to do this. But in what I do know (a little Greek, a little Latin, and of Old Norse very little indeed) I am not at all sure that I can. I can find in them lasciviousness, much brutal insensibility, cold cruelties taken for granted, but not this fury or luxury of hatred. I mean, of course, where writers are speaking in their own person; speeches put into the mouths of angry characters in a play are a different matter. One's first impres-sion is that the Jews were much more vindictive and vitriolic than the Pagans.

If we are not Christians we shall dismiss this with the old gibe 'How odd of God to choose the Jews'. That is impossible for us who believe that God chose that race for the vehicle of His own Incarnation, and who are indebted to Israel beyond all possible repayment.

Where we find a difficulty we may always expect that a discovery awaits us. Where there is cover we hope for game. This particular difficulty is well worth exploring.

It seems that there is a general rule in the moral universe which may be formulated, 'The higher, the more in danger'. The 'average sensual man' who is sometimes unfaithful to his wife, sometimes tipsy, always a little selfish, now and then (within the law) a trifle sharp in his deals, is certainly, by ordi-nary standards, a 'lower' type than the man whose soul is filled with some great Cause, to which he will subordinate his appetites, his fortune, and even his safety. But it is out of the second man that something really fiendish can be made; an Inquisitor, a Member of the Committee of Public Safety. It is great men, potential saints, not little men, who become merciless fanatics. Those who are readiest to die for a cause may easily become those who are readiest to kill for it. One sees the same principle at work in a field (comparatively) so unimportant as literary criticism; the most brutal work, the most rankling hatred of all other critics and of nearly all authors, may come from the most honest and disinterested critic, the man who cares most passionately and selflessly about literature. The higher the stakes, the greater the temptation to lose your temper over the game. We must not over-value the relative harmlessness of the little, sensual, frivolous people. They are not above, but below, some temptations.

If I am never tempted, and cannot even imagine myself being tempted, to gamble, this does not mean that I am better than those who are. The timidity and pessimism which exempt me from that temptation themselves tempt me to draw back from those risks and adventures which every man ought to take. In the same way we cannot be certain that the comparative absence of vindictiveness in the Pagans, though certainly a good thing in itself, is a good symptom. This was borne in upon me during a night journey taken early in the Second World War in a compartment full of young soldiers. Their conversation made it clear that they totally disbelieved all that they had read in the papers about the wholesale cruelties of the Nazi *régime*. They took it for granted, without argument, that this was all lies, all propaganda put out by our own government to 'pep up' our troops. And the shattering thing was, that, believing this, they expressed not the slightest anger. That our rulers should falsely attribute the worst of crimes to some of their fellow-men in order to induce other men to shed their blood seemed to them a matter of course. They weren't even particularly interested. They saw nothing wrong in it. Now it seemed to me that the most violent of the Psalmists – or, for that matter any child wailing out 'But it's not fair' – was in a more hopeful condition than these young men. If they had perceived, and felt as a man should feel, the diabolical wickedness which they believed our rulers to be committing, and then forgiven them, they would have been saints. But not to perceive it at all – not even to be tempted to resentment – to accept it as the most ordinary thing in the world – argues a terrifying insensibility. Clearly these young men had (on that subject anyway) no conception of good and evil whatsoever.

Thus the absence of anger, especially that sort of anger which we call *indignation*, can, in my opinion, be a most alarming symptom. And the presence of indignation may be a good one. Even when that indignation passes into bitter personal vindictiveness, it may still be a good symptom, though bad in itself. It is a sin; but it at least shows that those who commit it have not sunk below the level at which the temptation to that sin exists – just as the sins (often quite appalling) of the great patriot or great reformer point to something in him above mere self. If the Jews cursed more bitterly than the Pagans this was, I think, at least in part because they took right and wrong more seriously. For if we look at their railings we find they are usually angry not simply because these things have been done to them but because these things are manifestly wrong, are hateful to God as well as to the victim. The thought of the 'righteous Lord' – who surely must hate such doings as much as they do, who surely therefore must (but how terribly He delays!) 'judge' or avenge, is always there, if only in the background. Sometimes it comes into the foreground; as in Psalm 58:9, 10, 'The righteous shall rejoice when he seeth the vengeance ... so that a man shall say ... Doubtless there is a God that judgeth the earth.' This is something different from mere anger without indignation – the almost animal rage at finding that a man's enemy has done to him exactly what he would have done to his enemy if he had been strong enough or quick enough.

Different, certainly higher, a better symptom; yet also leading to a more terrible sin. For it encourages a man to think that his own worst passions are holy. It encourages him to add, explicitly or implicitly, 'Thus saith the Lord' to the expression of his own emotions or even his own opinions; as Carlyle and Kipling and some politicians, and even, in their own way, some modern critics, so horribly do. (It is this, by the way, rather than mere idle 'profane swearing' that we ought to mean by 'taking God's name in vain'. The man who says 'Damn that chair!' does not really wish that it should first be endowed with an immortal soul and then sent to eternal perdition.) For here also it is true, 'the higher, the more in danger'. The Jews sinned in this matter worse than the Pagans not because they were further from God but because they were nearer to Him. For the Supernatural, entering a human soul, opens to it new possibilities of both good and evil. From that point the road branches: one way to sanctity, love, humility, the other to spiritual pride, self-righteousness, persecuting zeal. And no way back to the mere humdrum virtues and vices of the unawakened soul. If the Divine call does not make us better, it will make us very much worse. Of all bad men religious bad men are the worst. Of all created beings the wickedest is one who originally stood in the immediate presence of God. There seems no way out of this. It gives a new application to Our Lord's words about 'counting the cost'.

For we can still see, in the worst of their maledictions, how these old poets were, in a sense, near to God. Though hideously distorted by the human instrument, something of the Divine voice can be heard in these passages. Not, we trust, that God looks upon their enemies as they do: He 'desireth not the death of a sinner'. But doubtless He has for the sin of those enemies just the implacable hostility which the poets express. Implacable? Yes, not to the sinner but to sin. It will not be tolerated nor condoned, no treaty will be made with it. That tooth must come out, that right hand must be amputated, if the man is to be saved. In that way the relentlessness of the Psalmists is far nearer to one side of the truth than many modern attitudes which can be mistaken, by those who hold them, for Christian charity. It is, for example, obviously nearer than the total moral indifference of the young soldiers. It is nearer than the pseudo-scientific tolerance which reduces all wickedness to neurosis (though of course some apparent wickedness is). It even contains a streak of sanity absent from the old woman presiding at a juvenile court who – I heard it myself – told some young hooligans, convicted of a well-planned robbery for gain (they had already sold the swag and some had previous convictions against them) that they must, they really must, give up such 'stupid pranks'. Against all this the ferocious parts of the Psalms serve as a reminder that there is in the world such a thing as wickedness and that it (if not its perpetrators) is hateful to God. In that way, however dangerous the human distortion may be, His word sounds through these passages too.

But can we, besides learning from these terrible Psalms, also use them in our devotional life? I believe we can; but that topic must be reserved for a later chapter.

4

DEATH IN THE PSALMS

According to my policy of taking first what is most unattractive, I should now proceed to the self-righteousness in many of the Psalms. But we cannot deal with that properly until some other matters have been noticed. I turn first to a very different subject.

Our ancestors seem to have read the Psalms and the rest of the Old Testament under the impression that the authors wrote with a pretty full understanding of Christian Theology; the main difference being that the Incarnation, which for us is something recorded, was for them something predicted. In particular, they seldom doubted that the old authors were, like ourselves, concerned with a life beyond death, that they feared damnation and hoped for eternal joy.

In our own Prayer Book version, and probably in many others, some passages make this impression almost irresistibly. Thus in Psalm 17:14, we read of wicked men 'which have their portion in this life'. The Christian reader inevitably reads into this (and Coverdale, the translator, obviously did so too) Our Lord's contrast between the Rich Man who had his good things here and Lazarus who had them hereafter; the same contrast which is implied in Luke 6:24 – 'Woe unto you that are rich, for ye have received your consolation.' But modern translators can find nothing like this in the actual Hebrew. In reality this passage is merely one of the cursings we were considering in the previous chapter. In Psalm 17:13 the poet prays God to 'cast down' (in Dr Moffatt, 'crush') the ungodly; in verse 14, a refinement occurs to him. Yes, crush them, but first let them 'have their portion in this life'. Kill them, but first give them a bad time while alive.

Again, in Psalm 49, we have, 'No man may deliver his brother ... for it cost more to redeem their souls; so that he must let that alone forever' (vv. 7, 8). Who would not think that this referred to the redeeming work of Christ? No man can 'save' the soul of another. The price of salvation is one that only the Son of God could pay; as the hymn says, there was no other 'good enough to pay the price'. The very phrasing of our version strengthens the effect – the verb 'redeem' which (outside the pawnbroking business) is now used only in a theological sense, and the past tense of 'cost'. Not it 'costs', but it did cost, more, once and for all on Calvary. But apparently the Hebrew poet meant something quite different and much more ordinary. He means merely that death is inevitable. As Dr Moffatt translates it: 'None can buy himself off. Not one can purchase for a price from God (soul's ransom is too dear) life that shall never end.'

At this point I can imagine a lifelong lover of the Psalms exclaiming: 'Oh bother the great scholars and modern translators! I'm not going to let them spoil the whole Bible for me. At least let me ask two questions. (i) Is it not stretching the arm of coincidence rather far to ask me to believe that, not once but twice, in the same book, mere accident (wrong translations, bad manuscripts, or what not) should have so successfully imitated the language of Christianity? (ii) Do you mean that the old meanings which we have always attached to these verses simply have to be scrapped?' Both questions will come up for consideration in a later chapter. For the moment I will only say that, to the second, my personal answer is a confident No. I return to what I believe to be the facts.

It seems quite clear that in most parts of the Old Testament there is little or no belief in a future life; certainly no belief that is of any religious importance. The word translated 'soul' in our version of the Psalms means simply 'life'; the word translated 'hell' means simply 'the land of the dead', the state of all the dead, good and bad alike, *Sheol*.

It is difficult to know how an ancient Jew thought of *Sheol*. He did not like thinking about it. His religion did not encourage him to think about it. No good could come of thinking about it. Evil might. It was a condition from which very wicked people like the Witch of Endor were believed to be able to conjure up a ghost. But the ghost told you nothing about Sheol; it was called up solely to tell you things about our own world. Or again, if you allowed yourself an unhealthy interest in Sheol you might be lured into one of the neighbouring forms of Paganism and 'eat the offerings of the dead' (Psalm 106:28).

Behind all this one can discern a conception not specifically Jewish but common to many ancient religions. The Greek Hades is the most familiar example to modern people. Hades is neither Heaven nor Hell; it is almost nothing. I am speaking of the popular beliefs; of course philosophers like Plato have a vivid and positive doctrine of immortality. And of course poets may write fantasies about the world of the dead. These have often no more to do with the real Pagan religion than the fantasies we may write about other planets have to do with real astronomy. In real Pagan belief, Hades was hardly worth talking about; a world of shadows, of decay. Homer (probably far closer to actual beliefs than the later and more sophisticated poets) represents the ghosts as witless. They gibber meaninglessly until some living man gives them sacrificial blood to drink. How the Greeks felt about it in his time is startlingly shown at the beginning of the *Iliad* where he says of men killed in battle that 'their souls' went to Hades but 'the men themselves' were devoured by dogs and carrion birds. It is the body, even the dead body which is the man himself; the ghost is only a sort of reflection or echo. (The grim impulse sometimes has crossed my mind to wonder whether all this was, is, in fact true; that the merely natural fate of humanity, the fate of unredeemed humanity, is just this – to disintegrate in soul as in body, to be a witless psychic sediment. If so, Homer's idea that only a drink of sacrificial blood can restore a ghost to rationality would be one of the most striking among many Pagan anticipations of the truth.)

Such a conception, vague and marginal even in Paganism, becomes more so in Judaism. Sheol is even dimmer, further in the background, than Hades. It is a thousand miles away from the centre of Jewish religion; especially in the Psalms. They speak of Sheol (or 'hell' or 'the pit') very much as a man speaks of 'death' or 'the grave' who has no belief in any sort of future state whatever – a man to whom the dead are simply dead, nothing, and there's no more to be said.

In many passages this is quite clear, even in our translation, to every attentive reader. The clearest of all is the cry in Psalm 89:46: 'O remember how short my time is: why hast thou made all men for nought?' We all come to nothing in the end. Therefore 'every man living is altogether vanity' (39:6). Wise and foolish have the same fate (49:10). Once dead, a man worships God no more: 'Shall the dust give thanks unto thee?' (30:10); 'for in death, no man remembereth thee' (6:5). Death is 'the land' where, not only worldly things, but all things, 'are forgotten' (88:12). When a man dies, 'all his thoughts perish' (146:3). Every man will 'follow the generation of his fathers, and shall never see light' (49:19): he goes into a darkness which will never end.

Elsewhere, I admit, it sounds as if the poet were praying for the 'salvation of his soul' in the Christian sense. Almost certainly he is not. In Psalm 30:3, 'Thou hast brought my soul out of hell' means 'you have saved me from death'. 'The snares of death compassed me round about, and the pains of hell gat hold upon me' (116:3) means 'Death was setting snares for me, I felt the anguish of a dying man' – as we should say, 'I was at death's door.'

As we all know from our New Testaments, Judaism had greatly changed in this respect by Our Lord's time. The Sadducees held to the old view. The Pharisees, and apparently many more, believed in the life of the world to come. When, and by what stages, and (under God) from what sources, this new belief crept in, is not part of our present subject. I am more concerned to try to understand the absence of such a belief, in the midst of intense religious feeling, over the earlier period. To some it may seem astonishing that God, having revealed so much of Himself to that people, should not have taught them this.

It does not now astonish me. For one thing there were nations close to the Jews whose religion was overwhelmingly concerned with the after life. In reading about ancient Egypt one gets the impression of a culture in which the main business of life was the attempt to secure the well-being of the dead. It looks as if God did not want the chosen people to follow that example. We may ask why. Is it possible for men to be too much concerned with their eternal destiny? In one sense, paradoxical though it sounds, I should reply, Yes.

For the truth seems to me to be that happiness or misery beyond death, simply in themselves, are not even religious subjects at all. A man who believes in them will of course be prudent to seek the one and avoid the other. But that seems to have no more to do with religion than looking after one's health or saving money for one's old age. The only difference here is that the stakes are so very much higher. And this means that, granted a real and steady conviction, the hopes and anxieties aroused are overwhelming. But they are not on that account the more religious. They are hopes for oneself, anxieties for oneself. God is not in the centre. He is still important only for the sake of something else. Indeed such a belief can exist without a belief in God at all. Buddhists are much concerned with what will happen to them after death, but are not, in any true sense, Theists.

It is surely, therefore, very possible that when God began to reveal Himself to men, to show them that He and nothing else is their true goal and the satisfaction of their needs, and that He has a claim upon them simply by being what He is, quite apart from anything He can bestow or deny, it may have been absolutely necessary that this revelation should not begin with any hint of future Beatitude or Perdition. These are not the right points to begin at. An effective belief in them, coming too soon, may even render almost impossible the development of (so to call it) the appetite for God; personal hopes and fears, too obviously exciting, have got in first. Later, when, after centuries of spiritual training, men have learned to desire and adore God, to pant after Him 'as pants the hart', it is another matter. For then those who love God will desire not only to enjoy Him but 'to enjoy Him forever', and will fear to lose Him. And it is by that door that a truly religious hope of Heaven and fear of Hell can enter; as corollaries to a faith already centred upon God, not as things of any independent or intrinsic weight. It is even arguable that the moment 'Heaven' ceases to mean union with God and 'Hell' to mean separation from Him, the belief in either is a mischievous superstition; for then we have, on the one hand, a merely 'compensatory' belief (a 'sequel' to life's sad story, in which everything will 'come all right') and, on the other, a nightmare which drives men into asylums or makes them persecutors.

Fortunately, by God's good providence, a strong and steady belief of that self-seeking and sub-religious kind is extremely difficult to maintain, and is perhaps possible only to those who are slightly neurotic. Most of us find that our belief in the future life is strong only when God is in the centre of our thoughts; that if we try to use the hope of 'Heaven' as a compensation (even for the most innocent and natural misery, that of bereavement) it crumbles away. It can, on those terms, be maintained only by arduous efforts of controlled imagination; and we know in our hearts that the imagination is our own. As for Hell, I have often been struck, in reading the 'hell-fire sermons' of our older divines, at the desperate efforts they make to render these horrors vivid to their hearers, at their astonishment that men, with such horrors hanging over them, can live as carelessly as they do. But perhaps it is not really astonishing. Perhaps the divines are appealing, on the level of self-centred prudence and self-centred terror, to a belief which, on that level, cannot really exist as a permanent influence on conduct – though doubtless it may be worked up for a few excited minutes or even hours.

All this is only one man's opinion. And it may be unduly influenced by my own experience. For I (I have said it in another book, but the repetition is unavoidable) was allowed for a whole year to believe in God and try – in some stumbling fashion – to obey Him before any belief in the future life was given me. And that year always seems to me to have been of very great value. It is therefore perhaps natural that I should suspect a similar value in the centuries during which the Jews were in the same position. Other views no doubt can be taken.

Of course among ancient Jews, as among us, there were many levels. They were not all of them, not perhaps any of them at all times, disinterested, any more than we. What then filled the place which was later taken by the hope of Heaven (too often, I am afraid, desired chiefly as an escape from Hell) was of course the hope of peace and plenty on earth. This was in itself no less (but really no more) sub-religious than prudential cares about the next world. It was not quite so personal and self-centred as our own wishes for earthly prosperity. The individual, as such, seems to have been less aware of himself, much less separated from others, in those ancient times. He did not so sharply distinguish his own prosperity from that of the nation and especially of his own descendants. Blessings on one's remote posterity were blessings on oneself. Indeed it is not always easy to know whether the speaker in a Psalm is the individual poet or Israel itself. I suspect that sometimes the poet had never raised the question.

But we should be quite mistaken if we supposed that these worldly hopes were the only thing in Judaism. They are not the characteristic thing about it, the thing that sets it apart from ancient religion in general. And notice here the strange roads by which God leads His people. Century after century, by blows which seem to us merciless, by defeat, deportation, and massacre, it was hammered into the Jews that earthly prosperity is not in fact the certain, or even the probable, reward of seeing God. Every hope was disappointed. The lesson taught in the Book of Job was grimly illustrated in practice. Such experience would surely have destroyed a religion which had no other centre than the hope of peace and plenty with 'every man under his own vine and his own fig tree'. We know that many did 'fall off'. But the astonishing thing is that the religion is not destroyed. In its best representatives it grows purer, stronger, and more profound. It is being, by this terrible discipline, directed more and more to its real centre. That will be the subject of the next chapter.

5

'THE FAIR BEAUTY
OF THE LORD'

'Now let us stint all this and speak of mirth.' So far – I couldn't help it – this book has been what the old woman in Scott described as 'a cauld clatter o' morality'. At last we can turn to better things. If we think 'mirth' an unsuitable word for them, that may show how badly we need something which the Psalms can give us perhaps better than any other book in the world.

David, we know, danced before the Ark. He danced with such abandon that one of his wives (presumably a more modern, though not a better type than he) thought he was making a fool of himself. David didn't care whether he was making a fool of himself or not. He was rejoicing in the Lord. This helps to remind us at the outset that Judaism, though it is the worship of the one true and eternal God, is an ancient religion. That means that its externals, and many of its attitudes, were much more like those of Paganism than they were like all that stuffiness – all that regimen of tiptoe tread and lowered voice – which the word 'religion' suggests to so many people now. In one way, of course, this puts a barrier between it and us. We should not have enjoyed the ancient rituals. Every temple in the world, the elegant Parthenon at Athens and the holy Temple at Jerusalem, was a sacred slaughterhouse. (Even the Jews seem to shrink from a return to this. They have not rebuilt the Temple nor revived the sacrifices.) But even that has two sides. If temples smelled of blood, they also smelled of roast meat; they struck a festive and homely note, as well as a sacred.

When I read the Bible as a boy I got the idea that the Temple of Jerusalem was related to the local synagogues very much as a great cathedral is related to the parish churches in a Christian country. In reality there is no such parallel. What happened in the synagogues was quite unlike what happened in the Temple. The synagogues were meeting-houses where the Law was read and where an address might be given – often by some distinguished visitor (as in Luke 4:20 or Acts 13:15). The Temple was the place of sacrifice, the place where the essential worship of Jahweh was enacted. Every parish church is the descendant of both. By its sermons and lessons it shows its ancestry in the synagogue. But because the Eucharist is celebrated and all other sacraments administered in it, it is like the Temple; it is a place where the adoration of the Deity can be fully enacted. Judaism without the Temple was mutilated, deprived of its central operation; any church, barn, sickroom, or field, can be the Christian's temple.

The most valuable thing the Psalms do for me is to express that same delight in God which made David dance. I am not saying that this is so pure or so profound a thing as the love of God reached by the greatest Christian saints and mystics. But I am not comparing it with that, I am comparing it with the merely dutiful 'churchgoing' and laborious 'saying our prayers' to which most of us are, thank God not always, but often, reduced. Against that it stands out as something astonishingly robust, virile, and spontaneous; something we may regard with an innocent envy and may hope to be infected by as we read.

For the reason I have given, this delight is very much centred on the Temple. The simpler poets do not in fact distinguish between the love of God in what we might (rather dangerously) call 'a spiritual sense' and their enjoyment of the festivals in the Temple. We must not misunderstand this. The Jews were not, like the Greeks, an analytical and logical people; indeed, except the Greeks, no ancient peoples were. The sort of distinction which we can easily make between those who are really worshipping God in church and those who enjoy 'a beautiful service' for musical, antiquarian, or merely sentimental reasons, would have been impossible to them. We get nearest to their state of mind if we think of a pious modern farm-labourer at church on Christmas Day or at the harvest thanksgiving. I mean, of course, one who really believes, who is a regular communicant; not one who goes only on these occasions and is thus (not in the worst but in the best sense of that word) a Pagan, practising Pagan piety, making his bow to the Unknown – and at other times Forgotten – on the great annual festivals. The man I picture is a real Christian. But you would do him wrong by asking him to separate out, at such moments, some exclusively religious element in his mind from all the rest – from his hearty social pleasure in a corporate act, his enjoyment of the hymns (and the crowd), his memory of other such services since childhood, his well-earned anticipation of rest after harvest or Christmas dinner after church. They are all one in his mind. This would have been even truer of any ancient man, and especially of an ancient Jew. He was a peasant, very close to the soil. He had never heard of music, or festivity, or agriculture as things separate from religion, nor of religion as something separate from them. Life was one. This assuredly laid him open to spiritual dangers which more sophisticated people can avoid; it also gave him privileges which they lack.

Thus when the Psalmists speak of 'seeing' the Lord, or long to 'see' Him, most of them mean something that happened to them in the Temple. The fatal way of putting this would be to say 'they only mean they have seen the festival'. It would be better to say, 'If we had been there we should have seen only the festival'. Thus in Psalm 68, 'It is well seen, O God, how thou goest[1] ... in the sanctuary ... the singers go before, the minstrels follow after; in the midst are the damsels playing with the timbrels' (vv. 24–25), it is almost as if the poet said, 'Look, here He comes'. If I had been there I should have seen the musicians and the girls with the tambourines; in addition, as another thing, I might or might not have (as we say) 'felt' the presence of God. The ancient worshipper would have been aware of no such dualism. Similarly, if a modern man wished to 'dwell in the house of the Lord all the days of his life, to behold the fair beauty of the Lord' (27:4), he would mean, I suppose, that he hoped to receive, not of course without the mediation of the sacraments and the help of other 'services', but as something distinguishable from them and not to be presumed upon as their inevitable result, frequent moments of spiritual vision and the 'sensible' love of God. But I suspect that the poet of that Psalm drew no distinction between 'beholding the fair beauty of the Lord' and the acts of worship themselves.

When the mind becomes more capable of abstraction and analysis this old unity breaks up. And no sooner is it possible to distinguish the rite from the vision of God than there is a danger of the rite becoming a substitute for, and a rival to, God Himself. Once it can be thought of separately, it will; and it may then take on a rebellious, cancerous life of its own. There is a stage in a child's life at which it cannot separate the religious from the merely festal character of Christmas or Easter. I have been told of a very small and very devout boy who was heard murmuring to himself on Easter morning a poem of his own composition which began 'Chocolate eggs and Jesus risen'. This seems to me, for his age, both admirable poetry and admirable piety. But of course the time will soon come when such a child can no longer effortlessly and spontaneously enjoy that unity. He will become able to distinguish the spiritual from the ritual and festal aspect of Easter; chocolate eggs will no longer be sacramental. And once he has distinguished he must put one or the other first. If he puts the spiritual first he can still taste something of Easter in the chocolate eggs; if he puts the eggs first they will soon be no more than any other sweetmeat. They have taken on an independent, and therefore a soon withering, life. Either at some period in Judaism, or else in the experience of some Jews, a roughly parallel situation occurred. The unity falls apart; the sacrificial rites become distinguishable from the

---

[1] This was perhaps sung while the Ark itself was carried round.

meeting with God. This does not unfortunately mean that they will cease or become less important. They may, in various evil modes, become even more important than before. They may be valued as a sort of commercial transaction with a greedy God who somehow really wants or needs large quantities of carcasses and whose favours cannot be secured on any other terms. Worse still, they may be regarded as the only thing He wants, so that their punctual performance will satisfy Him without obedience to His demands for mercy, 'judgement', and truth. To the priests themselves the whole system will seem important simply because it is both their art and their livelihood; all their pedantry, all their pride, all their economic position, is bound up with it. They will elaborate their art more and more. And of course the corrective to these views of sacrifice can be found within Judaism itself. The prophets continually fulminate against it. Even the Psalter, though largely a Temple collection, can do so; as in Psalm 50 where God tells His people that all this Temple worship, considered in itself, is not the real point at all, and particularly ridicules the genuinely Pagan notion that He really needs to be fed with roast meat. 'If I were hungry, do you think I would apply to *you*?' (v. 12). I have sometimes fancied He might similarly ask a certain type of modern clergyman, 'If I wanted music – if I were conducting research into the more recondite details of the history of the Western Rite – do you really think *you* are the source I would rely on?'

This possible degradation of sacrifice and the rebukes of it are, however, so well known that there is no need to stress them here. I want to stress what I think that we (or at least I) need more; the joy and delight in God which meet us in the Psalms, however loosely or closely, in this or that instance, they may be connected with the Temple. This is the living centre of Judaism. These poets knew far less reason than we for loving God. They did not know that He offered them eternal joy; still less that He would die to win it for them. Yet they express a longing for Him, for His mere presence, which comes only to the best Christians or to Christians in their best moments. They long to live all their days in the Temple so that they may constantly see 'the fair beauty of the Lord' (27:4). Their longing to go up to Jerusalem and 'appear before the presence of God' is like a physical thirst (42). From Jerusalem His presence flashes out 'in perfect beauty' (50:2). Lacking that encounter with Him, their souls are parched like a waterless countryside (63:2). They crave to be 'satisfied with the pleasures' of His house (65:4). Only there can they be at ease, like a bird in the nest (84:3). One day of those 'pleasures' is better than a lifetime spent elsewhere (v. 10).

I have rather – though the expression may seem harsh to some – called this the 'appetite for God' than 'the love of God'. The 'love of God' too easily suggests the word 'spiritual' in all those negative or restrictive senses which it has unhappily acquired. These old poets do not seem to think that they are meritorious or pious for having such feelings; nor, on the other hand, that they are privileged in being given the grace to have them. They are at once less priggish about it than the worst of us and less humble – one might almost say, less surprised – than the best of us. It has all the cheerful spontaneity of a natural, even a physical, desire. It is gay and jocund. They are glad and rejoice (9:2). Their fingers itch for the harp (43:4), for the lute and the harp – wake up, lute and harp! – (57:9); let's have a song, bring the tambourine, bring the 'merry harp with the lute', we're going to sing merrily and make a cheerful noise (81:1, 2). Noise, you may well say. Mere music is not enough. Let everyone, even the benighted Gentiles,[2] clap their hands (47:1). Let us have clashing cymbals, not only well tuned, but *loud*, and dances too (150:5). Let even the remote islands (all islands were remote, for the Jews were no sailors) share the exultation (97:1).

I am not saying that this gusto – if you like, this rowdiness – can or should be revived. Some of it cannot be revived because it is not dead but with us still. It would be idle to pretend that we Anglicans are a striking example. The Romans, the Orthodox, and the Salvation Army all, I think, have retained more of it than we. We have a terrible concern about good taste. Yet even we can still exult. The second reason goes far deeper. All Christians know something the Jews did not know about what it 'cost to redeem their souls'. Our life as Christians begins by being baptised into a death; our most joyous festivals begin with, and centre upon, the broken body and the shed blood. There is thus a tragic depth in our worship which Judaism lacked. Our joy has to be the sort of joy which can coexist with that; there is for us a spiritual counterpoint where they had simple melody. But this does not in the least cancel the delighted debt which I, for one, feel that I owe to the most jocund Psalms. There, despite the presence of elements we should now find it hard to regard as religious at all, and the absence of elements which some might think essential to religion, I find an experience fully God-centred, asking of God no gift more urgently than His presence, the gift of Himself, joyous to the highest degree, and unmistakably real. What I see (so to speak) in the faces of these old poets tells me more about the God whom they and we adore.

But this characteristically Hebraic delight or gusto finds also another channel. We must follow it in the next chapter.

---

[2] Not 'all ye people' as in our version, but 'all ye nations' (*Goyim*).

6

'SWEETER THAN HONEY'

In Racine's tragedy of *Athalie* the chorus of Jewish girls sing an ode about the original giving of the Law on Mount Sinai, which has the remarkable refrain *ô charmante loi* (Act 1, scene iv). Of course it will not do – it will border on the comic – to translate this 'oh charming Law'. *Charming* in English has come to be a tepid and even patronising word; we use it of a pretty cottage, of a book that is something less than great or a woman who is something less than beautiful. How we should translate *charmante* I don't know; 'enchanting'? 'delightful'? 'beautiful'? None of them quite fits. What is, however, certain is that Racine (a mighty poet and steeped in the Bible) is here coming nearer than any modern writer I know to a feeling very characteristic of certain Psalms. And it is a feeling which I at first found utterly bewildering.

'More to be desired are they than gold, yea than much fine gold: sweeter also than honey and the honey-comb' (19:10). One can well understand this being said of God's mercies, God's visitations, His attributes. But what the poet is actually talking about is God's law, His commands; His 'rulings' as Dr Moffatt well translates in verse 9 (for 'judgements' here plainly means decisions about conduct). What are being compared to gold and honey are those 'statutes' (in the Latin version 'decrees') which, we are told, 'rejoice the heart' (v. 8). For the whole poem is about the Law, not about 'judgement' in the sense to which Chapter 1 was devoted.

This was to me at first very mysterious. 'Thou shalt not steal, thou shalt not commit adultery' – I can understand that a man can, and must, respect these 'statutes', and try to obey them, and assent to them in his heart. But it is very hard to find how they could be, so to speak, delicious, how they exhilarate. If this is difficult at any time, it is doubly so when obedience to either is opposed to some strong, and perhaps *in itself* innocent, desire. A man held back by his unfortunate previous marriage to some lunatic or criminal who never dies from some woman whom he faithfully loves, or a hungry man left alone, without money, in a shop filled with the smell and sight of new bread, roasting coffee, or fresh strawberries – can these find the prohibition of adultery or of theft at all like honey? They may obey, they may still respect the 'statute'. But surely it could be more aptly compared to the dentist's forceps or the front line than to anything enjoyable and sweet.

A fine Christian and a great scholar to whom I once put this question said he thought that the poets were referring to the satisfaction men felt in knowing they had obeyed the Law; in other words, to the 'pleasures of a good conscience'. They would, on his view, be meaning something very like what Wordsworth meant when he said we know nothing more beautiful than the 'smile' on Duty's face – her smile when her orders have been carried out. It is rash for me to differ from such a man, and his view certainly makes excellent sense. The difficulty is that the Psalmists never seem to me to say anything very like this.

In Psalm 1:2 we are told that the good man's 'delight is in the law of the Lord, and in his law will he exercise himself day and night'. To 'exercise himself' in it apparently does not mean to obey it (though no doubt the good man will do that too) but to study it, as Dr Moffatt says to 'pore over it'. Of course 'the Law' does not here mean simply the ten commandments, it means the whole complex legislation (religious, moral, civil, criminal and even constitutional) contained in Leviticus, Numbers and Deuteronomy. The man who 'pores upon it' is obeying Joshua's command (Joshua 1:8), 'the book of the Law shall not depart out of thy mouth; but thou shalt meditate therein day and night.' This means, among other things, that the Law was a study or, as we should say, a 'subject'; a thing on which there would be commentaries, lectures, and examinations. There were. Thus part (religiously, the least important part) of what an ancient Jew meant when he said he 'delighted in the Law' was very like what one of us would mean if he said that somebody 'loved' history, or physics, or archaeology. This might imply a wholly innocent – though, of course, merely natural – delight in one's favourite subject; or, on the other hand, the pleasures of conceit, pride in one's own learning and consequent contempt for the outsiders who don't share it, or even a venal admiration for the studies which secure one's own stipend and social position.

The danger of this second development is obviously increased tenfold when the study in question is from the outset stamped as sacred. For then the danger of spiritual pride is added to that of mere ordinary pedantry and conceit. One is sometimes (not often) glad not to be a great theologian; one might so easily mistake it for being a good Christian. The temptations to which a great philologist or a great chemist is exposed are trivial in comparison. When the subject is sacred, proud and clever men may come to think that the outsiders who don't know it are not merely inferior to them in skill but lower in God's eyes; as the priests said (John 7:49), 'All that rabble who are not experts in the Torah are accursed.' And as this pride increases, the 'subject' or study which confers such privilege will grow more and more complicated, the list of things forbidden will increase, till to get through a single day without supposed sin becomes like an elaborate step-dance, and this horrible network breeds self-righteousness in some and haunting anxiety in others. Meanwhile the 'weightier matters of the Law', righteousness itself, shrinks into insignificance under this vast overgrowth, so that the legalists strain at a gnat and swallow a camel.

Thus the Law, like the sacrifice, can take on a cancerous life of its own and work against the thing for whose sake it existed. As Charles Williams wrote, 'When the means are autonomous they are deadly.' This morbid condition of the Law contributed to – I do not suggest it is the sole or main cause of – St Paul's joyous sense of Christ as the Deliverer from Law. It is against this same morbid condition that Our Lord uttered some of His sternest words; it is the sin, and simultaneously the punishment, of the Scribes and Pharisees. But that is not the side of the matter I want to stress here, nor does it by this time need stressing. I would rather let the Psalms show me again the good thing of which this bad thing is the corruption.

As everyone knows, the Psalm specially devoted to the Law is 119, the longest in the whole collection. And everyone has probably noticed that from the literary or technical point of view, it is the most formal and elaborate of them all. The technique consists in taking a series of words which are all, for purposes of this poem, more or less synonyms (*word, statutes, commandments, testimonies,* etc.), and ringing the changes on them through each of its eight-verse sections – which themselves correspond to the letters of the alphabet. (This may have given an ancient ear something of the same sort of pleasure we get from the Italian metre called the *Sestina,* where instead of rhymes we have the same end words repeated in varying orders in each stanza.) In other words, this poem is not, and does not pretend to be, a sudden outpouring of the heart like, say, Psalm 18. It is a pattern, a thing done like embroidery, stitch by stitch, through long, quiet hours, for love of the subject and for the delight in leisurely, disciplined craftsmanship.

Now this, in itself, seems to me very important because it lets us into the mind and mood of the poet. We can guess at once that he felt about the Law somewhat as he felt about his poetry; both involved exact and loving conformity to an intricate pattern. This at once suggests an attitude from which the Pharisaic conception could later grow but which in itself, though not necessarily religious, is quite innocent. It will look like priggery or pedantry (or else like a neurotic fussiness) to those who cannot sympathise with it, but it need not be any of these things. It may be the delight in Order, the pleasure in getting a thing 'just so' – as in dancing a minuet. Of course the poet is well aware that something incomparably more serious than a minuet is here in question. He is also aware that he is very unlikely, himself, to achieve this perfection of discipline: 'O that my ways *were* made so straight that I *might* keep thy statutes!' (v. 5). At present they aren't, and he can't. But his effort to do so does not spring from servile fear. The Order of the Divine mind, embodied in the Divine Law, is beautiful. What should a man do but try to reproduce it, so far as possible, in his daily life? His 'delight' is in those statutes (v. 16); to study them is like finding treasure (v. 14); they affect him like music, are his 'songs' (v. 54); they taste like honey (v. 103); they are better than silver and gold (v. 72). As one's eyes are more and more opened, one sees more and more in them, and it excites wonder (v. 18). This is not priggery nor even scrupulosity; it is the language of a man ravished by a moral beauty. If we cannot at all share his experience, we shall be the losers. Yet I cannot help fancying that a Chinese Christian – one whose own traditional culture had been the 'schoolmaster to bring him to Christ' – would appreciate this Psalm more than most of us; for it is an old idea in that culture that life should above all things be ordered and that its order should reproduce a Divine order.

But there is something else to our purpose in this grave poem. On three occasions the poet asserts that the Law is 'true' or 'the truth' (vv. 86, 138, 142). We find the same in Psalm 111:7, 'all his commandments are true'. (The word, I understand, could also be translated 'faithful', or 'sound'; what is, in the Hebrew sense, 'true' is what 'holds water', what doesn't 'give way' or collapse.) A modern logician would say that the Law is a command and that to call a command 'true' makes no sense; 'The door is shut' may be true or false but 'Shut the door' can't. But I think we all see pretty well what the Psalmists mean. They mean that in the Law you find the 'real' or 'correct' or stable, well-grounded, directions for living. The Law answers the question 'Wherewithal shall a young man cleanse his way?' (119:9). It is like a lamp, a guide (v. 105). There are many rival directions for living, as the Pagan cultures all round us show. When the poets call the directions or 'rulings' of Jahweh 'true' they are expressing the assurance that these, and not those others, are the 'real' or 'valid' or unassailable ones; that they are based on the very nature of things and the very nature of God.

By this assurance they put themselves, implicitly, on the right side of a controversy which arose far later among Christians. There were in the eighteenth century terrible theologians who held that 'God did not command certain things because they are right, but certain things are right because God commanded them.' To make the position perfectly clear, one of them even said that though God has, as it happens, commanded us to love Him and one another, He might equally well have commanded us to hate Him and one another, and hatred would then have been right. It was apparently a mere toss-up which He decided on. Such a view in effect makes God a mere arbitrary tyrant. It would be better and less irreligious to believe in no God and to have no ethics than to have such an ethics and such a theology as this. The Jews of course never discuss this in abstract and philosophical terms. But at once, and completely, they assume the right view, knowing better than they know. They know that the Lord (not merely obedience to the Lord) is 'righteous' and commands 'righteousness' because He loves it (11:8). He enjoins what is good because it is good, because He is good. Hence His laws have *emeth*, 'truth', intrinsic validity, rock-bottom reality, being rooted in His own nature, and are therefore as solid as that Nature which He has created. But the Psalmists themselves can say it best; 'thy righteousness standeth like the strong mountains, thy judgements are like the great deep' (36:6).[1] Their delight in the Law is a delight in having touched firmness; like the pedestrian's delight in feeling the hard road beneath his feet after a false short cut has long entangled him in muddy fields.

For there were other roads, which lacked 'truth'. The Jews had as their immediate neighbours, close to them in race as well as in position, Pagans of the worst kind, Pagans whose religion was marked by none of that beauty or (sometimes) wisdom which we can find among the Greeks. That background made the 'beauty' or 'sweetness' of the Law more visible; not least because these neighbouring Paganisms were a constant temptation to the Jew and may in some of their externals have been not unlike his own religion. The temptation was to turn to those terrible rites in times of terror – when, for example, the Assyrians were pressing on. We who not so long ago waited daily for invasion by enemies, like the Assyrians, skilled and constant in systematic cruelty, know how they may have felt. They were tempted, since the Lord seemed deaf, to try those appalling deities who demanded so much more and might therefore perhaps give more in return. But when a Jew in some happier hour, or a better Jew even in that hour, looked at those worships – when he thought of sacred prostitution, sacred sodomy, and the babies thrown into the fire for Moloch – his own 'Law' as he turned back to it must have shone with an extraordinary radiance. Sweeter than honey; or if that metaphor does not suit us who have not such a sweet tooth as all ancient peoples (partly because we have plenty of sugar), let us say like mountain water, like fresh air after a dungeon, like sanity after a nightmare. But, once again, the best image is in a Psalm, the 19th.[2]

I take this to be the greatest poem in the Psalter and one of the greatest lyrics in the world. Most readers will remember its structure; six verses about Nature, five about Law, and four of personal prayer. The actual words supply no logical connection between the first and second movements. In this way its technique resembles that of the most modern poetry. A modern

---

[1] See Appendix I, p. 720.
[2] See Appendix I, p. 719.

poet would pass with similar abruptness from one theme to another and leave you to find out the connecting link for yourself. But then he would possibly be doing this quite deliberately; he might have, though he chose to conceal, a perfectly clear and conscious link in his own mind which he could express to you in logical prose if he wanted to. I doubt if the ancient poet was like that. I think he felt, effortlessly and without reflecting on it, so close a connection, indeed (for his imagination) such an identity, between his first theme and his second that he passed from the one to the other without realising that he had made any transition. First he thinks of the sky; how, day after day, the pageantry we see there shows us the splendour of its Creator. Then he thinks of the sun, the bridal joyousness of its rising, the unimaginable speed of its daily voyage from east to west. Finally, of its heat; not of course the mild heats of our climate but the cloudless, blinding, tyrannous rays hammering the hills, searching every cranny. The key phrase on which the whole poem depends is 'there is nothing hid from the heat thereof'. It pierces everywhere with its strong, clean ardour. Then at once, in verse 7 he is talking of something else, which hardly seems to him something else because it is so like the all-piercing, all-detecting sunshine. The Law is 'undefiled', the Law gives light, it is clean and everlasting, it is 'sweet'. No one can improve on this and nothing can more fully admit us to the old Jewish feeling about the Law; luminous, severe, disinfectant, exultant. One hardly needs to add that this poet is wholly free from self-righteousness and the last section is concerned with his 'secret faults'. As he has felt the sun, perhaps in the desert, searching him out in every nook of shade where he attempted to hide from it, so he feels the Law searching out all the hiding-places of his soul.

In so far as this idea of the Law's beauty, sweetness, or preciousness, arose from the contrast of the surrounding Paganisms, we may soon find occasion to recover it. Christians increasingly live on a spiritual island; new and rival ways of life surround it in all directions and their tides come further up the beach every time. None of these new ways is yet so filthy or cruel as some Semitic Paganism. But many of them ignore all individual rights and are already cruel enough. Some give morality a wholly new meaning which we cannot accept, some deny its possibility. Perhaps we shall all learn, sharply enough, to value the clean air and 'sweet reasonableness' of the Christian ethics which in a more Christian age we might have taken for granted. But of course, if we do, we shall then be exposed to the danger of priggery. We might come to 'thank God that we are not as other men'. This introduces the greatest difficulty which the Psalms have raised in my mind.

7

CONNIVANCE

Every attentive reader of the Psalms will have noticed that they speak to us severely not merely about doing evil ourselves but about something else. In Psalm 26:4, the good man is not only free from 'vanity' (falsehood) but has not even 'dwelled with', been on intimate terms with, those who are 'vain'. He has 'hated' them (v. 5). So in 31:7, he has 'hated' idolaters. In 50:18, God blames a man not for being a thief but for 'consenting to' a thief (in Dr Moffatt, 'you are a friend to any thief you see'). In 141:4–6, where our translation appears to be rather wrong, the general sense nevertheless comes through and expresses the same attitude. Almost comically the Psalmist of 139 asks, 'Don't I hate those who hate thee, Lord? ... Why, I hate them as if they were *my* enemies!' (vv. 21, 22).

Now obviously all this – taking upon oneself to hate those whom one thinks God's enemies, avoiding the society of those one thinks wicked, judging our neighbours, thinking oneself 'too good' for some of them (not in the snobbish way, which is a trivial sin in comparison, but in the deepest meaning of the words 'too good') – is an extremely dangerous, almost a fatal, game. It leads straight to 'Pharisaism' in the sense which Our Lord's own teaching has given to that word. It leads not only to the wickedness but to the absurdity of those who in later times came to be called the 'unco guid'. This I assume from the outset, and I think that even in the Psalms this evil is already at work. But we must not be Pharisaical even to the Pharisees. It is foolish to read such passages without realising that a quite genuine problem is involved. And I am not at all confident about the solution.

We hear it said again and again that the editor of some newspaper is a rascal, that some politician is a liar, that some official person is a tyrannical Jack-in-office and even dishonest, that someone has treated his wife abominably, that some celebrity (film-star, author, or what not) leads a most vile and mischievous life. And the general rule in modern society is that no one refuses to meet any of these people and to behave towards them in the friendliest and most cordial manner. People will even go out of their way to meet them. They will not even stop buying the rascally newspaper, thus paying the owner for the lies, the detestable intrusions upon private life and private tragedy, the blasphemies and the pornography, which they profess to condemn.

I have said there is a problem here, but there are really two. One is social and almost political. It may be asked whether that state of society in which rascality undergoes no social penalty is a healthy one; whether we should not be a happier country if certain important people were pariahs as the hangman once was – blackballed at every club, dropped by every acquaintance, and liable to the print of riding-crop or fingers across the face if they were ever bold enough to speak to a respectable woman. It leads into the larger question whether the great evil of our civil life is not the fact that there seems now no medium between hopeless submission and full-dress revolution. Rioting has died out, moderate rioting. It can be argued that if the windows of various ministries and newspapers were more often broken, if certain people were more often put under pumps and (mildly – mud, not stones) pelted in the streets, we should get on a great deal better. It is not wholly desirable that any man should be allowed at once the pleasures of a tyrant or a wolf's-head and also those of an honest freeman among his equals. To this question I do not know the answer. The dangers of a change in the direction I have outlined are very great; so are the evils of our present tameness.

I am concerned here only with the problem that appears in our individual and private lives. How ought we to behave in the presence of very bad people? I will limit this by changing 'very bad people' to 'very bad people who are powerful, prosperous and impenitent'. If they are outcasts, poor and miserable, whose wickedness obviously has not 'paid', then every Christian knows the answer. Christ speaking to the Samaritan woman at the well, Christ with the woman taken in adultery, Christ dining with publicans, is our example. I mean, of course, that His humility, His love, His total indifference to the social discredit and misrepresentation He might incur are examples for us; not, Heaven knows, that any of us who was not specially qualified to do so by priesthood, age, old acquaintance, or the earnest request of the sinners themselves, could without insolence and presumption assume the least trace of His authority to rebuke and pardon. (One has to be very careful lest the desire to patronise and the itch to be a busybody should disguise itself as a vocation to help the 'fallen', or tend to obscure our knowledge that we are fallen – perhaps in God's eyes far more so – ourselves.) But we may be sure there were others who equally consorted with 'publicans and sinners' and whose motives were very unlike those of Our Lord.

The publicans were the lowest members of what may be called the Vichy or Collaborationist movement in Palestine; men who fleeced their fellow-countrymen to get money for the occupying power in return for a fat percentage of the swag. As such they were like the hangman, outside all decent social intercourse. But some of them did pretty well financially, and no doubt most of them enjoyed, up to a point, the protection and contemptuous favours of the Roman government. One may guess that some consorted with them for very bad reasons – to get 'pickings', to be on good terms with such dangerous neighbours. Besides Our Lord there would have been among their guests toadies and those who wanted to be 'on the bandwagon'; people in fact like a young man I once knew.

He had been a strict socialist at Oxford. Everything ought to be run by the State; private enterprise and independent professions were for him the great evil. He then went away and became a schoolmaster. After about ten years of that he came to see me. He said his political views had been wholly reversed. You never heard a fuller recantation. He now saw that State interference was fatal. What had converted him was his experience as a schoolmaster of the Ministry of Education – a set of ignorant meddlers armed with insufferable powers to pester, hamper and interrupt the work of real, practical teachers who knew the subjects they taught, who knew boys, parents, and all the real conditions of their work. It makes no difference to the point of the story whether you agree with his view of the Ministry; the important thing is that he held that view. For the real point of the story, and of his visit, when it came, nearly took my breath away. Thinking thus, he had come to see whether I had any influence which might help him to get a job in the Ministry of Education.

Here is the perfect band-wagoner. Immediately on the decision 'This is a revolting tyranny', follows the question 'How can I as quickly as possible cease to be one of the victims and become one of the tyrants?' If I had been able to introduce the young man to someone in the Ministry, I think we may be sure that his manners to that hated 'meddler' would have been genial and friendly in the extreme. Thus someone who had heard his previous invective against the meddling and then witnessed his actual behaviour to the meddler, might possibly (for charity 'believeth all things') have concluded that this young man was full of the purest Christianity and loved one he thought a sinner while hating what he thought his sin.

Of course this is an instance of band-wagoning so crude and unabashed as to be farcical. Not many of us perhaps commit the like. But there are subtler, more social or intellectual forms of band-wagoning which might deceive us. Many people have a very strong desire to meet celebrated or 'important' people, including those of whom they disapprove, from curiosity or vanity. It gives them something to talk or even (anyone may produce a book of reminiscences) to write about. It is felt to confer distinction if the great, though odious, man recognises you in the street. And where such motives are in play it is better still to know him quite well, to be intimate with him.

It would be delightful if he shouted out 'Hallo Bill' while you were walking down the Strand with an impressionable country cousin. I don't know that the desire is itself a very serious defect. But I am inclined to think a Christian would be wise to avoid, where he decently can, any meeting with people who are bullies, lascivious, cruel, dishonest, spiteful and so forth.

Not because we are 'too good' for them. In a sense because we are not good enough. We are not good enough to cope with all the temptations, nor clever enough to cope with all the problems, which an evening spent in such society produces. The temptation is to condone, to connive at; by our words, looks and laughter, to 'consent'. The temptation was never greater than now when we are all (and very rightly) so afraid of priggery or 'smugness'. And of course, even if we do not seek them out, we shall constantly be in such company whether we wish it or not. This is the real and unavoidable difficulty.

We shall hear vile stories told as funny; not merely licentious stories but (to me far more serious and less noticed) stories which the teller could not be telling unless he was betraying someone's confidence. We shall hear infamous detraction of the absent, often disguised as pity or humour. Things we hold sacred will be mocked. Cruelty will be slyly advocated by the assumption that its only opposite is 'sentimentality'. The very presuppositions of any possible good life – all disinterested motives, all heroism, all genuine forgiveness – will be, not explicitly denied (for then the matter could be discussed), but assumed to be phantasmal, idiotic, believed in only by children.

What is one to do? For on the one hand, quite certainly, there is a degree of unprotesting participation in such talk which is very bad. We are strengthening the hands of the enemy. We are encouraging him to believe that 'those Christians', once you get them off their guard and round a dinner table, really think and feel exactly as he does. By implication we are denying our Master; behaving as if we 'knew not the Man'. On the other hand is one to show that, like Queen Victoria, one is 'not amused'? Is one to be contentious, interrupting the flow of conversation at every moment with 'I don't agree, I don't agree'? Or rise and go away? But by these courses we may also confirm some of their worst suspicions of 'those Christians'. We are just the sort of ill-mannered prigs they always said.

Silence is a good refuge. People will not notice it nearly so easily as we tend to suppose. And (better still) few of us enjoy it as we might be in danger of enjoying more forcible methods. Disagreement can, I think, sometimes be expressed without the appearance of priggery, if it is done argumentatively not dictatorially; support will often come from some most unlikely member of the party, or from more than one, till we discover that those who were silently dissentient were actually a majority. A discussion of real interest may follow. Of course the right side may be defeated in it. That matters very much less than I used to think. The very man who has argued you down will sometimes be found, years later, to have been influenced by what you said.

There comes, however, a degree of evil against which a protest will have to be made, however little chance it has of success. There are cheery agreements in cynicism or brutality which one must contract out of unambiguously. If it can't be done without seeming priggish, then priggish we must seem.

For what really matters is not seeming but being a prig. If we sufficiently dislike making the protest, if we are strongly tempted not to, we are unlikely to be priggish in reality. Those who positively enjoy, as they call it, 'testifying' are in a different and more dangerous position. As for the mere seeming – well, though it is very bad to be a prig, there are social atmospheres so foul that in them it is almost an alarming symptom if a man has never been called one. Just in the same way, though pedantry is a folly and snobbery a vice, yet there are circles in which only a man indifferent to all accuracy will escape being called a pedant, and others where manners are so coarse, flashy and shameless that a man (whatever his social position) of any natural good taste will be called a snob.

What makes this contact with wicked people so difficult is that to handle the situation successfully requires not merely good intentions, even with humility and courage thrown in; it may call for social and even intellectual talents which God has not given us. It is therefore not self-righteousness but mere prudence to avoid it when we can. The Psalmists were not quite wrong when they described the good man as avoiding 'the seat of the scornful' and fearing to consort with the ungodly lest he should 'eat of' (shall we say, laugh at, admire, approve, justify?) 'such things as please them'. As usual in their attitude, with all its dangers, there is a core of very good sense. 'Lead us not into temptation' often means, among other things, 'Deny me those gratifying invitations, those highly interesting contacts, that participation in the brilliant movements of our age, which I so often, at such risk, desire.'

Closely connected with these warnings against what I have called 'connivance' are the protests of the Psalter[1] against other sins of the tongue. I think that when I began to read it these surprised me a little; I had half expected that in a simpler and more violent age when more evil was done with the knife, the big stick, and the firebrand, less would be done by talk. But in reality the Psalmists mention hardly any kind of evil more often than this one, which the most civilised societies share. 'Their throat is an open sepulchre, they flatter' (5:10), 'under his tongue is ungodliness and vanity', or 'perjury' as Dr Moffatt translates it (10:7), 'deceitful lips' (12:3), 'lying

---

[1] Some of these probably involve archaic, and even magical, ideas of a power intrinsic in words themselves, so that all blessings and cursings would be efficacious.

lips' (31:20), 'words full of deceit' (36:3), the 'whispering' of evil men (41:7), cruel lies that 'cut like a razor' (52:3), talk that sounds 'smooth as oil' and will wound like a sword (55:22), pitiless jeering (102:8). It is all over the Psalter. One almost hears the incessant whispering, tattling, lying, scolding, flattery, and circulation of rumours. No historical readjustments are here required, we are in the world we know. We even detect in that muttering and wheedling chorus voices which are familiar. One of them may be too familiar for recognition.

8

NATURE

Two factors determine the Psalmists' approach to Nature. The first they share with the vast majority of ancient writers; the second was in their time, if not absolutely unique, extremely rare.

(i) They belong to a nation chiefly of peasants. For us the very name Jew is associated with finance, shop-keeping, money-lending and the like. This however, dates from the Middle Ages when the Jews were not allowed to own land and were driven into occupations remote from the soil. Whatever characteristics the modern Jew has acquired from millennia of such occupations, they cannot have been those of his ancient ancestors. Those were peasants or farmers. When even a king covets a piece of his neighbour's property, the piece is a vineyard; he is more like a wicked squire than a wicked king. Everyone was close to the land; everyone vividly aware of our dependence on soils and weather. So, till a late age, was every Greek and Roman. Thus part of what we should now, perhaps, call 'appreciation of Nature' could not then exist – all that part which is really delight in 'the country' as a contrast to the town. Where towns are few and very small and where nearly everyone is on the land, one is not aware of any special thing called 'the country'. Hence a certain sort of 'nature poetry' never existed in the ancient world till really vast cities like Alexandria arose; and, after the fall of ancient civilisation, it never existed again until the eighteenth century. At other periods what we call 'the country' is simply the world, what water is to a fish. Nevertheless appreciation of Nature can exist; a delight which is both utilitarian and poetic. Homer can enjoy a landscape, but what he means by a beautiful landscape is one that is useful – good deep soil, plenty of fresh water, pasture that will make the cows really fat, and some nice timber. Being one of a seafaring race he adds, as a Jew would not, a good harbour. The Psalmists, who are writing lyrics not romances, naturally give us little landscape. What they do give us, far more sensuously and delightedly than anything I have seen in Greek, is the very feel of weather – weather seen with a real countryman's eyes, enjoyed almost as a vegetable might be

supposed to enjoy it. 'Thou art good to the earth ... thou waterest her furrows ... thou makest it soft with drops of rain ... the little hills shall rejoice
on every side ... the valleys shall stand so thick with corn that they shall
laugh and sing; (65:9–14). In 104:16 (better in Dr Moffatt than in the Prayer
Book), 'the great trees drink their fill'.

(ii) The Jews, as we all know, believed in one God, maker of heaven and
earth. Nature and God were distinct; the One had made the other; the One
ruled and the other obeyed. This, I say, we all know. But for various reasons
its real significance can easily escape a modern reader if his studies happen
not to have led him in certain directions.

In the first place it is for us a platitude. We take it for granted. Indeed I suspect that many people assume that some clear doctrine of creation underlies
all religions: that in Paganism the gods, or one of the gods, usually created the
world; even that religions normally begin by answering the question, 'Who
made the world?' In reality, creation, in any unambiguous sense, seems to be
a surprisingly rare doctrine; and when stories about it occur in Paganism they
are often religiously unimportant, not in the least central to the religions in
which we find them. They are on the fringe where religion tails off into what
was perhaps felt, even at the time, to be more like fairy-tale. In one Egyptian
story a god called Atum came up out of the water and, being apparently a
hermaphrodite, begot and bore the two next gods; after that, things could get
on. In another, the whole senate of the gods came up out of Nun, the Deep.
According to a Babylonian myth, before heaven and earth were made a being
called Apsu begot, and a being called Tiamat bore, Lahmu and Lahamu, who
in their turn produced Anshar and Kishar. We are expressly told that this pair
were greater than their parents, so that it is more like a myth of evolution
than of creation. In the Norse myth we begin with ice and fire, and indeed
with a north and south, amidst all which, somehow, a giant comes to life,
who bears (from his arm-pit) a son and daughter. Greek mythology starts
with heaven and earth already in existence.

I do not mention these myths to indulge in a cheap laugh at their crudity.
All our language about such things, that of the theologian as well as that of
the child, is crude. The real point is that the myths, even in their own terms,
do not reach the idea of Creation in our sense at all. Things 'come up out of'
something or 'are formed in' something. If the stories could, for the
moment, be supposed true, they would still be stories about very early
events in a process of development, a world-history, which was already
going on. When the curtain rises in these myths there are always some
'properties' already on the stage and some sort of drama is proceeding. You
may say they answer the question 'How did the play begin?' But that is an
ambiguous question. Asked by the man who arrived ten minutes late it
would be properly answered, say, with the words, 'Oh, first three witches

came in, and then there was a scene between an old king and a wounded soldier.' That is the sort of question the myths are in fact answering. But the very different question: 'How does a play originate? Does it write itself? Do the actors make it up as they go along? Or is there someone – not on the stage, not like the people on the stage – someone we don't see – who invented it all and caused it to be?' – this is rarely asked or answered.

Admittedly we find in Plato a clear Theology of Creation in the Judaic and Christian sense; the whole universe – the very conditions of time and space under which it exists – are produced by the will of a perfect, timeless, unconditioned God who is above and outside all that He makes. But this is an amazing leap (though not made without the help of Him who is the Father of lights) by an overwhelming theological genius; it is not ordinary Pagan religion.

Now we all understand of course the importance of this peculiarity in Judaic thought from a strictly and obviously religious point of view. But its total consequences, the ways in which it changes a man's whole mind and imagination, might escape us.

To say that God created Nature, while it brings God and Nature into relation, also separates them. What makes and what is made must be two, not one. Thus the doctrine of Creation in one sense empties Nature of divinity. How very hard this was to do and, still more, to keep on doing, we do not now easily realise. A passage from Job (not without its own wild poetry in it) may help us. 'If I beheld the sun when it shined, or the moon walking in brightness; and my heart hath been secretly enticed, or my mouth kissed my hand; this also would be an iniquity' (31:26–28). There is here no question of turning, in a time of desperate need, to devilish gods. The speaker is obviously referring to an utterly spontaneous impulse, a thing you might find yourself acting upon almost unawares. To pay some reverence to the sun or moon is apparently so natural; so apparently innocent. Perhaps in certain times and places it was really innocent. I would gladly believe that the gesture of homage offered to the moon was sometimes accepted by her Maker; in those times of ignorance which God 'winked at' (Acts 17:30). The author of Job, however, was not in that ignorance. If he had kissed his hand to the moon it would have been iniquity. The impulse was a temptation; one which no European has felt for the last thousand years.

But in another sense the same doctrine which empties Nature of her divinity also makes her an index, a symbol, a manifestation, of the Divine. I must recall two passages quoted in an earlier chapter. One is that from Psalm 19 where the searching and cleansing sun becomes an image of the searching and cleansing Law. The other is from Psalm 36: 'Thy mercy, O Lord, reacheth unto the heavens, and thy faithfulness unto the clouds. Thy righteousness standeth like the strong mountains, thy judgements are like the great deep'

(vv. 5, 6). It is surely just because the natural objects are no longer taken to be themselves Divine that they can now be magnificent symbols of Divinity. There is little point in comparing a Sun-god with the sun or Neptune with the great deep; there is much in comparing the Law with the sun or saying that God's judgements are an abyss and a mystery like the sea.

But of course the doctrine of Creation leaves Nature full of manifestations which show the presence of God, and created energies which serve Him. The light is His garment, the thing we partially see Him through (Psalm 104:2), the thunder can be His voice (29:3–5). He dwells in the dark thundercloud (18:11), the eruption of a volcano comes in answer to His touch (104:32). The world is full of his emissaries and executors. He makes winds His messengers and flames His servants (104:4), rides upon cherubim (18:10), commands the army of angels.

All this is clearly in one way very close to Paganism. Thor and Zeus also spoke in the thunder; Hermes or Iris was the messenger of the gods. But the difference, though subtle, is momentous, between hearing in the thunder the voice of God or the voice of a god. As we have seen, even in the creation-myths, gods have beginnings. Most of them have fathers and mothers; often we know their birth-places. There is no question of self-existence or the timeless. Being is imposed upon them, as upon us, by preceding causes. They are, like us, creatures or products; though they are luckier than we in being stronger, more beautiful, and exempt from death. They are, like us, actors in the cosmic drama, not its authors. Plato fully understood this. His God creates the gods and preserves them from death by His own power; they have no inherent immortality. In other words, the difference between believing in God and in many gods is not one of arithmetic. As someone has said 'gods' is not really the plural of God; God has no plural. Thus, when you hear in the thunder the voice of a god, you are stopping short, for the voice of a god is not really a voice from beyond the world, from the uncreated. By taking the god's voice away – or envisaging the god as an angel, a servant of that Other – you go further. The thunder becomes not less divine but more. By emptying Nature of divinity – or, let us say, of divinities – you may fill her with Deity, for she is now the bearer of messages. There is a sense in which Nature-worship silences her – as if a child or a savage were so impressed with the postman's uniform that he omitted to take in the letters.

Another result of believing in Creation is to see Nature not as a mere datum but as an achievement. Some of the Psalmists are delighted with its mere solidity and permanence. God has given to His works His own character of *emeth*; they are watertight, faithful, reliable, not at all vague or phantasmal. 'All His works are *faithful* – He spake and it was done, He commanded and it stood fast' (33:4, 9). By His might (Dr Moffatt's version) 'the mountains are made firm and strongly fixed' (65:6). God has laid the foundations of the earth with perfect thoroughness (104:5). He has made everything firm and permanent and imposed boundaries which limit each thing's operation (148:6). Notice how in Psalm 136 the poet passes from God's creation of Nature to the delivering of Israel out of Egypt: both are equally great deeds, great victories.

But the most surprising result of all is still to be mentioned. I said that the Jews, like nearly all the ancients, were agricultural and approached Nature with a gardener's and a farmer's interest, concerned with rain, with grass 'for the service of man', wine to cheer man up and olive-oil to make his face shine – to make it look, as Homer says somewhere, like a peeled onion (104:14, 15). But we find them led on beyond this. Their gusto, or even gratitude, embraces things that are no use to man. In the great Psalm especially devoted to Nature, from which I have just quoted (104),[1] we have not only the useful cattle, the cheering vine, and the nourishing corn. We have springs where the wild asses quench their thirst (v. 11), fir trees for the storks (v. 17), hill country for the wild goats and 'conies' (perhaps marmots, v. 18), finally even the lions (v. 21); and even with a glance far out to sea, where no Jew willingly went, the great whales playing, enjoying themselves (v. 26).

Of course this appreciation of, almost this sympathy with, creatures useless or hurtful or wholly irrelevant to man, is not our modern 'kindness to animals'. That is a virtue most easily practised by those who have never, tired and hungry, had to work with animals for a bare living, and who inhabit a country where all dangerous wild beasts have been exterminated.[2] The Jewish feeling, however, is vivid, fresh, and impartial. In Norse stories a pestilent creature such as a dragon tends to be conceived as the enemy not only of men but of gods. In classical stories, more disquietingly, it tends to be sent by a god for the destruction of men whom he has a grudge against. The Psalmist's clear objective view – noting the lions and whales side by side with men and men's cattle – is unusual. And I think it is certainly reached through the idea of God as Creator and sustainer of all. In 104:21, the point about the lions is that they, like us, 'do seek their meat from God'. All these creatures, like us, 'wait upon' God at feeding-time (v. 27). It is the same in 147:9; though the raven was an unclean bird to Jews, God 'feedeth the young ravens that call upon him'. The thought which gives these creatures a place in the Psalmist's gusto for Nature is surely obvious. They are our fellow-dependents; we all – lions, storks, ravens, whales – live, as our fathers said, 'at God's charges', and mention of all equally redounds to His praise.

---

[1] See Appendix 1, pp. 723–4.

[2] Heaven forbid, however, that I should be thought to slight it. I only mean that for those of us who meet beasts solely as pets it is not a costly virtue. We may properly be kicked if we lack it, but must not pat ourselves on the back for having it. When a hard-worked shepherd or carter remains kind to animals his back may well be patted; not ours.

One curious bit of evidence strengthens my belief that there is such a connection between this sort of nature poetry and the doctrine of creation; and it is also so interesting in itself that I think it worth a digression. I have said that Paganism in general fails to get out of nature something that the Jews got. There is one apparent instance to the contrary; one ancient Gentile poem which provides a fairly close parallel to Psalm 104. But then, when we come to examine it, we find that this poem is not Pagan in the sense of Polytheistic at all. It is addressed to a Monotheistic God and salutes Him as the Creator of the whole earth. It is therefore no exception to my generalisation. Where ancient Gentile literature (in some measure) anticipates the nature poetry of the Jews, it has also (in some measure) anticipated their theology. And that, in my view, is what we might have expected.

The poem in question is an Egyptian *Hymn to the Sun* dating from the 14th century BC. Its author is that Pharaoh whose real name was Amenhetep IV, but who called himself Akhenaten. Many of my readers will know his story already. He was a spiritual revolutionary. He broke away from the Polytheism of his fathers and nearly tore Egypt into shreds in his efforts to establish by force the worship of a single God. In the eyes of the established priesthood, whose property he transferred to the service of this new religion, he must have seemed a monster; a sort of Henry VIII plundering the abbeys. His Monotheism appears to have been of an extremely pure and conceptual kind. He did not, as a man of that age might have been expected to do, even identify God with the Sun. The visible disc was only His manifestation. It is an astonishing leap, more astonishing in some ways than Plato's, and, like Plato's, in sharp contrast to ordinary Paganism. And as far as we can see, it was a total failure. Akhenaten's religion died with him. Nothing, apparently, came of it.

Unless of course, as is just possible, Judaism itself partly came of it. It is conceivable that ideas derived from Akhenaten's system formed part of that Egyptian 'Wisdom' in which Moses was bred. There is nothing to disquiet us in such a possibility. Whatever was true in Akhenaten's creed came to him, in some mode or other, as all truth comes to all men, from God. There is no reason why traditions descending from Akhenaten should not have been among the instruments which God used in making Himself known to Moses. But we have no evidence that this is what actually happened. Nor do we know how fit Akhenatenism would really have been to serve as an instrument for this purpose. Its inside, its spirituality, the quality of life from which it sprang and which it encouraged, escape us. The man himself still has the power, after 34 centuries, to evoke the most violent, and contradictory, reactions. To one modern scholar he is the 'first individual' whom history records; to another, he is a crank, a faddist, half insane, possibly cretinous. We may well hope that he was accepted and blessed by God; but that his religion, at any rate on the historical level, was not so blessed and so accepted, is pretty clear. Perhaps the seed was good seed but fell on stony ground. Or perhaps it was not after all exactly the right sort of seed. To us moderns, no doubt, such a simple, enlightened, reasonable Monotheism looks very much more like the good seed than those earliest documents of Judaism in which Jahweh seems little more than a tribal deity. We might be wrong. Perhaps if Man is finally to know the bodiless, timeless, transcendent Ground of the whole universe not as a mere philosophical abstraction but as the Lord who, despite this transcendence, is 'not far from any one of us', as an utterly concrete Being (far more concrete than we) whom Man can fear, love, address, and 'taste', he must begin far more humbly and far nearer home, with the local altar, the traditional feast, and the treasured memories of God's judgements, promises, and mercies. It is possible that a certain sort of enlightenment can come too soon and too easily. At that early stage it may not be fruitful to typify God by anything so remote, so neutral, so international and (as it were) interdenominational, so featureless, as the solar disc. Since in the end we are to come to baptism and the Eucharist, to the stable at Bethlehem, the hill of Calvary, and the emptied rock-tomb, perhaps it is better to begin with circumcision, the Passover, the Ark, and the Temple. For 'the highest does not stand without the lowest'. Does not stand, does not stay; rises, rather, and expands, and finally loses itself in endless space. For the entrance is low: we must stoop till we are no taller than children in order to get in.

It would therefore be rash to assume that Akhenaten's Monotheism was, in those ways which are religiously most important, an exact anticipation of the Judaic; so that if only the priests and people of Egypt had accepted it, God could have dispensed with Israel altogether and revealed Himself to us henceforward through a long line of Egyptian prophets. What concerns us at the moment, however, is simply to note that Akhenaten's religion, being certainly in some respects like that of the Jews, sets him free to write nature-poetry in some degree like theirs. The degree could be exaggerated. The *Hymn to the Sun* remains different from the Psalms. It is magnificently like Psalm 139 (vv. 13–16) when it praises God for making the embryo grow in the mother's body, so that He is 'our nurse even in the womb': or for teaching the chick to break the eggshell and come forth 'chirping as loud as he can'. In the verse, 'Thou didst create the earth, according to thy desire,' Akhenaten even anticipates the New Testament – 'thou hast created all things, and for thy pleasure they are, and were created' (Revelation 4:11). But he does not quite see the lions as our fellow-pensioners. He brings them in, to be sure, but notice how: 'when thou settest, the world is in darkness like the dead. Out come the lions: all serpents sting.' Thus coupled with death and poisonous snakes, they are clearly envisaged in their capacity of enemies. It almost sounds as if the night itself were an enemy, out of God's reach. There is just a trace of dualism. But if there is difference, the likeness also is real. And it is the likeness which is relevant to the theme of this chapter. In Akhenaten as in the Psalms, a certain kind of poetry seems to go with a certain kind of theology. But the full and abiding development of both is Jewish.

(Meanwhile, what gentle heart can leave the topic without a prayer that this lonely ancient king, crank and doctrinaire though perhaps he was, has long seen and now enjoys the truth which so far transcends his own glimpse of it?)

9

A WORD ABOUT PRAISING

It is possible (and it is to be hoped) that this chapter will be unnecessary for most people. Those who were never thick-headed enough to get into the difficulty it deals with may even find it funny. I have not the least objection to their laughing; a little comic relief in a discussion does no harm, however serious the topic may be. (In my own experience the funniest things have occurred in the gravest and most sincere conversations.)

When I first began to draw near to belief in God and even for some time after it had been given to me, I found a stumbling block in the demand so clamorously made by all religious people that we should 'praise' God; still more in the suggestion that God Himself demanded it. We all despise the man who demands continued assurance of his own virtue, intelligence or delightfulness; we despise still more the crowd of people round every dictator, every millionaire, every celebrity, who gratify that demand. Thus a picture, at once ludicrous and horrible, both of God and of His worshippers, threatened to appear in my mind. The Psalms were especially troublesome in this way – 'Praise the Lord', 'O praise the Lord with me', 'Praise Him'. (And why, incidentally, did praising God so often consist in telling other people to praise Him? Even in telling whales, snowstorms, etc., to go on doing what they would certainly do whether we told them or not?) Worse still was the statement put into God's own mouth, 'whoso offereth me thanks and praise, he honoureth me' (50:23). It was hideously like saying, 'What I most want is to be told that I am good and great.' Worst of all was the suggestion of the very silliest Pagan bargaining, that of the savage who makes offerings to his idol when the fishing is good and beats it when he has caught nothing. More than once the Psalmists seemed to be saying, 'You like praise. Do this for me, and you shall have some.' Thus in Psalm 54 the poet begins 'save me' (v. 1), and in verse 6 adds an inducement, 'An offering of a free heart will I give thee, and praise thy Name.' Again and again the speaker asks to be saved from death on the ground that if God lets His suppliants die He will get no more praise from them, for the ghosts in Sheol

692

cannot praise (30:10; 88:10; 119:175). And mere quantity of praise seemed to count; 'seven times a day do I praise thee' (119:164). It was extremely distressing. It made one think what one least wanted to think. Gratitude to God, reverence to Him, obedience to Him, I thought I could understand; not this perpetual eulogy. Nor were matters mended by a modern author who talked of God's 'right' to be praised.

I still think 'right' is a bad way of expressing it, but I believe I now see what the author meant. It is perhaps easiest to begin with inanimate objects which can have no rights. What do we mean when we say that a picture is 'admirable'? We certainly don't mean that it is admired (that's as may be) for bad work is admired by thousands and good work may be ignored. Nor that it 'deserves' admiration in the sense in which a candidate 'deserves' a high mark from the examiners – i.e. that a human being will have suffered injustice if it is not awarded. The sense in which the picture 'deserves' or 'demands' admiration is rather this; that admiration is the correct, adequate or appropriate, response to it, that, if paid, admiration will not be 'thrown away', and that if we do not admire we shall be stupid, insensible, and great losers, we shall have missed something. In that way many objects both in Nature and in Art may be said to deserve, or merit, or demand, admiration. It was from this end, which will seem to some irreverent, that I found it best to approach the idea that God 'demands' praise. He is that Object to admire which (or, if you like, to appreciate which) is simply to be awake, to have entered the real world; not to appreciate which is to have lost the greatest experience, and in the end to have lost all. The incomplete and crippled lives of those who are tone-deaf, have never been in love, never known true friendship, never cared for a good book, never enjoyed the feel of the morning air on their cheeks, never (I am one of these) enjoyed football, are faint images of it.

But of course this is not all. God does not only 'demand' praise as the supremely beautiful and all-satisfying Object. He does apparently command it as lawgiver. The Jews were told to sacrifice. We are under an obligation to go to church. But this was a difficulty only because I did not then understand any of what I have tried to say above in Chapter 5. I did not see that it is in the process of being worshipped that God communicates His presence to men. It is not indeed the only way. But for many people at many times the 'fair beauty of the Lord' is revealed chiefly or only while they worship Him together. Even in Judaism the essence of the sacrifice was not really that men gave bulls and goats to God, but that by their so doing God gave Himself to men; in the central act of our own worship of course this is far clearer – there is manifestly, even physically, God who gives and we who receive. The miserable idea that God should in any sense need, or crave for, our worship like a vain woman wanting compliments, or a vain author presenting his new books to people who have never met or heard of him, is implicitly answered by the words, 'If I be hungry I will not tell *thee*' (50:12). Even if such an absurd Deity could be conceived, He would hardly come to *us*, the lowest of rational creatures, to gratify His appetite. I don't want my dog to bark approval of my books. Now that I come to think of it, there are some humans whose enthusiastically favourable criticism would not much gratify me.

But the most obvious fact about praise – whether of God or anything – strangely escaped me. I thought of it in terms of compliment, approval, or the giving of honour. I had never noticed that all enjoyment spontaneously overflows into praise unless (sometimes even if) shyness or the fear of boring others is deliberately brought in to check it. The world rings with praise – lovers praising their mistresses, readers their favourite poet, walkers praising the countryside, players praising their favourite game – praise of weather, wines, dishes, actors, motors, horses, colleges, countries, historical personages, children, flowers, mountains, rare stamps, rare beetles, even sometimes politicians or scholars. I had not noticed how the humblest, and at the same time most balanced and capacious, minds, praised most, while the cranks, misfits and malcontents praised least. The good critics found something to praise in many imperfect works; the bad ones continually narrowed the list of books we might be allowed to read. The healthy and unaffected man, even if luxuriously brought up and widely experienced in good cookery, could praise a very modest meal: the dyspeptic and the snob found fault with all. Except where intolerably adverse circumstances interfere, praise almost seems to be inner health made audible. Nor does it cease to be so when, through lack of skill, the forms of its expression are very uncouth or even ridiculous. Heaven knows, many poems of praise addressed to an earthly beloved are as bad as our bad hymns, and an anthology of love poems for public and perpetual use would probably be as sore a trial to literary taste as *Hymns Ancient and Modern*. I had not noticed either that just as men spontaneously praise whatever they value, so they spontaneously urge us to join them in praising it: 'Isn't she lovely? Wasn't it glorious? Don't you think that magnificent?' The Psalmists in telling everyone to praise God are doing what all men do when they speak of what they care about. My whole, more general, difficulty about the praise of God depended on my absurdly denying to us, as regards the supremely Valuable, what we delight to do, what indeed we can't help doing, about everything else we value.

I think we delight to praise what we enjoy because the praise not merely expresses but completes the enjoyment; it is its appointed consummation. It is not out of compliment that lovers keep on telling one another how beautiful they are; the delight is incomplete till it is expressed. It is frustrating to have discovered a new author and not to be able to tell anyone how good he is; to come suddenly, at the turn of the road, upon some mountain valley of unexpected grandeur and then to have to keep silent because the people with you care for it no more than for a tin can in the ditch; to hear a good joke and find no one to share it with (the perfect hearer died a year ago). This is so even when our expressions are inadequate, as of course they usually are. But how if one could really and fully praise even such things to perfection – utterly 'get out' in poetry or music or paint the upsurge of appreciation which almost bursts you? Then indeed the object would be fully appreciated and our delight would have attained perfect development. The worthier the object, the more intense this delight would be. If it were possible for a created soul fully (I mean, up to the full measure conceivable in a finite being) to 'appreciate', that is to love and delight in, the worthiest object of all, and simultaneously at every moment to give this delight perfect expression, then that soul would be in supreme beatitude. It is along these lines that I find it easiest to understand the Christian doctrine that 'Heaven' is a state in which angels now, and men hereafter, are perpetually employed in praising God. This does not mean, as it can so dismally suggest, that it is like 'being in church'. For our 'services' both in their conduct and in our power to participate, are merely attempts at worship; never fully successful, often 99.9 per cent failures, sometimes total failures. We are not riders but pupils in the riding school; for most of us the falls and bruises, the aching muscles and the severity of the exercise, far outweigh those few moments in which we were, to our own astonishment, actually galloping without terror and without disaster. To see what the doctrine really means, we must suppose ourselves to be in perfect love with God – drunk with, drowned in, dissolved by, that delight which, far from remaining pent up within ourselves as incommunicable, hence hardly tolerable, bliss, flows out from us incessantly again in effortless and perfect expression, our joy no more separable from the praise in which it liberates and utters itself than the brightness a mirror receives is separable from the brightness it sheds. The Scotch catechism says that man's chief end is 'to glorify God and enjoy Him forever'. But we shall then know that these are the same thing. Fully to enjoy is to glorify. In commanding us to glorify Him, God is inviting us to enjoy Him.

Meanwhile of course we are merely, as Donne says, tuning our instruments. The tuning up of the orchestra can be itself delightful, but only to those who can in some measure, however little, anticipate the symphony. The Jewish sacrifices, and even our own most sacred rites, as they actually occur in human experience, are, like the tuning, promise, not performance. Hence, like the tuning, they may have in them much duty and little delight; or none. But the duty exists for the delight. When we carry out our 'religious duties' we are like people digging channels in a waterless land, in order that when at last the water comes, it may find them ready. I mean, for the most part. There are happy moments, even now, when a trickle creeps along the dry beds; and happy souls to whom this happens often.

As for the element of bargaining in the Psalms (Do this and I will praise you), that silly dash of Paganism certainly existed. The flame does not ascend pure from the altar. But the impurities are not its essence. And we are not all in a position to despise even the crudest Psalmists on this score. Of course we would not blunder in our words like them. But there is, for ill as well as for good, a wordless prayer. I have often, on my knees, been shocked to find what sort of thoughts I have, for a moment, been addressing to God; what infantile placations I was really offering, what claims I have really made, even what absurd adjustments or compromises I was, half-consciously, proposing. There is a Pagan, savage heart in me somewhere. For unfortunately the folly and idiot-cunning of Paganism seem to have far more power of surviving than its innocent or even beautiful elements. It is easy, once you have power, to silence the pipes, still the dances, disfigure the statues, and forget the stories; but not easy to kill the savage, the greedy, frightened creature now cringing, now blustering, in one's soul – the creature to whom God may well say, 'thou thoughtest I am even such a one as thyself' (50:21).

But all this, as I have said, will be illuminating to only a few of my readers. To the others, such a comedy of errors, so circuitous a journey to reach the obvious, will furnish occasion for charitable laughter.

10

SECOND MEANINGS

I must now turn to something far more difficult. Hitherto we have been trying to read the Psalms as we suppose – or I suppose – their poets meant them to be read. But this of course is not the way in which they have chiefly been used by Christians. They have been believed to contain a second or hidden meaning, an 'allegorical' sense, concerned with the central truths of Christianity, with the Incarnation, the Passion, the Resurrection, the Ascension, and with the Redemption of man. All the Old Testament has been treated in the same way. The full significance of what the writers are saying is, on this view, apparent only in the light of events which happened after they were dead.

Such a doctrine, not without reason, arouses deep distrust in a modern mind. Because, as we know, almost anything can be read into any book if you are determined enough. This will be especially impressed on anyone who has written fantastic fiction. He will find reviewers, both favourable and hostile, reading into his stories all manner of allegorical meanings which he never intended. (Some of the allegories thus imposed on my own books have been so ingenious and interesting that I often wish I had thought of them myself.) Apparently it is impossible for the wit of man to devise a narrative in which the wit of some other man cannot, and with some plausibility, find a hidden sense.

The field for self-deception, once we accept such methods of interpretation, is therefore obviously very wide. Yet in spite of this I think it impossible – for a reason I will give later – to abandon the method wholly when we are dealing, as Christians, with the Bible. We have, therefore, a steep hill before us. I will not attempt the cliffs. I must take a roundabout route which will look first as if it could never lead us to the top at all.

I begin far away from Scripture and even from Christianity, with instances of something said or written which takes on a new significance in the light of later events.

One of the Roman historians tells us about a fire in a provincial town which was thought to have originated in the public baths. What gave some

697

colour to the suspicion of deliberate incendiarism was the fact that, earlier that day, a gentleman had complained that the water in the hot bath was only lukewarm and had received from an attendant the reply, *it will soon be hot enough*. Now of course if there really had been a plot, and the slave was in it, and fool enough to risk discovery by this veiled threat, then the story would not concern us. But let us suppose the fire was an accident (i.e. was intended by nobody). In that case the slave would have said something truer, or more importantly true, than he himself supposed. Clearly, there need to be nothing here but chance coincidence. The slave's reply is fully explained by the customer's complaint; it is just what any bath attendant would say. The deeper significance which his words turned out to have during the next few hours was, as we should say, accidental.

Now let us take a somewhat tougher instance. (The non-classical reader needs to know that to a Roman the 'age' or 'reign' of Saturn meant the lost age of innocence and peace. That is, it roughly corresponded to the Garden of Eden before the Fall; though it was never, except among the Stoics, of anything like comparable importance.) Virgil, writing not very long before the birth of Christ, begins a poem thus: 'The great procession of the ages begins anew. Now the Virgin returns, the reign of Saturn returns, and the new child is sent down from high heaven.' It goes on to describe the paradisal age which this nativity will usher in. And of course throughout the Middle Ages it was taken that some dim prophetic knowledge of the birth of Christ had reached Virgil, probably through the Sibylline Books. He ranked as a Pagan prophet. Modern scholars would, I suppose, laugh at the idea. They might differ as to what noble or imperial couple were being thus extravagantly complimented by a court poet on the birth of a son; but the resemblance to the birth of Christ would be regarded, once more, as an accident. To say the least of it, however, this is a much more striking accident than the slave's words to the man in the baths. If this is luck, it is extraordinary luck. If one were a fanatical opponent of Christianity one would be tempted to say, in an unguarded moment, that it was diabolically lucky.

I now turn to two examples which I think to be on a different level. In them, as in those we have been considering, someone says what is truer and more important than he knows; but it does not seem to me that he could have done so by chance. I hasten to add that the alternative to chance which I have in mind is not 'prophecy' in the sense of clear prevision, miraculously bestowed. Nor of course have I the slightest intention of using the examples I shall cite as evidences for the truth of Christianity. Evidences are not here our subject. We are merely considering how we should regard those second meanings which things said or written sometimes take on in the light of fuller knowledge than their author possessed. And I am suggesting that different instances demand that we should regard them in different ways.

Sometimes we may regard this overtone as the result of simple coincidence, however striking. But there are other cases in which the later truth (which the speaker did not know) is intimately related to the truth he did know; so that, in hitting on something like it, he was in touch with that very same reality in which the fuller truth is rooted. Reading his words in the light of that fuller truth and hearing it in them as an overtone or second meaning, we are not foisting on them something alien to his mind, an arbitrary addition. We are prolonging his meaning in a direction congenial to it. The basic reality behind his words and behind the full truth is one and the same.

The status I claim for such things, then, is neither that of coincidence on the one hand nor that of supernatural prevision on the other. I will try to illustrate it by three imaginable cases. (i) A holy person, explicitly claiming to prophesy by the Spirit, tells us that there is in the universe such and such a creature. Later we learn (which God forbid) to travel in space and distribute upon new worlds the vomit of our own corruption; and, sure enough, on the remote planet of some remote star, we find that very creature. This would be prophecy in the strictest sense. This would be evidence for the prophet's miraculous gift and strong presumptive evidence for the truth of anything else he had said. (ii) A wholly unscientific writer of fantasies invents a creature for purely artistic reasons. Later on, we find a creature recognisably like it. This would be just the writer's luck. A man who knows nothing about racing may once in his life back a winner. (iii) A great biologist, illustrating the relation between animal organisms and their environment, invents for this purpose a hypothetical animal adapted to a hypothetical environment. Later, we find a creature very like it (of course in an environment very like the one he had supposed). This resemblance is not in the least accidental. Insight and knowledge, not luck, led to his invention. The real nature of life explains both why there is such a creature in the universe and also why there was such a creature in his lectures. If, while we re-read the lectures, we think of the reality, we are not bringing arbitrary fancies of our own to bear on the text. This second meaning is congenial to it. The examples I have in mind correspond to this third case; though, as we shall see, something more sensitive and personal than scientific knowledge is involved – what the writer or speaker was, not only what he knew.

Plato in his *Republic* is arguing that righteousness is often praised for the rewards it brings – honour, popularity, and the like – but that to see it in its true nature we must separate it from all these, strip it naked. He asks us therefore to imagine a perfectly righteous man treated by all around him as a monster of wickedness. We must picture him, still perfect, while he is bound, scourged, and finally impaled (the Persian equivalent of crucifixion). At this passage a Christian reader starts and rubs his eyes. What is happening? Yet another of these lucky coincidences? But presently he sees that there is something here which cannot be called luck at all.

Virgil, in the poem I have quoted, may have been, and the slave in the baths almost certainly was, 'talking about something else', some matter other than that of which their words were most importantly true. Plato is talking, and knows he is talking, about the fate of goodness in a wicked and misunderstanding world. But that is not something simply other than the Passion of Christ. It is the very same thing of which that Passion is the supreme illustration. If Plato was in some measure moved to write of it by the recent death – we may almost say the martyrdom – of his master Socrates then that again is not something simply other than the Passion of Christ. The imperfect, yet very venerable, goodness of Socrates led to the easy death of the hemlock, and the perfect goodness of Christ led to the death of the cross, not by chance but for the same reason; because goodness is what it is, and because the fallen world is what it is. If Plato, starting from one example and from his insight into the nature of goodness and the nature of the world, was led on to see the possibility of a perfect example, and thus to depict something extremely like the Passion of Christ, this happened not because he was lucky but because he was wise. If a man who knew only England and had observed that, the higher a mountain was, the longer it retained the snow in early spring, were led on to suppose a mountain so high that it retained the snow all the year round, the similarity between his imagined mountain and the real Alps would not be merely a lucky accident. He might not know that there were any such mountains in reality; just as Plato probably did not know that the ideally perfect instance of crucified goodness which he had depicted would ever become actual and historical. But if that man ever saw the Alps he would not say, 'What a curious coincidence.' He would be more likely to say, 'There! What did I tell you?'

And what are we to say of those gods in various Pagan mythologies who are killed and rise again and who thereby renew or transform the life of their worshippers or of nature? The odd thing is that here those anthropologists who are most hostile to our faith would agree with many Christians in saying, 'The resemblance is not accidental.' Of course the two parties would say this for different reasons. The anthropologists would mean: 'All these superstitions have a common source in the mind and experience, especially the agricultural experience, of early man. Your myth of Christ is like the myth of Balder because it has the same origin. The likeness is a family likeness.' The Christians would fall into two schools of thought. The early Fathers (or some of them), who believed that Paganism was nothing but the direct work of the Devil, would say: 'The Devil has from the beginning tried to mislead humanity with lies. As all accomplished liars do, he makes his lies as like the truth as he can; provided they lead man astray on the main issue, the more closely they imitate truth the more effective they will be. That is why we call him God's Ape; he is always imitating God. The resemblance of Adonis to Christ is therefore not at all accidental; it is the resemblance we expect to find between a counterfeit and the real thing, between a parody and the original, between imitation pearls and pearls.' Other Christians who think, as I do, that in mythology divine and diabolical and human elements (the desire for a good story), all play a part, would say: 'It is not accidental. In the sequence of night and day, in the annual death and rebirth of the crops, in the myths which these processes gave rise to, in the strong, if half-articulate, feeling (embodied in many Pagan "Mysteries") that man himself must undergo some sort of death if he would truly live, there is already a likeness permitted by God to that truth on which all depends. The resemblance between these myths and the Christian truth is no more accidental than the resemblance between the sun and the sun's reflection in a pond, or that between a historical fact and the somewhat garbled version of it which lives in popular report, or between the trees and hills of the real world and the trees and hills in our dreams.' Thus all three views alike would regard the 'Pagan Christs' and the true Christ as things really related and would find the resemblance significant.

In other words, when we examine things said which take on, in the light of later knowledge, a meaning they could not have had for those who said them, they turn out to be of different sorts. To be sure, of whatever sort they may be, we can often profitably read them with that second meaning in mind. If I think (as I cannot help thinking) about the birth of Christ while I read that poem of Virgil's, or even if I make it a regular part of my Christmas reading, this may be quite a sensible and edifying thing to do. But the resemblance which makes such a reading possible may after all be a mere coincidence (though I am not sure that it is). I may be reading into Virgil what is wholly irrelevant to all he was, and did, and intended; irrelevant as the sinister meaning which the bathman's word in the Roman story acquired from later events may have been to anything that slave was or meant. But when I meditate on the Passion while reading Plato's picture of the Righteous One, or on the Resurrection while reading about Adonis or Balder, the case is altered. There is a real connection between what Plato and the myth-makers most deeply were and meant and what I believe to be the truth. I know that connection and they do not. But it is really there. It is not an arbitrary fancy of my own thrust upon the old words. One can, without any absurdity, imagine Plato or the myth-makers if they learned the truth, saying, 'I see ... so that was what I was really talking about. Of course. That is what my words really meant, and I never knew it.' The bath attendant if innocent, on hearing the second meaning given to his words, would no doubt have said, 'So help me, I never meant no such thing. Never come into my head. I hadn't a clue.' What Virgil would have said, if he had learned the truth, I have no idea. (Or may we more charitably speak, not of what Plato and Virgil and the myth-makers 'would have said' but of what they said? For we can pray with good hope that they now know and have long since welcomed the truth. 'Many shall come from the east and the west and sit down in the kingdom.')

Thus, long before we come to the Psalms or the Bible, there are good reasons for not throwing away all second meanings as rubbish. Keble said of the Pagan poets, 'Thoughts beyond their thoughts to those high bards were given.' But let us now turn to Scripture itself.

II

SCRIPTURE

I f even pagan utterances can carry a second meaning, not quite accidentally but because, in the sense I have suggested, they have a sort of right to
it, we shall expect the Scriptures to do this more momentously and more
often. We have two grounds for doing so if we are Christians.

(i) For us these writings are 'holy', or 'inspired', or, as St Paul says, 'the
Oracles of God'. But this has been understood in more than one way, and I
must try to explain how I understand it, at least so far as the Old Testament
is concerned. I have been suspected of being what is called a Fundamentalist.
That is because I never regard any narrative as unhistorical simply on the
ground that it includes the miraculous. Some people find the miraculous so
hard to believe that they cannot imagine any reason for my acceptance of
it other than a prior belief that every sentence of the Old Testament has
historical or scientific truth. But this I do not hold, any more than St Jerome
did when he said that Moses described Creation 'after the manner of a popular poet' (as we should say, mythically) or than Calvin did when he
doubted whether the story of Job were history or fiction. The real reason
why I can accept as historical a story in which a miracle occurs is that I have
never found any philosophical grounds for the universal negative proposition that miracles do not happen. I have to decide on quite other grounds (if
I decide at all) whether a given narrative is historical or not. The Book of Job
appears to me unhistorical because it begins about a man quite unconnected
with all history or even legend, with no genealogy, living in a country of
which the Bible elsewhere has hardly anything to say; because, in fact, the
author quite obviously writes as a story-teller not as a chronicler.

I have therefore no difficulty in accepting, say, the view of those scholars
who tell us that the account of Creation in Genesis is derived from earlier
Semitic stories which were Pagan and mythical. We must of course be quite
clear what 'derived from' means. Stories do not reproduce their species like
mice. They are told by men. Each re-teller either repeats exactly what his
predecessor had told him or else changes it. He may change it unknowingly

or deliberately. If he changes it deliberately, his invention, his sense of form, his ethics, his ideas of what is fit, or edifying, or merely interesting, all come in. If unknowingly, then his unconscious (which is so largely responsible for our forgettings) has been at work. Thus at every step in what is called – a little misleadingly – the 'evolution' of a story, a man, all he is and all his attitudes, are involved. And no good work is done anywhere without aid from the Father of Lights. When a series of such re-tellings turns a creation story which at first had almost no religious or metaphysical significance into a story which achieves the idea of true Creation and of a transcendent Creator (as Genesis does), then nothing will make me believe that some of the re-tellers, or some one of them, has not been guided by God.

Thus something originally merely natural – the kind of myth that is found amongst most nations – will have been raised by God above itself, qualified by Him and compelled by Him to serve purposes which of itself it would not have served. Generalising thus, I take it that the whole Old Testament consists of the same sort of material as any other literature – chronicle (some of it obviously pretty accurate), poems, moral and political diatribes, romances, and what not; but all taken into the service of God's word. Not all, I suppose, in the same way. There are prophets who write with the clearest awareness that Divine compulsion is upon them. There are chroniclers whose intention may have been merely to record. There are poets like those in the Song of Songs who probably never dreamed of any but a secular and natural purpose in what they composed. There is (and it is no less important) the work first of the Jewish and then of the Christian Church in preserving and canonising just these books. There is the work of redactors and editors in modifying them. On all of these I suppose a Divine pressure; of which not by any means all need have been conscious.

The human qualities of the raw materials show through. Naïvety, error, contradiction, even (as in the cursing Psalms) wickedness are not removed. The total result is not 'the Word of God' in the sense that every passage, in itself, gives impeccable science or history. It carries the Word of God; and we (under grace, with attention to tradition and to interpreters wiser than ourselves, and with the use of such intelligence and learning as we may have) receive that Word from it not by using it as an encyclopaedia or an encyclical but by steeping ourselves in its tone or temper and so learning its overall message.

To a human mind this working up (in a sense imperfectly), this sublimation (incomplete) of human material, seems, no doubt, an untidy and leaky vehicle. We might have expected, we may think we should have preferred, an unrefracted light giving us ultimate truth in systematic form – something we could have tabulated and memorised and relied on like the multiplication table. One can respect, and at moments envy, both the Fundamentalist's view of the Bible and the Roman Catholic's view of the Church. But there is one argument which we should beware of using for either position: God must have done what is best; this is best, therefore God has done this. For we are mortals and do not know what is best for us, and it is dangerous to prescribe what God must have done – especially when we cannot, for the life of us, see that He has after all done it.

We may observe that the teaching of Our Lord Himself, in which there is no imperfection, is not given us in that cut-and-dried, fool-proof, systematic fashion we might have expected or desired. He wrote no book. We have only reported sayings, most of them uttered in answer to questions, shaped in some degree by their context. And when we have collected them all we cannot reduce them to a system. He preaches but He does not lecture. He uses paradox, proverb, exaggeration, parable, irony; even (I mean no irreverence) the 'wisecrack'. He utters maxims which, like popular proverbs, if rigorously taken, may seem to contradict one another. His teaching therefore cannot be grasped by the intellect alone, cannot be 'got up' as if it were a 'subject'. If we try to do that with it, we shall find Him the most elusive of teachers. He hardly ever gave a straight answer to a straight question. He will not be, in the way we want, 'pinned down'. The attempt is (again, I mean no irreverence) like trying to bottle a sunbeam.

Descending lower, we find a somewhat similar difficulty with St Paul. I cannot be the only reader who has wondered why God, having given him so many gifts, withheld from him (what would to us seem so necessary for the first Christian theologian) that of lucidity and orderly exposition.

Thus on three levels, in appropriate degrees, we meet the same refusal of what we might have thought best for us – in the Word Himself, in the Apostle of the Gentiles, in Scripture as a whole. Since this is what God has done, this, we must conclude, was best. It may be that what we should have liked would have been fatal to us if granted. It may be indispensable that Our Lord's teaching, by that elusiveness (to our systematising intellect), should demand a response from the whole man, should make it so clear that there is no question of learning a subject but of steeping ourselves in a Personality, acquiring a new outlook and temper, breathing a new atmosphere, suffering Him, in His own way, to rebuild in us the defaced image of Himself. So in St Paul. Perhaps the sort of works I should wish him to have written would have been useless. The crabbedness, the appearance of inconsequence and even of sophistry, the turbulent mixture of petty detail, personal complaint, practical advice, and lyrical rapture, finally let through what matters more than ideas – a whole Christian life in operation – better say, Christ Himself operating in a man's life. And in the same way, the value of the Old Testament may be dependent on what seems its imperfection. It may repel one use in order that we may be forced to use it in another way – to find the Word in it, not without repeated and leisurely reading nor without discriminations made by our conscience and our critical faculties, to relive, while we read, the whole Jewish experience of God's gradual and graded self-revelation, to feel the very contentions between the Word and the human material through which it works. For here again, it is our total response that has to be elicited.

Certainly it seems to me that from having had to reach what is really the Voice of God in the cursing Psalms through all the horrible distortions of the human medium, I have gained something I might not have gained from a flawless, ethical exposition. The shadows have indicated (at least to my heart) something more about the light. Nor would I (now) willingly spare from my Bible something in itself so anti-religious as the nihilism of Ecclesiastes. We get there a clear, cold picture of man's life without God. That statement is itself part of God's word. We need to have heard it. Even to have assimilated Ecclesiastes and no other book in the Bible would be to have advanced further towards truth than some men do.

Admittedly these conjectures as to why God does what He does are probably of no more value than my dog's ideas of what I am up to when I sit and read. But though we can only guess the reasons, we can at least observe the consistency, of His ways. We read in Genesis (2:7) that God formed man of the dust and breathed life into him. For all the first writer knew of it, this passage might merely illustrate the survival, even in a truly creational story, of the Pagan inability to conceive true Creation, the savage, pictorial tendency to imagine God making things 'out of' something as the potter or the carpenter does. Nevertheless, whether by lucky accident or (as I think) by God's guidance, it embodies a profound principle. For on any view man is in one sense clearly made 'out of' something else. He is an animal; but an animal called to be, or raised to be, or (if you like) doomed to be, something more than an animal. On the ordinary biological view (what difficulties I have about evolution are not religious) one of the primates is changed so that he becomes man; but he remains still a primate and an animal. He is taken up into a new life without relinquishing the old. In the same way, all organic life takes up and uses processes merely chemical. But we can trace the principle higher as well as lower. For we are taught that the Incarnation itself proceeded 'not by the conversion of the godhead into flesh, but by taking of (the) manhood into God'; in it human life becomes the vehicle of Divine life. If the Scriptures proceed not by conversion of God's word into a literature but by taking up of a literature to be a vehicle of God's word, this is not anomalous.

Of course, on almost all levels, that method seems to us precarious or, as I have said, leaky. None of these up-gradings is, as we should have wished, self-evident. Because the lower nature, in being taken up and loaded with a new burden and advanced to a new privilege remains, and is not annihilated, it will always be possible to ignore the up-grading and see nothing but the lower. Thus men can read the life of Our Lord (because it is a human life) as nothing but a human life. Many, perhaps most, modern philosophies read human life merely as an animal life of unusual complexity. The Cartesians read animal life as mechanism. Just in the same way Scripture can be read as merely human literature. No new discovery, no new method, will ever give a final victory to either interpretation. For what is required, on all these levels alike, is not merely knowledge but a certain insight; getting the focus right. Those who can see in each of these instances only the lower will always be plausible. One who contended that a poem was nothing but black marks on white paper would be unanswerable if he addressed an audience who couldn't read. Look at it through microscopes, analyse the printer's ink and the paper, study it (in that way) as long as you like; you will never find something over and above all the products of analysis whereof you can say 'This is the poem'. Those who can read, however, will continue to say the poem exists.

If the Old Testament is a literature thus 'taken up', made the vehicle of what is more than human, we can hardly set any limit to the weight or multiplicity of meanings which may have been laid upon it. If any writer may say more than he knows and mean more than he meant, then these writers will be especially likely to do so. And not by accident.

(ii) The second reason for accepting the Old Testament in this way can be put more simply and is of course far more compulsive. We are committed to it in principle by Our Lord Himself. On that famous journey to Emmaus He found fault with the two disciples for not believing what the prophets had said. They ought to have known from their Bibles that the Anointed One, when He came, would enter his glory through suffering. He then explained, from 'Moses' (i.e. the Pentateuch) down, all the places in the Old Testament 'concerning Himself' (Luke 24:25–27). He clearly identified Himself with a figure often mentioned in the Scriptures; appropriated to Himself many passages where a modern scholar might see no such reference. In the predictions of His Own Passion which He had previously made to the disciples, He was obviously doing the same thing. He accepted – indeed He claimed to be – the second meaning of Scripture.

We do not know – or anyway I do not know – what all these passages were. We can be pretty sure about one of them. The Ethiopian eunuch who met Philip (Acts 8:27–38) was reading Isaiah 53. He did not know whether in that passage the prophet was talking about himself or about someone else. Philip, in answering the question, 'preached unto him Jesus'. The answer, in fact, was 'Isaiah is speaking of Jesus'. We need have no doubt that Philip's authority for this interpretation was Our Lord. (Our ancestors would have thought that Isaiah consciously foresaw the sufferings of Christ as people see the future in the sort of dreams recorded by Mr Dunne. Modern scholars would say, that on the conscious level, he was referring to Israel itself, the whole nation personified. I do not see that it matters which view we take.) We can, again, be pretty sure, from the words on the cross (Mark 15:34), that Our Lord identified Himself with the sufferer in Psalm 22. Or when He asked (Mark 12:35–36) how Christ could be both David's son and David's lord, He clearly identified Christ, and therefore Himself, with the 'my Lord' of Psalm 110 – was in fact hinting at the mystery of the Incarnation by pointing out a difficulty which only it could solve. In Matthew 4:6 the words of Psalm 91:11, 12, 'He shall give his angels charge over thee ... that thou hurt not thy foot against a stone,' are applied to Him, and we may be sure the application was His own since only He could be the source of the temptation story. In Mark 12:10 He implicitly appropriates to Himself the words of Psalm 118:22 about the stone which the builders rejected. 'Thou shalt not leave my soul in hell, neither shalt thou suffer thy Holy One to see corruption' (16:11) is treated as a prophecy of His Resurrection in Acts 2:27, and was doubtless so taken by Himself, since we find it so taken in the earliest Christian tradition – that is, by people likely to be closer both to the spirit and to the letter of His words than any scholarship (I do not say, 'any sanctity') will bring a modern. Yet it is, perhaps, idle to speak here of spirit and letter. There is almost no 'letter' in the words of Jesus. Taken by a literalist, He will always prove the most elusive of teachers. Systems cannot keep up with that darting illumination. No net less wide than a man's whole heart, nor less fine of mesh than love, will hold the sacred Fish.

12

SECOND MEANINGS

IN THE PSALMS

In a certain sense Our Lord's interpretation of the Psalms was common ground between Himself and His opponents. The question we mentioned a moment ago, how David can call Christ 'my Lord' (Mark 12:35–37), would lose its point unless it were addressed to those who took it for granted that the 'my Lord' referred to in Psalm 110 was the Messiah, the regal and anointed deliverer who would subject the world to Israel. This method was accepted by all. The 'scriptures' all had a 'spiritual' or second sense. Even a Gentile 'God-fearer'[1] like the Ethiopian eunuch (Acts 8:27–38) knew that the sacred books of Israel could not be understood without a guide, trained in the Judaic tradition, who could open the hidden meanings. Probably all instructed Jews in the first century saw references to the Messiah in most of those passages where Our Lord saw them; what was controversial was His identification of the Messianic King with another Old Testament figure and of both with Himself.

Two figures meet us in the Psalms, that of the sufferer and that of the conquering and liberating king. In 13, 28, 55 or 102, we have the Sufferer; in 2 or 72, the King. The Sufferer was, I think, by this time generally identified with (and may sometimes have originally been intended as) the whole nation, Israel itself – they would have said 'himself'. The King was the successor of David, the coming Messiah. Our Lord identified Himself with both these characters.

In principle, then, the allegorical way of reading the Psalms can claim the highest possible authority. But of course this does not mean that all the countless applications of it are fruitful, legitimate, or even rational. What we see when we think we are looking into the depths of Scripture may sometimes be only the reflection of our own silly faces. Many allegorical interpretations which were once popular seem to me, as perhaps to most moderns, to be

---

[1] The 'god-fearers' (*sebomenoi* or *metuentes*) were a recognised class of Gentiles who worshipped Jahveh without submitting to circumcision and the other ceremonial obligations of the Law. Cf. Psalm 118 (v. 2, Jewish laity, v. 3 Jewish priests; v. 4 God-fearers) and Acts 10:2.

strained, arbitrary and ridiculous. I think we may be sure that some of them really are; we ought to be much less sure that we know which. What seems strained – a mere triumph of perverse ingenuity – to one age, seems plain and obvious to another, so that our ancestors would often wonder how we could possibly miss what we wonder how they could have been silly-clever enough to find. And between different ages there is no impartial judge on earth, for no one stands outside the historical process; and of course no one is so completely enslaved to it as those who take our own age to be, not one more period, but a final and permanent platform from which we can see all other ages objectively.

Interpretations which were already established in the New Testament naturally have a special claim on our attention. We find in our Prayer Book that Psalm 110[2] is one of those appointed for Christmas Day. We may at first be surprised by this. There is nothing in it about peace and goodwill, nothing remotely suggestive of the stable at Bethlehem. It seems to have been originally either a coronation ode for a new king, promising conquest and empire, or a poem addressed to some king on the eve of a war, promising victory. It is full of threats. The 'rod' of the king's power is to go forth from Jerusalem, foreign kings are to be wounded, battle fields to be covered with carnage, skulls cracked. The note is not 'Peace and goodwill' but 'Beware. He's coming.' Two things attach it to Christ with an authority far beyond that of the Prayer Book. The first of course (already mentioned) is that He Himself did so; He is the 'lord' whom 'David' calls 'my Lord'. The second is the reference to Melchizedek (v. 4). The identification of this very mysterious person as a symbol or prophecy of Christ is made in Hebrews 7. The exact form of the comment there made on Genesis 14 is no doubt alien to our minds, but I think the essentials can all be retained in our own idiom. We should certainly not argue from the failure of Genesis to give Melchizedek any genealogy or even parents that he has neither beginning nor end (if it comes to that, Job has no genealogy either); but we should be vividly aware that his unrelated, unaccounted for, appearance sets him strangely apart from the texture of the surrounding narrative. He comes from nowhere, blesses in the name of the 'most high God, possessor of heaven and earth', and utterly disappears. This gives him the effect of belonging, if not to *the* Other World, at any rate to *another* world; other than the story of Abraham in general. He assumes without question, as the writer of Hebrews saw, a superiority over Abraham which Abraham accepts. He is an august, a 'numinous' figure. What the teller, or last re-teller, of Genesis would have said if we asked him why he brought

---

[2] See Appendix 1, p. 725.

this episode in or where he had got it from, I do not know. I think, as I have explained, that a pressure from God lay upon these tellings and re-tellings. And one effect which the episode of Melchizedek was to have is quite clear. It puts in, with unforgettable impressiveness, the idea of a priesthood, not Pagan but a priesthood to the one God, far earlier than the Jewish priesthood which descends from Aaron, independent of the call to Abraham, somehow superior to Abraham's vocation. And this older, pre-Judaic, priesthood is united with royalty; Melchizedek is a priest-king. In some communities priest-kings were normal, but not in Israel. It is thus simply a fact that Melchizedek resembles (in his peculiar way he is the only Old Testament character who resembles) Christ Himself. For He, like Melchizedek, claims to be Priest, though not of the priestly tribe, and also King. Melchizedek really does point to Him; and so of course does the hero of Psalm 110 who is a king but also has the same sort of priesthood.

For a Jewish convert to Christianity this was extremely important and removed a difficulty. He might be brought to see how Christ was the suc-cessor of David; it would be impossible to say that He was, in a similar sense, the successor of Aaron. The idea of His priesthood therefore involved the recognition of a priesthood independent of and superior to Aaron's. Melchizedek was there to give this conception the sanction of the Scriptures. For us Gentile Christians it is rather the other way round. We are more likely to start from the priestly, sacrificial, and intercessory char-acter of Christ and under-stress that of king and conqueror. Psalm 110, with three other Christmas Psalms, corrects this. In 45 we have again the almost threatening tone: 'Gird thee with thy sword upon thy thigh, O thou most mighty ... thy right hand shall teach thee terrible things ... thy arrows are very sharp' (vv. 4–6). In 89 we have the promises to David (who would certainly mean all, or any, of David's successors, just as 'Jacob' can mean all his descendants). Foes are to fall before him (v. 24). 'David' will call God 'Father', and God says 'I will make him my first-born' (vv. 27–28), that is 'I will make him an eldest son', make him my heir, give him the whole world. In 132 we have 'David' again; 'As for his enemies, I shall clothe them with shame, but upon himself shall his crown flourish' (v. 19). All this emphasises an aspect of the Nativity to which our later sentiment about Christmas (excellent in itself) does less than justice. For those who first read these Psalms as poems about the birth of Christ, that birth pri-marily meant something very militant; the hero, the 'judge' or champion or giant-killer, who was to fight and beat death, hell and the devils, had at last arrived, and the evidence suggests that Our Lord also thought of Himself in those terms. (Milton's poem on the *Nativity* well recaptures this side of Christmas.)

The assignment of Psalm 68[3] to Whitsunday has some obvious reasons, even at a first reading. Verse 8, 'The earth shook and the heavens dropped at the presence of God, even as Sinai also was moved,' was, no doubt, for the original writer a reference to the miracles mentioned in Exodus, and thus fore-shadows that very different descent of God which came with the tongues of fire. Verse 11 is a beautiful instance of the way in which the old texts, almost inevitably, charge themselves with the new weight of meaning. The Prayer Book version gives it as, 'The Lord gave the word, great was the company of the preachers.' The 'word' would be the order for battle and its 'preachers' (in rather a grim sense) the triumphant Jewish warriors. But that translation appears to be wrong. The verse really means that there were many to spread 'word' (i.e. the news) of the victory. This will suit Pentecost quite as well. But I think the real New Testament authority for assigning this Psalm to Whitsunday appears in verse 18 (in the Prayer Book, 'Thou art gone up on high, thou hast led captivity captive, and received gifts for men'). According to the scholars the Hebrew text here means that God, with the armies of Israel as his agents, had taken huge masses of prisoners and received 'gifts' (booty or tribute) *from* men. St Paul, however (Ephesians 4:8), quotes a different read-ing: 'When He ascended up on high He led captivity captive and *gave* gifts *to* men.' This must be the passage which first associated the Psalm with the com-ing of the Holy Ghost, for St Paul is there speaking of the gifts of the Spirit (vv. 4–7) and stressing the fact that they come after the Ascension. After ascending, as a result of ascending, Christ gives these gifts to men, or receives these gifts (notice how the Prayer Book version will now do well enough) from His Father 'for men', for the use of men, in order to transmit them to men. And this relation between the Ascension and the coming of the Spirit is of course in full accordance with Our Lord's own words, 'It is expedient for you that I go away, for if I go not away the Comforter will not come unto you' (John 16:7); as if the one were somehow impossible without the other, as if the Ascension, the withdrawal from the space–time in which our present senses operate, of the incarnate God, were the necessary condition of God's presence in another mode. There is a mystery here that I will not even attempt to sound.

That Psalm has led us through some complications; those in which Christ appears as the sufferer are very much easier. And it is here too that the sec-ond meaning is most inevitable. If Christ 'tasted death for all men', became the archetypal sufferer, then the expressions of all who ever suffered in the world are, from the very nature of things, related to His. Here (to speak in ludicrously human terms) we feel that it needed no Divine guidance to give the old texts their second meaning but would rather have needed a special

---

[3] See Appendix 1, p. 722.

miracle to keep it out. In Psalm 22, the terrible poem which Christ quoted in His final torture, it is not 'they pierced my hands and my feet' (v. 17), striking though this anticipation must always be, that really matters most. It is the union of total privation with total adherence to God, to a God who makes no response, simply because of what God is: 'and thou continuest holy' (v. 3). All the sufferings of the righteous speak here; but in 40:15, all the sufferings of the guilty too – 'my sins have taken such hold upon me that I am not able to look up.' But this too is for us the voice of Christ, for we have been taught that He who was without sin became sin for our sakes, plumbed the depth of that worst suffering which comes to evil men who at last know their own evil. Notice how this, in the original or literal sense, is hardly consistent with verses 8 and 9, and what counterpoint of truth this apparent contradiction takes on once the speaker is understood to be Christ.

But to say more of these suffering Psalms would be to labour the obvious. What I, at any rate, took longer to see was the full richness of that Christmas Psalm we have already mentioned, Psalm 45,[4] which shows us so many aspects of the Nativity we could never get from the carols or even (easily) from the Gospels. This in its original intention was obviously a laureate ode on a royal wedding. (We are nowadays surprised to find that such an official bit of work, made 'to order' by a court poet for a special occasion, should be good poetry. But in ages when the arts had their full health no one would have understood our surprise. All the great poets, painters, and musicians of old could produce great work 'to order'. One who could not would have seemed as great a humbug as a captain who could navigate or a farmer who could farm only when the fit took him.) And simply as a marriage ode – what the Greeks call an *Epithalamium* – it is magnificent. But it is far more valuable for the light it throws on the Incarnation.

Few things once seemed to me more frigid and far-fetched than those interpretations, whether of this Psalm or of the Song of Songs, which identify the Bridegroom with Christ and the Bride with the Church. Indeed, as we read the frank erotic poetry of the latter and contrast it with the edifying headlines in our Bibles, it is easy to be moved to a smile, even a cynically knowing smile, as if the pious interpreters were feigning an absurd innocence. I should still find it very hard to believe that anything like the 'spiritual' sense was remotely intended by the original writers. But no one now (I fancy) who accepts that spiritual or second sense is denying, or saying anything against, the very plain sense which the writers did intend. The Psalm remains a rich, festive Epithalamium, the Song remains fine, sometimes exquisite, love poetry, and this is not in the least obliterated by the burden of

[4] See Appendix I, p. 721.

the new meaning. (Man is still one of the primates; a poem is still black marks on white paper.) And later I began to see that the new meaning is not arbitrary and springs from depths I had not suspected. First, the language of nearly all great mystics, not even in a common tradition, some of them Pagan, some Islamic, most Christian, confronts us with evidence that the image of marriage, of sexual union, is not only profoundly natural but almost inevitable as a means of expressing the desired union between God and man. The very word 'union' has already entailed some such idea. Secondly, the god as bridegroom, his 'holy marriage' with the goddess, is a recurrent theme and a recurrent ritual in many forms of Paganism – Paganism not at what we should call its purest or most enlightened, but perhaps at its most religious, at its most serious and convinced. And if, as I believe, Christ, in transcending and thus abrogating, also fulfils, both Paganism and Judaism, then we may expect that He fulfils this side of it too. This, as well as all else, is to be 'summed up' in Him. Thirdly, the idea appears, in a slightly different form, within Judaism. For the mystics God is the Bridegroom of the individual soul. For the Pagans, the god is the bridegroom of the mother-goddess, the earth, but his union with her also makes fertile the whole tribe and its livestock, so that in a sense he is their bridegroom too. The Judaic conception is in some ways closer to the Pagan than to that of the mystics, for in it the Bride of God is the whole nation, Israel. This is worked out in one of the most moving and graphic chapters of the whole Old Testament (Ezekiel 16). Finally, this is transferred in the Apocalypse from the old Israel to the new, and the Bride becomes the Church, 'the whole blessed company of faithful people'. It is this which has, like the unworthy bride in Ezekiel, been rescued, washed, clothed, and married by God – a marriage like King Cophetua's. Thus the allegory which at first seemed so arbitrary – the ingenuity of some prudish commentator who was determined to force flat edifications upon the most unpromising texts – turned out, when you seriously tugged at it, to have roots in the whole history of religion, to be loaded with poetry, to yield insights. To reject it because it does not immediately appeal to our own age is to be provincial, to have the self-complacent blindness of the stay-at-home.

Read in this sense, the Psalm restores Christmas to its proper complexity. The birth of Christ is the arrival of the great warrior and the great king. Also of the Lover, the Bridegroom, whose beauty surpasses that of man. But not only the Bridegroom as the lover, the desired; the Bridegroom also as he who makes fruitful, the father of children still to be begotten and born. (Certainly the image of a Child in a manger by no means suggests to us a king, giant-killer, bridegroom, and father. But it would not suggest the eternal Word either – if we didn't know. All alike are aspects of the same central paradox.) Then the poet turns to the Bride, with the exhortation, 'forget also thine own people and thy father's house' (v. 11). This sentence has a plain, and to us painful, sense while we read the Psalm as the poet probably intended it. One thinks of home-sickness, of a girl (probably a mere child) secretly crying in a strange *hareem*, of all the miseries which may underlie any dynastic marriage, especially an Oriental one. The poet (who of course knew all about this – he probably had a daughter of his own) consoles her: 'Never mind, you have lost your parents but you will presently have children instead, and children who will be great men.' But all this has also its poignant relevance when the Bride is the Church. A vocation is a terrible thing. To be called out of nature into the supernatural life is at first (or perhaps not quite at first – the wrench of the parting may be felt later) a costly honour. Even to be called from one natural level to another is loss as well as gain. Man has difficulties and sorrows which the other primates escape. But to be called up higher costs still more. 'Get thee out of thy country, and from thy kindred, and from thy father's house,' said God to Abraham (Genesis 12:1). It is a terrible command; turn your back on all you know. The consolation (if it will at that moment console) is very like that which the Psalmist offers to the bride: 'I will make of thee a great nation.' This 'turn your back' is of course terribly repeated, one may say aggravated, by Our Lord – 'he that hateth not father and mother and his own life'. He speaks, as so often, in the proverbial, paradoxical manner; hatred (in cold prose) is not enjoined; only the resolute, the apparently ruthless, rejection of natural claims when, and if, the terrible choice comes to that point. (Even so, this text is, I take it, profitable only to those who read it with horror. The man who finds it easy enough to hate his father, the woman whose life is a long struggle not to hate her mother, had probably best keep clear of it.) The consolation of the Bride, in this allegory, consists, not (where the mystics would put it) in the embraces of the Spouse, but in her fruitfulness. If she does not bear fruit, is not the mother of saints and sanctity, it may be supposed that the marriage was an illusion – for 'a god's embraces never are in vain'.

The choice of Psalm 8⁵ for Ascension Day again depends on an interpretation found in the New Testament. In its literal sense this short, exquisite lyric is simplicity itself – an expression of wonder at man and man's place in Nature (there is a chorus in Sophocles not unlike it) and therefore at God who appointed it. God is wonderful both as champion or 'judge' and as Creator. When one looks up at the sky, and all the stars which are His work, it seems strange that He should be concerned at all with such things as man. Yet in fact, though He has made us inferior to the celestial beings, He has,

---

⁵ See Appendix 1, p. 719.

down here on earth, given us extraordinary honour – made us lords of all the other creatures. But to the writer of Hebrews (2:6–9) this suggested something which we, of ourselves, would never have thought of. The Psalmist said, 'Thou hast put all things in subjection under his (man's) feet' (v. 6). The Christian writer observes that, in the actual state of the universe, this is not strictly true. Man is often killed, and still more often defeated, by beasts, poisonous vegetables, weather, earthquakes, etc. It would seem to us merely perverse and captious thus to take a poetic expression as if it were intended for a scientific universal. We can get nearest to the point of view if we imagine the commentator arguing not (as I think he actually does), 'Since this is not true of the present, and since all the scriptures must be true, the statement must really refer to the future,' but rather, 'This is of course true in the poetic – and therefore, to a logician, the loose – sense which the poet intended; but how if it were far truer than he knew?' This will lead us, by a route that is easier for our habits of mind, to what he thinks the real meaning – or I should say the 'over-meaning', the new weight laid upon the poet's words. Christ has ascended into Heaven. And in due time all things, quite strictly all, will be subjected to Him. It is He who, having been made (for a while) 'lower than the angels', will become the conqueror and ruler of all things, including death and (death's patron) the devil.

To most of us this will seem a wire-drawn allegory. But it is the very same which St Paul obviously has in mind in 1 Corinthians 15:20–28. This, with the passage in Hebrews, makes it pretty certain that the interpretation was established in the earliest Christian tradition. It may even descend from Our Lord. There was, after all, no description of Himself which He delighted in more than the 'Son of Man'; and of course, just as 'daughter of Babylon' means Babylon, so 'Son of Man' means Man, the Man, the archetypal Man, in whose suffering, resurrection, and victories all men (unless they refuse) can share.

And it is this, I believe, that most modern Christians need to be reminded of. It seems to me that I seldom meet any strong or exultant sense of the continued, never-to-be-abandoned, Humanity of Christ in glory, in eternity. We stress the Humanity too exclusively at Christmas, and the Deity too exclusively after the Resurrection; almost as if Christ once became a man and then presently reverted to being simply a God. We think of the Resurrection and Ascension (rightly) as great acts of God; less often as the triumph of Man. The ancient interpretation of Psalm 8, however arrived at, is a cheering corrective. Nor, on further consideration, is the analogy of humanity's place in the universe (its greatness and littleness, its humble origins and – even on the natural level – amazing destiny) to the humiliation and victories of Christ, really strained and far-fetched. At least it does not seem so to me. As I have already indicated, there seems to me to be something more than analogy between the taking up of animality into man and the taking up of man into God.

But I walk in wonders beyond myself. It is time to conclude with a brief notice of some simpler things.

One is the apparent (and often no doubt real) self-righteousness of the Psalms: 'Thou shalt find no wickedness in me' (17:3), 'I have walked innocently' (26:1), 'Preserve thou my soul, for I am holy' (86:2). For many people it will not much mend matters if we say, as we probably can with truth, that sometimes the speaker was from the first intended to be Israel, not the individual; and even, within Israel, the faithful remnant. Yet it makes some difference; up to a certain point that remnant was holy and innocent compared with some of the surrounding Pagan cultures. It was often an 'innocent sufferer' in the sense that it had not deserved what was inflicted on it, nor deserved it at the hands of those who inflicted it. But of course there was to come a Sufferer who was in fact holy and innocent. Plato's imaginary case was to become actual. All these assertions were to become true in His mouth. And if true, it was necessary they should be made. The lesson that perfect, unretaliating, forgiving innocence can lead, as the world is, not to love but to the screaming curses of the mob and to death, is essential. Our Lord therefore becomes the speaker in these passages when a Christian reads them; by right – it would be an obscuring of the real issue if He did not. For He denied all sin of Himself. (That, indeed, is no small argument of His Deity. For He has not often made even on the enemies of Christianity the impression of arrogance; many of them do not seem as shocked as we should expect at His claim to be 'meek and lowly of heart'. Yet He said such things as, on any hypothesis but one, would be the arrogance of a paranoiac. It is as if, even where the hypothesis is rejected, some of the reality which implies its truth 'got across'.)

Of the cursing Psalms I suppose most of us make our own moral allegories – well aware that these are personal and on a quite different level from the high matters I have been trying to handle. We know the proper object of utter hostility – wickedness, especially our own. Thus in 36, 'My heart sheweth me the wickedness of the ungodly,' each can reflect that his own heart is the specimen of that wickedness best known to him. After that, the upward plunge at verse 5 into the mercy high as heaven and the righteousness solid as the mountains takes on even more force and beauty. From this point of view I can use even the horrible passage in 137 about dashing the Babylonian babies against the stones. I know things in the inner world which are like babies; the infantile beginnings of small indulgences, small resentments, which may one day become dipsomania or settled hatred, but which woo us and wheedle us with special pleadings and seem so tiny, so helpless that in resisting them we feel we are being cruel to animals. They begin whimpering to us, 'I don't ask much, but', or 'I had at least hoped', or 'you owe yourself *some* consideration'. Against all such pretty infants (the dears have such winning ways) the advice of the Psalm is the best. Knock the little bastards' brains out. And 'blessed' he who can, for it's easier said than done.

Sometimes with no prompting from tradition a second meaning will impose itself upon a reader irresistibly. When the poet of Psalm 84 said (v. 10), 'For one day in thy courts is better than a thousand,' he doubtless meant that one day there was better than a thousand elsewhere. I find it impossible to exclude while I read this the thought which, so far as I know, the Old Testament never quite reaches. It is there in the New, beautifully introduced not by laying a new weight on old words but more simply by adding to them. In Psalm 90 (v. 4) it had been said that a thousand years were to God like a single yesterday; in 2 Peter 3:8 – not the first place in the world where one would have looked for so metaphysical a theology – we read not only that a thousand years are as one day but also that 'one day is as a thousand years'. The Psalmist only meant, I think, that God was everlasting, that His life was infinite in time. But the epistle takes us out of the time-series altogether. As nothing outlasts God, so nothing slips away from Him into a past. The later conception (later in Christian thought – Plato had reached it) of the timeless as an eternal present has been achieved. Ever afterwards, for some of us, the 'one day' in God's courts which is better than a thousand, must carry a double meaning. The Eternal may meet us in what is, by our present measurements, a day, or (more likely) a minute or a second; but we have touched what is not in any way commensurable with lengths of time, whether long or short. Hence our hope finally to emerge, if not altogether from time (that might not suit our humanity) at any rate from the tyranny, the unlinear poverty, of time, to ride it not to be ridden by it, and so to cure that always aching wound ('the wound man was born for') which mere succession and mutability inflict on us, almost equally when we are happy and when we are unhappy. For we are so little reconciled to time that we are even astonished at it. 'How he's grown!' we exclaim, 'How time flies!' as though the universal form of our experience were again and again a novelty. It is as strange as if a fish were repeatedly surprised at the wetness of water. And that would be strange indeed; unless of course the fish were destined to become, one day, a land animal.

APPENDIX I

SELECTED PSALMS

PSALM 8 *Domine, Dominus noster*

O Lord our Governor, how excellent is thy Name in all the world: thou that hast set thy glory above the heavens!

2. Out of the mouth of very babes and sucklings hast thou ordained strength, because of thine enemies: that thou mightest still the enemy and the avenger.

3. For I will consider thy heavens, even the works of thy fingers: the moon and the stars, which thou hast ordained.

4. What is man, that thou art mindful of him: and the son of man, that thou visitest him?

5. Thou madest him lower than the angels: to crown him with glory and worship.

6. Thou makest him to have dominion of the works of thy hands: and thou hast put all things in subjection under his feet;

7. All sheep and oxen: yea, and the beasts of the field;

8. The fowls of the air, and the fishes of the sea: and whatsoever walketh through the paths of the seas.

9. O Lord our Governor: how excellent is thy Name in all the world!

PSALM 19 *Coeli enarrant*

The heavens declare the glory of God: and the firmament sheweth his handywork.

2. One day telleth another: and one night certifieth another.

3. There is neither speech nor language: but their voices are heard among them.

4. Their sound is gone out into all lands: and their words into the ends of the world.

5. In them hath he set a tabernacle for the sun: which cometh forth as a bridegroom out of his chamber, and rejoiceth as a giant to run his course.

6. It goeth forth from the uttermost part of the heaven, and runneth about unto the end of it again: and there is nothing hid from the heat thereof.

7. The law of the Lord is an undefiled law, converting the soul: the testimony of the Lord is sure, and giveth wisdom unto the simple.

8. The statutes of the Lord are right, and rejoice the heart: the commandment of the Lord is pure, and giveth light unto the eyes.

9. The fear of the Lord is clean, and endureth for ever: the judgements of the Lord are true, and righteous altogether.

10. More to be desired are they than gold, yea, than much fine gold: sweeter also than honey, and the honeycomb.

11. Moreover, by them is thy servant taught: and in keeping of them there is great reward.

12. Who can tell how oft he offendeth: O cleanse thou me from my secret faults.

13. Keep thy servant also from presumptuous sins, lest they get the dominion over me: so shall I be undefiled, and innocent from the great offence.

14. Let the words of my mouth, and the meditation of my heart: be alway acceptable in thy sight,

15. O Lord: my strength, and my redeemer.

PSALM 36 *Dixit injustus*

My heart sheweth me the wickedness of the ungodly: that there is no fear of God before his eyes.

2. For he flattereth himself in his own sight: until his abominable sin be found out.

3. The words of his mouth are unrighteous, and full of deceit: he hath left off to behave himself wisely, and to do good.

4. He imagineth mischief upon his bed, and hath set himself in no good way: neither doth he abhor any thing that is evil.

5. Thy mercy, O Lord, reacheth unto the heavens: and thy faithfulness unto the clouds.

6. Thy righteousness standeth like the strong mountains: thy judgements are like the great deep.

7. Thou, Lord, shalt save both man and beast; How excellent is thy mercy, O God: and the children of men shall put their trust under the shadow of thy wings.

8. They shall be satisfied with the plenteousness of thy house: and thou shalt give them drink of thy pleasures, as out of the river.

9. For with thee is the well of life: and in thy light shall we see light.

10. O continue forth thy loving-kindness unto them that know thee: and thy righteousness unto them that are true of heart.

11. O let not the foot of pride come against me: and let not the hand of the ungodly cast me down.

12. There are they fallen, all that work wickedness: they are cast down, and shall not be able to stand.

PSALM 45 *Eructavit cor meum*

My heart is inditing of a good matter: I speak of the things which I have made unto the King.

2. My tongue is the pen: of a ready writer.

3. Thou art fairer than the children of men: full of grace are thy lips, because God hath blessed thee for ever.

4. Gird thee with thy sword upon thy thigh, O thou most Mighty: according to thy worship and renown.

5. Good luck have thou with thine honour: ride on, because of the word of truth, of meekness, and righteousness; and thy right hand shall teach thee terrible things.

6. The arrows are very sharp, and the people shall be subdued unto thee: even in the midst among the King's enemies.

7. Thy seat, O God, endureth for ever: the sceptre of thy kingdom is a right sceptre.

8. Thou hast loved righteousness, and hated iniquity: wherefore God, even thy God, hath anointed thee with the oil of gladness above thy fellows.

9. All the garments smell of myrrh, aloes, and cassia: out of the ivory palaces, whereby they have made thee glad.

10. King's daughters were among thy honourable women: upon thy right hand did stand the queen in a vesture of gold, wrought about with divers colours.

11. Hearken, O daughter, and consider, incline thine ear: forget also thine own people, and thy father's house.

12. So shall the King have pleasure in thy beauty: for he is thy Lord God, and worship thou him.

13. And the daughter of Tyre shall be there with a gift: like as the rich also among the people shall make their supplication before thee.

14. The King's daughter is all glorious within: her clothing is of wrought gold.

15. She shall be brought unto the King in raiment of needlework: the virgins that be her fellows shall bear her company, and shall be brought unto thee.

16. With joy and gladness shall they be brought: and shall enter into the King's palace.

17. Instead of thy fathers thou shalt have children: whom thou mayest make princes in all lands.

18. I will remember thy Name from one generation to another: therefore shall the people give thanks unto thee, world without end.

PSALM 68 *Exurgat Deus*

Let God arise, and let his enemies be scattered: let them also that hate him flee before him.

2. Like as the smoke vanisheth, so shalt thou drive them away: and like as wax melteth at the fire, so let the ungodly perish at the presence of God.

3. But let the righteous be glad and rejoice before God: let them also be merry and joyful.

4. O sing unto God, and sing praises unto his Name: magnify him that rideth upon the heavens, as it were upon an horse; praise him in his Name JAH, and rejoice before him.

5. He is a Father of the fatherless, and defendeth the cause of the widows: even God in his Holy habitation.

6. He is the God that maketh men to be of one mind in an house, and bringeth the prisoners out of captivity: but letteth the runagates continue in scarceness.

7. O God, when thou wentest forth before the people: when thou wentest through the wilderness,

8. The earth shook, and the heavens dropped at the presence of God: even as Sinai also was moved at the presence of God, who is the God of Israel.

9. Thou, O God, sentest a gracious rain upon thine inheritance: and refreshedst it when it was weary.

10. Thy congregation shall dwell therein: for thou, O God, hast of thy goodness prepared for the poor.

11. The Lord gave the word: great was the company of the preachers.

12. Kings with their armies did flee, and were discomfited: and they of the household divided the spoil.

13. Though ye have lien among the pots, yet shall ye be as the wings of a dove: that is covered with silver wings, and her feathers like gold.

14. When the Almighty scattered kings for their sake: then were they as white as snow in Salmon.

15. As the hill of Basan, so is God's hill: even an high hill, as the hill of Basan.

16. Why hop ye so, ye high hills? this is God's hill, in which it pleaseth him to dwell: yea, the Lord will abide in it for ever.

17. The chariots of God are twenty thousand, even thousands of angels: and the Lord is among them, as in the holy place of Sinai.

18. Thou art gone up on high, thou hast led captivity captive, and received gifts for men: yea, even from thine enemies, that the Lord God might dwell among them.

19. Praised be the Lord daily: even the God who helpeth us, and poureth his benefits upon us.

20. He is our God, even the God of whom cometh salvation: God is the Lord, by whom we escape death.

21. God shall wound the head of his enemies: and the hairy scalp of such a one as goeth on still in wickedness.

22. The Lord hath said, I will bring my people again, as I did from Basan: mine own will I bring again, as I did sometime from the deep of the sea.

23. That thy foot may be dipped in the blood of thine enemies: and that the tongue of thy dogs may be red through the same.

24. It is well seen, O God, how thou goest: how thou, my God and King, goest in the sanctuary.

25. The singers go before, the minstrels follow after: in the midst are the damsels playing with the timbrels.

26. Give thanks, O Israel, unto God the Lord in the congregations: from the ground of the heart.

27. There is little Benjamin, their ruler, and the princes of Judah their counsel: the princes of Zabulon, and the princes of Nephthali.

28. Thy God hath sent forth strength for thee: stablish the thing, O God, that thou hast wrought in us.

29. For thy temple's sake at Jerusalem: so shall kings bring presents unto thee.

30. When the company of the spear-men, and multitude of the mighty are scattered abroad among the beasts of the people, so that they humbly bring pieces of silver: and when he hath scattered the people that delight in war;

31. Then shall the princes come out of Egypt: the Morians' land shall soon stretch out her hands unto God.

32. Sing unto God, O ye kingdoms of the earth: O sing praises unto the Lord;

33. Who sitteth in the heavens over all from the beginning: lo, he doth send out his voice, yea, and that a mighty voice.

34. Ascribe ye the power to God over Israel: his worship and strength is in the clouds.

35. O God, wonderful art thou in thy holy places: even the God of Israel; he will give strength and power unto his people; blessed be God.

PSALM 104 *Benedic, anima mea*

Praise the Lord, O my soul: O Lord my God, thou art become exceeding glorious; thou art clothed with majesty and honour.

2. Thou deckest thyself with light as it were with a garment: and spread-est out the heavens like a curtain.

3. Who layeth the beams of his chambers in the waters: and maketh the clouds his chariot, and walketh upon the wings of the wind.

4. He maketh his angels spirits: and his ministers a flaming fire.

5. He laid the foundations of the earth: that it never should move at any time.

6. Thou coveredst it with the deep like as with a garment: the waters stand in the hills.

7. At thy rebuke they flee: at the voice of thy thunder they are afraid.

8. They go up as high as the hills, and down to the valleys beneath: even unto the place which thou hast appointed for them.

9. Thou hast set them their bounds which they shall not pass: neither turn again to cover the earth.

10. He sendeth the springs into the rivers: which run among the hills.

11. All beasts of the field drink thereof: and the wild asses quench their thirst.

12. Beside them shall the fowls of the air have their habitation: and sing among the branches.

13. He watereth the hills from above: the earth is filled with the fruit of thy works.

14. He bringeth forth grass for the cattle: and green herb for the service of men.

15. That he may bring food out of the earth, and wine that maketh glad the heart of man: and oil to make him a cheerful countenance, and bread to strengthen man's heart.

16. The trees of the Lord also are full of sap: even the cedars of Libanus which he hath planted;

17. Wherein the birds make their nests: and the fir-trees are a dwelling for the stork.

18. The high hills are a refuge for the wild goats: and so are the stony rocks for the conies.

19. He appointed the moon for certain seasons: and the sun knoweth his going down.

20. Thou makest darkness that it may be night: wherein all the beasts of the forest do move.

21. The lions roaring after their prey: do seek their meat from God.

22. The sun ariseth, and they get them away together: and lay them down in their dens.

23. Man goeth forth to his work, and to his labour: until the evening.

24. O Lord, how manifold are thy works: in wisdom hast thou made them all; the earth is full of thy riches.

25. So is the great and wide sea also: wherein are things creeping innumerable, both small and great beasts.

26. There go the ships, and there is that Leviathan: whom thou hast made to take his pastime therein.

27. These wait all upon thee: that thou mayest give them their meat in due season.

28. When thou givest it them they gather it: and when thou openest thy hand they are filled with good.

29. When thou hidest thy face they are troubled: when thou takest away their breath they die, and are turned again to their dust.

30. When thou lettest thy breath go forth they shall be made: and thou shalt renew the face of the earth.

31. The glorious majesty of the Lord shall endure for ever: the Lord shall rejoice in his works.

32. The earth shall tremble at the look of him: if he do but touch the hills, they shall smoke.

33. I will sing unto the Lord as long as I live: I will praise my God while I have my being.

34. And so shall my words please him: my joy shall be in the Lord.

35. As for sinners, they shall be consumed out of the earth, and the ungodly shall come to an end: praise thou the Lord, O my soul, praise the Lord.

PSALM 110 *Dixit Dominus*

The Lord said unto my Lord: Sit thou on my right hand, until I make thine enemies thy footstool.

2. The Lord shall send the rod of thy power out of Sion: be thou ruler, even in the midst among thine enemies.

3. In the day of thy power shall the people offer thee free-will offerings with an holy worship: the dew of thy birth is of the womb of the morning.

4. The Lord sware, and will not repent: Thou art a Priest for ever after the order of Melchisedech.

5. The Lord upon thy right hand: shall wound even kings in the day of his wrath.

6. He shall judge among the heathen; he shall fill the places with the dead bodies: and smite in sunder the heads over divers countries.

7. He shall drink of the brook in the way: therefore shall he lift up his head.

APPENDIX II

PSALMS DISCUSSED

OR MENTIONED

THE SCREWTAPE
LETTERS

To J. R. R. Tolkien

'The best way to drive out the devil, if he will not yield to texts of Scripture, is to jeer and flout him, for he cannot bear scorn.'

LUTHER

'The devil ... the prowde spirite ... cannot endure to be mocked.'

THOMAS MORE

PREFACE TO THE
FIRST EDITION

I have no intention of explaining how the correspondence which I now offer to the public fell into my hands.

There are two equal and opposite errors into which our race can fall about the devils. One is to disbelieve in their existence. The other is to believe, and to feel an excessive and unhealthy interest in them. They themselves are equally pleased by both errors and hail a materialist or a magician with the same delight. The sort of script which is used in this book can be very easily obtained by anyone who has once learned the knack; but ill-disposed or excitable people who might make a bad use of it shall not learn it from me.

Readers are advised to remember that the devil is a liar. Not everything that Screwtape says should be assumed to be true even from his own angle. I have made no attempt to identify any of the human beings mentioned in the letters; but I think it very unlikely that the portraits, say, of Fr Spike or the patient's mother, are wholly just. There is wishful thinking in Hell as well as on Earth.

In conclusion, I ought to add that no effort has been made to clear up the chronology of the letters. Number XVII appears to have been composed before rationing became serious; but in general the diabolical method of dating seems to bear no relation to terrestrial time and I have not attempted to reproduce it. The history of the European War, except in so far as it happens now and then to impinge upon the spiritual condition of one human being, was obviously of no interest to Screwtape.

C. S. LEWIS

MAGDALEN COLLEGE, 5 JULY 1941

PREFACE TO THE
1961 EDITION

It was during the second German war that the letters of Screwtape appeared in the (now extinct) *Guardian*. I hope they did not hasten its death, but they certainly lost it one reader. A country clergyman wrote to the editor withdrawing his subscription on the ground that 'much of the advice given in these letters seemed to him not only erroneous but positively diabolical'.

In general, however, they had a reception I had never dreamed of. Reviews were either laudatory or filled with that sort of anger which tells an author that he has hit his target; sales were at first (by my standards) prodigious and have continued steady.

Of course, sales do not always mean what authors hope. If you gauged the amount of Bible-reading in England by the number of Bibles sold you would go far astray. Those of *Screwtape*, in their own little way, suffer from a similar ambiguity. It is the sort of book that gets given to god-children: the sort that gets read aloud at Retreats. It is even, as I have noticed with a chastened smile, the sort that gravitates towards spare bedrooms, there to live a life of undisturbed tranquility in company with *The Road Mender, John Inglesant* and *The Life of the Bee*. Sometimes it is bought for even more humiliating reasons. A lady whom I know discovered that the pretty little probationer who filled her hot water bottle in hospital had read *Screwtape*. She also discovered why. 'You see,' said the girl, 'we were warned that at interviews, after the real, technical questions are over, Matrons and People sometimes ask about your general interests. The best thing is to say you've read something. So they gave us a list of about ten books that usually go down pretty well and said we ought to read at least one of them.' 'And you chose *Screwtape*?' 'Well, of course; it was the shortest.'

Still, when all allowances have been made, the book had readers of the genuine sort sufficiently numerous to make it worth while answering some of the questions it has raised in their minds.

The commonest question is whether I really 'believe in the Devil'.

Now if by 'the Devil' you mean a power opposite to God and, like God, self-existent from all eternity, the answer is certainly 'No'. There is no uncreated being except God. God has no opposite. No being could attain a 'perfect badness' opposite to the perfect goodness of God; for when you have taken away every kind of good thing (intelligence, will, memory, energy, and existence itself) there would be none of him left.

The proper question is whether I believe in devils. I do. That is to say, I believe in angels and I believe that some of these, by the abuse of their free will, have become enemies to God and, as a corollary, to us. These we may call devils. They do not differ in nature from good angels, but their nature is depraved. *Devil* is the opposite of *angel* only as Bad Man is the opposite of Good Man. Satan, the leader or dictator of devils, is the opposite not of God but of Michael.

I believe this not in the sense that it is part of my creed, but in the sense that it is one of my opinions. My religion would not be in ruins if this opinion were shown to be false. Till that happens – and proofs of a negative are hard to come by – I shall retain it. It seems to me to explain a good many facts. It agrees with the plain sense of Scripture, the tradition of Christendom, and the beliefs of most men at most times. And it conflicts with nothing that any of the sciences has shown to be true.

It should be (but it is not) unnecessary to add that a belief in angels, whether good or evil, does not mean a belief in either as they are represented in art and literature. Devils are depicted with bats' wings and good angels with birds' wings not because anyone holds that moral deterioration would be likely to turn feathers into membrane, but because most men like birds better than bats. They are given wings at all in order to suggest the swiftness of unimpeded intellectual energy. They are given human form because man is the only rational creature we know. Creatures higher in the natural order than ourselves, either incorporeal or animating bodies of a sort we cannot experience, must be represented symbolically if they are to be represented at all.

These forms are not only symbolical but were always known to be symbolical by reflective people. The Greeks did not believe that the gods were really like the beautiful human shapes their sculptors gave them. In their poetry a god who wishes to 'appear' to a mortal temporarily assumes the likeness of a man. Christian theology has nearly always explained the 'appearance' of an angel in the same way. It is only the ignorant, says Dionysius in the fifth century, who dream that spirits are really winged men.

In the plastic arts these symbols have steadily degenerated. Fra Angelico's angels carry in their face and gesture the peace and authority of heaven. Later come the chubby infantile nudes of Raphael; finally the soft, slim, girlish, and consolatory angels of nineteenth-century art, shapes so feminine that they avoid being voluptuous only by their total insipidity – the frigid houris of a tea-table paradise. They are a pernicious symbol. In Scripture the visitation of an angel is always alarming; it has to begin by saying 'Fear not.' The Victorian angel looks as if it were going to say 'There, there.'

The literary symbols are more dangerous because they are not so easily recognised as symbolical. Those of Dante are the best. Before his angels we sink in awe. His devils, as Ruskin rightly remarked, in their rage, spite and obscenity, are far more like what the reality must be than anything in Milton. Milton's devils, by their grandeur and high poetry, have done great harm, and his angels owe too much to Homer and Raphael. But the really pernicious image is Goethe's Mephistopheles. It is Faust, not he, who really exhibits the ruthless, sleepless, unsmiling concentration upon self which is the mark of hell. The humorous, civilised, sensible, adaptable Mephistopheles has helped to strengthen the illusion that evil is liberating.

A little man may sometimes avoid some single error made by a great one, and I was determined that my own symbolism should at least not err in Goethe's way. For humour involves a sense of proportion and a power of seeing yourself from the outside. Whatever else we attribute to beings who sinned through pride, we must not attribute this. Satan, said Chesterton, fell through force of gravity. We must picture hell as a state where everyone is perpetually concerned about his own dignity and advancement, where everyone has a grievance, and where everyone lives in the deadly serious passions of envy, self-importance, and resentment. This, to begin with. For the rest, my own choice of symbols depended, I suppose, on temperament and on the age.

I like bats much better than bureaucrats. I live in the Managerial Age, in a world of 'Admin'. The greatest evil is not now done in those sordid 'dens of crime' that Dickens loved to paint. It is not done even in concentration camps and labour camps. In those we see its final result. But it is conceived and ordered (moved, seconded, carried, and minuted) in clean, carpeted, warmed and well-lighted offices, by quiet men with white collars and cut fingernails and smooth-shaven cheeks who do not need to raise their voice, Hence, naturally enough, my symbol for Hell is somethng like the bureau-cracy of a police state or the offices of a thoroughly nasty business concern.

Milton has told us that 'devil with devil damned Firm concord holds'. But how? Certainly not by friendship. A being which can still love is not yet a devil. Here again my symbol seemed to me useful. It enabled me, by earthly parallels, to picture an official society held together entirely by fear and greed. On the surface manners are normally suave. Rudeness to one's super-iors would obviously be suicidal; rudeness to one's equals might put them on their guard before you were ready to spring your mine. For of course 'Dog eat dog' is the principle of the whole organisation. Everyone wishes everyone else's discrediting, demotion, and ruin; everyone is an expert in the confidential report, the pretended alliance, the stab in the back. Over all this their good manners, their expressions of grave respect, their 'tributes' to one another's invaluable services, form a thin crust. Every now and then it gets punctured and the scalding lava of their hatred spurts out.

This symbol also enabled me to get rid of the absurd fancy that devils are engaged in the disinterested pursuit of something called Evil (the capital is essential). Mine have no use for any such turnip-ghost. Bad angels, like bad men, are entirely practical. They have two motives. The first is fear of punishment: for as totalitarian countries have their camps for torture, so my Hell contains deeper Hells, its 'houses of correction'. Their second motive is a kind of hunger. I feign that devils can, in a spiritual sense, eat one another; and us. Even in human life we have seen the passion to dominate, almost to digest, one's fellow; to make his whole intellectual and emotional life merely an extension of one's own – to hate one's hatreds and resent one's grievances and indulge one's egoism through him as well as through oneself. His own little store of passion must of course be suppressed to make room for ours. If he resists this suppression he is being very selfish.

On earth this desire is often called 'love'. In Hell I feign that they recognise it as hunger. But there the hunger is more ravenous and a fuller satisfaction is possible. There, I suggest, the stronger spirit – there are perhaps no bodies to impede the operation – can really and irrevocably suck the weaker into itself and permanently gorge its own being on the weaker's outraged individuality. It is (I feign) for this that devils desire human souls and the souls of one another. It is for this that Satan desires all his own followers and all the sons of Eve and all the host of heaven. His dream is of the day when all shall be inside him and all that says 'I' can say it only through him. This, I surmise, is the bloated-spider parody, the only imitation he can understand, of that unfathomed bounty whereby God turns tools into servants and servants into sons, so that they may be at last re-united to Him in the perfect freedom of a love offered from the height of the utter individualities which he has liberated them to be.

But, as in Grimm's story,* *das träumte mir nur*, this is all only myth and symbol. That is why the question of my own opinion about devils, though proper to be answered when once it was raised, is really of very minor importance to a reader of *Screwtape*. To those who share that opinion, my devils will be symbols of a concrete reality: to others, they will be personifications of abstractions and the book will be an allegory. But it makes little difference which way you read it. For of course its purpose was not to speculate about diabolical life but to throw light from a new angle on the life of men.

* *Der Räuberbräutigam*

I am told that I was not first in the field and that someone in the seventeenth century wrote letters from a devil. I have not seen that book. I believe its slant was mainly political. But I gladly acknowledge a debt to Stephen McKenna's *Confessions of a Well-Meaning Woman*. The connection may not be obvious, but you will find there the same moral inversion – the blacks all white and the whites all black – and the humour which comes of speaking through a totally humourless *persona*. I think my idea of spiritual cannibalism probably owes something to the horrible scenes of 'absorbing' in David Lindsay's neglected *Voyage to Arcturus*.

The names of my devils have excited a good deal of curiosity and there have been many explanations, all wrong. The truth is that I aimed merely at making them nasty – and here too I am perhaps indebted to Lindsay – by the sound. Once a name was invented, I might speculate like any one else (and with no more authority than any one else) as to the phonetic associations which caused the unpleasant effect. I fancy that *Scrooge, screw, thumbscrew, tapeworm* and *red tape* all do some work in my hero's name, and that *slob, slobber, slubber* and *gob* have all gone into *Slubgob*.

Some have paid me an undeserved compliment by supposing that my *Letters* were the ripe fruit of many years' study in moral and ascetic theology. They forgot that there is an equally reliable, though less creditable, way of learning how temptation works. 'My heart' – I need no other's – 'sheweth me the wickedness of the ungodly.'

I was often asked or advised to add to the original *Letters*, but for many years I felt not the least inclination to do it. Though I had never written anything more easily, I never wrote with less enjoyment. The ease came, no doubt, from the fact that the device of diabolical letters, once you have thought of it, exploits itself spontaneously, like Swift's big and little men, or the medical and ethical philosophy of *Erewhon*, or Anstey's Garuda Stone. It would run away with you for a thousand pages if you gave it its head. But though it was easy to twist one's mind into the diabolical attitude, it was not fun, or not for long. The strain produced a sort of spiritual cramp. The world into which I had to project myself while I spoke through Screwtape was all dust, grit, thirst and itch. Every trace of beauty, freshness and geniality had to be excluded. It almost smothered me before I was done. It would have smothered my readers if I had prolonged it.

I had, moreover, a sort of grudge against my book for not being a different book which no one could write. Ideally, Screwtape's advice to Wormwood should have been balanced by archangelical advice to the patient's guardian angel. Without this the picture of human life is lop-sided. But who could supply the deficiency? Even if a man – and he would have to be a far better man than I – could scale the spiritual heights required, what 'answerable style' could he use? For the style would really be part of the content. Mere advice would be no good; every sentence would have to smell of Heaven. And now-a-days even if you could write a prose like Traherne's, you wouldn't be allowed to, for the canon of 'functionalism' has disabled literature for half its functions. (At bottom, every ideal of style dictates not only how we should say things but what sort of things we may say.)

Then, as years went on and the stifling experience of writing the *Letters* became a weaker memory, reflections on this and that which seemed somehow to demand Screwtapian treatment began to occur to me. I was resolved never to write another *Letter*. The idea of something like a lecture or 'address' hovered vaguely in my mind, now forgotten, now recalled, never written. Then came an invitation from the *Saturday Evening Post*, and that pressed the trigger.

C. S. LEWIS

MAGDALENE COLLEGE, CAMBRIDGE, 18 MAY 1960

I

My dear Wormwood,

I note what you say about guiding your patient's reading and taking care that he sees a good deal of his materialist friend. But are you not being a trifle *naïve*? It sounds as if you supposed that *argument* was the way to keep him out of the Enemy's clutches. That might have been so if he had lived a few centuries earlier. At that time the humans still knew pretty well when a thing was proved and when it was not; and if it was proved they really believed it. They still connected thinking with doing and were prepared to alter their way of life as the result of a chain of reasoning. But what with the weekly press and other such weapons we have largely altered that. Your man has been accustomed, ever since he was a boy, to have a dozen incompatible philosophies dancing about together inside his head. He doesn't think of doctrines as primarily 'true' or 'false', but as 'academic' or 'practical', 'outworn' or 'contemporary', 'conventional' or 'ruthless'. Jargon, not argument, is your best ally in keeping him from the Church. Don't waste time trying to make him think that materialism is *true*! Make him think it is strong, or stark, or courageous – that it is the philosophy of the future. That's the sort of thing he cares about.

The trouble about argument is that it moves the whole struggle on to the Enemy's own ground. He can argue too; whereas in really practical propaganda of the kind I am suggesting He has been shown for centuries to be greatly the inferior of Our Father Below. By the very act of arguing, you awake the patient's reason; and once it is awake, who can foresee the result? Even if a particular train of thought can be twisted so as to end in our favour, you will find that you have been strengthening in your patient the fatal habit of attending to universal issues and withdrawing his attention from the stream of immediate sense experiences. Your business is to fix his attention on the stream. Teach him to call it 'real life' and don't let him ask what he means by 'real'.

Remember, he is not, like you, a pure spirit. Never having been a human (Oh that abominable advantage of the Enemy's!) you don't realise how enslaved they are to the pressure of the ordinary. I once had a patient, a sound atheist, who used to read in the British Museum. One day, as he sat reading, I saw a train of thought in his mind beginning to go the wrong way. The Enemy, of course, was at his elbow in a moment. Before I knew where I was I saw my twenty years' work beginning to totter. If I had lost my head and begun to attempt a defence by argument I should have been undone. But I was not such a fool. I struck instantly at the part of the man which I had best under my control and suggested that it was just about time he had some lunch. The Enemy presumably made the counter-suggestion (you know how one can never *quite* overhear what He says to them?) that this was more important than lunch. At least I think that must have been His line for when I said 'Quite. In fact much *too* important to tackle at the end of a morning,' the patient brightened up considerably; and by the time I had added 'Much better come back after lunch and go into it with a fresh mind,' he was already half way to the door. Once he was in the street the battle was won. I showed him a newsboy shouting the midday paper, and a No. 73 bus going past, and before he reached the bottom of the steps I had got into him an unalterable conviction that, whatever odd ideas might come into a man's head when he was shut up alone with his books, a healthy dose of 'real life' (by which he meant the bus and the newsboy) was enough to show him that all 'that sort of thing' just couldn't be true. He knew he'd had a narrow escape and in later years was fond of talking about 'that inarticulate sense for actuality which is our ultimate safeguard against the aberrations of mere logic'. He is now safe in Our Father's house.

You begin to see the point? Thanks to processes which we set at work in them centuries ago, they find it all but impossible to believe in the unfamiliar while the familiar is before their eyes. Keep pressing home on him the *ordinariness* of things. Above all, do not attempt to use science (I mean, the real sciences) as a defence against Christianity. They will positively encourage him to think about realities he can't touch and see. There have been sad cases among the modern physicists. If he must dabble in science, keep him on economics and sociology; don't let him get away from that invaluable 'real life'. But the best of all is to let him read no science but to give him a grand general idea that he knows it all and that everything he happens to have picked up in casual talk and reading is 'the results of modern investigation'. Do remember you are there to fuddle him. From the way some of you young fiends talk, anyone would suppose it was our job to *teach*!

Your affectionate uncle

SCREWTAPE

2

My dear Wormwood,

I note with grave displeasure that your patient has become a Christian. Do not indulge the hope that you will escape the usual penalties; indeed, in your better moments, I trust you would hardly even wish to do so. In the meantime we must make the best of the situation. There is no need to despair; hundreds of these adult converts have been reclaimed after a brief sojourn in the Enemy's camp and are now with us. All the *habits* of the patient, both mental and bodily, are still in our favour.

One of our great allies at present is the Church itself. Do not misunderstand me. I do not mean the Church as we see her spread out through all time and space and rooted in eternity, terrible as an army with banners. That, I confess, is a spectacle which makes our boldest tempters uneasy. But fortunately it is quite invisible to these humans. All your patient sees is the half-finished, sham Gothic erection on the new building estate. When he goes inside, he sees the local grocer with rather an oily expression on his face bustling up to offer him one shiny little book containing a liturgy which neither of them understands, and one shabby little book containing corrupt texts of a number of religious lyrics, mostly bad, and in very small print. When he gets to his pew and looks round him he sees just that selection of his neighbours whom he has hitherto avoided. You want to lean pretty heavily on those neighbours. Make his mind flit to and fro between an expression like 'the body of Christ' and the actual faces in the next pew. It matters very little, of course, what kind of people that next pew really contains. You may know one of them to be a great warrior on the Enemy's side. No matter. Your patient, thanks to Our Father Below, is a fool. Provided that any of those neighbours sing out of tune, or have boots that squeak, or double chins, or odd clothes, the patient will quite easily believe that their religion must therefore be somehow ridiculous. At his present stage, you see, he has an idea of 'Christians' in his mind which he supposes to be spiritual but which, in fact, is largely pictorial. His mind is full of togas and sandals and armour and bare legs and the mere fact that the other people in church wear modern clothes is a real – though of course an unconscious – difficulty to him.

Never let it come to the surface; never let him ask what he expected them to look like. Keep everything hazy in his mind now, and you will have all eternity wherein to amuse yourself by producing in him the peculiar kind of clarity which Hell affords.

Work hard, then, on the disappointment or anticlimax which is certainly coming to the patient during his first few weeks as a churchman. The Enemy allows this disappointment to occur on the threshold of every human endeavour. It occurs when the boy who has been enchanted in the nursery by *Stories from the Odyssey* buckles down to really learning Greek. It occurs when lovers have got married and begin the real task of learning to live together. In every department of life it marks the transition from dreaming aspiration to laborious doing. The Enemy takes this risk because He has a curious fantasy of making all these disgusting little human vermin into what He calls His 'free' lovers and servants – 'sons' is the word He uses, with His inveterate love of degrading the whole spiritual world by unnatural liaisons with the two-legged animals. Desiring their freedom, He therefore refuses to carry them, by their mere affections and habits, to any of the goals which He sets before them: He leaves them to 'do it on their own'. And there lies our opportunity. But also, remember, there lies our danger. If once they get through this initial dryness successfully, they become much less dependent on emotion and therefore much harder to tempt.

I have been writing hitherto on the assumption that the people in the next pew afford no *rational* ground for disappointment. Of course if they do – if the patient knows that the woman with the absurd hat is a fanatical bridge-player or the man with squeaky boots a miser and an extortioner – then your task is so much the easier. All you then have to do is to keep out of his mind the question 'If I, being what I am, can consider that I am in some sense a Christian, why should the different vices of those people in the next pew prove that their religion is mere hypocrisy and convention?' You may ask whether it is possible to keep such an obvious thought from occurring even to a human mind. It is, Wormwood, it is! Handle him properly and it simply won't come into his head. He has not been anything like long enough with the Enemy to have any real humility yet. What he says, even on his knees, about his own sinfulness is all parrot talk. At bottom, he still believes he has run up a very favourable credit-balance in the Enemy's ledger by allowing himself to be converted, and thinks that he is showing great humility and condescension in going to church with these 'smug', commonplace neighbours at all. Keep him in that state of mind as long as you can.

Your affectionate uncle

SCREWTAPE

744

3

My dear Wormwood,

I am very pleased by what you tell me about this man's relations with his mother. But you must press your advantage. The Enemy will be working from the centre outwards, gradually bringing more and more of the patient's conduct under the new standard, and may reach his behaviour to the old lady at any moment. You want to get in first. Keep in close touch with our colleague Glubose who is in charge of the mother, and build up between you in that house a good settled habit of mutual annoyance; daily pinpricks. The following methods are useful.

1. Keep his mind on the inner life. He thinks his conversion is something *inside* him and his attention is therefore chiefly turned at present to the states of his own mind – or rather to that very expurgated version of them which is all you should allow him to see. Encourage this. Keep his mind off the most elementary duties by directing it to the most advanced and spiritual ones. Aggravate that most useful human characteristic, the horror and neglect of the obvious. You must bring him to a condition in which he can practise self-examination for an hour without discovering any of those facts about himself which are perfectly clear to anyone who has ever lived in the same house with him or worked in the same office.

2. It is, no doubt, impossible to prevent his praying for his mother, but we have means of rendering the prayers innocuous. Make sure that they are always very 'spiritual', that he is always concerned with the state of her soul and never with her rheumatism. Two advantages will follow. In the first place, his attention will be kept on what he regards as her sins, by which, with a little guidance from you, he can be induced to mean any of her actions which are inconvenient or irritating to himself. Thus you can keep rubbing the wounds of the day a little sorer even while he is on his knees; the operation is not at all difficult and you will find it very entertaining. In the second place, since his ideas about her soul will be very crude and often erroneous, he will, in some degree, be praying for an imaginary person, and it will be

your task to make that imaginary person daily less and less like the real mother – the sharp-tongued old lady at the breakfast table. In time, you may get the cleavage so wide that no thought or feeling from his prayers for the imagined mother will ever flow over into his treatment of the real one. I have had patients of my own so well in hand that they could be turned at a moment's notice from impassioned prayer for a wife's or son's 'soul' to beating or insulting the real wife or son without a qualm.

3. When two humans have lived together for many years it usually happens that each has tones of voice and expressions of face which are almost unendurably irritating to the other. Work on that. Bring fully into the consciousness of your patient that particular lift of his mother's eyebrows which he learned to dislike in the nursery, and let him think how much he dislikes it. Let him assume that she knows how annoying it is and does it to annoy – if you know your job he will not notice the immense improbability of the assumption. And, of course, never let him suspect that he has tones and looks which similarly annoy her. As he cannot see or hear himself, this is easily managed.

4. In civilised life domestic hatred usually expresses itself by saying things which would appear quite harmless on paper (the *words* are not offensive) but in such a voice, or at such a moment, that they are not far short of a blow in the face. To keep this game up you and Glubose must see to it that each of these two fools has a sort of double standard. Your patient must demand that all his own utterances are to be taken at their face value and judged simply on the actual words, while at the same time judging all his mother's utterances with the fullest and most over-sensitive interpretation of the tone and the context and the suspected intention. She must be encouraged to do the same to him. Hence from every quarrel they can both go away convinced, or very nearly convinced, that they are quite innocent. You know the kind of thing: 'I simply ask her what time dinner will be and she flies into a temper.' Once this habit is well established you have the delightful situation of a human saying things with the express purpose of offending and yet having a grievance when offence is taken.

Finally, tell me something about the old lady's religious position. Is she at all jealous of the new factor in her son's life? – at all piqued that he should have learned from others, and so late, what she considers she gave him such good opportunity of learning in childhood? Does she feel he is making a great deal of 'fuss' about it – or that he's getting in on very easy terms? Remember the elder brother in the Enemy's story,

Your affectionate uncle

SCREWTAPE

746

4

My dear Wormwood,

The amateurish suggestions in your last letter warn me that it is high time for me to write to you fully on the painful subject of prayer. You might have spared the comment that my advice about his prayers for his mother 'proved singularly unfortunate'. That is not the sort of thing that a nephew should write to his uncle – nor a junior tempter to the under-secretary of a department. It also reveals an unpleasant desire to shift responsibility; you must learn to pay for your own blunders.

The best thing, where it is possible, is to keep the patient from the serious intention of praying altogether. When the patient is an adult recently reconverted to the Enemy's party, like your man, this is best done by encouraging him to remember, or to think he remembers, the parrot-like nature of his prayers in childhood. In reaction against that, he may be persuaded to aim at something entirely spontaneous, inward, informal, and unregularised; and what this will actually mean to a beginner will be an effort to produce in himself a vaguely devotional *mood* in which real concentration of will and intelligence have no part. One of their poets, Coleridge, has recorded that he did not pray 'with moving lips and bended knees' but merely 'composed his spirit to love' and indulged 'a sense of supplication'. That is exactly the sort of prayer we want; and since it bears a superficial resemblance to the prayer of silence as practised by those who are very far advanced in the Enemy's service, clever and lazy patients can be taken in by it for quite a long time. At the very least, they can be persuaded that the bodily position makes no difference to their prayers; for they constantly forget, what you must always remember, that they are animals and that whatever their bodies do affects their souls. It is funny how mortals always picture us as putting things into their minds: in reality our best work is done by keeping things out.

If this fails, you must fall back on a subtler misdirection of his intention. Whenever they are attending to the Enemy Himself we are defeated, but there are ways of preventing them from doing so. The simplest is to turn their gaze away from Him towards themselves. Keep them watching their own minds and trying to produce *feelings* there by the action of their own wills. When they meant to ask Him for charity, let them, instead, start trying to manufacture charitable feelings for themselves and not notice that this is what they are doing. When they meant to pray for courage, let them really be trying to feel brave. When they say they are praying for forgiveness, let them be trying to feel forgiven. Teach them to estimate the value of each prayer by their success in producing the desired feeling; and never let them suspect how much success or failure of that kind depends on whether they are well or ill, fresh or tired, at the moment.

But of course the Enemy will not meantime be idle. Whenever there is prayer, there is danger of His own immediate action. He is cynically indifferent to the dignity of His position, and ours, as pure spirits, and to human animals on their knees He pours out self-knowledge in a quite shameless fashion. But even if He defeats your first attempt at misdirection, we have a subtler weapon. The humans do not start from that direct perception of Him which we, unhappily, cannot avoid. They have never known that ghastly luminosity, that stabbing and searing glare which makes the background of permanent pain to our lives. If you look into your patient's mind when he is praying, you will not find *that*. If you examine the object to which he is attending, you will find that it is a composite object containing many quite ridiculous ingredients. There will be images derived from pictures of the Enemy as He appeared during the discreditable episode known as the Incarnation: there will be vaguer – perhaps quite savage and puerile – images associated with the other two Persons. There will even be some of his own reverence (and of bodily sensations accompanying it) objectified and attributed to the object revered. I have known cases where what the patient called his 'God' was actually *located* – up and to the left at the corner of the bedroom ceiling, or inside his own head, or in a crucifix on the wall. But whatever the nature of the composite object, you must keep him praying to *it* – to the thing that he has made, not to the Person who has made him. You may even encourage him to attach great importance to the correction and improvement of his composite object, and to keeping it steadily before his imagination during the whole prayer. For if he ever comes to make the distinction, if ever he consciously directs his prayers 'Not to what I think thou art but to what thou knowest thyself to be', our situation is, for the moment, desperate. Once all his thoughts and images have been flung aside or, if retained, retained with a full recognition of their merely subjective nature, and the man trusts himself to the completely real, external, invisible Presence, there with him in the room and never knowable by him as he is known by it – why, then it is that the incalculable may occur. In avoiding this situation – this real nakedness of the soul in prayer – you will be helped by the fact that the humans themselves do not desire it as much as they suppose. There's such a thing as getting more than they bargained for!

Your affectionate uncle

SCREWTAPE

My dear Wormwood,
    It is a little bit disappointing to expect a detailed report on your work and to receive instead such a vague rhapsody as your last letter. You say you are 'delirious with joy' because the European humans have started another of their wars. I see very well what has happened to you. You are not delirious; you are only drunk. Reading between the lines in your very unbalanced account of the patient's sleepless night, I can reconstruct your state of mind fairly accurately. For the first time in your career you have tasted that wine which is the reward of all our labours – the anguish and bewilderment of a human soul – and it has gone to your head. I can hardly blame you. I do not expect old heads on young shoulders. Did the patient respond to some of your terror-pictures of the future? Did you work in some good self-pitying glances at the happy past? – some fine thrills in the pit of his stomach, were there? You played your violin prettily, did you? Well, well, it's all very natural. But do remember, Wormwood, that duty comes before pleasure. If any present self-indulgence on your part leads to the ultimate loss of the prey, you will be left eternally thirsting for that draught of which you are now so much enjoying your first sip. If, on the other hand, by steady and cool-headed application here and now you can finally secure his soul, he will then be yours forever – a brim-full living chalice of despair and horror and astonishment which you can raise to your lips as often as you please. So do not allow any temporary excitement to distract you from the real business of undermining faith and preventing the formation of virtues. Give me without fail in your next letter a full account of the patient's reactions to the war, so that we can consider whether you are likely to do more good by making him an extreme patriot or an ardent pacifist. There are all sorts of possibilities. In the meantime, I must warn you not to hope too much from a war.

    Of course a war is entertaining. The immediate fear and suffering of the humans is a legitimate and pleasing refreshment for our myriads of toiling workers. But what permanent good does it do us unless we make use of it for bringing souls to Our Father Below? When I see the temporal suffering of humans who finally escape us, I feel as if I had been allowed to taste the first course of a rich banquet and then denied the rest. It is worse than not to have tasted it at all. The Enemy, true to His barbarous methods of warfare, allows us to see the short misery of His favourites only to tantalise and torment us – to mock the incessant hunger which, during this present phase of the great conflict, His blockade is admittedly imposing. Let us therefore think rather how to use, than how to enjoy, this European war. For it has certain tendencies inherent in it which are, in themselves, by no means in our favour. We may hope for a good deal of cruelty and unchastity. But, if we are not careful, we shall see thousands turning in this tribulation to the Enemy, while tens of thousands who do not go so far as that will nevertheless have their attention diverted from themselves to values and causes which they believe to be higher than the self. I know that the Enemy disapproves many of these causes. But that is where He is so unfair. He often makes prizes of humans who have given their lives for causes He thinks bad on the monstrously sophistical ground that the humans thought them good and were following the best they knew. Consider too what undesirable deaths occur in wartime. Men are killed in places where they knew they might be killed and to which they go, if they are at all of the Enemy's party, prepared. How much better for us if *all* humans died in costly nursing homes amid doctors who lie, nurses who lie, friends who lie, as we have trained them, promising life to the dying, encouraging the belief that sickness excuses every indulgence, and even, if our workers know their job, withholding all suggestion of a priest lest it should betray to the sick man his true condition! And how disastrous for us is the continual remembrance of death which war enforces. One of our best weapons, contented worldliness, is rendered useless. In wartime not even a human can believe that he is going to live forever.

I know that Scabtree and others have seen in wars a great opportunity for attacks on faith, but I think that view was exaggerated. The Enemy's human partisans have all been plainly told by Him that suffering is an essential part of what He calls Redemption; so that a faith which is destroyed by a war or a pestilence cannot really have been worth the trouble of destroying. I am speaking now of diffused suffering over a long period such as the war will produce. Of course, at the precise moment of terror, bereavement, or physical pain, you may catch your man when his reason is temporarily suspended. But even then, if he applies to Enemy headquarters, I have found that the post is nearly always defended,

Your affectionate uncle

SCREWTAPE

6

My dear Wormwood,

I am delighted to hear that your patient's age and profession make it possible, but by no means certain, that he will be called up for military service. We want him to be in the maximum uncertainty, so that his mind will be filled with contradictory pictures of the future, every one of which arouses hope or fear. There is nothing like suspense and anxiety for barricading a human's mind against the Enemy. He wants men to be concerned with what they do; our business is to keep them thinking about what will happen to them.

Your patient will, of course, have picked up the notion that he must submit with patience to the Enemy's will. What the Enemy means by this is primarily that he should accept with patience the tribulation which has actually been dealt out to him – the present anxiety and suspense. It is about *this* that he is to say 'Thy will be done', and for the daily task of bearing *this* that the daily bread will be provided. It is your business to see that the patient never thinks of the present fear as his appointed cross, but only of the things he is afraid of. Let him regard them as his crosses: let him forget that, since they are incompatible, they cannot all happen to him, and let him try to practise fortitude and patience to them all in advance. For real resignation, at the same moment, to a dozen different and hypothetical fates, is almost impossible, and the Enemy does not greatly assist those who are trying to attain it: resignation to present and actual suffering, even where that suffering consists of fear, is easier and is usually helped by this direct action.

An important spiritual law is here involved. I have explained that you can weaken his prayers by diverting his attention from the Enemy Himself to his own states of mind about the Enemy. On the other hand fear becomes easier to master when the patient's mind is diverted from the thing feared to the fear itself, considered as a present and undesirable state of his own mind; and when he regards the fear as his appointed cross he will inevitably think of it as a state of mind. One can therefore formulate the general rule; in all activities of mind which favour our cause, encourage the patient to be unself-conscious and to concentrate on the object, but in all activities favourable to the Enemy bend his mind back on itself. Let an insult or a woman's body so fix his attention outward that he does not reflect 'I am now entering into the state called Anger – or the state called Lust.' Contrariwise let the reflection 'My feelings are now growing more devout, or more charitable' so fix his attention inward that he no longer looks beyond himself to see our Enemy or his own neighbours.

As regards his more general attitude to the war, you must not rely too much on those feelings of hatred which the humans are so fond of discussing in Christian, or anti-Christian, periodicals. In his anguish, the patient can, of course, be encouraged to revenge himself by some vindictive feelings directed towards the German leaders, and that is good so far as it goes. But it is usually a sort of melodramatic or mythical hatred directed against imaginary scape-goats. He has never met these people in real life – they are lay figures modelled on what he gets from newspapers. The results of such fanciful hatred are often most disappointing, and of all humans the English are in this respect the most deplorable milksops. They are creatures of that miserable sort who loudly proclaim that torture is too good for their enemies and then give tea and ciga-rettes to the first wounded German pilot who turns up at the back door.

Do what you will, there is going to be some benevolence, as well as some malice, in your patient's soul. The great thing is to direct the malice to his immediate neighbours whom he meets every day and to thrust his benevo-lence out to the remote circumference, to people he does not know. The malice thus becomes wholly real and the benevolence largely imaginary. There is no good at all in inflaming his hatred of Germans if, at the same time, a pernicious habit of charity is growing up between him and his mother, his employer, and the man he meets in the train. Think of your man as a series of concentric circles, his will being the innermost, his intellect coming next, and finally his fantasy. You can hardly hope, at once, to exclude from all the circles everything that smells of the Enemy: but you must keep on shoving all the virtues outward till they are finally located in the circle of fantasy, and all the desirable qualities inward into the Will. It is only in so far as they reach the Will and are there embodied in habits that the virtues are really fatal to us. (I don't, of course, mean what the patient mis-takes for his Will, the conscious fume and fret of resolutions and clenched teeth, but the real centre, what the Enemy calls the Heart.) All sorts of virtues painted in the fantasy or approved by the intellect or even, in some measure, loved and admired, will not keep a man from Our Father's house: indeed they may make him more amusing when he gets there,

Your affectionate uncle

SCREWTAPE

7

My dear Wormwood,

I wonder you should ask me whether it is essential to keep the patient in ignorance of your own existence. That question, at least for the present phase of the struggle, has been answered for us by the High Command. Our policy, for the moment, is to conceal ourselves. Of course this has not always been so. We are really faced with a cruel dilemma. When the humans disbelieve in our existence we lose all the pleasing results of direct terrorism and we make no magicians. On the other hand, when they believe in us, we cannot make them materialists and sceptics. At least, not yet. I have great hopes that we shall learn in due time how to emotionalise and mythologise their science to such an extent that what is, in effect, a belief in us (though not under that name) will creep in while the human mind remains closed to belief in the Enemy. The 'Life Force', the worship of sex, and some aspects of Psychoanalysis, may here prove useful. If once we can produce our perfect work – the Materialist Magician, the man, not using, but veritably worshipping, what he vaguely calls 'Forces' while denying the existence of 'spirits' – then the end of the war will be in sight. But in the meantime we must obey our orders. I do not think you will have much difficulty in keeping the patient in the dark. The fact that 'devils' are predominantly *comic* figures in the modern imagination will help you. If any faint suspicion of your existence begins to arise in his mind, suggest to him a picture of something in red tights, and persuade him that since he cannot believe in that (it is an old textbook method of confusing them) he therefore cannot believe in you.

I had not forgotten my promise to consider whether we should make the patient an extreme patriot or an extreme pacifist. All extremes, except extreme devotion to the Enemy, are to be encouraged. Not always, of course, but at this period. Some ages are lukewarm and complacent, and then it is our business to soothe them yet faster asleep. Other ages, of which the present is one, are unbalanced and prone to faction, and it is our business to inflame them. Any small coterie, bound together by some interest which other men dislike or ignore, tends to develop inside itself a hothouse mutual admiration, and towards the outer world, a great deal of pride and hatred which is entertained without shame because the 'Cause' is its sponsor and it is thought to be impersonal. Even when the little group exists originally for the Enemy's own purposes, this remains true. We want the Church to be small not only that fewer men may know the Enemy but also that those who do may acquire the uneasy intensity and the defensive self-righteousness of a secret society or a clique. The Church herself is, of course, heavily defended and we have never yet quite succeeded in giving her *all* the characteristics of a faction; but subordinate factions within her have often produced admirable results, from the parties of Paul and of Apollos at Corinth down to the High and Low parties in the Church of England.

If your patient can be induced to become a conscientious objector he will automatically find himself one of a small, vocal, organised, and unpopular society, and the effects of this, on one so new to Christianity, will almost certainly be good. But only *almost* certainly. Has he had serious doubts about the lawfulness of serving in a just war before this present war began? Is he a man of great physical courage – so great that he will have no half-conscious misgivings about the real motives of his pacifism? Can he, when nearest to honesty (no human is ever *very* near), feel fully convinced that he is actuated wholly by the desire to obey the Enemy? If he is that sort of man, his pacifism will probably not do us much good, and the Enemy will probably protect him from the usual consequences of belonging to a sect. Your best plan, in that case, would be to attempt a sudden, confused, emotional crisis from which he might emerge as an uneasy convert to patriotism. Such things can often be managed. But if he is the man I take him to be, try Pacifism.

Whichever he adopts, your main task will be the same. Let him begin by treating the Patriotism or the Pacifism as a part of his religion. Then let him, under the influence of partisan spirit, come to regard it as the most important part. Then quietly and gradually nurse him on to the stage at which the religion becomes merely part of the 'cause', in which Christianity is valued chiefly because of the excellent arguments it can produce in favour of the British war-effort or of Pacifism. The attitude which you want to guard against is that in which temporal affairs are treated primarily as material for obedience. Once you have made the World an end, and faith a means, you have almost won your man, and it makes very little difference what kind of worldly end he is pursuing. Provided that meetings, pamphlets, policies, movements, causes, and crusades, matter more to him than prayers and sacraments and charity, he is ours – and the more 'religious' (on those terms) the more securely ours. I could show you a pretty cageful down here,

Your affectionate uncle

SCREWTAPE

8

My dear Wormwood,

So you 'have great hopes that the patient's religious phase is dying away', have you? I always thought the Training College had gone to pieces since they put old Slubgob at the head of it, and now I am sure. Has no one ever told you about the law of Undulation?

Humans are amphibians – half spirit and half animal. (The Enemy's determination to produce such a revolting hybrid was one of the things that determined Our Father to withdraw his support from Him.) As spirits they belong to the eternal world, but as animals they inhabit time. This means that while their spirit can be directed to an eternal object, their bodies, passions, and imaginations are in continual change, for to be in time means to change. Their nearest approach to constancy, therefore, is undulation – the repeated return to a level from which they repeatedly fall back, a series of troughs and peaks. If you had watched your patient carefully you would have seen this undulation in every department of his life – his interest in his work, his affection for his friends, his physical appetites, all go up and down. As long as he lives on earth periods of emotional and bodily richness and liveliness will alternate with periods of numbness and poverty. The dryness and dullness through which your patient is now going are not, as you fondly suppose, your workmanship; they are merely a natural phenomenon which will do us no good unless you make a good use of it.

To decide what the best use of it is, you must ask what use the Enemy wants to make of it, and then do the opposite. Now it may surprise you to learn that in His efforts to get permanent possession of a soul, He relies on the troughs even more than on the peaks; some of His special favourites have gone through longer and deeper troughs than anyone else. The reason is this. To us a human is primarily food; our aim is the absorption of its will into ours, the increase of our own area of selfhood at its expense. But the obedience which the Enemy demands of men is quite a different thing. One must face the fact that all the talk about His love for men, and His service being perfect freedom, is not (as one would gladly believe) mere propaganda, but an appalling truth. He really *does* want to fill the universe with a lot of loathsome little replicas of Himself – creatures whose life, on its miniature scale, will be qualitatively like His own, not because He has absorbed them but because their wills freely conform to His. We want cattle who can finally become food; He wants servants who can finally become sons. We want to suck in, He wants to give out. We are empty and would be filled; He is full and flows over. Our war aim is a world in which Our Father Below has drawn all other beings into himself: the Enemy wants a world full of beings united to Him but still distinct.

And that is where the troughs come in. You must have often wondered why the Enemy does not make more use of His power to be sensibly present to human souls in any degree He chooses and at any moment. But you now see that the Irresistible and the Indisputable are the two weapons which the very nature of His scheme forbids Him to use. Merely to override a human will (as His felt presence in any but the faintest and most mitigated degree would certainly do) would be for Him useless. He cannot ravish. He can only woo. For His ignoble idea is to eat the cake and have it; the creatures are to be one with Him, but yet themselves; merely to cancel them, or assimilate them, will not serve. He is prepared to do a little overriding at the beginning. He will set them off with communications of His presence which, though faint, seem great to them, with emotional sweetness, and easy conquest over temptation. But He never allows this state of affairs to last long. Sooner or later He withdraws, if not in fact, at least from their conscious experience, all those supports and incentives. He leaves the creature to stand up on its own legs – to carry out from the will alone duties which have lost all relish. It is during such trough periods, much more than during the peak periods, that it is growing into the sort of creature He wants it to be. Hence the prayers offered in the state of dryness are those which please Him best. We can drag our patients along by continual tempting, because we design them only for the table, and the more their will is interfered with the better. He cannot 'tempt' to virtue as we do to vice. He wants them to learn to walk and must therefore take away His hand; and if only the will to walk is really there He is pleased even with their stumbles. Do not be deceived, Wormwood. Our cause is never more in danger than when a human, no longer desiring, but still intending, to do our Enemy's will, looks round upon a universe from which every trace of Him seems to have vanished, and asks why he has been forsaken, and still obeys.

But of course the troughs afford opportunities to our side also. Next week I will give you some hints on how to exploit them,

Your affectionate uncle

SCREWTAPE

9

My dear Wormwood,

I hope my last letter has convinced you that the trough of dullness or 'dryness' through which your patient is going at present will not, of itself, give you his soul, but needs to be properly exploited. What forms the exploitation should take I will now consider.

In the first place I have always found that the trough periods of the human undulation provide excellent opportunity for all sensual temptations, particularly those of sex. This may surprise you, because, of course, there is more physical energy, and therefore more potential appetite, at the peak periods; but you must remember that the powers of resistance are then also at their highest. The health and spirits which you want to use in producing lust can also, alas, be very easily used for work or play or thought or innocuous merriment. The attack has a much better chance of success when the man's whole inner world is drab and cold and empty. And it is also to be noted that the trough sexuality is subtly different in quality from that of the peak – much less likely to lead to the milk and water phenomenon which the humans call 'being in love', much more easily drawn into perversions, much less contaminated by those generous and imaginative and even spiritual concomitants which often render human sexuality so disappointing. It is the same with other desires of the flesh. You are much more likely to make your man a sound drunkard by pressing drink on him as an anodyne when he is dull and weary than by encouraging him to use it as a means of merriment among his friends when he is happy and expansive. Never forget that when we are dealing with any pleasure in its healthy and normal and satisfying form, we are, in a sense, on the Enemy's ground. I know we have won many a soul through pleasure. All the same, it is His invention, not ours. He made the pleasures: all our research so far has not enabled us to produce one. All we can do is to encourage the humans to take the pleasures which our Enemy has produced, at times, or in ways, or in degrees, which He has forbidden. Hence we always try to work away from the natural condition of any pleasure to that in which it is least natural, least redolent of its Maker, and least pleasurable. An ever increasing craving for an ever diminishing pleasure is the formula. It is more certain; and it's better *style*. To get the man's soul and give him *nothing* in return – that is what really gladdens Our Father's heart. And the troughs are the time for beginning the process.

But there is an even better way of exploiting the trough; I mean through the patient's own thoughts about it. As always, the first step is to keep knowledge out of his mind. Do not let him suspect the law of undulation. Let him assume that the first ardours of his conversion might have been expected to last, and ought to have lasted, forever, and that his present dryness is an equally permanent condition. Having once got this misconception well fixed in his head, you may then proceed in various ways. It all depends on whether your man is of the desponding type who can be tempted to despair, or of the wishful-thinking type who can be assured that all is well. The former type is getting rare among the humans. If your patient should happen to belong to it, everything is easy. You have only got to keep him out of the way of experienced Christians (an easy task nowadays), to direct his attention to the appropriate passages in scripture, and then to set him to work on the desperate design of recovering his old feelings by sheer will-power, and the game is ours. If he is of the more hopeful type your job is to make him acquiesce in the present low temperature of his spirit and gradually become content with it, persuading himself that it is not so low after all. In a week or two you will be making him doubt whether the first days of his Christianity were not, perhaps, a little excessive. Talk to him about 'moderation in all things'. If you can once get him to the point of thinking that 'religion is all very well up to a point', you can feel quite happy about his soul. A moderated religion is as good for us as no religion at all – and more amusing.

Another possibility is that of direct attack on his faith. When you have caused him to assume that the trough is permanent, can you not persuade him that 'his religious phase' is just going to die away like all his previous phases? Of course there is no conceivable way of getting by reason from the proposition 'I am losing interest in this' to the proposition 'This is false'. But, as I said before, it is jargon, not reason, you must rely on. The mere word *phase* will very likely do the trick. I assume that the creature has been through several of them before – they all have – and that he always feels superior and patronising to the ones he has emerged from, not because he has really criticised them but simply because they are in the past. (You keep him well fed on hazy ideas of Progress and Development and the Historical Point of View, I trust, and give him lots of modern Biographies to read? The people in them are always emerging from Phases, aren't they?)

You see the idea? Keep his mind off the plain antithesis between True and False. Nice shadowy expressions – 'It was a phase' – 'I've been through all that' – and don't forget the blessed word 'Adolescent',
  Your affectionate uncle

SCREWTAPE

My dear Wormwood,

I was delighted to hear from Triptweeze that your patient has made some very desirable new acquaintances and that you seem to have used this event in a really promising manner. I gather that the middle-aged married couple who called at his office are just the sort of people we want him to know – rich, smart, superficially intellectual, and brightly sceptical about everything in the world. I gather they are even vaguely pacifist, not on moral grounds but from an ingrained habit of belittling anything that concerns the great mass of their fellow men and from a dash of purely fashionable and literary communism. This is excellent. And you seem to have made good use of all his social, sexual, and intellectual vanity. Tell me more. Did he commit himself deeply? I don't mean the words. There is a subtle play of looks and tones and laughs by which a mortal can imply that he is of the same party as those to whom he is speaking. That is the kind of betrayal you should specially encourage, because the man does not fully realise it himself; and by the time he does you will have made withdrawal difficult.

No doubt he must very soon realise that his own faith is in direct opposition to the assumptions on which all the conversation of his new friends is based. I don't think that matters much provided that you can persuade him to postpone any open acknowledgement of the fact, and this, with the aid of shame, pride, modesty and vanity, will be easy to do. As long as the postponement lasts he will be in a false position. He will be silent when he ought to speak and laugh when he ought to be silent. He will assume, at first only by his manner, but presently by his words, all sorts of cynical and sceptical attitudes which are not really his. But if you play him well, they may become his. All mortals tend to turn into the thing they are pretending to be. This is elementary. The real question is how to prepare for the Enemy's counterattack.

The first thing is to delay as long as possible the moment at which he realises this new pleasure as a temptation. Since the Enemy's servants have been preaching about 'the World' as one of the great standard temptations for two thousand years, this might seem difficult to do. But fortunately they have said very little about it for the last few decades. In modern Christian writings, though I see much (indeed more than I like) about Mammon, I see few of the old warnings about Worldly Vanities, the Choice of Friends, and the Value of Time. All that, your patient would probably classify as 'Puritanism' – and may I remark in passing that the value we have given to that word is one of the really solid triumphs of the last hundred years? By it we rescue annually thousands of humans from temperance, chastity, and sobriety of life.

Sooner or later, however, the real nature of his new friends must become clear to him, and then your tactics must depend on the patient's intelligence. If he is a big enough fool you can get him to realise the character of the friends only while they are absent; their presence can be made to sweep away all criticism. If this succeeds, he can be induced to live, as I have known many humans live, for quite long periods, two parallel lives; he will not only appear to be, but actually be, a different man in each of the circles he frequents. Failing this, there is a subtler and more entertaining method. He can be made to take a positive pleasure in the perception that the two sides of his life are inconsistent. This is done by exploiting his vanity. He can be taught to enjoy kneeling beside the grocer on Sunday just because he remembers that the grocer could not possibly understand the urbane and mocking world which he inhabited on Saturday evening; and contrariwise, to enjoy the bawdy and blasphemy over the coffee with these admirable friends all the more because he is aware of a 'deeper', 'spiritual' world within him which they cannot understand. You see the idea – the worldly friends touch him on one side and the grocer on the other, and he is the complete, balanced, complex man who sees round them all. Thus, while being permanently treacherous to at least two sets of people, he will feel, instead of shame, a continual undercurrent of self-satisfaction. Finally, if all else fails, you can persuade him, in defiance of conscience, to continue the new acquaintance on the ground that he is, in some unspecified way, doing these people 'good' by the mere fact of drinking their cocktails and laughing at their jokes, and that to cease to do so would be 'priggish', 'intolerant', and (of course) 'Puritanical'.

Meanwhile you will of course take the obvious precaution of seeing that this new development induces him to spend more than he can afford and to neglect his work and his mother. Her jealousy, and alarm, and his increasing evasiveness or rudeness, will be invaluable for the aggravation of the domestic tension,

Your affectionate uncle

SCREWTAPE

762

My dear Wormwood,
    Everything is clearly going very well. I am specially glad to hear that the two new friends have now made him acquainted with their whole set. All these, as I find from the record office, are thoroughly reliable people; steady, consistent scoffers and worldlings who without any spectacular crimes are progressing quietly and comfortably towards Our Father's house. You speak of their being great laughers. I trust this does not mean that you are under the impression that laughter as such is always in our favour. The point is worth some attention.

I divide the causes of human laughter into Joy, Fun, the Joke Proper, and Flippancy. You will see the first among friends and lovers reunited on the eve of a holiday. Among adults some pretext in the way of Jokes is usually provided, but the facility with which the smallest witticisms produce laughter at such a time shows that they are not the real cause. What that real cause is we do not know. Something like it is expressed in much of that detestable art which the humans call Music, and something like it occurs in Heaven – a meaningless acceleration in the rhythm of celestial experience, quite opaque to us. Laughter of this kind does us no good and should always be discouraged. Besides, the phenomenon is of itself disgusting and a direct insult to the realism, dignity, and austerity of Hell.

Fun is closely related to Joy – a sort of emotional froth arising from the play instinct. It is very little use to us. It can sometimes be used, of course, to divert humans from something else which the Enemy would like them to be feeling or doing: but in itself it has wholly undesirable tendencies; it promotes charity, courage, contentment, and many other evils.

The Joke Proper, which turns on sudden perception of incongruity, is a much more promising field. I am not thinking primarily of indecent or bawdy humour, which, though much relied upon by second-rate tempters, is often disappointing in its results. The truth is that humans are pretty clearly divided on this matter into two classes. There are some to whom 'no

passion is as serious as lust' and for whom an indecent story ceases to produce lasciviousness precisely in so far as it becomes funny: there are others
in whom laughter and lust are excited at the same moment and by the same
things. The first sort joke about sex because it gives rise to many incongruities: the second cultivate incongruities because they afford a pretext for
talking about sex. If your man is of the first type, bawdy humour will not
help you – I shall never forget the hours which I wasted (hours to me of
unbearable tedium) with one of my early patients in bars and smoking-
rooms before I learned this rule. Find out which group the patient belongs
to – and see that he does *not* find out.

The real use of Jokes or Humour is in quite a different direction, and it is
specially promising among the English who take their 'sense of humour' so
seriously that a deficiency in this sense is almost the only deficiency at
which they feel shame. Humour is for them the all-consoling and (mark
this) the all-excusing, grace of life. Hence it is invaluable as a means of
destroying shame. If a man simply lets others pay for him, he is 'mean'; if he
boasts of it in a jocular manner and twits his fellows with having been scored
off, he is no longer 'mean' but a comical fellow. Mere cowardice is shameful;
cowardice boasted of with humorous exaggerations and grotesque gestures
can be passed off as funny. Cruelty is shameful – unless the cruel man can
represent it as a practical joke. A thousand bawdy, or even blasphemous,
jokes do not help towards a man's damnation so much as his discovery that
almost anything he wants to do can be done, not only without the disapproval but with the admiration of his fellows, if only it can get itself treated
as a Joke. And this temptation can be almost entirely hidden from your
patient by that English seriousness about Humour. Any suggestion that
there might be too much of it can be represented to him as 'Puritanical' or as
betraying a 'lack of humour'.

But flippancy is the best of all. In the first place it is very economical.
Only a clever human can make a real Joke about virtue, or indeed about
anything else; any of them can be trained to talk *as if* virtue were funny.
Among flippant people the Joke is always assumed to have been made. No
one actually makes it; but every serious subject is discussed in a manner
which implies that they have already found a ridiculous side to it. If
prolonged, the habit of Flippancy builds up around a man the finest armour-
plating against the Enemy that I know, and it is quite free from the dangers
inherent in the other sources of laughter. It is a thousand miles away from
joy: it deadens, instead of sharpening, the intellect; and it excites no affection
between those who practise it,

Your affectionate uncle

SCREWTAPE

12

My dear Wormwood,

Obviously you are making excellent progress. My only fear is lest in attempting to hurry the patient you awaken him to a sense of his real position. For you and I, who see that position as it really is, must never forget how totally different it ought to appear to him. We know that we have introduced a change of direction in his course which is already carrying him out of his orbit around the Enemy; but he must be made to imagine that all the choices which have effected this change of course are trivial and revocable. He must not be allowed to suspect that he is now, however slowly, heading right away from the sun on a line which will carry him into the cold and dark of utmost space.

For this reason I am almost glad to hear that he is still a churchgoer and a communicant. I know there are dangers in this; but anything is better than that he should realise the break he has made with the first months of his Christian life. As long as he retains externally the habits of a Christian he can still be made to think of himself as one who has adopted a few new friends and amusements but whose spiritual state is much the same as it was six weeks ago. And while he thinks that, we do not have to contend with the explicit repentance of a definite, fully recognised, sin, but only with his vague, though uneasy, feeling that he hasn't been doing very well lately.

This dim uneasiness needs careful handling. If it gets too strong it may wake him up and spoil the whole game. On the other hand, if you suppress it entirely – which, by the by, the Enemy will probably not allow you to do – we lose an element in the situation which can be turned to good account. If such a feeling is allowed to live, but not allowed to become irresistible and flower into real repentance, it has one invaluable tendency. It increases the patient's reluctance to think about the Enemy. All humans at nearly all times have some such reluctance; but when thinking of Him involves facing and intensifying a whole vague cloud of half-conscious guilt, this reluctance is increased tenfold. They hate every idea that suggests Him, just as men in financial embarrassment hate the very sight of a pass-book. In this state your patient will not omit, but he will increasingly dislike, his religious duties. He will think about them as little as he feels he decently can beforehand, and forget them as soon as possible when they are over. A few weeks ago you had to *tempt* him to unreality and inattention in his prayers: but now you will find him opening his arms to you and almost begging you to distract his purpose and benumb his heart. He will *want* his prayers to be unreal, for he will dread nothing so much as effective contact with the Enemy. His aim will be to let sleeping worms lie.

As this condition becomes more fully established, you will be gradually freed from the tiresome business of providing Pleasures as temptations. As the uneasiness and his reluctance to face it cut him off more and more from all real happiness, and as habit renders the pleasures of vanity and excitement and flippancy at once less pleasant and harder to forgo (for that is what habit fortunately does to a pleasure) you will find that anything or nothing is sufficient to attract his wandering attention. You no longer need a good book, which he really likes, to keep him from his prayers or his work or his sleep; a column of advertisements in yesterday's paper will do. You can make him waste his time not only in conversation he enjoys with people whom he likes, but in conversations with those he cares nothing about on subjects that bore him. You can make him do nothing at all for long periods. You can keep him up late at night, not roistering, but staring at a dead fire in a cold room. All the healthy and out-going activities which we want him to avoid can be inhibited and *nothing* given in return, so that at least he may say, as one of my own patients said on his arrival down here, 'I now see that I spent most of my life in doing *neither* what I ought *nor* what I liked.' The Christians describe the Enemy as one 'without whom Nothing is strong'. And Nothing is very strong: strong enough to steal away a man's best years not in sweet sins but in a dreary flickering of the mind over it knows not what and knows not why, in the gratification of curiosities so feeble that the man is only half aware of them, in drumming of fingers and kicking of heels, in whistling tunes that he does not like, or in the long, dim labyrinth of reveries that have not even lust or ambition to give them a relish, but which, once chance association has started them, the creature is too weak and fuddled to shake off.

You will say that these are very small sins; and doubtless, like all young tempters, you are anxious to be able to report spectacular wickedness. But do remember, the only thing that matters is the extent to which you separate the man from the Enemy. It does not matter how small the sins are provided that their cumulative effect is to edge the man away from the Light and out into the Nothing. Murder is no better than cards if cards can do the trick. Indeed the safest road to Hell is the gradual one – the gentle slope, soft underfoot, without sudden turnings, without milestones, without signposts,

Your affectionate uncle

SCREWTAPE

13

M y dear Wormwood,
It seems to me that you take a great many pages to tell a very simple story. The long and the short of it is that you have let the man slip through your fingers. The situation is very grave, and I really see no reason why I should try to shield you from the consequences of your inefficiency. A repentance and renewal of what the other side call 'grace' on the scale which you describe is a defeat of the first order. It amounts to a second conversion – and probably on a deeper level than the first.

As you ought to have known, the asphyxiating cloud which prevented your attacking the patient on his walk back from the old mill, is a well-known phenomenon. It is the Enemy's most barbarous weapon, and generally appears when He is directly present to the patient under certain modes not yet fully classified. Some humans are permanently surrounded by it and therefore inaccessible to us.

And now for your blunders. On your own showing you first of all allowed the patient to read a book he really enjoyed, because he enjoyed it and not in order to make clever remarks about it to his new friends. In the second place, you allowed him to walk down to the old mill and have tea there – a walk through country he really likes, and taken alone. In other words you allowed him two real positive Pleasures. Were you so ignorant as not to see the danger of this? The characteristic of Pains and Pleasures is that they are unmistakably real, and therefore, as far as they go, give the man who feels them a touchstone of reality. Thus if you had been trying to damn your man by the Romantic method – by making him a kind of Childe Harold or Werther submerged in self-pity for imaginary distresses – you would try to protect him at all costs from any real pain; because, of course, five minutes' genuine toothache would reveal the romantic sorrows for the nonsense they were and unmask your whole stratagem. But you were trying to damn your patient by the World, that is by palming off vanity, bustle, irony, and expensive tedium as pleasures. How can you have failed to see that a *real* pleasure was the last thing you ought to have let him meet? Didn't you foresee that it would just kill by contrast all the trumpery which you have been so laboriously teaching him to value? And that the sort of pleasure which the book and the walk gave him was the most dangerous of all? That it would peel off from his sensibility the kind of crust you have been forming on it, and make him feel that he was coming home, recovering himself? As a preliminary to detaching him from the Enemy, you wanted to detach him from himself, and had made some progress in doing so. Now, all that is undone.

Of course I know that the Enemy also wants to detach men from themselves, but in a different way. Remember always, that He really likes the little vermin, and sets an absurd value on the distinctness of every one of them. When He talks of their losing their selves, He only means abandoning the clamour of self-will; once they have done that, He really gives them back all their personality, and boasts (I am afraid, sincerely) that when they are wholly His they will be more themselves than ever. Hence, while He is delighted to see them sacrificing even their innocent wills to His, He hates to see them drifting away from their own nature for any other reason. And we should always encourage them to do so. The deepest likings and impulses of any man are the raw material, the starting-point, with which the Enemy has furnished him. To get him away from those is therefore always a point gained; even in things indifferent it is always desirable to substitute the standards of the World, or convention, or fashion, for a human's own real likings and dislikings. I myself would carry this very far. I would make it a rule to eradicate from my patient any strong personal taste which is not actually a sin, even if it is something quite trivial such as a fondness for county cricket or collecting stamps or drinking cocoa. Such things, I grant you, have nothing of virtue in them; but there is a sort of innocence and humility and self-forgetfulness about them which I distrust. The man who truly and disinterestedly enjoys any one thing in the world, for its own sake, and without caring two-pence what other people say about it, is by that very fact fore-armed against some of our subtlest modes of attack. You should always try to make the patient abandon the people or food or books he really likes in favour of the 'best' people, the 'right' food, the 'important' books. I have known a human defended from strong temptations to social ambition by a still stronger taste for tripe and onions.

It remains to consider how we can retrieve this disaster. The great thing is to prevent his doing anything. As long as he does not convert it into action, it does not matter how much he thinks about this new repentance. Let the little brute wallow in it. Let him, if he has any bent that way, write a book about it; that is often an excellent way of sterilising the seeds which the Enemy plants in a human soul. Let him do anything but act. No amount of piety in his imagination and affections will harm us if we can keep it out of his will. As one of the humans has said, active habits are strengthened by repetition but passive ones are weakened. The more often he feels without acting, the less he will be able ever to act, and, in the long run, the less he will be able to feel,

Your affectionate uncle

SCREWTAPE ·

14

My dear Wormwood,

The most alarming thing in your last account of the patient is that he is making none of those confident resolutions which marked his original conversion. No more lavish promises of perpetual virtue, I gather; not even the expectation of an endowment of 'grace' for life, but only a hope for the daily and hourly pittance to meet the daily and hourly temptation! This is very bad.

I see only one thing to do at the moment. Your patient has become humble; have you drawn his attention to the fact? All virtues are less formidable to us once the man is aware that he has them, but this is specially true of humility. Catch him at the moment when he is really poor in spirit and smuggle into his mind the gratifying reflection, 'By jove! I'm being humble', and almost immediately pride – pride at his own humility – will appear. If he awakes to the danger and tries to smother this new form of pride, make him proud of his attempt – and so on, through as many stages as you please. But don't try this too long, for fear you awake his sense of humour and proportion, in which case he will merely laugh at you and go to bed.

But there are other profitable ways of fixing his attention on the virtue of Humility. By this virtue, as by all the others, our Enemy wants to turn the man's attention away from self to Him, and to the man's neighbours. All the abjection and self-hatred are designed, in the long run, solely for this end; unless they attain this end they do us little harm; and they may even do us good if they keep the man concerned with himself, and, above all, if self-contempt can be made the starting-point for contempt of other selves, and thus for gloom, cynicism, and cruelty.

You must therefore conceal from the patient the true end of Humility. Let him think of it not as self-forgetfulness but as a certain kind of opinion (namely, a low opinion) of his own talents and character. Some talents, I gather, he really has. Fix in his mind the idea that humility consists in trying to believe those talents to be less valuable than he believes them to be. No doubt they *are* in fact less valuable than he believes, but that is not the point. The great thing is to make him value an opinion for some quality other than truth, thus introducing an element of dishonesty and make-believe into the heart of what otherwise threatens to become a virtue. By this method thousands of humans have been brought to think that humility means pretty women trying to believe they are ugly and clever men trying to believe they are fools. And since what they are trying to believe may, in some cases, be manifest nonsense, they cannot succeed in believing it and we have the chance of keeping their minds endlessly revolving on themselves in an effort to achieve the impossible. To anticipate the Enemy's strategy, we must consider His aims. The Enemy wants to bring the man to a state of mind in which he could design the best cathedral in the world, and know it to be the best, and rejoice in the fact, without being any more (or less) or otherwise glad at having done it than he would be if it had been done by another. The Enemy wants him, in the end, to be so free from any bias in his own favour that he can rejoice in his own talents as frankly and gratefully as in his neighbour's talents – or in a sunrise, an elephant, or a waterfall. He wants each man, in the long run, to be able to recognise all creatures (even himself) as glorious and excellent things. He wants to kill their animal self-love as soon as possible; but it is His long-term policy, I fear, to restore to them a new kind of self-love – a charity and gratitude for all selves, including their own; when they have really learned to love their neighbours as themselves, they will be allowed to love themselves as their neighbours. For we must never forget what is the most repellent and inexplicable trait in our Enemy; He *really* loves the hairless bipeds He has created and always gives back to them with His right hand what He has taken away with His left.

His whole effort, therefore, will be to get the man's mind off the subject of his own value altogether. He would rather the man thought himself a great architect or a great poet and then forgot about it, than that he should spend much time and pains trying to think himself a bad one. Your efforts to instil either vainglory or false modesty into the patient will therefore be met from the Enemy's side with the obvious reminder that a man is not usually called upon to have an opinion of his own talents at all, since he can very well go on improving them to the best of his ability without deciding on his own precise niche in the temple of Fame. You must try to exclude this reminder from the patient's consciousness at all costs. The Enemy will also try to render real in the patient's mind a doctrine which they all profess but find it difficult to bring home to their feelings – the doctrine that they did not create themselves, that their talents were given them, and that they might as well be proud of the colour of their hair. But always and by all methods the Enemy's aim will be to get the patient's mind off such questions, and yours will be to fix it on them. Even of his sins the Enemy does not want him to think too much: once they are repented, the sooner the man turns his attention outward, the better the Enemy is pleased,

Your affectionate uncle

SCREWTAPE

15

My dear Wormwood,
    I had noticed, of course, that the humans were having a lull in their European war – what they naïvely call '*The War*'! – and am not surprised that there is a corresponding lull in the patient's anxieties. Do we want to encourage this, or to keep him worried? Tortured fear and stupid confidence are both desirable states of mind. Our choice between them raises important questions.

The humans live in time but our Enemy destines them to eternity. He therefore, I believe, wants them to attend chiefly to two things, to eternity itself, and to that point of time which they call the Present. For the Present is the point at which time touches eternity. Of the present moment, and of it only, humans have an experience analogous to the experience which our Enemy has of reality as a whole; in it alone freedom and actuality are offered them. He would therefore have them continually concerned either with eternity (which means being concerned with Him) or with the Present – either meditating on their eternal union with, or separation from, Himself, or else obeying the present voice of conscience, bearing the present cross, receiving the present grace, giving thanks for the present pleasure.

Our business is to get them away from the eternal, and from the Present. With this in view, we sometimes tempt a human (say a widow or a scholar) to live in the Past. But this is of limited value, for they have some real knowledge of the past and it has a determinate nature and, to that extent, resembles eternity. It is far better to make them live in the Future. Biological necessity makes all their passions point in that direction already, so that thought about the Future inflames hope and fear. Also, it is unknown to them, so that in making them think about it we make them think of unrealities. In a word, the Future is, of all things, the thing *least like* eternity. It is the most completely temporal part of time – for the Past is frozen and no longer flows, and the Present is all lit up with eternal rays. Hence the encouragement we have given to all those schemes of thought such as Creative Evolution, Scientific Humanism, or Communism, which fix men's affections on the

Future, on the very core of temporality. Hence nearly all vices are rooted in the future. Gratitude looks to the past and love to the present; fear, avarice, lust, and ambition look ahead. Do not think lust an exception. When the present pleasure arrives, the sin (which alone interests us) is already over. The pleasure is just the part of the process which we regret and would exclude if we could do so without losing the sin; it is the part contributed by the Enemy, and therefore experienced in a Present. The sin, which is our contribution, looked forward.

To be sure, the Enemy wants men to think of the Future too – just so much as is necessary for *now* planning the acts of justice or charity which will probably be their duty tomorrow. The duty of planning the morrow's work is *today's* duty; though its material is borrowed from the future, the duty, like all duties, is in the Present. This is now straw splitting. He does not want men to give the Future their hearts, to place their treasure in it. We do. His ideal is a man who, having worked all day for the good of posterity (if that is his vocation), washes his mind of the whole subject, commits the issue to Heaven, and returns at once to the patience or gratitude demanded by the moment that is passing over him. But we want a man hag-ridden by the Future – haunted by visions of an imminent heaven or hell upon earth – ready to break the Enemy's commands in the present if by so doing we make him think he can attain the one or avert the other – dependent for his faith on the success or failure of schemes whose end he will not live to see. We want a whole race perpetually in pursuit of the rainbow's end, never honest, nor kind, nor happy *now*, but always using as mere fuel wherewith to heap the altar of the future every real gift which is offered them in the Present.

It follows then, in general, and other things being equal, that it is better for your patient to be filled with anxiety or hope (it doesn't much matter which) about this war than for him to be living in the present. But the phrase 'living in the present' is ambiguous. It may describe a process which is really just as much concerned with the Future as anxiety itself. Your man may be untroubled about the Future, not because he is concerned with the Present, but because he has persuaded himself that the Future is going to be agreeable. As long as that is the real cause of his tranquillity, his tranquillity will do us good, because it is only piling up more disappointment, and therefore more impatience, for him when his false hopes are dashed. If, on the other hand, he is aware that horrors may be in store for him and is praying for the virtues, wherewith to meet them, and meanwhile concerning himself with the Present because there, and there alone, all duty, all grace, all knowledge, and all pleasure dwell, his state is very undesirable and should be attacked at once. Here again, our Philological Arm has done good work; try the word 'complacency' on him. But, of course, it is most likely that he is 'living in the Present' for none of these reasons but simply because his health is good and he is enjoying his work. The phenomenon would then be merely natural. All the same, I should break it up if I were you. No natural phenomenon is really in our favour. And anyway, why *should* the creature be happy?

Your affectionate uncle

SCREWTAPE

16

My dear Wormwood,
     You mentioned casually in your last letter that the patient has continued to attend one church, and one only, since he was converted, and that he is not wholly pleased with it. May I ask what you are about? Why have I no report on the causes of his fidelity to the parish church? Do you realise that unless it is due to indifference it is a very bad thing? Surely you know that if a man can't be cured of churchgoing, the next best thing is to send him all over the neighbourhood looking for the church that 'suits' him until he becomes a taster or connoisseur of churches.

The reasons are obvious. In the first place the parochial organisation should always be attacked, because, being a unity of place and not of likings, it brings people of different classes and psychology together in the kind of unity the Enemy desires. The congregational principle, on the other hand, makes each church into a kind of club, and finally, if all goes well, into a coterie or faction. In the second place, the search for a 'suitable' church makes the man a critic where the Enemy wants him to be a pupil. What He wants of the layman in church is an attitude which may, indeed, be critical in the sense of rejecting what is false or unhelpful, but which is wholly uncritical in the sense that it does not appraise – does not waste time in thinking about what it rejects, but lays itself open in uncommenting, humble receptivity to any nourishment that is going. (You see how grovelling, how unspiritual, how irredeemably vulgar He is!) This attitude, especially during sermons, creates the condition (most hostile to our whole policy) in which platitudes can become really audible to a human soul. There is hardly any sermon, or any book, which may not be dangerous to us if it is received in this temper. So pray bestir yourself and send this fool the round of the neighbouring churches as soon as possible. Your record up to date has not given us much satisfaction.

The two churches nearest to him, I have looked up in the office. Both have certain claims. At the first of these the Vicar is a man who has been so long engaged in watering down the faith to make it easier for a supposedly incredulous and hard-headed congregation that it is now he who shocks his parishioners with his unbelief, not *vice versa*. He has undermined many a soul's Christianity. His conduct of the services is also admirable. In order to spare the laity all 'difficulties' he has deserted both the lectionary and the appointed psalms and now, without noticing it, revolves endlessly round the little treadmill of his fifteen favourite psalms and twenty favourite lessons. We are thus safe from the danger that any truth not already familiar to him and to his flock should ever reach them through Scripture. But perhaps your patient is not quite silly enough for this church – or not yet?

At the other church we have Fr Spike. The humans are often puzzled to understand the range of his opinions – why he is one day almost a Communist and the next not far from some kind of theocratic Fascism – one day a scholastic, and the next prepared to deny human reason altogether – one day immersed in politics, and, the day after, declaring that all states of this world are *equally* 'under judgment'. We, of course, see the connecting link, which is Hatred. The man cannot bring himself to preach anything which is not calculated to shock, grieve, puzzle, or humiliate his parents and their friends. A sermon which such people could accept would be to him as insipid as a poem which they could scan. There is also a promising streak of dishonesty in him; we are teaching him to say 'The teaching of the Church is' when he really means 'I'm almost sure I read recently in Maritain or someone of that sort'. But I must warn you that he has one fatal defect: he really believes. And this may yet mar all.

But there is one good point which both these churches have in common – they are both party churches. I think I warned you before that if your patient can't be kept out of the Church, he ought at least to be violently attached to some party within it. I don't mean on really doctrinal issues; about those, the more lukewarm he is the better. And it isn't the doctrines on which we chiefly depend for producing malice. The real fun is working up hatred between those who *say* 'mass' and those who *say* 'holy communion' when neither party could possibly state the difference between, say, Hooker's doctrine and Thomas Aquinas', in any form which would hold water for five minutes. And all the purely indifferent things – candles and clothes and what not – are an admirable ground for our activities. We have quite removed from men's minds what that pestilent fellow Paul used to teach about food and other unessentials – namely, that the human without scruples should always give in to the human with scruples. You would think they could not fail to see the application. You would expect to find the 'low' churchman genuflecting and crossing himself lest the weak conscience of his 'high' brother should be moved to irreverence, and the 'high' one refraining from these exercises lest he should betray his 'low' brother into idolatry.

And so it would have been but for our ceaseless labour. Without that the variety of usage within the Church of England might have become a positive hotbed of charity and humility,

Your affectionate uncle

SCREWTAPE

17

My dear Wormwood,

The contemptuous way in which you spoke of gluttony as a means of catching souls, in your last letter, only shows your ignorance. One of the great achievements of the last hundred years has been to deaden the human conscience on that subject, so that by now you will hardly find a sermon preached or a conscience troubled about it in the whole length and breadth of Europe. This has largely been effected by concentrating all our efforts on gluttony of Delicacy, not gluttony of Excess. Your patient's mother, as I learn from the dossier and you might have learned from Glubose, is a good example. She would be astonished – one day, I hope, *will* be – to learn that her whole life is enslaved to this kind of sensuality, which is quite concealed from her by the fact that the quantities involved are small. But what do quantities matter, provided we can use a human belly and palate to produce querulousness, impatience, uncharitableness, and self-concern? Glubose has this old woman well in hand. She is a positive terror to hostesses and servants. She is always turning from what has been offered her to say with a demure little sigh and a smile 'Oh please, please ... *all* I want is a cup of tea, weak but not too weak, and the teeniest weeniest bit of really crisp toast.' You see? Because what she wants is smaller and less costly than what has been set before her, she never recognises as gluttony her determination to get what she wants, however troublesome it may be to others. At the very moment of indulging her appetite she believes that she is practising temperance. In a crowded restaurant she gives a little scream at the plate which some overworked waitress has set before her and says, 'Oh, that's far, far too much! Take it away and bring me about a quarter of it.' If challenged, she would say she was doing this to avoid waste; in reality she does it because the particular shade of delicacy to which we have enslaved her is offended by the sight of more food than she happens to want.

The real value of the quiet, unobtrusive work which Glubose has been doing for years on this old woman can be gauged by the way in which her belly now dominates her whole life. The woman is in what may be called the 'All-I-want' state of mind. *All* she wants is a cup of tea properly made, or an egg properly boiled, or a slice of bread properly toasted. But she never finds any servant or any friend who can do these simple things 'properly' – because her 'properly' conceals an insatiable demand for the exact, and almost impossible, palatal pleasures which she imagines she remembers from the past; a past described by her as 'the days when you could get good servants' but known to us as the days when her senses were more easily pleased and she had pleasures of other kinds which made her less dependent on those of the table. Meanwhile, the daily disappointment produces daily ill temper: cooks give notice and friendships are cooled. If ever the Enemy introduces into her mind a faint suspicion that she is too interested in food, Glubose counters it by suggesting to her that she doesn't mind what she eats herself but 'does like to have things nice for her boy'. In fact, of course, her greed has been one of the chief sources of his domestic discomfort for many years.

Now your patient is his mother's son. While working your hardest, quite rightly, on other fronts, you must not neglect a little quiet infiltration in respect of gluttony. Being a male, he is not so likely to be caught by the '*All* I want' camouflage. Males are best turned into gluttons with the help of their vanity. They ought to be made to think themselves very knowing about food, to pique themselves on having found the only restaurant in the town where steaks are really 'properly' cooked. What begins as vanity can then be gradually turned into habit. But, however you approach it, the great thing is to bring him into the state in which the denial of any one indulgence – it matters not which, champagne or tea, *sole colbert* or cigarettes – 'puts him out', for then his charity, justice, and obedience are all at your mercy.

Mere excess in food is much less valuable than delicacy. Its chief use is as a kind of artillery preparation for attacks on chastity. On that, as on every other subject, keep your man in a condition of false spirituality. Never let him notice the medical aspect. Keep him wondering what pride or lack of faith has delivered him into your hands when a simple enquiry into what he has been eating or drinking for the last twenty-four hours would show him whence your ammunition comes and thus enable him by a very little abstinence to imperil your lines of communication. If he *must* think of the medical side of chastity, feed him the grand lie which we have made the English humans believe, that physical exercise in excess and consequent fatigue are specially favourable to this virtue. How they can believe this, in face of the notorious lustfulness of sailors and soldiers, may well be asked. But we used the schoolmasters to put the story about – men who were really interested in chastity as an excuse for games and therefore recommended games as an aid to chastity. But this whole business is too large to deal with at the tail-end of a letter,

Your affectionate uncle

SCREWTAPE

18

My dear Wormwood,

Even under Slubgob you must have learned at college the routine technique of sexual temptation, and since, for us spirits, this whole subject is one of considerable tedium (though necessary as part of our training) I will pass it over. But on the larger issues involved I think you have a good deal to learn.

The Enemy's demand on humans takes the form of a dilemma; *either* complete abstinence *or* unmitigated monogamy. Ever since our Father's first great victory, we have rendered the former very difficult to them. The latter, for the last few centuries, we have been closing up as a way of escape. We have done this through the poets and novelists by persuading the humans that a curious, and usually shortlived, experience which they call 'being in love' is the only respectable ground for marriage; that marriage can, and ought to, render this excitement permanent; and that a marriage which does not do so is no longer binding. This idea is our parody of an idea that came from the Enemy.

The whole philosophy of Hell rests on recognition of the axiom that one thing is not another thing, and, specially, that one self is not another self. My good is my good and your good is yours. What one gains another loses. Even an inanimate object is what it is by excluding all other objects from the space it occupies; if it expands, it does so by thrusting other objects aside or by absorbing them. A self does the same. With beasts the absorption takes the form of eating; for us, it means the sucking of will and freedom out of a weaker self into a stronger. 'To be' *means* 'to be in competition'.

Now the Enemy's philosophy is nothing more nor less than one continued attempt to evade this very obvious truth. He aims at a contradiction. Things are to be many, yet somehow also one. The good of one self is to be the good of another. This impossibility He calls *love*, and this same monotonous panacea can be detected under all He does and even all He is – or claims to be. Thus He is not content, even Himself, to be a sheer arithmetical unity;

He claims to be three as well as one, in order that this nonsense about Love may find a foothold in His own nature. At the other end of the scale, He introduces into matter that obscene invention the organism, in which the parts are perverted from their natural destiny of competition and made to co-operate.

His real motive for fixing on sex as the method of reproduction among humans is only too apparent from the use He has made of it. Sex might have been, from our point of view, quite innocent. It might have been merely one more mode in which a stronger self preyed upon a weaker – as it is, indeed, among the spiders where the bride concludes her nuptials by eating the groom. But in the humans the Enemy has gratuitously associated affection between the parties with sexual desire. He has also made the offspring dependent on the parents and given the parents an impulse to support it – thus producing the Family, which is like the organism, only worse; for the members are more distinct, yet also united in a more conscious and responsible way. The whole thing, in fact, turns out to be simply one more device for dragging in Love.

Now comes the joke. The Enemy described a married couple as 'one flesh'. He did not say 'a happily married couple' or 'a couple who married because they were in love', but you can make the humans ignore that. You can also make them forget that the man they call Paul did not confine it to *married* couples. Mere copulation, for him, makes 'one flesh'. You can thus get the humans to accept as rhetorical eulogies of 'being in love' what were in fact plain descriptions of the real significance of sexual intercourse. The truth is that wherever a man lies with a woman, there, whether they like it or not, a transcendental relation is set up between them which must be eternally enjoyed or eternally endured. From the true statement that this transcendental relation was intended to produce, and, if obediently entered into, too often *will* produce, affection and the family, humans can be made to infer the false belief that the blend of affection, fear, and desire which they call 'being in love' is the only thing that makes marriage either happy or holy. The error is easy to produce because 'being in love' does very often, in Western Europe, precede marriages which are made in obedience to the Enemy's designs, that is, with the intention of fidelity, fertility and good will; just as religious emotion very often, but not always, attends conversion. In other words, the humans are to be encouraged to regard as the basis for marriage a highly-coloured and distorted version of something the Enemy really promises as its result. Two advantages follow. In the first place, humans who have not the gift of continence can be deterred from seeking marriage as a solution because they do not find themselves 'in love', and, thanks to us, the idea of marrying with any other motive seems to them low and cynical. Yes, they think that. They regard the intention of loyalty to a partnership for mutual help, for the preservation of chastity, and for the transmission of life, as something lower than a storm of emotion. (Don't neglect to make your man think the marriage-service very offensive.) In the second place any sexual infatuation whatever, so long as it intends marriage, will be regarded as 'love', and 'love' will be held to excuse a man from all the guilt, and to protect him from all the consequences, of marrying a heathen, a fool, or a wanton. But more of this in my next,

Your affectionate uncle

SCREWTAPE

19

My dear Wormwood,

I have been thinking very hard about the question in your last letter. If, as I have clearly shown, all selves are by their very nature in competition, and therefore the Enemy's idea of Love is a contradiction in terms, what becomes of my reiterated warning that He really loves the human vermin and really desires their freedom and continued existence? I hope, my dear boy, you have not shown my letters to anyone. Not that it matters of course. Anyone would see that the appearance of heresy into which I have fallen is purely accidental. By the way, I hope you understood, too, that some apparently uncomplimentary references to Slubgob were purely jocular. I really have the highest respect for him. And, of course, some things I said about not shielding you from the authorities were not seriously meant. You can trust me to look after your interests. But do keep everything under lock and key.

The truth is I slipped by mere carelessness into saying that the Enemy really loves the humans. That, of course, is an impossibility. He is one being, they are distinct from Him. Their good cannot be His. All His talk about Love must be a disguise for something else – He must have some *real* motive for creating them and taking so much trouble about them. The reason one comes to talk as if He really had this impossible Love is our utter failure to find out that real motive. What does He stand to make out of them? That is the insoluble question. I do not see that it can do any harm to tell you that this very problem was a chief cause of Our Father's quarrel with the Enemy. When the creation of man was first mooted and when, even at that stage, the Enemy freely confessed that He foresaw a certain episode about a cross, Our Father very naturally sought an interview and asked for an explanation. The Enemy gave no reply except to produce the cock-and-bull story about disinterested love which He has been circulating ever since. This Our Father naturally could not accept. He implored the Enemy to lay His cards on the table, and gave Him every opportunity. He admitted that he felt a real anxiety to know the secret; the Enemy replied 'I wish with all my heart that you did.' It was, I imagine, at this stage in the interview that Our Father's disgust at such an unprovoked lack of confidence caused him to remove himself an infinite distance from the Presence with a suddenness which has given rise to the ridiculous Enemy story that he was forcibly thrown out of Heaven. Since then, we have begun to see why our Oppressor was so secretive. His throne depends on the secret. Members of His faction have frequently admitted that if ever we came to understand what He means by love, the war would be over and we should re-enter Heaven. And there lies the great task. We know that He cannot really love: nobody can: it doesn't make sense. If we could only find out what He is *really* up to! Hypothesis after hypothesis has been tried, and still we can't find out. Yet we must never lose hope; more and more complicated theories, fuller and fuller collections of data, richer rewards for researchers who make progress, more and more terrible punishments for those who fail – all this, pursued and accelerated to the very end of time, cannot, surely, fail to succeed.

You complain that my last letter does not make it clear whether I regard *being in love* as a desirable state for a human or not. But really, Wormwood, that is the sort of question one expects *them* to ask! Leave them to discuss whether 'Love', or patriotism, or celibacy, or candles on altars, or teetotalism, or education, are 'good' or 'bad'. Can't you see there's no answer? Nothing matters at all except the tendency of a given state of mind, in given circumstances, to move a particular patient at a particular moment nearer to the Enemy or nearer to us. Thus it would be quite a good thing to make the patient decide that 'Love' is 'good' or 'bad'. If he is an arrogant man with a contempt for the body really based on delicacy but mistaken by him for purity – and one who takes pleasure in flouting what most of his fellows approve – by all means let him decide against love. Instil into him an overweening asceticism and then, when you have separated his sexuality from all that might humanise it, weigh in on him with it in some much more brutal and cynical form. If, on the other hand, he is an emotional, gullible man, feed him on minor poets and fifth-rate novelists of the old school until you have made him believe that 'Love' is both irresistible and somehow intrinsically meritorious. This belief is not much help, I grant you, in producing casual unchastity; but it is an incomparable recipe for prolonged, 'noble', romantic, tragic adulteries, ending, if all goes well, in murders and suicides. Failing that, it can be used to steer the patient into a useful marriage. For marriage, though the Enemy's invention, has its uses. There must be several young women in your patient's neighbourhood who would render the Christian life intensely difficult to him if only you could persuade him to marry one of them. Please send me a report on this when you next write. In the meantime, get it quite clear in your own mind that this state of *falling in love* is not, in itself, necessarily favourable either to us or to the other side. It is simply an occasion which we and the Enemy are both trying to exploit. Like most of the other things which humans are excited about, such as health and sickness, age and youth, or war and peace, it is, from the point of view of the spiritual life, mainly raw material,

Your affectionate uncle

SCREWTAPE

20

My dear Wormwood,

I note with great displeasure that the Enemy has, for the time being, put a forcible end to your direct attacks on the patient's chastity. You ought to have known that He always does in the end, and you ought to have stopped before you reached that stage. For as things are, your man has now discovered the dangerous truth that these attacks don't last forever; consequently you cannot use again what is, after all, our best weapon – the belief of ignorant humans, that there is no hope of getting rid of us except by yielding. I suppose you've tried persuading him that chastity is unhealthy?

I haven't yet got a report from you on young women in the neighbourhood. I should like it at once, for if we can't use his sexuality to make him unchaste we must try to use it for the promotion of a desirable marriage. In the meantime I would like to give you some hint about the type of woman – I mean the physical type – which he should be encouraged to fall in love with if 'falling in love' is the best we can manage.

In a rough and ready way, of course, this question is decided for us by spirits far deeper down in the Lowerarchy than you and I. It is the business of these great masters to produce in every age a general misdirection of what may be called sexual 'taste'. This they do by working through the small circle of popular artists, dressmakers, actresses and advertisers who determine the fashionable type. The aim is to guide each sex away from those members of the other with whom spiritually helpful, happy, and fertile marriages are most likely. Thus we have now for many centuries triumphed over nature to the extent of making certain secondary characteristics of the male (such as the beard) disagreeable to nearly all the females – and there is more in that than you might suppose. As regards the male taste we have varied a good deal. At one time we have directed it to the statuesque and aristocratic type of beauty, mixing men's vanity with their desires and encouraging the race to breed chiefly from the most arrogant and prodigal women. At another, we have selected an exaggeratedly feminine type, faint and languishing, so that folly and cowardice, and all the general falseness and littleness of mind which go with them, shall be at a premium. At present we are on the opposite tack. The age of jazz has succeeded the age of the waltz, and we now teach men to like women whose bodies are scarcely distinguishable from those of boys. Since this is a kind of beauty even more transitory than most, we thus aggravate the female's chronic horror of growing old (with many excellent results) and render her less willing and less able to bear children. And that is not all. We have engineered a great increase in the licence which society allows to the representation of the apparent nude (not the real nude) in art, and its exhibition on the stage or the bathing beach. It is all a fake, of course; the figures in the popular art are falsely drawn; the real women in bathing suits or tights are actually pinched in and propped up to make them appear firmer and more slender and more boyish than nature allows a full-grown woman to be. Yet at the same time, the modern world is taught to believe that it is being 'frank' and 'healthy' and getting back to nature. As a result we are more and more directing the desires of men to something which does not exist – making the rôle of the eye in sexuality more and more important and at the same time making its demands more and more impossible. What follows you can easily forecast!

That is the general strategy of the moment. But inside the framework you will still find it possible to encourage your patient's desires in one of two directions. You will find, if you look carefully into any human's heart, that he is haunted by at least two imaginary women – a terrestrial and an infernal Venus, and that his desire differs qualitatively according to its object. There is one type for which his desire is such as to be naturally amenable to the Enemy – readily mixed with charity, readily obedient to marriage, coloured all through with that golden light of reverence and naturalness which we detest; there is another type which he desires brutally, and desires to desire brutally, a type best used to draw him away from marriage altogether but which, even within marriage, he would tend to treat as a slave, an idol, or an accomplice. His love for the first might involve what the Enemy calls evil, but only accidentally; the man would wish that she was not someone else's wife and be sorry that he could not love her lawfully. But in the second type, the felt evil is what he wants; it is that 'tang' in the flavour which he is after. In the face, it is the visible animality, or sulkiness, or craft, or cruelty which he likes, and in the body, something quite different from what he ordinarily calls Beauty, something he may even, in a sane hour, describe as ugliness, but which, by our art, can be made to play on the raw nerve of his private obsession.

The real use of the infernal Venus is, no doubt, as prostitute or mistress. But if your man is a Christian, and if he has been well trained in nonsense about irresistible and all-excusing 'Love', he can often be induced to marry her. And that is very well worth bringing about. You will have failed as regards fornication and solitary vice; but there are other, and more indirect, methods of using a man's sexuality to his undoing. And, by the way, they are not only efficient, but delightful; the unhappiness produced is of a very lasting and exquisite kind,

Your affectionate uncle

SCREWTAPE

21

My dear Wormwood,

Yes. A period of sexual temptation is an excellent time for working in a subordinate attack on the patient's peevishness. It may even be the main attack, as long as he thinks it the subordinate one. But here, as in everything else, the way must be prepared for your moral assault by darkening his intellect.

Men are not angered by mere misfortune but by misfortune conceived as injury. And the sense of injury depends on the feeling that a legitimate claim has been denied. The more claims on life, therefore, that your patient can be induced to make, the more often he will feel injured and, as a result, ill-tempered. Now you will have noticed that nothing throws him into a passion so easily as to find a tract of time which he reckoned on having at his own disposal unexpectedly taken from him. It is the unexpected visitor (when he looked forward to a quiet evening), or the friend's talkative wife (turning up when he looked forward to a *tête-à-tête* with the friend), that throw him out of gear. Now he is not yet so uncharitable or slothful that these small demands on his courtesy are *in themselves* too much for it. They anger him because he regards his time as his own and feels that it is being stolen. You must therefore zealously guard in his mind the curious assumption 'My time is my own'. Let him have the feeling that he starts each day as the lawful possessor of twenty-four hours. Let him feel as a grievous tax that portion of this property which he has to make over to his employers, and as a generous donation that further portion which he allows to religious duties. But what he must never be permitted to doubt is that the total from which these deductions have been made was, in some mysterious sense, his own personal birthright.

You have here a delicate task. The assumption which you want him to go on making is so absurd that, if once it is questioned, even we cannot find a shred of argument in its defence. The man can neither make, nor retain, one moment of time; it all comes to him by pure gift; he might as well regard the

sun and moon as his chattels. He is also, in theory, committed to a total service of the Enemy; and if the Enemy appeared to him in bodily form and
demanded that total service for even one day, he would not refuse. He
would be greatly relieved if that one day involved nothing harder than listening to the conversation of a foolish woman; and he would be relieved
almost to the pitch of disappointment if for one half-hour in that day the
Enemy said 'Now you may go and amuse yourself'. Now if he thinks about
his assumption for a moment, even he is bound to realise that he is actually
in this situation every day. When I speak of preserving this assumption in
his mind, therefore, the last thing I mean you to do is to furnish him with
arguments in its defence. There aren't any. Your task is purely negative.
Don't let his thoughts come anywhere near it. Wrap a darkness about it, and
in the centre of that darkness let his sense of ownership-in-Time lie silent,
uninspected, and operative.

The sense of ownership in general is always to be encouraged. The humans
are always putting up claims to ownership which sound equally funny in
Heaven and in Hell and we must keep them doing so. Much of the modern
resistance to chastity comes from men's belief that they 'own' their bodies –
those vast and perilous estates, pulsating with the energy that made the
worlds, in which they find themselves without their consent and from which
they are ejected at the pleasure of Another! It is as if a royal child whom his
father has placed, for love's sake, in titular command of some great province,
under the real rule of wise counsellors, should come to fancy he really owns
the cities, the forests, and the corn, in the same way as he owns the bricks on
the nursery floor.

We produce this sense of ownership not only by pride but by confusion.
We teach them not to notice the different senses of the possessive pronoun –
the finely graded differences that run from 'my boots' through 'my dog',
'my servant', 'my wife', 'my father', 'my master' and 'my country', to 'my
God'. They can be taught to reduce all these senses to that of 'my boots', the
'my' of ownership. Even in the nursery a child can be taught to mean by 'my
teddy bear' *not* the old imagined recipient of affection to whom it stands in
a special relation (for that is what the Enemy will teach them to mean if we
are not careful) but 'the bear I can pull to pieces if I like'. And at the other
end of the scale, we have taught men to say 'my God' in a sense not really
very different from 'my boots', meaning 'the God on whom I have a claim
for my distinguished services and whom I exploit from the pulpit – the God
I have done a corner in'.

And all the time the joke is that the word 'Mine' in its fully possessive
sense cannot be uttered by a human being about anything. In the long run
either Our Father or the Enemy will say 'Mine' of each thing that exists, and
specially of each man. They will find out in the end, never fear, to whom

their time, their souls, and their bodies really belong – certainly not to *them*, whatever happens. At present the Enemy says 'Mine' of everything on the pedantic, legalistic ground that He made it: Our Father hopes in the end to say 'Mine' of all things on the more realistic and dynamic ground of conquest,

Your affectionate uncle

SCREWTAPE

22

My dear Wormwood,

So! Your man is in love – and in the worst kind he could possibly have fallen into – and with a girl who does not even appear in the report you sent me. You may be interested to learn that the little misunderstanding with the Secret Police which you tried to raise about some unguarded expressions in one of my letters has been tidied over. If you were reckoning on that to secure my good offices, you will find yourself mistaken. You shall pay for that as well as for your other blunders. Meanwhile I enclose a little booklet, just issued, on the new House of Correction for Incompetent Tempters. It is profusely illustrated and you will not find a dull page in it.

I have looked up this girl's dossier and am horrified at what I find. Not only a Christian but such a Christian – a vile, sneaking, simpering, demure, monosyllabic, mouse-like, watery, insignificant, virginal, bread-and-butter miss. The little brute. She makes me vomit. She stinks and scalds through the very pages of the dossier. It drives me mad, the way the world has worsened. We'd have had her to the arena in the old days. That's what her sort is made for. Not that she'd do much good there, either. A two-faced little cheat (I know the sort) who looks as if she'd faint at the sight of blood and then dies with a smile. A cheat every way. Looks as if butter wouldn't melt in her mouth and yet has a satirical wit. The sort of creature who'd find *ME* funny! Filthy insipid little prude – and yet ready to fall into this booby's arms like any other breeding animal. Why doesn't the Enemy blast her for it, if He's so moonstruck by virginity – instead of looking on there, grinning?

He's a hedonist at heart. All those fasts and vigils and stakes and crosses are only a façade. Or only like foam on the seashore. Out at sea, out in His sea, there is pleasure, and more pleasure. He makes no secret of it; at His right hand are 'pleasures for evermore'. Ugh! I don't think He has the least inkling of that high and austere mystery to which we rise in the Miserific Vision. He's vulgar, Wormwood. He has a bourgeois mind. He has filled His world full of pleasures. There are things for humans to do all day long without His minding in the least – sleeping, washing, eating, drinking, making love, playing, praying, working. Everything has to be *twisted* before it's any use to us. We fight under cruel disadvantages. Nothing is naturally on our side. (Not that that excuses *you*. I'll settle with you presently. You have always hated me and been insolent when you dared.)

Then, of course, he gets to know this woman's family and whole circle. Could you not see that the very house she lives in is one that he ought never to have entered? The whole place reeks of that deadly odour. The very gardener, though he has only been there five years, is beginning to acquire it. Even guests, after a weekend visit, carry some of the smell away with them. The dog and the cat are tainted with it. And a house full of the impenetrable mystery. We are certain (it is a matter of first principles) that each member of the family must in some way be making capital out of the others – but we can't find out how. They guard as jealously as the Enemy Himself the secret of what really lies behind this pretence of disinterested love. The whole house and garden is one vast obscenity. It bears a sickening resemblance to the description one human writer made of Heaven: 'the regions where there is only life and therefore all that is not music is silence'.

Music and silence – how I detest them both! How thankful we should be that ever since Our Father entered Hell – though longer ago than humans, reckoning in light years, could express – no square inch of infernal space and no moment of infernal time has been surrendered to either of those abominable forces, but all has been occupied by Noise – Noise, the grand dynamism, the audible expression of all that is exultant, ruthless, and virile – Noise which alone defends us from silly qualms, despairing scruples and impossible desires. We will make the whole universe a noise in the end. We have already made great strides in this direction as regards the Earth. The melodies and silences of Heaven will be shouted down in the end. But I admit we are not yet loud enough, or anything like it. Research is in progress. Meanwhile *you*, disgusting little –

[Here the MS breaks off and is resumed in a different hand.]

In the heat of composition I find that I have inadvertently allowed myself to assume the form of a large centipede. I am accordingly dictating the rest to my secretary. Now that the transformation is complete I recognise it as a periodical phenomenon. Some rumour of it has reached the humans and a distorted account of it appears in the poet Milton, with the ridiculous addition that such changes of shape are a 'punishment' imposed on us by the Enemy. A more modern writer – someone with a name like Pshaw – has, however, grasped the truth. Transformation proceeds from within and is a glorious manifestation of that Life Force which Our Father would worship if he worshipped anything but himself. In my present form I feel even more anxious to see you, to unite you to myself in an indissoluble embrace,

(Signed) TOADPIPE

For his Abysmal Sublimity Under Secretary Screwtape, TE, BS, etc.

23

My dear Wormwood,

Through this girl and her disgusting family the patient is now getting to know more Christians every day, and very intelligent Christians too. For a long time it will be quite impossible to *remove* spirituality from his life. Very well then; we must *corrupt* it. No doubt you have often practised transforming yourself into an angel of light as a parade-ground exercise. Now is the time to do it in the face of the Enemy. The World and the Flesh have failed us; a third Power remains. And success of this third kind is the most glorious of all. A spoiled saint, a Pharisee, an inquisitor, or a magician, makes better sport in Hell than a mere common tyrant or debauchee.

Looking round your patient's new friends I find that the best point of attack would be the borderline between theology and politics. Several of his new friends are very much alive to the social implications of their religion. That, in itself, is a bad thing; but good can be made out of it.

You will find that a good many Christian-political writers think that Christianity began going wrong, and departing from the doctrine of its Founder, at a very early stage. Now this idea must be used by us to encourage once again the conception of a 'historical Jesus' to be found by clearing away later 'accretions and perversions' and then to be contrasted with the whole Christian tradition. In the last generation we promoted the construction of such a 'historical Jesus' on liberal and humanitarian lines; we are now putting forward a new 'historical Jesus' on Marxian, catastrophic, and revolutionary lines. The advantages of these constructions, which we intend to change every thirty years or so, are manifold. In the first place they all tend to direct men's devotion to something which does not exist, for each 'historical Jesus' is unhistorical. The documents say what they say and cannot be added to; each new 'historical Jesus' therefore has to be got out of them by suppression at one point and exaggeration at another, and by that sort of guessing (*brilliant* is the adjective we teach humans to apply to it) on which no one would risk ten shillings in ordinary life, but which is enough to

797

produce a crop of new Napoleons, new Shakespeares, and new Swifts, in every publisher's autumn list. In the second place, all such constructions place the importance of their historical Jesus in some peculiar theory He is supposed to have promulgated. He has to be a 'great man' in the modern sense of the word – one standing at the terminus of some centrifugal and unbalanced line of thought – a crank vending a panacea. We thus distract men's minds from who He is, and what He did. We first make Him solely a teacher, and then conceal the very substantial agreement between His teachings and those of all other great moral teachers. For humans must not be allowed to notice that all great moralists are sent by the Enemy not to inform men but to remind them, to restate the primeval moral platitudes against our continual concealment of them. We make the Sophists: He raises up a Socrates to answer them. Our third aim is, by these constructions, to destroy the devotional life. For the real presence of the Enemy, otherwise experienced by men in prayer and sacrament, we substitute a merely probable, remote, shadowy, and uncouth figure, one who spoke a strange language and died a long time ago. Such an object cannot in fact be worshipped. Instead of the Creator adored by its creature, you soon have merely a leader acclaimed by a partisan, and finally a distinguished character approved by a judicious historian. And fourthly, besides being unhistorical in the Jesus it depicts, religion of this kind is false to history in another sense. No nation, and few individuals, are really brought into the Enemy's camp by the historical study of the biography of Jesus, simply as biography. Indeed materials for a full biography have been withheld from men. The earliest converts were converted by a single historical fact (the Resurrection) and a single theological doctrine (the Redemption) operating on a sense of sin which they already had – and sin, not against some new fancy-dress law produced as a novelty by a 'great man', but against the old, platitudinous, universal moral law which they had been taught by their nurses and mothers. The 'Gospels' come later and were written not to make Christians but to edify Christians already made.

The 'historical Jesus' then, however dangerous He may seem to be to us at some particular point, is always to be encouraged. About the general connection between Christianity and politics, our position is more delicate. Certainly we do not want men to allow their Christianity to flow over into their political life, for the establishment of anything like a really just society would be a major disaster. On the other hand we do want, and want very much, to make men treat Christianity as a means; preferably, of course, as a means to their own advancement, but, failing that, as a means to anything – even to social justice. The thing to do is to get a man at first to value social justice as a thing which the Enemy demands, and then work him on to the stage at which he values Christianity because it may produce social justice.

For the Enemy will not be used as a convenience. Men or nations who think they can revive the Faith in order to make a good society might just as well think they can use the stairs of Heaven as a short cut to the nearest chemist's shop. Fortunately it is quite easy to coax humans round this little corner. Only today I have found a passage in a Christian writer where he recommends his own version of Christianity on the ground that 'only such a faith can outlast the death of old cultures and the birth of new civilisations'. You see the little rift? 'Believe this, not because it is true, but for some other reason.' That's the game,

Your affectionate uncle

SCREWTAPE

24

M^y dear Wormwood,

y dear Wormwood,
    I have been in correspondence with Slumtrimpet who is in charge of your patient's young woman, and begin to see the chink in her armour. It is an unobtrusive little vice which she shares with nearly all women who have grown up in an intelligent circle united by a clearly defined belief; and it consists in a quite untroubled assumption that the outsiders who do not share this belief are really too stupid and ridiculous. The males, who habitually meet these outsiders, do not feel that way; their confidence, if they are confident, is of a different kind. Hers, which she supposes to be due to Faith, is in reality largely due to the mere colour she has taken from her surroundings. It is not, in fact, very different from the conviction she would have felt at the age of ten that the kind of fish-knives used in her father's house were the proper or normal or 'real' kind, while those of the neighbouring families were 'not real fish-knives' at all. Now the element of ignorance and naïvety in all this is so large, and the element of spiritual pride so small, that it gives us little hope of the girl herself. But have you thought of how it can be made to influence your own patient?

It is always the novice who exaggerates. The man who has risen in society is over-refined, the young scholar is pedantic. In this new circle your patient is a novice. He is there daily meeting Christian life of a quality he never before imagined and seeing it all through an enchanted glass because he is in love. He is anxious (indeed the Enemy commands him) to imitate this quality. Can you get him to imitate this *defect* in his mistress and to exaggerate it until what was venial in her becomes in him the strongest and most beautiful of the vices – Spiritual Pride?

The conditions seem ideally favourable. The new circle in which he finds himself is one of which he is tempted to be proud for many reasons other than its Christianity. It is a better educated, more intelligent, more agreeable society than any he has yet encountered. He is also under some degree of illusion as to his own place in it. Under the influence of 'love' he may still think himself unworthy of the girl, but he is rapidly ceasing to think himself unworthy of the others. He has no notion how much in him is forgiven because they are charitable and made the best of because he is now one of the family. He does not dream how much of his conversation, how many of his opinions, are recognised by them all as mere echoes of their own. Still less does he suspect how much of the delight he takes in these people is due to the erotic enhancement which the girl, for him, spreads over all her surroundings. He thinks that he likes their talk and way of life because of some congruity between their spiritual state and his, when in fact they are so far beyond him that if he were not in love he would be merely puzzled and repelled by much which he now accepts. He is like a dog which should imagine it understood fire-arms because its hunting instinct and love for its master enable it to enjoy a day's shooting!

Here is your chance. While the Enemy, by means of sexual love and of some very agreeable people far advanced in His service, is drawing the young barbarian up to levels he could never otherwise have reached, you must make him feel that he is finding his *own* level – that these people are 'his sort' and that, coming among them, he has come home. When he turns from them to other society he will find it dull; partly because almost any society within his reach is, in fact, much less entertaining, but still more because he will miss the enchantment of the young woman. You must teach him to mistake this contrast between the circle that delights and the circle that bores him for the contrast between Christians and unbelievers. He must be made to feel (he'd better not put it into words) 'how different we Christians are'; and by 'we Christians' he must really, but unknowingly, mean 'my set'; and by 'my set' he must mean not 'The people who, in their charity and humility, have accepted me', but 'The people with whom I associate by right'.

Success here depends on confusing him. If you try to make him explicitly and professedly proud of being a Christian, you will probably fail; the Enemy's warnings are too well known. If, on the other hand, you let the idea of 'we Christians' drop out altogether and merely make him complacent about 'his set', you will produce not true spiritual pride but mere social vanity which, by comparison, is a trumpery, puny little sin. What you want is to keep a sly self-congratulation mixing with all his thoughts and never allow him to raise the question 'What, precisely, am I congratulating myself *about*?' The idea of belonging to an inner ring, of being in a secret, is very sweet to him. Play on that nerve. Teach him, using the influence of this girl when she is silliest, to adopt an air of *amusement* at the things the unbelievers say. Some theories which he may meet in modern Christian circles may here prove helpful; theories, I mean, that place the hope of society in some inner ring of 'clerks', some trained minority of theocrats. It is no affair of yours whether those theories are true or false; the great thing is to make Christianity a mystery religion in which he feels himself one of the initiates.

Pray do not fill your letters with rubbish about this European War. Its final issue is, no doubt, important, but that is a matter for the High Command. I am not in the least interested in knowing how many people in England have been killed by bombs. In what state of mind they died, I can learn from the office at this end. That they were going to die sometime, I knew already. Please keep your mind on your work,

Your affectionate uncle

SCREWTAPE

25

My dear Wormwood,

The real trouble about the set your patient is living in is that it is *merely* Christian. They all have individual interests, of course, but the bond remains mere Christianity. What we want, if men become Christians at all, is to keep them in the state of mind I call 'Christianity And'. You know – Christianity and the Crisis, Christianity and the New Psychology, Christianity and the New Order, Christianity and Faith Healing, Christianity and Psychical Research, Christianity and Vegetarianism, Christianity and Spelling Reform. If they must be Christians let them at least be Christians with a difference. Substitute for the faith itself some Fashion with a Christian colouring. Work on their horror of the Same Old Thing.

The horror of the Same Old Thing is one of the most valuable passions we have produced in the human heart – an endless source of heresies in religion, folly in counsel, infidelity in marriage, and inconstancy in friendship. The humans live in time, and experience reality successively. To experience much of it, therefore, they must experience many different things; in other words, they must experience change. And since they need change, the Enemy (being a hedonist at heart) has made change pleasurable to them, just as He has made eating pleasurable. But since He does not wish them to make change, any more than eating, an end in itself, He has balanced the love of change in them by a love of permanence. He has contrived to gratify both tastes together in the very world He has made, by that union of change and permanence which we call Rhythm. He gives them the seasons, each season different yet every year the same, so that spring is always felt as a novelty yet always as the recurrence of an immemorial theme. He gives them in His Church a spiritual year; they change from a fast to a feast, but it is the same feast as before.

Now just as we pick out and exaggerate the pleasure of eating to produce gluttony, so we pick out this natural pleasantness of change and twist it into a demand for absolute novelty. This demand is entirely our workmanship. If we neglect our duty, men will be not only contented but transported by the mixed novelty and familiarity of snowdrops *this* January, sunrise *this* morning, plum pudding *this* Christmas. Children, until we have taught them better, will be perfectly happy with a seasonal round of games in which conkers succeed hopscotch as regularly as autumn follows summer. Only by our incessant efforts is the demand for infinite, or unrhythmical, change kept up.

This demand is valuable in various ways. In the first place it diminishes pleasure while increasing desire. The pleasure of novelty is by its very nature more subject than any other to the law of diminishing returns. And continued novelty costs money, so that the desire for it spells avarice or unhappiness or both. And again, the more rapacious this desire, the sooner it must eat up all the innocent sources of pleasure and pass on to those the Enemy forbids. Thus by inflaming the horror of the Same Old Thing we have recently made the Arts, for example, less dangerous to us than perhaps, they have ever been, 'low-brow' and 'high-brow' artists alike being now daily drawn into fresh, and still fresh, excesses of lasciviousness, unreason, cruelty, and pride. Finally, the desire for novelty is indispensable if we are to produce Fashions or Vogues.

The use of Fashions in thought is to distract the attention of men from their real dangers. We direct the fashionable outcry of each generation against those vices of which it is least in danger and fix its approval on the virtue nearest to that vice which we are trying to make endemic. The game is to have them all running about with fire extinguishers whenever there is a flood, and all crowding to that side of the boat which is already nearly gunwale under. Thus we make it fashionable to expose the dangers of enthusiasm at the very moment when they are all really becoming worldly and lukewarm; a century later, when we are really making them all Byronic and drunk with emotion, the fashionable outcry is directed against the dangers of the mere 'understanding'. Cruel ages are put on their guard against Sentimentality, feckless and idle ones against Respectability, lecherous ones against Puritanism; and whenever all men are really hastening to be slaves or tyrants we make Liberalism the prime bogey.

But the greatest triumph of all is to elevate this horror of the Same Old Thing into a philosophy so that nonsense in the intellect may reinforce corruption in the will. It is here that the general Evolutionary or Historical character of modern European thought (partly our work) comes in so useful. The Enemy loves platitudes. Of a proposed course of action He wants men, so far as I can see, to ask very simple questions; is it righteous? is it prudent? is it possible? Now if we can keep men asking 'Is it in accordance with the general movement of our time? Is it progressive or reactionary? Is this the way that History is going?' they will neglect the relevant questions. And the questions they *do* ask are, of course, unanswerable; for they do not know the future, and what the future will be depends very largely on just those choices which they now invoke the future to help them to make. As a result, while their minds are buzzing in this vacuum, we have the better chance to slip in and bend them to the action *we* have decided on. And great work has already been done. Once they knew that some changes were for the better, and others for the worse, and others again indifferent. We have largely removed this knowledge. For the descriptive adjective 'unchanged' we have substituted the emotional adjective 'stagnant'. We have trained them to think of the Future as a promised land which favoured heroes attain – not as something which everyone reaches at the rate of sixty minutes an hour, whatever he does, whoever he is,

Your affectionate uncle

SCREWTAPE

26

My dear Wormwood,
Yes; courtship is the time for sowing those seeds which will grow up ten years later into domestic hatred. The enchantment of unsatisfied desire produces results which the humans can be made to mistake for the results of charity. Avail yourself of the ambiguity in the word 'Love': let them think they have solved by Love problems they have in fact only waived or postponed under the influence of the enchantment. While it lasts you have your chance to foment the problems in secret and render them chronic.

The grand problem is that of 'Unselfishness'. Note, once again, the admirable work of our Philological Arm in substituting the negative unselfishness for the Enemy's positive Charity. Thanks to this you can, from the very outset, teach a man to surrender benefits not that others may be happy in having them but that he may be unselfish in forgoing them. That is a great point gained. Another great help, where the parties concerned are male and female, is the divergence of view about Unselfishness which we have built up between the sexes. A woman means by Unselfishness chiefly taking trouble for others; a man means not giving trouble to others. As a result, a woman who is quite far gone in the Enemy's service will make a nuisance of herself on a larger scale than any man except those whom Our Father has dominated completely; and, conversely, a man will live long in the Enemy's camp before he undertakes as much spontaneous work to please others as a quite ordinary woman may do every day. Thus while the woman thinks of doing good offices and the man of respecting other people's rights, each sex, without any obvious unreason, can and does regard the other as radically selfish.

On top of these confusions you can now introduce a few more. The erotic enchantment produces a mutual complaisance in which each is *really* pleased to give in to the wishes of the other. They also know that the Enemy demands of them a degree of charity which, if attained, would result in similar actions. You must make them establish as a Law for their whole married life that degree of mutual self-sacrifice which is at present sprouting naturally out of the enchantment, but which, when the enchantment dies away, they will not have charity enough to enable them to perform. They will not see the trap, since they are under the double blindness of mistaking sexual excitement for charity and of thinking that the excitement will last.

When once a sort of official, legal, or nominal Unselfishness has been established as a rule – a rule for the keeping of which their emotional resources have died away and their spiritual resources have not yet grown – the most delightful results follow. In discussing any joint action, it becomes obligatory that A should argue in favour of B's supposed wishes and against his own, while B does the opposite. It is often impossible to find out either party's real wishes; with luck, they end by doing something that neither wants, while each feels a glow of self-righteousness and harbours a secret claim to preferential treatment for the unselfishness shown and a secret grudge against the other for the ease with which the sacrifice has been accepted. Later on you can venture on what may be called the Generous Conflict Illusion. This game is best played with more than two players, in a family with grown-up children for example. Something quite trivial, like having tea in the garden, is proposed. One member takes care to make it quite clear (though not in so many words) that he would rather not but is, of course, prepared to do so out of 'Unselfishness'. The others instantly withdraw their proposal, ostensibly through their 'Unselfishness', but really because they don't want to be used as a sort of lay figure on which the first speaker practises petty altruisms. But he is not going to be done out of his debauch of Unselfishness either. He insists on doing 'what the others want'. They insist on doing what he wants. Passions are roused. Soon someone is saying 'Very well then, I won't have any tea at all!', and a real quarrel ensues with bitter resentment on both sides. You see how it is done? If each side had been frankly contending for its own real wish, they would all have kept within the bounds of reason and courtesy; but just because the contention is reversed and each side is fighting the other side's battle, all the bitterness which really flows from thwarted self-righteousness and obstinacy and the accumulated grudges of the last ten years is concealed from them by the nominal or official 'Unselfishness' of what they are doing or, at least, held to be excused by it. Each side is, indeed, quite alive to the cheap quality of the adversary's Unselfishness and of the false position into which he is trying to force them; but each manages to feel blameless and ill-used itself, with no more dishonesty than comes natural to a human.

A sensible human once said, 'If people knew how much ill-feeling Unselfishness occasions, it would not be so often recommended from the pulpit'; and again, 'She's the sort of woman who lives for others – you can always tell the others by their hunted expression.' All this can be begun even in the period of courtship. A little *real* selfishness on your patient's part is often of less value in the long run, for securing his soul, than the first beginnings of that elaborate and self-conscious unselfishness which may one day blossom into the sort of thing I have described. Some degree of mutual falseness, some surprise that the girl does not always notice just how Unselfish he is being, can be smuggled in already. Cherish these things, and, above all, don't let the young fools notice them. If they notice them they will be on the road to discovering that 'Love' is not enough, that charity is needed and not yet achieved and that no external law can supply its place. I wish Slumtrimpet could do something about undermining that young woman's sense of the ridiculous,

Your affectionate uncle

SCREWTAPE

27

My dear Wormwood,

You seem to be doing very little good at present. The use of his 'love' to distract his mind from the Enemy is, of course, obvious, but you reveal what poor use you are making of it when you say that the whole question of distraction and the wandering mind has now become one of the chief subjects of his prayers. That means you have largely failed. When this, or any other distraction, crosses his mind you ought to encourage him to thrust it away by sheer will power and to try to continue the normal prayer as if nothing had happened; once he accepts the distraction as his present problem and lays *that* before the Enemy and makes it the main theme of his prayers and his endeavours, then, so far from doing good, you have done harm. Anything, even a sin, which has the total effect of moving him close up to the Enemy, makes against us in the long run.

A promising line is the following. Now that he is in love, a new idea of *earthly* happiness has arisen in his mind: and hence a new urgency in his purely petitionary prayers – about this war and other such matters. Now is the time for raising intellectual difficulties about prayer of that sort. False spirituality is always to be encouraged. On the seemingly pious ground that 'praise and communion with God is the true prayer', humans can often be lured into direct disobedience to the Enemy who (in His usual flat, commonplace, uninteresting way) has definitely told them to pray for their daily bread and the recovery of their sick. You will, of course, conceal from him the fact that the prayer for daily bread, interpreted in a 'spiritual sense', is really just as crudely petitionary as it is in any other sense.

But since your patient has contracted the terrible habit of obedience, he will probably continue such 'crude' prayers whatever you do. But you can worry him with the haunting suspicion that the practice is absurd and can have no objective result. Don't forget to use the 'heads I win, tails you lose' argument. If the thing he prays for doesn't happen, then that is one more proof that petitionary prayers don't work; if it does happen, he will, of course, be able to see some of the physical causes which led up to it, and 'therefore it would have happened anyway', and thus a granted prayer becomes just as good a proof as a denied one that prayers are ineffective.

You, being a spirit, will find it difficult to understand how he gets into this confusion. But you must remember that he takes Time for an ultimate reality. He supposes that the Enemy, like himself, sees some things as present, remembers others as past, and anticipates others as future; or even if he believes that the Enemy does not see things that way, yet, in his heart of hearts, he regards this as a peculiarity of the Enemy's mode of perception – he doesn't really think (though he would say he did) that things as the Enemy sees them are things as they are! If you tried to explain to him that men's prayers today are one of the innumerable co-ordinates with which the Enemy harmonises the weather of tomorrow, he would reply that then the Enemy always knew men were going to make those prayers and, if so, they did not pray freely but were predestined to do so. And he would add that the weather on a given day can be traced back through its causes to the original creation of matter itself – so that the whole thing, both on the human and on the material side, is given 'from the word go'. What he ought to say, of course, is obvious to us; that the problem of adapting the particular weather to the particular prayers is merely the appearance, at two points in his temporal mode of perception, of the total problem of adapting the whole spiritual universe to the whole corporeal universe; that creation in its entirety operates at every point of space and time, or rather that their kind of consciousness forces them to encounter the whole, self-consistent creative act as a series of successive events. *Why* that creative act leaves room for their free will is the problem of problems, the secret behind the Enemy's nonsense about 'Love'. *How* it does so is no problem at all; for the Enemy does not *foresee* the humans making their free contributions in a future, but *sees* them doing so in His unbounded Now. And obviously to watch a man doing something is not to make him do it.

It may be replied that some meddlesome human writers, notably Boethius, have let this secret out. But in the intellectual climate which we have at last succeeded in producing throughout Western Europe, you needn't bother about that. Only the learned read old books and we have now so dealt with the learned that they are of all men the least likely to acquire wisdom by doing so. We have done this by inculcating the Historical Point of View. The Historical Point of View, put briefly, means that when a learned man is presented with any statement in an ancient author, the one question he never asks is whether it is true. He asks who influenced the ancient writer, and how far the statement is consistent with what he said in other books, and what phase in the writer's development, or in the general history of thought, it illustrates, and how it affected later writers, and how often it has been misunderstood (specially by the learned man's own colleagues) and what the general course of criticism on it has been for the last ten years, and what is the 'present state of the question'. To regard the ancient writer as a possible source of knowledge – to anticipate that what he said could possibly modify your thoughts or your behaviour – this would be rejected as unutterably simple-minded. And since we cannot deceive the whole human race all the time, it is most important thus to cut every generation off from all others; for where learning makes a free commerce between the ages there is always the danger that the characteristic errors of one may be corrected by the characteristic truths of another. But thanks be to Our Father and the Historical Point of View, great scholars are now as little nourished by the past as the most ignorant mechanic who holds that 'history is bunk',

Your affectionate uncle

SCREWTAPE

28

My dear Wormwood,

When I told you not to fill your letters with rubbish about the war, I meant, of course, that I did not want to have your rather infantile rhapsodies about the death of men and the destruction of cities. In so far as the war really concerns the spiritual state of the patient, I naturally want full reports. And on this aspect you seem singularly obtuse. Thus you tell me with glee that there is reason to expect heavy air raids on the town where the creature lives. This is a crying example of something I have complained about already – your readiness to forget the main point in your immediate enjoyment of human suffering. Do you not know that bombs kill men? Or do you not realise that the patient's death, at this moment, is precisely what we want to avoid? He has escaped the worldly friends with whom you tried to entangle him; he has 'fallen in love' with a very Christian woman and is temporarily immune from your attacks on his chastity; and the various methods of corrupting his spiritual life which we have been trying are so far unsuccessful. At the present moment, as the full impact of the war draws nearer and his worldly hopes take a proportionately lower place in his mind, full of his defence work, full of the girl, forced to attend to his neighbours more than he has ever done before and liking it more than he expected, 'taken out of himself' as the humans say, and daily increasing in conscious dependence on the Enemy, he will almost certainly be lost to us if he is killed tonight. This is so obvious that I am ashamed to write it. I sometimes wonder if you young fiends are not kept out on temptation-duty too long at a time – if you are not in some danger of becoming infected by the sentiments and values of the humans among whom you work. They, of course, do tend to regard death as the prime evil and survival as the greatest good. But that is because we have taught them to do so. Do not let us be infected by our own propaganda. I know it seems strange that your chief aim at the moment should be the very same thing for which the patient's lover and his mother are praying – namely his bodily safety. But so it is; you should be

812

guarding him like the apple of your eye. If he dies now, you lose him. If he survives the war, there is always hope. The Enemy has guarded him from you through the first great wave of temptations. But, if only he can be kept alive, you have time itself for your ally. The long, dull, monotonous years of middle-aged prosperity or middle-aged adversity are excellent campaigning weather. You see, it is so hard for these creatures to *persevere*. The routine of adversity, the gradual decay of youthful loves and youthful hopes, the quiet despair (hardly felt as pain) of ever overcoming the chronic temptations with which we have again and again defeated them, the drabness which we create in their lives and the inarticulate resentment with which we teach them to respond to it – all this provides admirable opportunities of wearing out a soul by attrition. If, on the other hand, the middle years prove prosperous, our position is even stronger. Prosperity knits a man to the World. He feels that he is 'finding his place in it', while really it is finding its place in him. His increasing reputation, his widening circle of acquaintances, his sense of importance, the growing pressure of absorbing and agreeable work, build up in him a sense of being really at home in earth, which is just what we want. You will notice that the young are generally less unwilling to die than the middle-aged and the old.

The truth is that the Enemy, having oddly destined these mere animals to life in His own eternal world, has guarded them pretty effectively from the danger of feeling at home anywhere else. That is why we must often wish long life to our patients; seventy years is not a day too much for the difficult task of unravelling their souls from Heaven and building up a firm attachment to the earth. While they are young we find them always shooting off at a tangent. Even if we contrive to keep them ignorant of explicit religion, the incalculable winds of fantasy and music and poetry – the mere face of a girl, the song of a bird, or the sight of a horizon – are always blowing our whole structure away. They *will* not apply themselves steadily to worldly advancement, prudent connections, and the policy of safety first. So inveterate is their appetite for Heaven that our best method, at this stage, of attaching them to earth is to make them believe that earth can be turned into Heaven at some future date by politics or eugenics or 'science' or psychology, or what not. Real worldliness is a work of time – assisted, of course, by pride, for we teach them to describe the creeping death as good sense or Maturity or Experience. *Experience*, in the peculiar sense we teach them to give it, is, by the by, a most useful word. A great human philosopher nearly let our secret out when he said that where Virtue is concerned 'Experience is the mother of illusion'; but thanks to a change in Fashion, and also, of course, to the Historical Point of View, we have largely rendered his book innocuous.

How valuable time is to us may be gauged by the fact that the Enemy allows us so little of it. The majority of the human race dies in infancy; of the survivors, a good many die in youth. It is obvious that to Him human birth is important chiefly as the qualification for human death, and death solely as the gate to that other kind of life. We are allowed to work only on a selected minority of the race, for what humans call a 'normal life' is the exception. Apparently He wants some – but only a very few – of the human animals with which He is peopling Heaven to have had the experience of resisting us through an earthly life of sixty or seventy years. Well, there is our opportunity. The smaller it is, the better we must use it. Whatever you do, keep your patient as safe as you possibly can,

Your affectionate uncle

SCREWTAPE

29

My dear Wormwood,

Now that it is certain the German humans will bombard your patient's town and that his duties will keep him in the thick of the danger, we must consider our policy. Are we to aim at cowardice – or at courage, with consequent pride – or at hatred of the Germans?

Well, I am afraid it is no good trying to make him brave. Our research department has not yet discovered (though success is hourly expected) how to produce *any* virtue. This is a serious handicap. To be greatly and effectively wicked a man needs some virtue. What would Attila have been without his courage, or Shylock without self-denial as regards the flesh? But as we cannot supply these qualities ourselves, we can only use them as supplied by the Enemy – and this means leaving Him a kind of foothold in those men whom, otherwise, we have made most securely our own. A very unsatisfactory arrangement, but, I trust, we shall one day learn to do better.

Hatred we can manage. The tension of human nerves during noise, danger, and fatigue, makes them prone to any violent emotion and it is only a question of guiding this susceptibility into the right channels. If conscience resists, muddle him. Let him say that he feels hatred not on his own behalf but on that of the women and children, and that a Christian is told to forgive his own, not other people's enemies. In other words let him consider himself sufficiently identified with the women and children to feel hatred on their behalf, but *not* sufficiently identified to regard their enemies as his own and therefore proper objects of forgiveness.

But hatred is best combined with Fear. Cowardice, alone of all the vices, is purely painful – horrible to anticipate, horrible to feel, horrible to remember; Hatred has its pleasures. It is therefore often the *compensation* by which a frightened man reimburses himself for the miseries of Fear. The more he fears, the more he will hate. And Hatred is also a great anodyne for shame. To make a deep wound in his charity, you should therefore first defeat his courage.

Now this is a ticklish business. We have made men proud of most vices, but not of cowardice. Whenever we have almost succeeded in doing so, the Enemy permits a war or an earthquake or some other calamity, and at once courage becomes so obviously lovely and important even in human eyes that all our work is undone, and there is still at least one vice of which they feel genuine shame. The danger of inducing cowardice in our patients, there-fore, is lest we produce real self-knowledge and self-loathing with conse-quent repentance and humility. And in fact, in the last war, thousands of humans, by discovering their own cowardice, discovered the whole moral world for the first time. In peace we can make many of them ignore good and evil entirely; in danger, the issue is forced upon them in a guise to which even we cannot blind them. There is here a cruel dilemma before us. If we promoted justice and charity among men, we should be playing directly into the Enemy's hands; but if we guide them to the opposite behaviour, this sooner or later produces (for He permits it to produce) a war or a revolu-tion, and the undisguisable issue of cowardice or courage awakes thousands of men from moral stupor.

This, indeed, is probably one of the Enemy's motives for creating a dangerous world – a world in which moral issues really come to the point. He sees as well as you do that courage is not simply *one* of the virtues, but the form of every virtue at the testing point, which means, at the point of highest reality. A chastity or honesty, or mercy, which yields to danger will be chaste or honest or merciful only on conditions. Pilate was merciful till it became risky.

It is therefore possible to lose as much as we gain by making your man a coward; he may learn too much about himself! There is, of course, always the chance, not of chloroforming the shame, but of aggravating it and pro-ducing Despair. This would be a great triumph. It would show that he had believed in, and accepted, the Enemy's forgiveness of his other sins only because he himself did not fully feel their sinfulness – that in respect of the one vice which he really understands in its full depth of dishonour he cannot seek, nor credit, the Mercy. But I fear you have already let him get too far in the Enemy's school, and he knows that Despair is a greater sin than any of the sins which provoke it.

As to the actual technique of temptations to cowardice, not much need be said. The main point is that precautions have a tendency to increase fear. The precautions publicly enjoined on your patient, however, soon become a matter of routine and this effect disappears. What you must do is to keep running in his mind (side by side with the conscious intention of doing his duty) the vague idea of all sorts of things he can do or not do, *inside* the framework of the duty, which seem to make him a little safer. Get his mind off the simple rule ('I've got to stay here and do so-and-so') into a series of imaginary life lines ('If A happened – though I very much hope it won't – I could do B – and if the worst came to the worst, I could always do C'). Superstitions, if not recognised as such, can be awakened. The point is to keep him feeling that he has *something*, other than the Enemy and courage the Enemy supplies, *to fall back on*, so that what was intended to be a total commitment to duty becomes honeycombed all through with little unconscious reservations. By building up a series of imaginary expedients to prevent 'the worst coming to the worst' you may produce, at that level of his will which he is not aware of, a determination that the worst *shall not* come to the worst. Then, at the moment of real terror, rush it out into his nerves and muscles and you may get the fatal act done before he knows what you're about. For remember, the *act* of cowardice is all that matters; the emotion of fear is, in itself, no sin and, though we enjoy it, does us no good,

Your affectionate uncle

SCREWTAPE

30

My dear Wormwood,

 I sometimes wonder whether you think you have been sent into the world for your own amusement. I gather, not from your miserably inadequate report but from that of the Infernal Police, that the patient's behaviour during the first raid has been the worst possible. He has been very frightened and thinks himself a great coward and therefore feels no pride; but he has done everything his duty demanded and perhaps a bit more. Against this disaster all you can produce on the credit side is a burst of ill temper with a dog that tripped him up, some excessive cigarette smoking, and the forgetting of a prayer. What is the use of whining to me about your difficulties? If you are proceeding on the Enemy's idea of 'justice' and suggesting that your opportunities and intentions should be taken into account, then I am not sure that a charge of heresy does not lie against you. At any rate, you will soon find that the justice of Hell is purely realistic, and concerned only with results. Bring us back food, or be food yourself.

 The only constructive passage in your letter is where you say that you still expect good results from the patient's fatigue. That is well enough. But it won't fall into your hands. Fatigue *can* produce extreme gentleness, and quiet of mind, and even something like vision. If you have often seen men led by it into anger, malice and impatience, that is because those men have had efficient tempters. The paradoxical thing is that moderate fatigue is a better soil for peevishness than absolute exhaustion. This depends partly on physical causes, but partly on something else. It is not fatigue simply as such that produces the anger, but unexpected demands on a man already tired. Whatever men expect they soon come to think they have a right to: the sense of disappointment can, with very little skill on our part, be turned into a sense of injury. It is after men have given in to the irremediable, after they have despaired of relief and ceased to think even a half-hour ahead, that the dangers of humbled and gentle weariness begin. To produce the best results from the patient's fatigue, therefore, you must feed him with false hopes. Put into his mind plausible reasons for believing that the air raid will not be repeated. Keep him comforting himself with the thought of how much he will enjoy his bed next night. Exaggerate the weariness by making him think it will soon be over; for men usually feel that a strain could have been endured no longer at the very moment when it is ending, or when they think it is ending. In this, as in the problem of cowardice, the thing to avoid is the total commitment. Whatever he *says*, let his inner resolution be not to bear whatever comes to him, but to bear it 'for a reasonable period' – and let the reasonable period be shorter than the trial is likely to last. It need not be *much* shorter; in attacks on patience, chastity, and fortitude, the fun is to make the man yield just when (had he but known it) relief was almost in sight.

I do not know whether he is likely to meet the girl under conditions of strain or not. If he does, make full use of the fact that up to a certain point, fatigue makes women talk more and men talk less. Much secret resentment, even between lovers, can be raised from this.

Probably the scenes he is now witnessing will not provide material for an *intellectual* attack on his faith – your previous failures have put that out of your power. But there is a sort of attack on the emotions which can still be tried. It turns on making him *feel*, when first he sees human remains plastered on a wall, that this is 'what the world is *really* like' and that all his religion has been a fantasy. You will notice that we have got them completely fogged about the meaning of the word 'real'. They tell each other, of some great spiritual experience, 'All that *really* happened was that you heard some music in a lighted building'; here 'real' means the bare physical facts, separated from the other elements in the experience they actually had. On the other hand, they will also say 'It's all very well discussing that high dive as you sit here in an armchair, but wait till you get up there and see what it's *really* like': here 'real' is being used in the opposite sense to mean, not the physical facts (which they know already while discussing the matter in armchairs) but the emotional effect those facts will have on a human consciousness. Either application of the word could be defended; but our business is to keep the two going at once so that the emotional value of the word 'real' can be placed now on one side of the account, now on the other, as it happens to suit us. The general rule which we have now pretty well established among them is that in all experiences which can make them happier or better only the physical facts are 'real' while the spiritual elements are 'subjective'; in all experiences which can discourage or corrupt them the spiritual elements are the main reality and to ignore them is to be an escapist. Thus in birth the blood and pain are 'real', the rejoicing a mere subjective point of view; in death, the terror and ugliness reveal what death 'really means'. The hatefulness of a hated person is 'real' – in hatred you see men as they are, you are disillusioned; but the loveliness of a loved person is merely a subjective haze concealing a 'real' core of sexual appetite or economic association. Wars and poverty are 'really' horrible; peace and plenty are mere physical facts about which men happen to have certain sentiments. The creatures are always accusing one another of wanting 'to eat the cake and have it'; but thanks to our labours they are more often in the predicament of paying for the cake and not eating it. Your patient, properly handled, will have no difficulty in regarding his emotion at the sight of human entrails as a revelation of Reality and his emotion at the sight of happy children or fair weather as mere sentiment,

Your affectionate uncle

SCREWTAPE

31

My dear, my very dear, Wormwood, my poppet, my pigsnie,
How mistakenly now that all is lost you come whimpering to ask
me whether the terms of affection in which I address you meant nothing
from the beginning. Far from it! Rest assured, my love for you and your
love for me are as like as two peas. I have always desired you, as you (pitiful
fool) desired me. The difference is that I am the stronger. I think they will
give you to me now; or a bit of you. Love you? Why, yes. As dainty a morsel
as ever I grew fat on.

You have let a soul slip through your fingers. The howl of sharpened
famine for that loss re-echoes at this moment through all the levels of the
Kingdom of Noise down to the very Throne itself. It makes me mad to
think of it. How well I know what happened at the instant when they
snatched him from you! There was a sudden clearing of his eyes (was there
not?) as he saw you for the first time, and recognised the part you had had in
him and knew that you had it no longer. Just think (and let it be the beginning of your agony) what he felt at that moment; as if a scab had fallen from
an old sore, as if he were emerging from a hideous, shell-like tetter, as if he
shuffled off for good and all a defiled, wet, clinging garment. By Hell, it is
misery enough to see them in their mortal days taking off dirtied and
uncomfortable clothes and splashing in hot water and giving little grunts of
pleasure – stretching their eased limbs. What, then, of this final stripping,
this complete cleansing?

The more one thinks about it, the worse it becomes. He got through so
easily! No gradual misgivings, no doctor's sentence, no nursing home, no
operating theatre, no false hopes of life; sheer, instantaneous liberation. One
moment it seemed to be all our world; the scream of bombs, the fall of
houses, the stink and taste of high explosive on the lips and in the lungs, the
feet burning with weariness, the heart cold with horrors, the brain reeling,
the legs aching; next moment all this was gone, gone like a bad dream, never
again to be of any account. Defeated, out-manoeuvred fool! Did you mark

how naturally – as if he'd been born for it – the earth-born vermin entered the new life? How all his doubts became, in the twinkling of an eye, ridiculous? I know what the creature was saying to itself! 'Yes. Of course. It always was like this. All horrors have followed the same course, getting worse and worse and forcing you into a kind of bottle-neck till, at the very moment when you thought you must be crushed, behold! you were out of the narrows and all was suddenly well. The extraction hurt more and more and then the tooth was out. The dream became a nightmare and then you woke. You die and die and then you are beyond death. How could I ever have doubted it?'

As he saw you, he also saw Them. I know how it was. You reeled back dizzy and blinded, more hurt by them than he had ever been by bombs. The degradation of it! – that this thing of earth and slime could stand upright and converse with spirits before whom you, a spirit, could only cower. Perhaps you had hoped that the awe and strangeness of it would dash his joy. But that is the cursed thing; the gods are strange to mortal eyes, and yet they are not strange. He had no faintest conception till that very hour of how they would look, and even doubted their existence. But when he saw them he knew that he had always known them and realised what part each one of them had played at many an hour in his life when he had supposed himself alone, so that now he could say to them, one by one, not 'Who *are* you?' but 'So it was *you* all the time.' All that they were and said at this meeting woke memories. The dim consciousness of friends about him which had haunted his solitudes from infancy was now at last explained; that central music in every pure experience which had always just evaded memory was now at last recovered. Recognition made him free of their company almost before the limbs of his corpse became quiet. Only you were left outside.

He saw not only Them; he saw Him. This animal, this thing begotten in a bed, could look on Him. What is blinding, suffocating fire to you, is now cool light to him, is clarity itself, and wears the form of a Man. You would like, if you could, to interpret the patient's prostration in the Presence, his self-abhorrence and utter knowledge of his sins (yes, Wormwood, a clearer knowledge even than yours) on the analogy of your own choking and paralysing sensations when you encounter the deadly air that breathes from the heart of Heaven. But it's all nonsense. Pains he may still have to encounter, but they *embrace* those pains. They would not barter them for any earthly pleasure. All the delights of sense, or heart, or intellect, with which you could once have tempted him, even the delights of virtue itself, now seem to him in comparison but as the half nauseous attractions of a raddled harlot would seem to a man who hears that his true beloved whom he has loved all his life and whom he had believed to be dead is alive and even now at his door. He is caught up into that world where pain and pleasure take on transfinite values and all our arithmetic is dismayed. Once more, the inexplicable meets us. Next to the curse of useless tempters like yourself the greatest curse upon us is the failure of our Intelligence Department. If only we could find out what He is really up to! Alas, alas, that knowledge, in itself so hateful and mawkish a thing, should yet be necessary for Power! Sometimes I am almost in despair. All that sustains me is the conviction that our Realism, our rejection (in the face of all temptations) of all silly nonsense and claptrap, *must* win in the end. Meanwhile, I have you to settle with. Most truly do I sign myself

Your increasingly and ravenously
affectionate uncle

SCREWTAPE

SCREWTAPE
PROPOSES A TOAST

PREFACE TO THE
REVISED EDITION

Screwtape Proposes a Toast was written years after the original *Screwtape Letters*. It takes over from them the technique of what may be called diabolical ventriloquism. Screwtape's outlook is like a photographic negative; his whites are our blacks and whatever he welcomes we ought to dread. But in the original *Letters* this device was applied to the religious and moral life of an individual. In the *Toast* the main subject is education.

In my view there is a sense in which education ought to be democratic and another sense in which it ought not. It ought to be democratic in the sense of being available, without distinction of sex, colour, class, race or religion, to all who can – and will – diligently accept it. But once the young people are inside the school there must be no attempt to establish a factitious egalitarianism between the idlers and dunces on the one hand and the clever and industrious on the other. A modern nation needs a very large class of genuinely educated people and it is the primary function of schools and universities to supply them. To lower standards or disguise inequalities is fatal.

If this sounds harsh, I would observe that opposite policy is really devised to soothe the inferiority complex not of the idlers and dunces but of their parents. Do not be in the least afraid that those who live out their schooldays – which should be brief – on the back bench of the lowest class will suffer any trauma when they see promotion and honours and official approval going to the diligent minority. They are stronger than it. They can punch its head and kick its stern. All the distinctions they really care about – the popularity and the success in games – go not to it but to them. They enjoy their school-days very much. Our real problem is to see that they impede as little as possible the purposes for which school really exists.

So far so good. But I had to face a tactical difficulty. The *Toast* was published in an American magazine. The tendency in education which I was deploring has gone further in America than anywhere else. If I had been writing 'straight' my article would have been an attack on the 'public schools' of America. It would indeed have raised nothing that educated

Americans do not fully admit. But it is one thing for them to say these things of their own country and another to hear them said by a foreigner! I therefore thought it neither good manners nor good tactics to make my point quite nakedly. Instead, I resorted to a further level of irony. Screwtape in fact describes American education; he affects to be holding English education up as the awful example. The most intelligent of my American readers would, I hoped, see the game I was playing and enjoy the joke. And if those who were a little duller really believed that 'democratic' education (in the true sense) had gone even further in England, they could not help seeing that their actual system was at least uncomfortably like the one Screwtape describes – and draw the moral.

C. S. LEWIS
MAGDALENE COLLEGE, CAMBRIDGE, 1962

828

SCREWTAPE PROPOSES

A TOAST

I was often asked or advised to add to the original 'Screwtape Letters', but for many years I felt not the least inclination to do it. Though I had never written anything more easily, I never wrote with less enjoyment. The ease came, no doubt, from the fact that the device of diabolical letters, once you have thought of it, exploits itself spontaneously, like Swift's big and little men, or the medical and ethical philosophy of 'Erewhon', as Anstey's Garuda Stone. It would run away with you for a thousand pages if you gave it its head. But though it was easy to twist one's mind into the diabolical attitude, it was not fun, or not for long. The strain produced a sort of spiritual cramp. The world into which I had to project myself while I spoke through Screwtape was all dust, grit, thirst and itch. Every trace of beauty, freshness and geniality had to be excluded. It almost smothered me before I was done. It would have smothered my readers if I had prolonged it.

I had, moreover, a sort of grudge against my book for not being a different book which no one could write. Ideally, Screwtape's advice to Wormwood should have been balanced by archangelical advice to the patient's guardian angel. Without this the picture of human life is lop-sided. But who could supply the deficiency? Even if a man – and he would have to be a far better man than I – could scale the spiritual heights required, what 'answerable style' could he use? For the style would really be part of the content. Mere advice would be no good; every sentence would have to smell of Heaven. And nowadays even if you could write prose like Traherne's, you wouldn't be allowed to, for the canon of 'functionalism' has disabled literature for half its functions. (At bottom, every ideal of style dictates not only how we should say things but what sort of things we may say.)

Then, as years went on and the stifling experience of writing the 'Letters' became a weaker memory, reflections on this and that which seemed somehow to demand Screwtapian treatment began to occur to me. I was resolved never to write another 'Letter'. The idea of something like a lecture or 'address' hovered vaguely in my mind, now forgotten, now recalled, never *written. Then came an invitation from* The Saturday Evening Post, *and that pressed the trigger.*

C.S.L.

The scene is in Hell at the annual dinner of the Tempters' Training College for young Devils. The Principal, Dr Slubgob, has just proposed the health of the guests. Screwtape, who is the guest of honour, rises to reply:

Mr Principal, your Imminence, your Disgraces, my Thorns, Shadies, and Gentledevils: It is customary on these occasions for the speaker to address himself chiefly to those among you who have just graduated and who will very soon be posted to official Tempt' on Earth. It is a custom I willingly obey. I well remember with what trepidation I awaited my own first appointment. I hope, and believe, that each one of you has the same uneasiness tonight. Your career is before you. Hell expects and demands that it should be – as Mine was – one of unbroken success. If it is not, you know what awaits you.

I have no wish to reduce the wholesome and realistic element of terror, the unremitting anxiety, which must act as the lash and spur to your endeavours. How often you will envy the humans their faculty of sleep! Yet at the same time I would wish to put before you a moderately encouraging view of the strategical situation as a whole.

Your dreaded Principal has included in a speech full of points something like an apology for the banquet which he has set before us. Well, gentledevils, no one blames *him*. But it would be vain to deny that the human souls on whose anguish we have been feasting tonight were of pretty poor quality. Not all the most skilful cookery of our tormentors could make them better than insipid.

Oh to get one's teeth again into a Farinata, a Henry VIII, or even a Hitler! There was real crackling there; something to crunch; a rage, an egotism, a cruelty only just less robust than our own. It put up a delicious resistance to being devoured. It warmed your innards when you'd got it down.

Instead of this, what have we had tonight? There was a municipal authority with Graft sauce. But personally I could not detect in him the flavour of a really passionate and brutal avarice such as delighted one in the great tycoons of the last century. Was he not unmistakably a Little Man – a creature of the petty rake-off pocketed with a petty joke in private and denied with the stalest platitudes in his public utterances – a grubby little nonentity who had drifted into corruption, only just realising that he was corrupt, and chiefly because everyone else did it? Then there was the lukewarm Casserole of Adulterers. Could you find in it any trace of a fully inflamed, defiant, rebellious, insatiable lust? I couldn't. They all tasted to me like under-sexed morons who had blundered or trickled into the wrong beds in automatic response to sexy advertisements, or to make themselves feel modern and emancipated, or to reassure themselves about their virility or their 'normalcy', or even because they had nothing else to do. Frankly, to me who have tasted Messalina and Casanova, they were nauseating. The Trade Unionist garnished with Claptrap was perhaps a shade better. He had done some real harm. He had, not quite unknowingly, worked for bloodshed, famine, and the extinction of liberty. Yes, in a way. But what a way! He thought of those ultimate objectives so little. Toeing the party line, self-importance, and above all mere routine, were what really dominated his life.

But now comes the point. Gastronomically, all this is deplorable. But I hope none of us puts gastronomy first. Is it not, in another and far more serious way, full of hope and promise?

Consider, first, the mere quantity. The quality may be wretched; but we never had souls (of a sort) in more abundance.

And then the triumph. We are tempted to say that such souls – or such residual puddles of what once was soul – are hardly worth damning. Yes, but the Enemy (for whatever inscrutable and perverse reason) thought them worth trying to save. Believe me, He did. You youngsters who have not yet been on active service have no idea with what labour, with what delicate skill, each of these miserable creatures was finally captured.

The difficulty lay in their very smallness and flabbiness. Here were vermin so muddled in mind, so passively responsive to environment, that it was very hard to raise them to that level of clarity and deliberateness at which mortal sin becomes possible. To raise them just enough; but not that fatal millimetre of 'too much'. For then, of course, all would possibly have been lost. They might have seen; they might have repented. On the other hand, if they had been raised too little, they would very possibly have qualified for Limbo, as creatures suitable neither for Heaven nor for Hell; things that, having failed to make the grade, are allowed to sink into a more or less contented sub-humanity forever.

In each individual choice of what the Enemy would call the 'wrong' turning such creatures are at first hardly, if at all, in a state of full spiritual responsibility. They do not understand either the source or the real character of the prohibitions they are breaking. Their consciousness hardly exists apart from the social atmosphere that surrounds them. And of course we have contrived that their very language should be all smudge and blur; what would be a *bribe* in someone else's profession is a *tip* or a *present* in theirs. The first job of their Tempters was to harden these choices of the Hell-ward roads into a habit by steady repetition. But then (and this was all-important) to turn the habit into a principle – a principle the creature is prepared to defend. After that, all will go well. Conformity to the social environment, at first merely instinctive or even mechanical – how should a *jelly* not conform? – now becomes an unacknowledged creed or ideal of Togetherness or Being Like Folks. Mere ignorance of the law they break now turns into a vague theory about it – remember they know no history – a theory expressed by calling it *conventional* or *puritan* or *bourgeois* 'morality'. Thus gradually there comes to exist at the centre of the creature a hard, tight, settled core of resolution to go on being what it is, and even to resist moods that might tend to alter it. It is a very small core; not at all reflective (they are too ignorant) nor defiant (their emotional and imaginative poverty excludes that); almost, in its own way, prim and demure; like a pebble, or a very young cancer. But it will serve our turn. Here at last is a real and deliberate, though not fully articulate, rejection of what the Enemy calls Grace.

These, then, are two welcome phenomena. First, the abundance of our captures; however tasteless our fare, we are in no danger of famine. And secondly, the triumph; the skill of our Tempters has never stood higher. But the third moral, which I have not yet drawn, is the most important of all.

The sort of souls on whose despair and ruin we have – well, I won't say feasted, but at any rate subsisted – tonight are increasing in numbers and will continue to increase. Our advices from Lower Command assure us that this is so; our directives warn us to orient all our tactics in view of this situation. The 'great' sinners, those in whom vivid and genial passions have been pushed beyond the bounds and in whom an immense concentration of will has been devoted to objects which the Enemy abhors, will not disappear. But they will grow rarer. Our catches will be ever more numerous; but they will consist increasingly of trash – trash which we should once have thrown to Cerberus and the hell-hounds as unfit for diabolical consumption. And there are two things I want you to understand about this. First, that however depressing it may seem, it is really a change for the better. And secondly, I would draw your attention to the means by which it has been brought about.

It is a change for the better. The great (and toothsome) sinners are made out of the very same material as those horrible phenomena, the great Saints. The virtual disappearance of such material may mean insipid meals for us. But is it not utter frustration and famine for the Enemy? He did not create the humans – He did not become one of them and die among them by torture – in order to produce candidates for Limbo; 'failed' humans. He wanted to make Saints; gods; things like Himself. Is the dullness of your present fare not a very small price to pay for the delicious knowledge that His whole great experiment is petering out? But not only that. As the great sinners grow fewer, and the majority lose all individuality, the great sinners become far more effective agents for us. Every dictator or even demagogue – almost every film-star or crooner–can now draw tens of thousands of the human sheep with him. They give themselves (what there is of them) to him; in him, to us. There may come a time when we shall have no need to bother about *individual* temptation at all, except for the few. Catch the bell-wether and his whole flock comes after him.

But do you realise how we have succeeded in reducing so many of the human race to the level of ciphers? This has not come about by accident. It has been our answer – and a magnificent answer it is – to one of the most serious challenges we ever had to face.

Let me recall to your minds what the human situation was in the latter half of the nineteenth century – the period at which I ceased to be a practising Tempter and was rewarded with an administrative post. The great movement towards liberty and equality among men had by then borne solid fruit and grown mature. Slavery had been abolished. The American War of Independence had been won. The French Revolution had succeeded. Religious toleration was almost everywhere on the increase. In that movement there had originally been many elements which were in our favour. Much Atheism, much Anti-Clericalism, much envy and thirst for revenge, even some (rather absurd) attempts to revive Paganism, were mixed in it. It was not easy to determine what our own attitude should be. On the one hand it was a bitter blow to us – it still is – that any sort of men who had been hungry should be fed or any who had long worn chains should have them struck off. But on the other hand, there was in the movement so much rejection of faith, so much materialism, secularism, and hatred, that we felt we were bound to encourage it.

But by the latter part of the century the situation was much simpler, and also much more ominous. In the English sector (where I saw most of my front-line service) a horrible thing had happened. The Enemy, with His usual sleight of hand, had largely appropriated this progressive or liberalising movement and perverted it to His own ends. Very little of its old anti-Christianity remained. The dangerous phenomenon called Christian Socialism was rampant. Factory owners of the good old type who grew rich on sweated labour, instead of being assassinated by their workpeople – we could have used that – were being frowned upon by their own class. The rich were increasingly giving up their powers not in the face of revolution and compulsion, but in obedience to their own consciences. As for the poor who benefited by this, they were behaving in a most disappointing fashion. Instead of using their new liberties – as we reasonably hoped and expected – for massacre, rape, and looting, or even for perpetual intoxication, they were perversely engaged in becoming cleaner, more orderly, more thrifty, better educated, and even more virtuous. Believe me, gentledevils, the threat of something like a really healthy state of society seemed then perfectly serious.

Thanks to Our Father Below the threat was averted. Our counter-attack was on two levels. On the deepest level our dealers contrived to call into full life an element which had been implicit in the movement from its earliest days. Hidden in the heart of this striving for Liberty there was also a deep hatred of personal freedom. That invaluable man Rousseau first revealed it. In his perfect democracy, you remember, only the state religion is permitted, slavery is restored, and the individual is told that he has really willed (though he didn't know it) whatever the Government tells him to do. From that starting point, *via* Hegel (another indispensable propagandist on our side) we easily contrived both the Nazi and the Communist state. Even in England we were pretty successful. I heard the other day that in that country a man could not, without a permit, cut down his own tree with his own axe, make it into planks with his own saw, and use the planks to build a tool-shed in his own garden.

Such was our counter-attack on one level. You, who are mere beginners, will not be entrusted with work of that kind. You will be attached as Tempters to private persons. Against them, or through them, our counter-attack takes a different form.

Democracy is the word with which you must lead them by the nose. The good work which our philological experts have already done in the corruption of human language makes it unnecessary to warn you that they should never be allowed to give this word a clear and definable meaning. They won't. It will never occur to them that *Democracy* is properly the name of a political system, even a system of voting, and that this has only the most remote and tenuous connection with what you are trying to sell them. Nor, of course, must they ever be allowed to raise Aristotle's question: whether 'democratic behaviour' means the behaviour that democracies like or the behaviour that will preserve a democracy. For if they did, it could hardly fail to occur to them that these need not be the same.

You are to use the word purely as an incantation; if you like, purely for its selling power. It is a name they venerate. And of course it is connected with the political ideal that men should be equally treated. You then make a stealthy transition in their minds from this political ideal to a factual belief that all men *are* equal. Especially the man you are working on. As a result you can use the word *Democracy* to sanction in his thought the most degrading (and also the least enjoyable) of all human feelings. You can get him to practise, not only without shame but with a positive glow of self-approval, conduct which, if undefended by the magic word, would be universally derided.

The feeling I mean is of course that which prompts a man to say *I'm as good as you*.

The first and most obvious advantage is that you thus induce him to enthrone at the centre of his life a good, solid resounding lie. I don't mean merely that his statement is false in fact, that he is no more equal to everyone he meets in kindness, honesty, and good sense than in height or waist-measurement. I mean that he does not believe it himself. No man who says *I'm as good as you* believes it. He would not say it if he did. The St Bernard never says it to the toy dog, nor the scholar to the dunce, nor the employable to the bum, nor the pretty woman to the plain. The claim to equality, outside the strictly political field, is made only by those who feel themselves to be in some way inferior. What it expresses is precisely the itching, smarting, writhing awareness of an inferiority which the patient refuses to accept.

And therefore resents. Yes, and therefore resents every kind of superiority in others; denigrates it; wishes its annihilation. Presently he suspects every mere difference of being a claim to superiority. No one must be different from himself in voice, clothes, manners, recreations, choice of food. 'Here is someone who speaks English rather more clearly and euphoniously than I – it must be a vile, upstage, lah-di-dah affectation. Here's a fellow who says he doesn't like hot dogs – thinks himself too good for them no doubt. Here's a man who hasn't turned on the jukebox – he must be one of those highbrows and is doing it to show off. If they were the right sort of chaps they'd be like me. They've no business to be different. It's undemocratic.'

Now this useful phenomenon is in itself by no means new. Under the name of Envy it has been known to the humans for thousands of years. But hitherto they always regarded it as the most odious, and also the most comical, of vices. Those who were aware of feeling it felt it with shame; those who were not gave it no quarter in others. The delightful novelty of the present situation is that you can sanction it – make it respectable and even laudable – by the incantatory use of the word *democratic*.

Under the influence of this incantation those who are in any or every way inferior can labour more wholeheartedly and successfully than ever before to pull down everyone else to their own level. But that is not all. Under the same influence, those who come, or could come, nearer to a full humanity, actually draw back from it for fear of being *undemocratic*. I am credibly informed that young humans now sometimes suppress an incipient taste for classical music or good literature because it might prevent their Being Like Folks; that people who would really wish to be – and are offered the Grace which would enable them to be – honest, chaste, or temperate, refuse it. To accept might make them Different, might offend again the Way of Life, take them out of Togetherness, impair their Integration with the Group. They might (horror of horrors!) become individuals.

All is summed up in the prayer which a young female human is said to have uttered recently: 'Oh God, make me a normal twentieth-century girl!' Thanks to our labours, this will mean increasingly, 'Make me a minx, a moron, and a parasite'.

Meanwhile, as a delightful by-product, the few (fewer every day) who will not be made Normal and Regular and Like Folks and Integrated, increasingly tend to become in reality the prigs and cranks which the rabble would in any case have believed them to be. For suspicion often creates what it suspects. ('Since, whatever I do, the neighbours are going to think me a witch, or a Communist agent, I might as well be hanged for a sheep as a lamb and become one in reality.') As a result we now have an intelligentsia which, though very small, is very useful to the cause of Hell.

But that is a mere by-product. What I want to fix your attention on is the vast, overall movement towards the discrediting, and finally the elimination, of every kind of human excellence – moral, cultural, social, or intellectual. And is it not pretty to notice how *Democracy* (in the incantatory sense) is now doing for us the work that was once done by the most ancient Dictatorships, and by the same methods? You remember how one of the Greek Dictators (they called them 'tyrants' then) sent an envoy to another Dictator to ask his advice about the principles of government. The second Dictator led the envoy into a field of corn, and there he snicked off with his cane the top of every stalk that rose an inch or so above the general level. The moral was plain. Allow no pre-eminence among your subjects. Let no man live who is wiser, or better, or more famous, or even handsomer than the mass. Cut them all down to a level; all slaves, all ciphers, all nobodies. All equals. Thus Tyrants could practise, in a sense, 'democracy'. But now 'democracy' can do the same work without any other tyranny than her own. No one need now go through the field with a cane. The little stalks will now of themselves bite the tops off the big ones. The big ones are beginning to bite off their own in their desire to Be Like Stalks.

I have said that to secure the damnation of these little souls, these creatures that have almost ceased to be individual, is a laborious and tricky work. But if proper pains and skill are expended, you can be fairly confident of the result. The great sinners *seem* easier to catch. But then they are incalculable. After you have played them for seventy years, the Enemy may snatch them from your claws in the seventy-first. They are capable, you see, of real repentance. They are conscious of real guilt. They are, if things take the wrong turn, as ready to defy the social pressures around them for the Enemy's sake as they were to defy them for ours. It is in some ways more troublesome to track and swat an evasive wasp than to shoot, at close range, a wild elephant. But the elephant is more troublesome if you miss.

My own experience, as I have said, was mainly on the English sector, and I still get more news from it than from any other. It may be that what I am now going to say will not apply so fully to the sectors in which some of you may be operating. But you can make the necessary adjustments when you get there. Some application it will almost certainly have. If it has too little, you must labour to make the country you are dealing with more like what England already is.

In that promising land the spirit of *I'm as good as you* has already become something more than a generally social influence. It begins to work itself into their educational system. How far its operations there have gone at the present moment, I would not like to say with certainty. Nor does it matter. Once you have grasped the tendency, you can easily predict its future developments; especially as we ourselves will play our part in the developing. The basic principle of the new education is to be that dunces and idlers must not be made to feel inferior to intelligent and industrious pupils. That would be 'undemocratic'. These differences between the pupils – for they are obviously and nakedly *individual* differences – must be disguised. This can be done on various levels. At universities, examinations must be framed so that nearly all the students get good marks. Entrance examinations must be framed so that all, or nearly all, citizens can go to universities, whether they have any power (or wish) to profit by higher education or not. At schools, the children who are too stupid or lazy to learn languages and mathematics and elementary science can be set to doing the things that children used to do in their spare time. Let them, for example, make mud-pies and call it modelling. But all the time there must be no faintest hint that they are inferior to the children who are at work. Whatever nonsense they are engaged in must have – I believe the English already use the phrase – 'parity of esteem'. An even more drastic scheme is not impossible. Children who are fit to proceed to a higher class may be artificially kept back, because the others would get a *trauma* – Beelzebub, what a useful word! – by being left behind. The bright pupil thus remains democratically fettered to his own age-group throughout his school career, and a boy who would be capable of tackling Aeschylus or Dante sits listening to his coaeval's attempts to spell out A CAT SAT ON THE MAT.

In a word, we may reasonably hope for the virtual abolition of education when *I'm as good as you* has fully had its way. All incentives to learn and all penalties for not learning will vanish. The few who might want to learn will be prevented; who are they to overtop their fellows? And anyway the teachers – or should I say, nurses? – will be far too busy reassuring the dunces and patting them on the back to waste any time on real teaching. We shall no longer have to plan and toil to spread imperturbable conceit and incurable ignorance among men. The little vermin themselves will do it for us.

Of course this would not follow unless all education became state education. But it will. That is part of the same movement. Penal taxes, designed for that purpose, are liquidating the Middle Class, the class who were prepared to save and spend and make sacrifices in order to have their children privately educated. The removal of this class, besides linking up with the abolition of education, is, fortunately, an inevitable effect of the spirit that says *I'm as good as you*. This was, after all, the social group which gave to the humans the overwhelming majority of their scientists, physicians, philosophers, theologians, poets, artists, composers, architects, jurists, and administrators. If ever there was a bunch of tall stalks that needed their tops knocked off, it was surely they. As an English politician remarked not long ago, 'A democracy does not want great men.'

It would be idle to ask of such a creature whether by *want* it means 'need' or 'like'. But you had better be clear. For here Aristotle's question comes up again.

We, in Hell, would welcome the disappearance of Democracy in the strict sense of that word; the political arrangement so called. Like all forms of government it often works to our advantage; but on the whole less often than other forms. And what we must realise is that 'democracy' in the diabolical sense (*I'm as good as you*, Being Like Folks, Togetherness) is the finest instrument we could possibly have for extirpating political Democracies from the face of the earth.

For 'democracy' or the 'democratic spirit' (diabolical sense) leads to a nation without great men, a nation mainly of subliterates, morally flaccid from lack of discipline in youth, full of the cocksureness which flattery breeds on ignorance, and soft from lifelong pampering. And that is what Hell wishes every democratic people to be. For when such a nation meets in conflict a nation where children have been made to work at school, where talent is placed in high posts, and where the ignorant mass are allowed no say at all in public affairs, only one result is possible.

One Democracy was surprised lately when it found that Russia had got ahead of it in science. What a delicious specimen of human blindness! If the whole tendency of their society is opposed to every sort of excellence, why did they expect their scientists to excel?

It is our function to encourage the behaviour, the manners, the whole attitude of mind, which democracies naturally like and enjoy, because these are the very things which, if unchecked, will destroy democracy. You would almost wonder that even humans don't see it themselves. Even if they don't read Aristotle (that would be undemocratic) you would have thought the French Revolution would have taught them that the behaviour aristocrats naturally like is not the behaviour that preserves aristocracy. They might then have applied the same principle to all forms of government.

But I would not end on that note. I would not – Hell forbid! – encourage in your own minds that delusion which you must carefully foster in the minds of your human victims. I mean the delusion that the fate of nations is *in itself* more important than that of individual souls. The overthrow of free peoples and the multiplication of slave-states are for us a means (besides, of course, being fun); but the real end is the destruction of individuals. For only individuals can be saved or damned, can become sons of the Enemy or food for us. The ultimate value, for us, of any revolution, war, or famine lies in the individual anguish, treachery, hatred, rage, and despair which it may produce. *I'm as good as you* is a useful means for the destruction of democratic societies. But it has a far deeper value as an end in itself, as a state of mind, which necessarily excluding humility, charity, contentment, and all the pleasures of gratitude or admiration, turns a human being away from almost every road which might finally lead him to Heaven.

But now for the pleasantest part of my duty. It falls to my lot to propose on behalf of the guests the health of Principal Slubgob and the Tempters' Training College. Fill your glasses. What is this I see? What is this delicious bouquet I inhale? Can it be? Mr Principal, I unsay all my hard words about the dinner. I see, and smell, that even under wartime conditions the College cellar still has a few dozen of sound old vintage *Pharisee*. Well, well, well. This is like old times. Hold it beneath your nostrils for a moment, gentledevils. Hold it up to the light. Look at those fiery streaks that writhe and tangle in its dark heart, as if they were contending. And so they are. You know how this wine is blended? Different types of Pharisee have been harvested, trodden, and fermented together to produce its subtle flavour. Types that were most antagonistic to one another on earth. Some were all rules and relics and rosaries; others were all drab clothes, long faces, and petty traditional abstinences from wine or cards or the theatre. Both had in common their self-righteousness and the almost infinite distance between their actual outlook and anything the Enemy really is or commands. The wickedness of other religions was the really live doctrine in the religion of each; slander was its gospel and denigration its litany. How they hated each other up there where the sun shone! How much more they hate each other now that they are forever conjoined but not reconciled. Their astonishment, their resentment, at the combination, the festering of their eternally impenitent spite, passing into our spiritual digestion, will work like fire. Dark fire. All said and done, my friends, it will be an ill day for us if what most humans mean by 'religion' ever vanishes from the Earth. It can still send us the truly delicious sins. The fine flower of unholiness can grow only in the close neighbourhood of the Holy. Nowhere do we tempt so successfully as on the very steps of the altar.

Your Imminence, your Disgraces, my Thorns, Shadies, and Gentledevils: I give you the toast of – Principal Slubgob and the College!

TILL WE HAVE FACES

A Myth Retold

Love is too young to know what conscience is
SHAKESPEARE

To Joy Davidman

NOTE

The story of Cupid and Psyche first occurs in one of the few surviving Latin novels, the *Metamorphoses* (sometimes called *The Golden Ass*) of Lucius Apuleius Platonicus, who was born about 125 A.D. The relevant parts are as follows:

A king and queen had three daughters of whom the youngest was so beautiful that men worshipped her as a goddess and neglected the worship of Venus for her sake. One result was that Psyche (as the youngest was called) had no suitors; men reverenced her supposed deity too much to aspire to her hand. When her father consulted the oracle of Apollo about her marriage he received the answer: 'Hope for no human son-in-law. You must expose Psyche on a mountain to be the prey of a dragon.' This he obediently did.

But Venus, jealous of Psyche's beauty, had already devised a different punishment for her, she had ordered her son Cupid to afflict the girl with an irresistible passion for the basest of men. Cupid set off to do so but, on seeing Psyche, fell in love with her himself. As soon as she was left on the mountain he therefore had her carried off by the West-Wind (Zephyrus) to a secret place where he had prepared a stately palace. Here he visited her by night and enjoyed her love; but he forbade her to see his face. Presently she begged that she might receive a visit from her two sisters. The god reluctantly consented and wafted them to her palace. Here they were royally feasted and expressed great delight at all the splendours they saw. But inwardly they were devoured with envy, for their husbands were not gods and their houses not so fine as hers.

They therefore plotted to destroy her happiness. At their next visit they persuaded her that her mysterious husband must really be a monstrous serpent. 'You must take into your bedroom tonight,' they said, 'a lamp covered with a cloak and a sharp knife. When he sleeps uncover the lamp – see the horror that is lying in your bed – and stab it to death.' All this the gullible Psyche promised to do.

When she uncovered the lamp and saw the sleeping god she gazed on him with insatiable love, till a drop of hot oil from her lamp fell on his shoulder and woke him. Starting up, he spread his shining wings, rebuked her, and vanished from her sight.

The two sisters did not long enjoy their malice, for Cupid took such measures as led both to their death. Psyche meanwhile wandered away, wretched and desolate, and attempted to drown herself in the first river she came to; but the god Pan frustrated her attempt and warned her never to repeat it. After many miseries she fell into the hands of her bitterest enemy, Venus, who seized her for a slave, beat her, and set her what were meant to be impossible tasks. The first, that of sorting out seeds into separate heaps, she did by the help of some friendly ants. Next, she had to get a hank of golden wool from some man-killing sheep; a reed by a river bank whispered to her that this could be achieved by plucking the wool off the bushes. After that, she had to fetch a cupful of the water of the Styx, which could be reached only by climbing certain impracticable mountains, but an eagle met her, took the cup from her hand, and returned with it full of the water. Finally she was sent down to the lower world to bring back to Venus, in a box, the beauty of Persephone, the Queen of the Dead. A mysterious voice told her how she could reach Persephone and yet return to our world; on the way she would be asked for help by various people who seemed to deserve her pity, but she must refuse them all. And when Persephone gave her the box (full of beauty) she must on no account open the lid to look inside. Psyche obeyed all this and returned to the upper world with the box; but then at last curiosity overcame her and she looked into it. She immediately lost consciousness.

Cupid now came to her again, but this time he forgave her. He interceded with Jupiter, who agreed to permit his marriage and make Psyche a goddess. Venus was reconciled and they all lived happily ever after.

The central alteration in my own version consists in making Psyche's palace invisible to normal, mortal eyes – if 'making' is not the wrong word for something which forced itself upon me, almost at my first reading of the story, as the way the thing must have been. This change of course brings with it a more ambivalent motive and a different character for my heroine and finally modifies the whole quality of the tale. I felt quite free to go behind Apuleius, whom I suppose to have been its transmitter, not its inventor. Nothing was further from my aim than to recapture the peculiar quality of the *Metamorphoses* – that strange compound of picaresque novel, horror comic, mystagogue's tract, pornography, and stylistic experiment. Apuleius was of course a man of genius: but in relation to my work he is a 'source', not an 'influence' nor a 'model'.

His version has been followed pretty closely by William Morris (in *The Earthly Paradise*) and by Robert Bridges (*Eros and Psyche*). Neither poem, in my opinion, shows its author at his best. The whole *Metamorphoses* was last translated by Mr Robert Graves (Penguin Books, 1950).

C.S.L.

On another occasion, C.S. Lewis wrote of TILL WE HAVE FACES:

This re-interpretation of an old story has lived in the author's mind, thickening and hardening with the years, ever since he was an undergraduate. That way, he could be said to have worked at it most of his life. Recently, what seemed to be the right form presented itself and themes suddenly interlocked: the straight tale of barbarism, the mind of an ugly woman, dark idolatry and pale enlightenment at war with each other and with vision, and the havoc which a vocation, or even a faith, works on human life.

PART I

PART 1

I

I am old now and have not much to fear from the anger of gods. I have neither husband nor child, nor hardly a friend, through whom they can hurt me. My body, this lean carrion that still has to be washed and fed and have clothes hung about it daily with so many changes, they may kill as soon as they please. The succession is provided for. My crown passes to my nephew.

Being, for all these reasons, free from fear, I will write in this book what no one who has happiness would dare to write. I will accuse the gods; especially the god who lives on the Grey Mountain. That is, I will tell all he has done to me from the very beginning, as if I were making my complaint of him before a judge. But there is no judge between gods and men, and the god of the mountain will not answer me. Terrors and plagues are not an answer. I write in Greek as my old master taught it to me. It may some day happen that a traveller from the Greeklands will again lodge in this palace and read the book. Then he will talk of it among the Greeks, where there is great freedom of speech even about the gods themselves. Perhaps their wise men will know whether my complaint is right or whether the god could have defended himself if he had made an answer

I was Orual the eldest daughter of Trom, King of Glome. The city of Glome stands on the left hand of the river Shennit to a traveller who is coming up from the south-east, not more than a day's journey above Ringal, which is the last town southward that belongs to the land of Glome. The city is built about as far back from the river as a woman can walk in the third of an hour; for the Shennit overflows her banks in the spring. In summer there was then dry mud on each side of it, and reeds, and plenty of waterfowl. About as far beyond the ford of the Shennit as our city is on this side of it you come to the holy house of Ungit. And beyond the house of Ungit (going all the time east and north) you come quickly to the foothills of the Grey Mountain. The god of the Grey Mountain, who hates me, is the son of Ungit. He does not, however, live in the house of Ungit, but Ungit sits there alone.

In the furthest recess of her house where she sits it is so dark that you cannot see her well, but in summer enough light may come down from the smoke-holes in the roof to show her a little. She is a black stone without head or hands or face, and a very great goddess. My old master, whom we called the Fox, said she was the same whom the Greeks call Aphrodite; but I write all the names of people and places in our own language.

I will begin my writing with the day my mother died, and they cut off my hair, as the custom is. The Fox – but he was not with us then – said it is a custom we learned from the Greeks. Batta, the nurse, shore me and my sister Redival outside the palace, at the foot of the garden which runs steeply up the hill behind. Redival was my sister, three years younger than I, and we two were still the only children. While Batta was using the shears many other of the slave women were standing round, from time to time wailing for the Queen's death and beating their breasts; but in between they were eating nuts and joking. As the shears snipped and Redival's curls fell off, the slaves said, 'Oh, what a pity! All the gold gone!' They had not said anything like that while I was being shorn. But what I remember best is the coolness of my head and the hot sun on the back of my neck when we were building mud houses, Redival and I, all that summer afternoon.

Our nurse Batta was a big-boned, fair-haired, hard-handed woman whom my father had bought from traders who got her further north. When we plagued her she would say, 'Only wait till your father brings home a new queen to be your stepmother. It'll be changed times for you then. You'll have hard cheese instead of honey-cakes then and skim milk instead of red wine. Wait and see.'

As things fell out, we got something else before we got a stepmother. There was a bitter frost that day. Redival and I were booted (we mostly went barefoot or sandalled) and trying to slide in the yard which is at the back of the oldest part of the palace, where the walls are wooden. There was ice enough all the way from the byre-door to the big dunghill, what with frozen spills of milk and puddles and the stale of the beasts; but too rough for sliding. And out comes Batta, with the cold reddening her nose, calling out, 'Quick, quick! Ah, you filthies! Come and be cleaned and then to the King. You'll see who's waiting for you there. My word! This'll be a change for you.'

'Is it the Stepmother?' said Redival.

'Oh, worse than that, worse than that; you'll see,' said Batta, polishing Redival's face with the end of her apron. 'Lots of whippings for the pair of you; lots of ear-pullings; lots of hard work.' Then we were led off and over to the new parts of the palace, where it is built of painted brick, and there were guards in their armour, and skins and heads of animals hung up on the walls. In the Pillar Room our father was standing by the hearth, and opposite him there were three men in travelling dress whom we knew well enough – traders who came to Glome three times a year. They were just packing up their scales, so we knew they had been paid for something, and one was putting up a fetter, so we knew they must have sold our father a slave. There was a short, thick-set man standing before them, and we knew this must be the man they had sold, for you could still see the sore places on his legs where the irons had been. But he did not look like any other slave we had ever known. He was very bright-eyed, and whatever of his hair and beard was not grey was reddish.

'Now, Greekling,' said my father to this man, 'I trust to beget a prince one of these days and I have a mind to see him brought up in all the wisdom of your people. Meanwhile practise on *them*.' (He pointed at us children.) 'If a man can teach a girl, he can teach anything.' Then, just before he sent us away, he said, 'Especially the elder. See if you can make her wise; it's about all she'll ever be good for.' I didn't understand that, but I knew it was like things I had heard people say of me ever since I could remember.

I loved the Fox, as my father called him, better than anyone I had yet known. You would have thought that a man who had been free in the Greeklands, and then been taken in war and sold far away among the barbarians, would be downcast. And so he was sometimes; possibly more often than I, in my childishness, guessed. But I never heard him complain; and I never heard him boast (as all the other foreign slaves did) about the great man he had been in his own country. He had all sorts of sayings to cheer himself up with: 'No man can be an exile if he remembers that all the world is one city,' and, 'Everything is as good or bad as our opinion makes it.' But I think what really kept him cheerful was his inquisitiveness. I never knew such a man for questions. He wanted to know everything about our country and language and ancestors and gods, and even our plants and flowers.

That was how I came to tell him all about Ungit, about the girls who are kept in her house, and the presents that brides have to make to her, and how we sometimes, in a bad year, have to cut someone's throat and pour the blood over her. He shuddered when I said that and muttered something under his breath; but a moment later he said, 'Yes, she is undoubtedly Aphrodite, though more like the Babylonian than the Greek. But come, I'll tell you a tale of our Aphrodite.'

Then he deepened and lilted his voice and told how their Aphrodite once fell in love with the prince Anchises while he kept his father's sheep on the slopes of a mountain called Ida. And as she came down the grassy slopes towards his shepherd's hut, lions and lynxes and bears and all sorts of beasts came about her fawning like dogs, and all went from her again in pairs to the delights of love. But she dimmed her glory and made herself like a mortal woman and came to Anchises and beguiled him and they went up together into his bed. I think the Fox had meant to end here, but the song now had him in its grip, and he went on to tell what followed; how Anchises woke from sleep and saw Aphrodite standing in the door of the hut, not now like a mortal but with the glory. So he knew he had lain with a goddess, and he covered his eyes and shrieked, 'Kill me at once.'

'Not that this ever really happened,' the Fox said in haste. 'It's only lies of poets, lies of poets, child. Not in accordance with nature.' But he had said enough to let me see that if the goddess was more beautiful in Greece than in Glome she was equally terrible in each.

It was always like that with the Fox; he was ashamed of loving poetry ('All folly, child') and I had to work much at my reading and writing and what he called philosophy in order to get a poem out of him. But thus, little by little, he taught me many. *Virtue, sought by man with travail and toil* was the one he praised most, but I was never deceived by that. The real lilt came into his voice and the real brightness into his eyes when we were off into *Take me to the apple-laden land* or

> *The Moon's gone down, but*
> *Alone I lie.*

He always sang that one very tenderly and as if he pitied me for something. He liked me better than Redival, who hated study and mocked and plagued him and set the other slaves on to play tricks on him.

We worked most often (in summer) on the little grass plot behind the pear trees, and it was there one day that the King found us. We all stood up of course, two children and a slave with our eyes on the ground and our hands crossed on our breasts. The King smacked the Fox heartily on the back and said, 'Courage, Fox. There'll be a prince for you to work on yet, please the gods. And thank them too, Fox, for it can't often have fallen to the lot of a mere Greekling to rule the grandson of so great a king as my father-in-law that is to be. Not that you'll know or care more about it than an ass. You're all pedlars and hucksters down in the Greeklands, eh?'

'Are not all men of one blood, Master?' said the Fox.

'Of one blood?' said the King with a stare and a great bull-laugh. 'I'd be sorry to think so.'

Thus in the end it was the King himself and not Batta who first told us that the Stepmother was really at hand. My father had made a great match. He was to have the third daughter of the King of Caphad, who is the biggest king in all our part of the world. (I know now why Caphad wanted an alliance with so poor a kingdom as we are, and I have wondered how my father did not see that his father-in-law must already be a sinking man. The marriage itself was a proof of it.)

It cannot have been many weeks before the marriage took place, but in my memory the preparations seem to have lasted for almost a year. All the brick work round the great gate was painted scarlet, and there were new hangings for the Pillar Room, and a great new royal bed which cost the King far more than he was wise to give. It was made of an eastern wood which was said to have such virtue that four of every five children begotten in such a bed would be male. ('All folly, child,' said the Fox, 'these things come about by natural causes.') And as the day drew nearer there was nothing but driving in of beasts and slaughtering of beasts – the whole courtyard reeked with the skins of them – and baking and brewing. But we children had not much time to wander from room to room and stare and hinder, for the King suddenly took it into his head that Redival and I and twelve other girls, daughters of nobles, were to sing the bridal hymn. And nothing would do him but a Greek hymn, which was a thing no other neighbouring king could have provided. 'But, Master—' said the Fox, almost with tears in his eyes. 'Teach 'em, Fox, teach 'em,' roared my father. 'What's the use of my spending good food and drink on your Greek belly if I'm not to get a Greek song out of you on my wedding night? What's that? No one's asking you to teach them Greek. Of course they won't understand what they're singing, but they can make the noises. See to it, or your back'll be redder than ever your beard was.'

It was a crazy scheme, and the Fox said afterwards that the teaching of that hymn to us barbarians was what greyed the last red hair. 'I was a fox,' he said, 'now I am a badger.'

When we had made some progress in our task the King brought the Priest of Ungit in to hear us. I had a fear of that Priest which was quite different from my fear of my father. I think that what frightened me (in those early days) was the holiness of the smell that hung about him – a temple-smell of blood (mostly pigeons' blood, but he had sacrificed men too) and burnt fat and singed hair and wine and stale incense. It is the Ungit smell. Perhaps I was afraid of his clothes too; all the skins they were made of, and the dried bladders, and the great mask shaped like a bird's head which hung on his chest. It looked as if there were a bird growing out of his body.

He did not understand a word of the hymn, nor the music either, but he asked, 'Are the young women to be veiled or unveiled?'

'Need you ask?' said the King with one of his great laughs, jerking his thumb in my direction. 'Do you think I want my queen frightened out of her senses? Veils of course. And good thick veils too.' One of the other girls tittered, and I think that was the first time I clearly understood that I am ugly.

This made me more afraid of the Stepmother than ever. I thought she would be crueller to me than to Redival because of my ugliness. It wasn't only what Batta had said that frightened me; I had heard of stepmothers in plenty of stories. And when the night came and we were all in the pillared porch, nearly dazzled with the torches and trying hard to sing our hymn as the Fox had taught us to – and he kept on frowning and smiling and nodding at us while we sang, and once he held up his hands in horror – pictures of things that had been done to girls in the stories were dancing in my mind. Then came the shouts from outside, and more torches, and next moment they were lifting the bride out of the chariot. She was as thickly veiled as we, and all I could see was that she was very small; it was as if they were lifting a child. That didn't ease my fears; 'the little are the spiteful', our proverb says. Then (still singing) we got her into the bridal chamber and took off her veil.

I know now that the face I saw was beautiful, but I did not think of that then. All I saw was that she was frightened, more frightened than I; indeed terrified. It made me see my father as he must have looked to her, a moment since, when she had her first sight of him standing to greet her in the porch. His was not a brow, a mouth, a girth, a stance, or a voice to quiet a girl's fear.

We took off layer after layer of her finery, making her yet smaller, and left the shivering, white body with its staring eyes in the King's bed, and filed out. We had sung very badly.

2

I can say very little about my father's second wife, for she did not live till the end of her first year in Glome. She was with child as soon as anyone could reasonably look for it, and the King was in high spirits and hardly ever ran across the Fox without saying something about the prince who was to be born. He made great sacrifices to Ungit every month after that. How it was between him and the Queen I do not know; except that once, after messengers had come from Caphad, I heard the King say to her, 'It begins to look, girl, as if I had driven my sheep to a bad market. I learn now that your father has lost two towns – no, three, though he tries to mince the matter. I would thank him to have told me he was sinking before he persuaded me to embark in the same bottom.' (I was leaning my head on my windowsill to dry my hair after the bath, and they were walking in the garden.) However that might be, it is certain that she was very homesick, and I think our winter was too hard for her southern body. She was soon pale and thin. I learned that I had nothing to fear from her. She was at first more afraid of me; after that, very loving in her timid way, and more like a sister than a stepmother.

Of course no one in the house went to bed on the night of the birth, for that, they say, will make the child refuse to wake into the world. We all sat in the great hall between the Pillar Room and the Bedchamber, in a red glare of birth-torches. The flames swayed and guttered terribly, for all doors must be open; the shutting of a door might shut up the mother's womb. In the middle of the hall burned a great fire. Every hour the Priest of Ungit walked round it nine times and threw in the proper things. The King sat in his chair and never moved all night, not even his head. I was sitting next to the Fox.

'Grandfather,' I whispered to him, 'I am terribly afraid.'

'We must learn, child, not to fear anything that nature brings,' he whispered back.

I must have slept after that, for the next thing I knew was the sound of women wailing and beating the breast as I had heard them do it the day my mother died. Everything had changed while I slept. I was shivering with cold.

The fire had sunk low, the King's chair was empty, the door of the Bedchamber was at last shut, and the terrible sounds from within it had stopped. There must have been some sacrifice too, for there was a smell of slaughtering, and blood on the floor, and the Priest was cleaning his holy knife. I was all in a daze from my sleep, for I started up with the wildest idea; I would go and see the Queen. The Fox was after me long before I reached the door of the Bedchamber. 'Daughter, daughter,' he was saying. 'Not now. Are you mad? The King—'

At that moment the door was flung open and out came my father. His face shocked me full awake, for he was in his pale rage. I knew that in his red rage he would storm and threaten, and little might come of it, but when he was pale he was deadly. 'Wine,' he said, not very loud; and that too was a bad sign. The other slaves pushed forward a boy who was rather a favourite, as slaves do when they are afraid. The child, white as his master and in all his finery (my father dressed the younger slaves very fine) came running with the flagon and the royal cup, slipped in the blood, reeled, and dropped both. Quick as thought, my father whipped out his dagger and stabbed him in the side. The boy dropped dead in the blood and wine, and the fall of his body sent the flagon rolling over and over. It made a great noise in that silence; I hadn't thought till then that the floor of the hall was so uneven. (I have re-paved it since.)

My father stared for a moment at his own dagger; stupidly, it seemed. Then he goes very gently up to the Priest.

'What have you to say for Ungit now?' he asked, still in that low voice. 'You had better recover what she owes me. When are you going to pay me for my good cattle?' Then, after a pause, 'Tell me, prophet, what would happen if I hammered Ungit into powder and tied you between the hammers and the stone?'

But the Priest was not in the least afraid of the King.

'Ungit hears, King, even at this moment,' he said. 'And Ungit will remember. You have already said enough to call down doom upon all your descendants.'

'Descendants,' says the King. 'You talk of descendants,' still very quiet, but now he was shaking. The ice of his rage would break any moment. The body of the dead boy caught his eye. 'Who did that?' he asked. Then he saw the Fox and me. All the blood rushed into his face, and now at last the voice came roaring out of his chest loud enough to lift the roof.

'Girls, girls, girls,' he bellowed. 'And now one girl more. Is there no end to it? Is there a plague of girls in heaven that the gods send me this flood of them? You – you—' He caught me by the hair, shook me to and fro, and flung me from him so that I fell in a heap. There are times when even a child knows better than to cry. When the blackness passed and I could see again, he was shaking the Fox by his throat.

'Here's an old babbler who has eaten my bread long enough,' he said. 'It would have paid me better to buy a dog as things turn out. But I'll feed you in idleness no longer. Some of you take him to the mines tomorrow. There might be a week's work in his old bones even now.'

Again there was dead silence in the hall. Suddenly the King flung up his hands, stamped, and cried, 'Faces, faces, faces! What are you all gaping at? It'd make a man mad. Be off! Away! Out of my sight, the whole pack of you!'

We were out of the hall as quick as the doorways would let us.

The Fox and I went out of the little door by the herb-garden on the east. It was nearly daylight now and there was a small rain beginning.

'Grandfather,' said I, sobbing, 'you must fly at once. This moment, before they come to take you to the mines.'

He shook his head. 'I'm too old to run far,' he said. 'And you know what the King does to runaway slaves.'

'But the mines, the mines! Look, I'll come with you. If we're caught I'll say I made you come. We shall be almost out of Glome once we're over *that*.' I pointed to the ridge of the Grey Mountain, now dark with a white day-break behind it, seen through the slanting rain.

'That is foolishness, daughter,' said he, petting me like a small child. 'They would think I was stealing you to sell. No; I must fly further. And help me you shall. Down by the river; you know the little plant with the purple spots on its stalks. It's the roots of it I need.'

'The poison?'

'Why, yes. (Child, child, don't cry so.) Have I not told you often that to depart from life of a man's own will when there's good reason is one of the things that are according to nature? We are to look on life as—'

'They say that those who go that way lie wallowing in filth – down there in the land of the dead.'

'Hush, hush. Are you also still a barbarian? At death we are resolved into our elements. Shall I accept birth and cavil at—'

'Oh, I know, I know. But, Grandfather, do you really in your heart believe nothing of what is said about the gods and Those Below? But you do, you do. You are trembling.'

'That's my disgrace. The body is shaking. I needn't let it shake the god within me. Have I not already carried this body too long if it makes such a fool of me at the end? But we are wasting time.'

'Listen!' said I. 'What's that?' For I was in a state to be scared by every sound.

'Horses,' said the Fox, peering through the quick-hedge with his eyes screwed up to see against the rain. 'They are coming to the great door. Messengers from Phars, by the look of them. And that will not sweeten the

King's mood either. Will you – ah, Zeus, it is already too late.' For there was a call from within doors, 'The Fox, the Fox, the Fox to the King.'

'As well go as be dragged,' said the Fox. 'Farewell, daughter,' and he kissed me, Greek fashion, on the eyes and the head. But I went in with him. I had an idea I would face the King; though whether I meant to beseech him or curse him or kill him I hardly knew. But as we came to the Pillar Room we saw many strangers within, and the King shouted through the open door, 'Here, Fox, I've work for you.' Then he saw me and said, 'And you, curd-face, be off to the women's quarters and don't come here to sour the morning drink for the men.'

I do not know that I have ever (to speak of things merely mortal) been in such dread as I was for the rest of that day; dread that feels as if there were an empty place between your belly and your chest. I didn't know whether I dared be comforted by the King's last words or not; for they sounded as if his anger had passed, but it might blaze out again. Moreover, I had known him do a cruel thing not in anger but in a kind of murderous joke, or because he remembered he had sworn to do it when he was angry. He had sent old house-slaves to the mines before. And I could not be alone with my terror, for now comes Batta to shear my head and Redival's again as they had been shorn when my mother died, and to make a great tale (clicking her tongue) of how the Queen was dead in childbed, which I had known ever since I heard the mourning, and how she had borne a daughter alive. I sat for the shearing and thought that, if the Fox must die in the mines, it was very fit I should offer my hair. Lank and dull and little it lay on the floor beside Redival's rings of gold.

In the evening the Fox came and told me that there was no more talk of the mines; for the present. A thing that had often irked me had now been our salvation. More and more, of late, the King had taken the Fox away from us girls to work for him in the Pillar Room; he had begun to find that the Fox could calculate and read and write letters (at first only in Greek but now in the speech of our parts too) and give advice better than any man in Glome. This very day the Fox had taught him to drive a better bargain with the King of Phars than he would ever have thought of for himself. The Fox was a true Greek; where my father could give only a Yes or a No to some neighbouring king or dangerous noble, he could pare the Yes to the very quick and sweeten the No till it went down like wine. He could make your weak enemy believe that you were his best friend and make your strong enemy believe you were twice as strong as you really were. He was far too useful to be sent to the mines.

They burnt the dead Queen on the third day, and my father named the child Istra. 'It is a good name,' said the Fox, 'a very good name. And you know enough now to tell me what it would be in Greek.'

'It would be Psyche, Grandfather,' said I.

New-born children were no rarity in the palace; the place sprawled with the slaves' babies and my father's bastards. Sometimes my father would say, 'Lecherous rascals! Anyone'd think this was Ungit's house, not mine,' and threaten to drown a dozen of them like blind puppies. But in his heart he thought the better of a man-slave if he could get half the maids in the place with child, especially if they bore boys. (The girls, unless they took his own fancy, were mostly sold when they were ripe; some were given to the house of Ungit.) Nevertheless, because I had (a little) loved the Queen, I went to see Psyche that very evening as soon as the Fox had set my mind at rest. And so, in one hour, I passed out of the worst anguish I had yet suffered into the beginning of all my joys.

The child was very big, not a wearish little thing as you might have expected from her mother's stature, and very fair of skin. You would have thought she made bright all the corner of the room in which she lay. She slept (tiny was the sound of her breathing). But there never was a child like Psyche for quietness in her cradle days. As I gazed at her the Fox came in on tiptoes and looked over my shoulder. 'Now by all the gods,' he whispered, 'old fool that I am, I could almost believe that there really is divine blood in your family. Helen herself, new-hatched, must have looked so.'

Batta had put her to nurse with a red-haired woman who was sullen and (like Batta herself) too fond of the wine-jar. I soon had the child out of their hands. I got for her nurse a free woman, a peasant's wife, as honest and wholesome as I could find, and after that both were in my own chamber day and night. Batta was only too pleased to have her work done for her, and the King knew and cared nothing about it. The Fox said to me, 'Don't wear yourself out, daughter, with too much toil, even if the child is as beautiful as a goddess.' But I laughed in his face. I think I laughed more in those days than in all my life before. Toil? I lost more sleep looking on Psyche for the joy of it than in any other way. And I laughed because she was always laughing. She laughed before the third month. She knew me for certain (though the Fox said not) before the second.

This was the beginning of my best times. The Fox's love for the child was wonderful; I guessed that long before, when he was free, he must have had a daughter of his own. He was like a true grandfather now. And it was now always we three – the Fox, and Psyche, and I – alone together. Redival had always hated our lessons and, but for the fear of the King, would never have come near the Fox. Now, it seemed, the King had put all his three daughters out of his mind, and Redival had her own way. She was growing tall, her breasts rounding, her long legs getting their shape. She promised to have beauty enough, but not like Psyche's.

859

Of Psyche's beauty – at every age the beauty proper to that age – there is only this to be said, that there were no two opinions about it, from man or woman, once she had been seen. It was beauty that did not astonish you till afterwards when you had gone out of sight of her and reflected on it. While she was with you, you were not astonished. It seemed the most natural thing in the world. As the Fox delighted to say, she was 'according to nature'; what every woman, or even every thing, ought to have been and meant to be, but had missed by some trip of chance. Indeed, when you looked at her you believed, for a moment, that they had not missed it. She made beauty all round her. When she trod on mud, the mud was beautiful; when she ran in the rain, the rain was silver. When she picked up a toad – she had the strangest and, I thought, unchanciest love for all manner of brutes – the toad became beautiful.

The years, doubtless, went round then as now, but in my memory it seems to have been all springs and summers. I think the almonds and the cherries blossomed earlier in those years and the blossoms lasted longer; how they hung on in such winds I don't know, for I see the boughs always rocking and dancing against blue-and-white skies, and their shadows flowing water-like over all the hills and valleys of Psyche's body. I wanted to be a wife so that I could have been her real mother. I wanted to be a boy so that she could be in love with me. I wanted her to be my full sister instead of my half sister. I wanted her to be a slave so that I could set her free and make her rich.

The Fox was so trusted by now that when my father did not need him he was allowed to take us anywhere, even miles from the palace. We were often out all day in summer on the hill-top to the south-west, looking down on all Glome and across to the Grey Mountain. We stared our eyes out on that jagged ridge till we knew every tooth and notch of it, for none of us had ever gone there or seen what was on the other side. Psyche, almost from the beginning (for she was a very quick, thinking child), was half in love with the Mountain. She made herself stories about it. 'When I'm big,' she said, 'I will be a great, great queen, married to the greatest king of all, and he will build me a castle of gold and amber up there on the very top.'

The Fox clapped his hands and sang, 'Prettier than Andromeda, prettier than Helen, prettier than Aphrodite herself.'

'Speak words of better omen, Grandfather,' I said, though I knew he would scold and mock me for saying it. For at his words, though on that summer day the rocks were too hot to touch, it was as if a soft, cold hand had been laid on my left side, and I shivered.

'Babai!' said the Fox. 'It is your words that are ill-omened. The divine nature is not like that. It has no envy.'

But whatever he said, I knew it is not good to talk that way about Ungit.

3

It was Redival who ended the good time. She had always been feather-headed and now grew wanton, and what must she do but stand kissing and whispering love-talk with a young officer of the guard (one Tarin) right under Batta's window an hour after midnight. Batta had slept off her wine in the earlier part of the night and was now wakeful. Being a busybody and tattler in grain, she went off straight and woke the King, who cursed her roundly but believed her. He was up, and had a few armed men with him, and was out into the garden and surprised the lovers before they knew that anything was amiss. The whole house was raised by the noise of it. The King had the barber to make a eunuch of Tarin there and then (as soon as he was healed, they sold him down at Ringal). The boy's screams had hardly sunk to a whimper before the King turned on the Fox and me, and made us to blame for the whole thing. Why had the Fox not looked to his pupil? Why had I not looked to my sister? The end of it was a strict command that we were never to let her out of our sight. 'Go where you will and do what you will,' said my father. 'But the salt bitch must be with you. I tell you, Fox, if she loses her maidenhead before I find her a husband, you'll yell louder for it than she. Look to your hide. And you, goblin daughter, do what you're good for, you'd best. Name of Ungit! if you with that face can't frighten the men away, it's a wonder.'

Redival was utterly cowed by the King's anger and obeyed him. She was always with us. And that soon cooled any love she had for Psyche or me. She yawned and she quarrelled and she mocked. Psyche, who was a child so merry, so truthful, so obedient that in her (the Fox said) Virtue herself had put on a human form, could do no right in Redival's eyes. One day Redival hit her. Then I hardly knew myself again till I found that I was astride of Redival, she on the ground with her face a lather of blood, and my hands about her throat. It was the Fox who pulled me off and, in the end, some kind of peace was made between us.

Thus all the comfort we three had had was destroyed when Redival joined us. And after that, little by little, one by one, came the first knocks of the hammer that finally destroyed us all.

The year after I fought Redival was the first of the bad harvests. That same year my father tried to marry himself (as the Fox told me) into two royal houses among the neighbouring kings, and they would have none of him. The world was changing, the great alliance with Caphad had proved a snare. The tide was against Glome.

That same year, too, a small thing happened which cost me many a shuddering. The Fox and I, up behind the pear trees, were deep in his philosophy. Psyche had wandered off, singing to herself, among the trees, to the edge of the royal gardens where they overlook the lane. Redival went after her. I had one eye on the pair of them, and one ear for the Fox. Then it seemed they were talking to someone in the lane, and shortly after that they came back.

Redival, sneering, bowed double before Psyche and went through the actions of pouring dust on her head. 'Why don't you honour the goddess?' she said to us.

'What do you mean, Redival?' asked I, wearily, for I knew she meant some new spite.

'Did you not know our stepsister had become a goddess?'

'What does she mean, Istra?' said I. (I never called her Psyche now that Redival had joined us.)

'Come on, stepsister goddess, speak up,' said Redival. 'I'm sure I've been told often enough how truthful you are, so you'll not deny that you have been worshipped.'

'It's not true,' said Psyche. 'All that happened was that a woman with child asked me to kiss her.'

'Ah, but why?' said Redival.

'Because – because she said her baby would be beautiful if I did.'

'*Because you are so beautiful yourself.* Don't forget that. She said that.'

'And what did you do, Istra?' asked I.

'I kissed her. She was a nice woman. I liked her.'

'And don't forget that she then laid down a branch of myrtle at your feet and bowed and put dust on her head,' said Redival.

'Has this happened before, Istra?' said I.

'Yes. Sometimes.'

'How often?'

'Don't know.'

'Twice before?'

'More than that.'

'Well, ten times?'

'No, more. I don't know. I can't remember. What are you looking at me like that for? Is it wrong?'

'Oh, it's dangerous, dangerous,' said I. 'The gods are jealous. They can't bear—'

'Daughter, it doesn't matter a straw,' said the Fox. 'The divine nature is without jealousy. Those gods – the sort of gods you are always thinking about – are all folly and lies of poets. We have discussed this a hundred times.'

'Heigh-ho,' yawns Redival, lying flat on her back in the grass and kicking her legs in the air till you could see all there was of her (which she did purely to put the Fox out of countenance, for the old man was very modest). 'Heigh-ho, a stepsister for goddess and a slave for counsellor. Who'd be a princess in Glome? I wonder what Ungit thinks of our new goddess.'

'It is not very easy to find out what Ungit thinks,' said the Fox.

Redival rolled round and laid her cheek on the grass. Then, looking up at him, she said softly, 'But it would be easy to find out what the Priest of Ungit thinks. Shall I try?'

All my old fear of the Priest, and more fears for the future than I could put a name to, stabbed into me.

'Sister,' said Redival to me, 'give me your necklace with the blue stones, the one our mother gave you.'

'Take it,' said I. 'I'll give it you when we go in.'

'And you, slave,' she said to the Fox. 'Mend your manners. And get my father to give me to some king in marriage; and it must be a young king, brave, yellow-bearded, and lusty. You can do what you like with my father when you're shut up with him in the Pillar Room. Everyone knows that you are the real King of Glome.'

The year after that we had rebellion. It came of my father's gelding Tarin. Tarin himself was of no great lineage (to be about a king's house at all) and the King had thought his father would have no power to avenge him. But the father made common cause with bigger men than himself, and about nine strong lords in our north-west rose against us. My father took the field himself (and when I saw him ride out in his armour, I came nearer to loving him than I had been yet) and beat the rebels; but with great slaughter on both parts and, I think, more slaughter of the beaten men than was needed. The thing left a stench and a disaffection behind it; when all was done, the King was weaker than he had been.

That year was the second bad harvest and the beginning of the fever. In the autumn the Fox took it and nearly died. I could not be with him, for as soon as the Fox fell sick the King said, 'Now, girl, you can read and write and chatter Greek. I'll have work for you. You must take the Fox's place.' So I was nearly always in the Pillar Room, for there was much business at the time. Though I was sick with fear for the Fox, the work with my father was far less dreadful to me than I expected. He came, for the time, to hate me less. In the end he would speak to me, not, certainly, with love, but friendly as one man might to another. I learned how desperate his affairs were. No neighbouring houses of divine blood (and ours cannot lawfully marry into any other) would take his daughters or give him theirs. The nobles were muttering about the succession. There were threats of war from every side, and no strength to meet any of them.

It was Psyche who nursed the Fox, however often forbidden. She would fight, yes, and bite, any who stood between her and his door; for she, too, had our father's hot blood, though her angers were all the sort that come from love. The Fox won through his illness, thinner and greyer than before. Now mark the subtlety of the god who is against us. The story of his recovery and Psyche's nursing got abroad; Batta alone was conduit-pipe enough, and there were a score of other talkers. It became a story of how the beautiful princess could cure the fever by her touch; soon, that her touch was the only thing that could cure it. Within two days half the city was at the palace gate – such scarecrows, risen from their beds, old dotards as eager to save their lives as if their lives in any event were worth a year's purchase, babies, sick men half dead and carried on beds. I stood looking at them from behind barred windows; all the pity and dread of it, the smell of sweat and fever and garlic and foul clothes.

'The Princess Istra,' they cried. 'Send out the Princess with her healing hands. We die! Healing, healing, healing!'

'And bread,' came other voices. 'The royal granaries! We are starving.'

This was at first, while they stood a little way off from the gate. But they got nearer. Soon they were hammering at it. Someone was saying, 'Bring fire.' But, behind them, the weaker voices wailed on, 'Heal us, heal us. The Princess with the healing hands!'

'She'll have to go out,' said my father. 'We can't hold them.' (Two-thirds of our guards were down with the fever.)

'Can she heal them?' said I to the Fox. 'Did she heal you?'

'It is possible,' said the Fox. 'It might be in accordance with nature that some hands can heal. Who knows?'

'Let me go out,' said Psyche. 'They are our people.'

'Our rump!' said my father. 'They shall smart for this day's work if ever I get the whip hand of them again. But quick. Dress the girl. She has beauty enough, that's one thing. And spirit.'

They put a queen's dress on her and a chaplet on her head and opened the door. You know how it is when you shed few tears or none, but there is a weight and pressure of weeping through your whole head. It is like that with me even now when I remember her going out, slim and straight as a sceptre, out of the darkness and cool of the hall into the hot, pestilential glare of that day. The people drew back, thrusting one another, the moment the doors opened. I think they expected a rush of spearmen. But a minute later the wailing and shouting died utterly away. Every man (and many a woman too) in that crowd was kneeling. Her beauty, which most of them had never seen, worked on them as a terror might work. Then a low murmur, almost a sob, began; swelled, broke into the gasping cry, 'A goddess, a goddess.' One woman's voice rang out clear. 'It is Ungit herself in mortal shape.'

Psyche went on, walking slowly and gravely, like a child going to say a lesson, right in among all the foulness. She touched and she touched. They fell at her feet and kissed her feet and the edge of her robe and her shadow and the ground where she had trodden. And still she touched and touched. There seemed to be no end of it; the crowd increased instead of diminishing. For hours she touched. The air was stifling even for us who stood in the shadow of the porch. The whole earth and air ached for the thunderstorm which (we knew now) would not come. I saw her growing paler and paler. Her walk had become a stagger.

'King,' said I, 'it will kill her.'

'Then more's the pity,' said the King. 'They'll kill us all if she stops.'

It was over in the end, somewhere about sunset. We carried her to her bed, and next day the fever was on her. But she won through it. In her wanderings she talked most of her gold and amber castle on the ridge of the Grey Mountain. At her worst, there was no look of death upon her face. It was as if he dared not come near her. And when her strength came back she was more beautiful than before. The childishness had gone. There was a new and severer radiance. 'Ah, no wonder,' sang the Fox, 'if the Trojans and the Achaeans suffer long woes for such a woman. Terribly does she resemble an undying spirit.'

Some of the sick in the town died and some recovered. Only the gods know if those who recovered were those whom Psyche had touched, and gods do not tell. But the people had, at first, no doubts. Every morning there were offerings left for her outside the palace; myrtle branches and garlands and soon honey-cakes and then pigeons, which are specially sacred to Ungit. 'Can this be well?' I said to the Fox.

'I should be greatly afraid,' said he, 'but for one thing. The Priest of Ungit lies sick with the fever himself. I do not think he can do us much mischief at present.'

About this time Redival became very pious and went often to the house of Ungit to make offerings. The Fox and I saw to it that she always had with her a trusty old slave who would let her get into no mischief. I thought she was praying for a husband (she wanted one badly since the King had, in a manner, chained her to the Fox and me) and also that she was as glad to be out of our sight for an hour as we were to be out of hers. Yet I warned her to speak to no one on the way.

'Oh, make your mind easy, Sister,' says Redival. 'It's not me they worship, you know. I'm not the goddess. The men are as likely to look at you as at me, now they've seen Istra.'

4

Up till now I had not known what the common people are like. That was why their adorings of Psyche, which in one way made me afraid, comforted me in another. For I was confused in my mind, sometimes thinking of what Ungit by her own divine power might do to any mortal who thus stole her honour, and sometimes of what the Priest and our enemies in the city (my father had many now) might do with their tongues, or stones, or spears. Against the latter the people's love for Psyche seemed to me a protection.

It did not last long. For one thing, the mob had now learned that a palace door can be opened by banging on it. Before Psyche was out of her fever they were back at our gates crying, 'Corn, corn! We are starving. Open the royal granaries.' That time the King gave them a dole. 'But don't come again,' he said. 'I've no more to give you. Name of Ungit! d'you think I can make corn if the fields don't bear it?'

'And why don't they?' said a voice from the back of the crowd.

'Where are your sons, King?' said another. 'Where's the prince?'

'The King of Phars has thirteen sons,' said another.

'Barren king makes barren land,' said a fourth. This time the King saw who had spoken and nodded to one of the bowmen who stood beside him. Before you'd wink the arrow went through the speaker's throat and the mob took to its heels. But it was foolishly done; my father ought to have killed either none of them or nearly all. He was right enough, though, in saying we could give them no more doles. This was the second of the bad harvests and there was little in the granary but our own seedcorn. Even in the palace we were already living for the most part on leeks and bean-bread and small beer. It took me endless contrivance to get anything good for Psyche when she was mending from the fever.

The next thing was this. Shortly after Psyche was well, I left the Pillar Room where I had been working for the King (and he still kept the Fox with him after he let me go) and set out to look for Redival, that care being always on my mind. The King would have thought nothing of keeping me away from her at his own business all the day and then blaming me for not having my eyes on her. But as it happened I met her at once, just coming in from one of her visits to the house of Ungit, and Batta with her. Batta and she were as thick as thieves these days.

'You needn't come looking for me, sister-jailer,' says Redival. 'I'm safe enough. It isn't here the danger lies. When did you last see the little goddess? Where's your darling stepsister?'

'In the gardens most likely,' said I. 'And as for *little*, she's half a head taller than yourself.'

'Oh mercy! Have I blasphemed? Will she smite me with thunder? Yes, she's tall enough. Tall enough to see her a long way off – half an hour ago – in a little lane near the market place. A king's daughter doesn't usually walk the back streets alone; but I suppose a goddess can.'

'Istra out in the town and alone?' said I.

'Indeed she was then,' chattered Batta. 'Scuttling along with her robe caught up. Like this … like this.' (Batta was a bad mimic but always mimicking; I remembered that from my earliest years.) 'I'd have followed her, the young boldface, but she went in at a doorway, so she did.'

'Well, well,' said I. 'The child ought to have known better. But she'll do no harm and come to none.'

'Come to no harm!' said Batta. 'That's more than any of us know.'

'You are mad, Nurse,' said I. 'The people were worshipping her not six days ago.'

'I don't know anything about that,' said Batta (who knew perfectly well). 'But she'll get little worship today. I knew what would come of all that touching and blessing. Fine goings on indeed! The plague's worse than ever it was. There were a hundred died yesterday, the smith's wife's brother-in-law tells me. They say the touchings didn't heal the fever but gave it. I've spoken to a woman whose old father was touched by the Princess, and he was dead before they had carried him home. And he wasn't the only one. If anyone had listened to old Batta—'

But I at least listened no more. I went out to the porch and looked towards the city; a long half-hour. I watched the shadows of the pillars slowly changing their position and it was then I first saw how the things we have known ever since we were weaned can look new and strange, like enemies. And at last I saw Psyche coming, very tired but in great haste. She caught me by the wrist and swallowed, like one that has a sob in the throat, and began leading me away and never stopped till we were in my own chamber. Then she put me in my chair and fell down and laid her head on my knees. I thought she was crying, but when at last she raised her face there were no tears on it.

'Sister,' she said. 'What is wrong? I mean, about me.'

'About you, Psyche?' said I. 'Nothing. What do you mean?'

'Why do they call me the Accursed?'

'Who has dared? We'll have his tongue torn out. Where have you been?'

Then it all came out. She had gone (very foolishly, I thought) into the city without a word to any of us. She had heard that her old nurse, the free-woman whom I had hired to suckle her and who now lived in town, was sick with the fever. And Psyche had gone to touch her – 'For they all said my hands cured it, and who knows? It might be. I felt as if they did.'

I told her she had done very wrong, and it was then that I fully perceived how much older she had grown since her sickness. For she neither accepted the rebuke like a child nor defended herself like a child, but looked at me with a grave quietness, almost as if she were older than I. It gave me a pang at the heart.

'But who cursed you?' I asked.

'Nothing happened till I had left Nurse's house; except that no one in the streets had saluted me, and I thought that one or two women gathered their skirts together and drew away from me as I passed. Well, on the way back, first there was a boy – a lovely boy he was, not eight years old – who stared at me and spat on the ground. 'Oh rude!' said I, and laughed and held out my hand to him. He scowled at me as black as a little fiend and then lost his courage and ran howling into a doorway. After that the street was empty for a space, but presently I had to pass a knot of men. They gave me black looks as I was passing, and as soon as my back was towards them they were all saying, 'The Accursed, the Accursed! She made herself a goddess.' And one said, 'She is the curse itself.' Then they threw stones. No, I'm not hurt. But I had to run. What does it mean? What did I do to them?'

'Do?' said I. 'You healed them, and blessed them, and took their filthy diseases upon yourself. And these are their thanks. Oh, I could tear them in pieces! Get up, child. Let me go. Even now – we are king's daughters still. I'll go to the King. He may beat me and drag me by the hair as he pleases, but this he shall hear. Bread for them indeed. I'll – I'll—'

'Hush, sister, hush,' said Psyche. 'I can't bear it when he hurts you. And I'm so tired. And I want my supper. There, don't be angry. You look just like our father when you say those things. Let us have supper here, you and I. There is some bad thing coming towards us – I have felt it a long time – but I don't think it will come tonight. I'll clap my hands to call your maids.'

Though the words *You look just like our father*, and from her, had hurt me with a wound that sometimes aches still, I let go my anger and yielded. We supped together and turned our poor meal into a joke and a game and were in a fashion happy. One thing the gods have not taken from me; I can remember all that she said or did that night and how she looked from moment to moment.

But whatever my heart boded, our ruin (and even now I had no clear foresight what it would be) did not fall upon us the next day. A whole train of days went past in which nothing happened, except for the slow, steady worsening of everything in Glome. The Shennit was now no more than a trickle between one puddle and another amid dry mud-flats; it was the corpse of a river and stank. Her fish were dead, her birds dead or gone away. The cattle had all died or been killed or were not worth the killing. The bees were dead. Lions, which had not been heard of in the land for forty years, came over the ridge of the Grey Mountain and took most of the few sheep we had left. The plague never ceased. All through these days I was waiting and listening, watching (when I could) everyone who went out of the palace or came in. It was well for me that the King found plenty of work both for the Fox and me in the Pillar Room. Messengers and letters from the neighbouring kings were coming in every day, demanding impossible things and contrary things, dragging up old quarrels or claiming old promises. They knew how things were in Glome and clustered round us like flies and crows round a dying sheep. My father would pass in and out of his rages a dozen times in one morning. When he was in them he would slap the Fox about the face and pull me by the ears or the hair; and then, between the fits, the tears would stand in his eyes, and he would speak to us more like a child imploring help than a king asking counsel.

'Trapped!' he would say. 'No way out. They will kill me by inches. What have I done that all these miseries should fall upon me? I've been a god-fearing man all my life.'

The only betterment in these days was that the fever seemed to have left the palace. We had lost a good many slaves, but we had better luck with the soldiers. Only one died and all the rest were now back at duty.

Then we heard that the Priest of Ungit had recovered from his fever. His sickness had been very long, for he had taken the fever and won over it and then taken it again, so that it was a wonder he should be alive. But it was noticed for a strange and unlucky thing about this sickness that it killed the young more easily than the old. On the seventh day after this news the Priest came to the palace. The King, who saw his coming (as I did too) from the windows of the Pillar Room, said, 'What does the old carrion mean by coming here with half an army?' There were indeed a good many spears behind his litter, for the house of Ungit has its own guards and he had brought a big handful with him. They grounded their spears some distance from our gates, and only the litter was carried to the porch. 'They'd better come no nearer,' said the King. 'Is this treason or only pride?' Then he gave some order to the captain of his own guard. I don't think he expected it would come to a fight, but that was what I, being still young, looked for. I had never seen men fight and, being as big a fool in that way as most girls, I felt no dread; rather, a little tingling that I liked well enough.

The bearers set down the litter and the Priest was lifted out of it. He was very old now and blind, and he had two temple girls with him to lead him. I had seen their kind before, but only by torchlight in the house of Ungit. They looked strange under the sun, with their gilt paps and their huge flaxen wigs and their faces painted till they looked like wooden masks. Only these two and the Priest, with one hand on a shoulder of each, came into the palace. As soon as they were in, my father called out to our men to shut and bar the door. 'The old wolf would hardly walk into such a trap if he meant mischief,' he said. 'But we'll make sure.'

The temple girls led the Priest into the Pillar Room, and a chair was set for him and he was helped into it. He was out of breath and sat for a long time before he spoke, making a chewing motion with his gums as old men do. The girls stood stiffly at each side of his chair, their meaningless eyes looking always straight ahead out of the mask of their painting. The smell of old age, and the smell of the oils and essences they put on those girls, and the Ungit smell, filled the room. It became very holy.

5

My father greeted the Priest and wished him joy of his recovery and called for wine to be given him. But the Priest held up his hand and said, 'No, King. I am under a strong vow, and neither food nor drink must pass my lips till I have given my message.' He spoke well enough now, though weakly, and I noticed how much thinner he was since his sickness.

'As you please, servant of Ungit,' said the King. 'What's this of a message?'

'I am speaking to you, King, with the voice of Ungit and the voice of all the people and elders and nobles of Glome.'

'Did all these, then, send you with a message?'

'Yes. We were all gathered – or those who could speak for all were gathered – last night, and even till this day's daybreak, in the house of Ungit.'

'Were you, death and scabs?' said my father, frowning. 'It's a new fashion to hold an assembly without the King's bidding; and newer still to hold it without bidding the King to it.'

'There would have been no reason in bidding you to it, King, seeing that we came together not to hear what you would say to us but to determine what we would say to you.'

My father's look grew very black.

'And being gathered together,' said the Priest, 'we reckoned up all the woes that have come upon us. First, the famine, which still increases. Second, the pestilence. Third, the drought. Fourth, the certain expectation of war by next spring at the latest. Fifth, the lions. And lastly, King, your own barrenness of sons which is hateful to Ungit—'

'That's enough,' shouted the King. 'You old fool, do you think I need you or any of the other wiseacres to tell me where my own belly aches? Hateful to Ungit, is it? Why does Ungit not mend it then? She's had bulls and rams and goats from me in plenty; blood enough to sail a ship on if all was reckoned.'

The Priest jerked up his head as if, though blind, he was looking at the King. And now I saw better how his thinness had changed him. He looked like a vulture. I was more afraid of him than I had been. The King dropped his eyes.

'Bulls and rams and goats will not win Ungit's favour while the land is impure,' said the Priest. 'I have served Ungit these fifty – no, sixty-three years, and I have learned one thing for certain. Her anger never comes upon us without cause, and it never ceases without expiation. I have made offerings to her for your father and your father's father, and it has always been the same. We were overthrown long before your day by the King of Essur; and that was because there was a man in your grandfather's army who had lain with his sister and killed the child. He was the Accursed. We found him out and expiated his sin, and then the men of Glome chased the men of Essur like sheep. Your father himself could have told you how one woman, little more than a child, cursed Ungit's son, the god of the Mountain, in secret. For her sake the floods came. She was the Accursed. We found her out and expiated her sin, and Shennit returned into her banks. And now, by all the signs I have reckoned over to you, we know that Ungit's anger is far greater than ever within my memory. Thus we all said in her house last night. We all said, We must find the Accursed. Though every man knew that he himself might be the Accursed, no man spoke against it. I too – I had not a word to say against it, though I knew that the Accursed might be I; or you, King. For we all knew (and you may hold it for certain) that there will be no mending of all our ills till the land is purged. Ungit will be avenged. It's not a bull or a ram that will quiet her now.'

'You mean she wants Man?' said the King.

'Yes,' said the Priest. 'Or Woman.'

'If they think I can get them a captive in war at present, they must be mad. The next time I take a thief you can cut his throat over Ungit if you like.'

'That is not enough, King. And you know it. We must find the Accursed. And she (or he) must die by the rite of the Great Offering. What is a thief more than a bull or a ram? This is not to be a common sacrifice. We must make the Great Offering. The Brute has been seen again. And when it comes the Great Offering must be made. That is how the Accursed must be offered.'

'The Brute? It's the first I've heard of it.'

'It may be so. Kings seem to hear very little. They do not know even what goes on in their own palaces. But I hear. I lie awake in the nights, very long awake, and Ungit tells me things. I hear of terrible doings in this land; mortals aping the gods and stealing the worship due to the gods—'

I looked at the Fox and said, soundlessly, by the shaping of my lips, 'Redival.'

The King was walking up and down the room with his hands clasped behind his back and his fingers working.

'You're doting,' he said. 'The Brute's a tale of my grandmother's.'

'It may well be,' said the Priest, 'for it was in her time that the Brute was last seen. And we made the Great Offering and it went away.'

'Who has ever seen this Brute?' asked by father. 'What is it like, eh?'

'Those who have seen it closest can least say what it is like, King. And many have seen it of late. Your own chief shepherd on the Grey Mountain saw it the night the first lion came. He fell upon the lion with a burning torch. And in the light of the torch he saw the Brute – behind the lion – very black and big, a terrible shape.'

As the Priest said this the King's walk had brought him close to the table where I and the Fox sat with our tablets and other tools for writing. The Fox slid along the bench and whispered something in my father's ear.

'Well said, Fox,' muttered my father. 'Speak up. Say it to the Priest.'

'By the King's permission,' said the Fox, 'the shepherd's tale is very questionable. If the man had a torch, of necessity the lion would have a big black shadow behind it. The man was scared and new waked from sleep. He took a shadow for a monster.'

'That is the wisdom of the Greeks,' said the Priest. 'But Glome does not take counsel with slaves, not even if they are king's favourites. And if the Brute was a shadow, King, what then? Many say it *is* a shadow. But if that shadow begins coming down into the city, look to yourself. You are of divine blood and doubtless fear nothing. But the people will fear. Their fear will be so great that not even I will be able to hold them. They will burn your palace about your ears. They will bar you in before they burn it. You would be wiser to make the Great Offering.'

'How is it made?' said the King. 'It has never happened in my time.'

'It is not done in the house of Ungit,' said the Priest. 'The victim must be given to the Brute. For the Brute is, in a mystery, Ungit herself or Ungit's son, the god of the Mountain; or both. The victim is led up the mountain to the Holy Tree, and bound to the Tree and left. Then the Brute comes. That is why you angered Ungit just now, King, when you spoke of offering a thief. In the Great Offering the victim must be perfect. For in holy language a man so offered is said to be Ungit's husband, and a woman is said to be the bride of Ungit's son. And both are called the Brute's Supper. And when the Brute is Ungit it lies with the man, and when it is her son it lies with the woman. And either way there is a devouring ... many different things are said ... many sacred stories ... many great mysteries. Some say the loving and the devouring are all the same thing. For in sacred language we say that a woman who lies with a man devours the man. That is why you are so wide of the mark, King, when you think a thief, or an old worn-out slave, or a coward taken in battle, would do for the Great Offering. The best in the land is not too good for this office.'

The King's forehead, I saw, was clammy now. The holiness and horror of divine things were continually thickening in that room. All at once, the Fox burst out, 'Master, Master, let me speak.'

'Speak on,' said the King.

'Do you not see, Master,' said the Fox, 'that the Priest is talking nonsense? A shadow is to be an animal which is also a goddess which is also a god, and loving is to be eating – a child of six would talk more sense. And a moment ago the victim of this abominable sacrifice was to be the Accursed, the wickedest person in the whole land, offered as a punishment. And now it is to be the best person in the whole land – the perfect victim – married to the god as a reward. Ask him which he means. It can't be both.'

If any hope had put up its head within me when the Fox began, it was killed. This sort of talk could do no good. I knew what had happened to the Fox; he had forgotten all his wiles, even, in a way, his love and fears for Psyche, simply because things such as the Priest had been saying put him beyond all patience. (I have noticed that all men, not only Greek men, if they have clear wits and ready tongues, will do the same.)

'We are hearing much Greek wisdom this morning, King,' said the Priest. 'And I have heard most of it before. I did not need a slave to teach it to me. It is very subtle. But it brings no rain and grows no corn; sacrifice does both. It does not even give them boldness to die. That Greek there is your slave because in some battle he threw down his arms and let them bind his hands and lead him away and sell him, rather than take a spear-thrust in his heart. Much less does it give them understanding of holy things. They demand to see such things clearly, as if the gods were no more than letters written in a book. I, King, have dealt with the gods for three generations of men, and I know that they dazzle our eyes and flow in and out of one another like eddies on a river, and nothing that is said clearly can be said truly about them. Holy places are dark places. It is life and strength, not knowledge and words, that we get in them. Holy wisdom is not clear and thin like water, but thick and dark like blood. Why should the Accursed not be both the best and the worst?'

The Priest looked more and more like a gaunt bird as he was speaking; not unlike the bird-mask that lay on his knees. And his voice, though not loud, was no longer shaking like an old man's. The Fox sat hunched together with his eyes fixed on the table. The taunt about being taken in war, I guessed, had been hot iron to some old ulcer in his soul. Certainly, I would that moment have hanged the Priest and made the Fox a king if power had been given me; but it was easy to see on which side the strength lay.

'Well, well,' says the King, quickening his stride, 'this may be all very true. I'm neither priest nor Greekling, I. They used to tell me I was the King. What's next?'

'Being determined, therefore,' said the Priest, 'to seek out the Accursed, we cast the holy lots. First we asked whether the Accursed were to be found among the commons. And the lots said No.'

'Go on, go on,' said the King.

'I cannot speak quickly,' said the Priest. 'I have not breath for it now. Then we asked if it was among the Elders. And the lots said No.'

There was a queer mottled colour on the King's face now; his fear and his anger were just on the balance, and neither he nor anyone else knew at all which would have the victory.

'Then we asked if it were among the nobles. And the lots said No.'

'And then you asked?' says the King, stepping up close to him and speaking low. And the Priest says:

'Then we asked, Is it in the King's house? And the lots said Yes.'

'Aye,' says the King, rather breathless. 'Aye. I thought as much. I smelled it from the beginning. Treason in a new cloak. Treason.' Then louder, 'Treason.' Next moment he was at the door, roaring, 'Treason! Treason! Guards! Bardia! Where are my guards? Where's Bardia? Send Bardia.'

There was a rush and a jingle of iron and guards came running. Bardia their captain, a very honest man, came in.

'Bardia,' said the King, 'there are too many people about my door today. Take what men you think you need and fall on those rebels who are standing with spears out yonder over against the gate. Don't scatter them but kill. Kill, do you see? Don't leave one of them alive.'

'Kill the temple guards, King?' said Bardia, looking from the King to the Priest and back at the King again.

'Temple rats! Temple pimps!' shouted the King. 'Are you deaf? Are you afraid? I – I—' And his rage choked him.

'This is foolishness, King,' said the Priest. 'All Glome is in arms. There is a party of armed men at every door of the palace by now. Your guards are outnumbered ten to one. And they won't fight. Would you fight against Ungit, Bardia?'

'Will you slink away from my side, Bardia?' said the King. 'After eating my bread? You were glad of my shield to cover you one day at Varin's wood.'

'You saved my head that day, King,' said Bardia. 'I'll never say otherwise. May Ungit send me to do as much for you (there may be chance enough next spring). I'm for the King of Glome and the gods of Glome while I live. But if the King and the gods fall out, you great ones must settle it between you. I'll not fight against powers and spirits.'

'You – you girl!' squealed the King, his voice shrill as a pipe. Then, 'Be off! I'll talk with you presently.' Bardia saluted and went out; you could see from his face that he cared no more for the insult than a great dog cares for a puppy making believe to fight him.

The moment the door was shut, the King, all quiet and white again, whipped out his dagger (the same he killed the page with the night Psyche was born), stepped up to the Priest's chair in three long cat's strides, shouldered the two girls away, and had the point of the dagger through the Priest's robes and his skin.

'You old fool,' he said. 'Where is your plot now? Eh? Can you feel my bodkin? Does it tickle you? As that? Or that? I can drive it into your heart as quickly or slowly as I please. The wasps may be outside but I've the queen wasp here. And now, what'll you do?'

I have never (to speak of things merely mortal) seen anything more wonderful than the Priest's stillness. Hardly any man can be quite still when a finger, much less a dagger, is thrust into the place between two ribs. The Priest was. Even his hands did not tighten on the arms of the chair. Never moving his head or changing his voice, he said:

'Drive it in, King, swift or slow, if it pleases you. It will make no difference. Be sure the Great Offering will be made whether I am dead or living. I am here in the strength of Ungit. While I have breath I am Ungit's voice. Perhaps longer. A priest does not wholly die. I may visit your palace more often, both by day and night, if you kill me. The others will not see me. I think you will.'

This was the worst yet. The Fox had taught me to think – at any rate to speak – of the Priest as of a mere schemer and a politic man who put into the mouth of Ungit whatever might most increase his own power and lands or most harm his enemies. I saw it was not so. He was sure of Ungit. Looking at him as he sat with the dagger pricking him and his blind eyes unwinking, fixed on the King, and his face like an eagle's face, I was sure too. Our real enemy was not a mortal. The room was full of spirits, and the horror of holiness.

With a beastly noise, all groan and snarl in one, my father turned away from the Priest and flung himself into his own chair and leaned back and passed his hands over his face and ruffled his hair like a man who is tired.

'Go on. Finish it,' he said.

'And then,' said the Priest, 'we asked whether it was the King who was the Accursed, and the lots said No.'

'What?' said the King. And this is the greatest shame I have to tell of in my whole life. His face cleared. He was only a hair's breadth from smiling. I had thought that he had seen the arrow pointed at Psyche all along, had been afraid for her, fighting for her. He had not thought of her at all, nor of any of us. Yet I am credibly told that he was a brave enough man in a fight.

'Go on,' he said. But his voice was changed; freshened, as if ten years of his age had slipped off him.

'The lot fell on your youngest daughter, King. She is the Accursed. The Princess Istra must be the Great Offering.'

'It's very hard,' said the King; gravely and glum enough, but I saw he was acting. He was hiding the greatness of his own relief. I went mad. In a moment I was at his feet, clinging to his knees as suppliants cling, babbling out I didn't know what, weeping, begging, calling him Father – a name I never used before. I believe he was glad of the diversion. He tried to kick me away, and when I still clung to his feet, rolling over and over, bruised in face and breast, he rose, gathered me up by my shoulders, and flung me from him with all his power.

'You!' he shouted. 'You! You to raise your voice among the counsels of men? You trull, you quean, you mandrake root! Have I not woes and miseries and horrors enough heaped upon me by the gods but you also must come scrabbling and clawing me? and it would have come to biting in a trice if I'd let you. There's vixen in your face this minute. For two straws I'd have you to the guardhouse to be flogged. Name of Ungit! are gods and priests and lions and shadowbrutes and traitors and cowards not enough unless I'm plagued with girls as well?'

I think he felt better the longer he railed. The breath had been knocked out of me so that I could neither sob nor rise nor speak. Somewhere above my head I heard them talking on, making all the plans for Psyche's death. She was to be kept prisoner in her chamber – or no, better in the room with five sides, which was more secure. The temple guards would reinforce our own; the whole house must be guarded, for the people were weathercocks – there might be a change of mood, even a rescue. They were talking soberly and prudently like men providing for a journey or a feast. Then I lost myself in darkness and a roaring noise.

6

'She's coming to her mind again,' said my father's voice. 'Take that side of her, Fox, and we'll get her to the chair.' The two of them were lifting me; my father's hands were gentler than I expected. I have found since that a soldier's hands often are. The three of us were alone.

'Here, lass, this'll do you good,' he said when they had put me in the chair, holding a cup of wine to my lips. 'Faugh, you're spilling it like a baby. Take it easy. So; that's better. If there's a bit of raw meat still to be had in this dog-hole of a palace, you must lay it on your bruises. And look, daughter, you shouldn't have crossed me like that. A man can't have women (and his own daughters, what's worse) meddling in business.'

There was a sort of shame about him; whether for beating me or for giving up Psyche without a struggle, who knows? He seemed to me now a very vile, pitiable king.

He set down the cup. 'The thing has to be done,' he said. 'Screaming and scrabbling won't help. Why, the Fox here was just telling me it's done even in your darling Greeklands – which I begin to think I was a fool ever to let you hear of.'

'Master,' said the Fox, 'I had not finished telling you. It is very true that a Greek king sacrificed his own daughter. But afterwards his wife murdered him, and his son murdered the wife, and Those Below drove the son mad.'

At this the King scratched his head and looked very blank. 'That's just like the gods,' he muttered. 'Drive you to do a thing and then punish you for doing it. The comfort is I've no wife or son, Fox.'

I had got my voice again now. 'King,' I said, 'you can't mean to do it. Istra is your daughter. You can't do it. You have not even tried to save her. There must be some way. Surely between now and the day—'

'Listen to her!' says the King. 'You fool, it's tomorrow they offer her.'

I was within an inch of fainting again. To hear this was as bad as to hear that she must be offered at all. As bad? It was worse. I felt that I had had no sorrow till now. I felt that if she could be spared only for a month – a month, why, a month was like eternity – we should all be happy.

'It's better so, dear,' whispered the Fox to me in Greek. 'Better for her and for us.'

'What are you mumbling about, Fox?' said the King. 'You both look at me as if I were some sort of two-headed giant they frighten children with, but what'd you have me do? What would you do yourself, Fox, with all your cleverness, if you were in my place?'

'I'd fight about the day first. I'd get a little time somehow. I'd say the Princess was at the wrong time of the month to be a bride. I'd say I'd been warned in a dream not to make the Great Offering till the new moon. I'd bribe men to swear that the Priest had cheated over the lots. There's half a dozen men across the river who hold land from him and don't love their landlord. I'd make a party. Anything to gain time. Give me ten days and I'd have a secret messenger to the King of Phars. I'd offer him all he wants without war – offer him anything if he'd come in and save the Princess – offer him Glome itself and my own crown.'

'What?' snarled the King. 'Be a little less free with other men's wealth, you'd best.'

'But, Master, I'd lose not only my throne but my life to save the Princess, if I were a king and a father. Let us fight. Arm the slaves and promise them their freedom if they play the man. We can make a stand, we of your household, even now. At the worst, we should all die innocent. Better than going Down Yonder with a daughter's blood on your hands.'

The King flung himself once more into his chair and began speaking with a desperate patience, like a teacher to a very stupid child (I had seen the Fox do it with Redival).

'I am a King. I have asked you for counsel. Those who counsel kings commonly tell them how to strengthen or save their kingship and their land. That is what counselling a king means. And your counsel is that I should throw my crown over the roof, sell my country to Phars, and get my throat cut. You'll tell me next that the best way to cure a man's headache is to cut off his head.'

'I see, Master,' said the Fox. 'I ask your pardon. I had forgotten that your own safety was the thing we must work for at all costs.' I, who knew the Fox so well, could see such a look in his face that he could not have done the King much more dishonour if he had spat on him. Indeed I had often seen him look at the King like that, and the King never knew. I was determined he should know something now.

'King,' said I, 'the blood of the gods is in us. Can such a house as ours bear the shame? How will it sound if men say when you are dead that you took shelter behind a girl to save your own life?'

'You hear her, Fox, you hear her,' said the King. 'And then she wonders that I black her eyes! I'll not say mar her face, for that's impossible. Look, mistress, I'd be sorry to beat you twice in a day, but don't try me too far.' He leaped up and began pacing the floor again.

'Death and scabs!' he said. 'You'd make a man mad. Anyone'd think it was *your* daughter they were giving to the Brute. Sheltering behind a girl, you say. No one seems to remember whose girl she is. She's mine; fruit of my own body. My loss. It's I who have a right to rage and blubber if anyone has. What did I beget her for if I can't do what I think best with my own? What is it to you? There's some cursed cunning that I haven't yet smelled out behind all your sobbing and scolding. You're not asking me to believe that any woman, let alone such a fright as you, has much love for a pretty half-sister. It's not in nature. But I'll sift you yet.'

I don't know whether he really believed this or not, but it is possible he did. He could believe anything in his moods, and everyone in the palace knew more than he about the life of us girls.

'Yes,' he said, more quietly now. 'It's I who should be pitied. It's I who am asked to give up part of myself. But I'll do my duty. I'll not ruin the land to save my own girl. The pair of you have talked me into making too much work about it. It has happened before. I'm sorry for the girl. But the Priest's right. Ungit must have her due. What's one girl – why, what would one man be – against the safety of us all? It's only sense that one should die for many. It happens in every battle.'

Wine and passion had brought my strength back. I rose from my chair and found that I could stand.

'Father,' said I. 'You are right. It is fit that one should die for the people. Give me to the Brute instead of Istra.'

The King, without a word, came up to me, took me (softly enough) by the wrist and led me the whole length of the room, to where his great mirror hung. You might wonder that he did not keep it in his bedchamber, but the truth is he was too proud of it for that and wanted every stranger to see it. It had been made in some distant land and no king in our parts had one to match it. Our common mirrors were false and dull; in this you could see your perfect image. As I had never been in the Pillar Room alone, I had never looked in it. He stood me before it and we saw our two selves, side by side.

'Ungit asked for the best in the land as her son's bride,' he said. 'And you'd give her *that*.' He held me there a full minute in silence; perhaps he thought I would weep or turn my eyes away. At last he said, 'Now be off. A man can't keep pace with your moods today. Get the beefsteak for your face. The Fox and I must be busy.'

As I came out of the Pillar Room I first noticed the pain in my side; I had twisted myself somehow in my fall. But I forgot it again when I saw how, in that little time, our house had changed. It seemed crowded. All the slaves, whether they had anything to do or not, were walking about and gathering in knots, wearing looks of importance; chattering under their breath, too, with a sort of mournful cheerfulness. (They always will when there's great news in a house, and now it troubles me not at all.) There were many of the temple guard lounging in the porch; some temple girls sitting in the hall. From the courtyard came the smell of incense, and sacrifice was going on. Ungit had taken the house; the reek of holiness was everywhere.

At the foot of the staircase who should meet me but Redival, running to me all in tears, and a great babble pouring out of her mouth – 'Oh Sister, Sister, how dreadful! Oh, poor Psyche! It's only Psyche, isn't it? They're not going to do it to all of us, are they? I never thought – I didn't mean any harm – it wasn't I – and oh, oh, oh....'

I put my face close up to hers and said very low but distinctly, 'Redival: if there is one single hour when I am queen of Glome, or even mistress of this house, I'll hang you by the thumbs at a slow fire till you die.'

'Oh, cruel, cruel,' sobbed Redival. 'How can you say such things, and when I'm so miserable already? Sister, don't be angry, comfort me—'

I pushed her away from me and passed on. I had known Redival's tears ever since I could remember. They were not wholly feigned; nor much dearer than ditchwater. I know now, as I felt sure then, that she had carried tattle about Psyche to the house of Ungit, and that with malice. It's likely enough she meant less mischief than she had done (she never knew how much she meant) and was now, in her fashion, sorry; but a new brooch, much more a new lover, would have had her drying her eyes and laughing in no time.

As I came to the top of the stairs (for we have upper rooms and even galleries in the palace; it is not like a Greek house) I was a little out of breath and the pain in my side came on me worse. I seemed to be somewhat lame in one foot too. I went on with all the haste I could to that five-sided room where they had shut Psyche up. The door was bolted on the outside (I have used that room for a courteous prison myself) and an armed man stood before it. It was Bardia.

'Bardia,' I panted, 'let me in. I must see the Princess Istra.'

He looked at me kindly but shook his head. 'It can't be done, Lady,' he said.

'But, Bardia, you can lock us both in. There's no way out but the door.'

'That's how all escapes begin, Lady. I am sorry for you and for the other Princess, but it can't be done. I'm under the sternest orders.'

'Bardia,' I said, with tears, my left hand to my side (for the pain was bad now), 'It's her last night alive.'

He looked away from me and said again, 'I'm sorry.'

I turned from him without another word. Though his was the kindest face (always excepting the Fox) I had seen that day, for the moment I hated him more than my father or the Priest or even Redival. What I did next shows how near I was to madness. I went as fast as I could to the Bedchamber. I knew the King had arms there. I took a plain, good sword, drew it, looked at it, and weighed it in my hand. It was not at all too heavy for me. I felt the edges and the point; they were what I then thought sharp, though a smart soldier would not have called them so. Quickly I was back at Psyche's door. Even in my woman's rage I had man enough about me to cry out, 'Ward yourself, Bardia,' before I fell on him.

It was of course the craziest attempt for a girl who had never had a weapon in her hand before. Even if I had known my work, the lame foot and the pain in my side (to breathe deep was agony) disabled me. Yet I made him use some of his skill; chiefly, of course, because he was not fighting to hurt me. In a moment he had twisted my sword out of my grip. I stood before him, with my hand pressed harder than ever to my side, all in a muck sweat and a tremble. His brow was dry and his breathing unchanged; it had been as easy as that for him. The knowledge that I was so helpless came over me like a new woe, or gathered the other woe up into itself. I burst into utterly childish weeping; like Redival.

'It's a thousand pities, Lady, that you weren't a man,' said Bardia. 'You've a man's reach and a quick eye. There are none of the recruits would do as well at a first attempt; I'd like to have the training of you. It's a thousand—'

'Ah, Bardia, Bardia,' I sobbed, 'if only you'd killed me. I'd be out of my misery now.'

'No, you wouldn't,' said he. 'You'd be dying, not dead. It's only in tales that a man dies the moment the steel's gone in and come out. Unless of course you swap off his head.'

I could talk no more at all now. The whole world seemed to me to be in my weeping.

'Curse it,' said Bardia, 'I can't bear this.' There were tears in his own eyes now; he was a very tender man. 'I wouldn't mind so much if the one weren't so brave and the other so beautiful. Here! Lady! Stop it. I'll risk my life, and Ungit's wrath too.'

I gazed at him, but was still not able to speak.

'I'd give my own life for the girl in there, if it would do any good. You may have wondered why I, the captain of the guard, am standing here like a common sentry. I wouldn't let anyone else do it. I thought if the poor girl called, or if I had to go in to her for any reason, I'd be homelier for her than a stranger. She sat on my knees when she was little. ... I wonder do the gods know what it feels like to be a man.'

'You'll let me in?' I said.

'On one condition, Lady. You must swear to come out when I knock. It's quiet up here now, but there'll be comings and goings later. There'll be two temple girls coming to her presently; I was warned of that. I'll give you as long as I can. But I must be sure of your coming out when I give the sign. Three knocks – like this.'

'I'll come out at once when you do that.'

'Swear it, Lady; here on my sword.'

I swore it. He looked to left and right, did back the bolt, and said, 'Quick. In you go. Heaven comfort you both.'

7

The window in that room is so small and high up that men need lights there at noon. That is why it can serve as a prison; it was built as the second story of a tower which my great-grandfather began and never finished.

Psyche sat upon the bed with a lamp burning beside her. Of course I was at once in her arms and saw this only in a flash; but the picture – Psyche, a bed, and a lamp – is everlasting.

Long before I could speak she said, 'Sister, what have they done to you? Your face, your eye! He has been beating you again.' Then I realised somewhat slowly that all this time she had been petting and comforting me as if it were I who was the child and the victim. And this, even in the midst of the great anguish, made its own little eddy of pain. It was so unlike the sort of love that used to be between us in our happy times.

She was so quick and tender that she knew at once what I was thinking, and at once she called me *Maia*, the old baby's name that the Fox had taught her. It was one of the first words she ever learned to say.

'Maia, Maia, tell me. What has he done to you?'

'Oh, Psyche,' said I, 'what does it matter? If only he had killed me! If only they would take me instead of you!'

But she would not be put off. She forced the whole tale out of me (how could one deny her?) wasting on it the little time we had.

'Sister, no more,' I said at last. 'What is it to me? What is he to either of us? I'll not shame your mother or mine to say he's not our father. If so, the name *father* is a curse. I'll believe now that he would hide behind a woman in a battle.'

And then (it was a kind of terror to me) she smiled. She had wept very little, and mostly, I think, for love and pity of me. Now she sat tall and queenly and still. There was no sign about her of coming death, except that her hands were very cold.

'Orual,' she said, 'you make me think I have learned the Fox's lessons better than you. Have you forgotten what we are to say to ourselves every morning? "Today I shall meet cruel men, cowards and liars, the envious and the drunken. They will be like that because they do not know what is good from what is bad. This is an evil which has fallen upon them not upon me. They are to be pitied, not—"' She was speaking with a loving mimicry of the Fox's voice; she could do this as well as Batta did it badly.

'Oh child, how can—' But I was choked again. All she was saying seemed to me so light, so far away from our sorrow. I felt we ought not to be talking that way, not now. What I thought it would be better to talk of, I did not know.

'Maia,' said Psyche. 'You must make me a promise. You'll not do anything outrageous? You'll not kill yourself? You mustn't, for the Fox's sake. We have been three loving friends.' (Why must she say bare *friends*?) 'Now it's only he and you; you must hold together and stand the closer. No, Maia, you must. Like soldiers in a hard battle.'

'Oh, your heart is of iron,' I said.

'As for the King, give him my duty – or whatever is proper. Bardia is a prudent and courteous man. He'll tell you what dying girls ought to say to fathers. One would not seem rude or ignorant at the last. But I can send the King no other message. The man is a stranger to me; I know the henwife's baby better than him. And for Redival—'

'Send her your curse. And if the dead can—'

'No, no. She also does what she doesn't know.'

'Not even for you, Psyche, will I pity Redival, whatever the Fox says.'

'Would you like to be Redival? What? No? Then she's pitiable. If I am allowed to give my jewels as I please, you must keep all the things that you and I have really loved. Let her have all that's big and costly and doesn't matter. You and the Fox take what you please.'

I could bear no more for a while, so I laid my head down in her lap and wept. If only she would so have laid her head in mine!

'Look up, Maia,' she said presently. 'You'll break my heart, and I to be a bride.' She could bear to say that. I could not bear to hear it.

'Orual,' she said, very softly, 'we are the blood of the gods. We must not shame our lineage. Maia, it was you who taught me not to cry when I fell.'

'I believe you are not afraid at all,' said I; almost, though I had not meant it to sound so, as if I were rebuking her for it.

'Only of one thing,' she said. 'There is a cold doubt, a horrid shadow, in some corner of my soul. Supposing – supposing – how if there were no god of the Mountain and even no holy Shadowbrute, and those who are tied to the tree only die, day by day, from thirst and hunger and wind and sun, or are eaten piecemeal by the crows and catamountains? And it is this – oh, Maia, Maia …'

And now she did weep and now she was a child again. What could I do but fondle and weep with her? But this is a great shame to write; there was now (for me) a kind of sweetness in our misery for the first time. This was what I had come to her in her prison to do.

She recovered before I did. She raised her head, queenlike again, and said, 'But I'll not believe it. The Priest has been with me. I never knew him before. He is not what the Fox thinks. Do you know, Sister, I have come to feel more and more that the Fox hasn't the whole truth. Oh, he has much of it. It'd be dark as a dungeon within me but for his teaching. And yet ... I can't say it properly. He calls the whole world a city. But what's a city built on? There's earth beneath. And outside the wall? Doesn't all the food come from there as well as all the dangers? ... things growing and rotting, strengthening and poisoning, things shining wet ... in one way (I don't know which way) more like, yes, even more like the House of—'

'Yes, of Ungit,' said I. 'Doesn't the whole land smell of her? Do you and I need to flatter gods any more? They're tearing us apart ... oh, how shall I bear it? ... and what worse can they do? Of course the Fox is wrong. He knows nothing about her. He thought too well of the world. He thought there were no gods, or else (the fool!) that they were better than men. It never entered his mind – he was too good – to believe that the gods are real, and viler than the vilest man.'

'Or else,' said Psyche, 'they are real gods but don't really do these things. Or even – mightn't it be – they do these things and the things are not what they seem to be? How if I am indeed to wed a god?'

She made me, in a way, angry. I would have died for her (this, at least, I know is true) and yet, the night before her death, I could feel anger. She spoke so steadily and thoughtfully; as if we had been disputing with the Fox, up behind the pear trees, with hours and days still before us. The parting between her and me seemed to cost her so little.

'Oh, Psyche,' I said, almost in a shriek, 'what can these things be except the cowardly murder they seem? To take you – you whom they have wor-shipped and who never hurt so much as a toad – to make you food for a monster ...'

You will say – I have said it many thousand times to myself – that, if I saw in her any readiness to dwell on the better part of the Priest's talk and to think she would be a god's bride more than a Brute's prey, I ought to have fallen in with her and encouraged it. Had I not come to her to give comfort, if I could? Surely not to take it away. But I could not rule myself. Perhaps it was a sort of pride in me, a little like her own; not to blind our eyes, not to hide terrible things; or a bitter impulse in anguish itself to say, and to keep on saying, the worst.

'I see,' said Psyche in a low voice. 'You think it devours the offering. I mostly think so myself. Anyway, it means death. Orual, you didn't think I was such a child as not to know that? How can I be the ransom for all Glome unless I die? And if I am to go to the god, of course it must be through death. That way, even what is strangest in the holy sayings might be true. To be eaten and to be married to the god might not be so different. We don't understand. There must be so much that neither the Priest nor the Fox knows.'

This time I bit my lip and said nothing. Unspeakable foulness seethed in my mind; did she think the Brute's lust better than its hunger? To be mated with a worm, or a giant eft, or a spectre?

'And as for death,' she said, 'why, Bardia there (I love Bardia) will look on it six times a day and whistle a tune as he goes to find it. We have made little use of the Fox's teaching if we're to be scared by death. And you know, Sister, he has sometimes let out that there were other Greek masters than those he follows himself; masters who have taught that death opens a door out of a little, dark room (that's all the life we have known before it) into a great, real place where the true sun shines and we shall meet—'

'Oh, cruel, cruel!' I wailed. 'Is it nothing to you that you leave me here alone? Psyche; did you ever love me at all?'

'Love you? Why, Maia, what have I ever had to love save you and our grandfather the Fox?' (But I did not want her to bring even the Fox in now.) 'But, Sister, you will follow me soon. You don't think any mortal life seems a long thing to me tonight? And how would it be better if I had lived? I suppose I should have been given to some king in the end; perhaps such another as our father. And there you can see again how little difference there is between dying and being married. To leave your home – to lose you, Maia, and the Fox – to lose one's maidenhead – to bear a child – they are all deaths. Indeed, indeed, Orual, I am not sure that this which I go to is not the best.'

'This!'

'Yes. What had I to look for if I lived? Is the world – this palace, this father – so much to lose? We have already had what would have been the best of our time. I must tell you something, Orual, which I never told to anyone, not even you.'

I know now that this must be so even between the lovingest hearts. But her saying it that night was like stabbing me.

'What is it?' said I, looking down at her lap where our four hands were joined.

'This,' she said, 'I have always – at least, ever since I can remember – had a kind of longing for death.'

'Ah, Psyche,' I said, 'have I made you so little happy as that?'

'No, no, no,' she said. 'You don't understand. Not that kind of longing. It was when I was happiest that I longed most. It was on happy days when we were up there on the hills, the three of us, with the wind and the sunshine ... where you couldn't see Glome or the palace. Do you remember? The colour and the smell, and looking across at the Grey Mountain in the distance? And because it was so beautiful, it set me longing, always longing. Somewhere else there must be more of it. Everything seemed to be saying, Psyche come! But I couldn't (not yet) come and I didn't know where I was to come to. It almost hurt me. I felt like a bird in a cage when the other birds of its kind are flying home.'

She kissed both my hands, flung them free, and stood up. She had her father's trick of walking to and fro when she talked of something that moved her. And from now till the end I felt (and this horribly) that I was losing her already, that the sacrifice tomorrow would only finish something that had already begun. She was (how long had she been, and I not to know?) out of my reach; in some place of her own.

Since I write this book against the gods, it is just that I should put into it whatever can be said against myself. So let me set this down; as she spoke I felt, amid all my love, a bitterness. Though the things she was saying gave her (that was plain enough) courage and comfort, I grudged her that courage and comfort. It was as if someone or something else had come in between us. If this grudging is the sin for which the gods hate me, it is one I have committed.

'Orual,' she said, her eyes shining. 'I am going, you see, to the Mountain. You remember how we used to look and long? And all the stories of my gold and amber house, up there against the sky, where we thought we should never really go? The greatest King of all was going to build it for me. If only you could believe it, Sister! No, listen. Do not let grief shut up your ears and harden your heart—'

'Is it *my* heart that is hardened?'

'Never to me; nor mine to you at all. But listen. Are these things so evil as they seemed? The gods will have mortal blood. But they say whose. If they had chosen any other in the land, that would have been only terror and cruel misery. But they chose me. And I am the one who has been made ready for it ever since I was a little child in your arms, Maia. The sweetest thing in all my life has been the longing – to reach the Mountain, to find the place where all the beauty came from—'

'And that was the sweetest? Oh, cruel, cruel. Your heart is not of iron; stone, rather,' I sobbed. I don't think she even heard me.

'— my country, the place where I ought to have been born. Do you think it all meant nothing, all the longing? The longing for home? For indeed it now feels not like going, but like going back. All my life the god of the Mountain has been wooing me. Oh, look up once at least before the end and wish me joy. I am going to my lover. Do you not see now—?'

'I only see that you have never loved me,' said I. 'It may well be you are going to the gods. You are becoming cruel like them.'

'Oh, Maia!' cried Psyche, tears at last coming into her eyes again. 'Maia, I—'

Bardia knocked on the door. No time for better words, no time to unsay anything. Bardia knocked again, and louder. My oath on his sword, itself like a sword, was upon us.

So, the last, spoiled embrace. Those are happy who have no such in their memory. For those who have – would they endure that I should write of it?

8

As soon as I was out in the gallery my pains, which I had not perceived while I was with Psyche, came strongly back upon me. My grief, even, was deadened for a while, though my wits became very sharp and clear. I was determined to go with Psyche to the Mountain and the Holy Tree, unless they bound me with chains. I even thought I might hide up there and set her free when the Priest and the King and all the rest had turned to come home. 'Or if there is a real Shadowbrute,' I thought, 'and I cannot save her from it, I'll kill her with my own hand before I'll leave her to its clutches.' To do all this I knew I must eat and drink and rest. (It was now nearly twilight and I was still fasting.) But first of all I must find out when their murder, their Offering, was to be. So I limped, holding my side, along the gallery and found an old slave, the King's butler, who was able to tell me all. The procession, he said, was to leave the palace an hour before sunrise. Then I went to my own chamber and told my women to bring me food. I sat down to wait till it came. A great dullness and heaviness crept over me; I thought and felt nothing, except that I was very cold. When the food came I could not eat, though I tried to force myself to it; it was like putting cloth in my mouth. But I drank; a little of the small beer which was all they had to give me, and then (for my stomach rose against the beer) a great deal of water. I must have been almost sleeping before I finished, for I remember that I knew I was in some great sorrow but I could not recall what it was.

They lifted me into the bed (I shrank and cried out a little at their touch) and I fell at once into a dead stupidity of sleep; so that it seemed only a heartbeat later that they were waking me – two hours before sunrise, as I had bidden them. I woke screaming, for all my sore places had stiffened while I slept and it was like hot pincers when I tried to move. One eye had closed up so that I might as well have been blind on that side. When they found how much they hurt me in raising me from the bed, they begged me to lie still. Some said it was useless for me to rise, for the King had said that neither of the Princesses should go to the Offering. One asked if she should bring Batta to me. I told that one, with bitter words, to hold her tongue, and if I had had the strength I would have hit her; which would have been ill done, for she was a good girl. (I have always been fortunate with my women since first I had them to myself and out of the reach of Batta's meddling.)

They dressed me somehow and tried to make me eat. One even had a little wine for me; stolen, I guess, from a flagon intended for the King. They were all weeping; I was not.

Dressing me (so sore I was) had taken a great time, so that I had hardly swallowed the wine before we heard the music beginning: temple music, Ungit's music, the drums and the horns and rattles and castanets, all holy, deadly; dark, detestable, maddening noises.

'Quick!' said I. 'It's time. They're going. Oh, I can't get up. Help me, girls. No, quicker! Drag me, if need be. Take no heed of my groaning and screaming.'

They got me with great torture as far as the head of the staircase. I could now see down into the great hall between the Pillar Room and the Bedchamber. It was ablaze with torches, and very crowded. There were many guards. There were some girls of noble blood veiled and chapleted like a bride's party. My father was there in very splendid robes. And there was a great bird-headed man. By the smell and the smoke there seemed to have been much killing already, at the altar in the courtyard. (Food for the gods must always be found somehow, even when the land starves.) The great gateway was opened. I could see cold, early twilight through it. Outside, priests and girls were singing. There must have been a great mob of the rabble too; in the pauses you could hear (who can mistake it?) their noise. No herd of other beasts, gathered together, has so ugly a voice as Man.

For a long time I could not see Psyche at all. The gods are cleverer than we and can always think of some vileness it never entered our heads to fear. When at last I saw her, that was the worst of all. She sat upright on an open litter between the King and the Priest. The reason I had not known her was that they had painted and gilded and be-wigged her like a temple girl. I could not even tell whether she saw me or not. Her eyes, peering out of the heavy, lifeless mask which they had made of her face, were utterly strange; you couldn't even see in what direction she was looking.

It is, in its way, admirable, this divine skill. It was not enough for the gods to kill her, they must make her father the murderer. It was not enough to take her from me, they must take her from me three times over, tear out my heart three times. First her sentence; then her strange, cold talk last night; and now this painted and gilded horror to poison my last sight of her. Ungit had taken the most beautiful thing that was ever born and made it into an ugly doll.

They told me afterwards that I tried to start going down the stairway, and fell. They carried me to my bed.

For many days after that I was sick, and most of them I do not remember. I was not in my right mind, and slept (they tell me) not at all. My ravings – what I can recall of them – were a ceaseless torture of tangled diversity, yet also of sameness. Everything changed into something else before you could understand it, yet the new thing always stabbed you in the very same place. One thread ran through all the delusions. Now mark yet again the cruelty of the gods. There is no escape from them into sleep or madness, for they can pursue you into them with dreams. Indeed you are then most at their mercy. The nearest thing we have to a defence against them (but there is no real defence) is to be very wide awake and sober and hard at work, to hear no music, never to look at earth or sky, and (above all) to love no one. And now, finding me heart-shattered for Psyche's sake, they made it the common burden of all my fantasies that Psyche was my greatest enemy. All my sense of intolerable wrong was directed against her. It was she who hated me; it was on her that I wanted to be revenged. Sometimes she and Redival and I were all children together, and then Psyche and Redival would drive me away and put me out of the game and stand with their arms linked laughing at me. Sometimes I was beautiful and had a lover who looked (absurdly) a little like poor, eunuch'd Tarin or a little like Bardia (I suppose because his was the last man's face, almost, that I had seen before I fell ill). But on the very threshold of the bridal chamber, or from the very bedside, Psyche, wigged and masked and no bigger than my forearm, would lead him away with one finger. And when they got to the door they would turn round and mock and point at me. But these were the clearest visions. More often it was all confused and dim – Psyche throwing me down high precipices, Psyche (now very like the King, but still Psyche) kicking me and dragging me by the hair, Psyche with a torch or a sword or a whip pursuing me over vast swamps and dark mountains; I running to save my life. But always wrong, hatred, mockery, and my determination to be avenged.

The beginning of my recovery was when the visions ceased and left behind them only a settled sense of some great injury that Psyche had done me, though I could not gather my wits to think what it was. They say I lay for hours saying, 'Cruel girl. Cruel Psyche. Her heart is of stone.' And soon I was in my right mind again and knew how I loved her and that she had never willingly done me any wrong; though it hurt me somewhat that she should have found time, at our last meeting of all, talking so little of me, to talk so much about the god of the Mountain, and the King, and the Fox, and Redival, and even Bardia.

Soon after that I was aware of a pleasant noise that had already been going on a long time.

'What is it?' I asked (and was astonished at the weak croak of my voice).

'What is what, child?' said the voice of the Fox; and I knew somehow that he had been sitting by my bed for many hours.

'The noise, Grandfather. Above our heads.'

'That is the rain, dear,' he said. 'Give thanks to Zeus for that and for your own recovery. And I – but you must sleep again. And drink this first.' I saw the tears on his face as he gave me the cup.

I had no broken bones, the bruises were gone, and my other pains with them. But I was very weak. Weakness, and work, are two comforts the gods have not taken from us. I'd not write it (it might move them to take these also away) except that they must know it already. I was too weak now to feel much grief or anger. These days, before my strength came back, were almost happy. The Fox was very loving and tender (and much weakened himself) and so were my women. I was loved; more than I had thought. And my sleeps were sweet now and there was much rain and, between-whiles, the kind south wind blowing in at the window; and sunshine. For a long time we never spoke of Psyche. We talked, when we talked at all, of common things.

They had much to tell me. The weather had changed the very day after my sickness began. The Shennit was full again. The breaking of the drought had come too late to save the crops (for the most part; one or two fields put up a little) but garden stuff was growing. Above all, the grass was reviving wonderfully; we should save far more of the cattle than we had hoped. And the fever was clean gone. My own sickness had been of another kind. And birds were coming back to Glome, so that every woman whose husband could shoot with a bow or set a snare might soon have something in the pot.

These things I heard of from the women as well as from the Fox. When we were alone he told me other news. My father was now, while it lasted, the darling of his people. It seemed (this was how we first came round to the matter nearest our hearts) he had been much pitied and praised at the Great Offering. Up there at the holy Tree he had wailed and wept and torn his robes and embraced Psyche countless times (he had never done it before) but said again and again that he would not withhold his heart's dearest when the good of the people called for her death. The whole crowd was in tears, as the Fox had been told; he himself, as a slave and an alien, had not been there.

'Did you know, Grandfather,' said I, 'that the King was such a mountebank?' (We were talking in Greek of course.)

'Not wholly that, child,' said the Fox. 'He believed it while he did it. His tears are no falser – or truer – than Redival's.'

Then he went on to tell me of the great news from Phars. A fool in the crowd had said the King of Phars had thirteen sons. The truth is he had begotten eight, whereof one died in childhood. The eldest was simple and could never rule, and the King (as some said their laws allowed him) had named Argan, the third, as his successor. And now, it seemed, his second son, Trunia, taking it ill to be put out of the succession – and, doubtless, fomenting some other discontents such as are never far to seek in any land –

had risen in rebellion, with a strong following, to recover what he called his right. The upshot was that all Phars was likely to be busy with civil war for a twelvemonth at least, and both parties were already as soft as butter towards Glome, so that we were safe from any threat in that quarter.

A few days later when the Fox was with me (often he could not be, for the King needed him) I said:

'Grandfather, do you still think that Ungit is only lies of poets and priests?'

'Why not, child?'

'If she were indeed a goddess what more could have followed my poor sister's death than has followed it? All the dangers and plagues that hung over us have been scattered. Why, the wind must have changed the very day after they had—' I found, now, I could not give it a name. The grief was coming back with my strength. So was the Fox's.

'Cursed chance, cursed chance,' he muttered, his face all screwed up, partly in anger and partly to keep back his tears (Greek men cry easily as women). 'It is these chances that nourish the beliefs of barbarians.'

'How often, Grandfather, you have told me there's no such thing as chance?'

'You're right. It was an old trick of the tongue. I meant that all these things had no more to do with that murder than with anything else. They and it are all part of the same web, which is called Nature, or the Whole. That south-west wind came over a thousand miles of sea and land. The weather of the whole world would have to have been different from the beginning if that wind was not to blow. It's all one web; you can't pick threads out nor put them in.'

'And so,' said I, raising myself on my elbow, 'she died to no purpose. If the King had waited a few days later we could have saved her, for all would have begun to go well of itself. And this you call comfort?'

'Not this. Their evil-doing was vain and ignorant, as all evil deeds are. This is our comfort, that the evil was theirs, not hers. They say there was not a tear in her eye, nor did so much as her hand shake, when they put her to the Tree. Not even when they turned away and left her did she cry out. She died full of all things that are really good; courage, and patience, and – and – Aiai! Aiai – oh Psyche, oh my little one—' Then his love got the better of his philosophy and he pulled his mantle over his head and at last, still weeping, left me.

Next day he said, 'You saw yesterday, Daughter, how little progress I have made. I began to philosophise too late. You are younger and can go further. To love, and to lose what we love, are equally things appointed for our nature. If we cannot bear the second well, that evil is ours. It did not befall Psyche. If we look at it with reason's eyes and not with our passions, what good that life offers did she not win? Chastity, temperance, prudence, meekness, clemency, valour – and, though fame is froth, yet, if we should reckon it at all, a name that stands with Iphigenia's and Antigone's.'

Of course he had long since told me those stories, so often that I had them by heart, mostly in the very words of the poets. Nevertheless, I asked him to tell me them again; chiefly for his sake, for I was now old enough to know that a man (above all, a Greek man) can find comfort in words coming out of his own mouth. But I was glad to hear them too. These were peaceful, familiar things and would keep at bay the great desolation which now, with my returning health, was beginning to mix itself in every thought.

Next day, being then for the first time risen, I said to him, 'Grandfather, I have missed being Iphigenia. I can be Antigone.'

'Antigone? How, child?'

'She gave her brother burial. I too – there may be something left. Even the Brute would not eat bones and all. I must go up to the Tree. I will bring it … them … back if I can and burn them rightly. Or, if there's too much, I'll bury it up there.'

'It would be pious,' said the Fox. 'It would accord with custom, if not with Nature. If you can. It's late in the year now for going up the Mountain.'

'That's why it must be done speedily. I think it will be about five-and-twenty days before the earliest snow.'

'If you can, child. You have been very sick.'

'It's all I can do,' said I.

9

I was soon able to go about the house and in the gardens again. I did it in some stealth, for the Fox told the King I was still sick. Otherwise he would have had me off to the Pillar Room to work for him. He often asked, 'Where's that girl got to? Does she mean to slug abed for the rest of her life? I'll not feed drones in my hive for ever.' The loss of Psyche had not at all softened him to Redival and me. Rather, the opposite. 'To hear him talk,' said the Fox, 'you'd think no father ever loved a child better than he Psyche.' The gods had taken his darling and left him the dross: the young whore (that was Redival) and the hobgoblin (which was I). But I could guess it all without the Fox's reports to help me.

For my own part, I was busily thinking out how I could make my journey to the Tree on the Mountain and gather whatever might remain of Psyche. I had talked lightly enough of doing this and was determined that I would do it, but the difficulties were very great. I had never been taught to ride any beast, so I must go on foot. I knew it would take a man who knew the way about six hours to go from the palace to the Tree. I, a woman, and one who had to find her way, must allow myself eight at the least. And two more for the work I went to do; and, say, six for the journey home. There were sixteen hours in all. It could not be done in one stitch. I must reckon to lie out a night on the Mountain, and must take food (water I should find) and warm clothing. It could not be done till I recovered my full strength.

And in truth (as I now see) I had the wish to put off my journey as long as I could. Not for any peril or labour it might cost; but because I could see nothing in the whole world for me to do once it was accomplished. As long as this act lay before me, there was, as it were, some barrier between me and the dead desert which the rest of my life must be. Once I had gathered Psyche's bones, then, it seemed, all that concerned her would be over and done with. Already, even with the great act still ahead, there was flowing in upon me, from the barren years beyond it, a dejection such as I had never conceived. It was not at all like the agonies I had endured before and have endured since. I did not weep nor wring my hands. I was like water put into a bottle and left in a cellar; utterly motionless, never to be drunk, poured out, spilled or shaken. The days were endless. The very shadows seemed nailed to the ground, as if the sun no longer moved.

One day when this deadness was at its worst I came into the house by the little door that leads into a narrow passage between the guards' quarters and the dairy. I sat down on the threshold, less weary of body (for the gods, not out of mercy, have made me strong) than unable to find a reason for going a step further in any direction or for doing anything at all. A fat fly was crawling up the doorpost. I remember thinking that its sluggish crawling, seemingly without aim, was like my life, or even the life of the whole world. 'Lady,' said a voice behind me. I looked up; it was Bardia.

'Lady,' he said, 'I'll make free with you. I've known sorrow too. I have been as you are now; I have sat and felt the hours drawn out to the length of years. What cured me was the wars. I don't think there's any other cure.'

'But I can't go to the wars, Bardia,' said I.

'You can, almost,' he said. 'When you fought me outside the other Princess's door (peace be on her, the Blessed!) I told you you had a good eye and a good reach. You thought I was saying it to cheer you. Well, so perhaps I was. But it was true too. There's no one in the quarters, and there are blunt swords. Come in and let me give you a lesson.'

'No,' said I dully. 'I don't want to. What would be the use?'

'Use? Try it and see. No one can be sad while they're using wrist and hand and eye and every muscle of their body. That's truth, Lady, whether you believe it or not. As well, it would be a hundred shames not to train anyone who has such a gift for the sport as you look like having.'

'No,' said I. 'Leave me alone. Unless we can use sharps and you would kill me.'

'That's women's talk, by your favour. You'd never say that again once you'd seen it done. Come. I'll not leave off till you do.'

A big, kindly man, some years older than herself, can usually persuade even a sad and sullen girl. In the end I rose and went in with him.

'That shield is too heavy,' he said. 'Here's the one for you. Slip it on, thus. And understand from the outset; your shield is a weapon, not a wall. You're fighting with it every bit as much as your sword. Watch me, now. You see the way I twist my shield – make it flicker like a butterfly. There'd be arrows and spears and sword points flying off it in every direction if we were in a hot engagement. Now: here's your sword. No, not like that. You want to grip it firm, but light. It's not a wild animal that's trying to run away from you. That's better. Now, your left foot forward. And don't look at my face, look at my sword. It isn't my face is going to fight you. And now, I'll show you a few guards.'

He kept me at it for a full half-hour. It was the hardest work I'd ever done, and, while it lasted, one could think of nothing else. I said not long before that work and weakness are comforters. But sweat is the kindest creature of the three; far better than philosophy, as a cure for ill thoughts.

'That's enough,' said Bardia. 'You shape very well. I'm sure now I can make a swordsman of you. You'll come again tomorrow? But your dress hampers you. It would be better if you could wear something that came only to your knee.'

I was in such a heat that I went across the passage into the dairy and drank a bowl of milk. It was the first food or drink that I had really relished ever since the bad times began. While I was in there, one of the other soldiers (I suppose he had had a sight of what we were doing) came into the passage and said something to Bardia. Bardia replied, I couldn't hear what. Then he spoke louder: 'Why, yes, it's a pity about her face. But she's a brave girl and honest. If a man was blind and she weren't the King's daughter, she'd make him a good wife.' And that is the nearest thing to a love-speech that was ever made me.

I had my lesson with Bardia every day after that. And I knew soon that he had been a good doctor to me. My grief remained, but the numbness was gone and time moved at its right pace again.

Soon I told Bardia how I wished to go to the Grey Mountain, and why.

'That's very well thought of, Lady,' he said. 'I'm ashamed I have not done it myself. We all owe the Blessed Princess that much at the least. But there's no need for you to go. I'll go for you.'

I said I would go.

'Then you must go with me,' he said. 'You'd never find the place by yourself. And you might meet a bear or wolves or a mountainy man, an outlaw, that'd be worse. Can you ride a horse, Lady?'

'No, I've never been taught.'

He wrinkled up his brow, thinking. 'One horse will do,' he said, 'I in the saddle and you behind me. And it won't take six hours getting up; there's a shorter way. But the work we have to do might take long enough. We'll need to sleep a night on the mountain.'

'Will the King let you be absent so long, Bardia?'

He chuckled. 'Oh, I'll spin the King a story easily enough. He isn't with us as he is with you, Lady. For all his hard words he's no bad master to soldiers, shepherds, huntsmen, and the like. He understands them and they him. You see him at his worst with women and priests and politic men. The truth is, he's half afraid of them.' This was very strange to me.

Six days after that, I and Bardia set out at the milking-time of the morning, the day being so cloudy that it was almost as dark as full night. No one in the palace knew of our going except the Fox and my own women. I had on a plain black cloak with a hood, and a veil over my face. Under the mantle I wore the short smock that I used for my fencing bouts, with a man's belt and a sword, this time a sharp one, at my side. 'Most likely we'll meet nothing worse than a wild cat or a fox,' Bardia had said. 'But no one, man or maid, ought to go weaponless up the hills.' I sat with both my legs on one side of the horse, and a hand on Bardia's girdle. With the other, I held on my knees an urn.

It was all silent in the city, but for the clatter of our own beast's hooves, though here and there you would see a light in a window. A sharp rain came on us from behind our backs as we went down from the city to the ford of the Shennit, but it ceased as we were crossing the water, and the clouds began to break. There was still no sign of dawn ahead, for it was in that direction the foul weather was packing off.

We passed the house of Ungit on our right. Its fashion is thus: great, ancient stones, twice the height of a man and four times the thickness of a man, set upright in an egg-shaped ring. These are very ancient, and no one knows who set them up or brought them into that place, or how. In between the stones it is filled up with brick to make the wall complete. The roof is thatched with rushes and not level but somewhat domed, so that the whole thing is a roundish hump, most like a huge slug lying on the field. This is a holy shape, and the priests say it resembles, or (in a mystery) that it really is, the egg from which the whole world was hatched or the womb in which the whole world once lay. Every spring the Priest is shut into it and fights, or makes believe to fight, his way out through the western door; and this means that the new year is born. There was smoke going up from it as we passed, for the fire before Ungit is always alight.

I found my mood changed as soon as we had left Ungit behind; partly because we were now going into country I had never known, and partly because I felt as if the air were sweeter as we got away from all that holiness. The Mountain, now bigger ahead of us, still shut out the brightening of the day; but when I looked back and saw, beyond the city, those hills where Psyche and I and the Fox used to wander, I perceived that it was already morning there. And further off still, the clouds in the western sky were beginning to turn pale rose.

We were going up and down little hills, but always more up than down, on a good enough road, with grass-lands on each side of us. There were dark woods on our left, and presently the road bent towards them. But here Bardia left the road and took to the grass.

'That's the Holy Road,' he said, pointing to the woods. 'That's the way they took the Blessed (peace be on her). Our way will be steeper and shorter.'

We now went for a long time over grass, gently but steadily upward, making for a ridge so high and so near that the true Mountain was quite out of sight. When we topped it, and stood for a while to let the horse breathe, everything was changed. And my struggle began.

We had come into the sunlight now, too bright to look into, and warm (I threw back my cloak). Heavy dew made the grass jewel-bright. The Mountain, far greater yet also far further off than I expected, seen with the sun hanging a hand-breath above its topmost crags, did not look like a solid thing. Between us and it was a vast tumble of valley and hill, woods and cliffs, more little lakes than I could count. To left and right, and behind us, the whole coloured world with all its hills was heaped up and up to the sky, with, far away, a gleam of what we call the sea (though it is not to be compared with the Great Sea of the Greeks). There was a lark singing; but for that, huge and ancient stillness.

And my struggle was this. You may well believe that I had set out sad enough; I came on a sad errand. Now, flung at me like frolic or insolence, there came as if it were a voice – no words, but if you made it into words it would be, 'Why should your heart not dance?' It's the measure of my folly that my heart almost answered, Why not? I had to tell myself over like a lesson the infinite reasons it had not to dance. My heart to dance? Mine whose love was taken from me, I, the ugly princess who must never look for other love, the drudge of the King, the jailer of hateful Redival, perhaps to be murdered or turned out as a beggar when my father died (for who knew what Glome would do then?). And yet, it was a lesson I could hardly keep in my mind. The sight of the huge world put mad ideas into me; as if I could wander away, wander for ever, see strange and beautiful things, one after the other to the world's end.

The freshness and wetness all about me (I had seen nothing but drought and withered things for many months before my sickness) made me feel that I had misjudged the world; it seemed kind, and laughing, as if its heart also danced. Even my ugliness I could not quite believe in. Who can *feel* ugly when the heart meets delight? It is as if, somewhere inside, within the hideous face and bony limbs, one is soft, fresh, lissom and desirable.

We had stood on the ridge only for a short time. But for hours later, while we went up and down, winding among great hills, often dismounting and leading the horse, sometimes on dangerous edges, the struggle went on.

Was I not right to struggle against this fool-happy mood? Mere seemliness, if nothing else, called for it. I would not go laughing to Psyche's burial. If I did, how should I ever again believe that I had loved her? Reason called for it. I knew the world too well to believe this sudden smiling. What woman can have patience with the man who can be yet again deceived by his doxy's fawning after he has thrice proved her false? I should be just like such a man if a mere burst of fair weather, and fresh grass after a long drought, and health after sickness, could make me friends again with this god-haunted, plague-breeding, decaying, tyrannous world. I had seen. I was not a fool. I did not know then, however, as I do now, the strongest reason for distrust. The gods never send us this invitation to delight so readily or so strongly as when they are preparing some new agony. We are their bubbles; they blow us big before they prick us.

But I held my own without that knowledge. I ruled myself. Did they think I was nothing but a pipe to be played on as their moment's fancy chose?

The struggle ended when we topped the last rise before the real Mountain. We were so high now that, though the sun was very strong, the wind blew bitterly cold. At our feet, between us and the Mountain, lay a cursed black valley: dark moss, dark peat-bogs, shingle, great boulders, and screes of stone sprawling down into it from the Mountain – as if the Mountain had sores and these were the stony issue from them. The great mass of it rose up (we tilted our heads back to look at it) into huge knobbles of stone against the sky, like an old giant's back teeth. The face it showed us was really no steeper than a roof, except for certain frightful cliffs on our left, but it looked as if it went up like a wall. It too was now black. Here the gods ceased trying to make me glad. There was nothing here that even the merriest heart could dance for.

Bardia pointed, ahead to our right. There the Mountain fell away in a smooth sweep to a saddle somewhat lower than the ground we stood on, but still with nothing behind it but the sky. Against the sky, on the saddle, stood a single leafless tree.

We went down into the black valley on our own feet, leading the horse, for the going was bad and stones slipped away from under us until, at the lowest place, we joined the sacred road (it came into the valley through the northern end, away to our left). We were so near now that we did not mount again. A few loops of the road led us up to the saddle and, once more, into the biting wind.

I was afraid, now that we were almost at the Tree. I can hardly say of what, but I know that to find the bones, or even the body, would have set my fear at rest. I believe I had a senseless child's fear that she might be neither living nor dead.

And now we were there. The iron girdle, and the chain that went from it about the gaunt trunk (there was no bark on the Tree) hung there and made a dull noise from time to time as they moved with the wind. There were no bones, nor rags of clothing, nor marks of blood, nor anything else.

'How do you read these signs, Bardia?' said I.

'The god's taken her,' said he, rather pale and speaking low (he was a god-fearing man). 'No natural beast would have licked his plate so clean. There'd be bones. A beast – any but the holy Shadow-brute itself – couldn't have got the whole body out of the irons. And it would have left the jewels. A man, now – but a man couldn't have freed her, unless he had tools with him.'

I had not thought of our journey's being so vain; nothing to do, nothing to gather. The emptiness of my life was to begin at once.

'We can search about a bit,' I said; foolishly, for I had no hope of finding anything.

'Yes, yes, Lady. We can search about,' said Bardia. I knew it was only his kindness that spoke.

And so we did; working round in circles, he one way and I the other, with our eyes on the ground; very cold, one's cloak flapping till leg and cheek smarted with the blows of it.

Bardia was ahead of me now, eastward and further across the saddle, when he called out. I had to thrust back the hair that was whipping about my face before I could see him. I rushed to him; half-flying, for the westwind made a sail of my cloak. He showed me what he had found – a ruby.

'I never saw her wear such a stone,' said I.

'She did though, Lady. On her last journey. They had put their own holy gear on her. The straps of the sandals were red with rubies.'

'Oh, Bardia! Then somebody – something – carried her thus far.'

'Or maybe carried only the sandals. A jackdaw'd do it.'

'We must go on; further on this line.'

'Carefully, Lady. If we must, I'll do it. You'd best stay behind.'

'Why, what's to fear? And anyway, I'll not stay behind.'

'I don't know that anyone's been over the saddle. At the Offering, even the priests come no further than the Tree. We are very near the bad part of the Mountain; I mean, the holy part. Beyond the Tree it's all gods' country, they say.'

'Then it is you must stay behind, Bardia. They can't do worse to me than they've done already.'

'I'll go where you go, Lady. But let's talk less of them, or not at all. And first, I must go back and get the horse.'

He went back (and for a moment out of sight – I stood alone on the edge of the perilous land) to where he had tied the horse to a little stunted bush. Then he rejoined me, leading it, very grave, and we went forward.

'Carefully,' he said again. 'We may find we're on the top of a cliff any moment.' And indeed it looked, for the next few paces, as if we were walking straight into the empty sky. Then suddenly we found we were on the brow of a steep slope; and at the same moment the sun – which had been overcast ever since we went down into the black valley – leaped out.

It was like looking down into a new world. At our feet, cradled amid a vast confusion of mountains, lay a small valley bright as a gem, but opening southward on our right. Through that opening there was a glimpse of warm, blue lands, hills and forests, far below us. The valley itself was like a cleft in the Mountain's southern chin. High though it was, the year seemed to have been kinder in it than down in Glome. I never saw greener turf. There was gorse in bloom, and wild vines, and many groves of flourishing trees; and plenty of bright water – pools, streams, and little cataracts. And when, after casting about a little to find where the slope would be easiest for the horse, we began descending, the air came up to us warmer and sweeter every minute. We were out of the wind now and could hear ourselves speak; soon we could hear the very chattering of the streams and the sound of bees.

'This may well be the secret valley of the god,' said Bardia, his voice hushed.

'It's secret enough,' said I.

Now we were at the bottom, and so warm that I had half a mind to dip my hands and face in the swift, amber water of the stream which still divided us from the main of the valley. I had already lifted my hand to put aside my veil when I heard two voices cry out; one, Bardia's. I looked. A quivering shock of feeling that has no name (but nearest terror) stabbed through me from head to foot. There, not six feet away, on the far side of the river, stood Psyche.

10

W hat I babbled, between tears and laughter, in the first wildness of my joy (the water still between us) I don't know. I was recalled by Bardia's voice.

'Careful, Lady. It may be her wraith. It may – ai! ai! – it is the bride of the god. It is a goddess.' He was deadly white, and bending down to throw earth on his forehead.

You could not blame him. She was so brightface, as we say in Greek. But I felt no holy fear. What? – I to fear the very Psyche whom I had carried in my arms and taught to speak and to walk? She was tanned by sun and wind, and clothed in rags; but laughing, her eyes like two stars, her limbs smooth and rounded, and (but for the rags) no sign of beggary or hardship about her.

'Welcome, welcome, welcome,' she was saying. 'Oh, Maia, I have longed for this. It was my only longing. I knew you would come. Oh, how happy I am! And good Bardia, too. It was he that brought you? Of course; I might have guessed it. Come, Orual, you must cross the stream. I'll show you where it's easiest. But, Bardia – I can't bid you across. Dear Bardia, it's not—'

'No, no, Blessed Istra,' said Bardia (and I thought he was very relieved). 'I'm only a soldier.' Then, in a lower voice, to me, 'Will you go, Lady? This is a very dreadful place. Perhaps—'

'Go?' said I. 'I'd go if the river flowed with fire instead of water.'

'Of course,' said he. 'It's not with you as with us. You have gods' blood in you. I'll stay here with the horse. We're out of the wind and there's good grass for him here.'

I was already on the edge of the river.

'A little further up, Orual,' Psyche was saying. 'Here's the best ford. Go straight ahead off that big stone. Gently! make your footing sure. No, not to your left. It's very deep in places. This way. Now, one step more. Reach out for my hand.'

I suppose the long bedridden and indoors time of my sickness had softened me. Anyhow, the coldness of that water shocked all the breath out of me; and the current was so strong that, but for Psyche's hand, I think it would have knocked me down and rolled me under. I even thought, momentarily amid a thousand other things, 'How strong she grows. She'll be a stronger woman than ever I was. She'll have that as well as her beauty.'

The next was all a confusion – trying to talk, to cry, to kiss, to get my breath back, all together. But she led me a few paces beyond the river and made me sit in the warm heather and sat beside me; our four hands joined in my lap, just as it had been that night in her prison.

'Why, Sister,' she said merrily, 'you have found my threshold cold and steep! You are breathless. But I'll refresh you.'

She jumped up, went a little way off, and came back, carrying something; the little cool, dark berries of the Mountain, in a green leaf. 'Eat,' she said. 'Is it not food fit for the gods?'

'Nothing sweeter,' said I. And indeed I was both hungry and thirsty enough by now, for it was noon or later. 'But oh, Psyche, tell me how—'

'Wait!' said she. 'After the banquet, the wine.' Close beside us a little silvery trickle came out from among stones mossed cushion-soft. She held her two hands under it till they were filled and raised them to my lips.

'Have you ever tasted a nobler wine?' she said. 'Or in a fairer cup?'

'It is indeed a good drink,' said I. 'But the cup is better. It is the cup I love best in the world.'

'Then it's yours, Sister.' She said it with such a pretty air of courtesy, like a queen and hostess giving gifts, that the tears came into my eyes again. It brought back so many of her plays in childhood.

'Thank you, child,' said I. 'I hope it is mine indeed. But, Psyche, we must be serious; yes, and busy too. How have you lived? How did you escape? And oh – we mustn't let the joy of the moment put it out of our minds – what are we to do now?'

'Do? Why, be merry, what else? Why should our hearts not dance?'

'They do dance. Do you not think – why, I could forgive the gods themselves. I'll shortly be able to forgive Redival; perhaps. But how can – it will be winter in a month or less. You can't – Psyche, how have you kept alive till now? I thought, I thought—' But to think of what I had thought overcame me.

'Hush, Maia, hush,' said Psyche (once more it was she who was comforting me). 'All those fears are over. All's well. I'll make it well for you too; I'll not rest till you're as happy as I. But you haven't yet even asked me my story. Weren't you surprised to find this fair dwelling-place, and me living here; like this? Have you no wonder?'

'Yes, Psyche, I am overwhelmed in it. Of course I want to hear your story. Unless we should make our plans first.'

'Solemn Orual,' said Psyche mockingly. 'You were always one for plans. And rightly too, Maia, with such a foolish child as me to bring up. And well you did it.' With one light kiss she put all those days, all of my life that I cared for, behind us, and began her story.

'I wasn't in my right mind when we left the palace. Before the two temple girls began painting and dressing me they gave me a sweet, sticky stuff to drink – a drug, as I guess, for soon after I had swallowed it everything went dreamlike, and more and more so for a long time. And I think, Sister, they must always give that to those whose blood is to be poured over Ungit, and that's why we see them die so patiently. And the painting on my face helped the dreaminess too. It made my face stiff till it didn't seem to be my own face. I couldn't feel it was I who was being sacrificed. And then the music and incense and the torches made it more so. I saw you, Orual, at the top of the stairway, but I couldn't lift even a hand to wave to you; my arms were as heavy as lead. And I thought it didn't matter much, because you too would wake up presently and find it was all a dream. And in a sense it was, wasn't it? And you are nearly awake now. What? still so grave? I must wake you more.

'You'd think the cold air would have given me my mind back when we came out of the great gates, but the drug must have been still coming to its full power. I had no fear; nor joy either. Sitting there on that litter, up above the heads of all that crowd, was a strange enough thing anyway ... and the horns and the rattles were going on all the time. I don't know whether the journey up the mountain was long or short. Each bit of it was long; I noticed every pebble on the road, I looked long, long at every tree as we passed it. Yet the whole journey seemed to take hardly any time. Yet long enough for me to get some of my wits back. I began to know that something dreadful was being done to me. Then for the first time I wanted to speak. I tried to cry out to them that there was some mistake, that I was only poor Istra and it couldn't be me they meant to kill. But nothing more than a kind of grunting or babbling came out of my mouth. Then a great bird-headed man, or a bird with a man's body—'

'That would be the Priest,' said I.

'Yes. If he is still the Priest when he puts on his mask; perhaps he becomes a god while he wears it. Anyway, it said, "Give her some more," and one of the younger priests got on someone else's shoulders and put the sweet sticky cup to my lips again. I didn't want to take it, but, you know, Maia, it all felt so like the time you had the barber to take that thorn out of my hand long ago – you remember, you holding me tight, and telling me to be good, and that it'd all be over in a moment. Well, it was like that, so I felt sure I'd better do whatever I was told.

'The next thing I knew – really knew – was that I was off the litter and on the hot earth, and they were fastening me to the Tree with iron round my waist. It was the sound of the iron that cleared the last of the drug out of my mind. And there was the King, shrieking and wailing and tearing his hair.

And do you know, Maia, he actually looked at me, really looked, and it seemed to me he was then seeing me for the first time. But all I wished was that he would stop it and then he and all the rest would go away and leave me alone to cry. I wanted to cry now. My mind was getting clearer and clearer and I was terribly afraid. I was trying to be like those girls in the Greek stories that the Fox is always telling us about, and I knew I could keep it up till they were gone, if only they would go quickly.'

'Oh, Psyche, you say all's well now. Forget that terrible time. Go on quickly and tell me how you were saved. We have so much to talk about and arrange. There's no time—'

'Orual! There's all the time there is. Don't you *want* to hear my story?'

'Of course I do. I want to hear every bit. When we're safe and—'

'Where shall we ever be safe if we're not safe here? This is my home, Maia. And you won't understand the wonder and glory of my adventure unless you listen to the bad part. It wasn't very bad, you know.'

'It's so bad I can hardly bear to listen to it.'

'Ah, but wait. Well, at last they were gone, and there I was alone under the glare of the sky with the great baked, parched mountain all round me, and not one noise to be heard. There wasn't a breath of wind even by the Tree; you remember what the last day of the drought was like. I was already thirsty – the sticky drink had done that. Then I noticed for the first time that they had so bound me that I couldn't sit down. That was when my heart really failed me. I did cry then; oh, Maia, how badly I wanted you and the Fox! And all I could do was to pray, pray, pray to the gods that whatever was going to happen to me might happen soon. But nothing happened, except that my tears made me thirstier. Then, a very long time after that, things began gathering round me.'

'Things?'

'Oh, nothing dreadful. Only the mountain cattle at first. Poor lean things they were. I was sorry for them, for I thought they were as thirsty as I. And they came nearer and nearer in a great circle, but never very near, and mooed at me. And after that there came a beast that I had never seen before, but I think it was a lynx. It came right up close. My hands were free and I wondered if I would be able to beat it off. But I had no need to. After advancing and drawing back I don't know how many times (I think it began by fearing me as much as I feared it) it came and sniffed at my feet, and then it stood up with its forepaws on me and sniffed again. Then it went away. I was sorry it had gone; it was a kind of company. And do you know what I was thinking all this time?'

'What?'

'At first I was trying to cheer myself with all that old dream of my gold and amber palace on the Mountain … and the god … trying to believe it. But

I couldn't believe in it at all. I couldn't understand how I ever had. All that, all my old longings, were clean gone.'

I pressed her hands and said nothing. But inwardly I rejoiced. It might have been good (I don't know) to encourage that fancy the night before the Offering, if it supported her. Now, I was glad she had got over it. It was a thing I could not like; unnatural and estranging. Perhaps this gladness of mine is one of the things the gods have against me. They never tell.

'The only thing that did me good,' she continued 'was quite different. It was hardly a thought, and very hard to put into words. There was a lot of the Fox's philosophy in it; things he says about gods or "the divine nature"; but mixed up with things the Priest said too, about the blood and the earth and how sacrifice makes the crops grow. I'm not explaining it well. It seemed to come from somewhere deep inside me; deeper than the part that sees pictures of gold and amber palaces, deeper than fears and tears. It was shapeless, but you could just hold on to it; or just let it hold on to you. Then the change came.'

'What change?' I didn't know well what she was talking about, but I saw she must have her way and tell the story in her own fashion.

'Oh, the weather of course. I couldn't see it, tied the way I was, but I could feel it. I was suddenly cool. Then I knew the sky must be filling with clouds, behind my back, over Glome, for all the colours on the Mountain went out and my own shadow vanished. And then – that was the first sweet moment – a sigh of wind – westwind – came at my back. Then more and more wind; you could hear and smell and feel the rain drawing near. So then I knew quite well that the gods really are, and that I was bringing the rain. And then the wind was roaring (but it's too soft a sound to call it a roar) all round me; and rain. The Tree kept some of it off me; I was holding out my hands all the time and licking the rain off them, I was so thirsty. The wind got wilder and wilder. It seemed to be lifting me off the ground so that, if it hadn't been for the iron round my waist, I'd have been blown right away, up in the air. And then – at last – for a moment – I saw him.'

'Saw whom?'

'The westwind.'

'*Saw* it?'

'Not it; him. The god of the wind: Westwind himself.'

'Were you awake, Psyche?'

'Oh, it was no dream. One can't dream things like that, because one's never seen things like that. He was in human shape. But you couldn't mistake him for a man. Oh, Sister, you'd understand if you'd seen. How can I make you understand? You've seen lepers?'

'Well, of course.'

'And you know how healthy people look beside a leper?'

'You mean – healthier, ruddier than ever?'

'Yes. Now we, beside the gods, are like lepers beside us.'

'Do you mean this god was so red?'

She laughed and clapped her hands. 'Oh, it's no use,' she said. 'I see I've not given you the idea at all. Never mind. You shall see gods for yourself, Orual. It must be so; I'll make it so. Somehow. There must be a way. Look, this may help you. When I saw Westwind I was neither glad nor afraid (at first). I felt ashamed.'

'But what of? Psyche, they hadn't stripped you naked or anything?'

'No, no, Maia. Ashamed of looking like a mortal; ashamed of being a mortal.'

'But how could you help that?'

'Don't you think the things people are most ashamed of are the things they can't help?'

I thought of my ugliness and said nothing.

'And he took me,' said Psyche, 'in his beautiful arms which seemed to burn me (though the burning didn't hurt) and pulled me right out of the iron girdle – and that didn't hurt either and I don't know how he did it – and carried me up into the air, far up above the ground, and whirled me away. Of course he was invisible again almost at once. I had seen him only as one sees a lightning flash. But that didn't matter. Now I knew it was he, not it, I wasn't in the least afraid of sailing along in the sky; even of turning head over heels in it.'

'Psyche, are you sure this happened? You must have been dreaming!'

'And if it was a dream, Sister, how do you think I came here? It's more likely everything that had happened to me before this was a dream. Why, Glome and the King and old Batta seem to me very like dreams now. But you hinder my tale, Maia. So he carried me through the air and set me down softly. At first I was all out of breath and too bewildered to see where I was; for Westwind is a merry, rough god. (Sister, do you think young gods have to be taught how to handle us? A hasty touch from hands like theirs and we'd fall to pieces.) But when I came to myself – ah, can you think what a moment that was! – and saw the House before me; I lying at the threshold. And it wasn't, you see, just the gold and amber House I used to imagine. If it had been just that, I might indeed have thought I was dreaming. But I saw it wasn't. And not quite like any house in this land, nor quite like those Greek houses the Fox describes to us. Something new, never conceived of – but, there, you can see for yourself; and I'll show you over every bit of it in a moment. Why need I try to show it in words?

'You could see it was a god's house at once. I don't mean a temple where a god is worshipped. A god's house, where he lives. I would not for any wealth have gone into it. But I had to, Orual. For there came a voice – sweet? oh, sweeter than any music, yet my hair rose at it too – and do you know, Orual, what it said? It said, "Enter your house" – yes, it called it *my* house – "Psyche, the bride of the god."

'I was ashamed again, ashamed of my mortality, and terribly afraid. But it would have been worse shame and worse fear to disobey. I went, cold, small, and shaking, up the steps and through the porch and into the courtyard. There was no one to be seen. But then the voices came. All round me, bidding me welcome.'

'What kind of voices?'

'Like women's voices – at least, as like women's voices as the wind-god was like a man. And they said, "Enter, Lady, enter, Mistress. Do not be afraid." And they were moving as the speakers moved, though I could see no one; and leading me by their movements. And so they brought me into a cool parlour with an arched roof, where there was a table set out with fruit and wine. Such fruits as never – but you shall see. They said, "Refresh yourself, Lady, before the bath; after it comes the feast." Oh, Orual, how can I tell you what it felt like? I knew they were all spirits and I wanted to fall at their feet. But I daren't; if they made me mistress of that house, mistress I should have to be. Yet all the time I was afraid there might be some bitter mockery in it and that at any moment terrible laughter might break out and—'

'Ah!' said I, with a long breath. How well I understood.

'Oh, but I was wrong, Sister. Utterly wrong. That's part of the mortal shame. They gave me fruit, they gave me wine—'

'The voices gave you?'

'The spirits gave them to me. I couldn't see their hands. Yet, you know, it never looked as if the plates or the cup were moving of themselves. You could see that hands were doing it. And, Orual' (her voice grew very low) 'When I took the cup, I – I – *felt* the other hands, touching my own. Again, that burning, though without pain. That was terrible.' She blushed suddenly and (I wondered why) laughed. 'It wouldn't be terrible now,' she said. 'Then they had me to the bath. You shall see it. It is in the delicatest pillared court, open to the sky, and the water is like crystal and smells as sweet as ... as sweet as this whole valley. I was terribly shy when it came to taking off my clothes, but—'

'You said they were all she-spirits.'

'Oh, Maia, you still don't understand. This shame has nothing to do with He or She. It's the being mortal; being, how shall I say it? ... insufficient. Don't you think a dream would feel shy if it were seen walking about in the waking world? And then' (she was speaking more and more quickly now) 'they dressed me again – in the most beautiful things – and then came the banquet – and the music – and then they had me to bed – and the night came – and then – he.'

'He?'

'The Bridegroom … the god himself. Don't look at me like that, Sister. I'm your own true Psyche still. Nothing will change that.'

'Psyche,' said I, leaping up, 'I can't bear this any longer. You have told me so many wonders. If this is all true, I've been wrong all my life. Everything has to be begun over again. Psyche, it is true? You're not playing a game with me? Show me. Show me your palace.'

'Of course I will,' she said, rising. 'Let us go in. And don't be afraid whatever you see or hear.'

'Is it far?' said I.

She gave me a quick, astonished look. 'Far to where?' she said.

'To the palace, to this god's house.'

You have seen a lost child in a crowd run up to a woman whom it takes for its mother, and how the woman turns round and shows the face of a stranger, and then the look in the child's eyes, silent a moment before it begins to cry. Psyche's face was like that; checked, blank; happiest assurance suddenly dashed all to pieces.

'Orual,' she said, beginning to tremble, 'what do you mean?'

I too became frightened, though I had yet no notion of the truth. 'Mean?' said I. 'Where is the palace? How far have we to go to reach it?'

She gave one loud cry. Then, with white face, staring hard into my eyes, she said, 'But *this* is it, Orual! It is here! You are standing on the stairs of the great gate.'

If anyone could have seen us at that moment I believe he would have thought we were two enemies met for a battle to the death. I know we stood like that, a few feet apart, every nerve taut, each with eyes fixed on the other in a terrible watchfulness.

And now we are coming to that part of my history on which my charge against the gods chiefly rests; and therefore I must try at any cost to write what is wholly true. Yet it is hard to know perfectly what I was thinking while those huge, silent moments went past. By remembering it too often I have blurred the memory itself.

I suppose my first thought must have been, 'She's mad.' Anyway, my whole heart leaped to shut the door against something monstrously amiss; not to be endured. And to keep it shut. Perhaps I was fighting not to be mad myself.

But what I said when I got my breath (and I know my voice came out in a whisper) was simply, 'We must go away at once. This is a terrible place.'

Was I believing in her invisible palace? A Greek will laugh at the thought. But it's different in Glome. There the gods are too close to us. Up in the Mountain, in the very heart of the Mountain, where Bardia had been afraid and even the priests don't go, anything was possible. No door could be kept shut. Yes, that was it; not plain belief, but infinite misgiving – the whole world (Psyche with it) slipping out of my hands.

Whatever I meant, she misunderstood me horribly.

'So,' she said, 'you do see it after all.'

'See what?' I asked. A fool's question. I knew what.

'Why, this, this,' said Psyche. 'The gates, the shining walls—'

For some strange reason, fury – my father's own fury – fell upon me when she said that. I found myself screaming (I am sure I had not meant to scream), 'Stop it! Stop it at once! There's nothing there.'

Her face flushed. For once, and for the moment only, she too was angry. 'Well, feel it, feel it, if you can't see,' she cried. 'Touch it. Slap it. Beat your head against it. Here—' She made to grab my hands. I wrenched them free.

'Stop it, stop it, I tell you! There's no such thing. You're pretending. You're trying to make yourself believe it.' But I was lying. How did I know whether she really saw invisible things or spoke in madness? Either way, something hateful and strange had begun. As if I could thrust it back by brute force, I fell upon Psyche. Before I knew what I was doing I had her by the shoulders and was shaking her as one shakes a child.

She was too big for that now and far too strong (stronger than I ever dreamt she could be) and she flung my grip off in a moment. We fell apart, both breathing hard, now more like enemies than ever. All at once a look came into her face that I had never seen there; sharp, suspicious.

'But you tasted the wine. Where do you think I got it from?'

'Wine? What wine? What are you talking about?'

'Orual! The wine I gave you. And the cup. I gave you the cup. And where is it? Where have you hidden it?'

'Oh, have done with it, child. I'm in no mood for nonsense. There was no wine.'

'But I gave it to you. You drank it. And the fine honey-cakes. You said—'

'You gave me water, cupped in your hands.'

'But you praised the wine; and the cup. You said—'

'I praised your hands. You were playing a game (you know you were) and I fell in with it.'

She gaped open-mouthed, yet beautiful even then.

'So that was all,' she said slowly. 'You mean you saw no cup? tasted no wine?'

I wouldn't answer. She had heard well enough what I said.

Presently her throat moved as if she were swallowing something (oh, the beauty of her throat!). She pressed down a great storm of passion and her mood changed; it was now sober sadness, mixed with pity. She struck her breast with her clenched fist as mourners do.

'Aiai!' she mourned, 'so this is what he meant. You can't see it. You can't feel it. For you, it is not there at all. Oh, Maia … I am very sorry.'

I came almost to a full belief. She was shaking and stirring me a dozen different ways. But I had not shaken her at all. She was as certain of her palace as of the plainest thing; as certain as the Priest had been of Ungit when my father's dagger was between his ribs. I was as weak beside her as the Fox beside the Priest. This valley was indeed a dreadful place; full of the divine, sacred, no place for mortals. There might be a hundred things in it that I could not see.

Can a Greek understand the horror of that thought? Years after, I dreamed, again and again, that I was in some well-known place – most often the Pillar Room – and everything I saw was different from what I touched. I would lay my hand on the table and feel warm hair instead of smooth wood, and the corner of the table would shoot out a hot, wet tongue and lick me. And I knew, by the mere taste of them that all those dreams came from that moment when I believed I was looking at Psyche's palace and did not see it. For the horror was the same; a sickening discord, a rasping together of two worlds, like the two bits of a broken bone.

But in the reality (not in the dreams), with the horror, came the inconsolable grief. For the world had broken in pieces and Psyche and I were not in the same piece. Seas, mountains, madness, death itself, could not have removed her from me to such a hopeless distance as this. Gods, and again gods, always gods ... they had stolen her. They would leave us nothing. A thought pierced up through the crust of my mind like a crocus coming up in the early year. Was she not worthy of the gods? Ought they not to have her? But instantly great, choking, blinding waves of sorrow swept it away and, 'Oh!' I cried. 'It's not right. It's not right. Oh, Psyche, come back! Where are you? Come back, come back.'

She had me in her arms at once. 'Maia – Sister,' she said. 'I'm here. Maia, don't. I can't bear it. I'll—'

'Yes ... oh, my child ... I do feel you ... I hold you. But oh ... it's only like holding you in a dream. You are leagues away. And I ...'

She led me a few paces further and made me sit down on a mossy bank and sat beside me. With words and touch she comforted me all she could. And as, in the centre of a storm or even of a battle, I have known sudden stillness for a moment, so now for a little I let her comfort me. Not that I took any heed of what she was saying. It was her voice, and her love in her voice, that counted. Her voice was very deep for a woman's. Sometimes even now the way she used to say this or that word comes back to me as warm and real as if she were beside me in the room; the softness of it, the richness as of corn grown from a deep soil.

What was she saying: '... and perhaps, Maia, you too will learn how to see. I will beg and implore him to make you able. He will understand. He warned me when I asked for this meeting that it might not turn out all as I hoped. I never thought ... I'm only simple Psyche, as he calls me ... never thought he meant you wouldn't even see it. So he must have known. He'll tell us ...'

He? I'd forgotten this *him*; or, if not forgotten, left him out of account ever since she first told me we were standing at his palace gates. And now she was saying *he* every moment, no other name but *he*, the way young wives talk. Something began to grow colder and harder inside me. And this also is like what I've known in wars; when that which was only *they* or *the enemy* all at once becomes the man, two feet away, who means to kill you.

'Who are you talking of?' I asked; but I meant, 'Why do you talk of him to me? What have I to do with him?'

'But, Maia,' she said, 'I've told you all my story. My god, of course. My lover. My husband. The master of my house.'

'Oh, I can't bear it,' said I, leaping up. Those last words of hers, spoken softly and with trembling, set me on fire. I could feel my rage coming back. Then (like a great light, a hope of deliverance, it came to me) I asked myself why I'd forgotten, and how long I'd forgotten, that first notion of her being mad. Madness; of course. The whole thing must be madness. I had been nearly as mad as she to think otherwise. At the very name *madness* the air of that valley seemed more breathable, seemed emptied of a little of its holiness and horror.

'Have done with it, Psyche,' I said sharply. 'Where is this god? Where the palace is? Nowhere – in your fancy. Where is he? Show him to me? What is he like?'

She looked a little aside and spoke, lower than ever but very clear, and as if all that had yet passed between us were of no account beside the gravity of what she was now saying. 'Oh, Orual,' she said, 'not even I have seen him ... yet. He comes to me only in the holy darkness. He says I mustn't ... not yet ... see his face or know his name. I'm forbidden to bring any light into his ... our ... chamber.'

Then she looked up, and as our eyes met for a moment I saw in hers unspeakable joy.

'There's no such thing,' I said, loud and stern. 'Never say these things again. Get up. It's time—'

'Orual,' said she, now at her queenliest, 'I have never told you a lie in my life.'

I tried to soften my manner. Yet the words came out cold and stern. 'No, you don't mean to lie. You're not in your right mind, Psyche. You have imagined things. It's the terror and the loneliness ... and that drug they gave you. We'll cure you.'

'Orual,' said she.

'What?'

'If it's all my fancy, how do you think I have lived these many days? Do I look as if I'd fed on berries and slept under the sky? Are my arms wasted? Or my cheeks fallen in?'

I would, I believe, have lied to her myself and said they were, but it was impossible. From the top of her head to her naked feet she was bathed in life and beauty and well-being. It was as if they flowed over her or from her. It was no wonder Bardia had worshipped her as a goddess. The very rags served only to show more of her beauty; all the honey-sweetness, all the rose-red and the ivory, the warm, breathing perfection of her. She even seemed ('But that's impossible,' I thought) taller than before. And as my lie died unspoken she looked at me with something like mockery in her face. Her mocking looks had always been some of her loveliest.

'You see?' she said. 'It's all true. And that – no, listen, Maia – that's why all will come right. We'll make – he will make you able to see, and then—'

'I don't want it!' I cried, putting my face close to hers, threatening her almost, till she drew back before my fierceness. 'I don't want it. I hate it. Hate it, hate it, hate it. Do you understand?'

'But ... Orual ... why? What do you hate?'

'Oh, the whole – what can I call it? You know very well. Or you used to. This, this—' And then something she had said about *him* (hardly noticed till now) began to work horribly in my mind. 'This thing that comes to you in the darkness ... and you're forbidden to see it. Holy darkness, you call it. What sort of thing? Faugh! it's like living in the house of Ungit. Everything's dark about the gods ... I think I can smell the very ...' The steadiness of her gaze, the beauty of her, so full of pity yet in a way so pitiless, made me dumb for a moment. Then my tears broke out again. 'Oh, Psyche,' I sobbed, 'you're so far away. Do you even hear me? I can't reach you. Oh, Psyche, Psyche ... you loved me once ... come back. What have we to do with gods and wonders and all these cruel, dark things? We're women, aren't we? Mortals. Oh, come back to the world. Leave all that alone. Come back where we were happy.'

'But Orual – think. How can I go back? This is my home. I am a wife.'

'Wife? Of what?' said I, shuddering.

'If you only knew him,' she said.

'You like it! Oh, Psyche!'

She would not answer me. Her face flushed. Her face, and her whole body, were the answer.

'Oh, you ought to have been one of Ungit's girls,' said I savagely. 'You ought to have lived in there – in the dark – all blood and incense and muttering and the reek of burnt fat. To like it ... living among things you can't see ... dark and holy and horrible. Is it nothing to you at all that you are leaving me ... going into all that ... turning your back on all our love?'

'No, no, Maia. I can't go back to you. How could I? But you must come to me.'

'Oh, it's madness,' said I.

Was it madness or not? Which was true? Which would be worse? I was at that very moment when, if they meant us well, the gods would speak. Mark what they did instead.

It began to rain. It was only a light rain, but it changed everything for me.

'Here, child,' said I, 'come under my cloak. Your poor rags! Quick. You'll be wet through.'

She gazed at me wonderingly. 'How should I get wet, Maia,' she said, 'when we are sitting indoors with a roof above us? And "rags"? – but I forgot. You can't see my robes either.' The rain shone on her cheeks as she spoke.

If that wise Greek who is to read this book doubts that this turned my mind right round, let him ask his mother or wife. The moment I saw her, my child whom I had cared for all her life, sitting there in the rain as if it meant no more to her than it does to cattle, the notion that her palace and her god could be anything but madness was at once unbelievable. All those wilder misgivings, all the fluttering to and fro between two opinions, was (for that time) quite over. I saw in a flash that I must choose one opinion or the other; and in the same flash knew which I had chosen.

'Psyche,' I said (and my voice had changed). 'This is sheer raving. You can't stay here. Winter'll be on us soon. It'll kill you.'

'I cannot leave my home, Maia.'

'Home! There's no home here. Get up. Here – under my cloak.'

She shook her head, a little wearily.

'It's no use, Maia,' she said. 'I see it and you don't. Who's to judge between us?'

'I'll call Bardia.'

'I'm not allowed to let him in. And he wouldn't come.'

That, I knew, was true.

'Get up, girl,' I said. 'Do you hear me? Do as you're told. Psyche, you never disobeyed me before.'

She looked up (wetter every moment) and said, very tender in voice but hard as a stone in her determination, 'Dear Maia, I am a wife now. It's no longer you that I must obey.'

I learned then how one can hate those one loves. My fingers were round her wrist in an instant, my other hand on her upper arm. We were struggling.

'You *shall* come,' I panted. 'We'll force you away – hide you somewhere – Bardia has a wife, I believe – lock you up – his house – bring you to your senses.'

It was useless. She was far stronger than I. ('Of course,' I thought, 'they say mad people have double strength.') We left marks on one another's skin. There was a thick, tangled sort of wrestling. Then we were apart again; she staring with reproach and wonder, I weeping (as I had wept at her prison door), utterly broken with shame and despair. The rain had stopped. It had, I suppose, done all the gods wanted.

And now there was nothing at all left that I could do.

Psyche, as always, recovered herself first. She laid her hand – there was a smear of blood on it; was it possible I could have scratched her? – across my shoulder.

'Dear Maia,' she said, 'you have very seldom been angry with me in all the years I can remember. Don't begin now. Look, the shadows have already crept nearly all the way across the courtyard. I had hoped that before this we should have feasted together and been merry. But, there – you would have tasted only berries and cold water. Bread and onions with Bardia will be more comfort to you. But I must send you away before the sun sets. I promised that I would.'

'Are you sending me away for ever, Psyche? And with nothing?'

'Nothing, Orual, but a bidding to come again as soon as you can. I'll work for you here. There must be some way. And then – oh, Maia – then we shall meet here again with no cloud between us. But now you must go.'

What could I do but obey her? In body she was stronger than I; her mind I could not reach. She was already leading me back to the river, back through the desolate valley she called her palace. The valley looked hideous to me now. There was a chill in the air. Sunset flamed up behind the black mass of the saddle.

She clung to me at the very edge of the water. 'You will come back soon, soon?' she said.

'If I can, Psyche. You know how it is in our house.'

'I think,' said she, 'the King will not be much hindrance to you in the next few days. Now, there's no more time. Kiss me again. Dear Maia. And now, lean on my hand. Feel for the flat stone with your foot.'

Again I endured the sword-cut of the icy water. From this side I looked back.

'Psyche, Psyche,' I broke out. 'There's still time. Come with me. Anywhere – I'll smuggle you out of Glome – we'll go for beggarwomen all over the world – or you can go to Bardia's house – anywhere, anything you like.'

She shook her head. 'How could I?' she said. 'I'm not my own. You forget, Sister, that I'm a wife. Yet always yours. Oh, if you knew, you'd be happy. Orual, don't look so sad. All will be well; all will be better than you can dream of. Come again soon. Farewell for a little.'

She went away from me into her terrible valley, and out of sight finally among the trees. It was already deep twilight on my side of the river, close in under the shadow of the saddle.

'Bardia,' I called. 'Bardia, where are you?'

Bardia, a grey shape in the twilight, came towards me.
'You have left the Blessed?' he said.

'Yes,' said I. I could not talk to him about it, I thought.

'Then we must speak of how to spend our night. We'd never find a way for the horse up to the saddle now, and if we did, we'd have to go down again beyond the Tree into the other valley. We couldn't sleep on the saddle itself; too much wind. It'll be cold enough here, where we're sheltered, in an hour or so. I fear we must lie here. Not where a man'd choose; too near the gods.'

'What does it matter?' said I. 'It will do as well as anywhere else.'

'Then come with me, Lady. I've gathered a few sticks.'

I followed him; and in that silence (there was nothing now but the chattering of the stream, and it seemed louder than ever) we could hear, long before we came to the horse, the sound of the grass torn up by his teeth.

A man and a soldier is a wonderful creature. Bardia had chosen a place where the bank was steepest, and two rocks close together made the next best thing to a cave. The sticks were all laid and the fire alight, though still sputtering from the late rain. And he brought out of the saddle-bags things better than bread and onions; even a flask of wine. I was still a girl (which in many matters is the same thing as a fool) and it seemed to me shameful that, in all my sorrow and care, I was so eager for the food when it came. I never tasted better. And that meal in the firelight (which had made all the rest of the world a mere darkness as soon as it blazed up) seemed to me very sweet and homelike; mortal food and warmth for mortal limbs and bellies, no need (for a space) to think of gods and riddles and wonders.

When we had ended Bardia said, somewhat shamefacedly, 'Lady, you're not used to lying in the open and you might be cruelly chilled before day. So I'll make so free – for I'm no more to you, Lady, than one of your father's big dogs – as to say we'd best lie close, back to back, the way men do in the wars. And both cloaks over us.'

I said yes to that, and indeed no woman in the world has so little reason as I to be chary in such matters. Yet it surprised me that he should have said it; for I did not yet know that, if you are ugly enough, all men (unless they hate you deeply) soon give up thinking of you as a woman at all.

Bardia rested as soldiers do; dead asleep in two breaths but ready (I have seen him tested since) to be wide awake in one if need were. I think I never slept at all. First there was the hardness and slope of the ground, and after that the cold. And besides these, fast and whirling thoughts, wakeful as a madman's; about Psyche and my hard riddle, and also of another thing.

At last the cold grew so bitter that I slipped from under the cloak – its outer side was wet with dew by now – and began walking to and fro. And now, let that wise Greek whom I look to as my reader and the judge of my cause, mark well what followed.

It was already twilight and there was much mist in the valley. The pools of the river as I went down to it to drink (for I was thirsty as well as cold) seemed to be dark holes in the greyness. And I got my drink, ice-cold, and I thought it steadied my mind. But would a river flowing in the god's secret valley do that, or the clean contrary? This is another of the things to be guessed. For when I lifted my head and looked once more into the mist across the water, I saw that which brought my heart into my throat. There stood the palace; grey, as all things were grey in that hour and place, but solid and motionless, wall within wall, pillar and arch and architrave, acres of it, a labyrinthine beauty. As she had said, it was like no house ever seen in our land or age. Pinnacles and buttresses leaped up – no memories of mine, you would think, could help me to imagine them – unbelievably tall and slender, pointed and prickly as if stone were shooting out into branch and flower. No light showed from any window. It was a house asleep. And somewhere within it, asleep also, someone or something – how holy, or horrible, or beautiful or strange? – with Psyche in its arms. And I, what had I done and said? what would it do to me for my blasphemies and unbelievings? I never doubted that I must now cross the river, or try to cross it, even if it should drown me. I must lie on the steps at the great gate of that house and make my petition. I must ask forgiveness of Psyche as well as of the god. I had dared to scold her – dared, what was worse, to try to comfort her as a child – but all the time she was far above me; herself now hardly mortal, if what I saw was real. I was in great fear. Perhaps it was not real. I looked and looked to see if it would not fade or change. Then as I rose (for all this time I was still kneeling where I had drunk), almost before I stood on my feet, the whole thing had vanished. There was a tiny space of time in which I thought I could see how some swirlings of the mist had looked, for the moment, like towers and walls. But very soon, no likeness at all. I was staring simply into fog, and my eyes smarting with it.

And now, you who read, give judgement. That moment when I either saw or thought I saw the House – does it tell against the gods or against me? Would they (if they answered) make it a part of their defence? – say it was a sign, a hint, beckoning me to answer the riddle one way rather than the other? I'll not grant them that. What is the use of a sign which is itself only another riddle? It might – I'll allow so much – it might have been a true seeing; the cloud over my mortal eyes may have been lifted for a moment. It might not; what would be easier than for one distraught and not, maybe, so fully waking as she seemed, gazing at a mist, in a half-light, to fancy what had filled her thoughts for so many hours? What easier, even, than for the gods themselves to send the whole ferly for a mockery? Either way, there's divine mockery in it. They set the riddle and then allow a seeming that can't be tested and can only quicken and thicken the tormenting whirlpool of your guess-work. If they had an honest intention to guide us, why is their guidance not plain? Psyche could speak plain when she was three; do you tell me the gods have not yet come so far?

When I came back to Bardia he was just awake. I did not tell him what I had seen; until I wrote it in this book, I have never told it to anyone.

Our journey down was comfortless, for there was no sun and the wind was always in our faces, with scudding showers at times. I, sitting behind Bardia, got less of it than he.

We halted somewhere about noon, under the lee of a small wood, to eat what was left of our food. Of course my riddle had been working in my mind all morning, and it was there, out of the wind for a little and somewhat warmer (was Psyche warm? and worse weather soon to come) that I made up my mind to tell him the whole story; always excepting that moment when I looked into the mist. I knew he was an honest man, and secret, and (in his own way) wise.

He listened to it all very diligently but said nothing when I had ended. I had to draw his answer out of him.

'How do you read it all, Bardia?'

'Lady,' says he, 'it's not my way to say more than I can help of gods and divine matters. I'm not impious. I wouldn't eat with my left hand, or lie with my wife when the moon's full, or slit open a pigeon to clean it with an iron knife, or do anything else that's unchancy and profane, even if the King himself were to bid me. And as for sacrifices, I've always done all that can be expected of a man on my pay. But for anything more – I think the less Bardia meddles with the gods, the less they'll meddle with Bardia.'

But I was determined to have his counsel.

'Bardia,' I said, 'do you think my sister is mad?'

'Look, Lady,' he answered, 'there at your very first word you say what's better unsaid. Mad? the Blessed, mad? Moreover, we've seen her and anyone could tell she was in her right mind.'

'Then you think there really was a palace in the valley though I couldn't see it?'

'I don't well know what's *really*, when it comes to houses of gods.'

'And what of this lover who comes to her in the dark?'

'I say nothing about him.'

'Oh, Bardia – and among the spears men say you're the bravest! Are you afraid even to whisper your thought to me? I am in desperate need of counsel.'

'Counsel about what, Lady? What is there to do?'

'How do you read this riddle? Does anyone really come to her?'

'She says so, Lady. Who am I to give the Blessed One the lie?'

'Who is he?'

'She knows that best.'

'She knows nothing. She confesses she has never seen him. Bardia, what kind of a lover must this be who forbids his bride to see his face?'

Bardia was silent. He had a pebble between his thumb and forefinger and was drawing little scratches in the earth.

'Well?' said I.

'There doesn't seem to be much of a riddle about it,' he said at last.

'Then what's your answer?'

'I should say – speaking as mortal man, and likely enough the gods know better – I should say it was one whose face and form would give her little pleasure if she saw them.'

'Some frightful thing?'

'They called her the Bride of the Brute, Lady. But it's time we were riding again. We're not much better than half-way home.' He got up as he spoke.

His thought was not new to me; it was only the most horrible of the guesses which had been jostling and wrangling in my head. But the shock of hearing it from his lips lay in this, that I knew he had no doubt of it. I had come to know Bardia very well by now, and I could clearly see that all my difficulty in drawing out his answer came from his fear to say the thing and not from any uncertainty. As he had said, my riddle was no riddle to him. And it was as though all the people of Glome had spoken to me through him. As he thought, so, doubtless, every prudent, god-fearing man of our nation and our time would think too. My other guesses would not even come into their minds; here was the plain answer, clear as noonday. Why seek further? The god and the Shadowbrute were all one. She had been given to it. We had got our rain and water and (as seemed likely) peace with Phars. The gods, for their share, had her away into their secret places where something, so foul it would not show itself, some holy and sickening thing, ghostly or demonlike or bestial – or all three (there's no telling, with gods) – enjoyed her at its will.

I was so dashed that, as we continued our journey, nothing in me even fought against this answer of Bardia's. I felt as, I suppose, a tortured prisoner feels when they dash water in his face to rouse him from his faint, and the truth, worse than all his fantasies, becomes clear and hard and unmistakable again around him. It now seemed to me that all my other guesses had been only self-pleasing dreams spun out of my wishes, but now I was awake. There never had been any riddle; the worst was the truth, and truth as plain as the nose on a man's face. Only terror would have blinded me to it so long.

My hand stole to the sword-hilt under my cloak. Before my sickness, I had sworn that, if there were no other way, I would have killed Psyche rather than leave her to the heat or hunger of a monster. Now again I made a deep resolve. I was half frightened when I perceived what I was resolving. 'So it might come even to that,' my heart said; even to killing her (Bardia had already taught me the straight thrust, and where to strike). Then my tenderness came over me again, and I cried, never more bitterly, till I could not tell whether it was tears or rain that had most drenched my veil. (It was settling down to steadier rain as the day went on.) And in that tenderness I even asked myself why I should save her from the Brute, or warn her against the Brute, or meddle with the matter at all. 'She is happy,' said my heart. 'Whether it's madness or a god or a monster, or whatever it is, she is happy. You have seen that for yourself. She is ten times happier, there in the Mountain, than you could ever make her. Leave her alone. Don't spoil it. Don't mar what you've learnt you can't make.'

We were down in the foothills now, almost (if one could have seen through the rain) in sight of the house of Ungit. My heart did not conquer me. I perceived now that there is a love deeper than theirs who seek only the happiness of their beloved. Would a father see his daughter happy as a whore? Would a woman see her lover happy as a coward? My hand went back to the sword. 'She shall not,' I thought. Come what might, she should not. However things might go, whatever the price, by her death or mine or a thousand deaths, by fronting the gods 'beard to beard' as the soldiers say, Psyche should not – least of all, contentedly – make sport for a demon.

'We are king's daughters still,' I said.

I had hardly said it when I had good cause to remember, in a different fashion, that I was a king's daughter, and what king's. For now we were fording the Shennit again and Bardia (whose mind was ever on next things) was saying that when we had passed the city, and before we had reached the palace, I had best slip off the horse and go up that little lane – where Redival first saw Psyche being worshipped – and so through the gardens and into the women's quarters by the back way. For it was easy to guess how my father would take it if he found that I (supposed too sick to work with him in the Pillar Room) had journeyed to the Holy Tree.

I3

It was nearly dark in the palace, and as I came to my chamber door a voice said in Greek, 'Well?' It was the Fox, who had been squatting there, as my women told me, like a cat at a mouse-hole.

'Alive, Grandfather,' said I, and kissed him. Then, 'Come back as soon as you can. I am wet as a fish and must wash and change and eat. I'll tell you all when you come.'

When I was re-clothed and finishing my supper, his knock came to the door. I made him come and sit with me at table and poured him drink. There was no one with us but little Poobi, my dark-skinned maid, who was faithful and loving and knew no Greek.

'You said *alive*,' the Fox began, raising his cup. 'See. I make a libation to Zeus the Saviour.' He did it Greek fashion with a clever twist of the cup that lets fall just one drop.

'Yes, Grandfather, alive and well and says she's happy.'

'I feel as if my heart would crack for joy, child,' said he. 'You tell me things almost beyond belief.'

'You've had the sweet, Grandfather. There's sour to follow.'

'Let me hear it. All is to be borne.'

Then I told him the whole story, always excepting that one glimpse in the fog. It was dreadful to me to see the light die out of his face as I went on, and to feel that I was darkening it. And I asked myself, 'If you can hardly bear to do this, how will you bear to wipe out Psyche's happiness?'

'Alas, alas, poor Psyche!' said the Fox. 'Our little child! And how she must have suffered! Hellebore's the right medicine; with rest, and peace, and loving care ... oh, we'd bring her into frame again, I don't doubt it, if we could nurse her well. But how are we to give her all or any of the things she needs? My wits are dry, daughter. We must think, though, contrive. I wish I were Odysseus, aye, or Hermes.'

'You think, then, she's mad, for certain?'

He darted a quick glance at me. 'Why, daughter, what then have you been thinking?'

'You'll call it folly, I suppose. But you weren't with her, Grandfather. She talked so calmly. There was nothing disordered in her speech. She could laugh merrily. Her glance wasn't wild. If I'd had my eyes shut, I would have believed her palace was as real as this.'

'But, your eyes being open, you saw no such thing.'

'You don't think – not possibly – not as a mere hundredth chance – there might be things that are real though we can't see them?'

'Certainly I do. Such things as Justice, Equality, the Soul, or musical notes.'

'Oh, Grandfather, I don't mean things like that. If there are souls, could there not be soul-houses?'

He ran his hands through his hair with an old, familiar gesture of teacher's dismay.

'Child,' he said, 'you make me believe that, after all these years, you have never even begun to understand what the word *soul* means.'

'I know well enough what you mean by it, Grandfather. But do you, even you, know all? Are there no things – I mean *things* – but what we see?'

'Plenty. Things behind our backs. Things too far away. And all things, if it's dark enough.' He leaned forward and put his hand on mine. 'I begin to think, daughter, that if I can get that hellebore, yours had better be the first dose,' he said.

I had had half a thought, at the outset, of telling him about the ferly, my glimpse of the palace. But I couldn't bring myself to it; he was the worst hearer in the world for such a story. Already he was making me ashamed of half the things I had been thinking. And now a more cheering thought came to me.

'Then, perhaps,' said I, 'this lover who comes to her in darkness is also part of the madness.'

'I wish I could believe it,' said the Fox.

'Why not, Grandfather?'

'You say she's plump and rosy? not starveling?'

'Never better.'

'Then who's fed her all this time?'

I was silenced.

'And who took her out of the irons?'

I had never thought of this question at all. 'Grandfather!' I said. 'What is in your mind? You – you of all men – are not hinting that it is the god. You'd laugh at me if I said so.'

'I'd be more likely to weep. Oh, child, child, child, when shall I have washed the nurse and the grandam and the priest and the soothsayer out of your soul? Do you think the Divine Nature – why, it's profane, ridiculous. You might as well say the universe itched or the Nature of Things sometimes tippled in the wine cellar.'

'I haven't said it was a god, Grandfather,' said I. 'I am asking who you think it was.'

'A man, a man, of course,' said the Fox, beating his hands on the table. 'What? Are you still a child? Didn't you know there were men on the Mountain?'

'Men!' I gasped.

'Yes. Vagabonds, broken men, outlaws, thieves. Where are your wits?'

Indignation came burning into my cheeks and I sprang up. For any daughter of our house to mix, even in lawful marriage, with those who have not (at least by one grandparent) divine descent, is an utter abomination. The Fox's thought was unendurable.

'What are you saying?' I asked him. 'Psyche would die on sharp stakes sooner than—'

'Peace, daughter,' said the Fox. 'Psyche doesn't know. As I read it, some robber or runaway has found the poor child, half-crazed with terror and loneliness, and with thirst too (likely enough), and got her out of her irons. And if she were not in her right mind, what would she most probably babble of in her ravings? Her gold and amber house on the Mountain, of course. She has had that fantasy from her childhood. The fellow would fall in with it. He'd be the god's messenger ... why, that's where her god of the westwind comes from. It would be the man himself. He'd take her to this valley. He'd whisper to her that the god, the bridegroom, would come to her that night. And after dark, he'd come back.'

'But the palace?'

'Her old fantasy, raised up by her madness and taken by her for reality. And whatever she tells the rascal about her fine house, he echoes it all. Perhaps adds more of his own. And so the delusion is built up stronger and stronger.'

For the second time that day I was utterly aghast. The Fox's explanation seemed too plain and evident to allow me any hope of doubt. While Bardia was speaking, his had seemed the same.

'It looks, Grandfather,' said I dully, 'as if you had read the riddle right.'

'It needs no Oedipus. But the real riddle's still to guess. What must we do? Oh, I'm barren, barren. I think your father has addled my brains with beating me about the ears. There must be some way ... yet we've so little time.'

'And so little freedom. I can't pretend to be on my sick-bed much longer. And once the King knows I'm whole, how shall I ever get to the Mountain again?'

'Oh, for that – but I'd forgotten. There's been news today. The lions have been seen again.'

'What?' I cried in terror. 'On the Mountain?'

'No, no, not so bad as that. Indeed, rather good than bad. Somewhere down south, and west of Ringal. The King will have a great lion-hunt.'

'The lions back ... so Ungit has played us false after all. Perhaps he'll sacrifice Redival this time. Is the King in a great rage?'

'Rage? No. Why, you'd think the loss of a herdsman and (what he values far more) some of the best dogs, and I don't know how many bullocks, was the best news he'd ever heard! I never saw him in better spirits. There's been nothing in his mouth all day but dogs and beaters and weather ... and such rummage and bustle – messages to this lord and that lord – deep talks with the huntsman – inspecting of kennels – shoeing of horses – beer flowing like water – even I have been slapped on the back in pure good-fellowship till my ribs ache with it. But what concerns us is that he'll be out at the hunting the next two days at least. With luck it might be five or six.'

'Then that's the time we have to work in.'

'No more than that. He goes at daybreak tomorrow. And anyway, we'd have little longer. She'll die if winter catches her on the Mountain. Living without a roof. And she'll be with child, no doubt, before we've time to look about us.'

It was as if I'd been hit about the heart. 'Leprosy and scabs on the man!' I gasped. 'Curse him, curse him! Psyche to carry a beggar's brat? We'll have him impaled if ever we catch him. He shall die for days. Oh, I could tear his body with my bare teeth.'

'You darken our counsels – and your own soul – with these passions,' said the Fox. 'If there were anywhere she could lie hidden (if we could get her)!'

'I had thought,' said I, 'we could hide her in Bardia's house.'

'Bardia! He'd never take one who's been sacrificed into his house. He's afraid of his own shadow where gods and old wives' tales are concerned. He's a fool.'

'That he is not,' said I; sharply enough, for the Fox often nettled me with his contempt for very brave and honest people if they had no tincture of his Greek wisdom.

'And if Bardia would,' the Fox added, 'that wife of his wouldn't let him. And everyone knows that Bardia's tied to his wife's apron-strings.'

'Bardia! And such a man. I couldn't have believed—'

'Pah! He's as amorous as Alcibiades. Why, the fellow married her undow-ered – for her beauty, if you please. The whole town knows of it. And she rules him like her slave.'

'She must be a very vile woman, Grandfather.'

928

'What does it matter to us whether she is or no? But you needn't think to find refuge for our darling in that house. I'll go further, daughter. There's nothing for it but to send her right out of Glome. If anyone in Glome knew that she had not died, they would seek her out and sacrifice her again. If we could get her to her mother's family ... but I see no way of doing it. Oh Zeus, Zeus, Zeus, if I had ten hoplites and a sane man to command them!'

'I can't see,' said I, 'even how to get her to leave the Mountain. She was obstinate, Grandfather. She obeys me no more. I think we must use force.'

'And we have no force. I am a slave and you are a woman. We can't lead a dozen spears up the Mountain. And if we could, the secret would never be kept.'

After that we sat silent for a long time; the fire flickering, Poobi sitting cross-legged by the hearth, feeding the logs into it, and playing a strange game of her own people's with beads (she once tried to teach it to me, but I could never learn). The Fox made as if to speak a dozen times but always checked himself. He was quick to devise plans, but no less quick to see the faults in them.

At last I said, 'It all comes to this, Grandfather. I must go back to Psyche. I must overrule her somehow. Once she is on our side, once she knows her shame and danger, then the three of us must devise as best we can. It may be that she and I must go out into the wide world together; wander like Oedipus.'

'And I with you,' said the Fox. 'You once bade me run away. This time I'll do it.'

'One thing's certain,' said I. 'She shall not be left to the felon who has abused her. I will choose any way – any way – rather than that. It rests on me. Her mother's dead (what mother but me has she ever known?). Her father's nothing; nothing for a father, and nothing for a king either. The honour of our house – the very being of Psyche – only I am left to care for them. She shall not be left. I'll – I'll—'

'What, child? You are pale! Are you fainting?'

'If there is no other way, I will kill her.'

'Babai!' said the Fox, so loud that Poobi stopped her game and stared at him. 'Daughter, daughter. You are transported beyond all reason and nature. Do you know what it is? There's one part love in your heart, and five parts anger, and seven parts pride. The gods know, I love Psyche too. And you know it; you know I love her as well as you do. It's a bitter grief that our child – our very Artemis and Aphrodite all in one – should live a beggar's life and lie in a beggar's arms. Yet even this ... it is not to be named beside such detested impieties as you speak of. Why, look at it squarely, as reason and nature have made it, not as passion would paint it. To be poor and in hardship, to be a poor man's wife—'

'Wife! You mean his trull, his drab, his whore, his slut.'

'Nature knows nothing of these names. What you call marriage is by law and custom, not nature. Nature's marriage is but the union of the man who persuades with the woman who consents. And so—'

'The man who persuades – or, more likely, forces or deceives – being some murderer, alien, traitor, runaway slave or other filth?'

'Filth? Perhaps I do not see it as you do. I am an alien and a slave myself; and ready to be a runaway – to risk the flogging and impaling – for your love and hers.'

'You are ten times my father,' said I, raising his hand to my lips. 'I meant no such thing. But, Grandfather, there are matters you don't understand. Psyche said so herself.'

'Sweet Psyche,' he said. 'I have often told her so. I am glad she has mastered the lesson. She was ever a good pupil.'

'You don't believe in the divine blood of our house,' I said.

'Oh yes. Of all houses. All men are of divine blood, for there is the god in every man. We are all one. Even the man who has taken Psyche. I have called him rascal and villain. Too likely he is. But it may not be. A good man might be an outlaw and a runaway.'

I was silent. All this meant nothing to me.

'Daughter,' said the Fox suddenly (I think no woman, at least no woman who loved you, would have done it). 'Sleep comes early to old men. I can hardly keep my eyes open. Let me go. Perhaps we shall see more clearly in the morning.'

What could I do but send him away? This is where men, even the trustiest, fail us. Their heart is never so wholly given to any matter but that some trifle of a meal, or a drink, or a sleep, or a joke, or a girl, may come in between them and it, and then (even if you are a queen) you'll get no more good out of them till they've had their way. In those days I had not yet understood this. Great desolation came over me.

'Everyone goes from me,' I said. 'None of them cares for Psyche. She lives at the very outskirts of their thoughts. She is less to them, far less, than Poobi is to me. They think of her a little and then get tired and go to something else; the Fox to his sleep, and Bardia to his doll or scold of a wife. You are alone, Orual. Whatever is to be done, you must devise and do it. No help will come. All gods and mortals have drawn away from you. You must guess the riddle. Not a word will come to you until you have guessed wrong and they all come crowding back to accuse and mock and punish you for it.'

I sent Poobi to bed. Then I did a thing which I think few have done. I spoke to the gods; myself, alone, in such words as came to me, not in a temple, without a sacrifice. I stretched myself face downward on the floor and called upon them with my whole heart. I took back every word I had said against them. I promised anything they might ask of me, if only they would send me a sign. They gave me none. When I began there was red fire-light in the room and rain on the roof; when I rose up again the fire had sunk a little lower, and the rain drummed on as before.

Now, when I knew that I was left utterly to myself, I said, 'I must do it … whatever I do … tomorrow. I must, then, rest tonight.' I lay down on the bed. I was in that state when the body is so tired that sleep comes soon, but the mind is in such anguish that it will wake you the moment the body's sated. It woke me a few hours past midnight, with no least possibility of further sleep in me. The fire was out; the rain had stopped. I went to my window and stood looking out into the gusty blackness, twisting my hair in my fists and my knuckles against my temples, and thought.

My mind was much clearer. I now saw that I had, strangely, taken both Bardia's explanation and the Fox's (each while it lasted) for certain truth. Yet one must be false. And I could not find out which, for each was well rooted in its own soil. If the things believed in Glome were true, then what Bardia said stood; if the Fox's philosophy were true, what the Fox said stood. But I could not find out whether the doctrines of Glome or the wisdom of Greece were right. I was the child of Glome and the pupil of the Fox; I saw that for years my life had been lived in two halves, never fitted together.

I must give up, then, trying to judge between Bardia and my master. And as soon as I said that, I saw (and wondered I had not seen before) that it made no difference. For there was one point on which both agreed. Both thought that some evil or shameful thing had taken Psyche for its own. Murdering thief or spectral Shadowbrute – did it matter which? The one thing neither of them had believed was that anything good or fair came to her in the night. No one but myself had dallied with that thought even for a moment. Why should they? Only my desperate wishes could have made it seem possible. The thing came in darkness and forbade itself to be seen. What lover would shun his bride's eyes unless he had some terrible reason for it?

Even I had thought the opposite only for an instant, while I looked at that likeness of a house across the river.

'It shall not have her,' I said. 'She shall not lie in those detestable embraces. Tonight must be the last night of that.'

Suddenly there rose up before me the memory of Psyche in the mountain valley, brightface, brimming over with joy. My terrible temptation came back; to leave her to that fool-happy dream, whatever came of it, to spare her, not to bring her down from it into misery. Must I be to her an avenging fury, not a gentle mother? And part of my mind now was saying, 'Do not meddle. Anything might be true. You are among marvels that you do not understand. Carefully, carefully. Who knows what ruin you might pull down on her head and yours?' But with the other part of me I answered that I was indeed her mother and her father too (all she had of either), that my love must be grave and provident, not slipshod and indulgent, that there is a time for love to be stern. After all, what was she but a child? If the present case were beyond my understanding, how much more must it be beyond hers? Children must obey. It had hurt me, long ago, when I made the barber pull out the thorn. Had I not none the less done well?

I hardened my resolution. I knew now what (which of two things) I must do; and no later than the day which would soon be breaking. Provided only that Bardia were not going on the lion-hunt; and that I could get him clear of this wife of his. As a man, even in great pain or sorrow, can still be fretted by a fly that buzzes in his face, I was fretted by the thought of this wife, this petted thing, suddenly starting up to delay or to hinder.

I lay down on my bed to wait for morning; calmed and quiet in a way, now that I knew what I would do.

14

It seemed long to me before the palace was stirring, though it stirred early because of the King's hunting. I waited till that noise was well begun. Then I rose and dressed in such clothes as I had worn the day before; and took the same urn. This time I put in it a lamp and a little pitcher of oil and a long band of linen about a span and a half broad, such as bridesmaids wear in Glome, wrapped over and over round them. Mine had lain in my chest ever since the marriage night of Psyche's mother. Then I called up Poobi and had food brought to me, of which I ate some, and some I put in the urn under the band. When I knew by the horse-hooves and horns and shoutings that the King's party was gone, I put on my veil and a cloak and went down. I sent the first slave I met to find whether Bardia were gone to the hunting; and if he were in the palace, to send him to me. I waited for him in the Pillar Room. It was a strange freedom to be in there alone; and indeed, amid all my cares, I could not help perceiving how the house was, as it were, lightened and set at liberty by the absence of the King. I thought, from their looks, that all the family felt it.

Bardia came to me.

'Bardia,' said I, 'I must go again to the Mountain.'

'It's impossible you should go with me, Lady,' he said. 'I was left out of the hunting (ill luck for me) for one purpose only; to watch over the house. I must even lie here at nights till the King's back.'

This dashed me very much. 'Oh, Bardia,' said I, 'what shall we do? I am in great straits. It's on my sister's business.'

Bardia rubbed his forefinger across his upper lip in a way he had when he was gravelled. 'And you can't ride,' he said. 'I wonder now – but no, that's foolishness. There's no horse to be trusted with a rider that can't ride. And a few days hence won't serve? The best would be to give you another man.'

'But, Bardia, it must be you. No one else would be able … it's a very secret errand.'

'I could let Gram off with you for two days and a night.'

'Who is Gram?'

'The small, dark one. He's a good man.'

'But can he hold his tongue?'

'It's more a question if he can ever loosen it. We get hardly ten words from him in as many days. But he's a true man; true to me, above all, for I once had the chance to do him a good turn.'

'It will not be like going with you, Bardia.'

'It's the best you can do, Lady, unless you can wait.'

But I said I could not wait, and Bardia had Gram called. He was a thin-faced man, very black-eyed, and (I thought) looked at me as if he feared me. Bardia told him to get his horse and await me where the little lane meets the road into the city.

As soon as he was gone, I said, 'Now, Bardia, get me a dagger.'

'A dagger, Lady? And for what?'

'To use as a dagger. Come Bardia, you know I mean no ill.'

He looked strangely at me, but got it. I put it on, at my belt, where the sword had hung yesterday. 'Farewell, Bardia,' said I.

'*Farewell*, Lady? Do you go for longer than a night?'

'I don't know, I don't know,' said I. Then, all in haste, and leaving him to wonder, I went out and went on foot, by the lane and joined Gram. He set me up on the horse (touching me, unless it was my fantasy, as one who touched a snake or a witch) and we began.

Nothing could be less like than that day's journey and the last. I never got more than 'Yes, Lady', or 'No, Lady', out of Gram all day. There was much rain and even between the showers the wind was wet. There was a grey, driving sky and the little hills and valleys, which had been so distinct with brightness and shade for Bardia and me the other day, were all sunk into one piece. We had started many hours later, and it was nearer evening than noon when we came down from the saddle into that secret valley. And there at last, as if by some trick of the gods (which perhaps it was), the weather cleared; so that it was hard not to think the valley had a sunlight of its own and the blustering rains merely ringed it about as the mountains did.

I brought Gram to the place where Bardia and I had passed the night and told him to await me there, and not to cross the river. 'I must go over it myself. It may be I shall re-cross it to your side by nightfall, or in the night. But I think that whatever time I spend on this side I will spend over yonder, near the ford. Do not come to me there unless I call you.'

He said, as always, 'Yes, Lady', and looked as if he liked this adventure very little.

I went to the ford; about a long bow-shot from Gram. My heart was still as ice, heavy as lead, cold as earth, but I was free now from all doubting and deliberating. I set my foot on the first stone of the crossing and called

Psyche's name. She must have been very close, for almost at once I saw her coming down to the bank. We might have been two images of love, the happy and the stern; she so young, so brightface, joy in her eyes and limbs; I, burdened and resolute, bringing pain in my hand.

'So I spoke truly, Maia,' she said as soon as I had crossed the water and we had embraced. 'The King has been no hindrance to you, has he? Salute me for a prophetess!'

This startled me for a moment, for I had forgotten her foretelling. But I put it aside to be thought of later. Now, I had my work to do; I must not, now of all times, begin doubting and pondering again.

She brought me a little way from the water – I don't know into what part of her phantom palace – and we sat down. I threw back my hood and put off my veil and set down the urn beside me.

'Oh, Orual,' said Psyche, 'what a storm-cloud in your face! That's how you looked when you were most angry with me as a child.'

'Was I ever angry? Ah, Psyche, do you think I ever scolded or denied you without grieving my heart ten times more than yours?'

'Sister, I meant to find no fault with you.'

'Then find no fault with me today either. For indeed we must talk very gravely. Now listen, Psyche. Our father is no father. Your mother (peace upon her!) is dead, and you have never seen her kindred. I have been – I have tried to be and still I must be – all the father and mother and kin you have. And all the King too.'

'Maia, you have been all this and more since the day I was born. You and the dear Fox are all I ever had.'

'Yes, the Fox. I'll have something to say of him too. And so, Psyche, if anyone is to care for you or counsel you or shield you, or if anyone is to tell you what belongs to the honour of our blood, it can be only I.'

'But why are you saying all this, Orual? You do not think I have left off loving you because I now have a husband to love as well? If you would understand it, that makes me love you – why, it makes me love everyone and everything – more.'

This made me shudder, but I hid it and went on. 'I know you love me, Psyche,' said I. 'And I think I should not live if you didn't. But you must trust me too.'

She said nothing. And now I was right on top of the terrible thing, and it almost struck me dumb. I cast about for ways to begin it.

'You spoke last time,' I said, 'of the day we got the thorn out of your hand. We hurt you that time, Psyche. But we did right. Those who love must hurt. I must hurt you again today. And, Psyche, you are still little more than a child. You cannot go your own way. You will let me rule and guide you.'

'Orual, I have a husband to guide me now.'

It was difficult not to be angered or terrified by her harping on it. I bit my lip; then said, 'Alas, child, it is about that very husband (as you call him) that I must grieve you.' I looked straight at her eyes and said sharply, 'Who is he? What is he?'

'A god,' she said, low and quivering. 'And I think, the god of the Mountain.'

'Alas, Psyche, you are deceived. If you knew the truth, you would die rather than lie in his bed.'

'The truth?'

'We must face it, child. Be very brave. Let me pull out this thorn. What sort of god would he be who dares not show his face?'

'*Dares not!* You come near to making me angry, Orual.'

'But think, Psyche. Nothing that's beautiful hides its face. Nothing that's honest hides its name. No, no, listen. In your heart you must see the truth, however you try to brazen it out with words. Think. Whose bride were you called? The Brute's. And think again. If it's not the Brute, who else dwells in these mountains? Thieves and murderers; men worse than brutes; and lecherous as goats, we may be sure. Are you a prize they'd let pass if you fell in their way? There's your lover, child. Either a monster – shadow and monster in one, maybe, a ghostly, un-dead thing – or a salt villain whose lips, even on your feet or the hem of your robe, would be a stain to our blood.'

She was silent a long time, her eyes on her lap.

'And so, Psyche,' I began at last, tenderly as I could – but she tossed away the hand that I had laid on hers.

'You mistake me, Orual. If I am pale, it is with anger. There, Sister; I have conquered it. I'll forgive you. You mean – I'll believe you mean – nothing but good. Yet how – or why – you can have blackened and tormented your soul with such thoughts ... but no more of that. If ever you loved me, put them away now.'

'Blackened my thoughts? They're not only mine. Tell me, Psyche, who are the two wisest men we know?'

'Why, the Fox for one. For the second – I know so few. I suppose Bardia is wise; in his own way.'

'You said yourself, that night in the five-walled room, that he was a prudent man. Now, Psyche, these two – so wise and so different – are both agreed with each other and with me concerning this love of yours. Agreed without doubt. All three of us are certain. Either Shadowbrute or felon.'

'You have told them my story, Orual? It was ill done. I gave you no leave. My lord gave no leave. Oh, Orual! It was more like Batta than you.'

I could not help it if my face reddened with anger, but I would not be turned aside. 'Doubtless,' I said. 'There is no end to the secrecy of this – this *husband* as you call him. Child, has his vile love so turned your brain that you can't see the plainest thing? A god? Yet on your own showing he hides and slinks and whispers "Mum", and "Keep counsel", and "Don't betray me", like a runaway slave.'

I am not certain that she had listened to this. What she said was, 'The Fox too! That is very strange. I never thought he would have believed in the Brute at all.'

I had not said he did. But if that was what she took out of my words, I thought it no part of my duty to set her right. It was an error helping her towards the main truth. I had need of all help to drive her thither.

'Neither he nor I nor Bardia,' said I, 'believes for one moment in your fancy that it is the god; no more than that this wild heath is a palace. And be sure, Psyche, that if we could ask every man and woman in Glome, all would say the same. The truth is too clear.'

'But what is all this to me? How should they know? I am his wife. I know.'

'How can you know if you have never seen him?'

'Orual, how can you be so simple? I – how could I not know?'

'But how, Psyche?'

'What am I to answer to such a question? It's not fitting ... it is ... and especially to you, Sister, who are a virgin.'

That matronly primness, from the child she was, went near to ending my patience. It was almost (but I think now she did not mean it so) as if she taunted me. Yet I ruled myself.

'Well, if you are so sure, Psyche, you will not refuse to put it to the test.'

'What test? Though I need none myself.'

'I have brought a lamp, and oil. See. Here they are.' (I set them down beside her.) 'Wait till he – or it – sleeps. Then look.'

'I cannot do that.'

'Ah! ... you see! You will abide no test. And why? Because you are not sure yourself. If you were, you'd be eager to do it. If he is, as you say, a god, one glimpse will set all our doubts at rest. What you call our dark thoughts will be put to flight. But you daren't.'

'Oh, Orual, what evil you think! The reason I cannot look at him – least of all by such trickery as you'd have me do – is that he has forbidden me.'

'I can think – Bardia and the Fox can think – of one reason only for such a forbidding. And of one only for your obeying it.'

'Then you know little of love.'

'You fling my virginity in my face again, do you? Better it than the stye you're in. So be it. Of what you now call love, I do know nothing. You can whisper about it to Redival better than to me – or to Ungit's girls, maybe, or the King's doxies. I know another sort of love. You shall find what it's like. You shall not—'

'Orual, Orual, you are raving,' said Psyche; herself unangered, gazing at me large-eyed, sorrowful, but nothing humble about her sorrow. You would have thought she was my mother, not I (almost) hers. I had known this long time that the old meek, biddable Psyche was gone for ever; yet it shocked me afresh.

'Yes,' I said. 'I was raving. You had made me angry. But I had thought (you will set me right, I don't doubt, if I am mistaken) that all loves alike were eager to clear the thing they loved of vile charges brought against it; if they could. Tell a mother her child is hideous. If it's beautiful she'll show it. No forbidding would stop her. If she keeps it hidden, the charge is true. You're afraid of the test, Psyche.'

'I am afraid – no, I am ashamed ... to disobey him.'

'Then, even at the best, look what you make of him! Something worse than our father. Who that loved you could be angry at your breaking so unreasonable a command – and for so good a reason?'

'Foolishness, Orual,' she answered, shaking her head. 'He is a god. He has good grounds for what he does, be sure. How should I know of them? I am only his simple Psyche.'

'Then you will not do it? You think – you say you think – that you can prove him a god and set me free from the fears that sicken my heart. But you will not do it.'

'I would if I could, Orual.'

I looked about me. The sun was almost setting behind the saddle. In a little while she would send me away. I rose up.

'An end of this must be made,' I said. 'You shall do it. Psyche, I command you.'

'Dear Maia, my duty is no longer to you.'

'Then my life shall end with it,' said I. I flung back my cloak further, thrust out my bare left arm, and struck the dagger into it till the point pricked out on the other side. Pulling the iron back through the wound was the worse pain; but I can hardly believe now how little I felt it.

'Orual! Are you mad?' cried Psyche, leaping up.

'You'll find linen in that urn. Tie up my wound,' said I, sitting down and holding the arm out to let the blood fall on the heather.

I had thought she might scream and wring her hands or faint. But I was deceived. She was pale enough but had all her wits about her. She bound my arm. The blood came seeping through fold after fold, but she staunched it in the end. (My stroke had been lucky enough. If I had known as much then as I do now about the inside of an arm, I might not – who knows? – have had the resolution to do it.)

The bandaging could not be done in a moment. The sun was lower and the air colder when we were able to talk again.

'Maia,' said Psyche, 'what did you do that for?'

'To show you I'm in earnest, girl. Listen. You have driven me to desperate courses. I give you your choice. Swear on this edge, with my blood still wet on it, that you will this very night do as I have commanded you; or else I'll first kill you and then myself.'

'Orual,' says she, very queenlike, raising her head, 'you might have spared that threat of killing me. All your power over me lies in the other.'

'Then swear, girl. You never knew me break my word.'

The look in her face now was one I did not understand. I think a lover – I mean, a man who loved – might look so on a woman who had been false to him. And at last she said:

'You are indeed teaching me about kinds of love I did not know. It is like looking into a deep pit. I am not sure whether I like your kind better than hatred. Oh, Orual – to take my love for you, because you know it goes down to my very roots and cannot be diminished by any other, newer love, and then to make of it a tool, a weapon, a thing of policy and mastery, an instrument of torture ... I begin to think I never knew you. Whatever comes after, something that was between us dies here.'

'Enough of your subtleties,' said I. 'Both of us die here, in plainest truth and blood, unless you swear.'

'If I do,' said she hotly, 'it will not be for any doubt of my husband or his love. It will only be because I think better of him than of you. He cannot be cruel like you. I'll not believe it. He will know how I was tortured into my disobedience. He will forgive me.'

'He need never know,' said I.

The look of scorn she gave me flayed my soul. And yet, this very noble-ness in her – had I not taught it to her? What was there in her that was not my work? And now she used it to look at me as if I were base beneath all baseness.

'You thought I would hide it? Thought I would not tell him?' she said; each word like the rubbing of a file across raw flesh. 'Well. It's all of a piece. Let us, as you say, make an end. You grow more and more a stranger to me at each word. And I had loved you so; loved, honoured, trusted, and (while it was fit) obeyed. And now; but I can't have your blood on my threshold. You chose your threat well. I'll swear. Where's your dagger?'

So I had won my victory and my heart was in torment. I had a terrible longing to unsay all my words and beg her forgiveness. But I held out the dagger. (The 'oath on edge', as we call it, is our strongest in Glome.)

'And even now,' said Psyche, 'I know what I do. I know that I am betray-ing the best of lovers and that perhaps, before sunrise, all my happiness may be destroyed for ever. This is the price you have put upon your life. Well, I must pay it.'

She took her oath. My tears burst out, and I tried to speak, but she turned her face away.

'The sun is almost down,' she said. 'Go. You have saved your life; go and live it as you can.'

I found I was becoming afraid of her. I made my way back to the stream; crossed it somehow. And the shadow of the saddle leaped across the whole valley as the sun set.

15

I think I must have fainted when I got to this side of the water, for there
seems to be some gap in my memory between the fording and being fully
aware again of three things: cold, and the pain in my arm, and thirst. I drank
ravenously. Then I wanted food, and now first remembered that I had left it
in the urn with the lamp. My soul rose up against calling Gram, who was
very irksome to me. I felt (though I saw it to be folly even at the time) that if
Bardia had come with me instead, all might have been different and better.
And away my thoughts wandered to imagine all he would be doing and
saying now if he had, till suddenly I remembered what business had brought
me there. I was ashamed that I had thought, even for a moment, of anything else.

My purpose was to sit by the ford, watching till I should see a light
(which would be Psyche lighting her lamp). It would vanish when she covered and hid it. Then, most likely far later, there would be a light again; she
would be looking at her vile master in its sleep. And after that – very, very
soon after it, I hoped – there would be Psyche creeping through the darkness and sending a sort of whispered call ('Maia, Maia') across the stream.
And I would be half-way over it in an instant. This time it would be I who
helped her at the ford. She would be all weeping and dismayed as I folded
her in my arms and comforted her; for now she would know who were her
true friends, and would love me again, and would thank me, shuddering, for
saving her from the thing the lamp had shown. These were dear thoughts to
me when they came and while they lasted.

But there were other thoughts too. Try as I would, I could not quite put
out of my head the fear that I had been wrong. A real god … was it impossible? But I could never dwell on that part of it. What came back and back to
my mind was the thought of Psyche herself somehow (I never knew well
how) ruined, lost, robbed of all joy, a wailing, wandering shape, for whom
I had wrecked everything. More times than I could count, that night, I had
the wish, tyrannously strong, to re-cross the cold water, to shout out that

I forgave her her promise, that she was not to light the lamp, that I had advised her wrongly. But I governed it.

Neither the one sort of thoughts nor the other were more than the surface of my mind. Beneath them, deep as the deep ocean-sea whereof the Fox spoke, was the cold, hopeless abyss of her scorn, her un-love, her very hatred.

How could she hate me, when my arm throbbed and burned with the wound I had given it for her love? 'Cruel Psyche, cruel Psyche,' I sobbed. But then I saw that I was falling back to the dreams of my sickness. So I set my wits against it and bestirred myself. Whatever happened I must watch and be sane.

The first light came soon enough; and vanished again. I said to myself – though indeed once I had her oath I never doubted her faith to it – 'So. All's well this far.' It made me wonder, as at a new question, what I meant by *well*. But the thought passed.

The cold grew bitter. My arm was a bar of fire, the rest of me an icicle, chained to that bar but never melted. I began to see that I was doing a perilous thing. I might die, thus wounded and fasting, or at least get such a chill as would bring my death soon after. And out of that seed there grew up, in one moment, a huge, foolish flower of fancies. For at once (leaping over all question of how it should come about) I saw myself laid on the pyre, and Psyche – she knew now, she loved me again now – beating her breast and weeping and repenting all her cruelties. The Fox and Bardia were there too; Bardia wept fast. Everyone loved me once I was dead. But I am ashamed to write all these follies.

What checked them was the next appearing of the light. To my eyes, long swilled with darkness, it seemed brighter than you would have thought possible. Bright and still, a homelike thing in that wild place. And for a time longer than I had expected, it shone and was still, and the whole world was still around it. Then the stillness broke.

The great voice, which rose up from somewhere close to the light, went through my whole body in such a swift wave of terror that it blotted out even the pain in my arm. It was no ugly sound; even in its implacable sternness it was golden. My terror was the salute that mortal flesh gives to immortal things. And after – barely after – the strong soaring of its incomprehensible speech, came the sound of weeping. I think (if those old words have a meaning) my heart broke then. But neither the immortal sound nor the tears of her who wept lasted for more than two heartbeats. Heartbeats, I say; but I think my heart did not beat till they were over.

A great flash laid the valley bare to my eyes. Then it thundered as if the sky broke in two straight above my head. Lightnings, thick-following one another, pricked the valley, left, right, near and far, everywhere. Each flash showed falling trees; the imagined pillars of Psyche's house were going down. They seemed to fall silently, for the thunder hid their crashing. But there was another noise it could not hide. Somewhere away on my left the walls of the Mountain itself were breaking. I saw (or I think I saw) fragments of rock hurled about and striking on other rocks and rising into the air again like a child's ball that bounces. The river rose, so quickly that I was overtaken by its rush before I could stumble back from it, wet to my middle; but that made little odds, for with the storm there had come a tyrannous pelting rain. Hair and clothes were already a mere sponge.

But, beaten and blinded though I was, I took these things for a good sign. They showed (so it seemed to me) that I was right. Psyche had roused some dreadful thing and these were its ragings. It had waked, she had not hidden her light soon enough; or else – yes, that was most likely – it had only feigned to be sleeping; it might be a thing that never needed sleep. It might, no doubt, destroy both her and me. But she would know. She would, at worst, die undeceived, disenchanted, reconciled to me. Even now, we might escape. Failing that, we could die together. I rose up, bent double under the battery of the rain, to cross the stream.

I believe I could never have crossed it – the deep, foaming death-race it had now become – even if I had been left free to try. I was not left free. There came as if it were a lightning that endured. That is, the look of it was the look of lightning, pale, dazzling, without warmth or comfort, showing each smallest thing with fierce distinctness, but it did not go away. This great light stood over me as still as a candle burning in a curtained and shuttered room. In the centre of the light was something like a man. It is strange that I cannot tell you its size. Its face was far above me, yet memory does not show the shape as a giant's. And I do not know whether it stood, or seemed to stand, on the far side of the water or on the water itself.

Though this light stood motionless, my glimpse of the face was as swift as a true flash of lightning. I could not bear it for longer. Not my eyes only, but my heart and blood and very brain were too weak for that. A monster – the Shadowbrute that I and all Glome had imagined – would have subdued me less than the beauty this face wore. And I think anger (what men call anger) would have been more supportable than the passionless and measureless rejection with which it looked upon me. Though my body crouched where I could almost have touched his feet, his eyes seemed to send me from him to an endless distance. He rejected, denied, answered, and (worst of all) he knew, all I had thought, done or been. A Greek verse says that even the gods cannot change the past. But is it true? He made it to be as if, from the beginning, I had known that Psyche's lover was a god, and as if all my doubtings, fears, guessings, debatings, questionings of Bardia, questionings of the Fox, all the rummage and business of it, had been trumped-up foolery, dust blown in my own eyes by myself. You, who read my book, judge. Was it so? Or, at least, had it been so in the very past, before this god changed the past? And if they can indeed change the past, why do they never do so in mercy?

The thunder had ceased, I think, the moment the still light came. There was great silence when the god spoke to me. And as there was no anger (what men call anger) in his face, so there was none in his voice. It was unmoved and sweet; like a bird singing on the branch above a hanged man.

'Now Psyche goes out in exile. Now she must hunger and thirst and tread hard roads. Those against whom I cannot fight must do their will upon her. You, woman, shall know yourself and your work. You also shall be Psyche.'

The voice and the light both ended together as if one knife had cut them short. Then, in the silence, I heard again the noise of the weeping.

I never heard weeping like that before or after; not from a child, nor a man wounded in the palm, nor a tortured man, nor a girl dragged off to slavery from a taken city. If you heard the woman you most hate in the world weep so, you would go to comfort her. You would fight your way through fire and spears to reach her. And I knew who wept, and what had been done to her, and who had done it.

I rose to go to her. But already the weeping was further away. She went wailing far off to my right, down to the end of the valley where I had never been, where doubtless it fell away, or dropped in sheer cliffs, towards the south. And I could not cross the stream. It would not even drown me. It would bruise and freeze and bemire me, but somehow whenever I grasped a rock – earth was no use now, for great slabs of the bank were slipping into the current every moment – I found I was still on this side. Sometimes I could not even find the river; I was so bewildered in the dark, and all the ground was now little better than a swamp, so that pools and new-formed brooks lured me now this way, now that.

I cannot remember more of that night. When day began to break, I could see what the god's anger had done to the valley. It was all bare rock, raw earth, and foul water; trees, bushes, sheep, and here and there a deer, floated in it. If I could have crossed the first river in the night it would not have profited me; I should have reached only the narrow bank of mud between it and the next. Even now I could not help calling out Psyche's name, calling till my voice was gone, but I knew it was foolishness. I had heard her leaving the valley. She had already gone into the exile which the god foretold. She had begun to wander, weeping, from land to land; weeping for her lover, not (I mustn't so cheat myself) for me.

I went and found Gram; a wet, shivering wretch he was, who gave one scared glance at my bandaged arm, and no more, and asked no questions. We ate food from the saddle-bags and began our journey. The weather was fair enough.

I looked on the things about me with a new eye. Now that I'd proved for certain that the gods are and that they hated me, it seemed that I had nothing to do but to wait for my punishment. I wondered on which dangerous edge the horse would slip and fling us down a few hundred feet into a gully; or what tree would drop a branch on my neck as we rode under it; or whether my wound would corrupt and I should die that way. Often, remembering that it is sometimes the god's way to turn us into beasts, I put my hand up under my veil to see if I could feel cat's fur, or dog's muzzle, or hog's tusks beginning to grow there. Yet with it all I was not afraid; never less. It is a strange, yet somehow a quiet and steady thing, to look round on earth and grass and the sky and say in one's heart to each, 'You are all my enemies now. None of you will ever do me good again. I see now only executioners.'

But I thought it most likely those words *You also shall be Psyche* meant that if she went into exile and wandering, I must do the same. And this, I had thought before, might very easily come about, if the men of Glome had no will to be ruled by a woman. But the god had been wide of the mark – so then they don't know all things? – if he thought he could grieve me most by making my punishment the same as Psyche's. If I could have borne hers as well as my own ... but next best was to share. And with this I felt a sort of hard and cheerless strength rising in me. I would make a good beggar-woman. I was ugly; and Bardia had taught me how to fight.

Bardia ... that set me thinking how much of my story I would tell him. Then, how much I would tell the Fox. I had not thought of this at all.

16

I crept in by the back parts of the palace and soon learned that my father had not yet come home from the hunting. But I went as soft and slinking to my place as if he had. When it became clear to my own mind (it did not at first) that I was hiding now not from the King but from the Fox, it was a trouble to me. Always before he had been my refuge and comforter.

Poobi cried over my wound and when she had the bandage off – that part was bad – laid good dressings on it. That was hardly done, and I was eating (hungrily enough) when the Fox came.

'Daughter, daughter,' he said. 'Praise the gods who have sent you back. I have been in pain for you all day. Where have you been?'

'To the Mountain, Grandfather,' said I, keeping my left arm out of sight. This was the first of my difficulties. I could not tell him of the self-wounding. I knew, now I saw him (I had not thought of it before), that he would rebuke me for putting that kind of force upon Psyche. One of his maxims was that if we cannot persuade our friends by reasons we must be content 'and not bring a mercenary army to our aid'. (He meant passions.)

'Oh, child, that was sudden,' he said. 'I thought we parted that night to talk it over again in the morning.'

'We parted to let you sleep,' said I. The words came fiercely, without my will and in my father's own voice. Then I was ashamed.

'So that's my sin,' said the Fox, smiling sadly. 'Well, Lady, you have punished it. But what's your news? Would Psyche hear you?'

I said nothing to that question but told him of the storm and the flood and how that mountain valley was now a mere swamp, and how I had tried to cross the stream and could not, and how I had heard Psyche go weeping away, on the south side of it, out of Glome altogether. There was no use in telling him about the god; he would have thought I had been mad or dreaming.

'Do you mean, child, you never came to speech with her at all?' said the Fox, looking very haggard.

'Yes,' I said. 'We did talk a little; earlier.'

'Child, what is wrong? Was there a quarrel? What passed between you?'

This was harder to answer. In the end, when he questioned me closely, I told him about my plan of the lamp.

'Daughter, daughter!' cried the Fox, 'what demon put such a device in your thoughts? What did you hope to do? Would not the villain by her side – he, a hunted man and an outlaw – be certain to wake? And what would he do then but snatch her up and drag her away to some other lair? Unless he stabbed her to the heart for fear she'd betray him to his pursuers. Why, the light alone would convince him she'd betrayed him already. How if it were a wound that made her weep? Oh, if you'd only taken counsel!'

I could say nothing. For now I wondered why indeed I had not thought of any of these things and whether I had ever at all believed her lover was a mountainy man.

The Fox stared at me, wondering more and more, I saw, at my silence. At last he said, 'Did you find it easy to make her do this?'

'No,' said I. I had taken off, while I ate, the veil I had worn all day; now I greatly wished I had it on.

'And how did you persuade her?' he asked.

This was the worst of all. I could not tell him what I had really done. Nor much of what I'd said. For when I told Psyche that he and Bardia were both agreed about her lover I meant what was very true; both agreed it was some shameful or dreadful thing. But if I said this to the Fox, he would say that Bardia's belief and his were sheer contraries, the one all old wives' tales and the other plain workaday probabilities. He would make it seem that I had lied. I could never make him understand how different it had looked on the Mountain.

'I – I spoke with her,' said I at last. 'I persuaded her.'

He looked long and searching at me, but never so tenderly since those old days when he used to sing *The Moon's gone down* ... I on his knee.

'Well. You have a secret from me,' he said in the end. 'No, don't turn away from me. Did you think I would try to press or conjure it out of you? Never that. Friends must be free. My tormenting you to find it would build a worse barrier between us than your hiding it. Some day – but you must obey the god within you, not the god within me. There, do not weep. I shall not cease to love you if you have a hundred secrets. I'm an old tree and my best branches were lopped off me the day I became a slave. You and Psyche were all that remained. Now – alas, poor Psyche! I see no way to her now. But I'll not lose you.'

He embraced me (I bit my lip not to scream when his arm touched the wound) and went away. I had hardly ever before been glad of his going. But I thought too how much kinder he was than Psyche.

I never told Bardia the story of that night at all.

I made one resolve before I slept, which, though it seems a small matter, made much difference to me in the years that followed. Hitherto, like all my countrywomen, I had gone bareface; on those two journeys up the Mountain I had worn a veil because I wished to be secret. I now determined that I would go always veiled. I have kept this rule, within doors and without, ever since. It is a sort of treaty made with my ugliness. There had been a time in childhood when I didn't yet know I was ugly. Then there was a time (for in this book I must hide none of my shames or follies) when I believed, as girls do – and as Batta was always telling me – that I could make it more tolerable by this or that done to my clothes or my hair. Now, I chose to be veiled. The Fox, that night, was the last man who ever saw my face; and not many women have seen it either.

My arm healed well (and so all wounds have done in my body) and when the King returned, about seven days later, I no longer pretended to be ill. He came home very drunk, for there'd been as much feasting as hunting on that party, and very out of humour, for they had killed only two lions and he'd killed neither and a favourite dog had been ripped up.

A few days later he sent for the Fox and me again to the Pillar Room. As soon as he saw me veiled, he shouted, 'Now, girl, what's this? Hung your curtains up, eh? Were you afraid we'd be dazzled by your beauty? Take off that frippery!'

It was then I first found what that night on the Mountain had done for me. No one who had seen and heard the god could much fear this roaring old King.

'It's hard if I'm to be scolded both for my face and for hiding it,' said I; putting no hand to the veil.

'Come here,' he said, not at all loud this time. I went up and stood so close to his chair that my knees almost touched his, still as a stone. To see his face while he could not see mine seemed to give me a kind of power. He was working himself into one of those white rages.

'Do you begin to set your wits against mine?' he said almost in a whisper.

'Yes,' said I, no louder than he, but very clearly. I had not known a moment before what I would do or say; that one little word came out of itself.

He stared at me while you could count seven and I half thought he might stab me dead. Then he shrugged, and snarled out, 'Oh, you're like all women. Talk, talk, talk ... you'd talk the moon out of the sky if a man'd listen to you. Here, Fox, are those lies you've been writing ready for her to copy?'

He never struck me, and I never feared him again. And from that day I never gave back an inch before him. Rather, I pressed on; so well that I told

him not long after how impossible it was that I and the Fox should guard
Redival if we were to work for him in the Pillar Room. He growled and
cursed, yet henceforth he made Batta her jailer. Batta had grown very familiar with him of late and spent many hours in the Bedchamber. Not, I suppose, that he had her to his bed – even in the best of her days she had
scarcely been what he called savoury – but she tattled and whispered and
flattered him and stirred his possets; for he began to show his years. She was
equally thick, for the most part, with Redival; but those were a pair who
could be ready to scratch each other's eyes out one moment, and snuggling
up for gossip and bawdy the next.

This, and all other things that were happening in the palace, mattered to
me not at all. I was like a condemned man waiting for his executioner, for
I believed that some sudden stroke of the gods would fall on me very soon.
But as day came after day and nothing happened, I began to see, at first very
unwillingly, that I might be doomed to live, and even to live an unchanged
life, some while longer.

When I understood this I went to Psyche's room, alone, and put everything in it as it had been before all our sorrows began. I found some verses in
Greek which seemed to be a hymn to the god of the Mountain. These I
burned. I did not choose that any of that part of her should remain. Even the
clothes that she had worn in the last year I burned also; but those she had
worn earlier, and especially what were left of those she wore in childhood,
and any jewels she had loved as a child, I hung in their proper places.
I wished all to be so ordered that if she could come back she would find all
as it had been when she was still happy, and still mine. Then I locked the
door and put a seal on it. And, as well as I could, I locked a door in my mind.
Unless I were to go mad I must put away all thoughts of her save those that
went back to her first, happy years. I never spoke of her. If my women mentioned her name I bade them be silent. If the Fox mentioned it I was silent
myself and led him to other things. There was less comfort than of old in
being with the Fox.

Yet I questioned him much about what he called the physical parts of philosophy, about the seminal fire, and how soul arises from blood, and the periods of the universe; and also about plants and animals, and the positions,
soils, airs, and governments of cities. I wanted hard things now, and to pile up
knowledge.

As soon as my wound was well enough I returned very diligently to my
fencing lessons with Bardia. I did it even before my left arm could bear a
shield, for he said that fighting without shields was also a skill that ought to be
learned. He said (and I now know it was true) that I made very good progress.

My aim was to build up more and more that strength, hard and joy-
less, which had come to me when I heard the god's sentence; by learning,

fighting, and labouring, to drive all the woman out of me. Sometimes at night, if the wind howled or the rain fell, there would leap upon me, like water from a bursting dam, a great and anguished wonder; whether Psyche was alive, and where she was on such a night, and whether hard wives of peasants were turning her, cold and famished, from their door. But then, after an hour or so of weeping and writhing and calling out upon the gods, I would set to and re-build the dam.

Soon Bardia was teaching me to ride on horseback as well as to fence with the sword. He used me, and talked to me, more and more like a man. And this both grieved and pleased me.

So things went on till the Midwinter, which is a great feast in our country. On the day after it the King came home from some revels he had been at in a lord's house, about three hours after noon, and in mounting the steps that go up into the porch he fell. It was so cold that day that the water the house-boys had used for scouring the steps had frozen on them. He fell with his right leg under him across the edge of a step, and when men ran to help him he roared out with pain and was ready to set his teeth in the hands of anyone who touched him. Next minute he was cursing them for leaving him to lie there and freeze. As soon as I came I nodded to the slaves to lift him up and carry him in, whatever he said or did. We got him to his bed, with great agony, and had the barber to him; who said (as we all guessed) that his thigh was broken. 'But I've no skill to set it, Lady, even if the King would let my fingers near it.' I sent a messenger over to the house of Ungit to the Second Priest, who had the name of a good surgeon. Before he came the King had filled himself up with enough strong wine to throw a sound man into a fever, and as soon as the Second Priest got his clothes out of the way and began handling the leg, he started screaming like a beast and tried to pluck out his dagger. Then Bardia and I whispered to one another, and we got in six of the guards and held the King down. Between his screams he kept on pointing at me with his eyes (they had his hands fast) and crying out:

'Take her away! Take away that one with the veil. Don't let her torture me. I know who she is. I know.'

He had no sleep that night or the day and night after (on top of the pain from his leg, he coughed as if his chest would burst), and whenever our backs were turned Batta would be taking him in more wine. I was not much in the Bedchamber myself, for the sight of me made him frantic. He kept on saying he knew who I was for all my veil.

'Master,' said the Fox, 'it is only the Princess Orual, your daughter.'

'Aye, so she tells you,' the King would say. 'But I know better. Wasn't she using red-hot iron on my leg all night? I know who she is … Aiai! Aiai! Guards! Bardia! Orual! Batta! Take her away!'

On the third night the Second Priest and Bardia and the Fox and I all stood just outside his door and talked in whispers. The Second Priest's name was Arnom; he was a dark man, no older than I, smooth-cheeked as a eunuch (which he cannot have been, for though Ungit has eunuchs, only a weaponed man can hold the full priesthood).

'It's likely,' said Arnom, 'that this will end in the King's death.'

'So,' thought I. 'This is how it will begin. There'll be a new world in Glome, and if I get off with my life, I shall be driven out. I too shall be a Psyche.'

'I think the same,' said the Fox. 'And it comes at a ticklish time. There's much business before us.'

'More than you think, Lysias,' said Arnom (I had never heard the Fox called by his real name before). 'The house of Ungit is in the very same plight as the King's house.'

'What do you mean, Arnom?' said Bardia.

'The Priest is dying at last. If I have any skill, he'll not last five days.'

'And you to succeed him?' said Bardia. The priest bowed his head.

'Unless the King forbids,' added the Fox. This was good law in Glome.

'It's very necessary,' said Bardia, 'that Ungit and the palace should be of one mind at such a moment. There are those who'd see their chance of setting Glome by the ears otherwise.'

'Yes, very necessary,' said Arnom. 'No one will rise against us both.'

'It's our good fortune,' said Bardia, 'that there's no cause of quarrel between the Queen and Ungit.'

'The Queen?' said Arnom.

'The Queen,' said Bardia and the Fox now both together.

'If only the Princess were married, now!' said Arnom, bowing very courteously. 'A woman cannot lead the armies of Glome in war.'

'This Queen can,' said Bardia; and the way he thrust out his lower jaw made him seem a whole army himself. I saw Arnom looking at me hard, and I think my veil served me better than the boldest countenance in the world; maybe better than beauty would have done.

'There is only one difference between Ungit and the King's house,' he said, 'and that concerns the Crumbles. But for the King's sickness and the Priest's I would have been here before now to speak of it.'

I knew all about this and saw now where we were. The Crumbles was good land on the far side of the river, and it had been a cat-and-dog quarrel ever since I started working for my father as to whether they belonged, or how much of them belonged, to the King or to Ungit. I had always thought (little cause as I had to love Ungit) that they should belong to her house; which was indeed poorly provided for the charge of continual sacrifices. And I thought too that if once Ungit were reasonably furnished with land, the priests could be stopped from wringing so much out of the common people by way of gifts.

'The King still lives,' said I; I had not spoken before, and my voice surprised them all. 'But because of his sickness I am now the King's mouth. It is his wish to give the Crumbles to Ungit, free and for ever, and the covenant to be cut in stone, upon one condition.'

Bardia and the Fox looked at me with wonder. But Arnom said, 'What is that, Lady?'

'That Ungit's guards be henceforward under the captain of the King's guard, and chosen by the King (or his successor), and under his obedience.'

'And paid by the King (or his successors) too?' says Arnom quick as lightning.

I had not thought of this stroke, but I judged any resolute answer better than the wisest pondering. 'That,' said I, 'must be according to the hours of duty they spend in Ungit's house and here.'

'You drive – that is, the King drives – a hard bargain, Lady,' said the priest. But I knew he would take it, for I knew that Ungit had more need of good land than of spears. Also, it would be hard for Arnom to succeed to the Priesthood if the palace was against him. Then my father began roaring out from within and the priest went back to him.

'Well done, daughter,' whispered the Fox.

'Long live the Queen,' whispered Bardia. Then they both followed Arnom.

I stood outside in the great hall, which was empty, and the fire low. It was as strange a moment as any in my life. To be a queen – that would not sweeten the bitter water against which I had been building the dam in my soul. It might strengthen the dam, though. Then, as a quite different thing, came the thought that my father would be dead. That struck me dizzy. The largeness of a world in which he was not ... the clear light of a sky in which that cloud would no longer hang ... freedom. I drew in a long breath; one way, the sweetest I had ever drawn. I came near to forgetting my great central sorrow.

But only for a moment. It was very still, and most of the household was in bed. I thought I heard a sound of weeping; a girl's weeping; the sound for which always, with or without my will, I was listening. It seemed to come from without, from behind the palace. Instantly crowns and policies and my father were a thousand leagues from my mind. In a torture of hope I went swiftly to the other end of the hall and then out by the little door between the dairy and the guard's quarters. The moon was shining, but the air was not so still as I thought. And where now was the weeping? Then I thought I heard it again. 'Psyche,' I called. 'Istra! Psyche!' I went to the sound. Now I was less sure what it was. I remembered that when the chains of the well swung a little (and there had been breeze enough to sway them just now) they could make a noise something like that. Oh, the cheat of it, the bitterness!

I stood and listened. There was no more weeping. But something was moving somewhere. Then I saw a cloaked form dart across a patch of moonlight and bury itself in some bushes. I was after it, quick as I could. Next moment I plunged my hand in among the branches. Another hand met it.

'Softly, sweetheart,' said a voice. 'Take me to the King's threshold.'

It was a wholly strange voice, and a man's.

17

'Who are you?' said I, wrenching my hand free and leaping back as if I had touched a snake. 'Come out and show yourself.' My thought was that it must be a lover of Redival's, and that Batta was playing bawd as well as jailer.

A slender, tall man stepped out. 'A suppliant,' he said, but with a merriment in his voice that did not sound like supplication. 'And one who never let a pretty girl go without a kiss.'

He'd have had an arm around my neck in a moment if I hadn't avoided him. Then he saw my dagger point twinkle in the moonlight; and laughed.

'You've good eyes if you can see beauty in this face,' said I, turning it on him to make sure he saw the blank wall of the veil.

'Only good ears, sister,' said he. 'I'll bet a girl with a voice like yours is beautiful.'

The whole adventure was, for such a woman as I, so unusual that I almost had a fool's wish to lengthen it. The very world was strange that night. But I came to my senses.

'Who are you?' I said. 'Tell me quick, or I'll call the guards.'

'I'm no thief, pretty one,' said he, 'though I confess you caught me slinking in a thief's fashion. I thought there might already be some kindred of my own in your garden whom I had no mind to meet. I am a suppliant to the King. Can you bring me to him?' He let me hear a couple of coins jingle in his hand.

'Unless the King's health mends suddenly, I am the Queen,' said I.

He gave a low whistle and laughed. 'If that's so, Queen,' he said, 'I've played the fool to admiration. Then it's your suppliant I am; suppliant for a few nights' – it might be only one – lodging and protection. I am Trunia of Phars.'

The news struck me almost stupid. I have written before how this prince was at war with his brother Argan and the old king their father.

'Defeated, then?' I said.

'Beaten in a cavalry skirmish,' he said, 'and had to ride for it, which would be little odds but that I missed my way and blundered into Glome. And then my horse went lame, not three miles back. The worst of it is, my brother's strength lies all along the border. If you can hide me for a day or so – his messengers will be at your door by daybreak, no doubt – so that I can get into Essur and so round to my main army in Phars, I'll soon show him and all the world whether I'm defeated.'

'This is all very well, Prince,' said I. 'But if we receive you as a suppliant we must, by all law, defend you. I'm not so young a queen as to think I can go to war with Phars at this time.'

'It's a cold night to lie out,' he said.

'You'd be very welcome if you were not a suppliant, Prince. But in that character you're too dangerous. I can give you lodging only as a prisoner.'

'Prisoner?' said he. 'Then, Queen, good night.'

He darted away as if he were not weary at all (though I had heard weariness in his voice) and ran as one who is used to it. But that flight was his undoing. I could have told him where the old millstone lay. He fell sprawling, made to leap up again with wonderful quickness, then gave a sharp hiss of pain, struggled, cursed, and was still.

'Sprained, if not broken,' he said. 'Plague on the god that invented man's ankle. Well, you may call your spears, Queen. Prisoner it is. And that prison leads to my brother's hangman?'

'We'll save you if we can,' said I. 'If we can do it any way without full war against Phars, we'll do it.'

The guards' quarters were on that side of the house, as I have said, and it was easy enough to go within calling distance of the men and yet keep my eye on the Prince. As soon as I heard them turning out I said, 'Pull your hood over your face. The fewer who know my prisoner's name, the freer my hands will be.'

They got him up and brought him hobbling into the hall and put him on the settle by the hearth, and I called for wine and victuals to be brought him, and for the barber to bind up his ankle. Then I went into the Bedchamber. Arnom had gone. The King was worse; his face a darker red, his breathing hoarse. It seemed he could not speak; but I wondered, as his eyes wandered from one to another of us three, what he thought and felt.

'Where have you been, daughter?' said the Fox. 'Here's terribly weighty news. A post has just ridden in to tell us that Argan of Phars with three – or maybe four – score of horse has crossed the border and now lies but ten miles away. He gives out that he is seeking his brother Trunia.'

How quickly we learn to queen or king it! Yesterday I should have cared little how many aliens in arms crossed our borders; tonight, it was as if someone had struck me in the face.

'And,' said Bardia, 'whether he really believes that we have Trunia here – or whether he's crossed the border of a crippled land only to make a cheap show of valour and mend his mouldy reputation – either way—'

'Trunia is here,' said I. Before their surprise let them speak, I made them come into the Pillar Room, for I found I could not bear my father's eyes on us. The others seemed to make no more account of him than of a dead man. I ordered lights and fire in the tower room, Psyche's old prison, and that the Prince should be taken there when he had eaten. Then we three went busily to our talking.

On three things we were all of one mind. First, that if Trunia weathered his present misfortune, he was likely enough to beat Argan in the end and rule Phars. The old king was in his dotage and counted for nothing. The longer the broils lasted, the more Trunia's party would probably increase, for Argan was false, cruel, and hated by many, and had, moreover, from his first battle (long before these troubles) an old slur of cowardice upon him which made him contemptible. Second, that Trunia as King of Phars would be a far better neighbour to us than Argan; especially if we had befriended him when he was lowest. But thirdly, that we were in no plight to take on a war with Phars, nor even with Argan's party in Phars; the pestilence had killed too many of our young men and we still had almost no corn.

Then a new thought, as if from nowhere, came scalding hot into my head.

'Bardia,' said I, 'what is Prince Argan worth as a swordsman?'

'There are two better at this table, Queen.'

'And he'd be very chary of doing anything that would revive the old story against his courage?'

'It's to be supposed so.'

'Then if we offered him a champion to fight against him for Trunia – pawned Trunia's head on the single combat – he'd be in a manner bound to take it up.'

Bardia thought for a time. 'Why,' he said, 'it sounds like something out of an old song. Yet, by the gods, the longer I look at it the better I like it. Weak though we are, he'll not want war with us while he has war at home. Not if we leave him any other choice. And his hope hangs on keeping or getting his people's favour. He has none of it to spare even now. And it's an odious thing to be pursuing his brother at our gates as if he were digging out a fox. That won't have made him more loved. If on top of it all he refuses the combat, his name will stink worse still. I think your plan has life in it, Queen.'

'This is very wise,' said the Fox. 'Even if our man's killed and we have to hand Trunia over, no man can say we've treated him ill. We save our good name and yet have no war with Phars.'

'And if our champion kills Argan,' said Bardia, 'then we've done the next thing to setting Trunia on the throne and earned a good friend; for all say Trunia's a right-minded man.'

'To make it surer still, friends,' said I, 'let our champion be one so contemptible that it would be shame beneath all shame for Argan to draw back.'

'That's too subtle, daughter,' said the Fox. 'And hard on Trunia. We don't want our man beaten.'

'What are you thinking of, Queen?' said Bardia, teasing his moustache in the old way. 'We can't ask him to fight a slave, if that's what you mean.'

'No. A woman,' said I.

The Fox stared in bewilderment. I had never told him of my exercises with the sword, partly because I had a tenderness about mentioning Bardia to him at all, for to hear Bardia called fool or barbarian angered me. (Bardia called the Fox Greekling and 'word-weaver' in return, but that never fretted me in the same way.)

'A woman?' said the Fox. 'Am I mad, or are you?'

And now a great smile that would do any heart good to see it broke over Bardia's face. But he shook his head.

'I've played chess too long to hazard my Queen,' he said.

'What, Bardia?' said I, steadying my voice as best I could. 'Were you only flattering when you said I was a better swordsman than Argan?'

'Not so. I'd lay my money on you if it came to a wager. But there's always luck as well as skill in these things.'

'And courage too, you'd say.'

'I've no fear of you for that, Queen.'

'I have no idea what you are both talking about,' said the Fox.

'The Queen wants to fight for Trunia herself, Fox,' said Bardia. 'And she could do it too. We've had scores of matches together. The gods never made anyone – man or woman – with a better natural gift for it. Oh, Lady, Lady, it's a thousand pities they didn't make you a man.' (He spoke it as kindly and heartily as could be; as if a man dashed a gallon of cold water in your broth and never doubted you'd like it all the better.)

'Monstrous – against all custom – and nature – and modesty,' said the Fox. On such matters he was a true Greek; he still thought it barbarous and scandalous that the women in our land go bareface. I had sometimes said to him when we were merry that I ought to call him not Grandfather but Grandam. That was another reason why I had never told him of the fencing.

'Nature's hand slipped when she made me anyway,' said I. 'If I'm to be hard-featured as a man, why shouldn't I fight like a man too?'

'Daughter, daughter,' said the Fox. 'In mercy to me, if for nothing else, put this horrible thought out of your head. The plan of a champion and a combat was good. How would this folly make it better?'

'It makes it far better,' said I. 'Do you think I'm so simple as to fancy I'm safe on my father's throne yet? Arnom is with me. Bardia is with me. But what of the nobles and the people? I know nothing of them nor they of me. If either of the King's wives had lived, I supposed I might have known the lords' wives and daughters. My father never let us see them; much less the lords themselves. I have no friends. Is this combat not the very thing to catch their fancy? Won't they like a woman for their ruler better if she has fought for Glome and killed her man?'

'Oh, for that,' said Bardia, 'it'd be incomparable. There'll be no one but you in their mouths and hearts for a twelvemonth.'

'Child, child,' said the Fox, his eyes full of tears, 'it's your life. Your life. First my home and freedom gone; then Psyche; now you. Will you not leave one leaf on this old tree?'

I could see right into his heart, for I knew he now implored me with the same anguish I had felt when I implored Psyche. The tears that stood in my eyes behind my veil were tears of pity for myself more than for him. I did not let them fall.

'My mind's made up,' I said. 'And none of you can think of a better way out of our dangers. Do we know where Argan lies, Bardia?'

'At the Red Ford, the post said.'

'Then let our herald be sent at once. The fields between the city and the Shennit to be the place of the combat. The time, the third day from now. The terms, these. If I fall, we deliver Trunia to him and condone his unlawful entering into our land. If he falls, Trunia is a free man and has a safe conduct to go over the border to his own people in Phars or where he will. Either way, all the aliens to be out of the land of Glome in two days.'

They both stared and said nothing.

'I'll go to bed now,' said I. 'See to the sending, Bardia, and then to bed yourself. A good night to you both.'

I knew from Bardia's face that he would obey, though he could not bring himself to assent in words. I turned quickly away and went to my own room.

To be alone there and in silence was like coming suddenly under the lee of a wall on a wild, windy day, so that one can breathe and collect oneself again. Ever since Arnom had said, hours ago, that the King was dying, there seemed to have been another woman acting and speaking in my place. Call her the Queen; but Orual was someone different and now I was Orual again. (I wondered if this was how all princes felt.) I looked back on the things the Queen had done and wondered at them. Did that Queen truly think she would kill Argan? I, Orual, as I now saw, did not believe it. I was not even sure that I could fight him. I had never used sharps before; nothing hung on my sham battles but the hope of pleasing my teacher (not that that was a small thing to me either). How would it be if, when the day came, and the trumpets had blown, and the swords were out, my courage failed me? I'd be the mockery of the whole world; I could see the shamed look on the Fox's face, on Bardia's. I could hear them saying, 'And yet how bravely her sister went to the offering! How strange that she, who was so meek and gentle, should have been the brave one after all!' And so she would be far above me in everything; in courage as well as in beauty and in those eyes which the gods favoured with sight of things invisible, and even in strength (I remembered her grip when we had wrestled). 'She shall not,' I said with my whole soul. 'Psyche? She's never had a sword in her hand in her life, never done man's work in the Pillar Room, never understood (hardly heard of) affairs of state ... a girl's life, a child's life ...'

I asked myself suddenly what I was thinking. 'Can it be my sickness coming back?' I thought. For it began to be like those vile dreams I had had in my ravings when the cruel gods put into my mind the horrible, mad fancy that it was Psyche who was my enemy. Psyche my enemy? – she, my child, the very heart of my heart, whom I had wronged and ruined, for whose sake the gods were right to kill me? And now I saw my challenge to the Prince quite differently. Of course he would kill me. He was the gods' executioner. And this would be the best thing in the world; far better than some of the dooms I had looked for. All my life must now be a sandy waste; who could have dared to hope it would be so short? And this accorded so well with all my daily thoughts since the god's sentence, that I now wondered how I could have forgotten that sandy waste for the past few hours.

It was queenship that had done it – all those decisions to make, coming pell-mell upon me without a breathing space, and so much hanging on each; all the speed, skill, peril, and dash of the game. I resolved that for the two days left to me I'd queen it with the best of them; and if by any chance Argan didn't kill me, I'd queen it as long as the gods let me. It was not pride – the glitter of the name – that moved me; or not much. I was taking to queenship as a stricken man takes to the wine-pot or as a stricken woman, if she had beauty, might take to lovers. It was an art that left you no time to mope. If Orual could vanish altogether into the Queen, the gods would almost be cheated.

But had Arnom said my father was dying? No; not quite that.

I rose up and went back to his Bedchamber; without a taper, feeling my way along the walls, for I would have been ashamed if anyone saw me. There were still lights in the Bedchamber. They had left Batta to be with him. She sat in his own chair, close to the fire, sleeping the noisy sleep of a sodden old woman. I went over to the bedside. He was seemingly wide awake. Whether the noises he was making were an attempt at speech, who knows? But the look in his eyes, when he saw me, was not to be mistaken.

It was terror. Did he know me and think I came to murder him? Did he think I was Psyche come back from the deadlands to bring him down there?

Some will say (perhaps the gods will say) that if I had murdered him indeed, I should have been no less impious than I was. For as he looked at me with fear, so I looked at him; but all my fear was lest he should live.

What do the gods expect of us? My deliverance was now so near. A prisoner may come to bear his dungeon with patience; but if he has almost escaped, tasted his first draught of the free air ... to be re-taken then, to go back to the clanking of that fetter, the smell of that straw?

I looked again at his face; terrified, idiotic, almost an animal's face. A thought of comfort came to me: 'Even if he lives, he will never have his mind again.'

I went back and slept soundly.

18

Next day I went as soon as I was risen to the Bedchamber to take my first look at the King; for indeed no lover nor doctor ever watched each change of a sick man's breath and pulse so closely as I. While I was still at his bedside (I could see no difference in him) in came Redival, all in a flurry and her face blubbered, and 'Oh, Orual,' she said, 'is the King dying? And what was going on all last night? And who's the young stranger? They say he's a wonderful, handsome man and looks as brave as a lion. Is he a prince? And oh, Sister, what will happen to us if the King dies?'

'I shall be Queen, Redival. Your treatment shall be according to your behaviour.'

Almost before the words were out of my mouth she was fawning upon me and kissing my hand and wishing me joy and saying she had always loved me better than anyone in the world. It sickened me. None of the slaves would cringe to me like that. Even when I was angry and they feared me, all knew better than to put on a beggar's whine; there's nothing moves my pity less.

'Don't be a fool, Redival,' said I, shoving her away from my hand. 'I'm not going to kill you. But if you put your nose out of the house without my leave, I'll have you whipped. Now be off.'

At the door she turned and said, 'But you'll get me a husband, Queen, won't you?'

'Yes; probably two,' said I. 'I've a dozen sons of kings hanging in my wardrobe. But go.'

Then came the Fox, who looked at the King, muttered, 'He might last for days yet,' and then said, 'Daughter, I did badly last night. I think this offer to fight the Prince yourself is foolish and, what's more, unseemly. But I was wrong to weep and beg and try to force you by your love. Love is not a thing to be so used.'

He broke off because just then Bardia came to the door. 'Here's a herald back from Argan already, Queen,' he said. 'Our man met the Prince (curse his insolence) a great deal nearer than ten miles.'

We went into the Pillar Room (my father's eyes followed me terribly) and had the herald in. He was a great, tall man, dressed as fine as a peacock. His message, stripped of many high words, was that his master accepted the combat. But he said his sword should not be stained with woman's blood, so he'd bring a rope with him to hang me when he'd disarmed me.

'That's a weapon in which I profess no skill,' said I. 'And therefore it's barely justice that your master should bring it. But then he's older than I (his first battle was, I think, long ago), so we'll concede it to make up for his years.'

'I can't say that to the Prince, Queen,' said the herald.

Then I thought I had done enough (I knew others would hear my gibe even if Argan didn't) and we went orderly to work on all the conditions of the fight and the hundred small things that had to be agreed on. It was the best part of an hour before the herald was gone. The Fox, I could see, was in great pain while all these provisions were being made; the thing growing more real and more irrevocable at each word. I was mostly the Queen now, but Orual would whisper a cold word in the Queen's ear at times.

After that came Arnom, and even before he spoke we knew the old Priest was dead and Arnom had succeeded him. He wore the skins and the bladders, the bird-mark hung at his chest. The sight of all that gave me a sudden shock, like a vile dream, forgotten on waking but suddenly remembered at noon. But my second glance braced me. He would never be terrible like the old Priest. He was only Arnom, with whom I had driven a very good bargain yesterday; there was no feeling that Ungit came into the room with him. And that started strange thoughts in my mind.

But I had no time to follow them. Arnom and the Fox went to the Bedchamber and fell into talk about the King's condition (those two seemed to understand each other well) and Bardia beckoned me out of the room. We went out by the little eastern door, where the Fox and I had gone on the morning Psyche was born, and there paced up and down between the herb-beds while we talked.

'Now, Queen,' said he, 'this is your first battle.'

'And you doubt my courage?'

'Not your courage to be killed, Queen. But you've never killed; and this must be a killing matter.'

'What then?'

'Why, just this. Women and boys talk easily about killing a man. Yet, believe me, it's a hard thing to do; I mean, the first time. There's something in a man that goes against it.'

'You think I'd pity him?'

'I don't know if it's pity. But the first time I did it – it was the hardest thing in the world to make my own hand plunge the sword into all that live flesh.'

'But you did.'

'Yes; my enemy was a bungler. But how if he'd been quick? That's the danger, you see. There's a moment when one pause – the fifth part of the time it takes to wink your eye – may lose a chance. And it might be your only chance, and then you'd have lost the battle.'

'I don't think my hand would delay, Bardia,' said I. I was trying to test it in my mind. I pictured my father, well again, and coming at me in one of his old rages; I felt sure my hand would not fail me to stab him. It had not failed when I stabbed myself.

'We'll hope not,' said Bardia. 'But you must go through the exercise. I make all the recruits do it.'

'The exercise?'

'Yes. You know they're to kill a pig this morning. You must be the butcher, Queen.'

I saw in a flash that if I shrank from this there would at once be less Queen and more Orual in me.

'I am ready,' said I. I understood the work pretty well, for of course we had seen the slaughtering of beasts ever since we were children. Redival had always watched and always screamed; I had watched less often and held my tongue. So now I went and killed my pig. (We kill pigs without sacrifice, for these beasts are an abomination to Ungit; there is a sacred story that explains why.) And I swore that if I came back alive from the combat Bardia and the Fox and Trunia and I should eat the choicest parts of it for our supper. Then, when I had taken off my butcher's apron and washed, I went back to the Pillar Room; for I had thought of something that must be done, now that my life might be only two days. The Fox was already there; I called Bardia and Arnom for witnesses and declared the Fox free.

Next moment I was plunged in despair. I cannot now understand how I had been so blind as not to foresee it. My only thought had been to save him from being mocked and neglected and perhaps sold by Redival if I were dead. But now, as soon as the other two were done wishing him joy and kissing him on the cheeks, it all broke on me. 'You'll be a loss to our councils—' 'There are many in Glome who'll be sorry to see you go—' 'Don't make your journey in winter—' What were they saying?

'Grandfather!' I cried, no Queen now; all Orual, even all child. 'Do they mean you'll leave me? Go away?'

The Fox raised towards me a face full of infinite trouble, twitching. 'Free?' he muttered. 'You mean I could ... I can ... it wouldn't matter much even if I died on the way. Not if I could get down to the sea. There'd be tunnies; olives. No, it'd be too early in the year for olives. But the smell of the harbours. And walking about the market talking; real talk. But you don't know, this is all foolishness, none of you know. I should be thanking you, daughter. But if ever you loved me, don't speak to me now. Tomorrow. Let me go.' He pulled his cloak over his head and groped his way out of the room.

And now this game of queenship, which had buoyed me up and kept me busy ever since I woke that morning, failed me utterly. We had made all our preparations for the combat. There was the rest of the day, and the whole of the next, to wait; and hanging over it, this new desolation, that if I lived I might have to live without the Fox.

I went out into the gardens. I would not go up to that plot behind the pear trees; that was where he, and Psyche, and I had often been happiest. I wandered, miserably, out on the other side, on the west of the apple orchard, till the cold drove me in; it was a bitter, black frost that day, with no sun. I am both ashamed and afraid to revive, by writing of them, the thoughts I had. In my ignorance I could not understand the strength of the desire which must be drawing my old master to his own land. I had lived in one place all my life; everything in Glome was to me stale, common, and taken for granted, even filled with memories of dread, sorrow, and humiliation. I had no notion how the remembered home looks to an exile. It embittered me that the Fox should even desire to leave me. He had been the central pillar of my whole life, something (I thought) as sure and established, and indeed as little thanked, as sunrise and the mere earth. In my folly I had thought I was to him as he was to me. 'Fool!' said I to myself. 'Have you not yet learned that you are that to no one? What are you to Bardia? as much perhaps as the old king was. His heart lies at home with his wife and her brats. If you mattered to him he'd never have let you fight. What are you to the Fox? His heart was always in the Greeklands. You were, maybe, the solace of his captivity. They say a prisoner will tame a rat. He comes to love the rat; after a fashion. But throw the door open, strike off his fetters, and how much'll he care for the rat then?' And yet, how could he leave us, after so much love? I saw him again with Psyche on his knees. 'Prettier than Aphrodite,' he had said. 'Yes, but that was Psyche,' said my heart. 'If she were still with us, he would stay. It was Psyche he loved. Never me.' I knew while I said it that it was false, yet I would not, or could not, put it out of my head.

But the Fox sought me out before I slept; his face very grey, and his manner very quiet. But that he did not limp, you would have thought he had been in the hands of the torturers. 'Wish me well, daughter,' he said. 'For I have won a battle. What's best for his fellows must be best for a man. I am but a limb of the whole and must work in the socket where I'm put. I'll stay, and—'

'Oh, Grandfather!' said I, and wept.

'Peace, peace,' he said, embracing me. 'What would I have done in Greece? My father is dead. My sons have, no doubt, forgotten me. My daughter ... should I not be only a trouble – *a dream strayed into daylight* as the verse says? Anyhow, it's a long journey and beset with dangers. I might never have reached the sea.'

And so he went on, making little of his deed, as if he feared I would dissuade him from it. But I, with my face on his breast, felt only the joy.

I went to look at my father many times that day, but could see no change in him.

That night I slept ill. It was not fear of the combat, but a restlessness that came from the manifold changes which the gods were sending upon me. The old Priest's death, by itself, would have been matter for a week's thought. I had hoped it before (and then, if he had died, it might have saved Psyche) but never really reckoned to see him go more than to wake one morning and find the Grey Mountain gone. The freeing of the Fox, though I had done it myself, felt to me like another impossible change. It was as if my father's sickness had drawn away some prop and the whole world – all the world I knew – had fallen to pieces. I was journeying into a strange, new land. It was so new and strange that I could not, that night, even feel my great sorrow. This astonished me. One part of me made to snatch that sorrow back; it said, 'Orual dies if she ceases to love Psyche.' But the other said, 'Let Orual die. She would never have made a queen.'

The last day, the eve of the battle, shows like a dream. Every hour made it more unbelievable. The noise and fame of my combat had got abroad (it was no part of our policy to be secret) and there were crowds of the common people at the palace gates. Though I valued their favour no more than it deserved – I remembered how they had turned against Psyche – yet, willynilly, their cheering quickened my pulse and sent a kind of madness into my brain. Some of the better sort, lords and elders, came to wait upon me. They all accepted me for Queen, and I spoke little but, I think, well – Bardia and the Fox praised it – and watched their eyes staring at my veil and manifestly wondering what it hid. Then I went to Prince Trunia in the tower room and told him we had found a champion (I did not say whom) to fight for him and how he would be brought in honourable custody to see the fight. Though this must have been uneasy news for him, he was too just a man not to see that we were using him as well as our weakness would bear. Then I called for wine that we might drink together. But when the door opened – this angered me for the moment – instead of my father's butler it was Redival who came in bearing the flagon and the cup. I was a fool not to have foreseen it. I knew her well enough to guess that once there was a strange man in the house she'd eat her way through stone walls in order to be seen. Yet even I was astonished to see what a meek, shy, modest, dutiful younger sister (perhaps even a somewhat downtrodden and spirit-broken sister) she could make of herself carrying that wine; with her downcast eyes (which missed nothing from Trunia's bandaged foot to the hair of his head) and her child's gravity.

'Who's that beauty?' said Trunia as soon as she was gone.

'That's my sister, the Princess Redival,' said I.

'Glome is a rose garden; even in winter,' said he. 'But why, cruel Queen, do you hide your own face?'

'If you become better known to my sister, she'll doubtless tell you,' said I; more sharply than I had intended.

'Why, that might be,' said the Prince. 'If your champion wins tomorrow; otherwise death's my wife. But if I live, Queen, I wouldn't let this friendship between our houses die away. Why should I not marry into your line? Perhaps yourself, Queen?'

'There's no room for two on my throne, Prince.'

'Your sister then?'

It was of course an offer to be seized. Yet for a moment, saying yes to it irked me; most likely because I thought this prince twenty times too good for her.

'For all I can see,' said I, 'this marriage can be made. I must speak to my wise men first. For my own part, I like it well.'

The day ended more strangely than it began. Bardia had had me into the quarters for my last practice. 'There's that old fault of yours, Queen,' he said, 'in the feint reverse. I think we've conquered it; but I must see you perfect.' We went at it for half an hour and when we stopped to breathe he said, 'That's as perfect as skill can go. It's my belief that if you and I were to fight with sharps you'd kill me. But there are two things more to say. This first. If it should happen, Queen – and most likely it won't happen to you, because of your divine blood – but if it should happen that when your cloak's off and the crowd's hushed and you're walking out into the empty space to meet your man – if you should then feel fear, never heed it. We've all felt it at our first fight. I feel it myself before every fight. And the second's this. That hauberk you've been wearing is excellent for weight and fit. But it's a poor thing to look at. A trace of gilding would suit a queen and a champion better. Let's see what the Bedchamber has.'

I have said before that the King kept all manner of arms and armours in there. So in we went. The Fox was sitting by the bedside; why, or with what thoughts, I don't know. It was not possible he should love his old master. 'Still no change,' he said. Bardia and I fell to rummaging among the mail, and soon to disputing; for I thought I'd be safer and more limber in the chain-shirt which I knew than in any other, and he kept on saying, 'But wait – wait – now here's a better.' And it was when we were most busied that the Fox's voice from behind said, 'It's finished.' We turned and looked. The thing on the bed which had been half-alive for so long was dead; had died (if he understood it) seeing a girl ransacking his armoury.

'Peace be upon him,' said Bardia. 'We'll be done here very shortly. Then the women can come and wash the body.' And we turned again at once to settle the matter of the hauberks.

And so the thing that I had thought of for so many years at last slipped by in a huddle of business which was, at that moment, of more consequence. An hour later, when I looked back, it astonished me. Yet I have often noticed since how much less stir nearly everyone's death makes than you might expect. Men better loved and more worth loving than my father go down making only a small eddy.

I kept to my old hauberk, but we told the armourer to scour it well, so that it might pass for silver.

19

On a great day the thing that makes it great may fill the least part of it, as a meal takes little time to eat, but the killing, baking and dressing, and the swilling and scraping after it, take long enough. My fight with the Prince took about the sixth part of an hour; yet the business about it, more than twelve.

First of all, now that the Fox was a freeman and the Queen's Lantern (so we call it, though my father had let the office sleep) I would have him at the fight and splendidly dressed. But you never had more trouble with a peevish girl going to her first feast. He said all barbarians' clothes were barbarous and the finer the worse. He would go in his old moth-eaten gown. And when we had brought him into some kind of order, then Bardia wanted me to fight without my veil. He thought it would blind me and did not see how it could well be worn either over or under my helmet. But I refused altogether to fight bareface. In the end I had Poobi to stitch me up a hood or mask of fine stuff, but such as could not be seen through; it had two eyeholes and covered the whole helmet. All this was needless, for I had fought Bardia himself in my old veil a dozen times; but the mask made me look very dreadful, as a ghost might look. 'If he's the coward they'd make him,' said Bardia, 'that'll cool his stomach.' And then we had to start very early, it seemed, for the crowd in the streets would make us ride slowly. So we had Trunia down and were all presently on horseback. There was some talk of dressing him fine too, but he refused this.

'Whether your champion kills or is killed,' he said, 'I'll fare no better in purple than in my old battle order. But where is your champion, Queen?'

'You shall see when we come to the field, Prince,' said I.

Trunia had started when he first saw me shrouded like a ghost; neither throat nor helmet to be seen, but two eyeholes in a white hummock; scarecrow or leper. I thought his starting boded well how it would taste to Argan.

Several lords and elders waited for us at the gate to bring us through the city. It's easy to guess what I was thinking. So Psyche had gone out that day to heal the people; and so she had gone out that other day to be offered to the Brute. Perhaps, thought I, this is what the god meant when he said *You also shall be Psyche*. I also might be an offering. That was a good, firm thought to lay hold of. But the thing was so near now that I could think very little of my own death or life. With all those eyes upon me, my only care was to make a brave show both now and in the fight. I'd have given ten talents to any prophet who could have foretold me that I'd fight well for five minutes and then be killed.

The lords who rode nearest me were very grave. I supposed (and indeed one or two confessed as much to me afterwards when I came to know them) they thought Argan would soon have me disarmed, but that my mad challenge was as good a way as any of getting him and Trunia both out of our country. But if the lords were glum, the common people in the streets were huzzaing and throwing caps in the air. It would have puffed me up if I had not looked in their faces. There, I could read their mind easily enough. Neither I nor Glome was in their thoughts. Any fight was a free show for them; and a fight of a woman with a man better still because an oddity; as those who can't tell one tune from another will crowd to hear the harp if a man plays it with his toes.

When at last we got down to the open field by the river there had to be more delays. Arnom was there, in his bird-mask, and there was a bull to be sacrificed; so well the gods have wound themselves into our affairs that nothing can be done but they have their bit. And opposite us, on the far side of the field, were the horsemen of Phars, and Argan sitting on his horse in the midst of them. It was the strangest thing in the world to look upon him, a man like any other man, and think that one of us presently would kill the other. *Kill*; it seemed like a word I'd never spoken before. He was a man with straw-coloured hair and beard, thin, yet somehow bloated, with pouting lips; a very unpleasing person. Then he and I dismounted and came close and each had to taste a tiny morsel of the bull's flesh, and take oaths on behalf of our peoples that all the agreements would be kept. And now, I thought, surely now they'll let us begin. (There was a pale white sun in a grey sky that day, and a biting wind; 'Do they want us to freeze before we fight?' I thought.) But now the people had to be pressed back with the butt-ends of spears, and the field cleared, and Bardia must go across and whisper something to Argan's chief man, and both of them must go and whisper to Arnom, and Argan's trumpeter and mine must be placed side by side.

'Now, Queen,' said Bardia suddenly, when I had half despaired of ever getting to the end of the preparations, 'the gods guard you.'

The Fox was standing with his face set like iron; he would have wept if he had tried to speak. I saw a great shock of surprise come over Trunia (and I never blamed him for turning pale) when I flung off my cloak, drew my sword, and stepped out on to the open grass.

The men from Phars roared with laughter. Our mob cheered. Argan was within ten paces of me, then five; then, we were at it.

I know he began despising me; there was a lazy insolence in his first passes. But I took the skin off his knuckles with one lucky stroke (and maybe numbed his hand a little) and that brought him to his senses. Though my eye never left his sword, yet I somehow saw his face as well. 'Cross-patch,' thought I. He had a puckered brow and a sort of blackguardly fret-fulness about his lip, which perhaps already masked some fear. For my part, I felt no fear because, now that we were really at it, I did not believe in the combat at all. It was so like all my sham fights with Bardia; the same strokes, feints, deadlocks. Even the blood on his knuckles made no difference; a blunt sword, or the flat of a sword, could have done as much.

You, the Greek for whom I write, may never have fought; or if you did you fought, most likely, as a hoplite. Unless I were with you and had a sword, or at least a stick, in my hand I could not make you understand the course of it. I soon felt sure he could not kill me. But I was less sure I could kill him. I was very afraid lest the thing should last too long and his greater strength would grind me down. What I shall remember for ever is the change that presently came over his face. It was to me an utter astonish-ment. I did not understand it. I should now. I have since seen the faces of other men as they began to believe, 'This is death.' You will know it if you have seen it; life more alive than ever, a raging, tortured intensity of life. Then he made his first bad mistake, and I missed my chance. It seemed a long time (it was a few minutes really) before he made it again. That time I was ready for it. I gave the straight thrust and then, all in one motion, wheeled my sword round and cut him deeply in the inner leg, where no surgery will stop the bleeding. I jumped back of course, lest his fall should bear me down with him; so my first man-killing bespattered me less than my first pig-killing.

People ran to him, but there was no possibility of saving his life. The shouting of the mob dinned in my ears, sounding strange as all things sound when you're in your helmet. I was scarcely out of breath even; most of my bouts with Bardia had been far longer. Yet I felt of a sudden very weak and my legs were shaking; and I felt myself changed too, as if something had been taken away from me. I have often wondered if women feel like that when they lose their virginity.

Bardia (the Fox close behind him) came running up to me, with tears in his eyes and joy all over his face. 'Blessed! Blessed!' he cried. 'Queen! Warrior! My best scholar! Gods, how prettily you did it! A stroke to remember all one's days.' And he raised my left hand to his lips. I wept hard and kept my head well down so that he should not see the tears dropping from under the mask. But long before I had my voice back they were all about me (Trunia still on horseback because he could not walk) with praises and thanks, till I was almost pestered with it, though a little sweet-sharp prickle of pride thrust up inside me. There was no peace. I must speak to the people, and to the men of Phars. I must, it seemed, do a score of things. And I thought, 'Oh, for that bowl of milk, drunk alone in the cool dairy, the first day I ever used a sword!'

As soon as I had my voice I called for my horse, mounted, brought it alongside Trunia's, and held out my hand to him. Thus we rode forward a few paces and faced the horsemen of Phars.

'Strangers,' said I, 'you have seen Prince Argan killed in clean combat. Is there any more debate concerning the succession of Phars?'

About half a dozen of them, who had, no doubt, been Argan's chief partisans, made no other answer than to wheel about and gallop off. The rest all raised their helmets on their spears and shouted for Trunia and peace. Then I let go his hand, and he rode forward and in among them and was soon talking with their captains.

'Now, Queen,' said Bardia in my ear, 'it's an absolute necessity that you should bid some of our notables and some of those from Phars (the Prince will tell us which) to a feast in the palace. And Arnom too.'

'A feast, Bardia? Of bean-bread? You know we've bare larders in Glome.'

'There's the pig, Queen. And Ungit must let us have a share of the bull; I'll speak to Arnom of it. You must let the King's cellar blood to some purpose tonight, and then the bread will be less noticed.' Thus my fancy of a snug supper with Bardia and the Fox was dashed, and my sword not yet wiped from the blood of my first battle before I found myself all woman again and caught up in housewife's cares. If only I could have ridden away from them all and got to the butler before they reached the palace and learned what wine we really had! My father (and doubtless Batta) had had enough to swim in during his last few days.

In the end there were five-and-twenty of us (counting in myself) who rode back from that field to the palace. The Prince was at my side, saying all manner of fine things about me (as indeed he had some reason) and always begging me to let him see my face. It was only a kind of courteous banter and would have been nothing to any other woman. To me it was so new and (I must confess this also) so sweet that I could not choose but keep the sport up a little. I had been happy, far happier than I could hope to be again, with Psyche and the Fox, long ago, before our troubles. Now, for the first time in all my life (and the last), I was gay. A new world, very bright, seemed to be opening all round me.

It was of course the gods' old trick; blow the bubble up big before you prick it.

They pricked it a moment after I had crossed the threshold of my house. A little girl whom I'd never seen before, a slave, came out from some corner where she'd been lurking and whispered in Bardia's ear. He had been very merry up till now; the sunlight went out of his face. Then he came up to me, and said, half shamefacedly, 'Queen, the day's work is over. You'll not need me now. I'd take it very kindly if you'll let me go home. My wife's taken with her pains. We had thought it could not be so soon. I'd be glad to be with her tonight.'

I understood in that moment all my father's rages. I put terrible constraint on myself and said, 'Why, Bardia, it is very fit you should. Commend me to your wife. And offer this ring to Ungit for her safe delivery.' The ring which I took off my finger was the choicest I had.

His thanks were hearty; yet he had hardly time to utter them before he was speeding away. I suppose he never dreamed what he had done to me with those words *the day's work is over*. Yes, that was it; the day's work. I was his work; he earned his bread by being my soldier. When his tale of work for the day was done, he went home, like other hired men, and took up his true life.

That night's banquet was the first I had ever been at and the last I ever sat through (we do not lie at table like Greeks but sit on chairs or benches). After this, though I gave many feasts, I never did more than to come in three times and pledge the most notable guests and speak to all and then out again; always with two of my women attending me. This has saved me much weariness, besides putting about a great notion either of my pride or my modesty which has been useful enough. That night I sat nearly to the end, the only woman in the whole mob of them. Three parts of me was a shamed and frightened Orual who looked forward to a scolding from the Fox for being there at all, and was bitterly lonely; the fourth part was Queen, proud (though dazed too) amid the heat and clamour, sometimes dreaming she could laugh loud and drink deep like a man and a warrior, next moment, more madly, answering to Trunia's daffing, as if her veil hid the face of a pretty woman.

When I got away and up into the cold and stillness of the gallery my head reeled and ached. And 'Faugh!' I thought. 'What vile things men are!' They were all drunk by now (except the Fox, who had gone early), but their drinking had sickened me less than their eating. I had never seen men at their pleasures before: the gobbling, snatching, belching, hiccuping, the greasiness of it all, the bones thrown on the floor, the dogs quarrelling under our feet. Were all men such? Would Bardia—? then back came my loneliness. My double loneliness, for Bardia, for Psyche. Not separable. The picture, the impossible fool's dream, was that all should have been different from the very beginning and he would have been my husband and Psyche our daughter. Then I would have been in labour ... with Psyche ... and to me he would have been coming home. But now I discovered the wonderful power of wine. I understand why men become drunkards. For the way it worked on me was not at all that it blotted out these sorrows, but that it made them seem glorious and noble, like sad music, and I somehow great and reverend for feeling them. I was a great, sad queen in a song. I did not check the big tears that rose in my eyes. I enjoyed them. To say all, I was drunk; I played the fool.

And so, to my fool's bed. What was that? No, no, not a girl crying in the garden. No one, cold, hungry, and banished, was shivering there, longing and not daring to come in. It was the chains swinging at the well. It would be folly to get up and go out and call again; Psyche, Psyche, my only love. I am a great queen. I have killed a man. I am drunk like a man. All warriors drink deep after the battle. Bardia's lips on my hand were like the touch of lightning. All great princes have mistresses or lovers. There's the crying again. No, it's only the buckets at the well. Shut the window, Poobi. To your bed, child. Do you love me, Poobi? Kiss me good night. Good night. The King's dead. He'll never pull my hair again. A straight thrust and then a cut in the leg. That would have killed him. I am the Queen; I'll kill Orual too.

20

On the next day we burnt the old King; on the day after that we betrothed Redival to Trunia (and the wedding was made a month later); the third day all the strangers rode off and we had the house to ourselves. My real reign began.

I must now pass quickly over many years (though they made up the longest part of my life) during which the Queen of Glome had more and more part in me and Orual had less and less. I locked her up or laid her asleep as best I could somewhere deep down inside me; she lay curled there. It was like being with child, but reversed; the thing I carried in me grew slowly smaller and less alive.

It may happen that someone who reads this book will have heard tales and songs about my reign and my wars and great deeds. Let him be sure that most of it is false, for I know already that the common talk, and especially in neighbouring lands, has doubled and trebled the truth, and my deeds, such as they were, have been mixed up with those of some great fighting queen who lived long ago and (I think) further north, and a fine patchwork of wonders and impossibilities made out of both. But the truth is that after my battle with Argan there were only three wars that I fought, and one of them, the last, against the Wagon Men who live beyond the Grey Mountain, was a very slight thing. And though I rode out with my men in all these wars, I was never such a fool as to think myself a great captain. All that part of it was Bardia's and Penuan's. (I met him first the night after I fought Argan, and he became the trustiest of my nobles.) I will also say this: I was never yet at any battle but that, when the lines were drawn up and the first enemy arrows came flashing in among us, and the grass and trees about you suddenly became a place, a Field, a thing to be put in chronicles, I wished very heartily that I had stayed at home. Nor did I ever do any notable deed with my own arm but once. That was in the war with Essur, when some of their horse came out of an ambush and Bardia, riding to his position, was surrounded all in a moment. Then I galloped in and hardly knew what I was doing till the matter was over, and they say I had killed seven men with my own strokes. (I was wounded that day.) But to hear the common rumour you would think I had planned every war and every battle and killed more enemies than all the rest of our army put together.

My real strength lay in two things. The first was that I had, and especially for the first years, two very good counsellors. You couldn't have had better yokefellows, for the Fox understood what Bardia did not, and neither cared a straw for his own dignity or advancement when my needs were in question. And I came to understand (what my girl's ignorance had once hidden from me) that their girding and mocking at one another was little more than a sort of game. They were no flatterers either. In this way I had some profit of my ugliness; they did not think of me as a woman. If they had, it is impossible that we three, alone, by the hearth in the Pillar Room (as we were often) should have talked with such freedom. I learned from them a thousand things about men.

My second strength lay in my veil. I could never have believed, till I had proof of it, what it would do for me. From the very first (it began that night in the garden with Trunia) as soon as my face was invisible, people began to discover all manner of beauties in my voice. At first it was 'deep as a man's, but nothing in the world less mannish'; later, and until it grew cracked with age, it was the voice of a spirit, a Siren, Orpheus, what you will. And as years passed and there were fewer in the city (and none beyond it) who remembered my face, the wildest stories got about as to what that veil hid. No one believed it was anything so common as the face of an ugly woman. Some said (nearly all the younger women said) that it was frightful beyond endurance; a pig's, bear's, cat's, or elephant's face. The best story was that I had no face at all; if you stripped off my veil you'd find emptiness. But another sort (there were more of the men among these) said that I wore a veil because I was of a beauty so dazzling that if I let it be seen all men in the world would run mad; or else that Ungit was jealous of my beauty and had promised to blast me if I went bareface. The upshot of all this nonsense was that I became something very mysterious and awful. I have seen ambassadors, who were brave men in battle, turn white like scared children in my Pillar Room when I turned and looked at them (and they couldn't see whether I was looking or not) and was silent. I have made the most seasoned liars turn red and blurt out the truth with the same weapon.

The first thing I did was to shift my own quarters over to the north side of the palace, in order to be out of that sound the chains made in the well. For though, by daylight, I knew well enough what made it, at night nothing I could do would cure me of taking it for the weeping of a girl. But the change of my quarters, and later changes (for I tried every side of the house) did no good. I discovered that there was no part of the palace from which the swinging of those chains could not be heard; at night, I mean, when the silence grows deep. It is a thing no one would have found out who was not always afraid of hearing one sound; and at the same time (that was Orual, Orual refusing to die) terribly afraid of not hearing it if for once – if possibly, at last, after ten thousand mockeries – it should be real, if Psyche had come back. But I knew this was foolishness. If Psyche were alive and able to come back, and wanted to come back, she would have done it long ago. She must be dead by now; or caught by someone and sold into slavery … When that thought came, my only resource was to rise, however late and cold it was, and go to my Pillar Room and find some work. I have read and written there till I could hardly see out of my eyes; my head on fire, my feet aching with cold.

Of course I had my bidders in every slave market, and my seekers in every land that I could reach, and listened to every traveller's tale that might put us on Psyche's track. I did these things for years, but they were infinitely irksome to me for I knew it was all hopeless.

Before I had reigned for a year (I remember the time well, for the men were picking the figs) I had Batta hanged. Following up a chance word which one of the horseboys said in my hearing, I found that she had long been the pest of the whole palace. No trifle could be given to any of the other slaves, and hardly a good bit could come on their trenchers, but Batta must have her share of it; otherwise she'd tell such tales of them as would lead to the whipping-post or the mines. And after Batta was hanged I went on and reduced the household to better order. There were far too many slaves. Some thieves and sluts I sold. Many of the good ones, both men and women, if they were sturdy and prudent (for otherwise to free a slave is but to have a new beggar at your door), I set free, and gave them land and cottages for their livelihood. I coupled them off in pairs and married them. Sometimes I even let them choose their own wives or husbands, which is a strange, unusual way of making even slaves' marriages, and yet it often turned out well enough. Though it was a great loss to me I set Poobi free, and she chose a very good man. Some of my happiest hours have been beside the fire in her cottage. And most of these freed people have become very thriving husbandmen, all living near the palace, and very faithful to me. It was like having a second body of guards.

I set the mines (they are silver mines) on a better footing. My father had never, it seems, thought of them save as a punishment. 'Take him to the mines!' he'd say. 'I'll teach him. Work him to death.' But there was more death than work in the mines, and the yield was light. As soon as I could get an honest overseer (Bardia was incomparable for finding out such men) I bought strong, young slaves for the mines, saw that they had dry lodging and good feeding, and let every man know that he should go free when he had, adding day by day, dug so much ore. The tale was such that a steady man could hope for his freedom in ten years; later, we brought it down to seven. This lowered the yield for the first year, but had raised it by a tenth in the third; now, it is half as great again as in my father's day. Ours is the best silver in all this part of the world, and a great root of our wealth.

I took the Fox out of the wretched dog-hole in which he had slept all these years and gave him noble apartments on the south side of the palace; and land for his living, so that he should not seem to hang by my bounties. I also put money into his hands for the buying (if it should prove possible) of books. It took a long time for traders, perhaps twenty kingdoms away, to learn that there was a vent for books in Glome, and longer still for the books to come up, changing hands many times and often delayed for a year or more on the journey. The Fox tore his hair at the cost of them. 'An obol's worth for a talent,' he said. We had to take what we could get, not what we chose. In this way we built up what was, for a barbarous land, a noble library: eighteen works in all. We had Homer's poetry about Troy, imperfect, coming down to that place where he brings in Patroclus weeping. We had two tragedies of Euripides, one about Andromeda and another where Dionysus says the prologue and the chorus is the wild women. Also a very good, useful book (without metre) about the breeding and drenching of horses and cattle, the worming of dogs, and such matters. Also, some of the conversations of Socrates; a poem in honour of Helen by Hesias Stesichorus; a book of Heraclitus; and a very long, hard book (without metre) which begins *All men by nature desire knowledge*. As soon as the books began to come in, Arnom would often be with the Fox, learning to read in them; and presently other men, mostly younger sons of nobles, came too.

And now I began to live as a Queen should, and to know my own nobles, and to show courtesies to the great ladies of the land. In this way, of necessity, I came to meet Bardia's wife, Ansit. I had thought she would be of dazzling beauty; but the truth is she was very short, and now, having borne eight children, very fat and unshapely. All the women of Glome splay out like that, pretty early in their lives. (That was one thing, perhaps, which helped the fantasy that I had a lovely face behind my veil. Being a virgin, I had kept my shape, and that – if you didn't see my face – was for a long time very tolerable.) I put great force upon myself to be courteous to Ansit; more than courteous, even loving. More than that, I would have loved her indeed, for Bardia's sake, if I could have done it. But she was mute as a mouse in my presence; afraid of me, I thought. When we tried to talk together, her eyes would wander round the room as if she were asking, 'Who will deliver me from this?' In a sudden flash, not without joy in it, the thought came to me, 'Can she be jealous?' And so it was, through all those years, whenever we met. Sometimes I would say to myself, 'She has lain in his bed, and that's bad. She has borne his children, and that's worse. But, has she ever crouched beside him in the ambush? Ever ridden knee to knee with him in the charge? Or shared a stinking water-bottle with him at the thirsty day's end? For all the dove's eyes they've made at one another, was there ever such a glance between them as well-proved comrades exchange in farewell when they ride different ways and both into desperate danger? I have known, I have had, so much of him that she could never dream of. She's his toy, his recreation, his leisure, his solace. I'm in his man's life.'

It's strange to think how Bardia went to and fro daily between Queen and wife, well assured he did his duty by both (as he did) and without thought, doubtless, of the pother he made between them. This is what it is to be a man. The one sin the gods never forgive us is that of being born women.

The duty of queenship that irked me most was going often to the house of Ungit and sacrificing. It would have been worse but that Ungit herself (or my pride made me think so) was now weakened. Arnom had opened new windows in the walls and her house was not so dark. He also kept it differently, scouring away the blood after each slaughter and sprinkling fresh water; it smelled cleaner and less holy. And Arnom was learning from the Fox to talk like a philosopher about the gods. The great change came when he proposed to set up an image of her – a woman-shaped image in the Greek fashion – in front of the old shapeless stone. I think he would like to have got rid of the stone altogether, but it is, in a manner, Ungit herself and the people would have gone mad if she were moved. It was a prodigious charge to get such an image as he wanted, for no one in Glome could make it; it had to be brought, not indeed from the Greeklands themselves, but from lands where men had learned of the Greeks. I was rich now and helped him with silver. I was not quite certain why I did this; I think I felt that an image of this sort would be somehow a defeat for the old, hungry, faceless Ungit whose terror had been over me in childhood. The new image, when at last it came, seemed to us barbarians wonderfully beautiful and lifelike, even when we brought her white and naked into her house; and when we had painted her and put her robes on, she was a marvel to all the lands about and pilgrims came to see her. The Fox, who had seen greater and more beautiful works at home, laughed at her.

I gave up trying to find a room where I should not hear that noise which was sometimes chains swinging in the wind and sometimes lost and beggared Psyche weeping at my door. Instead, I built stone walls round the well and put a thatched roof over it and added a door. The walls were very thick; my mason told me they were madly thick. 'You're wasting enough good stone, Queen,' he said, 'to have made ten new pigsties.' For a while after that an ugly fancy used to come to me in my dreams, or between sleeping and waking, that I had walled up, gagged with stone, not a well but Psyche (or

Orual) herself. But that also passed. I heard Psyche weeping no more. The year after that I defeated Essur.

The Fox was growing old now and needed rest; we had him less and less in my Pillar Room. He was very busy writing a history of Glome. He wrote it twice, in Greek and in our own tongue, which, he said, he now saw was capable of eloquence. It was strange for me to see our own speech written out in the Greek letters. I never told the Fox that he knew less of it than he believed, so that what he wrote in it was often laughable and most so where he thought it most eloquent. As he grew older he seemed to be ever less and less a philosopher, and to talk more of eloquence, and figures, and poetry. His voice grew always shriller and he talked more and more. He often mistook me for Psyche now; sometimes he called me Crethis, and sometimes even by boys' names like Charmides or Glaucon.

But I was too busy to be with him much. What did I not do? I had all the laws revised and cut in stone in the centre of the city. I narrowed and deepened the Shennit till barges could come up to our gates. I made a bridge where the old ford had been. I made cisterns so that we should not go thirsty whenever there was a dry year. I became wise about stock and bought in good bulls and rams and bettered our breeds. I did and I did and I did – and what does it matter what I did? I cared for all these things only as a man cares for a hunt or a game, which fills the mind and seems of some moment while it lasts, but then the beast's killed or the king's mated, and now who cares? It was so with me almost every evening of my life; one little stairway led me from feast or council, all the bustle and skill and glory of queenship, to my own chamber, to be alone with myself; that is, with a nothingness. Going to bed and waking in the morning (I woke, most often, too early) were bad times – so many hundreds of evenings and mornings. Sometimes I wondered who or what sends us this senseless repetition of days and nights and seasons and years; is it not like hearing a stupid boy whistle the same tune over and over, till you wonder how he can bear it himself?

The Fox died and I gave him a kingly funeral and made four Greek verses which were cut on his tomb; I will not write them here lest a true Greek should laugh at them. This happened about the end of harvest. The tomb is up behind the pear trees where he used to teach Psyche and me in summer. Then the days and months and years went on again as before, round and round like a wheel, till there came a day when I looked about me at the gardens and the palace and the ridge of the Grey Mountain out eastward, and thought I could no longer endure to see these same things every day till I died. The very blisters of the pitch on the wooden walls of the byres seemed to be the same ones I had seen before the Fox himself came to Glome. I resolved to go on a progress and travel in other lands. We were at peace with everyone. Bardia and Penuan and Arnom could do all that was needed while I was away; for indeed Glome had now been nursed and trained till it almost ruled itself.

I took with me Bardia's son Ilerdia, and Poobi's daughter Alit, and two of my women and a plump of spears (all honest men), and a cook and a groom with pack animals for the tents and victuals, and rode out of Glome three days later.

21

The thing for whose sake I tell of this journey happened at the very end of it; and even when I had thought it was finished. We had gone first into Phars, where they harvest later than we, so that it was like having that piece of the year twice over; we found what we had just left at home – the sound of the whetting, the singing of the reapers, the flats of stubble widening and the squares of standing corn diminishing, the piled wagons in the lanes, all the sweat and sunburn and merriment. We had lain ten nights or more in Trunia's palace, where I was astonished to see how Redival had grown fat and lost her beauty. She talked, as of old, everlastingly, but all about her children, and asked after no one in Glome except Batta. Trunia never listened to a word she said, but he and I had much talk together. I had already settled with my council that his second son, Daaran, was to be King of Glome after my day. This Daaran was (for the son of so silly a mother) a right-minded boy. I could have loved him if I had let myself and if Redival had been out of the way. But I would never give my heart again to any young creature.

Out of Phars we had turned westward into Essur by deep passes through the mountains. This was a country of forests greater than I had yet seen, and rushing rivers, with plenty of birds, deer, and other game. The people I had with me were all young and took great pleasure in their travels, and the journey itself had by now linked us all together; all burned brown, and with a world of hopes, cares, jests, and knowledge, all sprung up since we left home, and shared among us. At first they had been in awe of me and had ridden in silence; now we were good friends. My own heart lifted. The eagles wheeled above us and the waterfalls roared.

From the mountains we came down into Essur and lay three nights in the King's house. He was, I think, not a bad sort of man, but too slavish-courteous to me; for Glome and Phars in alliance had made Essur change her tune. His queen was manifestly terrified by my veil and by the stories she had heard of me. And from that house I had meant to turn homewards, but we

were told of a natural hot spring fifteen miles further to the west. I knew
Ilerdia longed to see it; and I thought (between sadness and smiling) how the
Fox would have scolded me if I had been so near any curious work of nature
and not examined it. So I said we would go the day's journey further and
turn then.

It was the calmest day; pure autumn; very hot, yet the sunlight on the stubble looked aged and gentle, not fierce like the summer heats. You would
think the year was resting, its work done. And I whispered to myself that
I too would begin to rest. When I was back at Glome I would no longer pile
task on task. I would let Bardia rest too (I had often thought he began to look
tired) and we would let younger heads be busy, while we sat in the sun and
talked of our old battles. What more was there for me to do? Why should
I not be at peace? I thought this was the wisdom of old age beginning.

The hot spring (like all such rarities) was only food for stupid wonder.
When we had seen it we went further down the warm, green valley in which
it rose and found a good camping place between a stream and a wood. While
my people were busied with the tents and the horses, I went a little way into
the wood and sat there in the coolness. Before long I heard the ringing of a
temple bell (all temples, nearly, have bells in Essur) from somewhere behind
me. Thinking it would be pleasant to walk a little after so many hours on
horseback, I rose and went slowly through the trees to find the temple; very
idly, not caring whether I found it or not. But in a few minutes I came out
into a mossy place free of trees, and there it was; no bigger than a peasant's
hut but built of pure white stone, with fluted pillars in the Greek style.
Behind it I could see a small thatched house where, no doubt, the priest
lived.

The place itself was quiet enough, but inside the temple there was a far
deeper silence and it was very cool. It was clean and empty and there were
none of the common temple smells about it, so that I thought it must belong
to one of those small, peaceful gods who are content with flowers and fruit
for sacrifice. Then I saw it must be a goddess, for there was on the altar the
image of a woman, about two feet high, carved in wood; not badly done and
all the fairer (to my mind) because there was no painting or gilding but only
the natural pale colour of the wood. The thing that marred it was a band or
scarf of some black stuff tied round the head of the image so as to hide its
face – much like my own veil, but that mine was white.

I thought how much better all this was than the house of Ungit, and how
unlike. Then I heard a step behind me and, turning, saw that a man in a black
robe had come in. He was an old man with quiet eyes; perhaps a little
simple.

'Does the Stranger want to make an offering to the goddess?' he asked.

I slipped a couple of coins into his hand and asked what goddess she was.

'Istra,' he said.

The name is not so uncommon in Glome and the neighbouring lands that I had much cause to be startled; but I said I had never heard of a goddess called that.

'Oh, that is because she is a very young goddess. She has only just begun to be a goddess. For you must know that, like many other gods, she began by being a mortal.'

'And how was she godded?'

'She is so lately godded that she is still a rather poor goddess, Stranger. Yet for one little silver piece I will tell you the sacred story. Thank you, kind Stranger, thank you. Istra will be your friend for this. Now I tell you the sacred story. Once upon a time in a certain land there lived a king and a queen who had three daughters, and the youngest was the most beautiful princess in the whole world ...'

And so he went on, as such priests do, all in a singsong voice, and using words which he clearly knew by heart. And to me it was as if the old man's voice, and the temple, and I myself and my journey, were all things in such a story; for he was telling the very history of our Istra, of Psyche herself – how Talapal (that's the Essurian Ungit) was jealous of her beauty and made her to be offered to a brute on a mountain, and how Talapal's son Ialim, the most beautiful of the gods, loved her and took her away to his secret palace. He even knew that Ialim had there visited her only in darkness and had forbidden her to see his face. But he had a childish reason for that: 'You see, Stranger, he had to be very secret because of his mother Talapal. She would have very angry with him if she had known he had married the woman she most hated in the world.'

I thought to myself, 'It's well for me I didn't hear this story fifteen years ago; yes, or even ten. It would have reawakened all my sleeping miseries. Now, it moves me hardly at all.' Then, suddenly struck afresh with the queerness of the thing, I asked him, 'Where did you learn all this?'

He stared at me as if he didn't well understand such a question. 'It's the sacred story,' he said. I saw that he was rather silly than cunning and that it would be useless to question him. As soon as I was silent he went on.

But now all the dreamlike feeling in me suddenly vanished. I was wide awake and I felt the blood rush into my face. He was telling it wrong; hideously and stupidly wrong. First of all, he made it that both Psyche's sisters had visited her in the secret palace of the god (to think of Redival going there!). 'And so,' he said, 'when her two sisters had seen the beautiful palace and been feasted and given gifts, they—'

'They *saw* the palace?'

'Stranger, you are hindering the sacred story. Of course they saw the palace. They weren't blind. And then—'

It was as if the gods themselves had first laughed, and then spat, in my face. So this was the shape the story had taken. You may say, the shape the gods had given it. For it must be they who had put it into the old fool's mind or into the mind of some other dreamer from whom he'd learned it. How could any mortal have known of that palace at all? That much of the truth they had dropped into someone's mind, in a dream, or an oracle, or however they do such things. That much; and wiped clean out the very meaning, the pith, the central knot, of the whole tale. Do I not do well to write a book against them, telling what they have kept hidden? Never, sitting on my judgement seat, had I caught a false witness in a more cunning half-truth. For if the true story had been like their story, no riddle would have been set me; there would have been no guessing and no guessing wrong. More than that; it's a story belonging to a different world, a world in which the gods show themselves clearly and don't torment men with glimpses, nor unveil to one what they hide from another, nor ask you to believe what contradicts your eyes and ears and nose and tongue and fingers. In such a world (is there such? it's not ours, for certain) I would have walked aright. The gods themselves would have been able to find no fault in me. And now to tell my story as if I had had the very sight they had denied me … is it not as if you told a cripple's story and never said he was lame, or told how a man betrayed a secret but never said it was after twenty hours of torture? And I saw all in a moment how the false story would grow and spread and be told all over the earth; and I wondered how many of the other sacred stories are just such twisted falsities as this.

'And so,' the priest was saying, 'when these two wicked sisters had made their plan to ruin Istra, they brought her the lamp and—'

'But why did she – they – want to separate her from the god, if they had seen the palace?'

'They wanted to destroy her *because* they had seen her palace.'

'But why?'

'Oh, because they were jealous. Her husband and her house were so much finer than theirs.'

That moment I resolved to write this book. For years now my old quarrel with the gods had slept. I had come into Bardia's way of thinking; I no longer meddled with them. Often, though I had seen a god myself, I was near to believing that there are no such things. The memory of his voice and face was kept in one of those rooms of my soul that I didn't lightly unlock. Now, instantly, I knew I was facing them; I with no strength and they with all; I visible to them, they invisible to me; I easily wounded (already so wounded all my life had been but a hiding and staunching of the wound), they invulnerable; I one, they many. In all these years they had only let me run away from them as far as the cat lets the mouse run; now, snatch! and the claw on me again. Well; I could speak. I could set down the truth. What had never perhaps been done in the world before should be done now. The case against them should be written.

Jealousy! I jealous of Psyche? I sickened not only at the vileness of the lie but at its flatness. It seemed as if the gods had minds just like the lowest of the people. What came easiest to them, what seemed the likeliest and simplest reason to put in a story, was the dull, narrow passion of the beggars' streets, the temple brothels, the slave, the child, the dog. Could they not lie, if lie they must, better than that?

'… and wanders over the earth, weeping, weeping, always weeping.' How long had the old man been going on? That one word rang in my ears as if he had repeated it a thousand times. I set my teeth and my soul stood on guard. A moment more and I should have begun to hear the sound myself again. She would have been weeping in that little wood outside the temple door.

'That's enough,' I shouted. 'Do you think I don't know a girl cries when her heart breaks? Go on, go on.'

'Wanders, weeping, weeping, always weeping,' he said. 'And falls under the power of Talapal, who hates her. And of course Ialim can't protect her because Talapal is his mother and he's afraid of her. So Talapal torments Istra and sets her to all manner of hard labours, things that seem impossible. But when Istra has done them all, then at last Talapal releases her, and she is reunited to Ialim and becomes a goddess. Then we take off her black veil, and I change my black robe for a white one, and we offer—'

'You mean she will some day be reunited to the god; and you will take off her veil then? When is this to happen?'

'We take off the veil and I change my robe in the spring.'

'Do you think I care what you do? Has the thing itself happened yet or not? Is Istra now wandering over the earth or has she already become a goddess?'

'But, Stranger, the sacred story is about the sacred things; the things we do in the temple. In spring, and all summer, she is a goddess. Then when harvest comes we bring a lamp into the temple in the night and the god flies away. Then we veil her. And all winter she is wandering and suffering; weeping, always weeping …'

He knew nothing. The story and the worship were all one in his mind. He could not understand what I was asking.

'I've heard your story told otherwise, old man,' said I. 'I think the sister – or the sisters – might have more to say for themselves than you know.'

'You may be sure that they would have plenty to say for themselves,' he replied. 'The jealous always have. Why, my own wife now—'

I saluted him and went out of that cold place into the warmth of the wood. I could see through the trees the red light of the fire my people had already kindled. The sun had set.

I hid all the things I was feeling – and indeed I did not know what they were, except that all the peace of that autumnal journey was shattered – so as not to spoil the pleasure of my people. Next day I understood more clearly. I could never be at peace again till I had written my charge against the gods. It burned me from within. It quickened; I was with book, as a woman is with child.

And so it comes about that I can tell nothing of our journey back to Glome. There were seven or eight days of it, and we passed many notable places in Essur; and in Glome, after we had crossed the border, we saw everywhere such good peace and plenty and such duty and, I think, love towards myself as ought to have gladdened me. But my eyes and ears were shut up. All day, and often all night too, I was recalling every passage of the true story, dragging up terrors, humiliations, struggles, and anguish that I had not thought of for years, letting Orual wake and speak, digging her almost out of a grave, out of the walled well. The more I remembered, the more still I could remember; often weeping beneath my veil as if I had never been Queen, yet never in so much sorrow that my burning indignation did not rise above it. I was in haste too. I must write it all quickly before the gods found some way to silence me. Whenever, towards evening, Ilerdia pointed and said, 'There, Queen, would be a good place for the tents,' I said (before I had thought what I would say), 'No, no. We can make three more miles tonight; or five.' Every morning I woke earlier. At first I endured the waiting; fretting myself in the cold mist, listening to the deep-breathed sleep of those young sleepers. But soon my patience would serve me no longer. I took to waking them. I woke them earlier each morning. In the end we were travelling like those who fly from a victorious enemy. I became silent, and this struck the others silent too. I could see they were bewildered and all the comfort of their travels was gone. I suppose they whispered together about the Queen's moods.

When I reached home, even then I could not set about it so suddenly as I had hoped. All manner of petty work had piled up. And now, when I most needed help, word was sent me that Bardia was a little sick and kept his bed. I asked Arnom about Bardia's sickness, and Arnom said, 'It's neither poison nor fever, Queen; a small matter for a strong man. But he'd best not rise. He's ageing, you know.' It would have given me a thrust of fear but that I already knew (and had seen growing signs of it lately) how that wife of his cockered and cosseted him, like a hen with one chicken; not, I'd swear, through any true fears, but to keep him at home and away from the palace.

Yet at last, after infinite hindrances, I made my book and here it stands. Now, you who read, judge between the gods and me. They gave me nothing in the world to love but Psyche and then took her from me. But that was not enough. They then brought me to her at such a place and time that it hung on my word whether she should continue in bliss or be cast out into misery. They would not tell me whether she was the bride of a god, or mad, or a brute's or villain's spoil. They would give no clear sign, though I begged for it. I had to guess. And because I guessed wrong they punished me; what's worse, punished me through her. And even that was not enough; they have now sent out a lying story in which I was given no riddle to guess, but knew and saw that she was the god's bride, and of my own will destroyed her, and that for jealousy. As if I were another Redival. I say the gods deal very unrightly with us. For they will neither (which would be best of all) go away and leave us to live our own short days to ourselves, nor will they show themselves openly and tell us what they would have us do. For that too would be endurable. But to hint and hover, to draw near us in dreams and oracles, or in a waking vision that vanishes as soon as seen, to be dead silent when we question them and then glide back and whisper (words we cannot understand) in our ears when we most wish to be free of them, and to show to one what they hide from another; what is all this but cat-and-mouse play, blindman's buff, and mere jugglery? Why must holy places be dark places?

I say, therefore, that there is no creature (toad, scorpion, or serpent) so noxious to man as the gods. Let them answer my charge if they can. It may well be that, instead of answering, they'll strike me mad or leprous or turn me into beast, bird, or tree. But will not all the world then know (and the gods will know it knows) that this is because they have no answer?

PART 2

I

Not many days have passed since I wrote those words *No answer*, but I must unroll my book again. It would be better to re-write it from the beginning, but I think there's no time for that. Weakness comes on me fast, and Arnom shakes his head and tells me I must rest. They think I don't know they have sent a message to Daaran.

Since I cannot mend the book, I must add to it. To leave it as it was would be to die perjured; I know so much more than I did about the woman who wrote it. What began the change was the very writing itself. Let no one lightly set about such a work. Memory, once waked, will play the tyrant. I found I must set down (for I was speaking as before judges and must not lie) passions and thoughts of my own which I had clean forgotten. The past which I wrote down was not the past that I thought I had (all these years) been remembering. I did not, even when I had finished the book, see clearly many things that I see now. The change which the writing wrought in me (and of which I did not write) was only a beginning; only to prepare me for the gods' surgery. They used my own pen to probe my wound.

Very early in the writing there came also a stroke from without. While I related my first years, when I wrote how Redival and I built mud houses in the garden, a thousand other things came back into my mind, all about those days when there was no Psyche and no Fox; only I and Redival. Catching tadpoles in the brook, hiding from Batta in the hay, waiting at the door of the hall when our father gave a feast and wheedling titbits out of the slaves as they went in and out. And I thought, how terribly she changed. This, all within my own mind. But then the stroke from without. On top of many other hindrances came word of an embassy from the Great King who lives to the South and East.

'Another plague,' said I. And when the strangers came (and there must be hours of talk, and a feast for them afterwards) I liked them none the better for finding that their chief man was a eunuch. Eunuchs are very great men at that court. This one was the fattest man I ever saw, so fat his eyes could hardly see over his cheeks, all shining and reeking with oil, and tricked out with as much doll-finery as one of Ungit's girls. But as he talked and talked I began to think there was a faint likeness in him to someone I had seen long ago. And, as we do, I chased it and gave it up, and chased it and gave it up again, till suddenly, when I least thought of it, the truth started into my mind and I shouted out, 'Tarin!'

'Oh yes, Queen, oh yes,' said he, spiteful-pleased (I thought) and leering. 'Oh yes, I was him you called Tarin. Your father did not love me, Queen, did he? But ... te-hee, te-hee ... he made my fortune. Oh yes, he set me on the right road. With two cuts of a razor. But for him I should not have been the great man I am now.'

I wished him joy of his advancement.

'Thank you, Queen, thank you. It is very good. And to think (te-hee) that but for your father's temper I might have gone on carrying a shield in the guard of a little barbarous king whose whole kingdom could be put into one corner of my master's hunting park and never be noticed! You will not be angry, no?'

I said I had always heard that the Great King had an admirable park.

'And your sister, Queen?' said the eunuch. 'Ah, she was a pretty little girl ... though, te-hee, te-hee, I've had finer women through my hands since ... is she still alive?'

'She is the Queen of Phars,' said I.

'Ah, so. Phars. I remember. One forgets the names of all these little countries. Yes ... a pretty little girl. I took pity on her. She was lonely.'

'Lonely?' said I.

'Oh yes, yes, very lonely. After the other princess, the baby, came. She used to say, "First of all Orual loved me much; then the Fox came and she loved me little; then the baby came and she loved me not at all." So she was lonely. I was sorry for her ... te-hee-hee ... Oh, I was a fine young fellow then. Half the girls in Glome were in love with me.' I led him back to our affairs of state.

This was only the first stroke, a light one; the first snowflake of the winter that I was entering, regarded only because it tells us what's to come. I was by no means sure that Tarin spoke truly. I am sure still that Redival was false and a fool. And for her folly the gods themselves cannot blame me; she had that from her father. But one thing was certain; I had never thought at all how it might be with her when I turned first to the Fox and then to Psyche. For it had been somehow settled in my mind from the very beginning that I was the pitiable and ill-used one. She had her gold curls, hadn't she?

So back to my writing. And the continual labour of mind to which it put me began to overflow into my sleep. It was a labour of sifting and sorting, separating motive from motive and both from pretext; and this same sorting went on every night in my dreams, but in a changed fashion. I thought I had before me a huge, hopeless pile of seeds, wheat, barley, poppy, rye, millet, what not? and I must sort them out and make separate piles, each all of one kind. Why I must do it, I did not know; but infinite punishment would fall upon me if I rested a moment from my labour or if, when all was done, a single seed were in the wrong pile. In waking life a man would know the task impossible. The torment of the dream was that, there, it could conceivably be done. There was one chance in ten thousand of finishing the labour in time, and one in a hundred thousand of making no mistake. It was all but certain I should fail, and be punished; but not certain. And so to it: searching, peering, picking up each seed between finger and thumb. Yet not always finger and thumb. For in some dreams, more madly still, I became a little ant, and the seeds were as big as millstones; and labouring with all my might, till my six legs cracked, I carried them to their places; holding them in front of me as ants do, loads bigger than myself.

One thing that shows how wholly the gods kept me to my two labours, the day's and the night's, is that all this time I hardly gave Bardia a thought, save to grumble at his absence because it meant that I was more hindered in my writing. While the rage of it lasted nothing seemed to matter a straw except finishing my book. Of Bardia I only said (once and again), 'Does he mean to slug abed for the rest of his life?' or, 'It's that wife of his.'

Then there came a day when that last line of the book (*they have no answer*) was still wet, and I found myself listening to Arnom and understanding, as if for the first time, what his looks and voice meant. 'Do you mean,' I cried, 'that the Lord Bardia is in danger?'

'He's very weak, Queen,' said the priest. 'I wish the Fox were with us. We are bunglers, we of Glome. It seems to me that Bardia has no strength or spirit to fight the sickness.'

'Good gods,' said I, 'why did you not make me understand this before? Ho! Slave! My horse. I will go and see him.'

Arnom was an old and trusted counsellor now. He laid his hand on my arm. 'Queen,' he said gently and very gravely, 'it would make him the less likely to recover if you now went to him.'

'Do I carry such an infection about me?' said I. 'Is there death in my aspect, even through a veil?'

'Bardia is your loyalest and most loving subject,' said Arnom. 'To see you would call up all his powers; perhaps crack them. He'd rouse himself to his duty and courtesy. A hundred affairs of state on which he meant to speak to you would crowd into his mind. He'd rack his brains to remember things he has forgotten for these last nine days. It might kill him. Leave him to drowse and dream. It's his best chance now.'

It was as bitter a truth as I'd ever tasted, but I drank it. Would I not have crouched silent in my own dungeons as long as Arnom bade me if it would add one featherweight to Bardia's chance of life? Three days I bore it (I, the old fool, with hanging dugs and shrivelled flanks). On the fourth I said, 'I can bear it no longer.' On the fifth Arnom came to me, himself weeping, and I knew his tidings without words. And this is a strange folly, that what seemed to me worst of all was that Bardia had died without ever hearing what it would have shamed him to hear. It seemed to me that all would be bearable if, once only, I could have gone to him and whispered in his ear, 'Bardia, I loved you.'

When they laid him on the pyre I could only stand by to honour him. Because I was neither his wife nor kin, I might not wail nor beat the breast for him. Ah, if I could have beaten the breast, I would have put on steel gloves or hedgehog skins to do it.

I waited three days, as the custom is, and then went to comfort (so they call it) his widow. It was not only duty and usage that drove me. Because he had loved her she was, in a way, surely enough, the enemy; yet who else in the whole world could now talk to me?

They brought me into the upper room in her house where she sat at her spinning; very pale, but very calm. Calmer than I. Once I had been surprised that she was so much less beautiful than report had made her. Now, in her later years, she had won a new kind of beauty; it was a proud, still sort of face.

'Lady – Ansit,' I said, taking both her hands (she had not time to get them away from me), 'what shall I say to you? How can I speak of him and not say that your loss is indeed without measure? And that's no comfort. Unless you can think even now that it is better to have had and lost such a husband than to enjoy any man else in the world for ever.'

'The Queen does me great honour,' said Ansit, pulling her hands out of mine so as to stand with them crossed on her breast, her eyes cast down, in the court fashion.

'Oh, dear Lady, un-queen me a little, I beseech you. Is it as if you and I had never met till yesterday? After yours (never think I'd compare them) my loss is greatest. I pray you, your seat again. And your distaff; we shall talk better to that movement. And you will let me sit here beside you?'

She sat down and resumed her spinning; her face at rest and her lips a little pursed, very housewifely. She would give me no help.

'It was very unlooked for,' said I. 'Did you at first see any danger in this sickness?'

'Yes.'

'Did you so? To me Arnom said it ought to have been a light matter.'

'He said that to me, Queen. He said it would be a light matter for a man who had all his strength to fight it.'

'Strength? But the Lord Bardia was a strong man.'

'Yes; as a tree that is eaten away within.'

'Eaten away? And with what? I never knew this.'

'I suppose not, Queen. He was tired. He had worked himself out; or been worked. Ten years ago he should have given over and lived as old men do. He was not made of iron or brass, but flesh.'

'He never looked nor spoke like an old man.'

'Perhaps you never saw him, Queen, at the times when a man shows his weariness. You never saw his haggard face in early morning. Nor heard his groan when you (because you had sworn to do it) must shake him and force him to rise. You never saw him come home late from the palace, hungry, yet too tired to eat. How should you, Queen? I was only his wife. He was too well-mannered, you know, to nod and yawn in a Queen's house.'

'You mean that his work—?'

'Five wars, thirty-one battles, nineteen embassies, taking thought for this and thought for that, speaking a word in one ear, and another, and another, soothing this man and scaring that and flattering a third, devising, consulting, remembering, guessing, forecasting ... and the Pillar Room and the Pillar Room. The mines are not the only place where a man can be worked to death.'

This was worse than the worst I had looked for. A flash of anger passed through me, then a horror of misgiving; could it (but that was fantastical) be true? But the misery of that mere suspicion made my own voice almost humble.

'You speak in your sorrow, Lady. But (forgive me) this is mere fantasy. I never spared myself more than him. Do you tell me a strong man'd break under the burden a woman's bearing still?'

'Who that knows men would doubt it? They're harder, but we're tougher. They do not live longer than we. They do not weather a sickness better. Men are brittle. And you, Queen, were the younger.'

My heart shrivelled up cold and abject within me. 'If this is true,' said I, 'I've been deceived. If he had dropped but a word of it, I'd have taken every burden from him; sent him home for ever, loaded with every honour I could give.'

'You know him little, Queen, if you think he'd ever have spoken that word. Oh, you have been a fortunate queen; no prince ever had more loving servants.'

'I know I have had loving servants. Do you grudge me that? Even now in your grief, will your heart serve you to grudge me that? Do you mock me because that is the only sort of love I ever had or could have? No husband; no child. And you – you who have had all—'

'All you left me, Queen.'

'Left you, fool? What mad thought is in your mind?'

'Oh, I know well enough that you were not lovers. You left me that. The divine blood will not mix with subjects', they say. You left me my share. When you had used him, you would let him steal home to me; until you needed him again. After weeks and months at the wars – you and he night and day together, sharing the councils, the dangers, the victories, the soldiers' bread, the very jokes – he could come back to me, each time a little thinner and greyer and with a few more scars; and fall asleep before his supper was down; and cry out in his dream, "Quick, on the right there. The Queen's in danger." And next morning – the Queen's a wonderful early riser in Glome – the Pillar Room again. I'll not deny it; I had what you left of him.'

Her look and voice now were such as no woman could mistake.

'What?' I cried. 'Is it possible you're jealous?'

She said nothing.

I sprang to my feet and pulled aside my veil. 'Look, look, you fool!' I cried. 'Are you jealous of this?'

She started back from me, gazing, so that for a moment I wondered if my face were a terror to her. But it was not fear that moved her. For the first time that prim mouth of hers twitched. The tears began to gather in her eyes. 'Oh,' she gasped, 'oh. I never knew … you also …?'

'What?'

'You loved him. You've suffered too. We both …'

She was weeping; and I. Next moment we were in each other's arms. It was the strangest thing that our hatred should die out at the very moment she first knew her husband was the man I loved. It would have been far otherwise if he were still alive; but on that desolate island (our blank, un-Bardia'd life) we were the only two castaways. We spoke a language, so to call it, which no one else in the huge heedless world could understand. Yet it was a language only of sobs. We could not even begin to speak of him in words; that would have unsheathed both daggers at once.

The softness did not last. I have seen something like this happen in a battle. A man was coming at me, I at him, to kill. Then came a sudden great gust of wind that wrapped our cloaks over our swords and almost over our eyes, so that we could do nothing to one another but must fight the wind itself. And that ridiculous contention, so foreign to the business we were on, set us both laughing, face to face; friends for a moment, and then at once enemies again and for ever. So here.

Presently (I have no memory how it came about) we were apart again; I now resuming my veil; her face hard and cold.

'Well!' I was saying. 'You have made me little better than the Lord Bardia's murderer. It was your aim to torture me. And you chose your torture well. Be content; you are avenged. But tell me this. Did you speak only to wound, or did you believe what you said?'

'Believe? I do not believe. I know, that your queenship drank up his blood year by year and ate out his life.'

'Then why did you not tell me? A word from you would have sufficed. Or are you like the gods who will speak only when it is too late?'

'Tell you?' she said, looking at me with a sort of proud wonder. 'Tell you? And so take away from him his work, which was his life (for what's any woman to a man and a soldier in the end?) and all his glory and his great deeds? Make a child and a dotard of him? Keep him to myself at that cost? Make him so mine that he was no longer his?'

'And yet – he would have been yours.'

'But I would be his. I was his wife, not his doxy. He was my husband, not my house-dog. He was to live the life he thought best and fittest for a great man; not that which would most pleasure me. You have taken Ilerdia now too. He will turn his back on his mother's house more and more; he will seek strange lands, and be occupied with matters I don't understand, and go where I can't follow, and be daily less mine; more his own and the world's. Do you think I'd lift up my little finger if lifting it would stop it?'

'And you could – and you can – bear that?'

'You ask that? Oh, Queen Orual, I begin to think you know nothing of love. Or no; I'll not say that. Yours is Queen's love, not commoners'. Perhaps you who spring from the gods love like the gods. Like the Shadow-brute. They say the loving and the devouring are all one, don't they?'

'Woman,' said I, 'I saved his life. Thankless fool! You'd have been widowed many a year sooner if I'd not been there one day on the field of Ingarn – and got that wound which still aches at every change of weather. Where are *your* scars?'

'Where a woman's are when she has borne eight children. Yes. Saved his life. Why, you had use for it. Thrift, Queen Orual. Too good a sword to throw away. Faugh! You're full fed. Gorged with other men's lives; women's too. Bardia's; mine; the Fox's; your sister's; both your sisters'.'

'It's enough,' I cried. The air in her room was shot with crimson. It came horribly in my mind that if I ordered her to torture and death no one could save her. Arnom would murmur. Ilerdia would turn rebel. But she'd be twisting (cockchafer-like) on a sharp stake before anyone could help her.

Something (if it was the gods, I bless their name) made me unable to do this. I got somehow to the door. Then I turned and said to her:

'If you had spoken thus to my father, he'd have had your tongue cut out.'

'What? Afraid of it?' said she.

As I rode homeward I said to myself, 'She shall have her Ilerdia back. He can go and live on his lands. Turn oaf. Grow fat and mumble between his belches about the price of bullocks. I would have made him a great man. Now he shall be nothing. He may thank his mother. She'll not have need to say again that I devour her men-folk.'

But I did none of these things to Ilerdia.

And now those divine Surgeons had me tied down and were at work. My anger protected me only for a short time; anger wearies itself out and truth comes in. For it was all true; truer than Ansit could know. I had rejoiced when there was a press of work, had heaped up needless work, to keep him late at the palace; plied him with questions for the mere pleasure of hearing his voice. Anything to put off the moment when he would go and leave me to my emptiness. And I had hated him for going. Punished him too. Men have a hundred ways of mocking a man who's thought to love his wife too well, and Bardia was defenceless; everyone knew he'd married an undowered girl, and Ansit boasted that she'd no need (like most) to seek out the ugliest girls in the slave market for her household. I never mocked him myself; but I had endless sleights and contrivances (behind my veil) for pushing the talk in such directions as, I knew, would make others mock him. I hated them for doing it, but I had a bittersweet pleasure at his clouded face. Did I hate him, then? Indeed, I believe so. A love can grow to be nine-tenths hatred and still call itself love. One thing's certain; in my mad midnight fantasies (Ansit dead, or, better still, proved whore, witch, or traitress) when he was at last to be seeking my love, I always had him begin by imploring my forgiveness. Sometimes he had hard work to get it. I would bring him within an ace of killing himself first.

But the result, when all those bitter hours were over, was a strange one. The craving for Bardia was ended. No one will believe this who has not lived long and looked hard, so that he knows how suddenly a passion which has for years been wrapped round the whole heart will dry up and wither. Perhaps in the soul, as in the soil, those growths that show the brightest colours and put forth the most overpowering smell have not always the deepest root. Or perhaps it's age that does it. But most of all, I think, it was this. My love for Bardia (not Bardia himself) had become to me a sickening thing. I had been dragged up and out on to such heights and precipices of truth, that I came into an air where it could not live. It stank; a gnawing greed for one to whom I could give nothing, of whom I craved all. Heaven knows how we had tormented him, Ansit and I. For it needs no Oedipus to guess that, many and many a night, her jealousy of me had welcomed him home, late from the palace, to a bitter hearth.

But when the craving went, nearly all that I called myself went with it. It was as if my whole soul had been one tooth and now that tooth was drawn. I was a gap. And now I thought I had come to the very bottom and that the gods could tell me no worse.

2

A few days after I had been with Ansit came the rite of the Year's birth. This is when the Priest is shut up in the house of Ungit from sunset, and on the following noon fights his way out and is said to be born. But of course, like all these sacred matters, it is and it is not (so that it was easy for the Fox to show its manifold contradictions). For the fight is with wooden swords, and instead of blood wine is poured over the combatants, and though they say he is shut into the house, it's only the great door to the city and the west that is shut, and the two smaller doors at the other end are open and common worshippers go in and out at will.

When there is a King in Glome he has to go in with the Priest at sunset and remain in the house till the Birth. But it is unlawful for a virgin to be present at the things which are done in the house that night; so I go in, by the north door, only an hour before the Birth. (The others who have to be there are one of the nobles, and one of the elders, and one of the people; chosen in a sacred manner of which I am not allowed to write.)

That year it was a fresh morning, very sweet, with a light wind from the south; and because of that freshness out of doors, I felt it, more than ever, a horrible thing to go into the dark holiness of Ungit's house. I have (I think) said before that Arnom had made it a little lighter and cleaner. But it was still an imprisoning, smothering sort of place; and especially on the morning of the Birth, when there had been censing and slaughtering, and pouring of wine and pouring of blood, and dancing and feasting and towsing of girls, and burning of fat, all night long. There was as much taint of sweat and foul air as (in a mortal's house) would have set the laziest slut to opening windows, scouring, and sweeping.

I came and sat on the flat stone which is my place, opposite the sacred stone which is Ungit herself; the new, woman-shaped image a little on my left. Arnom's seat was on my right. He was in his mask, of course, nodding with weariness. They were beating the drums, but not loud, and otherwise there was silence.

I saw the terrible girls sitting in rows down both sides of the house, each cross-legged at the door of her cell. Thus they sat year after year (and usually barren after a few seasons) till they turned into the toothless crones who were hobbling about the floor, tending fires and sweeping – sometimes, after a swift glance round, stooping as suddenly as a bird to pick up a coin or a half-gnawed bone and hide it in their gowns. And I thought how the seed of men that might have gone to make hardy boys and fruitful girls was drained into that house, and nothing given back; and how the silver that men had earned hard and needed was also drained in there, and nothing given back; and how the girls themselves were devoured and were given nothing back.

Then I looked at Ungit herself. She had not, like most sacred stones, fallen from the sky. The story was that, at the very beginning, she had pushed her way up out of the earth; a foretaste of, or an ambassador from, whatever things may live and work down there, one below the other, all the way down, under the dark and weight and heat. I have said she had no face; but that meant she had a thousand faces. For she was very uneven, lumpy and furrowed, so that, as when we gaze into a fire, you could always see some face or other. She was now more rugged than ever because of all the blood they had poured over her in the night. In the little clots and chains of it I made out a face; a fancy at one moment, but then, once you had seen it, not to be evaded. A face such as you might see in a loaf, swollen, brooding, infinitely female. It was a little like Batta as I remembered her in certain of her moods. Batta, when we were very small, had her loving moods, even to me. I have run out into the garden to get free – and to get, as it were, freshened and cleansed – from her huge, hot, strong yet flabby-soft embraces, the smothering engulfing tenacity of her.

'Yes,' I thought, 'Ungit is very like Batta today.'

'Arnom,' said I, whispering, 'who is Ungit?'

'I think, Queen,' said he (his voice strange out of the mask), 'she signifies the earth, which is the womb and mother of all living things.' This was the new way of talking about the gods which Arnom, and others, had learned from the Fox.

'If she is the mother of all things,' said I, 'in what way more is she the mother of the god of the Mountain?'

'He is the air and the sky; for we see the clouds coming up from the earth in mists and exhalations.'

'Then why do the stories sometimes say he's her husband too?'

'That means that the sky by its showers makes the earth fruitful.'

'If that's all they mean, why do they wrap it up in so strange a fashion?'

'Doubtless,' said Arnom (and I could tell that he was yawning inside the mask, being worn out with his vigil), 'doubtless to hide it from the vulgar.'

I would torment him no more, but I said to myself, 'It's very strange that our fathers should first think it worth telling us that rain falls out of the sky, and then, for fear such a notable secret should get out (why not hold their tongues?) wrap it up in a filthy tale so that no one could understand the telling.'

The drums went on. My back began to ache. Presently the little door on my right opened and a woman, a peasant, came in. You could see she had not come for the Birth feast, but on some more pressing matter of her own. She had done nothing (as even the poorest contrive for that feast) to make herself gay, and the tears were wet on her cheeks. She looked as if she had cried all night, and in her hands she held a live pigeon. One of the lesser priests came forward at once, took the tiny offering from her, slit it open with his stone knife, splashed the little shower of blood over Ungit (where it became like dribble from the mouth of the face I saw in her) and gave the body to one of the temple slaves. The peasant woman sank down on her face at Ungit's feet. She lay there a very long time, so shaking that anyone could tell how bitterly she wept. But the weeping ceased. She rose up on her knees and put back her hair from her face and took a long breath. Then she rose to go, and as she turned I could look straight into her eyes. She was grave enough; and yet (I was very close to her and could not doubt it) it was as if a sponge had been passed over her. The trouble was soothed. She was calm, patient, able for whatever she had to do.

'Has Ungit comforted you, child?' I asked.

'Oh yes, Queen,' said the woman, her face almost brightening, 'oh yes. Ungit has given me great comfort. There's no goddess like Ungit.'

'Do you always pray to *that* Ungit,' said I (nodding toward the shapeless stone), 'and not to *that*?' Here I nodded towards our new image, standing tall and straight in her robes and (whatever the Fox might say of it) the loveliest thing our land has ever seen.

'Oh, always this, Queen,' said she. 'That other, the Greek Ungit, she wouldn't understand my speech. She's only for nobles and learned men. There's no comfort in her.'

Soon after that it was noon and the sham fight at the western door had to be done and we all came out into the daylight, after Arnom. I had seen often enough before what met us there; the great mob, shouting, 'He is born! He is born!' and whirling their rattles, and throwing wheat-seed into the air; all sweaty and struggling and climbing on one another's backs to get a sight of Arnom and the rest of us. Today it struck me in a new way. It was the joy of the people that amazed me. There they stood, where they had waited for hours, so pressed together they could hardly breathe, each doubtless with a dozen cares and sorrows upon him (who has not?), yet every man and woman and the very children looking as if all the world was well because a

man dressed up as a bird had walked out of a door after striking a few blows
with a wooden sword. Even those who were knocked down in the press to
see us made light of it and indeed laughed louder than the others. I saw two
farmers whom I well knew for bitterest enemies (they'd wasted more of my
time when I sat in judgement than half the remainder of my people put
together) clap hands and cry, 'He's born!', brothers for the moment.

I went home and into my own chamber to rest, for now that I am old that
sitting on the flat stone wearies me cruelly. I sank into deep thought.

'Get up, girl,' said a voice. I opened my eyes. My father stood beside me.
And instantly all the long years of my queenship shrank up small like a
dream. How could I have believed in them? How could I ever have thought
I should escape from the King? I got up from my bed obediently and stood
before him. When I made to put on my veil, he said, 'None of that folly, do
you hear?' and I laid it obediently aside.

'Come with me to the Pillar Room,' he said.

I followed him down the stair (the whole palace was empty) and we went
into the Pillar Room. He looked all round him, and I became very afraid
because I felt sure he was looking for that mirror of his. But I had given it to
Redival when she became Queen of Phars; and what would he do to me
when he learned that I had stolen his favourite treasure? But he went to one
corner of the room and found there (which were strange things to find in
such a place) two pickaxes and a crowbar. 'To your work, goblin,' he said,
and made me take one of the picks. He began to break up the paved floor in
the centre of the room, and I helped him. It was very hard labour because of
the pain in my back. When we had lifted four or five of the big stone flags
we found a dark hole, like a wide well, beneath them.

'Throw yourself down,' said the King, seizing me by the hand. And however I struggled, I could not free myself, and we both jumped together. When
we had fallen a long way we alighted on our feet, nothing hurt by our fall. It
was warmer down here and the air was hard to breathe, but it was not so dark
that I could not see the place we were in. It was another Pillar Room, exactly
like the one we had left, except that it was smaller and all made (floor, walls,
and pillars) of raw earth. And here also my father looked about him, and once
again I was afraid he would ask what I had done with his mirror. But instead,
he went into a corner of the earthen room and there found two spades and
put one into my hand and said, 'Now, work. Do you mean to slug abed all
your life?' So then we had to dig a hole in the centre of the room. And this
time the labour was worse than before, for what we dug was all tough, clinging clay, so that you had rather to cut it out in squares with the spade than to
dig it. And the place was stifling. But at last we had done so much that
another black hole opened beneath us. This time I knew what he meant to do
to me, so I tried to keep my hand from his. But he caught it and said:

'Do you begin to set your wits against mine? Throw yourself down.'

'Oh no, no, no; no further down; mercy!' said I.

'There's no Fox to help you here,' said my father. 'We're far below any dens that foxes can dig. There's hundreds of tons of earth between you and the deepest of them.' Then we leaped down into the hole, and fell further than before, but again alighted unhurt. It was far darker here, yet I could see that we were in yet another Pillar Room; but this was of living rock, and water trickled down the walls of it. Though it was so like the two shallower rooms, this was far the smallest. And as I looked I could see that it was getting smaller still. The roof was closing in on us. I tried to cry out to him, 'If you're not quick, we shall be buried,' but I was smothering and no voice came from me. Then I thought, 'He doesn't care. It's nothing for him to be buried, for he's dead already.'

'Who is Ungit?' said he, still holding my hand.

Then he led me across the floor; and, a long way off before we came to it, I saw that mirror on the wall, just where it always had been. At the sight of it my terror increased, and I fought with all my strength not to go on. But his hand had grown very big now and it was as soft and clinging as Batta's arms, or as the tough clay we had been digging, or as the dough of a huge loaf. I was not so much dragged as sucked along till we stood right in front of the mirror. And in it I saw him, looking as he had looked that other day when he led me to the mirror long ago.

But my face was the face of Ungit as I had seen it that day in her house.

'Who is Ungit?' asked the King.

'I am Ungit.' My voice came wailing out of me and I found that I was in the cool daylight and in my own chamber. So it had been what we call a dream. But I must give warning that from this time onward they so drenched me with seeings that I cannot well discern dream from waking nor tell which is the truer. This vision, anyway, allowed no denial. Without question it was true. It was I who was Ungit. That ruinous face was mine. I was that Batta-thing, that all-devouring, womblike, yet barren, thing. Glome was a web; I the swollen spider, squat at its centre, gorged with men's stolen lives.

'I will not be Ungit,' said I. I got up, shivering as with fever, from my bed, and bolted the door. I took down my old sword, the very same that Bardia had taught me to use, and drew it. It looked such a happy thing (and it was indeed a most true, perfect, fortunate blade) that tears came into my eyes. 'Sword,' said I, 'you have had a happy life. You killed Argan. You saved Bardia. Now, for your masterpiece.'

It was all foolishness, though. The sword was too heavy for me now. My grip – think of a veined, claw-like hand, skinny knuckles – was childish. I would never be able to strike home; and I had seen enough of wars to know what a feeble thrust would do. This way of ceasing to be Ungit was now too hard for me. I sat down, the cold, small, helpless thing I was, on the edge of my bed, and thought again.

There must, whether the gods see it or not, be something great in the mortal soul. For suffering, it seems, is infinite, and our capacity without limit.

Of the things that followed I cannot at all say whether they were what men call real or what men call dream. And for all I can tell, the only difference is that what many see we call a real thing, and what one only sees we call a dream. But things that many see may have no taste or moment in them at all, and things that are shown only to one may be spears and waterspouts of truth from the very depth of truth.

The day passed somehow. All days pass, and that's great comfort; unless there should be some terrible region in the deadlands where the day never passes. But when the house slept I wrapped myself in a dark cloak and took a stick to lean on; for I think the bodily weakness, which I die of now, must have begun about that time. Then a new thought came to me. My veil was no longer a means to be unknown. It revealed me; all men knew the veiled Queen. My disguise now would be to go bareface; there was hardly anyone who had seen me unveiled. So, for the first time in many years, I went out bareface; showed that face which many had said, more truly than they could know, was too dreadful to be seen. It would have shamed me no more to go buff-naked. For I thought I would look as like Ungit to them as I had seen myself to be in that mirror beneath the earth. As like Ungit? I *was* Ungit; I in her and she in me. Perhaps if any saw me, they would worship me. I had become what the people, and the old Priest, called holy.

I went out, as often before, by the little eastern doorway that opens on the herb-garden. And thence, with endless weariness, through the sleeping city. I thought they would not sleep so sound if they knew what dark thing hobbled past their windows. Once I heard a child cry; perhaps it had dreamed of me. 'If the Shadowbrute begins coming down into the city, the people will be greatly afraid,' said the old Priest. If I were Ungit, I might be the Shadowbrute also. For the gods work in and out of one another as of us.

So at last, fainting with weariness, out beyond the city and down to the river; I myself had made it deep. The old Shennit, as she was before my works, would not, save in spate, have drowned even a crone.

I had to go a little way along the river to a place where I knew that the bank was high, so that I could fling myself down; for I doubted my courage to wade in and feel death first up to my knee, and then to my belly, and then to my neck, and still to go on. When I came to the high bank I took my girdle and tied my ankles together with it, lest, even in my old age, I might save my life, or lengthen my death, by swimming. Then I straightened myself, panting from the labour, and stood footfast, like a prisoner.

I hopped (what blending of misery and buffoonery it would have looked if I could have seen it!) – hopped with my strapped feet a little nearer to the edge.

A voice came from beyond the river: 'Do not do it.'

Instantly – I had been freezing cold till now – a wave of fire passed over me; even down to my numb feet. It was the voice of a god. Who should know better than I? A god's voice had once shattered my whole life. They are not to be mistaken. It may well be that, by trickery of priests, men have sometimes taken a mortal's voice for a god's. But it will not work the other way. No one who hears a god's voice takes it for a mortal's.

'Lord, who are you?' said I.

'Do not do it,' said the god. 'You cannot escape Ungit by going to the deadlands, for she is there also. Die before you die. There is no chance after.'

'Lord, I am Ungit.'

But there was no answer. And that is another thing about the voices of the gods; when once they have ceased, though it is only a heartbeat ago and the bright, hard syllables, the heavy bars or mighty obelisks of sound, are still master in your ears, it is as if they had ceased a thousand years before, and to expect further utterance is like asking for an apple from a tree that fruited the day the world was made.

The voice of the god had not changed in all those years, but I had. There was no rebel in me now. I must not drown and doubtless should not be able to.

I crawled home, troubling the quiet city once more with my dark witch-shape and my tapping stick. And when I laid my head on my pillow it seemed but a moment before my women came to wake me; whether because the whole journey had been a dream or because my weariness (which would be no wonder) threw me into a very fast sleep.

3

Then the gods left me for some days to chew the strange bread they had given me. I was Ungit. What did it mean? Do the gods flow in and out of us as they flow in and out of each other? And again, they would not let me die till I had died. I knew there were certain initiations, far away at Eleusis in the Greeklands, whereby a man was said to die and live again before the soul left the body. But how could I go there? Then I remembered that conversation which his friends had with Socrates before he drank the hemlock, and how he said that true wisdom is the skill and practice of death. And I thought Socrates understood such matters better than the Fox, for in the same book he has said how the soul 'is dragged back through the fear of the invisible'; so that I even wondered if he had not himself tasted this horror as I had tasted it in Psyche's valley. But by the death which is wisdom I supposed he meant the death of our passions and desires and vain opinions. And immediately (it is terrible to be a fool) I thought I saw my way clear and not impossible. To say that I was Ungit meant that I was as ugly in soul as she; greedy, blood-gorged. But if I practised true philosophy, as Socrates meant it, I should change my ugly soul into a fair one. And this, the gods helping me, I would do. I would set about it at once.

The gods helping ... but would they help? Nevertheless I must begin. And it seemed to me they would not help. I would set out boldly each morning to be just and calm and wise in all my thoughts and acts; but before they had finished dressing me I would find that I was back (and knew not how long I had been back) in some old rage, resentment, gnawing fantasy, or sullen bitterness. I could not hold out half an hour. And a horrible memory crept into my mind of those days when I had tried to mend the ugliness of my body with new devices in the way I did my hair or the colours I wore. I'd a cold fear that I was at the same work again. I could mend my soul no more than my face. Unless the gods helped. And why did the gods not help?

Babai! A terrible, sheer thought, huge as a cliff, towered up before me; infinitely likely to be true. No man will love you, though you gave your life for him, unless you have a pretty face. So (might it not be?) the gods will not love you (however you try to pleasure them, and whatever you suffer) unless you have that beauty of soul. In either race, for the love of men or the love of a god, the winners and losers are marked out from birth. We bring our ugliness, in both kinds, with us into the world; with it our destiny. How bitter this was, every ill-favoured woman will know. We have all had our dream of some other land, some other world, some other way of giving the prizes, which would bring us in as the conquerors; leave the smooth, rounded limbs, and the little pink and white faces, and the hair like burnished gold, far behind; their day ended, and ours come. But how if it's not so at all? How if we were made to be dregs and refuse everywhere and everyway?

About this time there came (if you call it so) another dream. But it was not like a dream, for I went into my chamber an hour after noon (none of my women being there) and without lying down, or even sitting down, walked straight into the vision by merely opening the door. I found myself standing on the bank of a bright and great river. And on the further bank I saw a flock; of sheep, I thought. Then I considered them more closely, and I saw that they were all rams, high as horses, mightily horned, and their fleeces such bright gold that I could not look steadily at them. (There was deep, blue sky above them, and the grass was a luminous green like emerald, and there was a pool of very dark shadow, clear-edged, under every tree. The air of that country was sweet as music.) 'Now those,' thought I, 'are the rams of the gods. If I can steal but one golden flock off their sides, I shall have beauty. Redival's ringlets were nothing to that wool.' And in my vision I was able to do what I had feared to do at the Shennit; for I went into the cold water, up to my knee, up to my belly, up to my neck, and then lost the bottom and swam and found the bottom again and came up out of the river into the pastures of the gods. And I walked forward over that holy turf with a good and glad heart. But all the golden rams came at me. They drew closer to one another as their onrush brought them closer to me, till it was a solid wall of living gold. And with terrible force their curled horns struck me and knocked me flat and their hooves trampled me. They were not doing it in anger. They rushed over me in their joy; perhaps they did not see me; certainly I was nothing in their minds. I understood it well. They butted and trampled me because their gladness led them on; the Divine Nature wounds and perhaps destroys us merely by being what it is. We call it the wrath of the gods; as if the great cataract in Phars were angry with every fly it sweeps down in its green thunder.

Yet they did not kill me. When they had gone over me, I lived and knew myself, and presently could stand on my feet. Then I saw that there was another mortal woman with me in the field. She did not seem to see me. She was walking slowly, carefully, along the hedge which bordered that grassland, scanning it like a gleaner, picking something out of it. Then I saw what. Bright gold hung in flecks upon the thorns. Of course! The rams had left some of their golden wool on them as they raced past. This she was gleaning, handful after handful, a rich harvest. What I had sought in vain by meeting the joyous and terrible brutes, she took at her leisure. She won without effort what utmost effort would not win for me.

I now despaired of ever ceasing to be Ungit. Though it was spring without, in me a winter which, I thought, must be everlasting, locked up all my powers. It was as if I were dead already, but not as the god, or Socrates, bade me die. Yet all the time I was able to go about my work, doing and saying whatever was needful, and no one knew that there was anything amiss. Indeed the dooms I gave, sitting on my judgement seat, about this time, were thought to be even wiser and more just than before; it was work on which I spent much pains and I know I did it well. But the prisoners and plaintiffs and witnesses and the rest now seemed to me more like shadows than real men. I did not care a straw (though I still laboured to discern) who had a right to the little field or who had stolen the cheeses.

I had only one comfort left me. However I might have devoured Bardia, I had at least loved Psyche truly. There, if nowhere else, I had the right of it and the gods were in the wrong. And as a prisoner in a dungeon or a sick man on his bed makes much of any little shred of pleasure he still has, so I made much of this. And one day, when my work had been very wearisome, I took this book, as soon as I was free, and went out into the garden to comfort myself, and gorge myself with comfort, by reading over how I had cared for Psyche and taught her and tried to save her and wounded myself for her sake.

What followed was certainly vision and no dream. For it came upon me before I had sat down or unrolled the book. I walked into the vision with my bodily eyes wide open.

I was walking over burning sands, carrying an empty bowl. I knew well what I had to do. I must find the spring that rises from the river that flows in the deadlands, and fill it with the water of death and bring it back without spilling a drop and give it to Ungit. For in this vision it was not I who was Ungit; I was Ungit's slave or prisoner, and if I did all the tasks she set me perhaps she would let me go free. So I walked in the dry sand up to my ankles, white with sand to my middle, my throat rough with sand; unmitigated noon above me, and the sun so high that I had no shadow. And I longed for the water of death; for however bitter it was, it must surely be cold, coming from the sunless country. I walked for a hundred years. But at last the desert ended at the foot of some great mountains; crags and pinnacles and rotting cliffs that no one could climb. Rocks were loosened and fell from the heights all the time; their booming and clanging, as they bounced from one jag to another, and the thud when they fell on the sand, were the only sounds there. Looking at the waste of rock, I first thought it empty, and that what flickered over its hot surface were the shadows of clouds. But there were no clouds. Then I saw what it really was. Those mountains were alive with innumerable serpents and scorpions that scuttled and slithered over them continually. The place was a huge torture chamber, but the instruments were all living. And I knew that the well I was looking for rose in the very heart of these mountains.

'I can never get up,' said I.

I sat upon the sand gazing up at them, till I felt as if the flesh would be burned off my bones. Then at last there came a shadow. Oh, mercy of the gods, could it be a cloud? I looked up at the sky and was nearly blinded, for the sun was still straight above my head; I had come, it seemed, into that country where the day never passes. Yet at last, though the terrible light seemed to bore through my eyeballs into my brain, I saw something; black against the blue, but far too small for a cloud. Then by its circlings I knew it to be a bird. Then it wheeled and came lower and at last was plainly an eagle; but an eagle from the gods, far greater than those of the highlands in Phars. It lighted on the sand and looked at me. Its face was a little like the old Priest's, but it was not he; it was a divine creature.

'Woman,' it said, 'who are you?'

'Orual, Queen of Glome,' said I.

'Then it is not you that I was sent to help. What is that roll you carry in your hands?'

I now saw, with great dismay, that what I had been carrying all this time was not a bowl but a book. This ruined everything.

'It is my complaint against the gods,' said I.

The eagle clapped his wings and lifted his head and cried out with a loud voice, 'She's come at last. Here is the woman who has a complaint against the gods.'

Immediately a hundred echoes roared from the face of the mountain, 'Here is the woman ... a complaint against the gods ... plaint against the gods.'

'Come,' said the eagle.

'Where?' said I.

'Come into court. Your case is to be heard.' And he called aloud once more, 'She's come. She's come.' Then from every crack and hole in the mountains there came out dark things like men, so that there was a crowd of them all round me before I could fly. They seized on me and hustled me and passed me on from one to another, each shouting, towards the mountain-face, 'Here she comes. Here is the woman'; and voices (as it seemed) from within the mountain answered them, 'Bring her in. Bring her into court. Her case is to be heard.' I was dragged and pushed and sometimes lifted, up among the rocks, till at last a great black hole yawned before me. 'Bring her in. The court waits,' came the voices. And with a sudden shock of cold I was hurried in out of the burning sunlight into the dark inwards of the mountain, and then further and further in, always in haste, always passed from hand to hand, and always with that din of shouts: 'Here she is. She's come at last. To the judge, to the judge.' Then the voices changed and grew quieter; and now it was, 'Let her go. Make her stand up. Silence in the court. Silence for her complaint.'

I was free now from all their hands, alone (as I thought) in silent darkness. Then a sort of grey light came. I stood on a platform or pillar of rock in a cave so great that I could see neither the sides nor the roof of it. All round me, below me, up to the very edges of the stone I stood on, there surged a sort of unquiet darkness. But soon my eyes grew able to see things in that half-light. The darkness was alive. It was a great assembly, all staring upon me, and I uplifted on my perch above their heads. Never in peace or war have I seen so vast a concourse. There were tens of thousands of them, all silent; every face watching me. Among them I saw Batta, and the King my father, and the Fox, and Argan. They were all ghosts. In my foolishness I had not thought before how many dead there must be. The faces, one above the other (for the place was shaped that way) rose and rose and receded in the greyness till the very thought of counting – not the faces, that would be madness – but the mere ranks of them, was tormenting. The endless place was packed full as it could hold. The court had met.

But on the same level with me, though far away, sat the judge. Male or female, would could say? Its face was veiled. It was covered from crown to toe in sweepy black.

'Uncover her,' said the judge.

Hands came from behind me and tore off my veil; after it, every rag I had on. The old crone with her Ungit face stood naked before those countless gazers. No thread to cover me, no bowl in my hand to hold the water of death; only my book.

'Read your complaint,' said the judge.

I looked at the roll in my hand and saw at once that it was not the book I had written. It couldn't be; it was far too small. And too old – a little, shabby, crumpled thing, nothing like my great book that I had worked on all day, day after day, while Bardia was dying. I thought I would fling it down and trample on it. I'd tell them someone had stolen my complaint and slipped this thing into my hand instead. Yet I found myself unrolling it. It was written all over inside, but the hand was not like mine. It was all a vile scribble; each stroke mean and yet savage, like the snarl of my father's voice, like the ruinous faces one could make out in the Ungit stone. A great terror and loathing came over me. I said to myself, 'Whatever they do to me, I will never read out this stuff. Give me back my Book.' But already I heard myself reading it. And what I read out was like this:

'I know what you'll say. You will say the real gods are not at all like Ungit, and that I was shown a real god and the house of a real god and ought to know it. Hypocrites! I do know it. As if that would heal my wounds! I could have endured it if you were things like Ungit and the Shadowbrute. You know well that I never really began to hate you until Psyche began talking of her palace and her lover and her husband. Why did you lie to me? You said a brute would devour her. Well, why didn't it? I'd have wept for her and buried what was left and built her a tomb and … and … But to steal her love from me! Can it be that you really don't understand? Do you think we mortals will find you gods easier to bear if you're beautiful? I tell you that if that's true we'll find you a thousand times worse. For then (I know what beauty does) you'll lure and entice. You'll leave us nothing; nothing that's worth our keeping or your taking. Those we love best – whoever's most worth loving – those are the very ones you'll pick out. Oh, I can see it happening, age after age, and growing worse and worse the more you reveal your beauty; the son turning his back on the mother and the bride on her groom, stolen away by this everlasting calling, calling, calling of the gods. Taken where we can't follow. It would be far better for us if you were foul and ravening. We'd rather you drank their blood than stole their hearts. We'd rather they were ours and dead than yours and made immortal. But to steal her love from me, to make her see things I couldn't see … oh, you'll say (you've been whispering it to me these forty years) that I'd signs enough her palace was real; could have known the truth if I'd wanted. But how could I want to know it? Tell me that. The girl was mine. What right had you to steal her away into your dreadful heights? You'll say I was jealous. Jealous of Psyche? Not while she was mine. If you'd gone the other way to work – if it was my eyes you had opened – you'd soon have seen how I would have shown her and told her and taught her and led her up to my level. But to hear a chit of a girl who had (or ought to have had) no thought in her head that I'd not put there, setting up for a seer and a prophetess and next thing to a goddess … how could anyone endure it? That's why I say it makes no difference whether you're fair or foul. That there should be gods at all, there's our misery and bitter wrong. There's no room for you and us in the same world. You're a tree in whose shadow we can't thrive. We want to be our own. I was my own and Psyche was mine and no one else had any right to her. Oh, you'll say you took her away into bliss and joy such as I could never have given her, and I ought to have been glad of it for her sake. Why? What should I care for some horrible, new happiness which I hadn't given her and which separated her from me? Do you think I wanted her to be happy, that way? It would have been better if I'd seen the Brute tear her in pieces before my eyes. You stole her to make her happy, did you? Why, every wheedling, smiling, catfoot rogue who lures away another man's wife or slave or dog might say the same. Dog, now. That's very much to the purpose. I'll thank you to let me feed my own; it needed no titbits from your table. Did you ever remember whose the girl was? She was mine. *Mine*; do you not know what the word means? Mine! You're thieves, seducers. That's my wrong. I'll not complain (not now) that you're blood-drinkers and man-eaters. I'm past that…'

'Enough,' said the judge.

There was utter silence all round me. And now for the first time I knew what I had been doing. While I was reading, it had, once and again, seemed strange to me that the reading took so long; for the book was a small one. Now I knew that I had been reading it over and over; perhaps a dozen times. I would have read it for ever, quick as I could, starting the first word again almost before the last was out of my mouth, if the judge had not stopped me. And the voice I read it in was strange to my ears. There was given to me a certainty that this, at last, was my real voice.

There was silence in the dark assembly long enough for me to have read my book out yet again. At last the judge spoke.

'Are you answered?' he said.

'Yes,' said I.

4

The complaint was the answer. To have heard myself making it was to be answered. Lightly men talk of saying what they mean. Often when he was teaching me to write in Greek the Fox would say, 'Child, to say the very thing you really mean, the whole of it, nothing more or less or other than what you really mean; that's the whole art and joy of words.' A glib saying. When the time comes to you at which you will be forced at last to utter the speech which has lain at the centre of your soul for years, which you have, all that time, idiot-like, been saying over and over, you'll not talk about joy of words. I saw well why the gods do not speak to us openly, nor let us answer. Till that word can be dug out of us, why should they hear the babble that we think we mean? How can they meet us face to face till we have faces?

'Best leave the girl to me,' said a well-known voice. 'I'll lesson her.' It was the spectre which had been my father.

Then a new voice spoke from beneath me. It was the Fox's. I thought he too was going to give some terrible evidence against me. But he said, 'Oh Minos, or Rhadamanthus, or Persephone, or by whatever name you are called, I am to blame for most of this, and I should bear the punishment. I taught her, as men teach a parrot, to say "Lies of poets", and "Ungit's a false image". I made her think that ended the question. I never said, too true an image of the demon within. And then the other face of Ungit (she has a thousand) … something live anyway. And the real gods more alive. Neither they nor Ungit mere thoughts or words. I never told her why the old Priest got something from the dark House that I never got from my trim sentences. She never asked me (I was content she shouldn't ask) why the people got something from the shapeless stone which no one every got from that painted doll of Arnom's. Of course, I didn't know; but I never told her I didn't know. I don't know now. Only that the way to the true gods is more like the House of Ungit … oh, it's unlike too, more unlike than we yet dream, but that's the easy knowledge, the first lesson; only a fool would stay there, posturing and repeating it. The Priest knew at least that there must be sacrifices. They will have sacrifice; will have man. Yes, and the very heart, centre, ground, roots of a man; dark and strong and costly as blood. Send me away, Minos, even to Tartarus, if Tartarus can cure glibness. I made her think that a prattle of maxims would do, all thin and clear as water. For of course water's good; and it didn't cost much, not where I grew up. So I fed her on words.'

I wanted to cry out that it was false, that he had fed me not on words but on love, that he had given, if not to the gods, yet to me, all that was costliest. But I had not time. The trial, it seemed, was over.

'Peace,' said the judge. 'The woman is a plaintiff, not a prisoner. It is the gods who have been accused. They have answered her. If they in turn accuse her, a greater judge and a more excellent court must try the case. Let her go.'

Which way should I turn, set up on that pillar of rock? I looked on every side. Then, to end it, I flung myself down into the black sea of spectres. But before I reached the floor of the cavern one rushed forward and caught me in strong arms. It was the Fox.

'Grandfather!' I cried. 'But you're real and warm. Homer said one could not embrace the dead … they were only shadows.'

'My child, my beloved,' said the Fox, kissing my eyes and head in the old way. 'One thing that I told you was true. The poets are often wrong. But for all the rest – ah, you'll forgive me?'

'I to forgive you, Grandfather? No, no, I must speak. I knew at the time that all those good reasons you gave for staying in Glome after you were a freeman were only disguises for your love. I knew you stayed only in pity and love for me. I knew you were breaking your heart for the Greeklands. I ought to have sent you away. I lapped up all you gave me like a thirsty animal. Oh, Grandfather, Ansit's right. I've battened on the lives of men. It's true. Isn't it true?'

'Why, child, it is. I could almost be glad; it gives me something to forgive. But I'm not your judge. We must go to your true judges now. I am to bring you there.'

'My judges?'

'Why, yes, child. The gods have been accused by you. Now's their turn.'

'I cannot hope for mercy.'

'Infinite hopes – and fears – may both be yours. Be sure that, whatever else you get, you will not get justice.'

'Are the gods not just?'

'Oh no, child. What would become of us if they were? But come and see.'

He was leading me somewhere and the light was strengthening as we went. It was a greenish, summery light. In the end it was sunshine falling through vine leaves. We were in a cool chamber, walls on three sides of us, but on the fourth side only pillars and arches with a vine growing over them on the outside. Beyond, and between, the light pillars and the soft leaves I saw level grass and shining water.

'We must wait here till you are sent for,' said the Fox. 'But there is plenty here that's worth studying.'

I now saw that the walls of the place were all painted with stories. We have little skill with painting in Glome, so that it's small praise to say they seemed wonderful to me. But I think all mortals would have wondered at these.

'They begin here,' said the Fox, taking me by the hand and leading me to part of the wall. For an instant I was afraid that he was leading me to a mirror as my father had twice done. But before we came near enough to the picture to understand it, the mere beauty of the coloured wall put that out of my head.

Now we were before it and I could see the story it told. I saw a woman coming to the river bank. I mean that by her painted posture I could see it was a picture of one walking. That at first. But no sooner had I understood this than it became alive, and the ripples of the water were moving and the reeds stirred with the water and the grass stirred with the breeze, and the woman moved on and came to the river's edge. There she stood and stooped down and seemed to be doing something – I could not at first tell what – with her feet. She was tying her ankles together with her girdle. I looked closer at her. She was not I. She was Psyche.

I am too old, and I have no time, to begin to write all over again of her beauty. But nothing less would serve, and no words I have would serve even then, to tell you how beautiful she was. It was as though I had never seen her before. Or had I forgotten … no, I could never have forgotten her beauty, by day or by night, for one heartbeat. But all this was a flash of thought, swallowed up at once in my horror of the thing she had come to that river to do.

'Do not do it. Do not do it,' I cried out; madly, as if she could hear me. Nevertheless she stopped, and untied her ankles and went away. The Fox led me to the next picture. And it too came alive, and there in some dark place, cavern or dungeon, when I looked hard into the murk I could see that what was moving in it was Psyche; Psyche in rags and iron fetters, sorting out the seeds into their proper heaps. But the strangest thing was that I saw in her face no such anguish as I looked for. She was grave; her brow knitted as I have seen it knitted over a hard lesson when she was a child (and that look became her well; what look did not?). Yet I thought there was no despair in it. Then of course I saw why. Ants were helping her. The floor was black with them.

'Grandfather,' said I, 'did—'

'Hush,' said the Fox, laying his thick old finger (the very feel of that finger again, after so many years!) on my lips. He led me to the next.

Here we were back in the pasture of the gods. I saw Psyche creeping, cautious as a cat, along the hedgerow; then standing, her finger at her lip, wondering how she could ever get one curl of their golden wool. Yet now again, only more than last time, I marvelled at her face. For though she looked puzzled, it was only as if she were puzzled at some game; as she and I had both been puzzled over the game Poobi used to play with her beads. It was even as if she laughed inwardly a little at her own bewilderment. (And that too I'd seen in her before, when she blundered over her tasks as a child; she was never out of patience with herself, no more than with her teacher.) But she did not puzzle long. For the rams scented some intruder and turned their tails to Psyche and all lifted their terrible heads, and then lowered them again for battle, and all charged away together to the other end of the meadow, drawing nearer to their enemy, so that an unbroken wave or wall of gold overwhelmed her. Then Psyche laughed and clapped her hands and gathered her bright harvest off the hedge at ease.

In the next picture I saw both Psyche and myself; but I was only a shadow. We toiled together over those burning sands, she with her empty bowl, I with the book full of my poison. She did not see me. And though her face was pale with the heat and her lips cracked with thirst, she was no more pitiable than when I have seen her, often pale with heat and thirsty, come back with the Fox and me from a summer day's ramble on the old hills. She was merry and in good heart. I believe, from the way her lips moved, she was singing. When she came to the foot of the precipices I vanished away. But the eagle came to her, and took her bowl, and brought it back to her brim-full of the water of death.

We had now travelled round two of the three walls and the third remained.

'Child,' said the Fox, 'have you understood?'

'But are these pictures true?'

'All here's true.'

'But how could she – did she really – do such things and go to such places – and not …? Grandfather, she was all but unscathed. She was almost happy.'

'Another bore nearly all the anguish.'

'I? Is it possible?'

'That was one of the true things I used to say to you. Don't you remember? We're all limbs and parts of one Whole. Hence, of each other. Men, and gods, flow in and out and mingle.'

'Oh, I give thanks. I bless the gods. Then it was really I—'

'Who bore the anguish. But she achieved the tasks. Would you rather have had justice?'

'Would you mock me, Grandfather? Justice? Oh, I've been a queen and I know the people's cry for justice must be heard. But not my cry. A Batta's muttering, a Redival's whining: "Why can't I?" "Why should she?" "It's not fair." And over and over. Faugh!'

'That's well, daughter. But now, be strong and look upon the third wall.'

We looked and saw Psyche walking alone in a wide way under the earth; a gentle slope, but downwards, always downwards.

'This is the last of the tasks that Ungit has set her. She must—'

'Then there is a real Ungit?'

'All, even Psyche, are born into the house of Ungit. And all must get free from her. Or say that Ungit in each must bear Ungit's son and die in childbed – or change. And now Psyche must go down into the deadlands to get beauty in a casket from the Queen of the Deadlands, from death herself; and bring it back to give it to Ungit so that Ungit will become beautiful. But this is the law for her journey. If, for any fear or favour or love or pity, she speaks to anyone on the way, then she will never come back to the sunlit lands again. She must keep straight on, in silence, till she stands before the throne of the Queen of Shadows. All's at stake. Now watch.'

He needed not to tell me that. We both watched. Psyche went on and on, deeper into the earth; colder, deeper, darker. But at last there came a chilly light on one side of her way, and there (I think) the great tunnel or gallery in which she journeyed opened out. For there, in that cold light, stood a great crowd of rabble. Their speech and clothes showed me at once that they were people of Glome. I saw the faces of some I knew.

'Istra! Princess! Ungit!' they called out, stretching their hands towards her. 'Stay with us. Be our goddess. Rule us. Speak oracles to us. Receive our sacrifices. Be our goddess.'

Psyche walked on and never looked at them.

'Whoever the enemy is,' said I, 'he's not very clever if he thinks she would falter for that.'

'Wait,' said the Fox.

Psyche, her eyes fixed straight ahead, went further on and further down, and again, on the left side of her road, there came a light. One figure rose up in it. I was startled at this one, and looked to my side. The Fox was with me still; but he who rose up in the cold light to meet Psyche by the wayside was also the Fox – but older, greyer, paler than the Fox who was with me.

'Oh Psyche, Psyche,' said the Fox in the picture (say, in that other world; it was no painted thing), 'what folly is this? What are you doing, wandering through a tunnel beneath the earth? What? You think it is the way to the Deadlands? You think the gods have sent you there? All lies of priests and poets, child. It is only a cave or a disused mine. There are no deadlands such as you dream of, and no such gods. Has all my teaching taught you no more than this? The god within you is the god you should obey; reason, calmness, self-discipline. Fie, child, do you want to be a barbarian all your days?

I would have given you a clear, Greek, full-grown soul. But there's still time. Come to me and I'll lead you out of all this darkness; back to the grass plot behind the pear trees, where all was clear, hard, limited, and simple.

But Psyche walked on and never looked at him. And presently she came to a third place where there was a little light on the left of the dark road. Amid that light something like a woman rose up; its face was unknown to me. When I looked at it I felt a pity that nearly killed my heart. It was not weeping, but you could see from its eyes that it had already wept them dry. Despair, humiliation, entreaty, endless reproach: all these were in it. And now I trembled for Psyche. I knew the thing was there only to entrap her and turn her from her path. But did she know it? And if she did, could she, so loving and so full of pity, pass it by? It was too hard a test. Her eyes looked straight forward; but of course she had seen it out of the corner of her eye. A quiver ran through her. Her lip twitched, threatened with sobbing. She set her teeth in the lip to keep it straight. 'O great gods, defend her,' I said to myself. 'Hurry, hurry her past.'

The woman held out her hands to Psyche, and I saw that her left arm dripped with blood. Then came her voice, and what a voice it was! So deep, yet so womanlike, so full of passion, it would have moved you even if it spoke happy or careless things. But now (who could resist it?) it would have broken a heart of iron.

'Oh, Psyche,' it wailed. 'Oh, my own child, my only love. Come back. Come back. Back to the old world where we were happy together. Come back to Maia.'

Psyche bit her lip till the blood came and wept bitterly. I thought she felt more grief than that wailing Orual. But that Orual had only to suffer; Psyche had to keep on her way as well. She kept on; went on out of sight, journeying always further into death. That was the last of the pictures.

The Fox and I were alone again.

'Did we really do these things to her?' I asked.

'Yes. All here's true.'

'And we said we loved her.'

'And we did. She had no more dangerous enemies than us. And in that far distant day when the gods become wholly beautiful, or we at last are shown how beautiful they always were, this will happen more and more. For mortals, as you said, will become more and more jealous. And mother and wife and child and friend will all be in league to keep a soul from being united with the Divine Nature.'

'And Psyche, in that old terrible time when I thought her cruel ... she suffered more than I, perhaps?'

'She bore much for you then. You have borne something for her since.'

'And will the gods one day grow thus beautiful, Grandfather?'

'They say ... but even I, who am dead, do not understand more than a few broken words of their language. Only this I know. This age of ours will one day be the distant past. And the Divine Nature can change the past. Nothing is yet in its true form.'

But as he said this many voices from without, sweet and to be feared, took up the cry, 'She comes. Our lady returns to her house; the goddess Psyche, back from the lands of the dead, bringing the casket of beauty from the Queen of Shadows.'

'Come,' said the Fox. I think I had no will in me at all. He took my hand and led me out between the pillars (the vine leaves brushed my hair) into the warm sunlight. We stood in a fair, grassy court, with blue, fresh sky above us; mountain sky. In the centre of the court was a bath of clear water in which many could have swum and sported together. Then there was a moving and rustling of invisible people, and more voices (now somewhat hushed). Next moment I was flat on my face; for Psyche had come and I was kissing her feet.

'Oh, Psyche, oh, goddess,' I said. 'Never again will I call you mine; but all there is of me shall be yours. Alas, you know now what it's worth. I never wished you well, never had one selfless thought of you. I was a craver.'

She bent over me to lift me up. Then, when I would not rise, she said, 'But Maia, dear Maia, you must stand up. I have not given you the casket. You know I went a long journey to fetch the beauty that will make Ungit beautiful.'

I stood up then; all wet in a kind of tears that do not flow in this country. She stood before me, holding out something for me to take. Now I knew that she was a goddess indeed. Her hands burned me (a painless burning) when they met mine. The air that came from her clothes and limbs and hair was wild and sweet; youth seemed to come into my breast as I breathed it. And yet (this is hard to say) with all this, even because of all this, she was the old Psyche still; a thousand times more her very self than she had been before the Offering. For all that had then but flashed out in a glance or a gesture, all that one meant most when one spoke her name, was now wholly present, not to be gathered up from hints nor in shreds, not some of it in one moment and some in another. Goddess? I had never seen a real woman before.

'Did I not tell you, Maia,' she said, 'that a day was coming when you and I would meet in my house and no cloud between us?'

Joy silenced me. And I thought I had now come to the highest, and to the utmost fullness of being which the human soul can contain. But now, what was this? You have seen the torches grow pale when men open the shutters and broad summer morning shines in on the feasting-hall? So now. Suddenly, from a strange look in Psyche's face (I could see she knew something she had not spoken of), or from a glorious and awful deepening of the blue sky above us, or from a deep breath like a sigh uttered all round us by invisible lips, or from a deep, doubtful, quaking and surmise in my own heart, I knew that all this had been only a preparation. Some far greater matter was upon us. The voices spoke again; but not loud this time. They were awed and trembled. 'He is coming,' they said. 'The god is coming into his house. The god comes to judge Orual.'

If Psyche had not held me by the hand I should have sunk down. She had brought me now to the very edge of the pool. The air was growing brighter and brighter about us; as if something had set it on fire. Each breath I drew let into me new terror, joy, overpowering sweetness. I was pierced through and through with the arrows of it. I was being unmade. I was no one. But that's little to say; rather, Psyche herself was, in a manner, no one. I loved her as I would once have thought it impossible to love; would have died any death for her. And yet, it was not, not now, she that really counted. Or if she counted (and oh, gloriously she did) it was for another's sake. The earth and stars and sun, all that was or will be, existed for his sake. And he was coming. The most dreadful, the most beautiful, the only dread and beauty there is, was coming. The pillars on the far side of the pool flushed with his approach. I cast down my eyes.

Two figures, reflections, their feet to Psyche's feet and mine, stood head downward in the water. But whose were they? Two Psyches, the one clothed, the other naked? Yes, both Psyches, both beautiful (if that mattered now) beyond all imagining, yet not exactly the same.

'You also are Psyche,' came a great voice. I looked up then, and it's strange that I dared. But I saw no god, no pillared court. I was in the palace gardens, my foolish book in my hand. The vision to the eye had, I think, faded one moment before the oracle to the ear. For the words were still sounding.

That was four days ago. They found me lying on the grass, and I had no speech for many hours. The old body will not stand many more such seeings; perhaps (but who can tell?) the soul will not need them. I have got the truth out of Arnom; he thinks I am very near my death now. It's strange he should weep; and my women too. What have I ever done to please them? I ought to have had Daaran here and learned to love him and taught him, if I could, to love them.

I ended my first book with the words No answer. I know now, Lord, why you utter no answer. You are yourself the answer. Before your face questions die away. What other answer would suffice? Only words, words; to be led out to battle against other words. Long did I hate you, long did I fear you. I might—

(I, Arnom, priest of Aphrodite, saved this roll and put it in the temple. From the other markings after the word *might*, we think the Queen's head must have fallen forward on them as she died and we cannot read them. This book was all written by Queen Orual of Glome, who was the most wise, just, valiant, fortunate, and merciful of all the princes known in our parts of the world. If any stranger who intends the journey to Greece finds this book let him take it to Greece with him, for that is what she seems mostly to have desired. The Priest who comes after me has it in charge to give up the book to any stranger who will take an oath to bring it into Greece.)

THE GREAT DIVORCE

A Dream

No, there is no escape. There is no heaven with a little of hell in it – no plan to retain this or that of the devil in our hearts or our pockets. Out Satan must go, every hair and feather.

GEORGE MACDONALD

To Barbara Wall
Best and most long-suffering of scribes

PREFACE

Blake wrote the Marriage of Heaven and Hell. If I have written of their Divorce, this is not because I think myself a fit antagonist for so great a genius, nor even because I feel at all sure that I know what he meant. But in some sense or other the attempt to make that marriage is perennial. The attempt is based on the belief that reality never presents us with an absolutely unavoidable 'either-or'; that, granted skill and patience and (above all) time enough, some way of embracing both alternatives can always be found; that mere development or adjustment or refinement will somehow turn evil into good without our being called on for a final and total rejection of anything we should like to retain. This belief I take to be a disastrous error. You cannot take all luggage with you on all journeys; on one journey even your right hand and your right eye may be among the things you have to leave behind. We are not living in a world where all roads are radii of a circle and where all, if followed long enough, will therefore draw gradually nearer and finally meet at the centre: rather in a world where every road, after a few miles, forks into two, and each of those into two again, and at each fork you must make a decision. Even on the biological level life is not like a river but like a tree. It does not move towards unity but away from it and the creatures grow further apart as they increase in perfection. Good, as it ripens, becomes continually more different not only from evil but from other good.

I do not think that all who choose wrong roads perish; but their rescue consists in being put back on the right road. A sum can be put right: but only by going back till you find the error and working it afresh from that point, never by simply *going on*. Evil can be undone, but it cannot 'develop' into good. Time does not heal it. The spell must be unwound, bit by bit, 'with backward mutters of dissevering power' – or else not. It is still 'either-or'. If we insist on keeping Hell (or even earth) we shall not see Heaven: if we accept Heaven we shall not be able to retain even the smallest and most intimate souvenirs of Hell. I believe, to be sure, that any man who reaches

Heaven will find that what he abandoned (even in plucking out his right eye) has not been lost: that the kernel of what he was really seeking even in his most depraved wishes will be there, beyond expectation, waiting for him in 'the High Countries'. In that sense it will be true for those who have completed the journey (and for no others) to say that good is everything and Heaven everywhere. But we, at this end of the road, must not try to anticipate that retrospective vision. If we do, we are likely to embrace the false and disastrous converse and fancy that everything is good and everywhere is Heaven.

But what, you ask, of earth? Earth, I think, will not be found by anyone to be in the end a very distinct place. I think earth, if chosen instead of Heaven, will turn out to have been, all along, only a region in Hell: and earth, if put second to Heaven, to have been from the beginning a part of Heaven itself.

There are only two things more to be said about this small book. Firstly, I must acknowledge my debt to a writer whose name I have forgotten and whom I read several years ago in a highly coloured American magazine of what they call 'Scientifiction'. The unbendable and unbreakable quality of my heavenly matter was suggested to me by him, though he used the fancy for a different and most ingenious purpose. His hero travelled into the *past*: and there, very properly, found raindrops that would pierce him like bullets and sandwiches that no strength could bite – because, of course, nothing in the past can be altered. I, with less originality but (I hope) equal propriety, have transferred this to the eternal. If the writer of that story ever reads these lines I ask him to accept my grateful acknowledgement. The second thing is this. I beg readers to remember that this is a fantasy. It has of course – or I intended it to have – a moral. But the transmortal conditions are solely an imaginative supposal: they are not even a guess or a speculation at what may actually await us. The last thing I wish is to arouse factual curiosity about the details of the after-world.

C.S. LEWIS
April, 1945

THE GREAT DIVORCE

I

I seemed to be standing in a busy queue by the side of a long, mean street. Evening was just closing in and it was raining. I had been wandering for hours in similar mean streets, always in the rain and always in evening twilight. Time seemed to have paused on that dismal moment when only a few shops have lit up and it is not yet dark enough for their windows to look cheering. And just as the evening never advanced to night, so my walking had never brought me to the better parts of the town. However far I went I found only dingy lodging houses, small tobacconists, hoardings from which posters hung in rags, windowless warehouses, goods stations without trains, and bookshops of the sort that sell *The Works of Aristotle*. I never met anyone. But for the little crowd at the bus stop, the whole town seemed to be empty. I think that was why I attached myself to the queue.

I had a stroke of luck right away, for just as I took my stand a little waspish woman who would have been ahead of me snapped out at a man who seemed to be with her, 'Very well, then. I won't go at all. So there,' and left the queue. 'Pray don't imagine,' said the man, in a very dignified voice, 'that I care about going in the least. I have only been trying to please *you*, for peace sake. My own feelings are of course a matter of no importance, I quite understand *that*' – and suiting the action to the word he also walked away. 'Come,' thought I, 'that's two places gained.' I was now next to a very short man with a scowl who glanced at me with an expression of extreme disfavour and observed, rather unnecessarily loudly, to the man beyond him, 'This sort of thing really makes one think twice about going at all.' 'What sort of thing?' growled the other, a big beefy person. 'Well,' said the Short Man, 'this is hardly the sort of society I'm used to as a matter of fact.' 'Huh!' said the Big Man: and then added with a glance at me, 'Don't you stand any sauce from *him*, Mister. You're not *afraid* of him, are you?' Then, seeing I made no move, he rounded suddenly on the Short Man and said, 'Not good enough for you, aren't we? Like your lip.' Next moment he had fetched the Short Man one on the side of the face that sent him sprawling into the gutter. 'Let him lay, let him lay,' said the Big Man to no one in particular. 'I'm a plain man that's what I am and I got to have my rights same as anyone else, see?' As the Short Man showed no disposition to rejoin the queue and soon began limping away, I closed up, rather cautiously, behind the Big Man and congratulated myself on having gained yet another step. A moment later two young people in front of him also left us arm in arm. They were both so trousered, slender, giggly and falsetto that I could be sure of the sex of neither, but it was clear that each for the moment preferred the other to the chance of a place in the bus. 'We shall never all get in,' said a female voice with a whine in it from some four places ahead of me. 'Change places with you for five bob, lady,' said someone else. I heard the clink of money and then a scream in the female voice, mixed with roars of laughter from the rest of the crowd. The cheated woman leaped out of her place to fly at the man who had bilked her, but the others immediately closed up and flung her out ... So what with one thing and another the queue had reduced itself to manageable proportions long before the bus appeared.

It was a wonderful vehicle, blazing with golden light, heraldically coloured. The Driver himself seemed full of light and he used only one hand to drive with. The other he waved before his face as if to fan away the greasy steam of the rain. A growl went up from the queue as he came in sight. 'Looks as if *he* had a good time of it, eh? ... Bloody pleased with himself, I bet ... My dear, why can't he behave *naturally*? – Thinks himself too good to look at us ... Who does he imagine he is? ... All that gilding and purple, I call it a wicked waste. Why don't they spend some of the money on their house property down here? – God! I'd like to give him one in the ear-'ole.' I could see nothing in the countenance of the Driver to justify all this, unless it were that he had a look of authority and seemed intent on carrying out his job.

My fellow passengers fought like hens to get on board the bus though there was plenty of room for us all. I was the last to get in. The bus was only half full and I selected a seat at the back, well away from the others. But a tousle-haired youth at once came and sat down beside me. As he did so we moved off.

'I thought you wouldn't mind my tacking on to you,' he said, 'for I've noticed that you feel just as I do about the present company. Why on earth they insist on coming I can't imagine. They won't like it at all when we get there, and they'd really be much more comfortable at home. It's different for you and me.'

'Do they *like* this place?' I asked.

'As much as they'd like anything,' he answered. 'They've got cinemas and fish and chip shops and advertisements and all the sorts of things they want. The appalling lack of any intellectual life doesn't worry *them*. I realised as soon as I got here that there'd been some mistake. I ought to have taken the first bus but I've fooled about trying to wake people up here. I found a few fellows I'd known before and tried to form a little circle, but they all seem to have sunk to the level of their surroundings. Even before we came here I'd had some doubts about a man like Cyril Blellow. I always thought he was working in a false idiom. But he was at least intelligent: one could get some criticism worth hearing from him, even if he was a failure on the creative side. But now he seems to have nothing left but his self-conceit. The last time I tried to read him some of my own stuff ... but wait a minute, I'd just like you to look at it.'

Realising with a shudder that what he was producing from his pocket was a thick wad of type-written paper, I muttered something about not having my spectacles and exclaimed, 'Hullo! We've left the ground.'

It was true. Several hundred feet below us, already half hidden in the rain and mist, the wet roofs of the town appeared, spreading without a break as far as the eye could reach.

I was not left very long at the mercy of the Tousle-Headed Poet, because
another passenger interrupted our conversation: but before that happened I had learned a good deal about him. He appeared to be a singularly
ill-used man. His parents had never appreciated him and none of the five
schools at which he had been educated seemed to have made any provision
for a talent and temperament such as his. To make matters worse he had
been exactly the sort of boy in whose case the examination system works
out with the maximum unfairness and absurdity. It was not until he
reached the university that he began to recognise that all these injustices
did not come by chance but were the inevitable results of our economic
system. Capitalism did not merely enslave the workers, it also vitiated
taste and vulgarised intellect: hence our educational system and hence the
lack of 'Recognition' for new genius. This discovery had made him a
Communist. But when the war came along and he saw Russia in alliance
with the capitalist governments, he had found himself once more isolated
and had to become a conscientious objector. The indignities he suffered at
this stage of his career had, he confessed, embittered him. He decided he
could serve the cause best by going to America: but then America came
into the war too. It was at this point that he suddenly saw Sweden as the
home of a really new and radical art, but the various oppressors had given
him no facilities for going to Sweden. There were money troubles. His
father, who had never progressed beyond the most atrocious mental complacency and smugness of the Victorian epoch, was giving him a ludicrously inadequate allowance. And he had been very badly treated by a
girl too. He had thought her a really civilised and adult personality, and
then she had unexpectedly revealed that she was a mass of bourgeois prejudices and monogamic instincts. Jealousy, possessiveness, was a quality he
particularly disliked. She had even shown herself, at the end, to be mean
about money. That was the last straw. He had jumped under a train ...

I gave a start, but he took no notice.

Even then, he continued, ill luck had continued to dog him. He'd been sent to the grey town. But of course it was a mistake. I would find, he assured me, that all the other passengers would be with me on the return journey. But he would not. He was going to stay 'there'. He felt quite certain that he was going where, at last, his finely critical spirit would no longer be outraged by an uncongenial environment – where he would find 'Recognition' and 'Appreciation'. Meanwhile, since I hadn't got my glasses, he would read me the passage about which Cyril Blellow had been so insensitive …

It was just then that we were interrupted. One of the quarrels which were perpetually simmering in the bus had boiled over and for a moment there was a stampede. Knives were drawn: pistols were fired: but it all seemed strangely innocuous and when it was over I found myself unharmed, though in a different seat and with a new companion. He was an intelligent-looking man with a rather bulbous nose and a bowler hat. I looked out of the windows. We were now so high that all below us had become featureless. But fields, rivers, or mountains I did not see, and I got the impression that the grey town still filled the whole field of vision.

'It seems the deuce of a town,' I volunteered, 'and that's what I can't understand. The parts of it that I saw were so empty. Was there once a much larger population?'

'Not at all,' said my neighbour. 'The trouble is that they're so quarrelsome. As soon as anyone arrives he settles in some street. Before he's been there twenty-four hours he quarrels with his neighbour. Before the week is over he's quarrelled so badly that he decides to move. Very likely he finds the next street empty because all the people there have quarrelled with *their* neighbours – and moved. If so he settles in. If by any chance the street is full, he goes further. But even if he stays, it makes no odds. He's sure to have another quarrel pretty soon and then he'll move on again. Finally he'll move right out to the edge of the town and build a new house. You see, it's easy here. You've only got to *think* a house and there it is. That's how the town keeps on growing.'

'Leaving more and more empty streets?'

'That's right. And time's sort of odd here. That place where we caught the bus is thousands of miles from the Civic Centre where all the newcomers arrive from earth. All the people you've met were living near the bus stop: but they'd taken centuries – of our time – to get there, by gradual removals.'

'And what about the earlier arrivals? I mean – there must be people who came from Earth to your town even longer ago.'

'That's right. There are. They've been moving on and on. Getting further apart. They're so far off by now that they could never think of coming to the bus stop at all. Astronomical distances. There's a bit of rising ground near

where I live and a chap has a telescope. You can see the lights of the inhabited houses, where those old ones live, millions of miles away. Millions of
miles from us and from one another. Every now and then they move further
still. That's one of the disappointments. I thought you'd meet interesting
historical characters. But you don't: they're too far away.'

'Would they get to the bus stop in time, if they ever set out?'

'Well – theoretically. But it'd be a distance of light-years. And they
wouldn't want to by now: not those old chaps like Tamberlaine and
Genghiz Khan, or Julius Caesar, or Henry the Fifth.'

'Wouldn't want to?'

'That's right. The nearest of those old ones is Napoleon. We know that
because two chaps made the journey to see him. They'd started long before
I came, of course, but I was there when they came back. About fifteen thousand years of our time it took them. We've picked out the house by now.
Just a little pin prick of light and nothing else near it for millions of miles.'

'But they got there?'

'That's right. He'd built himself a huge house all in the Empire style –
rows of windows flaming with light, though it only shows as a pin prick
from where I live.'

'Did they see Napoleon?'

'That's right. They went up and looked through one of the windows.
Napoleon was there all right.'

'What was he doing?'

'Walking up and down – up and down all the time – left-right, left-right –
never stopping for a moment. The two chaps watched him for about a year
and he never rested. And muttering to himself all the time. "It was Soult's
fault. It was Ney's fault. It was Josephine's fault. It was the fault of the
Russians. It was the fault of the English." Like that all the time. Never
stopped for a moment. A little, fat man and he looked kind of tired. But he
didn't seem able to stop it.'

From the vibrations I gathered that the bus was still moving, but there
was now nothing to be seen from the windows which confirmed this – nothing but grey void above and below.

'Then the town will go on spreading indefinitely?' I said.

'That's right,' said the Intelligent Man. 'Unless someone can do something about it.'

'How do you mean?'

'Well, as a matter of fact, between you and me and the wall, that's my job
at the moment. What's the trouble about this place? Not that people are
quarrelsome – that's only human nature and was always the same even on
Earth. The trouble is they have no Needs. You get everything you want (not
very good quality, of course) by just imagining it. That's why it never costs

any trouble to move to another street or build another house. In other words, there's no proper economic basis for any community life. If they needed real shops, chaps would have to stay near where the real shops were. If they needed real houses they'd have to stay near where builders were. It's scarcity that enables a society to exist. Well, that's where I come in. I'm not going on this trip for my health. As far as that goes I don't think it would suit me up there. But if I can come back with some *real* commodities – anything at all that you could really bite or drink or sit on – why, at once you'd get a demand down in our town. I'd start a little business. I'd have something to sell. You'd soon get people coming to live near – centralisation. Two fully-inhabited streets would accommodate the people that are now spread over a million square miles of empty streets. I'd make a nice little profit and be a public benefactor as well.'

'You mean, if they *had* to live together they'd gradually learn to quarrel less?'

'Well, I don't know about that. I daresay they could be kept a bit quieter. You'd have a chance to build up a police force. Knock some kind of discipline into them. Anyway' (here he dropped his voice) 'it'd be *better*, you know. Everyone admits that. Safety in numbers.'

'Safety from what?' I began, but my companion nudged me to be silent. I changed my question.

'But look here,' said I, 'if they can get everything just by imagining it, why would they want any *real* things, as you call them?'

'Eh? Oh well, they'd like houses that really kept out the rain.'

'Their present houses don't?'

'Well, of course not. How could they?'

'What the devil is the use of building them, then?' The Intelligent Man put his head closer to mine. 'Safety again,' he muttered. 'At least, the feeling of safety. It's all right *now*: but later on ... you understand.'

'What?' said I, almost involuntarily sinking my own voice to a whisper.

He articulated noiselessly as if expecting that I understood lip-reading. I put my ear up close to his mouth. 'Speak up,' I said. 'It will be dark presently,' he mouthed.

'You mean the evening *is* really going to turn into a night in the end?'

He nodded.

'What's that got to do with it?' said I.

'Well ... no one wants to be out of doors when that happens.'

'Why?'

His reply was so furtive that I had to ask him several times to repeat it. When he had done so, being a little annoyed (as one so often is with whisperers), I replied without remembering to lower my voice.

'Who are "They"?' I asked. 'And what are you afraid they'll do to you?

And why should they come out when it's dark? And what protection could an imaginary house give if there was any danger?'

'Here!' shouted the Big Man. 'Who's talking all that stuff? You stop your whispering, you two, if you don't want a hiding, see? Spreading rumours, that's what I call it. You shut your face, Ikey, see?'

'Quite right. Scandalous. Ought to be prosecuted. How did they get on the bus?' growled the passengers.

A fat clean-shaven man who sat on the seat in front of me leaned back and addressed me in a cultured voice.

'Excuse me,' he said, 'but I couldn't help overhearing parts of your conversation. It is astonishing how these primitive superstitions linger on. I beg your pardon? Oh, God bless my soul, that's all it is. There is not a shred of evidence that this twilight is ever going to turn into a night. There has been a revolution of opinion on that in educated circles. I am surprised that you haven't heard of it. All the nightmare fantasies of our ancestors are being swept away. What we now see in this subdued and delicate half-light is the promise of the dawn: the slow turning of a whole nation towards the light. Slow and imperceptible, of course. "And not through Eastern windows only, When day-light comes, comes in the light." And that passion for "real" commodities which our friend speaks of is only materialism, you know. It's retrogressive. Earth-bound! A hankering for matter. But *we* look on this spiritual city – for with all its faults it *is* spiritual – as a nursery in which the creative functions of man, now freed from the clogs of matter, begin to try their wings. A sublime thought.'

Hours later there came a change. It began to grow light in the bus. The greyness outside the windows turned from mud-colour to mother of pearl, then to faintest blue, then to a bright blueness that stung the eyes. We seemed to be floating in a pure vacancy. There were no lands, no sun, no stars in sight: only the radiant abyss. I let down the window beside me. Delicious freshness came in for a second, and then –

'What the hell are you doing?' shouted the Intelligent Man, leaning roughly across me and pulling the window sharply up. 'Want us all to catch our death of cold?'

'Hit him a biff,' said the Big Man.

I glanced round the bus. Though the windows were closed, and soon muffed, the bus was full of light. It was cruel light. I shrank from the faces and forms by which I was surrounded. They were all fixed faces, full not of possibilities but impossibilities, some gaunt, some bloated, some glaring with idiotic ferocity, some drowned beyond recovery in dreams; but all, in one way or another, distorted and faded. One had a feeling that they might fall to pieces at any moment if the light grew much stronger. Then – there was a mirror on the end wall of the bus – I caught sight of my own.

And still the light grew.

3

A cliff had loomed up ahead. It sank vertically beneath us so far that I could not see the bottom, and it was dark and smooth. We were mounting all the time. At last the top of the cliff became visible like a thin line of emerald green stretched tight as a fiddle-string. Presently we glided over that top: we were flying above a level, grassy country through which there ran a wide river. We were losing height now: some of the tallest tree tops were only twenty feet below us. Then, suddenly we were at rest. Everyone had jumped up. Curses, taunts, blows, a filth of vituperation, came to my ears as my fellow-passengers struggled to get out. A moment later, and they had all succeeded. I was alone in the bus, and through the open door there came to me in the fresh stillness the singing of a lark.

I got out. The light and coolness that drenched me were like those of summer morning, early morning a minute or two before the sunrise, only that there was a certain difference. I had the sense of being in a larger space, perhaps even a larger *sort* of space, than I had ever known before: as if the sky were further off and the extent of the green plain wider that they could be on this little ball of earth. I had got 'out' in some sense which made the Solar System itself seem an indoor affair. It gave me a feeling of freedom, but also of exposure, possibly of danger, which continued to accompany me through all that followed. It is the impossibility of communicating that feeling, or even of inducing you to remember it as I proceed, which makes me despair of conveying the real quality of what I saw and heard.

At first, of course, my attention was caught by my fellow-passengers, who were still grouped about in the neighbourhood of the omnibus, though beginning, some of them, to walk forward into the landscape with hesitating steps. I gasped when I saw them. Now that they were in the light, they were transparent – fully transparent when they stood between me and it, smudgy and imperfectly opaque when they stood in the shadow of some tree. They were in fact ghosts: man-shaped stains on the brightness of that air. One could attend to them or ignore them at will as you do with the dirt on a window pane. I noticed that the grass did not bend under their feet: even the dew drops were not disturbed.

Then some re-adjustment of the mind or some focussing of my eyes took place, and I saw the whole phenomenon the other way round. The men were as they had always been; as all the men I had known had been perhaps. It was the light, the grass, the trees that were different; made of some different substance, so much solider than things in our country that men were ghosts by comparison. Moved by a sudden thought, I bent down and tried to pluck a daisy which was growing at my feet. The stalk wouldn't break. I tried to twist it, but it wouldn't twist. I tugged till the sweat stood out on my forehead and I had lost most of the skin off my hands. The little flower was hard, not like wood or even like iron, but like diamond. There was a leaf – a young tender beech-leaf, lying in the grass beside it. I tried to pick the leaf up: my heart almost cracked with the effort, and I believe I did just raise it. But I had to let it go at once; it was heavier than a sack of coal. As I stood, recovering my breath with great gasps and looking down at the daisy, I noticed that I could see the grass not only between my feet but *through* them. I also was a phantom. Who will give me words to express the terror of that discovery? 'Golly!' thought I, 'I'm in for it this time.'

'I don't like it! I don't like it,' screamed a voice. 'It gives me the pip!' One of the ghosts had darted past me, back into the bus. She never came out of it again as far as I know.

The others remained, uncertain.

'Hi, Mister,' said the Big Man, addressing the Driver, 'when have we got to be back?'

'You need never come back unless you want to,' he replied. 'Stay as long as you please.' There was an awkward pause.

'This is simply ridiculous,' said a voice in my ear. One of the quieter and more respectable ghosts had sidled up to me. 'There must be some mismanagement,' he continued. 'What's the sense of allowing all that riff-raff to float about here all day? Look at them. They're not enjoying it. They'd be far happier at home. They don't even know what to do.'

'I don't know very well myself,' said I. 'What does one do?'

'Oh me? I shall be met in a moment or two. I'm expected. I'm not bothering about that. But it's rather unpleasant on one's first day to have the whole place crowded out with trippers. Damn it, one's chief object in coming here at all was to avoid them!'

He drifted away from me. And I began to look about. In spite of his reference to a 'crowd', the solitude was so vast that I could hardly notice the knot of phantoms in the foreground. Greenness and light had almost swallowed them up. But very far away I could see what might be either a great bank of cloud or a range of mountains. Sometimes I could make out in it steep forests, far-withdrawing valleys, and even mountain cities perched on inaccessible summits. At other times it became indistinct. The height was so enormous that my waking sight could not have taken in such an object at all. Light brooded on the top of it: slanting down thence it made long shadows behind every tree on the plain. There was no change and no progression as the hours passed. The promise – or the threat – of sunrise rested immovably up there.

Long after that I saw people coming to meet us. Because they were bright I saw them while they were still very distant, and at first I did not know that they were people at all. Mile after mile they drew nearer. The earth shook under their tread as their strong feet sank into the wet turf. A tiny haze and a sweet smell went up where they had crushed the grass and scattered the dew. Some were naked, some robed. But the naked ones did not seem less adorned, and the robes did not disguise in those who wore them the massive grandeur of muscle and the radiant smoothness of flesh. Some were bearded but no one in that company struck me as being of any particular age. One gets glimpses, even in our country, of that which is ageless – heavy thought in the face of an infant, and frolic childhood in that of a very old man. Here it was all like that. They came on steadily. I did not entirely like it. Two of the ghosts screamed and ran for the bus. The rest of us huddled closer to one another.

4

As the solid people came nearer still I noticed that they were moving with order and determination as though each of them had marked his man in our shadowy company. 'There are going to be affecting scenes,' I said to myself. 'Perhaps it would not be right to look on.' With that, I sidled away on some vague pretext of doing a little exploring. A grove of huge cedars to my right seemed attractive and I entered it. Walking proved difficult. The grass, hard as diamonds to my unsubstantial feet, made me feel as if I were walking on wrinkled rock, and I suffered pains like those of the mermaid in Hans Andersen. A bird ran across in front of me and I envied it. It belonged to that country and was as real as the grass. It could bend the stalks and spatter itself with the dew.

Almost at once I was followed by what I have called the Big Man – to speak more accurately, the Big Ghost. He in his turn was followed by one of the bright people. 'Don't you know me?' he shouted to the Ghost: and I found it impossible not to turn and attend. The face of the solid spirit – he was one of those that wore a robe – made me want to dance, it was so jocund, so established in its youthfulness.

'Well, I'm damned,' said the Ghost. 'I wouldn't have believed it. It's a fair knock-out. It isn't right, Len, you know. What about poor Jack, eh? You look pretty pleased with yourself, but what I say is, What about poor Jack?'

'He is here,' said the other. 'You will meet him soon, if you stay.'

'But you murdered him.'

'Of course I did. It is all right now.'

'All right, is it? All right for you, you mean. But what about the poor chap himself, laying cold and dead?'

'But he isn't. I have told you, you will meet him soon. He sent you his love.'

'What I'd like to understand,' said the Ghost, 'is what you're here for, as pleased as Punch, you, a bloody murderer, while I've been walking the streets down there and living in a place like a pigstye all these years.'

'That is a little hard to understand at first. But it is all over now. You will be pleased about it presently. Till then there is no need to bother about it.'

'No need to bother about it? Aren't you ashamed of yourself?'

'No. Not as you mean. I do not look at myself. I have given up myself. I had to, you know, after the murder. That was what it did for me. And that was how everything began.'

'Personally,' said the Big Ghost with an emphasis which contradicted the ordinary meaning of the word, 'Personally, I'd have thought you and I ought to be the other way round. That's my personal opinion.'

'Very likely we soon shall be,' said the other. 'If you'll stop thinking about it.'

'Look at me, now,' said the Ghost, slapping its chest (but the slap made no noise). 'I gone straight all my life. I don't say I was a religious man and I don't say I had no faults, far from it. But I done my best all my life, see? I done my best by everyone, that's the sort of chap I was. I never asked for anything that wasn't mine by rights. If I wanted a drink I paid for it and if I took my wages I done my job, see? That's the sort I was and I don't care who knows it.'

'It would be much better not to go on about that now.'

'Who's going on? I'm not arguing. I'm just telling you the sort of chap I was, see? I'm asking for nothing but my rights. You may think you can put me down because you're dressed up like that (which you weren't when you worked under me) and I'm only a poor man. But I got to have my rights same as you, see?'

'Oh no. It's not so bad as that. I haven't got my rights, or I should not be here. You will not get yours either. You'll get something far better. Never fear.'

'That's just what I say. I haven't got my rights. I always done my best and I never done nothing wrong. And what I don't see is why I should be put below a bloody murderer like you.'

'Who knows whether you will be? Only be happy and come with me.'

'What do you keep on arguing for? I'm only telling you the sort of chap I am. I only want my rights. I'm not asking for anybody's bleeding charity.'

'Then do. At once. Ask for the Bleeding Charity. Everything is here for the asking and nothing can be bought.'

'That may do very well for you, I daresay. If they choose to let in a bloody murderer all because he makes a poor mouth at the last moment, that's their look out. But I don't see myself going in the same boat as you, see? Why should I? I don't want charity. I'm a decent man and if I had my rights I'd have been here long ago and you can tell them I said so.'

The other shook his head. 'You can never do it like that,' he said. 'Your feet will never grow hard enough to walk on our grass that way. You'd be tired out before we got to the mountains. And it isn't exactly true, you know.' Mirth danced in his eyes as he said it.

'What isn't true?' asked the Ghost sulkily.

'You weren't a decent man and you didn't do your best. We none of us were and none of us did. Lord bless you, it doesn't matter. There is no need to go into it all now.'

'You!' gasped the Ghost. '*You* have the face to tell *me* I wasn't a decent chap?'

'Of course. Must I go into all that? I will tell you one thing to begin with. Murdering old Jack wasn't the worst thing I did. That was the work of a moment and I was half mad when I did it. But I murdered you in my heart, deliberately, for years. I used to lie awake at nights thinking what I'd do to you if I ever got the chance. That is why I have been sent to you now: to ask your forgiveness and to be your servant as long as you need one, and longer if it pleases you. I was the worst. But all the men who worked under you felt the same. You made it hard for us, you know. And you made it hard for your wife too and for your children.'

'You mind your own business, young man,' said the Ghost. 'None of your lip, see? Because I'm not taking any impudence from you about my private affairs.'

'There are no private affairs,' said the other.

'And I'll tell you another thing,' said the Ghost. 'You can clear off, see? You're not wanted. I may be only a poor man but I'm not making pals with a murderer, let alone taking lessons from him. Made it hard for you and your like, did I? If I had you back there I'd show you what work is.'

'Come and show me now,' said the other with laughter in his voice. 'It will be joy going to the mountains, but there will be plenty of work.'

'You don't suppose I'd go with you?'

'Don't refuse. You will never get there alone. And I am the one who was sent to you.'

'So that's the trick, is it?' shouted the Ghost, outwardly bitter, and yet I thought there was a kind of triumph in its voice. It had been entreated: it could make a refusal: and this seemed to it a kind of advantage. 'I thought there'd be some damned nonsense. It's all a clique, all a bloody clique. Tell them I'm not coming, see? I'd rather be damned than go along with you. I came here to get my rights, see? Not to go snivelling along on charity tied onto your apron-strings. If they're too fine to have me without you, I'll go home.' It was almost happy now that it could, in a sense, threaten. 'That's what I'll do,' it repeated, 'I'll go home. I didn't come here to be treated like a dog. I'll go home. That's what I'll do. Damn and blast the whole pack of you …' In the end, still grumbling, but whimpering also a little as it picked its way over the sharp grasses, it made off.

5

For a moment there was silence under the cedar trees and then – *pad, pad, pad* – it was broken. Two velvet-footed lions came bouncing into the open space, their eyes fixed upon each other, and started playing some solemn romp. Their manes looked as if they had been just dipped in the river whose noise I could hear close at hand, though the tree hid it. Not greatly liking my company, I moved away to find that river, and after passing some thick flowering bushes, I succeeded. The bushes came almost down to the brink. It was as smooth as the Thames but flowed swiftly like a mountain stream: pale green where trees overhung it but so clear that I could count the pebbles at the bottom. Close beside me I saw another of the Bright People in conversation with a ghost. It was that fat ghost with the cultured voice who had addressed me in the bus, and it seemed to be wearing gaiters.

'My dear boy, I'm delighted to see you,' it was saying to the Spirit, who was naked and almost blindingly white. 'I was talking to your poor father the other day and wondering where you were.'

'You didn't bring him?' said the other.

'Well, no. He lives a long way from the bus, and, to be quite frank, he's been getting a little eccentric lately. A little difficult. Losing his grip. He never was prepared to make any great efforts, you know. If you remember, he used to go to sleep when you and I got talking seriously! Ah, Dick, I shall never forget some of our talks. I expect you've changed your views a bit since then. You became rather narrow-minded towards the end of your life: but no doubt you've broadened out again.'

'How do you mean?'

'Well, it's obvious by now, isn't it, that you weren't quite right. Why, my dear boy, you were coming to believe in a literal Heaven and Hell!'

'But wasn't I right?'

'Oh, in a spiritual sense, to be sure. I still believe in them in that way. I am still, my dear boy, looking for the Kingdom. But nothing superstitious or mythological ...'

'Excuse me. Where do you imagine you've been?'

'Ah, I see. You mean that the grey town with its continual hope of morning (we must all live by hope, must we not?), with its field for indefinite progress, is, in a sense, Heaven, if only we have eyes to see it? That is a beautiful idea.'

'I didn't mean that at all. Is it possible you don't know where you've been?'

'Now that you mention it, I don't think we ever do give it a name. What do you call it?'

'We call it Hell.'

'There is no need to be profane, my dear boy. I may not be very orthodox, in your sense of that word, but I do feel that these matters ought to be discussed simply, and seriously, and reverently.'

'Discuss Hell *reverently*? I meant what I said. You have been in Hell: though if you don't go back you may call it Purgatory.'

'Go on, my dear boy, go on. That is *so* like you. No doubt you'll tell me why, on your view, I was sent there. I'm not angry.'

'But don't you know? You went there because you are an apostate.'

'Are you serious, Dick?'

'Perfectly.'

'This is worse that I expected. Do you really think people are penalised for their honest opinions? Even assuming, for the sake of argument, that those opinions were mistaken.'

'Do you really think there are no sins of intellect?'

'There are indeed, Dick. There is hide-bound prejudice, and intellectual dishonesty, and timidity, and stagnation. But honest opinions fearlessly followed – they are not sins.'

'I know we used to talk that way. I did it too until the end of my life when I became what you call narrow. It all turns on what are honest opinions.'

'Mine certainly were. They were not only honest but heroic. I asserted them fearlessly. When the doctrine of the Resurrection ceased to commend itself to the critical faculties which God had given me, I openly rejected it. I preached my famous sermon. I defied the whole chapter. I took every risk.'

'What risk? What was at all likely to come of it except what actually came – popularity, sales for your books, invitations, and finally a bishopric?'

'Dick, this is unworthy of you. What are you suggesting?'

'Friend, I am not suggesting at all. You see, I *know* now. Let us be frank. Our opinions were not honestly come by. We simply found ourselves in contact with a certain current of ideas and plunged into it because it seemed modern and successful. At College, you know, we just started automatically writing the kind of essays that got good marks and saying the kind of things that won applause. When, in our whole lives, did we honestly face, in solitude, the one question on which all turned: whether after all the Super-natural might not in fact occur? When did we put up one moment's real resistance to the loss of our faith?'

'If this is meant to be a sketch of the genesis of liberal theology in general, I reply that it is a mere libel. Do you suggest that men like …'

'I have nothing to do with any generality. Nor with any man but you and me. Oh, as you love your own soul, remember. You know that you and I were playing with loaded dice. We didn't *want* the other to be true. We were afraid of crude salvationism, afraid of a breach with the spirit of the age, afraid of ridicule, afraid (above all) of real spiritual fears and hopes.'

'I'm far from denying that young men may make mistakes. They may well be influenced by current fashions of thought. But it's not a question of how the opinions are formed. The point is that they were my honest opin-ions, sincerely expressed.'

'Of course. Having allowed oneself to drift, unresisting, unpraying, accepting every half-conscious solicitation from our desires, we reached a point where we no longer believed the Faith. Just in the same way, a jealous man, drifting and unresisting, reaches a point at which he believes lies about his best friend: a drunkard reaches a point at which (for the moment) he actually believes that another glass will do him no harm. The beliefs are sin-cere in the sense that they do occur as psychological events in the man's mind. If that's what you mean by sincerity they are sincere, and so were ours. But errors which are sincere in that sense are not innocent.'

'You'll be justifying the Inquisition in a moment!'

'Why? Because the Middle Ages erred in one direction, does it follow that there is no error in the opposite direction?'

'Well, this is extremely interesting,' said the Episcopal Ghost. 'It's a point of view. Certainly, it's a point of view. In the meantime …'

'There is no meantime,' replied the other. 'All that is over. We are not playing now. I have been talking of the past (your past and mine) only in order that you may turn from it forever. One wrench and the tooth will be out. You can begin as if nothing had ever gone wrong. White as snow. It's all true, you know. He is in me, for you, with that power. And – I have come a long journey to meet you. You have seen Hell: you are in sight of Heaven. Will you, even now, repent and believe?'

'I'm not sure that I've got the exact point you are trying to make,' said the Ghost.

'I am not trying to make any point,' said the Spirit. 'I am telling you to repent and believe.'

'But my dear boy, I believe already. We may not be perfectly agreed, but you have completely misjudged me if you do not realise that my religion is a very real and a very precious thing to me.'

'Very well,' said the other, as if changing his plan. 'Will you believe in *me*?'

'In what sense?'

'Will you come with me to the mountains? It will hurt at first, until your feet are hardened. Reality is harsh to the feet of shadows. But will you come?'

'Well, that is a plan. I am perfectly ready to consider it. Of course I should require some assurances … I should want a guarantee that you are taking me to a place where I shall find a wider sphere of usefulness – and scope for the talents that God has given me – and an atmosphere of free inquiry – in short, all that one means by civilisation and – er – the spiritual life.'

'No,' said the other. 'I can promise you none of these things. No sphere of usefulness: you are not needed there at all. No scope for your talents: only forgiveness for having perverted them. No atmosphere of inquiry, for I will bring you to the land not of questions but of answers, and you shall see the face of God.'

'Ah, but we must all interpret those beautiful words in our own way! For me there is no such thing as a final answer. The free wind of inquiry must *always* continue to blow through the mind, must it not? "Prove all things" … to travel hopefully is better than to arrive.'

'If that were true, and known to be true, how could anyone travel hopefully? There would be nothing to hope for.'

'But you must feel yourself that there is something stifling about the idea of finality? Stagnation, my dear boy, what is more soul-destroying than stagnation?'

'You think that, because hitherto you have experienced truth only with the abstract intellect. I will bring you where you can taste it like honey and be embraced by it as by a bridegroom. Your thirst shall be quenched.'

'Well, really, you know, I am not aware of a thirst for some ready-made truth which puts an end to intellectual activity in the way you seem to be describing. Will it leave me the free play of Mind, Dick? I must insist on that, you know.'

'Free, as a man is free to drink while he is drinking. He is not free still to be dry.' The Ghost seemed to think for a moment. 'I can make nothing of that idea,' it said.

'Listen!' said the White Spirit. 'Once you were a child. Once you knew what inquiry was for. There was a time when you asked questions because you wanted answers, and were glad when you had found them. Become that child again: even now.'

'Ah, but when I became a man I put away childish things.'

'You have gone far wrong. Thirst was made for water; inquiry for truth. What you now call the free play of inquiry has neither more nor less to do with the ends for which intelligence was given you than masturbation has to do with marriage.'

'If we cannot be reverent, there is at least no need to be obscene. The suggestion that I should return at my age to the mere factual inquisitiveness of boyhood strikes me as preposterous. In any case, that question-and-answer conception of thought only applies to matters of fact. Religious and speculative questions are surely on a different level.'

'We know nothing of religion here: we think only of Christ. We know nothing of speculation. Come and see. I will bring you to Eternal Fact, the Father of all other facthood.'

'I should object very strongly to describing God as a "fact". The Supreme Value would surely be a less inadequate description. It is hardly ...'

'Do you not even believe that He exists?'

'Exists? What does Existence mean? You *will* keep on implying some sort of static, ready-made reality which is, so to speak, "there", and to which our minds have simply to conform. These great mysteries cannot be approached in that way. If there were such a thing (there is no need to interrupt, my dear boy) quite frankly, I should not be interested in it. It would be of no *religious* significance. God, for me, is something purely spiritual. The spirit of sweetness and light and tolerance – and, er, service, Dick, service. We mustn't forget that, you know.'

'If the thirst of the Reason is really dead ... ,' said the Spirit, and then stopped as though pondering. Then suddenly he said, 'Can you, at least, still desire happiness?'

'Happiness, my dear Dick,' said the Ghost placidly, 'happiness, as you will come to see when you are older, lies in the path of duty. Which reminds me ... Bless my soul, I'd nearly forgotten. Of course I can't come with you. I have to be back next Friday to read a paper. We have a little Theological Society down there. Oh yes! there is plenty of intellectual life. Not of a very high quality, perhaps. One notices a certain lack of grip – a certain confusion of mind. That is where I can be of some use to them. There are even regrettable jealousies ... I don't know why, but tempers seem less controlled than they used to be. Still, one mustn't expect too much of human nature. I feel I can do a great work among them. But you've never asked me what my paper is about! I'm taking the text about growing up to the measure of the stature of Christ and working out an idea which I feel sure you'll be interested in. I'm going to point out how people always forget that Jesus (here the Ghost bowed) was a comparatively young man when he died. He would have outgrown some of his earlier views, you know, if he'd lived. As he might have done, with a little more tact and patience. I am going to ask my audience to consider what his mature views would have been. A profoundly interesting question. What a different Christianity we might have had if only the Founder had reached his full stature! I shall end up by pointing out how this deepens the significance of the Crucifixion. One feels for the first time what a disaster it was: what a tragic waste ... so much promise cut short. Oh, must you be going? Well, so must I. Goodbye, my dear boy. It has been a great pleasure. Most stimulating and provocative. Goodbye, goodbye, goodbye.'

The Ghost nodded its head and beamed on the Spirit with a bright clerical smile – or with the best approach to it which such unsubstantial lips could manage – and then turned away humming softly to itself 'City of God, how broad and far.'

But I did not watch him for long, for a new idea had just occurred to me. If the grass were hard as rock, I thought, would not the water be hard enough to walk on? I tried it with one foot, and my foot did not go in. Next moment I stepped boldly out on the surface. I fell on my face at once and got some nasty bruises. I had forgotten that though it was, to me, solid, it was not the less in rapid motion. When I had picked myself up I was about thirty yards further down-stream than the point where I had left the bank. But this did not prevent me from walking up-stream: it only meant that by walking very fast indeed I made very little progress.

6

The cool smooth skin of the bright water was delicious to my feet and I walked on it for about an hour, making perhaps a couple of hundred yards. Then the going became difficult. The current grew swifter. Great flakes or islands of foam came swirling down towards me, bruising my shins like stones if I did not get out of their way. The surface became uneven, rounded itself into lovely hollows and elbows of water which distorted the appearance of the pebbles on the bottom and threw me off my balance, so that I had to scramble to shore. But as the banks hereabouts consisted of great flat stones, I continued my journey without much hurt to my feet. An immense yet lovely noise vibrated through the forest. Hours later I rounded a bend and saw the explanation.

Before me green slopes made a wide amphitheatre, enclosing a frothy and pulsating lake into which, over many-coloured rocks, a waterfall was pouring. Here once again I realised that something had happened to my senses so that they were now receiving impressions which would normally exceed their capacity. On Earth, such a waterfall could not have been perceived at all as a whole; it was too big. Its sound would have been a terror in the woods for twenty miles. Here, after the first shock, my sensibility 'took' both as a well-built ship takes a huge wave. I exulted. The noise, though gigantic, was like giants' laughter: like the revelry of a whole college of giants together laughing, dancing, singing, roaring at their high works.

Near the place where the fall plunged into the lake there grew a tree. Wet with the spray, half-veiled in foam-bows, flashing with the bright, innumerable birds that flew among its branches, it rose in many shapes of billowy foliage, huge as a fen-land cloud. From every point apples of gold gleamed through the leaves.

Suddenly my attention was diverted by a curious appearance in the foreground. A hawthorn bush not twenty yards away seemed to be behaving oddly. Then I saw that it was not the bush but something standing close to the bush and on this side of it. Finally I realised that it was one of the

Ghosts. It was crouching as if to conceal itself from something beyond the bush, and it was looking back at me and making signals. It kept on signing to me to duck down. As I could not see what the danger was, I stood fast.

Presently the Ghost, after peering around in every direction, ventured beyond the hawthorn bush. It could not get on very fast because of the torturing grasses beneath its feet, but it was obviously going as fast as it possibly could, straight for another tree. There it stopped again, standing straight upright against the trunk as though it were taking cover. Because the shadow of the branches now covered it, I could see it better: it was my bowler-hatted companion, the one whom the Big Ghost had called Ikey. After it had stood panting at the tree for about ten minutes and carefully reconnoitred the ground ahead, it made a dash for another tree – such a dash as was possible to it. In this way, with infinite labour and caution, it had reached the great Tree in about an hour. That is, it had come within ten yards of it.

Here it was checked. Round the Tree grew a belt of lilies: to the Ghost an insuperable obstacle. It might as well have tried to tread down an anti-tank trap as to walk *on* them. It lay down and tried to crawl between them but they grew too close and they would not bend. And all the time it was apparently haunted by the terror of discovery. At every whisper of the wind it stopped and cowered: once, at the cry of a bird, it struggled back to its last place of cover: but then desire hounded it out again and it crawled once more to the Tree. I saw it clasp its hands and writhe in the agony of its frustration.

The wind seemed to be rising. I saw the Ghost wring its hand and put its thumb into its mouth – cruelly pinched, I doubt not, between two stems of the lilies when the breeze swayed them. Then came a real gust. The branches of the Tree began to toss. A moment later and half a dozen apples had fallen round the Ghost and on it. He gave a sharp cry, but suddenly checked it. I thought the weight of the golden fruit where it had fallen on him would have disabled him: and certainly, for a few minutes, he was unable to rise. He lay whimpering, nursing his wounds. But soon he was at work again. I could see him feverishly trying to fill his pockets with the apples. Of course it was useless. One could see how his ambitions were gradually forced down. He gave up the idea of a pocketful: two would have to do. He gave up the idea of two, he would take one, the largest one. He gave up that hope. He was now looking for the smallest one. He was trying to find if there was one small enough to carry.

The amazing thing was that he succeeded. When I remembered what the leaf had felt like when I tried to lift it, I could hardly help admiring this unhappy creature when I saw him rise staggering to his feet actually holding the smallest of the apples in his hands. He was lame from his hurts, and the weight bent him double. Yet even so, inch by inch, still availing himself of every scrap of cover, he set out on his *via dolorosa* to the bus, carrying his torture.

'Fool. Put it down,' said a great voice suddenly. It was quite unlike any other voice I had heard so far. It was a thunderous yet liquid voice. With an appalling certainty I knew that the waterfall itself was speaking: and I saw now (though it did not cease to look like a waterfall) that it was also a bright angel who stood, like one crucified, against the rocks and poured himself perpetually down towards the forest with loud joy.

'Fool', he said, 'put it down. You cannot take it back. There is not room for it in Hell. Stay here and learn to eat such apples. The very leaves and the blades of grass in the wood will delight to teach you.'

Whether the Ghost heard or not, I don't know. At any rate, after pausing for a few minutes, it braced itself anew for its agonies and continued with even greater caution till I lost sight of it.

7

Although I watched the misfortunes of the Ghost in the Bowler with some complacency, I found, when we were left alone, that I could not bear the presence of the Water-Giant. It did not appear to take any notice of me, but I became self-conscious; and I rather think there was some assumed nonchalance in my movements as I walked away over the flat rocks, downstream again. I was beginning to be tired. Looking at the silver fish which darted over the river-bed, I wished greatly that to me also that water were permeable. I should have liked a dip.

'Thinking of going back?' said a voice close at hand. I turned and saw a tall ghost standing with its back against a tree, chewing a ghostly cheroot. It was that of a lean hard-bitten man with grey hair and a gruff, but not uneducated voice: the kind of man I have always instinctively felt to be reliable.

'I don't know,' said I. 'Are you?'

'Yes,' it replied. 'I guess I've seen about all there is to see.'

'You don't think of staying?'

'That's all propaganda,' it said. 'Of course there never was any question of our staying. You can't eat the fruit and you can't drink the water and it takes you all your time to walk on the grass. A human being couldn't live here. All that idea of staying is only an advertisement stunt.'

'They why did you come?'

'Oh, I don't know. Just to have a look round. I'm the sort of chap who likes to see things for himself. Wherever I've been I've always had a look at anything that was being cracked up. When I was out East, I went to see Pekin. When ...'

'What was Pekin like?'

'Nothing to it. Just one darn wall inside another. Just a trap for tourists. I've been pretty well everywhere. Niagara Falls, the Pyramids, Salt Lake City, the Taj Mahal ...'

'What was *it* like?'

'Not worth looking at. They're all advertisement stunts. All run by the same people. There's a combine, you know, a World Combine, that just takes an Atlas and decides where they'll have a Sight. Doesn't matter what they choose: anything'll do as long as the publicity's properly managed.'

'And you've lived – er – *down there* – in the Town – for some time?'

'In what they call Hell? Yes. It's a flop too. They lead you to expect red fire and devils and all sorts of interesting people sizzling on grids – Henry VIII and all that – but when you get there it's just like any other town.'

'I prefer it up here,' said I.

'Well, I don't see what all the talk is about,' said the Hard-Bitten Ghost. 'It's as good as any other park to look at, and darned uncomfortable.'

'There seems to be some idea that if one stays here one would get – well, solider – grow acclimatised.'

'I know all about that,' said the Ghost. 'Same old lie. People have been telling me that sort of thing all my life. They told me in the nursery that if I were good I'd be happy. And they told me at school that Latin would get easier as I went on. After I'd been married a month some fool was telling me that there were always difficulties at first, but with Tact and Patience I'd soon "settle down" and like it! And all through two wars what didn't they say about the the good time coming if only I'd be a brave boy and go on being shot at? Of course they'll play the old game here if anyone's fool enough to listen.'

'But who are "They"? This might be run by someone different?'

'Entirely new management, eh? Don't you believe it! It's *never* a new management. You'll always find the same old Ring. I know all about dear, kind Mummie coming up to your bedroom and getting all she wants to know out of you: but you always found she and Father were the same firm really. Didn't we find that both sides in all the wars were run by the same Armament Firms? or the same Firm, which is behind the Jews and the Vatican and the Dictators and the Democracies and all the rest of it. All this stuff up here is run by the same people as the Town. They're just laughing at us.'

'I thought they were at war?'

'Of course you did. That's the official version. But who's ever seen any signs of it? Oh, I know that's how they *talk*. But if there's a real war why don't they do anything? Don't you see that if the official version were true these chaps up here would attack and sweep the Town out of existence? They've got the strength. If they wanted to rescue *us* they could do it. But obviously the last thing they want is to end their so-called "war". The whole game depends on keeping it going.'

This account of the matter struck me as uncomfortably plausible. I said nothing.

'Anyway,' said the Ghost, 'who wants to be rescued? What the hell would there be to *do* here?'

'Or there?' said I.

'Quite,' said the Ghost. 'They've got you either way.'

'What would you like to do if you had your choice?' I asked.

'There you go!' said the Ghost with a certain triumph. 'Asking *me* to make a plan. It's up to the Management to find something that doesn't bore us, isn't it? It's their job. Why should we do it for them? That's just where all the parsons and moralists have got the thing upside down. They keep on asking *us* to alter ourselves. But if the people who run the show are so clever and so powerful, why don't they find something to suit their public? All this poppycock about growing harder so that the grass doesn't hurt our feet, now! There's an example. What would you say if you went to a hotel where the eggs were all bad and when you complained to the Boss, instead of apologising and changing his dairyman, he just told you that if you tried you'd get to like bad eggs in time?'

'Well, I'll be getting along,' said the Ghost after a short silence. 'You coming my way?'

'There doesn't seem to be much point in going anywhere on your showing,' I replied. A great depression had come over me. 'And at least it's not raining here.'

'Not at the moment,' said the Hard-Bitten Ghost. 'But I never saw one of those bright mornings that didn't turn to rain later on. And, by gum, when it does rain here! Ah, you hadn't thought of that? It hadn't occurred to you that with the sort of water they have here every raindrop will make a hole in you, like a machine-gun bullet. That's their little joke, you see. First of all tantalise you with ground you can't walk on and water you can't drink and then drill you full of holes. But they won't catch *me* that way.'

A few minutes later he moved off.

8

I sat still on a stone by the river's side feeling as miserable as I ever felt in my life. Hitherto it had not occurred to me to doubt the intentions of the Solid People, nor to question the essential goodness of their country even if it were a country which I could not long inhabit. It had indeed once crossed my mind that if these Solid People were as benevolent as I had heard one or two of them claim to be, they might have done something to help the inhabitants of the Town – something more than meeting them on the plain. Now a terrible explanation came into my mind. How if this whole trip were allowed the Ghosts merely to mock them? Horrible myths and doctrines stirred in my memory. I thought how the Gods had punished Tantalus. I thought of the place in the Book of Revelation where it says that the smoke of Hell goes up forever in the sight of the blessed spirits. I remembered how poor Cowper, dreaming that he was not after all doomed to perdition, at once knew the dream to be false and said, 'These are the sharpest arrows in His quiver.' And what the Hard-Bitten Ghost had said about the rain was clearly true. Even a shower of dew-drops from a branch might tear me in pieces. I had not thought of this before. And how easily I might have ventured into the spray of the waterfall!

The sense of danger, which had never been entirely absent since I left the bus, awoke with sharp urgency. I gazed around on the trees, the flowers, and the talking cataract: they had begun to look unbearably sinister. Bright insects darted to and fro. If one of those were to fly into my face, would it not go right through me? If it settled on my head, would it crush me to earth? Terror whispered, 'This is no place for you.' I remembered also the lions.

With no very clear plan in my mind, I rose and began walking away from the river in the direction where the trees grew closest together. I had not fully made up my mind to go back to the bus, but I wanted to avoid open places. If only I could find a trace of evidence that it was really possible for a Ghost to stay – that the choice was not only a cruel comedy – I would not go back. In the meantime I went on, gingerly, and keeping a sharp look-out. In about half an hour I came to a little clearing with some bushes in the centre. As I stopped, wondering if I dared cross it, I realised that I was not alone.

A Ghost hobbled across the clearing – as quickly as it could on that uneasy soil – looking over its shoulder as if it were pursued. I saw that it had been a woman: a well-dressed woman, I thought, but its shadows of finery looked ghastly in the morning light. It was making for the bushes. It could not really get in among them – the twigs and leaves were too hard – but it pressed as close up against them as it could. It seemed to believe it was hiding.

A moment later I heard the sound of feet, and one of the Bright People came in sight: one always noticed that sound there, for we Ghosts made no noise when we walked.

'Go away!' squealed the Ghost. 'Go away! Can't you see I want to be alone?'

'But you need help,' said the Solid One.

'If you have the least trace of decent feeling left,' said the Ghost, 'you'll keep away. I don't want help. I want to be left alone. Do go away. You know I can't walk fast enough on those horrible spikes to get away from you. It's abominable of you to take advantage.'

'Oh, that!' said the Spirit. 'That'll soon come right. But you're going in the wrong direction. It's back there – to the mountains – you need to go. You can lean on me all the way. I can't absolutely *carry* you, but you need have almost no weight on your own feet: and it will hurt less at every step.'

'I'm not afraid of being hurt. You know that.'

'Then what is the matter?'

'Can't you understand *anything*? Do you really suppose I'm going out there among all those people, like *this*?'

'But why not?'

'I'd never have come at all if I'd known you were all going to be dressed like that.'

'Friend, you see I'm not dressed at all.'

'I didn't mean that. Do go away.'

'But can't you even tell me?'

'If you can't understand, there'd be no good trying to explain it. How *can* I go out like this among a lot of people with real solid bodies? It's far worse than going out with nothing on would have been on Earth. Have everyone staring *through* me.'

'Oh, I see. But we were all a bit ghostly when we first arrived, you know. That'll wear off. Just come out and try.'

'But they'll *see* me.'

'What does it matter if they do?'

'I'd rather die.'

'But you've died already. There's no good trying to go back to that.'

The Ghost made a sound something between a sob and a snarl. 'I wish I'd never been born,' it said. 'What *are* we born for?'

'For infinite happiness,' said the Spirit. 'You can step out into it at any moment ...'

'But, I tell you, they'll *see* me.'

'An hour hence and you will not care. A day hence and you will laugh at it. Don't you remember on earth – there were things too hot to touch with your finger but you could drink them all right? Shame is like that. If you will accept it – if you will drink the cup to the bottom – you will find it very nourishing: but try to do anything else with it and it scalds.'

'You really mean? ...' said the Ghost, and then paused. My suspense was strained up to the height. I felt that my own destiny hung on her reply. I could have fallen at her feet and begged her to yield.

'Yes,' said the Spirit. 'Come and try.'

Almost, I thought the Ghost had obeyed. Certainly it had moved: but suddenly it cried out, 'No, I can't. I tell you I can't. For a moment, while you were talking, I almost thought ... but when it comes to the point ... You've no right to ask me to do a thing like that. It's disgusting. I should never forgive myself if I did. Never, never. And it's not fair. They ought to have warned us. I'd never have come. And now – please, please go away!'

'Friend,' said the Spirit. 'Could you, only for a moment, fix your mind on something not yourself?'

'I've already given you my answer,' said the Ghost, coldly but still tearful.

'Then only one expedient remains,' said the Spirit, and to my great surprise he set a horn to his lips and blew. I put my hands over my ears. The earth seemed to shake: the whole wood trembled and dindled at the sound. I suppose there must have been a pause after that (though there seemed to be none) before I heard the thudding of hoofs – far off at first, but already nearer before I had well identified it, and soon so near that I began to look about for some place of safety. Before I had found one the danger was all about us. A herd of unicorns came thundering through the glades: twenty-seven hands high the smallest of them and white as swans but for the red gleam in eyes and nostrils and the flashing indigo of their horns. I can still remember the squelching noise of the soft wet turf under their hoofs, the breaking of the undergrowth, the snorting and the whinneyings; how their hind legs went up and their horned heads down in mimic battle. Even then I wondered for what real battle it might be the rehearsal. I heard the Ghost scream, and I think it made a bolt away from the bushes ... perhaps towards the Spirit, but I don't know. For my own nerve failed and I fled, not heeding, for the moment, the horrible going underfoot, and not once daring to pause. So I never saw the end of that interview.

9

'Where are ye going?' said a voice with a strong Scotch accent. I stopped and looked. The sound of the unicorns had long since died away and my flight had brought me to open country. I saw the mountains where the unchanging sunrise lay, and in the foreground two or three pines on a little knoll, with some large smooth rocks, and heather. On one of the rocks sat a very tall man, almost a giant, with a flowing beard. I had not yet looked one of the Solid People in the face. Now, when I did so, I discovered that one sees them with a kind of double vision. Here was an enthroned and shining god, whose ageless spirit weighed upon mine like a burden of solid gold: and yet, at the very same moment, here was an old weatherbeaten man, one who might have been a shepherd – such a man as tourists think simple because he is honest and neighbours think 'deep' for the same reason. His eyes had the far-seeing look of one who has lived long in open, solitary places; and somehow I divined the network of wrinkles which must have surrounded them before re-birth had washed him in immortality.

'I – I don't quite know,' said I.

'Ye can sit and talk to me then,' he said, making room for me on the stone.

'I don't know you, Sir,' said I, taking my seat beside him.

'My name is George,' he answered. 'George MacDonald.'

'Oh!' I cried. 'Then you can tell me! You at least will not deceive me.' Then, supposing that these expressions of confidence needed some explanation, I tried, trembling, to tell this man all that his writings had done for me. I tried to tell how a certain frosty afternoon at Leatherhead Station when I first bought a copy of *Phantastes* (being then about sixteen years old) had been to me what the first sight of Beatrice had been to Dante: *Here begins the New Life.* I started to confess how long that Life had delayed in the region of imagination merely: how slowly and reluctantly I had come to admit that his Christendom had more than an accidental connexion with it, how hard I had tried not to see that the true name of the quality which first met me in his books is Holiness. He laid his hand on mine and stopped me.

'Son,' he said, 'Your love – all love – is of inexpressible value to me. But it may save precious time' (here he suddenly looked very Scotch) 'if I inform ye that I am already well acquainted with these biographical details. In fact, I have noticed that your memory misleads you in one or two particulars.'

'Oh!' said I, and became still.

'Ye had started,' said my Teacher, 'to talk of something more profitable.'

'Sir,' said I, 'I had almost forgotten it, and I have no anxiety about the answer now, though I have still a curiosity. It is about these Ghosts. *Do* any of them stay? *Can* they stay? Is any real choice offered to them? How do they come to be here?'

'Did ye never hear of the *Refrigerium*? A man with your advantages might have read of it in Prudentius, not to mention Jeremy Taylor.'

'The name is familiar, Sir, but I'm afraid I've forgotten what it means.'

'It means that the damned have holidays – excursions, ye understand.'

'Excursions to *this* country?'

'For those that will take them. Of course most of the silly creatures don't. They prefer taking trips back to Earth. They go and play tricks on the poor daft women ye call mediums. They go and try to assert their ownership of some house that once belonged to them: and then ye get what's called a Haunting. Or they go to spy on their children. Or literary ghosts hang about public libraries to see if anyone's still reading their books.'

'But if they come here they can really stay?'

'Aye. Ye'll have heard that the emperor Trajan did.'

'But I don't understand. Is judgement not final? Is there really a way out of Hell into Heaven?

'It depends on the way ye're using the words. If they leave that grey town behind it will not have been Hell. To any that leaves it, it is Purgatory. And perhaps ye had better not call this country Heaven. Not *Deep Heaven*, ye understand.' (Here he smiled at me.) 'Ye can call it the Valley of the Shadow of Life. And yet to those who stay here it will have been Heaven from the first. And ye can call those sad streets in the town yonder the Valley of the Shadow of Death: but to those who remain there they will have been Hell even from the beginning.'

I suppose he saw that I looked puzzled, for presently he spoke again.

'Son,' he said, 'ye cannot in your present state understand eternity: when Anodos looked through the door of the Timeless he brought no message back. But ye can get some likeness of it if ye say that both good and evil, when they are full grown, become retrospective. Not only this valley but all their earthly past will have been Heaven to those who are saved. Not only the twilight in that town, but all their life on Earth too, will then be seen by the damned to have been Hell. That is what mortals misunderstand. They say of some temporal suffering, "No future bliss can make up for it," not knowing that Heaven, once attained, will work backwards and turn even that agony into a glory. And of some sinful pleasure they say "Let me have but *this* and I'll take the consequences": little dreaming how damnation will spread back and back into their past and contaminate the pleasure of the sin. Both processes begin even before death. The good man's past begins to change so that his forgiven sins and remembered sorrows take on the quality of Heaven: the bad man's past already conforms to his badness and is filled only with dreariness. And that is why, at the end of all things, when the sun rises here and the twilight turns to blackness down there, the Blessed will say "We have never lived anywhere except in Heaven," and the Lost, "We were always in Hell." And both will speak truly.'

'Is that not very hard, Sir?'

'I mean, that is the real sense of what they will say. In the actual language of the Lost, the words will be different, no doubt. One will say he has always served his country right or wrong; and another that he has sacrificed everything to his Art; and some that they've never been taken in, and some that, thank God, they've always looked after Number One, and nearly all, that, at least they've been true to themselves.'

'And the Saved?'

'Ah, the Saved … what happens to them is best described as the opposite of a mirage. What seemed, when they entered it, to be the vale of misery turns out, when they look back, to have been a well; and where present experience saw only salt deserts, memory truthfully records that the pools were full of water.'

'Then those people are right who say that Heaven and Hell are only states of mind?'

'Hush,' he said sternly. 'Do not blaspheme. Hell is a state of mind – ye never said a truer word. And every state of mind, left to itself, every shutting up of the creature within the dungeon of its own mind – is, in the end, Hell. But Heaven is not a state of mind. Heaven is reality itself. All that is fully real is Heavenly. For all that can be shaken will be shaken and only the unshakeable remains.'

'But there is a real choice after death? My Roman Catholic friends would be surprised, for to them souls in Purgatory are already saved. And my Protestant friends would like it no better, for they'd say that the tree lies as it falls.'

'They're both right, maybe. Do not fash yourself with such questions. Ye cannot fully understand the relations of choice and Time till you are beyond both. And ye were not brought here to study such curiosities. What concerns you is the nature of the choice itself: and that ye can watch them making.'

'Well, Sir,' I said, 'That also needs explaining. What do they choose, these souls who go back (I have yet seen no others)? And how *can* they choose it?'

'Milton was right,' said my Teacher. 'The choice of every lost soul can be expressed in the words "Better to reign in Hell than serve in Heaven." There is always something they insist on keeping, even at the price of misery. There is always something they prefer to joy – that is, to reality. Ye see it easily enough in a spoiled child that would sooner miss its play and its supper than say it was sorry and be friends. Ye call it the Sulks. But in adult life it has a hundred fine names – Achilles' wrath and Coriolanus' grandeur, Revenge and Injured Merit and Self-Respect and Tragic Greatness and Proper Pride.'

'Then is no one lost through the undignified vices, Sir? Through mere sensuality?'

'Some are, no doubt. The sensualist, I'll allow ye, begins by pursuing a real pleasure, though a small one. His sin is the less. But the time comes on when, though the pleasure becomes less and less and the craving fiercer and fiercer, and though he knows that joy can never come that way, yet he prefers to joy the mere fondling of unappeasable lust and would not have it taken from him. He'd fight to the death to keep it. He'd like well to be able to scratch; but even when he can scratch no more he'd rather itch than not.'

He was silent for a few minutes, and then began again.

'Ye'll understand, there are innumerable forms of this choice. Sometimes forms that one hardly thought of at all on Earth. There was a creature came here not long ago and went back – Sir Archibald they called him. In his earthly life he'd been interested in nothing but Survival. He'd written a whole shelf-full of books about it. He began by being philosophical, but in the end he took up Psychical Research. It grew to be his only occupation – experimenting, lecturing, running a magazine. And travelling too: digging out queer stories among Thibetan lamas and being initiated into brotherhoods in Central Africa. Proofs – and more proofs – and then more proofs again – were what he wanted. It drove him mad if ever he saw anyone taking an interest in anything else. He got into trouble during one of your wars for running up and down the country telling them not to fight because it wasted a lot of money that ought to be spent on Research. Well, in good time, the poor creature died and came here: and there was no power in the universe would have prevented him staying and going on to the mountains. But do ye think that did him any good? This country was no use to him at all. Everyone here had "survived" already. Nobody took the least interest in the question. There was nothing more to prove. His occupation was clean gone. Of course if he would only have admitted that he'd mistaken the means for the end and had a good laugh at himself he could have begun all over again like a little child and entered into joy. But he would not do that. He cared nothing about joy. In the end he went away.'

'How fantastic!' said I.

'Do ye think so?' said the Teacher with a piercing glance. 'It is nearer to such as you than ye think. There have been men before now who got so interested in proving the existence of God that they came to care nothing for God Himself ... as if the good Lord had nothing to do but *exist*! There have been some who were so occupied in spreading Christianity that they never gave a thought to Christ. Man! Ye see it in smaller matters. Did ye never know a lover of books that with all his first editions and signed copies had lost the power to read them? Or an organiser of charities that had lost all love for the poor? It is the subtlest of all the snares.'

Moved by a desire to change the subject, I asked why the Solid People, since they were full of love, did not go down into Hell to rescue the Ghosts. Why were they content simply to meet them on the plain? One would have expected a more militant charity.

'Ye will understand that better, perhaps, before ye go,' said he. 'In the meantime, I must tell ye they have come further for the sake of the Ghosts than ye can understand. Every one of us lives only to journey further and further into the mountains. Every one of us has interrupted that journey and retraced immeasurable distances to come down to-day on the mere chance of saving some Ghost. Of course it is also joy to do so, but ye cannot blame us for that! And it would be no use to come further even if it were possible. The sane would do no good if they made themselves mad to help madmen.'

'But what of the poor Ghosts who never get into the omnibus at all?'

'Everyone who wishes it does. Never fear. There are only two kinds of people in the end: those who say to God, "Thy will be done," and those to whom God says, in the end, "*Thy* will be done." All that are in Hell, choose it. Without that self-choice there could be no Hell. No soul that seriously and constantly desires joy will ever miss it. Those who seek find. To those who knock it is opened.'

At this moment we were suddenly interrupted by the thin voice of a Ghost talking at an enormous speed. Looking behind us we saw the creature. It was addressing one of the Solid People and was doing so too busily to notice us. Every now and then the Solid Spirit tried to get in a word but without success. The Ghost's talk was like this:

'Oh, my dear, I've had such a dreadful time, I don't know how I ever got here at all, I was coming with Elinor Stone and we'd arranged the whole thing and we were to meet at the corner of Sink Street; I made it perfectly plain because I knew what she was like and if I told her once I told her a thousand times I would *not* meet her outside that dreadful Marjoribanks woman's house, not after the way she'd treated me ... that was one of the most dreadful things that happened to me; I've been dying to tell you because I felt sure you'd tell me I acted rightly; no, wait a moment, dear, till I've told you – I tried living with her when I first came and it was all fixed up, she was to do the cooking and I was to look after the house and I *did* think I was going to be comfortable after all I'd been through but she turned out to be *so* changed, absolutely selfish, and not a particle of sympathy for anyone but herself – and as I once said to her "I *do* think I'm entitled to a little consideration because you at least lived out your time, but I oughtn't to have been here for years and years yet" – oh but of course I'm forgetting you don't know – I was murdered, simply murdered, dear, that man should never have operated, I ought to be alive to-day and they simply *starved* me in that dreadful nursing home and no one ever came near me and ...'

The shrill monotonous whine died away as the speaker, still accompanied by the bright patience at her side, moved out of hearing.

'What troubles ye, son?' asked my Teacher.

'I am troubled, Sir,' said I, 'because that unhappy creature doesn't seem to me to be the sort of soul that ought to be even in danger of damnation. She isn't wicked: she's only a silly, garrulous old woman who has got into a habit of grumbling, and feels that a little kindness, and rest, and change would put her all right.'

'That is what she once was. That is maybe what she still is. If so, she certainly will be cured. But the whole question is whether she *is* now a grumbler.'

'I should have thought there was no doubt about that!'

'Aye, but ye misunderstand me. The question is whether she is a grumbler, or only a grumble. If there is a real woman – even the least trace of one – still there inside the grumbling, it can be brought to life again. If there's one wee spark under all those ashes, we'll blow it till the whole pile is red and clear. But if there's nothing but ashes we'll not go on blowing them in our own eyes forever. They must be swept up.'

'But how can there be a grumble without a grumbler?'

'The whole difficulty of understanding Hell is that the thing to be understood is so nearly Nothing. But ye'll have had experiences ... it begins with a grumbling mood, and yourself still distinct from it: perhaps criticising it. And yourself, in a dark hour, may will that mood, embrace it. Ye can repent and come out of it again. But there may come a day when you can do that no longer. Then there will be no *you* left to criticise the mood, nor even to enjoy it, but just the grumble itself going on forever like a machine. But come! Ye are here to watch and listen. Lean on my arm and we will go for a little walk.'

I obeyed. To lean on the arm of someone older than myself was an experience that carried me back to childhood, and with this support I found the going tolerable: so much so, indeed, that I flattered myself my feet were already growing more solid, until a glance at the poor transparent shapes convinced me that I owed all this ease to the strong arm of the Teacher. Perhaps it was because of his presence that my other senses also appeared to be quickened. I noticed scents in the air which had hitherto escaped me, and the country put on new beauties. There was water everywhere and tiny flowers quivering in the early breeze. Far off in the woods we saw the deer glancing past, and, once, a sleek panther came purring to my companion's side. We also saw many of the Ghosts.

I think the most pitiable was a female Ghost. Her trouble was the very opposite of that which afflicted the other, the lady frightened by the Unicorns. This one seemed quite unaware of her phantasmal appearance. More than one of the Solid People tried to talk to her, and at first I was quite at a loss to understand her behaviour to them. She appeared to be contorting her all but invisible face and writhing her smokelike body in a quite meaningless fashion. At last I came to the conclusion – incredible as it seemed – that she supposed herself still capable of attracting them and was trying to do so. She was a thing that had become incapable of conceiving conversation save as a means to that end. If a corpse already liquid with decay had arisen from the coffin, smeared its gums with lipstick, and attempted a flirtation, the result could not have been more appalling. In the end she muttered, 'Stupid creatures,' and turned back to the bus.

This put me in mind to ask my Teacher what he thought of the affair with the Unicorns. 'It will maybe have succeeded,' he said. 'Ye will have divined that he meant to frighten her; not that fear itself could make her less a Ghost, but if it took her mind a moment off herself, there might, in that moment, be a chance. I have seen them saved so.'

We met several Ghosts that had come so near to Heaven only in order to tell the Celestials about Hell. Indeed this is one of the commonest types. Others, who had perhaps been (like myself) teachers of some kind actually wanted to give lectures about it: they brought fat notebooks full of statistics, and maps, and (one of them) a magic lantern. Some wanted to tell anecdotes of the notorious sinners of all ages whom they had met below. But the most part seemed to think that the mere fact of having contrived for themselves so much misery gave them a kind of superiority. 'You have led a sheltered life!' they bawled. 'You don't know the seamy side. We'll tell you. We'll give you some hard facts' – as if to tinge Heaven with infernal images and colours had been the only purpose for which they came. All alike, so far as I could judge from my own exploration of the lower world, were wholly unreliable, and all equally incurious about the country in which they had arrived. They repelled every attempt to teach them, and when they found that nobody listened to them they went back, one by one, to the bus.

This curious wish to describe Hell turned out, however, to be only the mildest form of a desire very common among the Ghosts – the desire to *extend* Hell, to bring it bodily, if they could, into Heaven. There were tub-thumping Ghosts who in thin, bat-like voices urged the blessed spirits to shake off their fetters, to escape from their imprisonment in happiness, to tear down the mountains with their hands, to seize Heaven 'for their own': Hell offered her co-operation. There were planning Ghosts who implored them to dam the river, cut down the trees, kill the animals, build a mountain railway, smooth out the horrible grass and moss and heather with asphalt. There were materialistic Ghosts who informed the immortals that they were deluded: there was no life after death, and this whole country was a hallucination. There were Ghosts, plain and simple: mere bogies, fully conscious of their own decay, who had accepted the traditional rôle of the spectre, and seemed to hope they could frighten someone. I had had no idea that this desire was possible. But my Teacher reminded me that the pleasure of frightening is by no means unknown on Earth, and also of Tacitus' saying: 'They terrify lest they should fear.' When the *débris* of a decayed human soul finds itself crumbled into ghosthood and realises 'I myself am now that which all humanity has feared, I am just that cold churchyard shadow, that horrible thing which cannot be, yet somehow is', then to terrify others appears to it an escape from the doom of being a Ghost yet still fearing Ghosts – fearing even the Ghost it is. For to be afraid of oneself is the last horror.

But, beyond all these, I saw other grotesque phantoms in which hardly a trace of the human form remained; monsters who had faced the journey to the bus stop – perhaps for them it was thousands of miles – and come up to the country of the Shadow of Life and limped far into it over the torturing grass, only to spit and gibber out in one ecstasy of hatred their envy and (what is harder to understand) their contempt of joy. The voyage seemed to them a small price to pay if once, only once, within sight of that eternal dawn, they could tell the prigs, the toffs, the sanctimonious humbugs, the snobs, the 'haves', what they thought of them.

'How do they come to be here at all?' I asked my Teacher.

'I have seen that kind converted,' said he, 'when those ye would think less deeply damned have gone back. Those that hate goodness are sometimes nearer than those that know nothing at all about it and think they have it already.'

'Whisht, now!' said my Teacher suddenly. We were standing close to some bushes and beyond them I saw one of the Solid People and a Ghost who had apparently just that moment met. The outlines of the Ghost looked vaguely familiar, but I soon realised that what I had seen on Earth was not the man himself but photographs of him in the papers. He had been a famous artist.

'God!' said the Ghost, glancing round the landscape.

'God what?' asked the Spirit.

'What do you mean, "God what"?' asked the Ghost.

'In our grammar *God* is a noun.'

'Oh – I see. I only meant "By Gum" or something of the sort. I meant … well, all *this*. It's … it's … I should like to paint this.'

'I shouldn't bother about that just at present if I were you.'

'Look here; isn't one going to be allowed to go on painting?'

'Looking comes first.'

'But I've had my look. I've seen just what I want to do. God! – I wish I'd thought of bringing my things with me!'

The Spirit shook his head, scattering light from his hair as he did so. 'That sort of thing's no good here,' he said.

'What do you mean?' said the Ghost.

'When you painted on earth – at least in your earlier days – it was because you caught glimpses of Heaven in the earthly landscape. The success of your painting was that it enabled others to see the glimpses too. But here you are having the thing itself. It is from here that the messages came. There is no good *telling* us about this country, for we see it already. In fact we see it better than you do.'

'Then there's never going to be any point in painting here?'

'I don't say that. When you've grown into a Person (it's all right, we all had to do it) there'll be some things which you'll see better than anyone else. One of the things you'll want to do will be to tell us about them. But not yet. At present your business is to see. Come and see. He is endless. Come and feed.'

There was a little pause. 'That will be delightful,' said the Ghost presently in a rather dull voice.

'Come, then,' said the Spirit, offering it his arm.

'How soon do you think I *could* begin painting?' it asked.

The Spirit broke into laughter. 'Don't you see you'll never paint at all if that's what you're thinking about?' he said.

'What do you mean?' asked the Ghost.

'Why, if you are interested in the country only for the sake of painting it, you'll never learn to see the country.'

'But that's just how a real artist *is* interested in the country.'

'No. You're forgetting,' said the Spirit. 'That was not how you began. Light itself was your first love: you loved paint only as a means of telling about light.'

'Oh, that's ages ago,' said the Ghost. 'One grows out of that. Of course, you haven't seen my later works. One becomes more and more interested in paint for its own sake.'

'One does, indeed. I also have had to recover from that. It was all a snare. Ink and catgut and paint were necessary down there, but they are also dangerous stimulants. Every poet and musician and artist, but for Grace, is drawn away from love of the thing he tells, to love of the telling till, down in

Deep Hell, they cannot be interested in God at all but only in what they say about Him. For it doesn't stop at being interested in paint, you know. They sink lower – become interested in their own personalities and then in nothing but their own reputations.'

'I don't think I'm much troubled in *that* way,' said the Ghost stiffly.

'That's excellent,' said the Spirit. 'Not many of us had quite got over it when we first arrived. But if there is any of that inflammation left it will be cured when you come to the fountain.'

'What fountain's that?'

'It is up there in the mountains,' said the Spirit. 'Very cold and clear, between two green hills. A little like Lethe. When you have drunk of it you forget forever all proprietorship in your own works. You enjoy them just as if they were someone else's: without pride and without modesty.'

'That'll be grand,' said the Ghost without enthusiasm.

'Well, come,' said the Spirit: and for a few paces he supported the hobbling shadow forward to the East.

'Of course,' said the Ghost, as if speaking to itself, 'there'll always be interesting people to meet…'

'Everyone will be interesting.'

'Oh – ah – yes, to be sure. I was thinking of people in our own line. Shall I meet Claude? Or Cézanne? Or –.'

'Sooner or later – if they're here.'

'But don't you know?'

'Well, of course not. I've only been here a few years. All the chances are against my having run across them … there are a good many of us, you know.'

'But surely in the case of distinguished people, you'd hear?'

'But they aren't distinguished – no more than anyone else. Don't you understand? The Glory flows into everyone, and back from everyone: like light and mirrors. But the light's the thing.'

'Do you mean there are no famous men?'

'They are all famous. They are all known, remembered, recognised by the only Mind that can give a perfect judgement.'

'Oh, of course, in *that* sense …' said the Ghost.

'Don't stop,' said the Spirit, making to lead him still forward.

'One must be content with one's reputation among posterity, then,' said the Ghost.

'My friend,' said the Spirit. 'Don't you know?'

'Know what?'

'That you and I are already completely forgotten on the Earth?'

'Eh? What's that?' exclaimed the Ghost, disengaging its arm. 'Do you mean those damned Neo-Regionalists have won after all?'

'Lord love you, yes!' said the Spirit, once more shaking and shining with laughter. 'You couldn't get five pounds for any picture of mine or even of yours in Europe or America to-day. We're dead out of fashion.'

'I must be off at once,' said the Ghost. 'Let me go! Damn it all, one has one's duty to the future of Art. I must go back to my friends. I must write an article. There must be a manifesto. We must start a periodical. We must have publicity. Let me go. This is beyond a joke!'

And without listening to the Spirit's reply, the spectre vanished.

10

This conversation also we overheard.

'That is quite, *quite* out of the question,' said a female Ghost to one of the bright Women, 'I should not dream of staying if I'm expected to meet Robert. I am ready to forgive him, of course. But anything more is quite impossible. How he comes to be here … but that is your affair.'

'But if you have forgiven him,' said the other, 'surely —.'

'I forgive him as a Christian,' said the Ghost. 'But there are some things one can never forget.'

'But I don't understand …' began the She-Spirit.

'Exactly,' said the Ghost with a little laugh. 'You never did. You always thought Robert could do no wrong. *I* know. Please don't interrupt for *one* moment. You haven't the faintest conception of what I went through with your dear Robert. The ingratitude! It was I who made a man of him! Sacrificed my whole life to him! And what was my reward? Absolute, utter selfishness. No, but listen. He was pottering along on about six hundred a year when I married him. And mark my words, Hilda, he'd have been in that position to the day of his death if it hadn't been for me. It was I who had to drive him every step of the way. He hadn't a spark of ambition. It was like try-ing to lift a sack of coal. I had to positively nag him to take on that extra work in the other department, though it was really the beginning of everything for him. The laziness of men! He said, if you please, he couldn't work more than thirteen hours a day! As if I weren't working far longer. For *my* day's work wasn't over when his was. I had to keep him going all evening, if you under-stand what I mean. If he'd had his way he'd have just sat in an armchair and sulked when dinner was over. It was I who had to draw him out of himself and brighten him up and make conversation. With no help from him, of course. Sometimes he didn't even listen. As I said to him, I should have thought good manners, if nothing else … he seemed to have forgotten that I was a lady even if I *had* married him, and all the time I was working my fingers to the bone for him: and without the slightest appreciation. I used to spend simply *hours* arranging flowers to make that poky little house nice, and instead of thanking me, what do you think he said? He said he wished I wouldn't fill up the writing desk with them when he wanted to use it: and there was a perfectly frightful fuss one evening because I'd spilled one of the vases over some papers of his. It was all nonsense really, because they weren't anything to do with his work. He had some silly idea of writing a book in those days … as if he could. I cured him of that in the end.

'No, Hilda, you *must* listen to me. The trouble I went to, entertaining! Robert's idea was that he'd just slink off by himself every now and then to see what he called his old friends … and leave me to amuse myself! But I knew from the first that those friends were doing him no good. "No, Robert," said I, "your friends are now mine. It is my duty to have them *here*, however tired I am and however little we can afford it." You'd have thought that would have been enough. But they did come for a bit. That is where I had to use a certain amount of tact. A woman who has her wits about her can always drop in a word here and there. I wanted Robert to see them against a different background. They weren't quite at their ease, somehow, in my drawing-room: not at their best. I couldn't help laughing sometimes. Of course Robert was uncomfortable while the treatment was going on, but it was all for his own good in the end. None of that set were friends of his any longer by the end of the first year.

'And then, he got the new job. A great step up. But what *do* you think? Instead of realising that we now had a chance to spread out a bit, all he said was "Well *now*, for God's sake let's have some peace." That nearly finished me. I nearly gave him up altogether: but I knew my duty. I have always done my duty. You can't believe the work I had getting him to agree to a bigger house, and then finding a house. I wouldn't have grudged it one scrap if only he'd taken it in the right spirit – if only he'd seen the *fun* of it all. If he'd been a different sort of man it *would* have been fun meeting him on the doorstep as he came back from the office and saying, "Come along, Bobs, no time for dinner to-night. I've just heard of a house near Watford and I've got the keys and we can get there and back by one o'clock." But with *him*! It was perfect misery, Hilda. For by this time your wonderful Robert was turning into the sort of man who cares about nothing but food.

'Well, I got him into the new house at last. Yes, I know. It was a little more than we could really afford at the moment, but all sorts of things were opening out before him. And, of course, I began to entertain properly. No more of his sort of friends, thank you. I was doing it all for his sake. Every useful friend he ever made was due to me. Naturally, I had to dress well. They ought to have been the happiest years of both our lives. If they weren't, he had no one but himself to thank. Oh, he was a maddening man, simply maddening! He just set himself to get old and silent and grumpy. Just sank into himself. He could have looked years younger if he'd taken the trouble. He needn't have walked with a stoop – I'm sure I warned him about that often enough. He was the most miserable host. Whenever we gave a party everything rested on my shoulders: Robert was simply a wet blanket. As I said to him (and if I said it once, I said it a hundred times) he hadn't always been like that. There had been a time when he took an interest in all sorts of things and had been quite ready to make friends. "What on earth is coming over you?" I used to say. But now he just didn't answer at all. He would sit staring at me with his great big eyes (I came to hate a man with dark eyes) and – I know it now – just hating me. That was my reward. After all I'd done. Sheer wicked, senseless hatred: at the very moment when he was a richer man that he'd ever dreamed of being! As I used to say to him, "Robert, you're simply letting yourself go to seed." The younger men who came to the house – it wasn't my fault if they liked me better than my old bear of a husband – used to laugh at him.

'I did my duty to the very end. I *forced* him to take exercise – that was really my chief reason for keeping a great Dane. I kept on giving parties. I took him for the most wonderful holidays. I saw that he didn't drink too much. Even, when things became desperate, I encouraged him to take up his writing again. It couldn't do any harm by then. How could I help it if he *did* have a nervous breakdown in the end? My conscience is clear. I've done my duty by him, if ever a woman has. So you see why it would be impossible to ...

'And yet ... I don't know. I believe I have changed my mind. I'll make them a fair offer. Hilda. I will *not* meet him, if it means just meeting him and no more. But if I'm given a free hand I'll take charge of him again. I will take up my burden once more. But I must have a free hand. With all the time one would have here, I believe I could still make something of him. Somewhere quiet to ourselves. Wouldn't that be a good plan? He's not fit to be on his own. Put me in charge of him. He wants firm handling. I know him better than you do. What's that? No, give him to me, do you hear? Don't consult *him*: just give him to me. I'm his wife, aren't I? I was only beginning. There's lots, lots, lots of things I still want to do with him. No, listen, Hilda. Please, please! I'm so miserable. I must have someone to – to do things to. It's simply frightful down there. No one minds about me at all. I can't alter them. It's dreadful to see them all sitting about and not be able to do anything with them. Give him back to me. Why should he have everything his own way? It's not good for him. It isn't right, it's not fair. I want Robert. What right have you to keep him from me? I hate you. How can I pay him out if you won't let me have him?'

The Ghost which had towered up like a dying candle-flame snapped suddenly. A sour, dry smell lingered in the air for a moment and then there was no Ghost to be seen.

One of the most painful meetings we witnessed was between a woman's Ghost and a Bright Spirit who had apparently been her brother. They must have met only a moment before we ran across them, for the Ghost was just saying in a tone of unconcealed disappointment, 'Oh … Reginald! It's *you*, is it?'

'Yes, dear,' said the Spirit. 'I know you expected someone else. Can you … I hope you can be a little glad to see even me; for the present.'

'I did think Michael would have come,' said the Ghost; and then, almost fiercely, 'He is *here*, of course?'

'He's there – far up in the mountains.'

'Why hasn't he come to meet me? Didn't he know?'

'My dear (don't worry, it will all come right presently) it wouldn't have done. Not yet. He wouldn't be able to see or hear you as you are at present. You'd be totally invisible to Michael. But we'll soon build you up.'

'I should have thought if *you* can see me, my own son could!'

'It doesn't always happen like that. You see, I have specialised in this sort of work.'

'Oh, it's work, is it?' snapped the Ghost. Then, after a pause, 'Well. When *am* I going to be allowed to see him?'

'There's no question of being *allowed*, Pam. As soon as it's possible for him to see you, of course he will. You need to be thickened up a bit.'

'How?' said the Ghost. The monosyllable was hard and a little threatening.

'I'm afraid the first step is a hard one,' said the Spirit. 'But after that you'll go on like a house on fire. You will become solid enough for Michael to perceive you when you learn to want Someone Else besides Michael. I don't say "more than Michael", not as a beginning. That will come later. It's only the little germ of a desire for God that we need to start the process.'

'Oh, you mean religion and all that sort of thing? This is hardly the moment … and from *you*, of all people. Well, never mind. I'll do whatever's necessary. What do you want me to do? Come on. The sooner I begin it, the sooner they'll let me see my boy. I'm quite ready.'

'But, Pam, do think! Don't you see you are not beginning at all as long as you are in that state of mind? You're treating God only as a means to Michael. But the whole thickening treatment consists in learning to want God for His own sake.'

'You wouldn't talk like that if you were a mother.'

'You mean, if I were *only* a mother. But there is no such thing as being only a mother. You exist as Michael's mother only because you first exist as God's creature. That relation is older and closer. No, listen, Pam! He also loves. He also has suffered. He also has waited a long time.'

'If He loved me He'd let me see my boy. If He loved me why did He take Michael away from me? I wasn't going to say anything about that. But it's pretty hard to forgive, you know.'

'But He had to take Michael away. Partly for Michael's sake ...'

'I'm sure I did my best to make Michael happy. I gave up my whole life ...'

'Human beings can't make one another really happy for long. And secondly, for your sake. He wanted your merely instinctive love for your child (tigresses share *that*, you know!) to turn into something better. He wanted you to love Michael as He understands love. You cannot love a fellow-creature fully till you love God. Sometimes this conversion can be done while the instinctive love is still gratified. But there was, it seems, no chance of that in your case. The instinct was uncontrolled and fierce and mono-maniac. (Ask your daughter, or your husband. Ask our own mother. You haven't once thought of *her*.) The only remedy was to take away its object. It was a case for surgery. When that first kind of love was thwarted, then there was just a chance that in the loneliness, in the silence, something else might begin to grow.'

'This is all nonsense – cruel and wicked nonsense. What *right* have you to say things like that about Mother-love? It is the highest and holiest feeling in human nature.'

'Pam, Pam – no natural feelings are high or low, holy or unholy, in themselves. They are all holy when God's hand is on the rein. They all go bad when they set up on their own and make themselves into false gods.'

'My love for Michael would never have gone bad. Not if we'd lived together for millions of years.'

'You are mistaken. And you must know. Haven't you met – down there – mothers who have their sons with them, in Hell? Does *their* love make them happy?'

'If you mean people like the Guthrie woman and her dreadful Bobby, of course not. I hope you're not suggesting ... If I had Michael I'd be perfectly happy, even in that town. I wouldn't be always talking about him till everyone hated the sound of his name, which is what Winifred Guthrie does about *her* brat. I wouldn't quarrel with people for not taking enough notice of him and then be furiously jealous if they did. I wouldn't go about whining and complaining that he wasn't nice to me. Because, of course, he would be nice. Don't you dare to suggest that Michael could ever become like the Guthrie boy. There are some things I won't stand.'

'What you have seen in the Guthries is what natural affection turns to in the end if it will not be converted.'

'It's a lie. A wicked, cruel lie. How could anyone love their son more than I did? Haven't I lived only for his memory all these years?'

'That was rather a mistake, Pam. In your heart of hearts you know it was.'

'What was a mistake?'

'All that ten years' ritual of grief. Keeping his room exactly as he'd left it; keeping anniversaries; refusing to leave that house though Dick and Muriel were both wretched there.'

'Of course they didn't care. I know that. I soon learned to expect no real sympathy from them.'

'You're wrong. No man ever felt his son's death more than Dick. Not many girls loved their brothers better than Muriel. It wasn't against Michael they revolted: it was against you – against having their whole life dominated by the tyranny of the past: and not really even Michael's past, but your past.'

'You are heartless. Everyone is heartless. The past was all I had.'

'It was all you chose to have. It was the wrong way to deal with a sorrow. It was Egyptian – like embalming a dead body.'

'Oh, of course. I'm wrong. Everything I say or do is wrong, according to you.'

'But of course!' said the Spirit, shining with love and mirth so that my eyes were dazzled. 'That's what we all find when we reach this country. We've all been wrong! That's the great joke. There's no need to go on pretending one was right! After that we begin living.'

'How dare you laugh about it? Give me my boy. Do you hear? I don't care about all your rules and regulations. I don't believe in a God who keeps mother and son apart. I believe in a God of love. No one had a right to come between me and my son. Not even God. Tell Him that to His face. I want my boy, and I mean to have him. He is mine, do you understand? Mine, mine, mine, for ever and ever.'

'He will be, Pam. Everything will be yours. God Himself will be yours. But not that way. Nothing can be yours by nature.'

'What? Not my own son, born out of my own body?'

'And where is your own body now? Didn't you know that Nature draws to an end? Look! The sun is coming, over the mountains there: it will be up any moment now.'

'Michael is mine.'

'How yours? You didn't make him. Nature made him to grow in your body without your will. Even against your will … you sometimes forget that you didn't intend to have a baby then at all. Michael was originally an Accident.'

'Who told you that?' said the Ghost: and then, recovering itself, 'It's a lie. It's not true. And it's no business of yours. I hate your religion and I hate and despise your God. I believe in a God of Love.'

'And yet, Pam, you have no love at this moment for your own mother or for me.'

'Oh, I see! *That's* the trouble, is it? *Really*, Reginald! The idea of your being hurt because …'

'Lord love you!' said the Spirit with a great laugh. 'You needn't bother about that! Don't you know that you *can't* hurt anyone in this country?'

The Ghost was silent and open-mouthed for a moment; more wilted, I thought, by this re-assurance than by anything else that had been said.

'Come. We will go a bit further,' said my Teacher, laying his hand on my arm.

'Why did you bring me away, Sir?' said I when we had passed out of earshot of this unhappy Ghost.

'It might take a long while, that conversation,' said my Teacher. 'And ye have heard enough to see what the choice is.'

'Is there any hope for her, Sir?'

'Aye, there's some. What she calls her love for her son has turned into a poor, prickly, astringent sort of thing. But there's still a wee spark of something that's not just herself in it. That might be blown into a flame.'

'Then some natural feelings are really better than others – I mean, are a better starting-point for the real thing?'

'Better *and* worse. There's something in natural affection which will lead it on to eternal love more easily than natural appetite could be led on. But there's also something in it which makes it easier to stop at the natural level and mistake it for the heavenly. Brass is mistaken for gold more easily than clay is. And if it finally refuses conversion its corruption will be worse than the corruption of what ye call the lower passions. It is a stronger angel, and therefore, when it falls, a fiercer devil.'

'I don't know that I dare repeat this on Earth, Sir,' said I. 'They'd say I was inhuman: they'd say I believed in total depravity: they'd say I was attacking the best and the holiest things. They'd call me …'

'It might do you no harm if they did,' said he with (I really thought) a twinkle in his eye.

'But could one dare – could one have the face – to go to a bereaved mother, in her misery – when one's not bereaved oneself? …'

'No, no, Son, that's no office of yours. You're not a good enough man for that. When your own heart's been broken it will be time for you to think of talking. But someone must say in general what's been unsaid among you this many a year: that love, as mortals understand the word, isn't enough. Every natural love will rise again and live forever in this country: but none will rise again until it has been buried.'

'The saying is almost too hard for us.'

'Ah, but it's cruel not to say it. They that know have grown afraid to speak. That is why sorrows that used to purify now only fester.'

'Keats was wrong, then, when he said he was certain of the holiness of the heart's affections.'

'I doubt if he knew clearly what he meant. But you and I must be clear. There is but one good; that is God. Everything else is good when it looks to Him and bad when it turns from Him. And the higher and mightier it is in the natural order, the more demoniac it will be if it rebels. It's not out of bad mice or bad fleas you make demons, but out of bad archangels. The false religion of lust is baser than the false religion of mother-love or patriotism or art: but lust is less likely to be made into a religion. But look!'

I saw coming towards us a Ghost who carried something on his shoulder. Like all the Ghosts, he was unsubstantial, but they differed from one another as smokes differ. Some had been whitish; this one was dark and oily. What sat on his shoulder was a little red lizard, and it was twitching its tail like a whip and whispering things in his ear. As we caught sight of him he turned his head to the reptile with a snarl of impatience. 'Shut up, I tell you!' he said. It wagged its tail and continued to whisper to him. He ceased snarling, and presently began to smile. Then he turned and started to limp westward, away from the mountains.

'Off so soon?' said a voice.

The speaker was more or less human in shape but larger than a man, and so bright that I could hardly look at him. His presence smote on my eyes and on my body too (for there was heat coming from him as well as light) like the morning sun at the beginning of a tyrannous summer day.

'Yes. I'm off,' said the Ghost. 'Thanks for all your hospitality. But it's no good, you see. I told this little chap' (here he indicated the Lizard) 'that he'd have to be quiet if he came – which he insisted on doing. Of course his stuff won't do here: I realise that. But he won't stop. I shall just have to go home.'

'Would you like me to make him quiet?' said the flaming Spirit – an angel, as I now understood.

'Of course I would,' said the Ghost.

'Then I will kill him,' said the Angel, taking a step forward.

'Oh – ah – look out! You're burning me. Keep away,' said the Ghost, retreating.

'Don't you *want* him killed?'

'You didn't say anything about *killing* him at first. I hardly meant to bother you with anything so drastic as that.'

'It's the only way,' said the Angel, whose burning hands were now very close to the Lizard. 'Shall I kill it?'

'Well, that's a further question. I'm quite open to consider it, but it's a new point, isn't it? I mean, for the moment I was only thinking about silencing it because up here – well, it's so damned embarrassing.'

'May I kill it?'

'Well, there's time to discuss that later.'

'There is no time. May I kill it?'

'Please, I never meant to be such a nuisance. Please – really – don't bother. Look! It's gone to sleep of its own accord. I'm sure it'll be all right now. Thanks ever so much.'

'May I kill it?'

'Honestly, I don't think there's the slightest necessity for that. I'm sure I shall be able to keep it in order now. I think the gradual process would be far better than killing it.'

'The gradual process is of no use at all.'

'Don't you think so? Well, I'll think over what you've said very carefully. I honestly will. In fact I'd let you kill it now, but as a matter of fact I'm not feeling frightfully well to-day. It would be most silly to do it *now*. I'd need to be in good health for the operation. Some other day, perhaps.'

'There is no other day. All days are present now.'

'Get back! You're burning me. How can I tell you to kill it? You'd kill *me* if you did.'

'It is not so.'

'Why, you're hurting me now.'

'I never said it wouldn't hurt you. I said it wouldn't kill you.'

'Oh, I know. You think I'm a coward. But it isn't that. Really it isn't. I say! Let me run back by to-night's bus and get an opinion from my own doctor. I'll come again the first moment I can.'

'This moment contains all moments.'

'Why are you torturing me? You are jeering at me. How *can* I let you tear me in pieces? If you wanted to help me, why didn't you kill the damned thing without asking me – before I knew? It would be all over by now if you had.'

'I cannot kill it against your will. It is impossible. Have I your permission?'

The Angel's hands were almost closed on the Lizard, but not quite. Then the Lizard began chattering to the Ghost so loud that even I could hear what it was saying.

'Be careful,' it said. 'He can do what he says. He can kill me. One fatal word from you and he *will*! Then you'll be without me for ever and ever. It's not natural. How could you live? You'd be only a sort of ghost, not a real man as you are now. He doesn't understand. He's only a cold, bloodless abstract thing. It may be natural for him, but it isn't for us. Yes, yes. I know there are no real pleasures now, only dreams. But aren't they better than nothing? And I'll be so good. I admit I've sometimes gone too far in the past, but I promise I won't do it again. I'll give you nothing but really nice dreams – all sweet and fresh and almost innocent. You might say, quite innocent ...'

'Have I your permission?' said the Angel to the Ghost.

'I know it will kill me.'

'It won't. But supposing it did?'

'You're right. It would be better to be dead than to live with this creature.'

'Then I may?'

'Damn and blast you! Go on, can't you? Get it over. Do what you like,' bellowed the Ghost: but ended, whimpering, 'God help me. God help me.'

Next moment the Ghost gave a scream of agony such as I never heard on Earth. The Burning One closed his crimson grip on the reptile: twisted it, while it bit and writhed, and then flung it, broken-backed, on the turf.

'Ow! That's done for me,' gasped the Ghost, reeling backwards.

For a moment I could make out nothing distinctly. Then I saw, between me and the nearest bush, unmistakably solid but growing every moment solider, the upper arm and the shoulder of a man. Then, brighter still and stronger, the legs and hands. The neck and golden head materialised while I watched, and if my attention had not wavered I should have seen the actual completing of a man – an immense man, naked, not much smaller than the Angel. What distracted me was the fact that at the same moment something seemed to be happening to the Lizard. At first I thought the operation had failed. So far from dying, the creature was still struggling and even growing bigger as it struggled. And as it grew it changed. Its hinder parts grew rounder. The tail, still flickering, became a tail of hair that flickered between huge and glossy buttocks. Suddenly I started back, rubbing my eyes. What stood before me was the greatest stallion I have ever seen, silvery white but with mane and tail of gold. It was smooth and shining, rippled with swells of flesh and muscle, whinneying and stamping with its hoofs. At each stamp the land shook and the trees dindled.

The new-made man turned and clapped the new horse's neck. It nosed his bright body. Horse and master breathed each into the other's nostrils. The man turned from it, flung himself at the feet of the Burning One, and embraced them. When he rose I thought his face shone with tears, but it may have been only the liquid love and brightness (one cannot distinguish them in that country) which flowed from him. I had not long to think about it. In joyous haste the young man leaped upon the horse's back. Turning in his seat he waved a farewell, then nudged the stallion with his heels. They were off before I knew well what was happening. There was riding if you like! I came out as quickly as I could from among the bushes to follow them with my eyes; but already they were only like a shooting star far off on the green plain, and soon among the foothills of the mountains. Then, still like a star, I saw them winding up, scaling what seemed impossible steeps, and quicker every moment, till near the dim brow of the landscape, so high that I must strain my neck to see them, they vanished, bright themselves, into the rose-brightness of that everlasting morning.

While I still watched, I noticed that the whole plain and forest were shaking with a sound which in our world would be too large to hear, but there I could take it with joy. I knew it was not the Solid People who were singing. It was the voice of that earth, those woods and those waters. A strange archaic, inorganic noise, that came from all directions at once. The Nature or Arch-Nature of that land rejoiced to have been once more ridden, and therefore consummated, in the person of the horse. It sang,

'The Master says to our master, Come up. Share my rest and splendour till all natures that were your enemies become slaves to dance before you and backs for you to ride, and firmness for your feet to rest on.

'From beyond all place and time, out of the very Place, authority will be given you: the strengths that once opposed your will shall be obedient fire in your blood and heavenly thunder in your voice.

'Overcome us that, so overcome, we may be ourselves: we desire the beginning of your reign as we desire dawn and dew, wetness at the birth of light.

'Master, your Master has appointed you for ever: to be our King of Justice and our high Priest.'

'Do ye understand all this, my Son?' said the Teacher.

'I don't know about all, Sir,' said I. 'Am I right in thinking the Lizard really turned into the Horse?'

'Aye. But it was killed first. Ye'll not forget that part of the story?'

'I'll try not to, Sir. But does it mean that everything – everything – that is in us can go on to the Mountains?'

'Nothing, not even the best and noblest, can go on as it now is. Nothing, not even what is lowest and most bestial, will not be raised again if it submits to death. It is sown a natural body, it is raised a spiritual body. Flesh and blood cannot come to the Mountains. Not because they are too rank, but because they are too weak. What is a lizard compared with a stallion? Lust is a poor, weak, whimpering, whispering thing compared with that richness and energy of desire which will arise when lust has been killed.'

'But am I to tell them at home that this man's sensuality proved less of an obstacle than that poor woman's love for her son? For that was, at any rate, an excess of *love*.'

'Ye'll tell them no such thing,' he replied sternly. 'Excess of love, did ye say? There was no excess, there was defect. She loved her son too little, not too much. If she had loved him more there'd be no difficulty. I do not know how her affair will end. But it may well be that at this moment she's demanding to have him down with her in Hell. That kind is sometimes perfectly ready to plunge the soul they say they love in endless misery if only they can still in some fashion possess it. No, no. Ye must draw another lesson. Ye must ask, if the risen body even of appetite is as grand a horse as ye saw, what would the risen body of maternal love or friendship be?'

But once more my attention was diverted. 'Is there *another* river, Sir?' I asked.

12

The reason why I asked if there were another river was this. All down one long aisle of the forest the under-sides of the leafy branches had begun to tremble with dancing light; and on Earth I knew nothing so likely to produce this appearance as the reflected lights cast upward by moving water. A few moments later I realised my mistake. Some kind of procession was approaching us, and the light came from the persons who composed it.

First came bright Spirits, not the Spirits of men, who danced and scattered flowers – soundlessly falling, lightly drifting flowers, though by the standards of the ghost-world each petal would have weighed a hundred-weight and their fall would have been like the crashing of boulders. Then, on the left and right, at each side of the forest avenue, came youthful shapes, boys upon one hand, and girls upon the other. If I could remember their singing and write down the notes, no man who read that score would ever grow sick or old. Between them went musicians: and after these a lady in whose honour all this was being done.

I cannot now remember whether she was naked or clothed. If she were naked, then it must have been the almost visible penumbra of her courtesy and joy which produces in my memory the illusion of a great and shining train that followed her across the happy grass. If she were clothed, then the illusion of nakedness is doubtless due to the clarity with which her innermost spirit shone through the clothes. For clothes in that country are not a disguise: the spiritual body lives along each thread and turns them into living organs. A robe or a crown is there as much one of the wearer's features as a lip or an eye.

But I have forgotten. And only partly do I remember the unbearable beauty of her face.

'Is it? ... is it?' I whispered to my guide.

'Not at all,' said he. 'It's someone ye'll never have heard of. Her name on Earth was Sarah Smith and she lived at Golders Green.'

'She seems to be … well, a person of particular importance?'

'Aye. She is one of the great ones. Ye have heard that fame in this country and fame on Earth are two quite different things.'

'And who are these gigantic people … look! They're like emeralds … who are dancing and throwing flowers before her?'

'Haven't ye read your Milton? *A thousand liveried angels lackey her.*'

'And who are all these young men and women on each side?'

'They are her sons and daughters.'

'She must have had a very large family, Sir.'

'Every young man or boy that met her became her son – even if it was only the boy that brought the meat to her back door. Every girl that met her was her daughter.'

'Isn't that a bit hard on their own parents?'

'No. There *are* those that steal other people's children. But her motherhood was of a different kind. Those on whom it fell went back to their natural parents loving them more. Few men looked on her without becoming, in a certain fashion, her lovers. But it was the kind of love that made them not less true, but truer, to their own wives.'

'And how … but hullo! What are all these animals? A cat – two cats – dozens of cats. And all these dogs … why, I can't count them. And the birds. And the horses.'

'They are her beasts.'

'Did she keep a sort of zoo? I mean, this is a bit too much.'

'Every beast and bird that came near her had its place in her love. In her they became themselves. And now the abundance of life she has in Christ from the Father flows over into them.'

I looked at my Teacher in amazement.

'Yes,' he said. 'It is like when you throw a stone into a pool, and the concentric waves spread out further and further. Who knows where it will end? Redeemed humanity is still young, it has hardly come to its full strength. But already there is joy enough in the little finger of a great saint such as yonder lady to waken all the dead things of the universe into life.'

While we spoke the Lady was steadily advancing towards us, but it was not at us she looked. Following the direction of her eyes, I turned and saw an oddly-shaped phantom approaching. Or rather two phantoms: a great tall Ghost, horribly thin and shaky, who seemed to be leading on a chain another Ghost no bigger than an organ-grinder's monkey. The taller Ghost wore a soft black hat, and he reminded me of something that my memory could not quite recover. Then, when he had come within a few feet of the Lady he spread out his lean, shaky hand flat on his chest with the fingers wide apart, and exclaimed in a hollow voice, 'At last!' All at once I realised what it was that he had put me in mind of. He was like a seedy actor of the old school.

'Darling! At last!' said the Lady. 'Good Heavens!' thought I. 'Surely she can't —', and then I noticed two things. In the first place, I noticed that the little Ghost was not being led by the big one. It was the dwarfish figure that held the chain in its hand and the theatrical figure that wore the collar round its neck. In the second place, I noticed that the Lady was looking solely at the dwarf Ghost. She seemed to think it was the Dwarf who had addressed her, or else she was deliberately ignoring the other. On the poor dwarf she turned her eyes. Love shone not from her face only, but from all her limbs, as if it were some liquid in which she had just been bathing. Then, to my dismay, she came nearer. She stooped down and kissed the Dwarf. It made one shudder to see her in such close contact with that cold, damp, shrunken thing. But she did not shudder.

'Frank,' she said, 'before anything else, forgive me. For all I ever did wrong and for all I did not do right since the first day we met, I ask your pardon.'

I looked properly at the Dwarf for the first time now: or perhaps, when he received her kiss he became a little more visible. One could just make out the sort of face he must have had when he was a man: a little, oval, freckled face with a weak chin and a tiny wisp of unsuccessful moustache. He gave her a glance, not a full look. He was watching the Tragedian out of the corner of his eyes. Then he gave a jerk to the chain: and it was the Tragedian, not he, who answered the Lady.

'There, there,' said the Tragedian. 'We'll say no more about it. We all make mistakes.' With the words there came over his features a ghastly contortion which, I think, was meant for an indulgently playful smile. 'We'll say no more,' he continued. 'It's not myself I'm thinking about. It is you. That is what has been continually on my mind – all these years. The thought of you – you here alone, breaking your heart about me.'

'But now,' said the Lady to the Dwarf, 'you can set all that aside. Never think like that again. It is all over.'

Her beauty brightened so that I could hardly see anything else, and under that sweet compulsion the Dwarf really looked at her for the first time. For a second I thought he was growing more like a man. He opened his mouth. He himself was going to speak this time. But oh, the disappointment when the words came!

'You missed me?' he croaked in a small, bleating voice.

Yet even then she was not taken aback. Still the love and courtesy flowed from her.

'Dear, you will understand about that very soon,' she said. 'But to-day —.'

What happened next gave me a shock. The Dwarf and Tragedian spoke in unison, not to her but to one another. 'You'll notice,' they warned one another, 'she hasn't answered our question.' I realised then that they were one person, or rather that both were the remains of what had once been a person. The Dwarf again rattled the chain.

'You missed me?' said the Tragedian to the Lady, throwing a dreadful theatrical tremor into his voice.

'Dear friend,' said the Lady, still attending exclusively to the Dwarf, 'you may be happy about that and about everything else. Forget all about it for ever.'

And really, for a moment, I thought the Dwarf was going to obey: partly because the outlines of his face became a little clearer, and partly because the invitation to all joy, singing out of her whole being like a bird's song on an April evening, seemed to me such that no creature could resist it. Then he hesitated. And then – once more he and his accomplice spoke in unison.

'Of course it would be rather fine and magnanimous not to press the point,' they said to one another. 'But can we be sure she'd notice? We've done these sort of things before. There was the time we let her have the last stamp in the house to write to her mother and said nothing although she *had* known we wanted to write a letter ourself. We'd thought she'd remember and see how unselfish we'd been. But she never did. And there was the time ... oh, lots and lots of times!' So the Dwarf gave a shake to the chain and —

'I can't forget it,' cried the Tragedian. 'And I won't forget it, either. I could forgive them all they've done to me. But for your miseries —.'

'Oh, don't you understand?' said the Lady. 'There *are* no miseries here.'

'Do you mean to say,' answered the Dwarf, as if this new idea had made him quite forget the Tragedian for a moment, 'do you mean to say you've been *happy*?'

'Didn't you want me to be? But no matter. Want it now. Or don't think about it at all.'

The Dwarf blinked at her. One could see an unheard-of idea trying to enter his little mind: one could see even that there was for him some sweetness in it. For a second he had almost let the chain go: then, as if it were his life-line, he clutched it once more.

'Look here,' said the Tragedian. 'We've got to face this.' He was using his 'manly' bullying tone this time: the one for bringing women to their senses.

'Darling,' said the Lady to the Dwarf, 'there's nothing to face. You don't want me to have been miserable for misery's sake. You only think I must have been if I loved you. But if you'll only wait you'll see that isn't so.'

'Love!' said the Tragedian striking his forehead with his hand: then, a few notes deeper, 'Love! Do you know the meaning of the word?'

'How should I not?' said the Lady. 'I am in love. *In* love, do you understand? Yes, now I love truly.'

'You mean,' said the Tragedian, 'you mean – you did *not* love me truly in the old days.'

'Only in a poor sort of way,' she answered. 'I have asked you to forgive me. There was a little real love in it. But what we called love down there was mostly the craving to be loved. In the main I loved you for my own sake: because I needed you.'

'And now!' said the Tragedian with a hackneyed gesture of despair. 'Now, you need me no more?'

'But of course not!' said the Lady; and her smile made me wonder how both the phantoms could refrain from crying out with joy.

'What needs could I have,' she said, 'now that I have all? I am full now, not empty. I am in Love Himself, not lonely. Strong, not weak. You shall be the same. Come and see. We shall have no *need* for one another now: we can begin to love truly.'

But the Tragedian was still striking attitudes. 'She needs me no more – no more. No more,' he said in a choking voice to no one in particular. 'Would to God,' he continued, but he was now pronouncing it *Gud* – 'would to Gud I had seen her lying dead at my feet before I heard those words. Lying dead at my feet. Lying dead at my feet.'

I do not know how long the creature intended to go on repeating the phrase, for the Lady put an end to that. 'Frank! Frank!' she cried in a voice that made the whole wood ring. 'Look at me. *Look* at me. What are you doing with that great, ugly doll? Let go of the chain. Send it away. It is *you* I want. Don't you see what nonsense it's talking?' Merriment danced in her eyes. She was sharing a joke with the Dwarf, right over the head of the Tragedian. Something not at all unlike a smile struggled to appear on the Dwarf's face. For he *was* looking at her now. Her laughter was past his first defences. He was struggling hard to keep it out, but already with imperfect success. Against his will, he was even growing a little bigger. 'Oh, you great goose,' said she. 'What is the good of talking like that here? You know as well as I do that you *did* see me lying dead years and years ago. Not "at your feet", of course, but on a bed in a nursing home. A very good nursing home it was too. Matron would never have dreamed of leaving bodies lying about the floor! It's ridiculous for that doll to try to be impressive about death *here*. It just won't work.'

13

I do not know that I ever saw anything more terrible than the struggle of that Dwarf Ghost against joy. For he had almost been overcome. Somewhere, incalculable ages ago, there must have been gleams of humour and reason in him. For one moment, while she looked at him in her love and mirth, he saw the absurdity of the Tragedian. For one moment he did not at all misunderstand her laughter: he too must once have known that no people find each other more absurd than lovers. But the light that reached him, reached him against his will. This was not the meeting he had pictured; he would not accept it. Once more he clutched at his death-line, and at once the Tragedian spoke.

'You dare to laugh at it!' it stormed. 'To my face? And this is my reward. Very well. It is fortunate that you give yourself no concern about my fate. Otherwise you might be sorry afterwards to think that you had driven me back to Hell. What? Do you think I'd stay *now*? Thank you. I believe I'm fairly quick at recognising where I'm not wanted. "Not needed" was the exact expression, if I remember rightly.'

From this time on the Dwarf never spoke again: but still the Lady addressed it.

'Dear, no one sends you back. Here is all joy. Everything bids you stay.' But the Dwarf was growing smaller even while she spoke.

'Yes,' said the Tragedian. 'On terms you might offer to a dog. I happen to have some self-respect left, and I see that my going will make no difference to you. It is nothing to you that I go back to the cold and the gloom, the lonely, lonely streets —.'

'Don't, don't, Frank,' said the Lady. 'Don't let it talk like that.' But the Dwarf was now so small that she had dropped on her knees to speak to it. The Tragedian caught her words greedily as a dog catches a bone.

'Ah, you can't bear to hear it!' he shouted with miserable triumph. 'That was always the way. *You* must be sheltered. Grim realities must be kept out of *your* sight. You who can be happy without me, forgetting me! You don't want even to hear of my sufferings. You say, *don't*. Don't tell you. Don't make you unhappy. Don't break in on your sheltered, self-centred little heaven. And this is the reward —.'

She stooped still lower to speak to the Dwarf which was now a figure no bigger than a kitten, hanging on the end of the chain with his feet off the ground.

'That wasn't why I said, Don't,' she answered. 'I meant, stop acting. It's no good. He is killing you. Let go of that chain. Even now.'

'Acting,' screamed the Tragedian. 'What do you mean?'

The Dwarf was now so small that I could not distinguish him from the chain to which he was clinging. And now for the first time I could not be certain whether the Lady was addressing him or the Tragedian.

'Quick,' she said. 'There is still time. Stop it. Stop it at once.'

'Stop what?'

'Using pity, other people's pity, in the wrong way. We have all done it a bit on earth, you know. Pity was meant to be a spur that drives joy to help misery. But it can be used the wrong way round. It can be used for a kind of blackmailing. Those who choose misery can hold joy up to ransom, by pity. You see, I know now. Even as a child you did it. Instead of saying you were sorry, you went and sulked in the attic ... because you knew that sooner or later one of your sisters would say, "I can't bear to think of him sitting up there alone, crying." You used their pity to blackmail them, and they gave in in the end. And afterwards, when we were married ... oh, it doesn't matter, if only you will *stop* it.'

'And *that*,' said the Tragedian, 'that is all you have understood of me, after all these years.' I don't know what had become of the Dwarf Ghost by now. Perhaps it was climbing up the chain like an insect: perhaps it was somehow absorbed into the chain.

'No, Frank, not *here*,' said the Lady. 'Listen to reason. Did you think joy was created to live always under that threat? Always defenceless against those who would rather be miserable than have their self-will crossed? For it was real misery. I know that now. You made yourself really wretched. That you can still do. But you can no longer communicate your wretchedness. Everything becomes more and more itself. Here is joy that cannot be shaken. Our light can swallow up your darkness: but your darkness cannot now infect our light. No, no, no. Come to us. We will not go to you. Can you really have thought that love and joy would always be at the mercy of frowns and sighs? Did you not know they were stronger than their opposites?'

'Love? How dare *you* use that sacred word?' said the Tragedian. At the same moment he gathered up the chain which had now for some time been swinging uselessly at his side, and somehow disposed of it. I am not quite sure, but I think he swallowed it. Then for the first time it became clear that the Lady saw and addressed him only.

'Where is Frank?' she said. 'And who are you, Sir? I never knew you. Perhaps you had better leave me. Or stay, if you prefer. If it would help you and if it were possible I would go down with you into Hell: but you cannot bring Hell into me.'

'You do not love me,' said the Tragedian in a thin bat-like voice: and he was now very difficult to see.

'I cannot love a lie,' said the Lady. 'I cannot love the thing which is not. I am in Love, and out of it I will not go.'

There was no answer. The Tragedian had vanished. The Lady was alone in that woodland place, and a brown bird went hopping past her, bending with its light feet the grasses I could not bend.

Presently the lady got up and began to walk away. The other Bright Spirits came forward to receive her, singing as they came:

> 'The Happy Trinity is her home: nothing can trouble her joy.
> She is the bird that evades every net: the wild deer that leaps every
>   pitfall.
> Like the mother bird to its chickens or a shield to the arm'd knight: so is
>   the Lord to her mind, in His unchanging lucidity.
> Bogies will not scare her in the dark: bullets will not frighten her in the
>   day.
> Falsehoods tricked out as truths assail her in vain: she sees through the lie
>   as if it were glass.
> The invisible germ will not harm her: nor yet the glittering
>   sun-stroke.
> A thousand fail to solve the problem, ten thousand choose the wrong
>   turning: but she passes safely through.
> He details immortal gods to attend her: upon every road where she must
>   travel.
> They take her hand at hard places: she will not stub her toes in the dark.
> She may walk among Lions and rattlesnakes: among dinosaurs and
>   nurseries of lionets.
> He fills her brim-full with immensity of life: he leads her to see the
>   world's desire.

'And yet ... and yet ... ,' said I to my Teacher, when all the shapes and the singing had passed some distance away into the forest, 'even now I am not quite sure. Is it really tolerable that she should be untouched by his misery, even his self-made misery?'

'Would ye rather he still had the power of tormenting her? He did it many a day and many a year in their earthly life.'

'Well, no. I suppose I don't want that.'

'What then?'

'I hardly know, Sir. What some people say on Earth is that the final loss of one soul gives the lie to all the joy of those who are saved.'

'Ye see it does not.'

'I feel in a way that it ought to.'

'That sounds very merciful: but see what lurks behind it.'

'What?'

'The demand of the loveless and the self-imprisoned that they should be allowed to blackmail the universe: that till they consent to be happy (on their own terms) no one else shall taste joy: that theirs should be the final power; that Hell should be able to *veto* Heaven.'

'I don't know what I want, Sir.'

'Son, son, it must be one way or the other. Either the day must come when joy prevails and all the makers of misery are no longer able to infect it: or else for ever and ever the makers of misery can destroy in others the happiness they reject for themselves. I know it has a grand sound to say ye'll accept no salvation which leaves even one creature in the dark outside. But watch that sophistry or ye'll make a Dog in a Manger the tyrant of the universe.'

'But dare one say – it is horrible to say – that Pity must ever die?'

'Ye must distinguish. The action of Pity will live for ever: but the passion of Pity will not. The passion of Pity, the Pity we merely suffer, the ache that draws men to concede what should not be conceded and to flatter when they should speak truth, the pity that has cheated many a woman out of her virginity and many a statesman out of his honesty – that will die. It was used as a weapon by bad men against good ones: their weapon will be broken.'

'And what is the other kind – the action?'

'It's a weapon on the other side. It leaps quicker than light from the highest place to the lowest to bring healing and joy, whatever the cost to itself. It changes darkness into light and evil into good. But it will not, at the cunning tears of Hell, impose on good the tyranny of evil. Every disease that submits to a cure shall be cured: but we will not call blue yellow to please those who insist on still having jaundice, nor make a midden of the world's garden for the sake of some who cannot abide the smell of roses.'

'You say it will go down to the lowest, Sir. But she didn't go down with him to Hell. She didn't even see him off by the bus.'

'Where would ye have had her go?'

'Why, where we all came from by that bus. The big gulf, beyond the edge of the cliff. Over there. You can't see it from here, but you must know the place I mean.'

My Teacher gave a curious smile. 'Look,' he said, and with the word he went down on his hands and knees. I did the same (how it hurt my knees!)

and presently saw that he had plucked a blade of grass. Using its thin end as a pointer, he made me see, after I had looked very closely, a crack in the soil so small that I could not have identified it without this aid.

'I cannot be certain,' he said, 'that this *is* the crack ye came up through. But through a crack no bigger than that ye certainly came.'

'But – but,' I gasped with a feeling of bewilderment not unlike terror. 'I saw an infinite abyss. And cliffs towering up and up. And then *this* country on top of the cliffs.'

'Aye. But the voyage was not mere locomotion. That bus, and all you inside it, were increasing *in size*.[1]

'Do you mean then that Hell – all that infinite empty town – is down in some little crack like this?'

'Yes. All Hell is smaller than one pebble of your earthly world: but it is smaller than one atom of *this* world, the Real World. Look at yon butterfly. If it swallowed all Hell, Hell would not be big enough to do it any harm or to have any taste.'

'It seems big enough when you're in it, Sir.'

'And yet all loneliness, angers, hatreds, envies and itchings that it contains, if rolled into one single experience and put into the scale against the least moment of the joy that is felt by the least in Heaven, would have no weight that could be registered at all. Bad cannot succeed even in being bad as truly as good is good. If all Hell's miseries together entered the consciousness of yon wee yellow bird on the bough there, they would be swallowed up without trace, as if one drop of ink had been dropped into that Great Ocean to which your terrestrial Pacific itself is only a molecule.'

'I see,' said I at last. 'She couldn't *fit* into Hell.'

He nodded. 'There's not room for her,' he said. 'Hell could not open its mouth wide enough.'

'And she couldn't make herself smaller? – like Alice, you know.'

'Nothing like small enough. For a damned soul is nearly nothing: it is shrunk, shut up in itself. Good beats upon the damned incessantly as sound waves beat on the ears of the deaf, but they cannot receive it. Their fists are clenched, their teeth are clenched, their eyes fast shut. First they will not, in the end they cannot, open their hands for gifts, or their mouth for food, or their eyes to see.'

'Then no one can ever reach them?'

'Only the Greatest of all can make Himself small enough to enter Hell. For the higher a thing is, the lower it can descend – a man can sympathise with a horse but a horse cannot sympathise with a rat. Only One has descended into Hell.'

---

[1] This method of travel also I learned from the 'scientifictionists'.

'And will He ever do so again?'

'It was not once long ago that He did it. Time does not work that way when once ye have left the Earth. All moments that have been or shall be were, or are, present in the moment of His descending. There is no spirit in prison to Whom He did not preach.'

'And some hear him?'

'Aye.'

'In your own books, Sir,' said I, 'you were a Universalist. You talked as if all men would be saved. And St. Paul too.'

'Ye can know nothing of the end of all things, or nothing expressible in those terms. It may be, as the Lord said to the Lady Julian, that all will be well, and all will be well, and all manner of thing will be well. But it's ill talking of such questions.'

'Because they are too terrible, Sir?'

'No. Because all answers deceive. If ye put the question from within Time and are asking about possibilities, the answer is certain. The choice of ways is before you. Neither is closed. Any man may choose eternal death. Those who choose it will have it. But if ye are trying to leap on into eternity, if ye are trying to see the final state of all things as it *will* be (for so ye must speak) when there are no more possibilities left but only the Real, then ye ask what cannot be answered to mortal ears. Time is the very lens through which ye see – small and clear, as men see through the wrong end of a telescope – something that would otherwise be too big for ye to see at all. That thing is Freedom: the gift whereby ye most resemble your Maker and are yourselves parts of eternal reality. But ye can see it only through the lens of Time, in a little clear picture, through the inverted telescope. It is a picture of moments following one another and yourself in each moment making some choice that might have been otherwise. Neither the temporal succession nor the phantom of what ye might have chosen and didn't is itself Freedom. They are a lens. The picture is a symbol: but it's truer than any philosophical theorem (or, perhaps, than any mystic's vision) that claims to go behind it. For every attempt to see the shape of eternity except through the lens of Time destroys your knowledge of Freedom. Witness the doctrine of Predestination which shows (truly enough) that eternal reality is not waiting for a future in which to be real; but at the price of removing Freedom which is the deeper truth of the two. And wouldn't Universalism do the same? Ye *cannot* know eternal reality by a definition. Time itself, and all acts and events that fill Time, are the definition, and it must be lived. The Lord said we were gods. How long could ye bear to look (without Time's lens) on the greatness of your own soul and the eternal reality of her choice?'

14

And suddenly all was changed. I saw a great assembly of gigantic forms all motionless, all in deepest silence, standing forever about a little silver table and looking upon it. And on the table there were little figures like chessmen who went to and fro doing this and that. And I knew that each chessman was the *idolum* or puppet representative of some of the great presences that stood by. And the acts and motions of each chessman were a moving portrait, a mimicry or pantomime, which delineated the inmost nature of his giant master. And these chessmen are men and women as they appear to themselves and to one another in this world. And the silver table is Time. And those who stand and watch are the immortal souls of those same men and women. Then vertigo and terror seized me and, clutching at my Teacher, I said, 'Is *that* the truth? Then is all that I have been seeing in this country false? These conversations between the Spirits and the Ghosts – were they only the mimicry of choices that had really been made long ago?'

'Or might ye not as well say, anticipations of a choice to be made at the end of all things? But ye'd do better to say neither. Ye saw the choices a bit more clearly than ye could see them on Earth: the lens was clearer. But it was still seen through the lens. Do not ask of a vision in a dream more than a vision in a dream can give.'

'A dream? Then – then – am I not really here, Sir?'

'No, Son,' said he kindly, taking my hand in his. 'It is not so good as that. The bitter drink of death is still before you. Ye are only dreaming. And if ye come to tell of what ye have seen, make it plain that it was but a dream. See ye make it very plain. Give no poor fool the pretext to think ye are claiming knowledge of what no mortal knows. I'll have no Swedenborgs and no Vale Owens among my children.'

'God forbid, Sir,' said I, trying to look very wise.

'He *has* forbidden it. That's what I'm telling ye.' As he said this he looked more Scotch than ever. I was gazing steadfastly on his face. The vision of the chessmen had faded, and once more the quiet woods in the cool light before sunrise were about us. Then, still looking at his face, I saw there something that sent a quiver through my whole body. I stood at that moment with my back to the East and the mountains, and he, facing me, looked towards them. His face flushed with a new light. A fern, thirty yards behind him, turned golden. The eastern side of every tree-trunk grew bright. Shadows deepened. All the time there had been bird noises, trillings, chatterings, and the like; but now suddenly the full chorus was poured from every branch; cocks were crowing, there was music of hounds, and horns; above all this ten thousand tongues of men and woodland angels and the wood itself sang. 'It comes, it comes!' they sang. 'Sleepers awake! It comes, it comes, it comes.' One dreadful glance over my shoulder I essayed – not long enough to see (or did I see?) the rim of the sunrise that shoots Time dead with golden arrows and puts to flight all phantasmal shapes. Screaming, I buried my face in the fold of my Teacher's robe. 'The morning! The morning!' I cried, 'I am caught by the morning and I am a ghost.' But it was too late. The light, like solid blocks, intolerable of edge and weight, came thundering upon my head. Next moment the folds of my Teacher's garment were only the folds of the old ink-stained cloth on my study table which I had pulled down with me as I fell from my chair. The blocks of light were only the books which I had pulled off with it, falling about my head. I awoke in a cold room, hunched on the floor beside a black and empty grate, the clock striking three, and the siren howling overhead.

MIRACLES

A preliminary study

To
Cecil and Daphne Harwood

Among the hills a meteorite
Lies huge; and moss has overgrown,
And wind and rain with touches light
Made soft, the contours of the stone.

Thus easily can Earth digest
A cinder of sidereal fire,
And make her translunary guest
The native of an English shire.

Nor is it strange these wanderers
Find in her lap their fitting place,
For every particle that's hers
Came at the first from outer space.

All that is Earth has once been sky;
Down from the sun of old she came,
Or from some star that travelled by
Too close to his entangling flame.

Hence, if belated drops yet fall
From heaven, on these her plastic power
Still works as once it worked on all
The glad rush of the golden shower.

C.S.L.

Reprinted by permission of *Time and Tide*

Contents

THE SCOPE OF THIS BOOK

*Those who wish to succeed must ask
the right preliminary questions.*
ARISTOTLE, *Metaphysics, II,* (III), 1.

In all my life I have met only one person who claims to have seen a ghost. And the interesting thing about the story is that that person disbelieved in the immortal soul before she saw the ghost and still disbelieves after seeing it. She says that what she saw must have been an illusion or a trick of the nerves. And obviously she may be right. Seeing is not believing.

For this reason, the question whether miracles occur can never be answered simply by experience. Every event which might claim to be a miracle is, in the last resort, something presented to our senses, something seen, heard, touched, smelled, or tasted. And our senses are infallible. If anything extraordinary seems to have happened, we can always say that we have been the victims of an illusion. If we hold a philosophy which excludes the supernatural, this is what we always shall say. What we learn from experience depends on the kind of philosophy we bring to experience. It is therefore useless to appeal to experience before we have settled, as well as we can, the philosophical question.

If immediate experience cannot prove or disprove the miraculous, still less can history do so. Many people think one can decide whether a miracle occurred in the past by examining the evidence 'according to the ordinary rules of historical inquiry'. But the ordinary rules cannot be worked until we have decided whether miracles are possible, and if so, how probable they are. For if they are impossible, then no amount of historical evidence will convince us. If they are possible but immensely improbable, then only mathematically demonstrative evidence will convince us: and since history never provides that degree of evidence for any event, history can never convince us that a miracle occurred. If, on the other hand, miracles are not intrinsically improbable, then the existing evidence will be sufficient to convince us that quite a number of miracles have occurred. The result of our historical enquiries thus depends on the philosophical views which we have been holding before we even began to look at the evidence. This philosophical question must therefore come first.

Here is an example of the sort of thing that happens if we omit the preliminary philosophical task, and rush on to the historical. In a popular commentary on the Bible you will find a discussion of the date at which the Fourth Gospel was written. The author says it must have been written after the execution of St Peter, because, in the Fourth Gospel, Christ is represented as predicting the execution of St Peter. 'A book', thinks the author, 'cannot be written *before* events which it refers to'. Of course it cannot – unless real predictions ever occur. If they do, then this argument for the date is in ruins. And the author has not discussed at all whether real predictions are possible. He takes it for granted (perhaps unconsciously) that they are not. Perhaps he is right: but if he is, he has not discovered this principle by historical inquiry. He has brought his disbelief in predictions to his historical work, so to speak, ready made. Unless he had done so his historical conclusion about the date of the Fourth Gospel could not have been reached at all. His work is therefore quite useless to a person who wants to know *whether* predictions occur. The author gets to work only after he has already answered that question in the negative, and on grounds which he never communicates to us.

This book is intended as a preliminary to historical inquiry. I am not a trained historian and I shall not examine the historical evidence for the Christian miracles. My effort is to put my readers in a position to do so. It is no use going to the texts until we have some idea about the possibility or probability of the miraculous. Those who assume that miracles cannot happen are merely wasting their time by looking into the texts: we know in advance what results they will find for they have begun by begging the question.

THE NATURALIST

AND THE SUPERNATURALIST

'Gracious!' exclaimed Mrs Snip, 'and is there
a place where people venture to live above
ground?' 'I never heard of people living
under ground,' replied Tim, 'before I came
to Giant-Land.' 'Came to Giant-Land!'
cried Mrs Snip, 'why, isn't everywhere
Giant-Land?'
ROLAND QUIZZ, *Giant Land,* chap xxxii.

I use the word *Miracle* to mean an interference with Nature by supernatural power.[1] Unless there exists, in addition to Nature, something else which we may call the supernatural, there can be no miracles. Some people believe that nothing exists except Nature; I call these people *Naturalists.* Others think that, besides Nature, there exists something else: I call them *Supernaturalists.* Our first question, therefore, is whether the Naturalists or the Supernaturalists are right. And here comes our first difficulty.

Before the Naturalist and the Supernaturalist can begin to discuss their difference of opinion, they must surely have an agreed definition both of Nature and of Supernature. But unfortunately it is almost impossible to get such a definition. Just because the Naturalist thinks that nothing but Nature exists, the word *Nature* means to him merely 'everything' or 'the whole show' or 'whatever there is'. And if that is what we mean by Nature, then of course nothing else exists. The real question between him and the Supernaturalist has evaded us. Some philosophers have defined Nature as 'What we perceive with our five senses'. But this also is unsatisfactory; for we do not perceive our own emotions in that way, and yet they are presumably 'natural' events. In order to avoid this deadlock and to discover

---

[1] This definition is not that which would be given by many theologians. I am adopting it not because I think it an improvement upon theirs but precisely because, being crude and 'popular', it enables me most easily to treat those questions which 'the common reader' probably has in mind when he takes up a book on Miracles.

what the Naturalist and the Supernaturalist are really differing about, we must approach our problem in a more roundabout way.

I begin by considering the following sentences (1) Are those his natural teeth or a set? (2) The dog in his natural state is covered with fleas. (3) I love to get away from tilled lands and metalled roads and be alone with Nature. (4) Do be natural. Why are you so affected? (5) It may have been wrong to kiss her but it was very natural.

A common thread of meaning in all these usages can easily be discovered. The natural teeth are those which grow in the mouth; we do not have to design them, make them, or fit them. The dog's natural state is the one he will be in if no one takes soap and water and prevents it. The countryside where Nature reigns supreme is the one where soil, weather and vegetation produce their results unhelped and unimpeded by man. Natural behaviour is the behaviour which people would exhibit if they were not at pains to alter it. The natural kiss is the kiss which will be given if moral or prudential considerations do not intervene. In all the examples Nature means what happens 'of itself' or 'of its own accord': what you do not need to labour for; what you will get if you take no measures to stop it. The Greek word for Nature (Physis) is connected with the Greek verb for 'to grow'; Latin *Natura,* with the verb 'to be born'. The Natural is what springs up, or comes forth, or arrives, or goes on, *of its own accord*: the given, what is there already: the spontaneous, the unintended, the unsolicited.

What the Naturalist believes is that the ultimate Fact, the thing you can't go behind, is a vast process in space and time which is *going on of its own accord.* Inside that total system every particular event (such as your sitting reading this book) happens because some other event has happened; in the long run, because the Total Event is happening. Each particular thing (such as this page) is what it is because other things are what they are; and so, eventually, because the whole system is what it is. All the things and events are so completely interlocked that no one of them can claim the slightest independence from 'the whole show'. None of them exists 'on its own' or 'goes on of its own accord' except in the sense that it exhibits, at some particular place and time, that general 'existence on its own' or 'behaviour of its own accord' which belongs to 'Nature' (the great total interlocked event) as a whole. Thus no thoroughgoing Naturalist believes in free will: for free will would mean that human beings have the power of independent action, the power of doing something more or other than what was involved by the total series of events. And any such separate power of originating events is what the Naturalist denies. Spontaneity, originality, action 'on its own', is a privilege reserved for 'the whole show', which he calls *Nature.*

The Supernaturalist agrees with the Naturalist that there must be something which exists in its own right; some basic Fact whose existence it would be nonsensical to try to explain because this Fact is itself the ground or starting-point of all explanations. But he does not identify this Fact with 'the whole show'. He thinks that things fall into two classes. In the first class we find either things or (more probably) One Thing which is basic and original, which exists on its own. In the second we find things which are merely derivative from that One Thing. The one basic Thing has caused all the other things to be. It exists on its own; they exist because it exists. They will cease to exist if it ever ceases to maintain them in existence; they will be altered if it ever alters them.

The difference between the two views might be expressed by saying that Naturalism gives us a democratic, Supernaturalism a monarchical, picture of reality. The Naturalist thinks that the privilege of 'being on its own' resides in the total mass of things, just as in a democracy sovereignty resides in the whole mass of the people. The Supernaturalist thinks that this privilege belongs to some things or (more probably) One Thing and not to others – just as, in a real monarchy, the king has sovereignty and the people have not. And just as, in a democracy, all citizens are equal, so for the Naturalist one thing or event is as good as another, in the sense that they are all equally dependent on the total system of things. Indeed each of them is only the way in which the character of that total system exhibits itself at a particular point in space and time. The Supernaturalist, on the other hand, believes that the one original or self-existent thing is on a different level from, and more important than, all other things.

At this point a suspicion may occur that Supernaturalism first arose from reading into the universe the structure of monarchical societies. But then of course it may with equal reason be suspected that Naturalism has arisen from reading into it the structure of modern democracies. The two suspicions thus cancel out and give us no help in deciding which theory is more likely to be true. They do indeed remind us that Supernaturalism is the characteristic philosophy of a monarchical age and Naturalism of a democratic, in the sense that Supernaturalism, even if false, would have been believed by the great mass of unthinking people four hundred years ago, just as Naturalism, even if false, will be believed by the great mass of unthinking people today.

Everyone will have seen that the One Self-existent Thing – or the small class of self-existent things – in which Supernaturalists believe, is what we call God or the gods. I propose for the rest of this book to treat only that form of Supernaturalism which believes in one God; partly because polytheism is not likely to be a live issue for most of my readers, and partly because those who believed in many gods very seldom, in fact, regarded their gods as creators of the universe and as self-existent. The gods of Greece were not really supernatural in the strict sense which I am giving to the word. They were products of the total system of things and included within it. This introduces an important distinction.

The difference between Naturalism and Supernaturalism is not exactly the same as the difference between belief in a God and disbelief. Naturalism, without ceasing to be itself, could admit a certain kind of God. The great interlocking event called Nature might be such as to produce at some stage a great cosmic consciousness, an indwelling 'God' arising from the whole process as human mind arises (according to the Naturalists) from human organisms. A Naturalist would not object to that sort of God. The reason is this. Such a God would not stand outside Nature or the total system, would not be existing 'on his own'. It would still be 'the whole show' which was the basic Fact, and such a God would merely be one of the things (even if he were the most interesting) which the basic Fact contained. What Naturalism cannot accept is the idea of a God who stands outside Nature and made it.

We are now in a position to state the difference between the Naturalist and the Supernaturalist despite the fact that they do not mean the same by the word Nature. The Naturalist believes that a great process, of 'becoming', exists 'on its own' in space and time, and that nothing else exists – what we call particular things and events being only the parts into which we analyse the great process or the shapes which that process takes at given moments and given points in space. This single, total reality he calls Nature. The Supernaturalist believes that one Thing exists on its own and has produced the framework of space and time and the procession of systematically connected events which fill them. This framework, and this filling, he calls Nature. It may, or may not, be the only reality which the one Primary Thing has produced. There might be other systems in addition to the one we call Nature.

In that sense there might be several 'Natures'. This conception must be kept quite distinct from what is commonly called 'plurality of worlds' – i.e. different solar systems or different galaxies, 'island universes' existing in widely separated parts of a single space and time. These, however remote, would be parts of the same Nature as our own sun: it and they would be interlocked by being in relations to one another, spatial and temporal relations and casual relations as well. And it is just this reciprocal interlocking within a system which makes it what we call a Nature. Other Natures might not be spatio-temporal at all: or, if any of them were, their space and time would have no spatial or temporal relation to ours. It is just this discontinuity, this failure of interlocking, which would justify us in calling them different Natures. This does not mean that there would be absolutely no relation between them; they would be related by their common derivation from a single Supernatural source. They would, in this respect, be like different novels by a single author; the events in one story have no relation to the events in another *except* that they are invented by the same author. To find the relation between them you must go right back to the author's mind: there is no cutting across from anything Mr Pickwick says in *Pickwick Papers* to anything Mrs Gamp hears in *Martin Chuzzlewit*. Similarly there would be no normal cutting across from an event in one Nature to an event in any other. By a 'normal' relation I mean one which occurs in virtue of the character of the two systems. We have to put in the qualification 'normal' because we do not know in advance that God might not bring two Natures into partial contact at some particular point: that is, He might allow *selected* events in the one to produce results in the other. There would thus be, at certain points, a partial interlocking; but this would not turn the two Natures into one, for the total reciprocity which makes a Nature would still be lacking, and the anomalous interlockings would arise not from what either system was in itself but from the Divine act which was bringing them together. If this occurred each of the two Natures would be 'supernatural' in relation to the other: but the fact of their contact would be supernatural in a more absolute sense – not as being beyond this or that Nature but beyond any and every Nature. It would be one kind of miracle. The other kind would be Divine 'interference' not by the bringing together of two Natures, but simply.

All this is, at present purely speculative. It by no means follows from Supernaturalism that Miracles of any sort do in fact occur. God (the primary thing) may never in fact interfere with the natural system He has created. If He has created more natural systems than one, He may never cause them to impinge on one another.

But that is a question for further consideration. If we decide that Nature is not the only thing there is, then we cannot say in advance whether she is safe from miracles or not. There are things outside her: we do not yet know whether they can get in. The gates may be barred, or they may not. But if Naturalism is true, then we do know in advance that miracles are impossible: nothing can come into Nature from the outside because there is nothing outside to come in, Nature being everything. No doubt, events which we in our ignorance should mistake for miracles might occur: but they would in reality be (just like the commonest events) an inevitable result of the character of the whole system.

Our first choice, therefore, must be between Naturalism and Supernaturalism.

3

THE CARDINAL DIFFICULTY
OF NATURALISM

We cannot have it both ways, and no sneers
at the limitations of logic . . . amend the
dilemma.
I. A. RICHARDS, *Principles of Literary Criticism,*
chap. xxv.

If Naturalism is true, every finite thing or event must be (in principle) explicable in terms of the Total System. I say 'explicable *in principle*' because of course we are not going to demand that naturalists, at any given moment, should have found the detailed explanation of every phenomenon. Obviously many things will only be explained when the sciences have made further progress. But if Naturalism is to be accepted we have a right to demand that every single thing should be such that we see, in general, how it could be explained in terms of the Total System. If any one thing exists which is of such a kind that we see in advance the impossibility of ever giving it *that kind* of explanation, then Naturalism would be in ruins. If necessities of thought force us to allow to any one thing any degree of independence from the Total System – if any one thing makes good a claim to be on its own, to be something more than an expression of the character of Nature as a whole – then we have abandoned Naturalism. For by Naturalism we mean the doctrine that only Nature – the whole interlocked system – exists. And if that were true, every thing and event would, if we knew enough, be explicable without remainder (no *heel-taps*) as a necessary product of the system. The whole system being what it is, it ought to be a contradiction in terms if you were not reading this book at the moment; and, conversely, the only cause why you are reading it ought to be that the whole system, at such and such a place and hour, was bound to take that course.

One threat against strict Naturalism has recently been launched on which I myself will base no argument, but which it will be well to notice. The older scientists believed that the smallest particles of matter moved according to strict laws: in other words, that the movements of each particle were 'interlocked' with the total system of Nature. Some modern scientists seem to think – if I understand them – that this is not so. They seem to think that the individual unit of matter (it would be rash to call it any longer a 'particle') moves in an indeterminate or random fashion; moves, in fact, 'on its own' or 'of its own accord'. The regularity which we observe in the movements of the smallest visible bodies is explained by the fact that each of these contains millions of units and that the law of averages therefore levels out the idiosyncrasies of the individual unit's behaviour. The movement of one unit is incalculable, just as the result of tossing a coin once is incalculable: the majority movement of a billion units can however be predicted, just as, if you tossed a coin a billion times, you could predict a nearly equal number of heads and tails. Now it will be noticed that if this theory is true we have really admitted something other than Nature. If the movements of the individual units are events 'on their own', events which do not interlock with all other events, then these movements are not part of Nature. It would be, indeed, too great a shock to our habits to describe them as *super*-natural. I think we should have to call them *sub*-natural. But all our confidence that Nature has no doors, and no reality outside herself for doors to open on, would have disappeared. There is apparently *something* outside her, the Subnatural; it is indeed from this Subnatural that all events and all 'bodies' are, as it were, fed into her. And clearly if she thus has a back door opening on the Subnatural, it is quite on the cards that she may also have a front door opening on the Supernatural – and events might be fed into her at that door too.

I have mentioned this theory because it puts in a fairly vivid light certain conceptions which we shall have to use later on. But I am not, for my own part, assuming its truth. Those who like myself have had a philosophical rather than a scientific education find it almost impossible to believe that the scientists really mean what they seem to be saying. I cannot help thinking they mean no more than that the movements of individual units are permanently incalculable *to us*, not that they are in themselves random and lawless. And even if they mean the latter, a layman can hardly feel any certainty that some new scientific development may not tomorrow abolish this whole idea of a lawless Subnature. For it is the glory of science to progress. I therefore turn willingly to other ground.

It is clear that everything we know, beyond our own immediate sensations, is inferred from those sensations. I do not mean that we begin as children, by regarding our sensations as 'evidence' and thence arguing consciously to the existence of space, matter, and other people. I mean that if, after we are old enough to understand the question, our confidence in the existence of anything else (say, the solar system or the Spanish Armada) is challenged, our argument in defence of it will have to take the form of inferences from our immediate sensations. Put in its most general form the inference would run, 'Since I am presented with colours, sounds, shapes, pleasures and pains which I cannot perfectly predict or control, and since the more I investigate them the more regular their behaviour appears, therefore there must exist something other than myself and it must be systematic'. Inside this very general inference, all sorts of special trains of inference lead us to more detailed conclusions. We infer Evolution from fossils: we infer the existence of our own brains from what we find inside the skulls of other creatures like ourselves in the dissecting room.

All possible knowledge, then, depends on the validity of reasoning. If the feeling of certainty which we express by words like *must be* and *therefore* and *since* is a real perception of how things outside our own minds really 'must' be, well and good. But if this certainty is merely a feeling *in* our own minds and not a genuine insight into realities beyond them – if it merely represents the way our minds happen to work – then we can have no knowledge. Unless human reasoning is valid no science can be true.

It follows that no account of the universe can be true unless that account leaves it possible for our thinking to be a real insight. A theory which explained everything else in the whole universe but which made it impossible to believe that our thinking was valid, would be utterly out of court. For that theory would itself have been reached by thinking, and if thinking is not valid that theory would, of course, be itself demolished. It would have destroyed its own credentials. It would be an argument which proved that no argument was sound – a proof that there are no such things as proofs – which is nonsense.

Thus a strict materialism refutes itself for the reason given long ago by Professor Haldane: 'If my mental processes are determined wholly by the motions of atoms in my brain, I have no reason to suppose that my beliefs are true ... and hence I have no reason for supposing my brain to be composed of atoms.' (*Possible Worlds*, p. 209)

But Naturalism, even if it is not purely materialistic, seems to me to involve the same difficulty, though in a somewhat less obvious form. It discredits our processes of reasoning or at least reduces their credit to such a humble level that it can no longer support Naturalism itself.

The easiest way of exhibiting this is to notice the two senses of the word *because*. We can say, 'Grandfather is ill today *because* he ate lobster yesterday.' We can also say, 'Grandfather must be ill today *because* he hasn't got up yet (and we know he is an invariably early riser when he is well).' In the first sentence *because* indicates the relation of Cause and Effect: The eating made him ill. In the second, it indicates the relation of what logicians call Ground and Consequent. The old man's late rising is not the cause of his disorder but the reason why we believe him to be disordered. There is a similar difference between 'He cried out *because* it hurt him' (Cause and Effect) and 'It must have hurt him *because* he cried out' (Ground and Consequent). We are especially familiar with the Ground and Consequent *because* in mathematical reasoning: 'A = C *because*, as we have already proved, they are both equal to B.'

The one indicates a dynamic connection between events or 'states of affairs'; the other, a logical relation between beliefs or assertions.

Now a train of reasoning has no value as a means of finding truth unless each step in it is connected with what went before in the Ground-Consequent relation. If our B does not follow logically from our A, we think in vain. If what we think at the end of our reasoning is to be true, the correct answer to the question, 'Why do you think this?' must begin with the Ground-Consequent *because*.

On the other hand, every event in Nature must be connected with previous events in the Cause and Effect relation. But our acts of thinking are events. Therefore the true answer to 'Why do you think this?' must begin with the Cause-Effect *because*.

Unless our conclusion is the logical consequent from a ground it will be worthless and could be true only by a fluke. Unless it is the effect of a cause, it cannot occur at all. It looks, therefore, as if, in order for a train of thought to have any value, these two systems of connection must apply simultaneously to the same series of mental acts.

But unfortunately the two systems are wholly distinct. To be caused is not to be proved. Wishful thinkings, prejudices, and the delusions of madness, are all caused, but they are ungrounded. Indeed to be caused is so different from being proved that we behave in disputation as if they were mutually exclusive. The mere existence of causes for a belief is popularly treated as raising a presumption that it is groundless, and the most popular way of discrediting a person's opinions is to explain them causally – 'You say that *because* (Cause and Effect) you are a capitalist, or a hypochondriac, or a mere man, or only a woman'. The implication is that if causes fully account for a belief, then, since causes work inevitably, the belief would have had to arise whether it had grounds or not. We need not, it is felt, consider grounds for something which can be fully explained without them.

But even if grounds do exist, what exactly have they got to do with the actual occurrence of the belief as a psychological event? If it is an event it must be caused. It must in fact be simply one link in a causal chain which stretches back to the beginning and forward to the end of time. How could such a trifle as lack of logical grounds prevent the belief's occurrence or how could the existence of grounds promote it?

There seems to be only one possible answer. We must say that just as one way in which a mental event causes a subsequent mental event is by Association (when I think of parsnips I think of my first school), so another way in which it can cause it, is simply by being a ground for it. For then being a cause and being a proof would coincide.

But this, as it stands, is clearly untrue. We know by experience that a thought does not necessarily cause all, or even any, of the thoughts which logically stand to it as Consequents to Ground. We should be in a pretty pickle if we could never think 'This is glass' without drawing all the inferences which could be drawn. It is impossible to draw them all; quite often we draw none. We must therefore amend our suggested law. One thought can cause another not by *being*, but by being *seen to be*, a ground for it.

If you distrust the sensory metaphor in *seen*, you may substitute *apprehended* or *grasped* or simply *known*. It makes little difference for all these words recall us to what thinking really is. Acts of thinking are no doubt events; but they are a very special sort of events. They are 'about' something other than themselves and can be true or false. Events in general are not 'about' anything and cannot be true or false. (To say 'these events, or facts are false' means of course that someone's account of them is false.) Hence acts of inference can, and must, be considered in two different lights. On the one hand they are subjective events, items in somebody's psychological history. On the other hand, they are insights into, or knowings of, something other than themselves. What from the first point of view is the psychological transition from thought A to thought B, at some particular moment in some particular mind, is, from the thinker's point of view a perception of an implication (if A, then B). When we are adopting the psychological point of view we may use the past tense. 'B *followed* A in my thoughts.' But when we assert the implication we always use the present – 'B *follows* from A.' If it ever 'follows from' in the logical sense, it does so always. And we cannot possibly reject the second point of view as a subjective illusion without discrediting all human knowledge. For we can know nothing, beyond our own sensations at the moment unless the act of inference is the real insight that it claims to be.

But it can be this only on certain terms. An act of knowing must be determined, in a sense, solely by what is known; we must know it to be thus solely because it *is* thus. That is what knowing means. You may call this a Cause and Effect *because,* and call 'being known' a mode of causation if you like. But it is a unique mode. The act of knowing has no doubt various conditions, without which it could not occur: attention, and the states of will and health which this presupposes. But its positive character must be determined by the truth it knows. If it were totally explicable from other sources it would cease to be knowledge, just as (to use the sensory parallel) the ringing in my ears ceases to be what we mean by 'hearing' if it can be fully explained from causes other than a noise in the outer world – such as, say, the *tinnitus* produced by a bad cold. If what seems an act of knowledge is partially explicable from other sources, then the knowing (properly so called) in it is just what they leave over, just what demands, for its explanation, the thing known, as real hearing is what is left after you have discounted the *tinnitus*. Any thing which professes to explain our reasoning fully without introducing an act of knowing thus solely determined by what is known, is really a theory that there is no reasoning.

But this, as it seems to me, is what Naturalism is bound to do. It offers what professes to be a full account of our mental behaviour; but this account, on inspection, leaves no room for the acts of knowing or insight on which the whole value of our thinking, as a means to truth, depends.

It is agreed on all hands that reason, and even sentience, and life itself are late comers in Nature. If there is nothing but Nature, therefore, reason must have come into existence by a historical process. And of course, for the Naturalist, this process was not designed to produce a mental behaviour that can find truth. There was no Designer; and indeed, until there were thinkers, there was no truth or falsehood. The type of mental behaviour we now call rational thinking or inference must therefore have been 'evolved' by natural selection, by the gradual weeding out of types less fitted to survive.

Once, then, our thoughts were not rational. That is, all our thoughts once were, as many of our thoughts still are, merely subjective events, not apprehensions of objective truth. Those which had a cause external to ourselves at all were (like our pains) responses to stimuli. Now natural selection could operate only by eliminating responses that were biologically hurtful and multiplying those which tended to survival. But it is not conceivable that any improvement of responses could ever turn them into acts of insight, or even remotely tend to do so. The relation between response and stimulus is utterly different from that between knowledge and the truth known. Our physical vision is a far more useful response to light than that of the cruder organisms which have only a photo-sensitive spot. But neither this improvement nor any possible improvements we can suppose could bring it an inch nearer to being a knowledge of light. It is admittedly something without which we could not have had that knowledge. But the knowledge is achieved by experiments and inferences from them, not by refinement of the response. It is not men with specially good eyes who know about light, but men who have studied the relevant sciences. In the same way our psychological responses to our environment – our curiosities, aversions, delights, expectations – could be indefinitely improved (from the biological point of view) without becoming anything more than responses. Such perfection of the non-rational responses, far from amounting to their conversion into valid inferences, might be conceived as a different method of achieving survival – an alternative to reason. A conditioning which secured that we never felt delight except in the useful nor aversion save from the dangerous, and that the degrees of both were exquisitely proportional to the degree of real utility or danger in the object, might serve us as well as reason or in some circumstances better.

Besides natural selection there is, however, experience – experience originally individual but handed on by tradition and instruction. It might be held that this, in the course of millennia, could conjure the mental behaviour we call reason – in other words, the practice of inference – out of a mental behaviour which was originally not rational. Repeated experiences of finding fire (or the remains of fire) where he had seen smoke would condition a man to expect fire whenever he saw smoke. This expectation, expressed in the form 'If smoke, then fire' becomes what we call inference. Have all our inferences originated in that way?

But if they did they are all invalid inferences. Such a process will no doubt produce expectation. It will train men to expect fire when they see smoke in just the same way as it trained them to expect that all swans would be white (until they saw a black one) or that water would always boil at 212° (until someone tried a picnic on a mountain). Such expectations are not inferences and need not be true. The assumption that things which have been conjoined in the past will always be conjoined in the future is the guiding principle not of rational but of animal behaviour. Reason comes in precisely when you make the inference 'Since always conjoined, therefore probably connected' and go on to attempt the discovery of the connection. When you have discovered what smoke is you may then be able to replace the mere expectation of fire by a genuine inference. Till this is done reason recognises the expectation as a mere expectation. Where this does not need to be done – that is, where the inference depends on an axiom – we do not appeal to past experience at all. My belief that things which are equal to the same thing are equal to one another is not at all based on the fact that I have never caught them behaving otherwise. I see that it 'must' be so. That some people nowadays call axioms tautologies seems to me irrelevant. It is by means of such 'tautologies' that we advance from knowing less to knowing more. And to call them tautologies is another way of saying that they are completely and certainly known. To see fully that A implies B does (once you have seen it) involve the admission that the assertion of A and the assertion of B are at bottom in the same assertion. The degree to which any true proportion is a tautology depends on the degree of your insight into it. $9 \times 7 = 63$ is a tautology to the perfect arithmetician, but not to the child learning its tables nor to the primitive calculator who reached it, perhaps, by adding seven nines together. If Nature is a totally interlocked system, then every true statement about her (e.g. there was a hot summer in 1959) would be a tautology to an intelligence that could grasp that system in its entirety. 'God is love' may be a tautology to the seraphim; not to men.

'But', it will be said, 'it is incontestable that we do in fact reach truths by inferences'. Certainly. The Naturalist and I both admit this. We could not discuss anything unless we did. The difference I am submitting is that he gives, and I do not, a history of the evolution of reason which is inconsistent with the claims that he and I both have to make for inference as we actually practise it. For his history is, and from the nature of the case can only be, an account, in Cause and Effect terms, of how people came to think the way they do. And this of course leaves in the air the quite different question of how they could possibly be justified in so thinking. This imposes on him the very embarrassing task of trying to show how the evolutionary product which he has described could also be a power of 'seeing' truths.

But the very attempt is absurd. This is best seen if we consider the humblest and almost the most despairing form in which it could be made. The Naturalist might say, 'Well, perhaps we cannot exactly see – not yet – how natural selection would turn sub-rational mental behaviour into inferences that reach truth. But we are certain that this in fact has happened. For natural selection is bound to preserve and increase useful behaviour. And we also find that our habits of inference are in fact useful. And if they are useful they must reach truth.' But notice what we are doing. Inference itself is on trial: that is, the Naturalist has given an account of what we thought to be our inferences which suggests that they are not real insights at all. We, and he, want to be reassured. And the reassurance turns out to be one more inference (if useful, then true) – as if this inference were not, once we accept his evolutionary picture, under the same suspicion as all the rest. If the value of our reasoning is in doubt, you cannot try to establish it by reasoning. If, as I said above, a proof that there are no proofs is nonsensical, so is a proof that there are proofs. Reason is our starting point. There can be no question either of attacking or defending it. If by treating it as a mere phenomenon you put yourself outside it, there is then no way, except by begging the question, of getting inside again.

A still humbler position remains. You may, if you like, give up all claim to truth. You may say simply 'Our way of thinking is useful' – without adding, even under your breath, 'and therefore true'. It enables us to set a bone and build a bridge and make a Sputnik. And that is good enough. The old, high pretensions of reason must be given up. It is a behaviour evolved entirely as an aid to practice. That is why, when we use it simply for practice, we get along pretty well; but when we fly off into speculation and try to get general views of 'reality' we end in the endless, useless, and probably merely verbal, disputes of the philosopher. We will be humbler in future. Goodbye to all that. No more theology, no more ontology, no more metaphysics...

But then, equally, no more Naturalism. For of course Naturalism is a prime specimen of that towering speculation, discovered from practice and going far beyond experience, which is now being condemned. Nature is not an object that can be presented either to the senses or the imagination. It can be reached only by the most remote inferences. Or not reached, merely approached. It is the hoped for, the assumed, unification in a single inter-locked system of all the things inferred from our scientific experiments. More than that, the Naturalist, not content to assert this, goes on to the sweeping negative assertion. 'There is nothing except this' – an assertion surely, as remote from practice, experience, and any conceivable verification as has ever been made since men began to use their reason speculatively. Yet on the present view, the very first step into such a use was an abuse, the per-version of a faculty merely practical, and the source of all chimeras.

On these terms the Theist's position must be a chimera nearly as outrageous as the Naturalist's. (Nearly, not quite; it abstains from the crowning audacity of a huge negative). But the Theist need not, and does not, grant these terms. He is not committed to the view that reason is a comparatively recent devel-opment moulded by a process of selection which can select only the biologi-cally useful. For him, reason – the reason of God – is older than Nature, and from it the orderliness of Nature, which alone enables us to know her, is derived. For him, the human mind in the act of knowing is illuminated by the Divine reason. It is set free, in the measure required, from the huge nexus of non-rational causation; free from this to be determined by the truth known. And the preliminary processes within Nature which led up to this liberation, if there were any, were designed to do so.

To call the act of knowing – the act, not of remembering that something was so in the past, but of 'seeing' that it must be so always and in any possi-ble world – to call this act 'supernatural', is some violence to our ordinary linguistic usage. But of course we do not mean by this that it is spooky, or sensational, or even (in any religious sense) 'spiritual'. We mean only that it 'won't fit in'; that such an act, to be what it claims to be – and if it is not, all our thinking is discredited – cannot be merely the exhibition at a particular place and time of that total, and largely mindless, system of events called 'Nature'. It must break sufficiently free from that universal chain in order to be determined by what it knows.

It is of some importance here to make sure that, if vaguely spatial imagery intrudes (and in many minds it certainly will), it should not be of the wrong kind. We had better not envisage our acts of reason as something 'above' or 'behind' or 'beyond' Nature. Rather 'this side of Nature' – if you must picture spatially, picture them between us and her. It is by inferences that we build up the idea of Nature at all. Reason is given before Nature and on reason our concept of Nature depends. Our acts of inference are prior to our picture of Nature almost as the telephone is prior to the friend's voice we hear by it. When we try to fit these acts into the picture of Nature we fail.

The item which we put into that picture and label 'Reason' always turns out to be somehow different from the reason we ourselves are enjoying and exercising while we put it in. The description we have to give of thought as an evolutionary phenomenon always makes a tacit exception in favour of the thinking which we ourselves perform at that moment. For the one can only, like any other particular feat, exhibit, at particular moments in particular consciousnesses, the general and for the most part non-rational working of the whole interlocked system. The other, our present act, claims and must claim, to be an act of insight, a knowledge sufficiently free from non-rational causation to be determined (positively) only by the truth it knows. But the imagined thinking which we put into the picture depends – because our whole idea of Nature depends – on the thinking we are actually doing, not vice versa. This is the prime reality, on which the attribution of reality to anything else rests. If it won't fit into Nature, we can't help it. We will certainly not, on that account, give it up. If we do, we should be giving up Nature too.

4

NATURE AND SUPERNATURE

*Throughout the long tradition of European
thought it has been said, not by everyone but
by most people, or at any rate by most of
those who have proved that they have a
right to be heard, that Nature, though it is a
thing that really exists, is not a thing that
exists in itself or in its own right, but a thing
which depends for its existence upon
something else.*
R. G. COLLINGWOOD, *The Idea of Nature*, III iii.

If our argument has been sound, acts of reasoning are not interlocked with
the total interlocking system of Nature as all its other items are interlocked with one another. They are connected with it in a different way; as
the understanding of a machine is certainly connected with the machine but
not in the way the parts of the machine are connected with each other. The
knowledge of a thing is not one of the thing's parts. In this sense something
beyond Nature operates whenever we reason. I am not maintaining that
consciousness as a whole must necessarily be put in the same position.
Pleasures, pains, fears, hopes, affections and mental images need not. No
absurdity would follow from regarding them as parts of Nature. The distinction we have to make is not one between 'mind' and 'matter', much less
between 'soul' and 'body' (hard words, all four of them) but between
Reason and Nature: the frontier coming not where the 'outer world' ends
and what I should ordinarily call 'myself' begins, but between reason and
the whole mass of non-rational events whether physical or psychological.

At that frontier we find a great deal of traffic but it is all one-way traffic.
It is a matter of daily experience that rational thoughts induce and enable us
to alter the course of Nature – of physical nature when we use mathematics
to build bridges, or of psychological nature when we apply arguments to
alter our own emotions. We succeed in modifying physical nature more
often and more completely than we succeed in modifying psychological
nature, but we do at least a little to both. On the other hand, Nature is quite
powerless to produce rational thought: not that she never modifies our
thinking but that the moment she does so, it ceases (for that very reason) to

be rational. For, as we have seen, a train of thought loses all rational credentials as soon as it can be shown to be wholly the result of non-rational causes. When Nature, so to speak, attempts to do things to rational thoughts she only succeeds in killing them. That is the peculiar state of affairs at the frontier. Nature can only raid Reason to kill; but Reason can invade Nature to take prisoners and even to colonise. Every object you see before you at this moment – the walls, ceiling, and furniture, the book, your own washed hands and cut fingernails, bears witness to the colonisation of Nature by Reason: for none of this matter would have been in these states if Nature had had her way. And if you are attending to my argument as closely as I hope, that attention also results from habits which Reason has imposed on the natural ramblings of consciousness. If, on the other hand, a toothache or an anxiety is at this very moment preventing you from attending, then Nature is indeed interfering with your consciousness: but not to produce some new variety of reasoning, only (as far as in her lies) to suspend Reason altogether.

In other words the relation between Reason and Nature is what some people call an Unsymmetrical Relation. Brotherhood is a symmetrical relation because if A is the brother of B, B is the brother of A. Father-and-son is an unsymmetrical relation because if A is the father of B, B is *not* the father of A. The relation between Reason and Nature is of this kind. Reason is not related to Nature as Nature is related to Reason.

I am only too well aware how shocking those who have been brought up to Naturalism will find the picture which begins to show itself. It is, frankly, a picture in which Nature (at any rate on the surface of our own planet) is perforated or pock-marked all over by little orifices at each of which something of a different kind from herself – namely reason – can do things to her. I can only beg you, before you throw the book away, to consider seriously whether your instinctive repugnance to such a conception is really rational, or whether it is only emotional or aesthetic. I know that the hankering for a universe which is all of a piece, and in which everything is the same sort of thing as everything else – a continuity, a seamless web, a democratic universe – is very deep-seated in the modern heart: in mine, no less than in yours. But have we any real assurance that things are like that? Are we mistaking for an intrinsic probability what is really a human desire for tidiness and harmony? Bacon warned us long ago that 'the human understanding is of its own nature prone to suppose the existence of more order and regularity in the world than it finds. And though there be many things which are singular and unmatched, yet it devises for them parallels and conjugates and relatives which do not exist. Hence the fiction that all celestial bodies move in perfect circles' (*Novum Organum,* I, 45). I think Bacon was right. Science itself has already made reality appear less homogeneous than we expected it to be:

Newtonian atomism was much more the sort of thing we expected (and desired) than Quantum physics.

If you can, even for the moment, endure the suggested picture of Nature, let us now consider the other factor – the Reasons, or instances of Reason, which attack her. We have seen that rational thought is not part of the system of Nature. Within each man there must be an area (however small) of activity which is outside or independent of her. In relation to Nature, rational thought goes on 'of its own accord' or exists 'on its own'. It does not follow that rational thought exists *absolutely* on its own. It might be independent of Nature by being dependent on something else. For it is not dependence simply but dependence on the non-rational which undermines the credentials of thought. One man's reason has been led to see things by the aid of another man's reason, and is none the worse for that. It is thus still an open question whether each man's reason exists absolutely on its own or whether it is the result of some (rational) cause – in fact, of some other Reason. That other Reason might conceivably be found to depend on a third, and so on; it would not matter how far this process was carried provided you found Reason coming from Reason at each stage. It is only when you are asked to believe in Reason coming from non-reason that you must cry Halt, for, if you don't, all thought is discredited. It is therefore obvious that sooner or later you must admit a Reason which exists absolutely on its own. The problem is whether you or I can be such a self-existent Reason.

This question almost answers itself the moment we remember what existence 'on one's own' means. It means that kind of existence which Naturalists attribute to 'the whole show' and Supernaturalists attribute to God. For instance, what exists on its own must have existed from all eternity; for if anything else could make it begin to exist then it would not exist on its own but because of something else. It must also exist incessantly: that is, it cannot cease to exist and then begin again. For having once ceased to be, it obviously could not recall itself to existence, and if anything else recalled it it would then be a dependent being. Now it is clear that my Reason has grown up gradually since my birth and is interrupted for several hours each night. I therefore cannot be that eternal self-existent Reason which neither slumbers nor sleeps. Yet if any thought is valid, such a Reason must exist and must be the source of my own imperfect and intermittent rationality. Human minds, then, are not the only supernatural entities that exist. They do not come from nowhere. Each has come into Nature from Supernature: each has its tap-root in an eternal, self-existent, rational Being, whom we call God. Each is an offshoot, or spearhead, or incursion of that Supernatural reality into Nature.

Some people may here raise the following question. If Reason is sometimes present in my mind and sometimes not, then, instead of saying that 'I' am a product of eternal Reason, would it not be wiser to say simply that eternal Reason itself occasionally works through my organism, leaving me a merely natural being? A wire does not become something other than a wire because an electric current has passed through it. But to talk thus is, in my opinion, to forget what reasoning is like. It is not an object which knocks against us, nor even a sensation which we feel. Reasoning doesn't 'happen to' us: we *do* it. Every train of thought is accompanied by what Kant called 'the *I think*'. The traditional doctrine that I am a creature to whom God has given reason but who is distinct from God seems to me much more philosophical than the theory that what appears to be my thinking is only God's thinking through me. On the latter view it is very difficult to explain what happens when I think correctly but reach a false conclusion because I have been misinformed about facts. Why God – who presumably knows the real facts – should be at pains to think one of His perfectly rational thoughts through a mind in which it is bound to produce error, I do not understand. Nor indeed do I understand why, if all 'my' valid thinking is really God's, He should either Himself mistake it for mine or cause me to mistake it for mine. It seems much more likely that human thought is not God's but God-kindled.

I must hasten, however, to add that this is a book about miracles, not about everything. I am attempting no full doctrine of man:[1] and I am not in the least trying to smuggle in an argument for the 'immortality of the soul'. The earliest Christian documents give a casual and unemphatic assent to the belief that the supernatural part of a man survives the death of the natural organism. But they are very little interested in the matter. What they are intensely interested in is the restoration or 'resurrection' of the whole composite creature by a miraculous divine act: and until we have come to some conclusion about miracles in general we shall certainly not discuss that. At this stage the supernatural element in man concerns us solely as evidence that something beyond Nature exists. The dignity and destiny of man have, at present, nothing to do with the argument. We are interested in man only because his rationality is the little tell-tale rift in Nature which shows that there is something beyond or behind her.

In a pond whose surface was completely covered with scum and floating vegetation, there might be a few water-lilies. And you might of course be interested in them for their beauty. But you might also be interested in them because from their structure you could deduce that they had stalks underneath which went down to roots in the bottom. The Naturalist thinks that the pond (Nature – the great event in space and time) is of an indefinite depth – that there is nothing but water however far you go down. My claim

---

[1] See Appendix A.

is that some of the things on the surface (i.e. in our experience) show the contrary. These things (rational minds) reveal, on inspection, that they at least are not floating but attached by stalks to the bottom. Therefore the pond has a bottom. It is not pond, pond for ever. Go deep enough and you will come to something that is not pond – to mud and earth and then to rock and finally the whole bulk of Earth and the subterranean fire.

At this point it is tempting to try whether Naturalism cannot still be saved. I pointed out in Chapter II that one could remain a Naturalist and yet believe in a certain kind of God – a cosmic consciousness to which 'the whole show' somehow gave rise: what we might call an *Emergent* God. Would not an Emergent God give us all we need? Is it really necessary to bring in a *super*-natural God, distinct from and outside the whole inter-locked system? (Notice, Modern Reader, how your spirits rise – how much more at home you would feel with an emergent, than with a transcendent, God – how much less primitive, repugnant, and naïf the emergent conception seems to you. For by that, as you will see later, there hangs a tale.)

But I am afraid it will not do. It is, of course, possible to suppose that when all the atoms of the universe got into a certain relation (which they were bound to get into sooner or later) they would give rise to a universal consciousness. And it might have thoughts. And it might cause those thoughts to pass through our minds. But unfortunately its own thoughts, on this supposition, would be the product of non-rational causes and therefore, by the rule which we use daily, they would have no validity. This cosmic mind would be, just as much as our own minds, the product of mindless Nature. We have not escaped from the difficulty, we have only put it a stage further back. The cosmic mind will help us only if we put it at the beginning, if we suppose it to be, not the product of the total system, but the basic, original, self-existent Fact which exists in its own right. But to admit *that* sort of cosmic mind is to admit a God outside Nature, a transcendent and supernatural God. This route, which looked like offering an escape, really leads us round again to the place we started from.

There is, then, a God who is not a part of Nature. But nothing has yet been said to show that He must have created her. Might God and Nature be both self-existent and totally independent of each other? If you thought they were you would be a Dualist and would hold a view which I consider manlier and more reasonable than any form of Naturalism. You might be many worse things than a Dualist, but I do not think Dualism is true. There is an enormous difficulty in conceiving two things which simply co-exist and have no other relation. If this difficulty sometimes escapes our notice, that is because we are the victims of picture-thinking. We really imagine them side by side in some kind of space. But of course if they were both in a common space, or a common time, or in any kind of common medium whatever, they would both be parts of a system, in fact of a 'Nature'. Even if we succeed in eliminating such pictures, the mere fact of our trying to think of them together slurs over the real difficulty because, for that moment anyway, our own mind is the common medium. If there can be such a thing as sheer 'otherness', if things can co-exist and no more, it is at any rate a conception which my mind cannot form. And in the present instance it seems specially gratuitous to try to form it, for we already know that God and Nature have come into a certain relation. They have, at the very least, a relation – almost, in one sense, a common frontier – in every human mind.

The relations which arise at that frontier are indeed of a most complicated and intimate sort. That spearhead of the Supernatural which I call my reason links up with all my natural contents – my sensations, emotions, and the like – so completely that I call the mixture by the single word 'me'. Again, there is what I have called the unsymmetrical character of the frontier relations. When the physical state of the brain dominates my thinking, it produces only disorder. But my brain does not become any less a brain when it is dominated by Reason: nor do my emotions and sensations become any the less emotions and sensations. Reason saves and strengthens my whole system, psychological and physical, whereas that whole system, by rebelling against Reason, destroys both Reason and itself. The military metaphor of a spearhead was apparently ill-chosen. The supernatural Reason enters my natural being not like a weapon – more like a beam of light which illuminates or a principle of organisation which unifies and develops. Our whole picture of Nature being 'invaded' (as if by a foreign enemy) was wrong. When we actually examine one of these invasions it looks much more like the arrival of a king among his own subjects or a mahout visiting his own elephant. The elephant may run amuck, Nature may be rebellious. But from observing what happens when Nature obeys it is almost impossible not to conclude that it is her very 'nature' to be a subject. All happens *as if* she had been designed for that very role.

To believe that Nature produced God, or even the human mind, is, as we have seen, absurd. To believe that the two are both independently self-existent is impossible: at least the attempt to do so leaves me unable to say that I am thinking of anything at all. It is true that Dualism has a certain theological attraction; it seems to make the problem of evil easier. But if we cannot, in fact, think Dualism out to the end, this attractive promise can never be kept, and I think there are better solutions of the problem of evil. There remains, then, the belief that God created Nature. This at once supplies a relation between them and gets rid of the difficulty of sheer 'otherness'. This also fits in with the observed frontier situation, in which everything looks as if Nature were not resisting an alien invader but rebelling against a lawful sovereign. This, and perhaps this alone, fits in with the fact that Nature, though not apparently intelligent, is intelligible – that events in the remotest parts of space appear to obey the laws of rational thought. Even the act of creation itself presents none of the intolerable difficulties which seem to meet us on every other hypothesis. There is in our own human minds something that bears a faint resemblance to it. We can imagine: that is, we can cause to exist the mental pictures of material objects, and even human characters, and events. We fall short of creation in two ways. In the first place we can only re-combine elements borrowed from the real universe: no one can imagine a new primary colour or a sixth sense. In the second place, what we imagine exists only for our own consciousness – though we can, by words, induce other people to build for themselves pictures in their own minds which may be roughly similar to it. We should have to attribute to God the power both of producing the basic elements, of inventing not only colours but colour itself, the senses themselves, space, time and matter themselves, and also of imposing what He has invented on created minds. This seems to me no intolerable assumption. It is certainly easier than the idea of God and Nature as wholly unrelated entities, and far easier than the idea of Nature producing valid thought.

I do not maintain that God's creation of Nature can be proved as rigorously as God's existence, but it seems to me overwhelmingly probable, so probable that no one who approached the question with an open mind would very seriously entertain any other hypothesis. In fact one seldom meets people who have grasped the existence of a supernatural God and yet deny that He is the Creator. All the evidence we have points in that direction, and difficulties spring up on every side if we try to believe otherwise. No philosophical theory which I have yet come across is a radical improvement on the words of Genesis, that 'In the beginning God made Heaven and Earth'. I say 'radical' improvement, because the story in Genesis – as St Jerome said long ago – is told in the manner 'of a popular poet', or as we should say, in the form of folk tale. But if you compare it with the creation legends of other peoples – with all these delightful absurdities in which giants to be cut up and floods to be dried up are made to exist *before* creation – the depth and originality of this Hebrew folk tale will soon be apparent. The idea of *creation* in the rigorous sense of the word is there fully grasped.

5

A FURTHER DIFFICULTY

IN NATURALISM

*Even as rigorous a determinist as Karl Marx,
who at times described the social behaviour
of the bourgeoisie in terms which suggested a
problem in social physics, could subject it at
other times to a withering scorn which only
the presupposition of moral responsibility
could justify.*
R. NIEBUHR, *An Interpretation of Christian Ethics*, chap. iii.

Some people regard logical thinking as the deadest and driest of our activities and may therefore be repelled by the privileged position I gave it in the last chapter. But logical thinking – Reasoning – had to be the pivot of the argument because, of all the claims which the human mind puts forward, the claim of Reasoning to be valid is the only one which the Naturalist cannot deny without (philosophically speaking) cutting his own throat. You cannot, as we saw, prove that there are no proofs. But you can if you wish regard all human ideals as illusions and all human loves as biological by-products. That is, you can do so without running into flat self-contradiction and nonsense. Whether you can do so without extreme unplausibility – without accepting a picture of things which no one really believes – is another matter.

Besides reasoning about matters of fact, men also make moral judgements – 'I ought to do this' – 'I ought not to do that' – 'This is good' – 'That is evil.' Two views have been held about moral judgements. Some people think that when we make them we are not using our Reason, but are employing some different power. Other people think that we make them by our Reason. I myself hold this second view. That is, I believe that the primary moral principles on which all others depend are rationally perceived. We 'just see' that there is no reason why my neighbour's happiness should be sacrificed to my own, as we 'just see' that things which are equal to the same thing are equal to one another. If we cannot prove either axiom, that is not because they are irrational but because they are self-evident and all proofs depend on them. Their intrinsic reasonableness shines by its own light. It is because all morality is based on such self-evident principles that we say to a man, when we would recall him to right conduct, 'Be reasonable.'

But this is by the way. For our present purpose it does not matter which of these two views you adopt. The important point is to notice that moral judgements raise the same sort of difficulty for Naturalism as any other thoughts. We always assume in discussions about morality, as in all other discussions, that the other man's views are worthless if they can be fully accounted for by some non-moral and non-rational cause. When two men differ about good and evil we soon hear this principle being brought into play. 'He believes in the sanctity of property because he's a millionaire' – 'He believes in Pacifism because he's a coward' – 'He approves of corporal punishment because he's a sadist.' Such taunts may often be untrue: but the mere fact that they are made by the one side, and hotly rebutted by the other, shows clearly what principle is being used. Neither side doubts that if they were true they would be decisive. No one (in real life) pays attention to any moral judgement which can be shown to spring from non-moral and non-rational causes. The Freudian and the Marxist attack traditional morality precisely on this ground – and with wide success. All men accept the principle.

But, of course, what discredits particular moral judgements must equally discredit moral judgement as a whole. If the fact that men have such ideas as *ought* and *ought not* at all can be fully explained by irrational and non-moral causes, then those ideas are an illusion. The Naturalist is ready to explain how the illusion arose. Chemical conditions produce life. Life, under the influence of natural selection, produces consciousness. Conscious organisms which behave in one way live longer than those which behave in another. Living longer, they are more likely to have offspring. Inheritance, and sometimes teaching as well, pass on their mode of behaviour to their young. Thus in every species a pattern of behaviour is built up. In the human species conscious teaching plays a larger part in building it up, and the tribe further strengthens it by killing individuals who don't conform. They also invent gods who are said to punish departures from it. Thus, in time, there comes to exist a strong human impulse to conform. But since this impulse is often at variance with the other impulses, a mental conflict arises, and the man expresses it by saying 'I want to do A but I ought to do B.'

This account may (or may not) explain why men do in fact make moral judgements. It does not explain how they could be right in making them. It excludes, indeed, the very possibility of their being right. For when men say 'I ought' they certainly think they are saying something, and something true, about the nature of the proposed action, and not merely about their own feelings. But if Naturalism is true, 'I ought' is the same sort of statement as 'I itch' or 'I'm going to be sick.' In real life when a man says 'I ought' we may reply, 'Yes. You're right. That *is* what you ought to do,' or else, 'No. I think you're mistaken.' But in a world of Naturalists (if Naturalists really remembered their philosophy out of school) the only sensible reply would be, 'Oh, are you?' All moral judgements would be statements about the speaker's feelings, mistaken by him for statements about something else (the real moral quality of actions) which does not exist.

Such a doctrine, I have admitted, is not flatly self-contradictory. The Naturalist can, if he chooses, brazen it out. He can say, 'Yes. I quite agree that there is no such thing as wrong and right. I admit that no moral judgement can be "true" or "correct" and, consequently, that no one system of morality can be better or worse than another. All ideas of good and evil are hallucinations – shadows cast on the outer world by the impulses which we have been conditioned to feel.' Indeed many Naturalists are delighted to say this.

But then they must stick to it; and fortunately (though inconsistently) most real Naturalists do not. A moment after they have admitted that good and evil are illusions, you will find them exhorting us to work for posterity, to educate, revolutionise, liquidate, live and die for the good of the human race. A Naturalist like Mr H. G. Wells spent a long life doing so with passionate eloquence and zeal. But surely this is very odd? Just as all the books about spiral nebulae, atoms and cave men would really have led you to suppose that the Naturalists claimed to be able to know something, so all the books in which Naturalists tell us what we ought to do would really make you believe that they thought some ideas of good (their own, for example) to be somehow preferable to others. For they write with indignation like men proclaiming what is good in itself and denouncing what is evil in itself, and not at all like men recording that they personally like mild beer but some people prefer bitter. Yet if the 'oughts' of Mr Wells and, say, Franco are both equally the impulses which Nature has conditioned each to have and both tell us nothing about any objective right or wrong, whence is all the fervour? Do they remember while they are writing thus that when they tell us we 'ought to make a better world' the words 'ought' and 'better' must, on their own showing, refer to an irrationally conditioned impulse which cannot be true or false any more than a vomit or a yawn?

My idea is that sometimes they do forget. That is their glory. Holding a philosophy which excludes humanity, they yet remain human. At the sight of injustice they throw all their Naturalism to the winds and speak like men and like men of genius. They know far better than they think they know. But at other times, I suspect they are trusting in a supposed way of escape from their difficulty.

It works – or *seems* to work – like this. They say to themselves, 'Ah, yes. Morality' – or 'bourgeois morality' or 'conventional morality' or 'traditional morality' or some such addition – 'Morality *is* an illusion. But we have found out what modes of behaviour will in fact preserve the human race alive. That is the behaviour we are pressing you to adopt. Pray don't mistake us for moralists. We are under an entirely new management' … just as if this would help. It would help only if we grant, firstly, that life is better than death and, secondly, that we ought to care for the lives of our descendants as much as, or more than, for our own. And both these are moral judgements which have, like all others, been explained away by Naturalism. Of course, having been conditioned by Nature in a certain way, we do feel thus about life and about posterity. But the Naturalists have cured us of mistaking these feelings for insights into what we once called 'real value'. Now that I know that my impulse to serve posterity is just the same kind of thing as my fondness for cheese – now that its transcendental pretensions have been exposed for a sham – do you think I shall pay much attention to it? When it happens to be strong (and it has grown considerably weaker since you explained to me its real nature) I suppose I shall obey it. When it is weak, I shall put my money into cheese. There can be no reason for trying to whip up and encourage the one impulse rather than the other. Not now that I know what they both are. The Naturalists must not destroy all my reverence for conscience on Monday and expect to find me still venerating it on Tuesday.

There is no escape along those lines. If we are to continue to make moral judgements (and whatever we say we shall in fact continue) then we must believe that the conscience of man is not a product of Nature. It can be valid only if it is an offshoot of some absolute moral wisdom, a moral wisdom which exists absolutely 'on its own' and is not a product of non-moral, non-rational Nature. As the argument of the last chapter led us to acknowledge a supernatural source for rational thought, so the argument of this leads us to acknowledge a supernatural source for our ideas of good and evil. In other words, we now know something more about God. If you hold that moral judgement is a different thing from Reasoning you will express this new knowledge by saying, 'We now know that God has at least one other attribute than rationality.' If, like me, you hold that moral judgement is a kind of Reasoning, then you will say, 'We now know more about the Divine Reason.'

And with this we are almost ready to begin our main argument. But before doing so it will be well to pause for the consideration of some misgivings or misunderstandings which may have already arisen.

6

ANSWERS TO MISGIVINGS

*For as bats' eyes are to daylight so is our
intellectual eye to those truths which are, in
their own nature, the most obvious of all.*
ARISTOTLE, *Metaphysics*, I (Brevior) i.

I t must be clearly understood that the argument so far leads to no conception of 'souls' or 'spirits' (words I have avoided) floating about in the
realm of Nature with no relation to their environment. Hence we do not
deny – indeed we must welcome – certain considerations which are often
regarded as proofs of Naturalism. We can admit, and even insist, that
Rational Thinking can be shown to be conditioned in its exercise by a natural object (the brain). It is temporarily impaired by alcohol or a blow on
the head. It wanes as the brain decays and vanishes when the brain ceases to
function. In the same way the moral outlook of a community can be shown
to be closely connected with its history, geographical environment, economic structure, and so forth. The moral ideas of the individual are equally
related to his general situation: it is no accident that parents and schoolmasters so often tell us that they can stand any vice rather than lying, the lie
being the only defensive weapon of the child. All this, far from presenting us
with a difficulty, is exactly what we should expect.

The rational and moral element in each human mind is a point of force
from the Supernatural working its way into Nature, exploiting at each point
those conditions which Nature offers, repulsed where the conditions are
hopeless and impeded when they are unfavourable. A man's Rational thinking is *just so much* of his share in eternal Reason as the state of his brain
allows to become operative: it represents, so to speak, the bargain struck or
the frontier fixed between Reason and Nature at that particular point. A
nation's moral outlook is just so much of its share in eternal Moral Wisdom
as its history, economics etc. lets through. In the same way the voice of the
Announcer is just so much of a human voice as the receiving set lets
through. Of course it varies with the state of the receiving set, and deterio-
rates as the set wears out and vanishes altogether if I throw a brick at it. It is
conditioned by the apparatus but not originated by it. If it were – if we knew
that there was no human being at the microphone – we should not attend to
the news. The various and complex conditions under which Reason and

Morality appear are the twists and turns of the frontier between Nature and Supernature. That is why, if you wish, you can always ignore Supernature and treat the phenomena purely from the Natural side; just as a man studying on a map the boundaries of Cornwall and Devonshire can always say, 'What you call a bulge in Devonshire is really a dent in Cornwall.' And in a sense you can't refute him. What we call a bulge in Devonshire always *is* a dent in Cornwall. What we call rational thought in a man always involves a state of the brain, in the long run a relation of atoms. But Devonshire is none the less something more than 'where Cornwall ends', and Reason is something more than cerebral biochemistry.

I now turn to another possible misgiving. To some people the great trouble about any argument for the Supernatural is simply the fact that argument should be needed at all. If so stupendous a thing exists, ought it not to be obvious as the sun in the sky? Is it not intolerable, and indeed incredible, that knowledge of the most basic of all Facts should be accessible only by wire-drawn reasonings for which the vast majority of men have neither leisure nor capacity? I have great sympathy with this point of view. But we must notice two things.

When you are looking at a garden from a room upstairs it is obvious (once you think about it) that you are looking through a window. But if it is the garden that interests you, you may look at it for a long time without thinking of the window. When you are reading a book it is obvious (once you attend to it) that you are using your eyes: but unless your eyes begin to hurt you, or the book is a text book on optics, you may read all evening without once thinking of eyes. When we talk we are obviously using language and grammar: and when we try to talk a foreign language we may be painfully aware of the fact. But when we are talking English we don't notice it. When you shout from the top of the stairs, 'I'm coming in half a moment,' you are not usually conscious that you have made the singular *am* agree with the singular *I*. There is indeed a story told about a Redskin who, having learned several other languages, was asked to write a grammar of the language used by his own tribe. He replied, after some thought, that it had no grammar. The grammar he had used all his life had escaped his notice all his life. He knew it (in one sense) so well that (in another sense) he did not know it existed.

All these instances show that the fact which is in one respect the most obvious and primary fact, and through which alone you have access to all the other facts, may be precisely the one that is most easily forgotten – forgotten not because it is so remote or abstruse but because it is so near and so obvious. And that is exactly how the Supernatural has been forgotten. The Naturalists have been engaged in thinking about Nature. They have not attended to the fact that they were *thinking*. The moment one attends to this it is obvious that one's own thinking cannot be merely a natural event, and that therefore something other than Nature exists. The Supernatural is not remote and abstruse: it is a matter of daily and hourly experience, as intimate as breathing. Denial of it depends on a certain absent-mindedness. But this absent-mindedness is in no way surprising. You do not need – indeed you do not wish – to be always thinking about windows when you are looking at gardens or always thinking about eyes when you are reading. In the same way the proper procedure for all limited and particular inquiries is to ignore the fact of your own thinking, and concentrate on the object. It is only when you stand back from particular inquiries and try to form a complete philosophy that you must take it into account. For a complete philosophy must get in *all* the facts. In it you turn away from specialised or truncated thought to total thought: and one of the facts total thought must think about is Thinking itself. There is thus a tendency in the study of Nature to make us forget the most obvious fact of all. And since the sixteenth century, when Science was born, the minds of men have been increasingly turned outward, to know Nature and to master her. They have been increasingly engaged on those specialised inquiries for which truncated thought is the correct method. It is therefore not in the least astonishing that they should have forgotten the evidence for the Supernatural. The deeply ingrained habit of truncated thought – what we call the 'scientific' habit of mind – was indeed certain to lead to Naturalism, unless this tendency were continually corrected from some other source. But no other source was at hand, for during the same period men of science were coming to be metaphysically and theologically uneducated.

That brings me to the second consideration. The state of affairs in which ordinary people can discover the Supernatural only by abstruse reasoning is recent and, by historical standards, abnormal. All over the world, until quite modern times, the direct insight of the mystics and the reasonings of the philosophers percolated to the mass of the people by authority and tradition; they could be received by those who were no great reasoners themselves in the concrete form of myth and ritual and the whole pattern of life. In the conditions produced by a century or so of Naturalism, plain men are being forced to bear burdens which plain men were never expected to bear before. We must get the truth for ourselves or go without it. There may be two explanations for this. It might be that humanity, in rebelling against tradition and authority, have made a ghastly mistake; a mistake which will not be the less fatal because the corruptions of those in authority rendered it very excusable. On the other hand, it may be that the Power which rules our species is at this moment carrying out a daring experiment. Could it be intended that the whole mass of the people should now move forward and occupy for themselves those heights which were once reserved only for the sages? Is the distinction between wise and simple to disappear because all are now expected to become wise? If so, our present blunderings would be but growing pains. But let us make no mistake about our necessities. If we are content to go back and become humble plain men obeying a tradition, well. If we are ready to climb and struggle on till we become sages ourselves, better still. But the man who will neither obey wisdom in others nor adventure for her/himself is fatal. A society where the simple many obey the few seers can live: a society where all were seers could live even more fully. But a society where the mass is still simple and the seers are no longer attended to can achieve only superficiality, baseness, ugliness, and in the end extinction. On or back we must go; to stay here is death.

One other point that may have raised doubt or difficulty should here be dealt with. I have advanced reasons for believing that a supernatural element is present in every rational man. The presence of human rationality in the world is therefore a Miracle by the definition given in Chapter II. On realising this the reader may excusably say, 'Oh, if *that's* all he means by a Miracle ...' and fling the book away. But I ask him to have patience. Human Reason and Morality have been mentioned not as instances of Miracle (at least, not of the kind of Miracle you wanted to hear about) but as proofs of the Supernatural: not in order to show that Nature ever is invaded but that there is a possible invader. Whether you choose to call the regular and familiar invasion by human Reason a Miracle or not is largely a matter of words. Its regularity – the fact that it regularly enters by the same door, human sexual intercourse – may incline you not to do so. It looks as if it were (so to speak) the very nature of Nature to suffer *this* invasion. But then we might later find that it was the very nature of Nature to suffer Miracles in general. Fortunately the course of our argument will allow us to leave this question of terminology on one side. We are going to be concerned with other invasions of Nature – with what everyone would call Miracles. Our question could, if you liked, be put in the form, 'Does Supernature ever produce particular results in space and time *except* through the instrumentality of human brains acting on human nerves and muscles?'

I have said '*particular* results' because, on our view, Nature as a whole is herself one huge result of the Supernatural: God created her. God pierces her wherever there is a human mind. God presumably maintains her in existence. The question is whether He ever does anything else to her. Does He, besides all this, ever introduce into her events of which it would not be true to say, 'This is simply the working out of the general character which He gave to Nature as a whole in creating her'? Such events are what are popularly called Miracles: and it will be in this sense only that the word Miracle will be used for the rest of the book.

7

A CHAPTER OF
RED HERRINGS

Thence came forth Maul, a giant.
This Maul did use to spoil young
Pilgrims with sophistry.
BUNYAN

From the admission that God exists and is the author of Nature, it by no means follows that miracles must, or even can, occur. God Himself might be a being of such a kind that it was contrary to His character to work miracles. Or again, He might have made Nature the sort of thing that cannot be added to, subtracted from, or modified. The case against Miracles accordingly relies on two different grounds. You either think that the character of God excludes them or that the character of Nature excludes them. We will begin with the second which is the more popular ground. In this chapter I shall consider forms of it which are, in my opinion, very superficial – which might even be called misunderstandings or Red Herrings.

The first Red Herring is this. Any day you may hear a man (and not necessarily a disbeliever in God) say of some alleged miracle, 'No. Of course I don't believe that. We know it is contrary to the laws of Nature. People could believe it in olden times because they didn't know the laws of Nature. We know now that it is a scientific impossibility'.

By the 'laws of Nature' such a man means, I think, the observed course of Nature. If he means anything more than that he is not the plain man I take him for but a philosophic Naturalist and will be dealt with in the next chapter. The man I have in view believes that mere experience (and specially those artificially contrived experiences which we call Experiments) can tell us what regularly happens in Nature. And he thinks that what we have discovered excludes the possibility of Miracle. This is a confusion of mind.

Granted that miracles *can* occur, it is, of course, for experience to say whether one has done so on any given occasion. But mere experience, even if prolonged for a million years, cannot tell us whether the thing is possible. Experiment finds out what regularly happens in Nature: the norm or rule to which she works. Those who believe in miracles are not denying that there is such a norm or rule: they are only saying that it can be suspended. A miracle is by definition an exception. How can the discovery of the rule tell you whether, granted a sufficient cause, the rule can be suspended? If we said that the rule was A, then experience might refute us by discovering that it was B. If we said that there was no rule, then experience might refute us by observing that there is. But we are saying neither of these things. We agree that there is a rule and that the rule is B. What has that got to do with the question whether the rule can be suspended? You reply, 'But experience shows that it never has'. We reply, 'Even if that were so, this would not prove that it never can. But does experience show that it never has? The world is full of stories of people who say they have experienced miracles. Perhaps the stories are false: perhaps they are true. But before you can decide on that historical question, you must first (as was pointed out in Chapter 1) discover whether the thing is possible, and if possible, how probable.'

The idea that the progress of science has somehow altered this question is closely bound up with the idea that people 'in olden times' believe in them 'because they didn't know the laws of Nature'. Thus you will hear people say, 'The early Christians believed that Christ was the son of a virgin, but we know that this is a scientific impossibility.' Such people seem to have an idea that belief in miracles arose at a period when men were so ignorant of the course of nature that they did not perceive a miracle to be contrary to it. A moment's thought shows this to be nonsense: and the story of the Virgin Birth is a particularly striking example. When St Joseph discovered that his fiancée was going to have a baby, he not unnaturally decided to repudiate her. Why? Because he knew just as well as any modern gynaecologist that in the ordinary course of nature women do not have babies unless they have lain with men. No doubt the modern gynaecologist knows several things about birth and begetting which St Joseph did not know. But those things do not concern the main point – that a virgin birth is contrary to the course of nature. And St Joseph obviously knew *that*. In any sense in which it is true to say now, 'The thing is scientifically impossible', he would have said the same: the thing always was, and was always known to be, impossible *unless* the regular processes of nature were, in this particular case, being over-ruled or supplemented by something from beyond nature. When St Joseph finally accepted the view that his fiancée's pregnancy was due not to unchastity but to a miracle, he accepted the miracle as something contrary to the known order of nature. All records of miracles teach the same thing. In such stories the miracles excite fear and wonder (that is what the very word *miracle* implies) among the spectators, and are taken as evidence of supernatural power. If they were not known to be contrary to the laws of nature how could they suggest the presence of the supernatural? How could they be surprising unless they were seen to be exceptions to the rules? And how can anything be seen to be an exception till the rules are known? If there ever were men who did not know the laws of nature *at all*, they would have no idea of a miracle and feel no particular interest in one if it were performed before them. Nothing can seem extraordinary until you have discovered what is ordinary. Belief in miracles, far from depending on an ignorance of the laws of nature, is only possible in so far as those laws are known. We have already seen that if you begin by ruling out the supernatural you will perceive no miracles. We must now add that you will equally perceive no miracles until you believe that nature works according to regular laws. If you have not yet noticed that the sun always rises in the East you will see nothing miraculous about his rising one morning in the West.

If the miracles were offered us as events that normally occurred, then the progress of science, whose business is to tell us what normally occurs, would render belief in them gradually harder and finally impossible. The progress of science has in just this way (and greatly to our benefit) made all sorts of things incredible which our ancestors believed; man-eating ants and gryphons in Scythia, men with one single gigantic foot, magnetic islands that draw all ships towards them, mermaids and fire-breathing dragons. But those things were never put forward as supernatural interruptions of the course of nature. They were put forward as items within her ordinary course – in fact as 'science'. Later and better science has therefore rightly removed them. Miracles are in a wholly different position. If there were fire-breathing dragons our big-game hunters would find them: but no one ever pretended that the Virgin Birth or Christ's walking on the water could be reckoned on to recur. When a thing professes from the very outset to be a unique invasion of Nature by something from outside, increasing knowledge of Nature can never make it either more or less credible than it was at the beginning. In this sense it is mere confusion of thought to suppose that advancing science has made it harder for us to accept miracles. We always knew they were contrary to the natural course of events; we know still that if there is something beyond Nature, they are possible. Those are the bare bones of the question; time and progress and science and civilisation have not altered them in the least. The grounds for belief and disbelief are the same today as they were two thousand – or ten thousand – years ago. If St Joseph had lacked faith to trust God or humility to perceive the holiness of his spouse, he could have disbelieved in the miraculous origin of her Son as easily as any modern man; and any modern man who believes in God can accept the miracle as easily as St Joseph did. You and I may not agree, even by the end of this book, as to whether miracles happen or not. But at least let us not talk nonsense. Let us not allow vague rhetoric about the march of science to fool us into supposing that the most complicated account of birth, in terms of genes and spermatozoa, leaves us any more convinced than we were before that *nature* does not send babies to young women who 'know not a man'.

The second Red Herring is this. Many people say, 'They could believe in miracles in olden times because they had a false conception of the universe. They thought the Earth was the largest thing in it and Man the most important creature. It therefore seemed reasonable to suppose that the Creator was specially interested in Man and might even interrupt the course of Nature for his benefit. But now that we know the real immensity of the universe – now that we perceive our own planet and even the whole Solar System to be only a speck – it becomes ludicrous to believe in them any longer. We have discovered our significance and can no longer suppose that God is so drastically concerned in our petty affairs'.

Whatever its value may be as an argument, it may be stated at once that this view is quite wrong about facts. The immensity of the universe is not a recent discovery. More than seventeen hundred years ago Ptolemy taught that in relation to the distance of the fixed stars the whole Earth must be regarded as a point with no magnitude. His astronomical system was universally accepted in the Dark and Middle Ages. The insignificance of Earth was as much a commonplace to Boethius, King Alfred, Dante, and Chaucer as it is to Mr H. G. Wells or Professor Haldane. Statements to the contrary in modern books are due to ignorance.

The real question is quite different from what we commonly suppose. The real question is why the spatial insignificance of Earth, after being asserted by Christian philosophers, sung by Christian poets, and commented on by Christian moralists for some fifteen centuries, without the slightest suspicion that it conflicted with their theology, should suddenly in quite modern times have been set up as a stock argument against Christianity and enjoyed, in that capacity, a brilliant career. I will offer a guess at the answer to this question presently. For the moment, let us consider the strength of this stock argument.

When the doctor at a post-mortem looks at the dead man's organs and diagnoses poison he has a clear idea of the different state in which the organs would have been if the man had died a natural death. If from the vastness of the universe and the smallness of Earth we diagnose that Christianity is false we ought to have a clear idea of the sort of universe we should have expected if it were true. But have we? Whatever space may really be, it is certain that our perceptions make it appear three dimensional; and to a three-dimensional space no boundaries are conceivable. By the very forms of our perceptions therefore we must feel as if we lived somewhere in infinite space: and whatever size the Earth happens to be, it must of course be very small in comparison with infinity. And this infinite space must either be empty or contain bodies. If it were empty, if it contained nothing but our own Sun, then that vast vacancy would certainly be used as an argument against the very existence of God. Why, it would be asked, should He create one speck and leave all the rest of space to nonentity? If, on the other hand, we find (as we actually do) countless bodies floating in space, they must be either habitable or uninhabitable. Now the odd thing is that *both* alternatives are equally used as objections to Christianity. If the universe is teeming with life other than ours, then this, we are told, makes it quite ridiculous to believe that God should be so concerned with the human race as to 'come down from Heaven' and be made man for its redemption. If, on the other hand, our planet is really unique in harbouring organic life, then this is thought to prove that life is only an accidental by-product in the universe and so again to disprove our religion. We treat God as the policeman in the story treated the suspect; whatever he does 'will be used in evidence against Him'. This kind of objection to the Christian faith is not really based on the observed nature of the actual universe at all. You can make it without waiting to find out what the universe is like, for it will fit any kind of universe we choose to imagine. The doctor here can diagnose poison without looking at the corpse for he has a theory of poison which he will maintain *whatever* the state of the organs turns out to be.

The reason why we cannot even imagine a universe so built as to exclude these objections is, perhaps, as follows. Man is a finite creature who has sense enough to know that he is finite: therefore, on any conceivable view, he finds himself dwarfed by reality as a whole. He is also a derivative being: the cause of his existence lies not in himself but (immediately) in his parents and (ultimately) *either* in the character of Nature as a whole *or* (if there is a God) in God. But there must be something, whether it be God or the totality of Nature, which exists in its own right or goes on 'of its own accord'; not as the product of causes beyond itself, but simply because it does. In the face of that something, whichever it turns out to be, man must feel his own derived existence to be unimportant, irrelevant, almost accidental. There is no question of religious people fancying that all exists for man and scientific people discovering that it does not. Whether the ultimate and inexplicable being – that which simple *is* – turns out to be God or 'the whole show', of course it does not exist for us. On either view we are faced with something which existed before the human race appeared and will exist after the Earth has become uninhabitable; which is utterly independent of us though we are totally dependent on it; and which, through vast ranges of its being, has no relevance to our own hopes and fears. For no man was, I suppose, ever so mad as to think that man, or all creation, *filled* the Divine Mind; if we are a small thing to space and time, space and time are a much smaller thing to God. It is a profound mistake to imagine that Christianity ever intended to dissipate the bewilderment and even the terror, the sense of our own nothingness, which come upon us when we think about the nature of things. It comes to intensify them. Without such sensations there is no religion. Many a man, brought up in the glib profession of some shallow form of Christianity, who comes through reading Astronomy to realise for the first time how majestically indifferent most reality is to man, and who perhaps abandons his religion on that account, may at that moment be having his first genuinely religious experience.

Christianity does not involve the belief that all things were made for man. It does involve the belief that God loves man and for his sake became man and died. I have not yet succeeded in seeing how what we know (and have known since the days of Ptolemy) about the size of the universe affects the credibility of this doctrine one way or the other.

The sceptic asks how we can believe that God so 'came down' to this one tiny planet. The question would be embarrassing if we knew (1) that there are rational creatures on any of the other bodies that float in space; (2) that they have, like us, fallen and need redemption; (3) that their redemption must be in the same mode as ours; (4) that redemption in this mode has been withheld from them. But we know none of them. The universe may be full of happy lives that never needed redemption. It may be full of lives that have been redeemed in modes suitable to their condition, of which we can form no conception. It may be full of lives that have been redeemed in the very same mode as our own. It may be full of things quite other than life in which God is interested though we are not.

If it is maintained that anything so small as the Earth must, in any event, be too unimportant to merit the love of the Creator, we reply that no Christian ever supposed we did merit it. Christ did not die for men because they were intrinsically worth dying for, but because He is intrinsically love, and therefore loves infinitely. And what, after all, does the *size* of a world or a creature tell us about its 'importance' or value?

There is no doubt that we all *feel* the incongruity of supposing, say, that the planet Earth might be more important than the Great Nebula in Andromeda. On the other hand, we are all equally certain that only a lunatic would think a man six feet high necessarily more important than a man five feet high, or a horse necessarily more important than a man, or a man's legs than his brain. In other words this supposed ratio of size to importance feels plausible only when one of the sizes involved is very great. And that betrays the true basis of this type of thought. When a relation is perceived by Reason, it is perceived to hold good universally. If our Reason told us that size was proportional to importance, then small differences in size would be accompanied by small differences in importance just as surely as great differences in size were accompanied by great differences in importance. Your six-foot man would have to be slightly more valuable than the man of five feet, and your leg slightly more important than your brain – which everyone knows to be nonsense. The conclusion is inevitable: the importance we attach to great differences of size is an affair not of reason but of emotion – of that peculiar emotion which superiorities in size begin to produce in us only after a certain point of absolute size has been reached.

We are inveterate poets. When a quantity is very great we cease to regard it as a mere quantity. Our imaginations awake. Instead of mere quantity, we now have a quality – the Sublime. But for this, the merely arithmetical greatness of the Galaxy would be no more impressive than the figures in an account book. To a mind which did not share our emotions and lacked our imaginative energies, the argument against Christianity from the size of the universe would be simply unintelligible. It is therefore from ourselves that the material universe derives its power to overawe us. Men of sensibility look up on the night sky with awe: brutal and stupid men do not. When the silence of the eternal spaces terrified Pascal, it was Pascal's own greatness that enabled them to do so; to be frightened by the bigness of the nebulae is, almost literally, to be frightened at our own shadow. For light years and geological periods are mere arithmetic until the shadow of man, the poet, the maker of myths, falls upon them. As a Christian I do not say we are wrong to tremble at that shadow, for I believe it to be the shadow of an image of God. But if the vastness of Nature ever threatens to overcrow our spirits, we must remember that it is only Nature spiritualised by human imagination which does so.

This suggests a possible answer to the question raised a few pages ago – why the size of the universe, known for centuries, should first in modern times become an argument against Christianity. Has it perhaps done so because in modern times the imagination has become more sensitive to bigness? From this point of view the argument from size might almost be regarded as a by-product of the Romantic Movement in poetry. In addition to the absolute increase of imaginative vitality on this topic, there has pretty certainly been a decline on others. Any reader of old poetry can see that brightness appealed to ancient and medieval man more than bigness, and more than it does to us. Medieval thinkers believed that the stars must be somehow superior to the Earth because they looked bright and it did not. Moderns think that the Galaxy ought to be more important than the Earth because it is bigger. Both states of mind can produce good poetry. Both can supply mental pictures which rouse very respectable emotions – emotions of awe, humility, or exhilaration. But taken as serious philosophical argument both are ridiculous. The atheist's argument from size is, in fact, an instance of just that picture-thinking to which, as we shall see in a later chapter, the Christian is *not* committed. It is the particular mode in which picture-thinking appears in the twentieth century: for what we fondly call 'primitive' errors do not pass away. They merely change their form.

8

MIRACLES AND THE
LAWS OF NATURE

It's a very odd thing –
As odd as can be –
That whatever Miss T. eats
Turns into Miss T.

W. DE LA MARE

Having cleared out of the way those objections which are based on a popular and confused notion that the 'progress of science' has somehow made the world safe against Miracle, we must now consider the subject on a somewhat deeper level. The question is whether Nature can be known to be of such a kind that supernatural interferences with her are impossible. She is already known to be, in general, regular: she behaves according to fixed laws, many of which have been discovered, and which interlock with one another. There is, in this discussion, no question of mere failure or inaccuracy to keep these laws on the part of Nature, no question of chancy or spontaneous variation.[1] The only question is whether, granting the existence of a Power outside Nature, there is any intrinsic absurdity in the idea of its intervening to produce within Nature events which the regular 'going on' of the whole natural system would never have produced.

Three conceptions of the 'Laws' of Nature have been held. (1) That they are mere brute facts, known only by observation, with no discoverable rhyme or reason about them. We know *that* Nature behaves thus and thus; we do not know why she does and can see no reason why she should not do the opposite. (2) That they are applications of the law of averages. The foundations of Nature are in the random and lawless. But the number of units we are dealing with are so enormous that the behaviour of these crowds (like the behaviour of very large masses of men) can be calculated with practical accuracy. What we call 'impossible events' are events so overwhelmingly improbable – by actuarial standards – that we do not need to take them into

---

[1] If any region of reality is in fact chancy or lawless then it is a region which, so far from admitting Miracle with special ease, renders the word 'Miracle' meaningless throughout that region.

account. (3) That the fundamental laws of Physics are really what we call 'necessary truths' like the truths of mathematics – in other words, that if we clearly understand what we are saying we shall see that the opposite would be meaningless nonsense. Thus it is a 'law' that when one billiard ball shoves another the amount of momentum lost by the first ball must exactly equal the amount gained by the second. People who hold that the laws of Nature are necessary truths would say that all we have done is to split up the single events into two halves (adventures of ball A, and adventures of ball B) and then discover that 'the two sides of the account balance'. When we understand this we see that of course they *must* balance. The fundamental laws are in the long run merely statements that every event is itself and not some different event.

It will at once be clear that the first of these three theories gives no assurance against Miracles – indeed no assurance that, even apart from Miracles, the 'laws' which we have hitherto observed will be obeyed tomorrow. If we have no notion why a thing happens, then of course we know no reason why it should not be otherwise, and therefore have no certainty that it might not some day be otherwise. The second theory, which depends on the law of averages, is in the same position. The assurance it gives us is of the same general kind as our assurance that a coin tossed a thousand times will not give the same result, say, nine hundred times: and that the longer you toss it the more nearly the numbers of Heads and Tails will come to being equal. But this is so only provided the coin is an honest coin. If it is a loaded coin our expectations may be disappointed. But the people who believe in miracles are maintaining precisely that the coin *is* loaded. The expectations based on the law of averages will work only for *undoctored* Nature. And the question whether miracles occur is just the question whether Nature is ever doctored.

The third view (that laws of Nature are necessary truths) seems at first sight to present an insurmountable obstacle to miracle. The breaking of them would, in that case, be a self-contradiction and not even Omnipotence can do what is self-contradictory. Therefore the Laws cannot be broken. And therefore, we shall conclude, no miracle can ever occur?

We have gone too quickly. It is certain that the billiard balls will behave in a particular way, just as it is certain that if you divided a shilling unequally between two recipients then A's share must exceed the half and B's share fall short of it by exactly the same amount. Provided, of course, that A does not by sleight of hand steal some of B's pennies at the very moment of the transaction. In the same way, you know what will happen to the two billiard balls – provided nothing interferes. If one ball encounters a roughness in the cloth which the other does not, their motion will not illustrate the law in the way you had expected. Of course what happens as a result of the roughness in the cloth will illustrate the law in some other way, but your original prediction will have been false. Or again, if I snatch up a cue and give one of the balls a little help, you will get a third result: and that third result will equally illustrate the laws of physics, and equally falsify your prediction. I shall have 'spoiled the experiment'. All interferences leave the law perfectly true. But every prediction of what will happen in a given instance is made under the proviso 'other things being equal' or ' if there are no interferences'. Whether other things *are equal* in a given case and whether interferences may occur is another matter. The arithmetician, as an arithmetician, does not know how likely A is to steal some of B's pennies when the shilling is being divided; you had better ask a criminologist. The physicist, as a physicist, does not know how likely I am to catch up a cue and 'spoil' his experiment with the billiard balls: you had better ask someone who knows *me*. In the same way the physicist, as such, does not know how likely it is that some supernatural power is going to interfere with them: you had better ask a metaphysician. But the physicist does know, just because he is a physicist, that if the billiard balls are tampered with by any agency, natural or supernatural, which he has not taken into account, then their behaviour must differ from what he expected. Not because the law is false, but because it is true. The more certain we are of the law the more clearly we know that if new factors have been introduced the result will vary accordingly. What we do not know, as physicists, is whether Supernatural power might be one of the new factors.

If the laws of Nature are necessary truths, no miracle can break them: but then no miracle needs to break them. It is with them as with the laws of arithmetic. If I put six pennies into a drawer on Monday and six more on Tuesday, the laws decree that – *other things being equal* – I shall find twelve pennies there on Wednesday. But if the drawer has been robbed I may in fact find only two. Something will have been broken (the lock of the drawer or the laws of England) but the laws of arithmetic will not have been broken. The new situation created by the thief will illustrate the laws of arithmetic just as well as the original situation. But if God comes to work miracles, He comes 'like a thief in the night'. Miracle is, from the point of view of the scientist, a form of doctoring, tampering, (if you like) cheating. It introduces a new factor into the situation, namely supernatural force, which the scientist had not reckoned on. He calculates what will happen, or what must have happened on a past occasion, in the belief that the situation, at that point of space and time, is or was A. But if supernatural force has been added, then the situation really is or was AB. And no one knows better than the scientist that AB *cannot* yield the same result as A. The necessary truth of the laws, far from making it impossible that miracles should occur, makes it certain that if the Supernatural is operating they must occur. For if the natural situation by itself, and the natural situation *plus* something else, yielded only the same result, it would be then that we should be faced with a lawless and unsystematic universe. The better you know that two and two make four, the better you know that two and three don't.

This perhaps helps to make a little clearer what the laws of Nature really are. We are in the habit of talking as if they caused events to happen; but they have never caused any event at all. The laws of motion do not set billiard balls moving: they analyse the motion after something else (say, a man with a cue, or a lurch of the liner, or, perhaps, supernatural power) has provided it. They produce no events: they state the pattern to which every event – if only it can be induced to happen – must conform, just as the rules of arithmetic state the pattern to which all transactions with money must conform – if only you can get hold of any money. Thus in one sense the laws of Nature cover the whole field of space and time; in another, what they leave out is precisely the whole real universe – the incessant torrent of actual events which makes up true history. That must come from somewhere else. To think the laws can produce it is like thinking that you can create real money by simply doing sums. For every law, in the last resort, says 'If you have A, then you will get B'. But first catch your A: the laws won't do it for you.

It is therefore inaccurate to define a miracle as something that breaks the laws of Nature. It doesn't. If I knock out my pipe I alter the position of a great many atoms: in the long run, and to an infinitesimal degree, of all the atoms there are. Nature digests or assimilates this event with perfect ease and harmonises it in a twinkling with all other events. It is one more bit of raw material for the laws to apply to, and they apply. I have simply thrown one event into the general cataract of events and it finds itself at home there and conforms to all other events. If God annihilates or creates or deflects a unit of matter He has created a new situation at that point. Immediately all Nature domiciles this new situation, makes it at home in her realm, adapts all other events to it. It finds itself conforming to all the laws. If God creates a miraculous spermatozoon in the body of a virgin, it does not proceed to break any laws. The laws at once take it over. Nature is ready. Pregnancy follows, according to all the normal laws, and nine months later a child is born. We see every day that physical nature is not in the least incommoded by the daily inrush of events from biological nature or from psychological nature. If events ever come from beyond Nature altogether, she will be no more incommoded by them. Be sure she will rush to the point where she is invaded, as the defensive forces rush to a cut in our finger, and there hasten to accommodate the newcomer. The moment it enters her realm it obeys all her laws. Miraculous wine will intoxicate, miraculous conception will lead to pregnancy, inspired books will suffer all the ordinary processes of textual corruption, miraculous bread will be digested. The divine art of miracle is not an art of suspending the pattern to which events conform but of feeding new events into that pattern. It does not violate the law's proviso, 'If A, then

B': it says, 'But this time instead of A, A2,' and Nature, speaking through all her laws, replies 'Then B2' and naturalises the immigrant, as she well knows how. She is an accomplished hostess.

A miracle is emphatically not an event without cause or without results. Its cause is the activity of God: its results follow according to Natural law. In the forward direction (i.e. during the time which follows its occurrence) it is interlocked with all Nature just like any other event. Its peculiarity is that it is not in that way interlocked backwards, interlocked with the previous history of Nature. And this is just what some people find intolerable. The reason they find it intolerable is that they start by taking Nature to be the whole of reality. And they are sure that all reality must be interrelated and consistent. I agree with them. But I think they have mistaken a partial system within reality, namely Nature, for the whole. That being so, the miracle and the previous history of Nature may be interlocked after all but not in the way the Naturalist expected: rather in a much more roundabout fashion. The great complex event called Nature, and the new particular event introduced into it by the miracle, are related by their common origin in God, and doubtless, if we knew enough, most intricately related in His purpose and design, so that a Nature which had had a different history, and therefore been a different Nature, would have been invaded by different miracles or by none at all. In that way the miracles and the previous course of Nature are as well interlocked as any other two realities, but you must go back as far as their common Creator to find the interlocking. You will not find it *within* Nature. The same sort of thing happens with any partial system. The behaviour of fishes which are being studied in a tank makes a relatively closed system. Now suppose that the tank is shaken by a bomb in the neighbourhood of the laboratory. The behaviour of the fishes will now be no longer fully explicable by what was going on in the tank before the bomb fell: there will be a failure of backward interlocking. This does not mean that the bomb and the previous history of events within the tank are totally and finally unrelated. It does mean that to find their relation you must go back to the much larger reality which includes both the tank and the bomb – the reality of wartime England in which bombs are falling but some laboratories are still at work. You would never find it within the history of the tank. In the same way, the miracle is not *naturally* interlocked in the backward direction. To find out how it is interlocked with the previous history of Nature you must replace both Nature and the miracle in a larger context. Everything *is* connected with everything else: but not all things are connected by the short and straight roads we expected.

The rightful demand that all reality should be consistent and systematic does not therefore exclude miracles: but it has a very valuable contribution to make to our conception of them. It reminds us that miracles, if they occur, must, like all events, be revelations of that total harmony of all that exists. Nothing arbitrary, nothing simply 'stuck on' and left unreconciled with the texture of total reality, can be admitted. By definition, miracles must of course interrupt the usual course of Nature; but if they are real they must, in the very act of so doing, assert all the more the unity and self-consistency of total reality at some deeper level. They will not be like unmetrical lumps of prose breaking the unity of a poem; they will be like that crowning metrical audacity which, though it may be paralleled nowhere else in the poem, yet, coming just where it does, and effecting just what it effects, is (to those who understand) the supreme revelation of the unity in the poet's conception. If what we call Nature is modified by supernatural power, then we may be sure that the capability of being so modified is of the essence of Nature – that the total events, if we could grasp it, would turn out to involve, by its very character, the possibility of such modifications. If Nature brings forth miracles then doubtless it is as 'natural' for her to do so when impregnated by the masculine force beyond her as it is for a woman to bear children to a man. In calling them miracles we do not mean that they are contradictions or outrages; we mean that, left to her own resources, she could never produce them.

9

A CHAPTER NOT

STRICTLY NECESSARY

And there we saw the giants, the sons of
Anak; which come of the giants: and we
were in our own sight as grasshoppers,
and so we were in their sight
Numbers 13:33

The last two chapters have been concerned with objections to Miracle, made, so to speak, from the side of Nature; made on the ground that she is the sort of system which could not admit miracles. Our next step, if we followed a strict order, would be to consider objections from the opposite side – in fact, to inquire whether what is beyond Nature can reasonably be supposed to be the sort of being that could, or would, work miracles. But I find myself strongly disposed to turn aside and face first an objection of a different sort. It is a purely emotional one; severer readers may skip this chapter. But I know it is one which weighed very heavily with me at a certain period of my life, and if others have passed through the same experience they may care to read of it.

One of the things that held me back from Supernaturalism was a deep repugnance to the view of Nature which, as I thought, Supernaturalism entailed. I passionately desired that Nature should exist 'on her own'. The idea that she had been made, and could be altered, by God, seemed to take from her all that spontaneity which I found so refreshing. In order to breathe freely I wanted to feel that in Nature one reached at last something that simply *was*: the thought that she had been manufactured or 'put there', and put there with a purpose, was suffocating. I wrote a poem in those days about a sunrise, I remember, in which, after describing the scene, I added that some people liked to believe there was a Spirit behind it all and that this Spirit was communicating with them. But, said I, that was exactly what I did not want. The poem was not much good and I have forgotten most of it: but it ended up by saying how much rather I would feel

That in their own right earth and sky
Continually do dance
For their own sakes – and here crept I
To watch the world by chance.

'*By chance!*' – one could not bear to feel that the sunrise had been in any way 'arranged' or had anything to do with oneself. To find that it had not simply happened, that it had been somehow contrived, would be as bad as finding that the fieldmouse I saw beside some lonely hedge was really a clockwork mouse put there to amuse me, or (worse still) to point some moral lesson. The Greek poet asks, 'If water sticks in your throat, what will you take to wash it down?' I likewise asked, 'If Nature herself proves artificial, where will you go to seek wildness? Where is the real out-of-doors?' To find that all the woods, and small streams in the middle of the woods, and odd corners of mountain valleys, and the wind and the grass were only a sort of *scenery*, only backcloths for some kind of play, and that play perhaps one with a moral – what flatness, what an anti-climax, what an unendurable bore!

The cure of this mood began years ago: but I must record that the cure was not complete until I began to study this question of Miracles. At every stage in the writing of this book I have found my idea of Nature becoming more vivid and more concrete. I set out on a work which seemed to involve reducing her status and undermining her walls at every turn: the paradoxical result is a growing sensation that if I am not very careful she will become the heroine of my book. She has never seemed to me more great or more real than at this moment.

The reason is not far to seek. As long as one is a Naturalist, 'Nature' is only a word for 'everything'. And Everything is not a subject about which anything very interesting can be said or (save by illusion) felt. One aspect of things strikes us and we talk of the 'peace' of Nature; another strikes us and we talk of her cruelty. And then, because we falsely take her for the ultimate and self-existent Fact and cannot quite repress our high instinct to worship the Self-existent, we are all at sea and our moods fluctuate and Nature means to us whatever we please as the moods select and slur. But everything becomes different when we recognise that Nature is a *creature*, a created thing, with its own particular tang or flavour. There is no need any longer to select and slur. It is not in her, but in Something far beyond her, that all lines meet and all contrasts are explained. It is no more baffling that the creature called Nature should be both fair and cruel than that the first man you meet in the train should be a dishonest grocer and a kind husband. For she is not the Absolute: she is one of the creatures, with her good points and her bad points and her own unmistakable flavour running through them all.

To say that God has created her is not to say that she is unreal, but precisely that she is real. Would you make God less creative than Shakespeare or Dickens? What He creates is created in the round: it is far more concrete than Falstaff or Sam Weller. The theologians certainly tell us that He created Nature freely. They mean that He was not forced to do so by any external necessity. But we must not interpret freedom negatively, as if Nature were a mere construction of parts arbitrarily stuck together. God's creative freedom is to be conceived as the freedom of a poet: the freedom to create a consistent, positive thing with its own inimitable flavour. Shakespeare need not create Falstaff: but if he does, Falstaff *must* be fat. God need not create this Nature. He might have created others, He may have created others. But granted *this* Nature, then doubtless no smallest part of her is there except because it expresses the character He chose to give her. It would be a miserable error to suppose that the dimensions of space and time, the death and rebirth of vegetation, the unity in multiplicity of organisms, the union in opposition of sexes, and the colour of each particular apple in Herefordshire this autumn, were merely a collection of useful devices forcibly welded together. They are the very idiom, almost the facial expression, the smell or taste, of an individual thing. The *quality* of Nature is present in them all just as the Latinity of Latin is present in every inflection or the 'Correggiosity' of Correggio in every stroke of the brush.

Nature is by human (and probably by Divine) standards partly good and partly evil. We Christians believe that she has been corrupted. But the same tang or flavour runs through both her corruptions and her excellences. Everything is in character. Falstaff does not sin in the same way as Othello. Othello's fall bears a close relation to his virtues. If Perdita had fallen she would not have been bad in the same way as Lady Macbeth: if Lady Macbeth had remained good her goodness would have been quite different from that of Perdita. The evils we see in Nature are, so to speak, the evils proper to *this* Nature. Her very character decreed that if she were corrupted the corruption would take this form and not another. The horrors of parasitism and the glories of motherhood are good and evil worked out of the same basic scheme or idea.

I spoke just now about the Latinity of Latin. It is more evident to us than it can have been to the Romans. The Englishness of English is audible only to those who know some other language as well. In the same way and for the same reason, only Supernaturalists really see Nature. You must go a little away from her, and then turn round, and look back. Then at last the true landscape will become visible. You must have tasted, however briefly, the pure water from beyond the world before you can be distinctly conscious of the hot, salty tang of Nature's current. To treat her as God, or as Everything, is to lose the whole pith and pleasure of her. Come out, look back, and then you will see ... this astonishing cataract of bears, babies, and bananas: this immoderate deluge of atoms, orchids, oranges, cancers, canaries, fleas, gases, tornadoes and toads. How could you ever have thought this was the ultimate reality? How could you ever have thought that it was merely a stage-set for the moral drama of men and women? She is herself. Offer her neither worship nor contempt. Meet her and know her. If we are immortal, and if she is doomed (as the scientists tell us) to run down and die, we shall miss this half-shy and half-flamboyant creature, this ogress, this hoyden, this incorrigible fairy, this dumb witch. But the theologians tell us that she, like ourselves, is to be redeemed. The 'vanity' to which she was subjected was her disease, not her essence. She will be cured in character: not tamed (Heaven forbid) nor sterilised. We shall still be able to recognise our old enemy, friend, playfellow and foster-mother, so perfected as to be not less, but more, herself. And that will be a merry meeting.

10

'HORRID RED THINGS'

*We can call the attempt to refute theism by
displaying the continuity of the belief in God
with primitive delusion the method of
Anthropological intimidation.*
EDWYN BEVAN, *Symbolism and Belief*, chap. ii.

I have argued that there is no security against Miracle to be found by the
study of Nature. She is not the whole of reality but only a part; for all we
know she might be a small part. If that which is outside her wishes to invade
her she has, so far as we can see, no defences. But of course many who disbelieve in Miracles would admit all this. Their objection comes from the other
side. They think that the Supernatural would not invade: they accuse those
who say that it has done so of having a childish and unworthy notion of the
Supernatural. They therefore reject all forms of Supernaturalism which assert
such interference and invasions: and specially the form called Christianity,
for in it the Miracles, or at least some Miracles, are more closely bound up
with the fabric of the whole belief than in any other. All the essentials of
Hinduism would, I think, remain unimpaired if you subtracted the miraculous, and the same is almost true of Mohammedanism. But you cannot do
that with Christianity. It is precisely the story of a great Miracle. A naturalistic Christianity leaves out all that is specifically Christian.

The difficulties of the unbeliever do not begin with questions about this
or that particular miracle; they begin much further back. When a man who
has had only the ordinary modern education looks into any authoritative
statement of Christian doctrine, he finds himself face to face with what
seems to him a wholly 'savage' or 'primitive' picture of the universe. He
finds that God is supposed to have had a 'Son', just as if God were a mythological deity like Jupiter or Odin. He finds that this 'Son' is supposed to
have 'come down from Heaven', just as if God had a palace in the sky from
which He had sent down His 'Son' like a parachutist. He finds that this
'Son' then 'descended into Hell' – into some land of the dead under the surface of a (presumably) flat earth – and thence 'ascended' again, as if by a balloon, into his Father's sky-palace, where He finally sat down in a decorated
chair placed a little to His Father's right. Everything seems to presuppose a
conception of reality which the increase of our knowledge has been steadily

refuting for the last two thousand years and which no honest man in his senses could return to today.

It is this impression which explains the contempt, and even disgust, felt by many people for the writings of modern Christians. When once a man is convinced that Christianity *in general* implies a local 'Heaven', a flat earth, and a God who can have children, he naturally listens with impatience to our solutions of particular difficulties and our defences against particular objections. The more ingenious we are in such solutions and defences the more perverse we seem to him. 'Of course,' he says, 'once the doctrines are there, clever people can invent clever arguments to defend them, just as, when once a historian has made a blunder he can go on inventing more and more elaborate theories to make it appear that it was not a blunder. But the real point is that none of these elaborate theories would have been thought of if he had read his documents correctly in the first instance. In the same way, is it not clear that Christian theology would never have come into existence at all if the writers of the New Testament had had the slightest knowledge of what the real universe is actually like?' Thus, at any rate, I used to think myself. The very man who taught me to think – a hard, satirical atheist (ex-Presbyterian) who doted on the *Golden Bough* and filled his house with the products of the Rationalist Press Association – thought in the same way; and he was a man as honest as the daylight, to whom I here willingly acknowledge an immense debt. His attitude to Christianity was for me the starting point of adult thinking; you may say it is bred in my bones. And yet, since those days, I have come to regard that attitude as a total misunderstanding.

Remembering, as I do, from within, the attitude of the impatient sceptic, I realise very well how he is forearmed against anything I may say for the rest of this chapter. 'I know exactly what this man is going to do,' he murmurs. 'He is going to start explaining all these mythological statements away. It is the invariable practice of these Christians. On any matter whereon science has not yet spoken and on which they cannot be checked, they will tell you some preposterous fairytale. And then, the moment science makes a new advance and shows (as it invariably does) their statement to be untrue, they suddenly turn round and explain that they didn't mean what they said, that they were using a poetic metaphor or constructing an allegory, and that all they really intended was some harmless moral platitude. We are sick of this theological thimble-rigging'. Now I have a great deal of sympathy with that sickness and I freely admit that 'modernist' Christianity has constantly played just the game of which the impatient sceptic accuses it. But I also think there is a kind of explaining which is not explaining away. In one sense I am going to do just what the sceptic thinks I am going to do: that is, I am going to distinguish what I regard as the 'core' or 'real meaning' of the doctrines from that in their expression which I regard as inessential and possibly even capable of being changed without damage. But then, what will drop away from the 'real meaning' under my treatment will precisely *not* be the miraculous. It is the core itself, the core scraped as clean of inessentials as we can scrape it, which remains for me entirely miraculous, supernatural – nay, if you will, 'primitive' and even 'magical'.

In order to explain this I must now touch on a subject which has an importance quite apart from our present purpose and of which everyone who wishes to think clearly should make himself master as soon as he possibly can. And he ought to begin by reading Mr Owen Barfield's *Poetic Diction* and Mr Edwyn Bevan's *Symbolism and Belief*. But for the present argument it will be enough to leave the deeper problems on one side and proceed in a 'popular' and unambitious manner.

When I think about London I usually see a mental picture of Euston Station. But when I think (as I do) that London has several million inhabitants, I do not mean that there are several million images of people contained in my image of Euston Station. Nor do I mean that several millions of real people live in the real Euston Station. In fact though I have the image while I am thinking about London, what I think or say is not *about* that image, and would be manifest nonsense if it were. It makes sense because it is not about my own mental pictures but about the real London, outside my imagination, of which no one can have an adequate mental picture at all. Or again, when we say that the Sun is ninety-odd million miles away, we understand perfectly clearly what we mean by this number; we can divide and multiply it by other numbers and we can work out how long it would take to travel that distance at any given speed. But this clear *thinking* is accompanied by *imagining* which is ludicrously false to what we know that the reality must be.

To think, then, is one thing, and to imagine is another. What we think or say can be, and usually is, quite different from what we imagine or picture; and what we mean may be true when the mental images that accompany it are entirely false. It is, indeed, doubtful whether anyone except an extreme visualist who is also a trained artist ever has mental images which are particularly like the things he is thinking about.

In these examples the mental image is not only unlike the reality but is known to be unlike it, at least after a moment's reflection. I know that London is not merely Euston Station. Let us now go on to a slightly different predicament. I once heard a lady tell her young daughter that you would die if you ate too many tablets of aspirin. 'But why?' asked the child, 'it isn't poisonous'. 'How do you know it isn't poisonous?' said the mother. 'Because', said the child, 'when you crush an aspirin tablet you don't find horrid red things inside it'. Clearly, when this child thought of poison she had a mental picture of Horrid Red Things, just as I have a picture of Euston when I think of London. The difference is that whereas I know my image to be very unlike the real London, the child thought that poison was *really red*. To that extent she was mistaken. But this does not mean that everything she thought or said about poison was necessarily nonsensical. She knew perfectly well that a poison was something which killed you or made you ill if you swallowed it; and she knew, to some extent, which of the substances in her mother's house were poisonous. If a visitor to that house had been warned by the child, 'Don't drink that. Mother says it is poison', he would have been ill advised to neglect the warning on the ground that 'This child has a primitive idea of poison as Horrid Red Things, which my adult scientific knowledge has long since refuted.'

We can now add to our previous statement (that thinking may be sound where the images that accompany it are false) the further statement: thinking may be sound in certain respects where it is accompanied not only by false images but by false images mistaken for true ones.

There is still a third situation to be dealt with. In our two previous examples we have been concerned with thought and imagination, but not with language. I had to picture Euston Station, but I did not need to *mention* it; the child thought that poison was Horrid Red Things, but she could talk about poison without saying so. But very often when we are talking about something which is not perceptible by the five senses we use words which, in one of their meanings, refer to things or actions that are. When a man says that he grasps an argument he is using a verb (*grasp*) which literally means to take something in the hands, but he is certainly not thinking that his mind has hands or that an argument can be seized like a gun. To avoid the word *grasp* he may change the form of expression and say, 'I see your point,' but he does not mean that a pointed object has appeared in his visual field. He may have a third shot and say, 'I follow you,' but he does not mean that he is walking behind you along a road. Everyone is familiar with this linguistic phenomenon and the grammarians call it metaphor. But it is a serious mistake to think that metaphor is an optional thing which poets and orators may put into their work as a decoration and plain speakers can do without. The truth is that if we are going to talk at all about things which are not perceived by the senses, we are forced to use language metaphorically. Books on psychology or economics or politics are as continuously metaphorical as books of poetry or devotion. There is no other way of talking, as every philologist is aware. Those who wish can satisfy themselves on the point by reading the books I have already mentioned and the other books to which those two will lead them on. It is a study for a lifetime and I must here content myself with the mere statement; all speech about supersensibles is, and must be, metaphorical in the highest degree.

We have now three guiding principles before us. (1) That thought is distinct from the imagination which accompanies it. (2) That thought may be in the main sound even when the false images that accompany it are mistaken by the thinker for true ones. (3) That anyone who talks about things that cannot be seen, or touched, or heard, or the like, must inevitably talk as *if they could be* seen or touched or heard (e.g. must talk of 'complexes' and 'repressions' *as if* desires could really be tied up in bundles or shoved back; of 'growth' and 'development' *as if* institutions could really grow like trees or unfold like flowers; of energy being 'released' *as if* it were an animal let out of a cage).

Let us now apply this to the 'savage' or 'primitive' articles of the Christian creed. And let us admit at once that many Christians (though by no means all) when they make these assertions do have in mind just those crude mental pictures which so horrify the sceptic. When they say that Christ 'came down from Heaven' they do have a vague image of something shooting or floating downwards out of the sky. When they say that Christ is the 'Son' of 'the Father' they may have a picture of two human forms, the one looking rather older than the other. But we now know that the mere presence of these mental pictures does not, of itself, tell us anything about the reasonableness or absurdity of the thoughts they accompany. If absurd images meant absurd thought, then we should all be thinking nonsense all the time. And the Christians themselves make it clear that the images are not to be identified with the thing believed. They may picture the Father as a human form, but they also maintain that He has no body. They may picture Him older than the son, but they also maintain the one did not exist before the other, both having existed from all eternity. I am speaking, of course, about Christian adults. Christianity is not to be judged from the fancies of children any more than medicine from the ideas of the little girl who believed in horrid red things.

At this stage I must turn aside to deal with a rather simple-minded illusion. When we point out that what the Christians mean is not to be identified with their mental pictures, some people say, 'In that case, would it not be better to get rid of the mental pictures, and of the language which suggests them, altogether?' But this is impossible. The people who recommend it have not noticed that when they try to get rid of man-like, or as they are called, 'anthropomorphic', images they merely succeed in substituting images of some other kind. 'I don't believe in a personal God,' says one, 'but I do believe in a great spiritual force'. What he has not noticed is that the word 'force' has let in all sorts of images about winds and tides and electricity and gravitation. 'I don't believe in a personal God,' says another, 'but I do believe we are all parts of one great Being which moves and works through us all' – not noticing that he has merely exchanged the image of a fatherly and royal-looking man for the image of some widely extended gas or fluid. A girl

I knew was brought up by 'higher thinking' parents to regard God as a perfect 'substance'; in later life she realised that his had actually led her to think of Him as something like a vast tapioca pudding. (To make matters worse, she disliked tapioca.) We may feel ourselves quite safe from this degree of absurdity, but we are mistaken. If a man watches his own mind, I believe he will find that what profess to be specially advanced or philosophic conceptions of God are, in his thinking, always accompanied by vague images which, if inspected, would turn out to be even more absurd than the man-like images aroused by Christian theology. For man, after all, is the highest of the things we meet in sensuous experience. He has, at least, conquered the globe, honoured (though not followed) virtue, achieved knowledge, made poetry, music and art. If God exists at all it is not unreasonable to suppose that we are less unlike Him than anything else we know. No doubt we are unspeakably different from Him; to that extent all man-like images are false. But those images of shapeless mists and irrational forces which, unacknowledged, haunt the mind when we think we are rising to the conception of impersonal and absolute Being, must be very much more so. For images, of the one kind or of the other, will come; we cannot jump off our own shadow.

As far, then, as the adult Christian of modern times is concerned, the absurdity of the images does not imply absurdity in the doctrines; but it may be asked whether the early Christian was in the same position. Perhaps he mistook the images for true ones, and really believed in the sky-palace or the decorated chair. But as we have seen from the example of the Horrid Red Things, even this would not necessarily invalidate everything that he thought on these subjects. The child in our example might know many truths about poison and even, in some particular cases, truths which a given adult might not know. We can suppose a Galilean peasant who thought that Christ had literally and physically 'sat down at the right hand of the Father'. If such a man had then gone to Alexandria and had a philosophical education he would have discovered that the Father had no right hand and did not sit on a throne. Is it conceivable that he would regard this as making any difference to what he had really intended and valued, in the doctrine during the days of his naïvety? For unless we suppose him to have been not only a peasant but a fool (two very different things) physical details about a supposed celestial throne-room would not have been what he cared about. What mattered must have been the belief that a person whom he had known as a man in Palestine had, as a person, survived death and was now operating as the supreme agent of the supernatural Being who governed and maintained the whole field of reality. And that belief would survive substantially unchanged after the falsity of the earlier images had been recognised.

Even if it could be shown, then, that the early Christians accepted their imagery literally, this would not mean that we are justified in relegating their doctrines as a whole to the lumber-room. Whether they actually did, is another matter. The difficulty here is that they were not writing as philosophers to satisfy speculative curiosity about the nature of God and of the universe. They *believed* in God; and once a man does that, philosophical definiteness can never be the *first* necessity. A drowning man does not analyse the rope that is flung at him, nor an impassioned lover consider the chemistry of his mistress's complexion. Hence the sort of question we are now considering is never raised by the New Testament writers. When once it is raised, Christianity decides quite clearly that the naïf images are false. The sect in the Egyptian desert which thought that God was like a man is condemned: the desert monk who felt he had lost something by its correction is recognised as 'muddle-headed'.[1] All three Persons of the Trinity are declared 'incomprehensible'.[2] God is pronounced 'inexpressible, unthinkable, invisible to all created beings'.[3] The Second Person is not only bodiless but so unlike man that if self-revelation had been His sole purpose He would not have chosen to be incarnate in a human form.[4] We do not find similar statements in the New Testament, because the issue has not yet been made explicit: but we do find statements which make it certain how that issue will be decided when once it becomes explicit. The title 'Son' may sound 'primitive' or 'naïf'. But already in the New Testament this 'Son' is identified with the Discourse or Reason or Word which was eternally 'with God' and yet also *was* God.[5] He is the all-pervasive principle of concretion or cohesion whereby the universe holds together.[6] All things, and specially Life, arose *within* Him,[7] and within Him all things will reach their conclusion – the final statement of what they have been trying to express.[8]

It is, of course, always possible to imagine an earlier stratum of Christianity from which such ideas were absent; just as it is always possible to say that anything you dislike in Shakespeare was put in by an 'adapter' and the original play was free from it. But what have such assumptions to do with serious inquiry? And here the fabrication of them is specially perverse, since even if we go back beyond Christianity into Judaism itself, we shall not find the unambiguous anthropomorphism (or man-likeness) we are looking for. Neither, I admit, shall we find its denial. We shall find, on the one hand, God pictured as living above 'in the high and holy place': we shall

---

[1] *Senex mente confusus* Cassian quoted in Gibbon, cap. xlvii.
[2] Athanasian Creed.
[3] St Chrysostom *De Incomprehensibili* quoted in Otto, *Idea of the Holy*, Appendix 1.
[4] Athanasius *De Incarnatione* viii.
[5] John 1:1.
[6] Colossians 1:17.
[7] Colossians 1 ἐν αὐτῷ ἐκτίσθη. John 1:4.
[8] Ephesians 1:10.

find, on the other, 'Do not I fill heaven and earth? saith the Lord'.[9] We shall find that in Ezekiel's vision God appeared (notice the hesitating words) in 'the likeness as the appearance of a man'.[10] But we shall find also the warning, 'Take ye therefore good heed unto yourselves. For ye saw no manner of similitude on the day that the Lord spake unto you in Horeb out of the midst of the fire – lest ye corrupt yourselves and make a graven image'.[11] Most baffling of all to a modern literalist, the God who seems to live locally in the sky, also *made* it.[12]

The reason why the modern literalist is puzzled is that he is trying to get out of the old writers something which is not there. Starting from a clear modern distinction between material and immaterial he tries to find out on which side of that distinction the ancient Hebrew conception fell. He forgets that the distinction itself has been made clear only by later thought.

We are often told that primitive man could not conceive pure spirit; but then neither could he conceive mere matter. A throne and a local habitation are attributed to God only at that stage when it is still impossible to regard the throne, or palace even of an earthly king as merely physical objects. In earthly thrones and palaces it was the spiritual significance – as we should say, the 'atmosphere' – that mattered to the ancient mind. As soon as the contrast of 'spiritual' and 'material' was before their minds, they knew God to be 'spiritual' and realised that their religion had implied this all along. But at an earlier stage that contrast was not there. To regard that earlier stage as unspiritual because we find there no clear assertion of unembodied spirit, is a real misunderstanding. You might just as well call it spiritual because it contained no clear consciousness of mere matter. Mr Barfield has shown, as regards the history of language, that words did not start by referring merely to physical objects and then get extended by metaphor to refer to emotions, mental states and the like. On the contrary, what we now call the 'literal and metaphorical' meanings have both been disengaged by analysis from an ancient unity of meaning which was neither or both. In the same way it is quite erroneous to think that man started with a 'material' God or 'Heaven' and gradually spiritualised them. He could not have started with something 'material' for the 'material', as we understand it, comes to be realised only by contrast to the 'immaterial', and the two sides of the contrast grow at the same speed. He started with something which was neither and both. As long as we are trying to read back into that ancient unity either the one or the other of the two opposites which have since been analysed out of it, we shall

---

[9] Jeremiah 23:24.
[10] Ezekiel 1:26.
[11] Deuteronomy 4:15.
[12] Genesis 1:1.

misread all early literature and ignore many states of consciousness which we ourselves still from time to time experience. The point is crucial not only for the present discussion but for any sound literary criticism or philosophy.

The Christian doctrines, and even the Jewish doctrines which preceded them, have always been statements about spiritual reality, not specimens of primitive physical science. Whatever is positive in the conception of the spiritual has always been contained in them; it is only its negative aspect (immateriality) which has had to wait for recognition until abstract thought was fully developed. The material imagery has never been taken literally by anyone who had reached the stage when he could understand what 'taking it literally' meant. And now we come to the difference between 'explaining' and 'explaining away'. It shows itself in two ways. (1) Some people when they say that a thing is meant 'metaphorically' conclude from this that it is hardly meant at all. They rightly think that Christ spoke metaphorically when he told us to carry the cross: they wrongly conclude that carrying the cross means nothing more than leading a respectable life and subscribing moderately to charities. They reasonably think that hell 'fire' is a metaphor – and unwisely conclude that it means nothing more serious than remorse. They say that the story of the Fall in Genesis is not literal; and then go on to say (I have heard them myself) that it was really a fall upwards – which is like saying that because 'My heart is broken' contains a metaphor, it therefore means 'I feel very cheerful'. This mode of interpretation I regard, frankly, as nonsense. For me the Christian doctrines which are 'metaphorical' – or which have become metaphorical with the increase of abstract thought – mean something which is just as 'supernatural' or shocking after we have removed the ancient imagery as it was before. They mean that in addition to the physical or psycho-physical universe known to the sciences, there exists an uncreated and unconditioned reality which causes the universe to be; that this reality has a positive structure or constitution which is usefully, though doubtless not completely, described in the doctrine of the Trinity; and that this reality, at a definite point in time, entered the universe we know by becoming one of its own creatures and there produced effects on the historical level which the normal workings of the natural universe do not produce; and that this has brought about a change in our relations to the unconditioned reality. It will be noticed that our colourless 'entered the universe' is not a whit less metaphorical than the more picturesque 'came down from Heaven'. We have only substituted a picture of horizontal or unspecified movement for one of vertical movement. And every attempt to improve the ancient language will have the same result. These things not only cannot be asserted – they cannot even be presented for discussion – without metaphor. We can make our speech duller; we cannot make it more literal. (2) These statements concern two things – the supernatural, unconditioned reality, and those events on the historical level which its irruption into the natural universe is held to have produced. The first thing is indescribable in 'literal' speech, and therefore we rightly interpret all that is said about it metaphorically. But the second thing is in a wholly different position. Events on the historical level are the sort of things we can talk about literally. If they occurred, they were perceived by the senses of men. Legitimate 'explanation' degenerates into muddled or dishonest 'explaining away' as soon as we start applying to these events the metaphorical interpretation which we rightly apply to the statements about God. The assertion that God has a Son was never intended to mean that He is a being propagating His kind by sexual intercourse: and so we do not alter Christianity by rendering explicit the fact that 'sonship' is not used of Christ in exactly the same sense in which it is used of men. But the assertion that Jesus turned water into wine was meant perfectly literally, for this refers to something which, if it happened, was well within the reach of our senses and our language. When I say, 'My heart is broken,' you know perfectly well that I don't mean anything you could verify at a post-mortem. But when I say, 'My bootlace is broken,' then, if your own observation shows it to be intact, I am either lying or mistaken. The accounts of the 'miracles' in first-century Palestine are either lies, or legends, or history. And if all, or the most important, of them are lies or legends then the claim which Christianity has been making for the last two thousand years is simply false. No doubt it might even so contain noble sentiments and moral truths. So does Greek mythology; so does Norse. But that is quite a different affair.

Nothing in this chapter helps us to a decision about the probability or improbability of the Christian claim. We have merely removed a misunderstanding in order to secure for that question a fair hearing.

CHRISTIANITY AND
'RELIGION'

*Those who make religion their god will
not have God for their religion.*
THOMAS ERSKINE OF LINLATHEN

Having eliminated the confusions which come from ignoring the relations of thought, imagination, and speech, we may now return to our
question. The Christians say that God has done miracles. The modern
world, even when it believes in God, and even when it has seen the defence-
lessness of Nature, does not. It thinks God would not do that sort of thing.
Have we any reason for supposing that the modern world is right? I agree
that the sort of God conceived by the popular 'religion' of our own times
would almost certainly work no miracles. The question is whether that popular religion is at all likely to be true.

I call it 'religion' advisedly. We who defend Christianity find ourselves
constantly opposed not by the irreligion of our hearers but by their real religion. Speak about beauty, truth and goodness, or about a God who is simply
the indwelling principle of these three, speak about a great spiritual force
pervading all things, a common mind of which we are all parts, a pool of
generalised spirituality to which we can all flow, and you will command
friendly interest. But the temperature drops as soon as you mention a God
who has purposes and performs particular actions, who does one thing and
not another, a concrete, choosing, commanding, prohibiting God with a
determinate character. People become embarrassed or angry. Such a conception seems to them primitive and crude and even irreverent. The popular
'religion' excludes miracles because it excludes the 'living God' of
Christianity and believes instead in a kind of God who obviously would not
do miracles, or indeed anything else. This popular 'religion' may roughly be
called Pantheism, and we must now examine its credentials.

In the first place it is usually based on a quite fanciful picture of the history of religion. According to this picture, Man starts by inventing 'spirits'
to explain natural phenomena; and at first he imagines these spirits to be
exactly like himself. As he gets more enlightened they become less man-like,

less 'anthropomorphic' as the scholars call it. Their anthropomorphic attributes drop off one by one – first the human shape, the human passions, the personality, will, activity – in the end every concrete or positive attribute whatever. There is left in the end a pure abstraction – mind as such, spirituality as such. God, instead of being a particular entity with a real character of its own, becomes simply 'the whole show' looked at in a particular way or the theoretical point at which all the lines of human aspiration would meet if produced to infinity. And since, on the modern view, the final stage of anything is the most refined and civilised stage, this 'religion' is held to be a more profound, more spiritual, and more enlightened belief than Christianity.

Now this imagined history of religion is not true. Pantheism certainly is (as its advocates would say) congenial to the modern mind; but the fact that a shoe slips on easily does not prove that it is a new shoe – much less that it will keep your feet dry. Pantheism is congenial to our minds not because it is the final stage in a slow process of enlightenment, but because it is almost as old as we are. It may even be the most primitive of all religions, and the *orenda* of a savage tribe has been interpreted by some to be an 'all-pervasive spirit'. It is immemorial in India. The Greeks rose above it only at their peak, in the thought of Plato and Aristotle; their successors relapsed into the great Pantheistic system of the Stoics. Modern Europe escaped it only while she remained predominantly Christian; with Giordano Bruno and Spinoza it returned. With Hegel it became almost the agreed philosophy of highly educated people, while the more popular Pantheism of Wordsworth, Carlyle and Emerson conveyed the same doctrine to those on a slightly lower cultural level. So far from being the final religious refinement, Pantheism is in fact the permanent natural bent of the human mind; the permanent ordinary level below which man sometimes sinks, under the influence of priestcraft and superstition, but above which his own unaided efforts can never raise him for very long. Platonism and Judaism, and Christianity (which has incorporated both) have proved the only things capable of resisting it. It is the attitude into which the human mind automatically falls when left to itself. No wonder we find it congenial. If 'religion' means simply what man says about God, and not what God does about man, then Pantheism almost *is* religion. And 'religion' in that sense has, in the long run, only one really formidable opponent – namely Christianity.[1] Modern philosophy has rejected Hegel and modern science started out with no bias in favour of religion; but they

---

[1] Hence, if a Minister of Education professes to value religion and at the same time takes steps to suppress Christianity, it does not necessarily follow that he is a hypocrite or even (in the ordinary this-wordly sense of the word) a fool. He may sincerely desire more 'religion' and rightly see that the suppression of Christianity is a necessary preliminary to his design.

have both proved quite powerless to curb the human impulse toward Pantheism. It is nearly as strong today as it was in ancient India or in ancient Rome. Theosophy and the worship of the life-force are both forms of it: even the German worship of a racial spirit is only Pantheism truncated or whittled down to suit barbarians. Yet, by a strange irony, each new relapse into this immemorial 'religion' is hailed as the last word in novelty and emancipation.

This native bent of the mind can be paralleled in quite a different field of thought. Men believed in atoms centuries before they had any experimental evidence of their existence. It was apparently natural to do so. And the sort of atoms we naturally believe in are little hard pellets – just like the hard substances we meet in experience, but too small to see. The mind reaches this conception by an easy analogy from grains of sand or of salt. It explains a number of phenomena; and we feel at home with atoms of that sort – we can picture them. The belief would have lasted forever if later science had not been so troublesome as to find out what atoms are *really* like. The moment it does that, all our mental comfort, all the immediate plausibility and obviousness of the old atomic theory, is destroyed. The real atoms turn out to be quite alien from our natural mode of thought. They are not even made of hard 'stuff' or 'matter' (as the imagination understands 'matter') at all: they are not simple, but have a structure: they are not all the same: and they are unpicturable. The old atomic theory is in physics what Pantheism is in religion – the normal, instinctive guess of the human mind, not utterly wrong, but needing correction. Christian theology, and quantum physics, are both, by comparison with the first guess, hard, complex, dry and repellent. The first shock of the object's real nature, breaking in on our spontaneous dreams of what that object ought to be, always has these characteristics. You must not expect Schrödinger to be as plausible as Democritus; he knows too much. You must not expect St Athanasius to be as plausible as Mr Bernard Shaw: he also knows too much.

The true state of the question is often misunderstood because people compare an adult knowledge of Pantheism with a knowledge of Christianity which they acquired in their childhood. They thus get the impression that Christianity gives the 'obvious' account of God, the one that is too easy to be true, while Pantheism offers something sublime and mysterious. In reality, it is the other way round. The apparent profundity of Pantheism thinly veils a mass of spontaneous picture-thinking and owes its plausibility to that fact. Pantheists and Christians agree that God is present everywhere. Pantheists conclude that He is 'diffused' or 'concealed' in all things and therefore a universal medium rather that a concrete entity, because their minds are really dominated by the picture of a gas, or fluid, or space itself. The Christian, on the other hand, deliberately rules out such images by saying that God is totally present at every point of space and time, and *locally* present in none. Again the Pantheist and Christian agree that we are all dependent on God and intimately related to Him. But the Christian defines this relation in terms of Maker and made, whereas the Pantheist (at least of the popular kind) says, we are 'parts' of Him, or are contained in Him. Once more, the picture of a vast extended something which can be divided into areas has crept in. Because of this fatal picture Pantheism concludes that God must be equally present in what we call evil and what we call good and therefore indifferent to both (ether permeates the mud and the marble impartially). The Christian has to reply that this is far too simple; God is present in a great many different modes: not present in matter as He is present in man, not present in all men as in some, not present in any other man as in Jesus. Pantheist and Christian also agree that God is super-personal. The Christian means by this that God has a positive structure which we could never have guessed in advance, any more than a knowledge of squares would have enabled us to guess at a cube. He contains 'persons' (three of them) while remaining one God, as a cube contains six squares while remaining one solid body. We cannot comprehend such a structure any more than the Flatlanders could comprehend a cube. But we can at least comprehend our incomprehension, and see that if there is something beyond personality it *ought* to be incomprehensible in that sort of way. The Pantheist, on the other hand, though he may say 'super-personal' really conceives God in terms of what is sub-personal – as though the Flatlanders thought a cube existed in *fewer* dimensions than a square.

At every point Christianity has to correct the natural expectations of the Pantheist and offer something more difficult, just as Schrödinger has to correct Democritus. At every moment he has to multiply distinctions and rule out false analogies. He has to substitute the mappings of something that has a positive, concrete, and highly articulated character for the formless generalities in which Pantheism is at home. Indeed, after the discussion has been going on for some time, the Pantheist is apt to change his ground and where he before accused us of childish naïvety now to blame us for the pedantic complexity of our 'cold Christs and tangled Trinities'. And we may well sympathise with him. Christianity, faced with popular 'religion' is continuously troublesome. To the large well-meant statements of 'religion' it finds itself forced to reply again and again, 'Well, not quite like that,' or 'I should hardly put it that way'. This troublesomeness does not of course prove it to be true; but if it were true it would be bound to have this troublesomeness. The real musician is similarly troublesome to a man who wishes to indulge in untaught 'musical appreciation'; the real historian is similarly a nuisance when we want to romance about 'the old days' or ' the ancient Greeks and Romans'. The ascertained nature of any real thing is always at first a nuisance to our natural fantasies – a wretched, pedantic, logic-chopping intruder upon a conversation which was getting on famously without it.

But 'religion' also claims to base itself on experience. The experiences of the mystics (that ill-defined but popular class) are held to indicate that God is the God of 'religion' rather than of Christianity; that He – or It – is not a concrete Being but 'being in general' about which nothing can be truly asserted. To everything which we try to say about Him, the mystics tend to reply, 'Not thus'. What all these negatives of the mystics really mean I shall consider in a moment: but I must first point out why it seems to me impossible that they should be true in the sense popularly understood.

It will be agreed that, however they came there, concrete, individual, determinate things do now exist: things like flamingoes, German generals, lovers, sandwiches, pineapples, comets and kangaroos. These are not mere principles or generalities or theorems, but things – facts – real, resistant existences. One might even say *opaque* existences, in the sense that each contains something which our intelligence cannot completely digest. In so far as they illustrate general laws it can digest them: but then they are never mere illustrations. Above and beyond that there is in each of them the 'opaque' brute fact of existence, the fact that it is actually there and is itself. Now this opaque fact, this concreteness, is not in the least accounted for by the laws of Nature or even by the laws of thought. Every law can be reduced to the form 'If A, then B'. Laws give us only a universe of 'Ifs and Ands': not this universe which actually exists. What we know through laws and general principles is a series of connections. But in order for there to be a real universe the connections must be given something to connect; a torrent of opaque actualities must be fed into the pattern. If God created the world, then He is precisely the source of this torrent, and it alone gives our truest principles anything to be true *about*. But if God is the ultimate source of all concrete, individual things and events, then God Himself must be concrete, and individual in the highest degree. Unless the origin of all other things were itself concrete and individual, nothing else could be so; for there is no conceivable means whereby what is abstract or general could itself produce concrete reality. Bookkeeping, continued to all eternity, could never produce one farthing. Metre, of itself, could never produce a poem. Bookkeeping needs something else (namely, real money put into the account) and metre needs something else (real words, fed into it by a poet) before any income or any poem can exist. If anything is to exist at all, then the Original Thing must be, not a principle nor a generality, much less an 'ideal' or a 'value', but an utterly concrete fact.

Probably no thinking person would, in so many words, deny that God is concrete and individual. But not all thinking people, and certainly not all who believe in 'religion', keep this truth steadily before their minds. We must beware, as Professor Whitehead says, of paying God ill-judged 'metaphysical compliments'. We say that God is 'infinite'. In the sense that His knowledge and power extend not to some things but to all, this is true. But if by using the word 'infinite' we encourage ourselves to think of Him as a formless 'everything' about whom nothing in particular and everything in general is true, then it would be better to drop that word altogether. Let us dare to say that God is a particular Thing. Once He was the only Thing: but He is creative. He made other things to be. He is not those other things. He is not 'universal being': if He were there would be no creatures, for a generality can make nothing. He is 'absolute being' – or rather *the* Absolute Being – in the sense that He alone exists in His own right. But there are things which God is not. In that sense He has a determinate character. Thus He is righteous, not amoral; creative, not inert. The Hebrew writings here observe an admirable balance. Once God says simply I AM, proclaiming the mystery of self-existence. But times without number He says 'I am the Lord' – I, the ultimate Fact, have *this* determinate character, and not *that*. And men are exhorted to ' know the Lord', to discover and experience this particular character.

The error which I am here trying to correct is one of the most sincere and respectable errors in the world; I have sympathy enough with it to feel shocked at the language I have been driven to use in stating the opposite view, which I believe to be the true one. To say that God 'is a particular Thing' does seem to obliterate the immeasurable difference not only between what He is and what all other things are but between the very mode of His existence and theirs. I must at once restore the balance by insisting that derivative things, from atoms to archangels, hardly attain to existence at all in comparison with their Creator. Their principle of existence is not in themselves. You can distinguish *what* they are from the fact *that* they are. The definition of them can be understood and a clear idea of them formed without even knowing *whether* they are. Existence is an 'opaque' addition to the idea of them. But with God it is not so: if we fully understood *what* God is we should see that there is no question *whether* He is. It would always have been impossible that He should not exist. He is the opaque centre of all existences, the thing that simply and entirely *is*, the fountain of facthood. And yet, now that He has created, there is a sense in which we must say that He is a particular Thing and even one Thing among others. To say this is not to lessen the immeasurable difference between Him and them. On the contrary, it is to recognise in Him a positive perfection which Pantheism has obscured; the perfection of being creative. He is so brimfull of existence that He can give existence away, can cause things to be, and to be really other than Himself, can make it untrue to say that He is everything.

It is clear that there never was a time when nothing existed; otherwise nothing would exist now. But to exist means to be a positive Something, to have (metaphorically) a certain shape or structure, to be this and not that. The Thing which always existed, namely God, has therefore always had His own positive character. Throughout all eternity certain statements about Him would have been true and others false. And from the mere fact of our own existence and Nature's we already know to some extent which are which. We know that He invents, acts, creates. After that there can be no ground for assuming in advance that He does not do miracles.

Why, then, do the mystics talk of Him as they do, and why are many people prepared in advance to maintain that, whatever else God may be, He is not the concrete, living, willing, and acting God of Christian theology? I think the reason is as follows. Let us suppose a mystical limpet, a sage among limpets, who (rapt in vision) catches a glimpse of what Man is like. In reporting it to his disciples, who have some vision themselves (though less than he) he will have to use many negatives. He will have to tell them that Man has no shell, is not attached to a rock, is not surrounded by water. And his disciples, having a little vision of their own to help them, do get some idea of Man. But then there come erudite limpets, limpets who write histories of philosophy and give lectures on comparative religion, and who have never had any vision of their own. What they get out of the prophetic limpet's words is simply and solely the negatives. From these, uncorrected by any positive insight, they build up a picture of Man as a sort of amorphous jelly (he has no shell) existing nowhere in particular (he is not attached to a rock) and never taking nourishment (there is no water to drift it towards him). And having a traditional reverence for Man they conclude that to be a famished jelly in a dimensionless void is the supreme mode of existence, and reject as crude, materialistic superstition any doctrine which would attribute to Man a definite shape, a structure, and organs.

Our own situation is much like that of the erudite limpets. Great prophets and saints have an intuition of God which is positive and concrete in the highest degree. Because, just touching the fringes of His being, they have seen that He is plenitude of life and energy and joy, therefore (and for no other reason) they have to pronounce that He transcends those limitations which we call personality, passion, change, materiality, and the like. The positive quality in Him which repels these limitations is their only ground for all the negatives. But when we come limping after and try to construct an intellectual or 'enlightened' religion, we take over these negatives (infinite, immaterial, impassible, immutable, etc.) and use them unchecked by any positive intuition. At each step we have to strip off from our idea of God some human attribute. But the only real reason for stripping off the human attribute is to make room for putting in some positive divine attribute. In St Paul's language, the purpose of all this unclothing is not that our idea of God should reach nakedness but that it should be reclothed. But unhappily we have no means of doing the reclothing. When we have removed from our idea of God some puny human characteristic, we (as merely erudite or intelligent enquirers) have no resources from which to supply that blindingly real and concrete attribute of Deity which ought to replace it. Thus at each step in the process of refinement our idea of God contains less, and the fatal pictures come in (an endless, silent sea, an empty sky beyond all stars, a dome of white radiance) and we reach at last mere zero and worship a nonentity. And the understanding, left to itself, can hardly help following this path. That is why the Christian statement that only He who does the will of the Father will ever know the true doctrine is philosophically accurate. Imagination may help a little: but in the moral life, and (still more) in the devotional life we touch something concrete which will at once begin to correct the growing emptiness of our idea of God. One moment even of feeble contrition or blurred thankfulness will, at least in some degree, head us off from the abyss of abstraction. It is Reason herself which teaches us not to rely on Reason only in this matter. For Reason knows that she cannot work without materials. When it becomes clear that you cannot find out by reasoning whether the cat is in the linen-cupboard, it is Reason herself who whispers, 'Go and look. This is not my job: it is a matter for the senses'. So here. The materials for correcting our abstract conception of God cannot be supplied by Reason: she will be the first to tell you to go and try experience – 'Oh, taste and see!' For of course she will have already pointed out that your present position is absurd. As long as we remain Erudite Limpets we are forgetting that if no one had ever seen more of God than we, we should have no reason even to believe Him immaterial, immutable, impassible and all the rest of it. Even that negative knowledge which seems to us so enlightened is only a relic left over from the positive knowledge of better men – only the pattern which that heavenly wave left on the sand when it retreated.

'A Spirit and a Vision,' said Blake, ' are not, as the modern philosophy supposes, a cloudy vapour, or a nothing. They are organised and minutely articulated beyond all that the mortal and perishing nature can produce'.[2] He is speaking only of how to draw pictures of apparitions which may well have been illusory, but his words suggest a truth on the metaphysical level also. God is basic Fact or Actuality, the source of all other facthood. At all costs therefore He must not be thought of as a featureless generality. If He exists at all, He is the most concrete thing there is, the most individual, 'organised and minutely articulated'. He is unspeakable not by being

[2] *A Descriptive Catalogue.* Number IV.

indefinite but by being too definite for the unavoidable vagueness of language. The words *incorporeal* and *impersonal* are misleading, because they suggest that He lacks some reality which we possess. It would be safer to call Him *trans-corporeal, trans-personal*. Body and personality as we know them are the real negatives – they are what is left of positive being when it is sufficiently diluted to appear in temporal or finite forms. Even our sexuality should be regarded as the transposition into a minor key of that creative joy which in Him is unceasing and irresistible. Grammatically, the things we say of Him are 'metaphorical': but in a deeper sense it is our physical and psychic energies that are mere 'metaphors' of the real Life which is God. Divine Sonship is, so to speak, the solid of which biological sonship is merely a diagrammatic representation on the flat.

And here the subject of imagery, which crossed our path in the last chapter, can be seen in a new light. For it is just the recognition of God's positive and concrete reality which the religious imagery preserves. The crudest Old Testament picture of Jahweh thundering and lightning out of dense smoke, making mountains skip like rams, threatening, promising, pleading, even changing His mind, transmits that sense of *living* Deity which evaporates in abstract thought. Even sub-Christian images – even a Hindu idol with a hundred hands – gets in *something* which mere 'religion' in our own days has left out. We rightly reject it, for by itself it would encourage the most blackguardly of superstitions, the adoration of mere power. Perhaps we may rightly reject much of the Old Testament imagery. But we must be clear why we are doing so: not because the images are too strong but because they are too weak. The ultimate spiritual reality is not vaguer, more inert, more transparent than the images, but more positive, more dynamic, more opaque. Confusion between Spirit and soul (or 'ghost') has here done much harm. Ghosts must be pictured, if we are to picture them at all, as shadowy and tenuous, for ghosts are half-men, one element abstracted from a creature that ought to have flesh. But Spirit, if pictured at all, must be pictured in the very opposite way. Neither God nor even the gods are 'shadowy' in traditional imagination: even the human dead, when glorified in Christ, cease to be 'ghosts' and become 'saints'. The difference of atmosphere which even now surrounds the words 'I saw a ghost' and the words 'I saw a saint' – all the pallor and insubstantiality of the one, all the gold and blue of the other – contains more wisdom than whole libraries of 'religion'. If we must have a mental picture to symbolise Spirit, we should represent it as something *heavier* than matter.

And if we say that we are rejecting the old images in order to do more justice to the moral attributes of God, we must again be careful of what we are really meaning. When we wish to learn of the love and goodness of God by *analogy* – by imagining parallels to them in the realm of human relations –

we turn of course to the parables of Christ. But when we try to conceive the reality as it may be in itself, we must beware lest we interpret 'moral attributes' in terms of mere conscientiousness or abstract benevolence. The mistake is easily made because we (correctly) deny that God has passions; and with us a love that is not passionate means a love that is something less. But the reason why God has no passions is that passions imply passivity and intermission. The passion of love is something that happens to us, as 'getting wet' happens to a body: and God is exempt from that 'passion' in the same way that water is exempt from 'getting wet'. He cannot be affected with love, because He *is* love. To imagine that love as something less torrential or less sharp than our own temporary and derivative 'passions' is a most disastrous fantasy.

Again, we may find a violence in some of the traditional imagery which tends to obscure the changelessness of God, the peace, which nearly all who approach Him have reported – the 'still, small voice'. And it is here, I think, that the pre-Christian imagery is least suggestive. Yet even here, there is a danger lest the half conscious picture of some huge thing at rest – a clear, still ocean, a dome of 'white radiance' – should smuggle in ideas of inertia or vacuity. The stillness in which the mystics approach Him is intent and alert – at the opposite pole from sleep or reverie. They are becoming like Him. Silences in the physical world occur in empty places: but the ultimate Peace is silent through very density of life. Saying is swallowed up in being. There is no movement because His action (which is Himself) is timeless. You might, if you wished, call it movement at an infinite speed, which is the same thing as rest, but reached by a different – perhaps a less misleading – way of approach.

Men are reluctant to pass over from the notion of an abstract and negative deity to the living God. I do not wonder. Here lies the deepest tap-root of Pantheism and of the objection to traditional imagery. It was hated not, at bottom, because it pictured Him as man but because it pictured Him as king, or even as warrior. The Pantheist's God does nothing, demands nothing. He is there if you wish for Him, like a book on a shelf. He will not pursue you. There is no danger that at any time heaven and earth should flee away at His glance. If He were the truth, then we could really say that all the Christian images of kingship were a historical accident of which our religion ought to be cleansed. It is with a shock that we discover them to be indispensable. You have had a shock like that before, in connection with smaller matters – when the line pulls at your hand, when something breathes beside you in the darkness. So here; the shock comes at the precise moment when the thrill of *life* is communicated to us along the clue we have been following. It is always shocking to meet life where we thought we were alone. 'Look out!' we cry, 'it's *alive*'. And therefore this is the very point at which so many draw back – I would have done so myself if I could – and proceed no further with Christianity. An 'impersonal God' – well and good. A subjective God of beauty, truth and goodness, inside our own heads – better still. A formless life-force surging through us, a vast power which we can tap – best of all. But God Himself, alive, pulling at the other end of the cord, perhaps approaching at an infinite speed, the hunter, king, husband – that is quite another matter. There comes a moment when the children who have been playing at burglars hush suddenly: was that a *real* footstep in the hall? There comes a moment when people who have been dabbling in religion ('Man's search for God!') suddenly draw back. Supposing we really found Him? We never meant it to come to *that*! Worse still, supposing He had found us?

So it is a sort of Rubicon. One goes across; or not. But if one does, there is no manner of security against miracles. One may be in for *anything*.

12

THE PROPRIETY
OF MIRACLES

*The Principle at the same moment that it
explains the Rules supersedes them.*
SEELEY, *Ecce Homo*, chap. xvi.

If the ultimate Fact is not an abstraction but the living God, opaque by the
very fullness of His blinding actuality, then He might do things. He
might work miracles. But would He? Many people of sincere piety feel that
He would not. They think it unworthy of Him. It is petty and capricious
tyrants who break their own laws: good and wise kings obey them. Only an
incompetent workman will produce work which needs to be interfered
with. And people who think in this way are not satisfied by the assurance
given them in Chapter VIII that miracles do not, in fact, break the laws of
Nature. That may be undeniable. But it will still be felt (and justly) that miracles interrupt the orderly march of events, the steady development of
Nature according to her own inherent genius or character. That regular
march seems to such critics as I have in mind more impressive than any miracle. Looking up (like Lucifer in Meredith's sonnet) at the night sky, they
feel it almost impious to suppose that God should sometimes unsay what
He has once said with such magnificence. This feeling springs from deep and
noble sources in the mind and must always be treated with respect. Yet it is,
I believe, founded on an error.

When schoolboys begin to be taught to make Latin verses at school they
are very properly forbidden to have what is technically called 'a spondee in
the fifth foot'. It is a good rule for boys because the normal hexameter does
not have a spondee there: if boys were allowed to use this abnormal form
they would be constantly doing it for convenience and might never get the
typical music of the hexameter into their heads at all. But when the boys
come to read Virgil they find that Virgil does the very thing they have been
forbidden to do – not very often, but not so very rarely either. In the same
way, young people who have just learned how to write English rhyming
verse, may be shocked at finding 'bad' rhymes (i.e. half-rhymes) in the great
poets. Even in carpentry or car-driving or surgery there are, I expect,

'licenses' – abnormal ways of doing things – which the master will use himself both safely and judiciously but which he would think it unwise to teach his pupils.

Now one often finds that the beginner, who has just mastered the strict formal rules, is over-punctilious and pedantic about them. And the mere critic, who is never going to begin himself, may be more pedantic still. The classical critics were shocked at the 'irregularity' or 'licenses' of Shakespeare. A stupid schoolboy might think that the abnormal hexameters in Virgil, or the half-rhymes in English poets, were due to incompetence. In reality, of course, every one of them is there for a purpose and breaks the superficial regularity of the metre in obedience to a higher and subtler law: just as the irregularities in *The Winter's Tale* do not impair, but embody and perfect, the inward unity of its spirit.

In other words, there are rules behind the rules, and a unity which is deeper than uniformity. A supreme workman will never break by one note or one syllable or one stroke of the brush the living and inward law of the work he is producing. But he will break without scruple any number of those superficial regularities and orthodoxies which little, unimaginative critics mistake for its laws. The extent to which one can distinguish a just 'license' from a mere botch or failure of unity depends on the extent to which one has grasped the real and inward significance of the work as a whole. If we had grasped as a whole the innermost spirit of that 'work which God worketh from the beginning to the end', and of which Nature is only a part and perhaps a small part, we should be in a position to decide whether miraculous interruptions of Nature's history were mere improprieties unworthy of the Great Workman or expressions of the truest and deepest unity in His total work. In fact, of course, we are in no such position. The gap between God's mind and ours must, on any view, be incalculably greater than the gap between Shakespeare's mind and that of the most peddling critics of the old French school.

For who can suppose that God's external act, seen from within, would be that same complexity of mathematical relations which Nature, scientifically studied, reveals? It is like thinking that a poet builds up his line out of those metrical feet into which we can analyse it, or that living speech takes grammar as its starting point. But the best illustration of all is Bergson's. Let us suppose a race of people whose peculiar mental limitation compels them to regard a painting as something made up of little coloured dots which have been put together like a mosaic. Studying the brushwork of a great painting, through their magnifying glasses, they discover more and more complicated relations between the dots, and sort these relations out, with great toil, into certain regularities. Their labour will not be in vain. These regularities will in fact 'work'; they will cover most of the facts. But if they go on to conclude that any departure from them would be unworthy of the painter, and an arbitrary breaking of his own rules, they will be far astray. For the regularities they have observed never were the rule the painter was following. What they painfully reconstruct from a million dots, arranged in an agonising complexity, he really produced with a single lightning-quick turn of the wrist, his eye meanwhile taking in the canvas as a whole and his mind obeying laws of composition which the observers, counting their dots, have not yet come within sight of, and perhaps never will. I do not say that the normalities of Nature are unreal. The living fountain of divine energy, solidified for purposes of this spatio-temporal Nature into bodies moving in space and time, and thence, by our abstract thought, turned into mathematical formulae, does in fact for us, commonly fall into such and such patterns. In finding out those patterns we are therefore gaining real, and often useful, knowledge. But to think that a disturbance of them would constitute a breach of the living rule and organic unity whereby God, from His own point of view, works, is a mistake. If miracles do occur then we may be sure that *not* to have wrought them would be the real inconsistency.

How a miracle can be no inconsistency, but the highest consistency, will be clear to those who have read Miss Dorothy Sayers' indispensable book, *The Mind of the Maker*. Miss Sayers' thesis is based on the analogy between God's relation to the world, on the one hand, and an author's relation to his book on the other. If you are writing a story, miracles or abnormal events may be bad art, or they may not. If, for example, you are writing an ordinary realistic novel and have got your characters into a hopeless muddle, it would be quite intolerable if you suddenly cut the knot and secured a happy ending by having a fortune left to the hero from an unexpected quarter. On the other hand there is nothing against taking as your subject from the outset the adventures of a man who inherits an unexpected fortune. The unusual event is perfectly permissible if it is what you are really writing *about*: it is an artistic crime if you simply drag it in by the heels to get yourself out of a hole. The ghost story is a legitimate form of art; but you must not bring a ghost into an ordinary novel to get over a difficulty in the plot. Now there is no doubt that a great deal of the modern objection to miracles is based on the suspicion that they are marvels of the wrong sort; that a story of a certain kind (Nature) is arbitrarily interfered with, to get the characters out of a difficulty, by events that do not really belong to that kind of story. Some people probably think of the Resurrection as a desperate last moment expedient to save the Hero from a situation which had got out of the Author's control.

The reader may set his mind at rest. If I thought miracles were like that, I should not believe in them. If they have occurred, they have occurred because they are the very thing this universal story is about. They are not exceptions (however rarely they occur) not irrelevancies. They are precisely those chapters in this great story on which the plot turns. Death and Resurrection are what the story is about; and had we but eyes to see it, this has been hinted on every page, met us, in some disguise, at every turn, and even been muttered in conversations between such minor characters (if they are minor characters) as the vegetables. If you have hitherto disbelieved in miracles, it is worth pausing a moment to consider whether this is not chiefly because you thought you had discovered what the story was really about? – that atoms, and time and space and economics and politics were the main plot? And is it certain you were right? It is easy to make mistakes in such matters. A friend of mine wrote a play in which the main idea was that the hero had a pathological horror of trees and a mania for cutting them down. But naturally other things came in as well; there was some sort of love story mixed up with it. And the trees killed the man in the end. When my friend had written it, he sent it an older man to criticise. It came back with the comment, 'Not bad. But I'd cut out those bits of *padding* about the trees'. To be sure, God might be expected to make a better story than my friend. But it is a very *long* story, with a complicated plot; and we are not, perhaps, very attentive readers.

13

ON PROBABILITY

*Probability is founded on the presumption
of a resemblance between those objects of
which we have had experience and those
of which we have had none; and therefore
it is impossible that this presumption can
arise from probability.*
HUME, *Treatise of Human Nature*, I, iii,vi.

The argument up to date shows that miracles are possible and that there is
nothing antecedently ridiculous in the stories which say that God has
sometimes performed them. This does not mean, of course, that we are committed to believing all stories of miracles. Most stories about miraculous
events are probably false: if it comes to that, most stories about natural events
are false. Lies, exaggerations, misunderstandings and hearsay make up perhaps
more than half of all that is said and written in the world. We must therefore
find a criterion whereby to judge any particular story of the miraculous.

In one sense, of course, our criterion is plain. Those stories are to be
accepted for which the historical evidence is sufficiently good. But then, as
we saw at the outset, the answer to the question, 'How much evidence
should we require for this story?' depends on our answer to the question,
'How far is this story intrinsically probable?' We must therefore find a
criterion of probability.

The ordinary procedure of the modern historian, even if he admits the
possibility of miracle, is to admit no particular instance of it until every possibility of 'natural' explanation has been tried and failed. That is, he will
accept the most improbable 'natural' explanations rather than say that a miracle occurred. Collective hallucination, hypnotism of unconsenting spectators, widespread instantaneous conspiracy in lying by persons not otherwise
known to be liars and not likely to gain by the lie – all these are known to be
very improbable events: so improbable that, except for the special purpose
of excluding a miracle, they are never suggested. But they are preferred to
the admission of a miracle.

Such a procedure is, from the purely historical point of view, sheer midsummer madness *unless* we start by knowing that any Miracle whatever is
more improbable than the most improbable natural event. Do we know this?

We must distinguish the different kinds of improbability. Since miracles are, by definition, rarer than other events, it is obviously improbable beforehand that one will occur at any given place and time. In that sense every miracle is improbable. But that sort of improbability does not make the story that a miracle *has* happened incredible; for in the same sense all events whatever were once improbable. It is immensely improbable beforehand that a pebble dropped from the stratosphere over London will hit any given spot or that any one particular person will win a large lottery. But the report that the pebble has landed outside such and such a shop or that Mr So-and-So has won the lottery is not at all incredible. When you consider the immense number of meetings and fertile unions between ancestors which were necessary in order that you should be born, you perceive that it was once immensely improbable that such a person as you should come to exist: but once you are here, the report of your existence is not in the least incredible. With probability of this kind – antecedent probability of chances – we are not here concerned. Our business is with historical probability.

Ever since Hume's famous *Essay* it has been believed that historical statements about miracles are the most intrinsically improbable of all historical statements. According to Hume, probability rests on what may be called the majority vote of our past experiences. The more often a thing has been known to happen, the more probable it is that it should happen again; and the less often the less probable. Now the regularity of Nature's course, says Hume, is supported by something better than the majority vote of past experiences: it is supported by their unanimous vote, or, as Hume says, by 'firm and unalterable experience'. There is, in fact, 'uniform experience' against Miracle; otherwise, says Hume, it would not be a Miracle. A miracle is therefore the most improbable of all events. It is always more probable that the witnesses were lying or mistaken than that a miracle occurred.

Now of course we must agree with Hume that if there is absolutely 'uniform experience' against miracles, if in other words they have never happened, why then they never have. Unfortunately we know the experience against them to be uniform only if we know that all the reports of them are false. And we can know all the reports to be false only if we know already that miracles have never occurred. In fact, we are arguing in a circle.

There is also an objection to Hume which leads us deeper into our problem. The whole idea of Probability (as Hume understands it) depends on the principle of the Uniformity of Nature. Unless Nature always goes on in the same way, the fact that a thing had happened ten million times would not make it a whit more probable that it would happen again. And how do we know the Uniformity of Nature? A moment's thought shows that we do not know it by experience. We observe many regularities in Nature. But of course all the observations that men have made or will make while the race lasts cover only a minute fraction of the events that actually go on. Our observations would therefore be of no use unless we felt sure that Nature when we are not watching her behaves in the same way as when we are: in other words, unless we believed in the Uniformity of Nature. Experience therefore cannot prove uniformity, because uniformity has to be assumed before experience proves anything. And mere length of experience does not help matters. It is no good saying, 'Each fresh experience confirms our belief in uniformity and therefore we reasonably expect that it will always be confirmed'; for that argument works only on the assumption that the future will resemble the past – which is simply the assumption of Uniformity under a new name. Can we say that Uniformity is at any rate very probable? Unfortunately not. We have just seen that all probabilities depend on *it*. Unless Nature is uniform, nothing is either probable or improbable. And clearly the assumption which you have to make before there is any such thing as probability cannot itself be probable.

The odd thing is that no man knew this better than Hume. His *Essay on Miracles* is quite inconsistent with the more radical, and honourable, scepticism of his main work.

The question, 'Do miracles occur?' and the question, 'Is the course of Nature absolutely uniform?' are the same question asked in two different ways. Hume, by sleight of hand, treats them as two different questions. He first answers 'Yes,' to the question whether Nature is absolutely uniform: and then uses this 'Yes' as a ground for answering, 'No,' to the question, 'Do miracles occur?' The single real question which he set out to answer is never discussed at all. He gets the answer to one form of the question by assuming the answer to another form of the same question.

Probabilities of the kind that Hume is concerned with hold inside the framework of an assumed Uniformity of Nature. When the question of miracles is raised we are asking about the validity or perfection of the frame itself. No study of probabilities inside a given frame can ever tell us how probable it is that the frame itself can be violated. Granted a school timetable with French on Tuesday morning at ten o'clock, it is really probable that Jones, who always skimps his French preparation, will be in trouble next Tuesday, and that he was in trouble on any previous Tuesday. But what does this tell us about the probability of the timetable's being altered? To find that out you must eavesdrop in the masters' common-room. It is no use studying the timetable.

If we stick to Hume's method, far from getting what he hoped (namely, the conclusion that all miracles are infinitely improbable) we get a complete deadlock. The only kind of probability he allows holds exclusively within the frame of uniformity. When uniformity is itself in question (and it is in question the moment we ask whether miracles occur) this kind of probability is suspended. And Hume knows no other. By his method, therefore, we cannot say that uniformity is either probable or improbable; and equally we cannot say that miracles are either probable or improbable. We have impounded *both* uniformity *and* miracles in a sort of limbo where probability and improbability can never come. This result is equally disastrous for the scientist and the theologian; but along Hume's lines there is nothing whatever to be done about it.

Our only hope, then, will be to cast about for some quite different kind of Probability. Let us for the moment cease to ask what right we have to believe in the Uniformity of Nature and ask why in fact men do believe in it. I think the belief has three causes, two of which are irrational. In the first place we are creatures of habit. We expect new situations to resemble old ones. It is a tendency which we share with animals; one can see it working, often to very comic results, in our dogs and cats. In the second place, when we plan our actions, we have to leave out of account the theoretical possibility that Nature might not behave as usual tomorrow, because we can do nothing about it. It is not worth bothering about because no action can be taken to meet it. And what we habitually put out of our minds we soon forget. The picture of uniformity thus comes to dominate our minds without rival and we believe it. Both these causes are irrational and would be just as effective in building up a false belief as in building up a true one.

But I am convinced that there is a third cause. 'In science,' said the late Sir Arthur Eddington, 'we sometimes have convictions which we cherish but cannot justify; we are influenced by some innate sense of the fitness of things'. This may sound a perilously subjective and aesthetic criterion; but can one doubt that it is a principal source of our belief in Uniformity? A universe in which unprecedented and unpredictable events were at every moment flung into Nature would not merely be inconvenient to us: it would be profoundly repugnant. We will not accept such a universe on any terms whatever. It is utterly detestable to us. It shocks our 'sense of the fitness of things'. In advance of experience, in the teeth of many experiences, we are already enlisted on the side of uniformity. For of course science actually proceeds by concentrating not on the regularities of Nature but on her apparent irregularities. It is the apparent irregularity that prompts each new hypothesis. It does so because we refuse to acquiesce in irregularities: we never rest till we have formed and verified a hypothesis which enables us to say that they were not really irregularities at all. Nature as it comes to us looks at first like a mass of irregularities. The stove which lit all right yesterday won't light today; the water which was wholesome last year is poisonous this year. The whole mass of seemingly irregular experience could never have been turned into scientific knowledge at all unless from the very start we had brought to it a faith in uniformity which almost no number of disappointments can shake.

This faith – the preference – is it a thing we can trust? Or is it only the way our minds happen to work? It is useless to say that it has hitherto always been confirmed by the event. That is no good unless you (at least silently) add, 'And therefore always will be': and you cannot add that unless you know already that our faith in uniformity is well grounded. And that is just what we are now asking. Does this sense of fitness of ours correspond to anything in external reality?

The answer depends on the Metaphysic one holds. If all that exists is Nature, the great mindless interlocking event, if our own deepest convictions are merely the by-products of an irrational process, then clearly there is not the slightest ground for supposing that our sense of fitness and our consequent faith in uniformity tell us anything about a reality external to ourselves. Our convictions are simply a fact *about us* – like the colour of our hair. If Naturalism is true we have no reason to trust our conviction that Nature is uniform. It can be trusted only if quite a different Metaphysic is true. If the deepest thing in reality, the Fact which is the source of all other facthood, is a thing in some degree like ourselves – if it is a Rational Spirit and we derive our rational spirituality from It – then indeed our conviction can be trusted. Our repugnance to disorder is derived from Nature's Creator and ours. The disorderly world which we cannot endure to believe in is the disorderly world He would not have endured to create. Our conviction that the timetable will not be perpetually or meaninglessly altered is sound because we have (in a sense) eavesdropped in the Masters' common-room.

The sciences logically require a metaphysic of this sort. Our greatest natural philosopher thinks it is also the metaphysic out of which they originally grew. Professor Whitehead points out[1] that centuries of belief in a God who combined 'the personal energy of Jehovah' with 'the rationality of a Greek philosopher' first produced that firm expectation of systematic order which rendered possible the birth of modern science. Men became scientific because they expected Law in Nature, and they expected Law in Nature because they believed in a Legislator. In most modern scientists this belief has died: it will be interesting to see how long their confidence in uniformity survives it. Two significant developments have already appeared – the hypothesis of a lawless sub-nature, and the surrender of the claim that science is true. We may be living nearer than we suppose to the end of the Scientific Age.

But if we admit God, must we admit Miracle? Indeed, indeed, you have no security against it. That is the bargain. Theology says to you in effect, 'Admit God and with Him the risk of a few miracles, and I in return will ratify your faith in uniformity as regards the overwhelming majority of

---

[1] *Science and the Modern World*, Chapter II.

events.' The philosophy which forbids you to make uniformity absolute is also the philosophy which offers you solid grounds for believing it to be general, to be *almost* absolute. The Being who threatens Nature's claim to omnipotence confirms her in her lawful occasions. Give us this ha'porth of tar and we will save the ship. The alternative is really much worse. Try to make Nature absolute and you find that her uniformity is not even probable. By claiming too much, you get nothing. You get the deadlock, as in Hume. Theology offers you a working arrangement, which leaves the scientist free to continue his experiments and the Christian to continue his prayers.

We have also, I suggest, found what we were looking for – a criterion whereby to judge the intrinsic probability of an alleged miracle. We must judge it by our 'innate sense of the fitness of things', that same sense of fitness which led us to anticipate that the universe would be orderly. I do not mean, of course, that we are to use this sense in deciding whether miracles in general are possible: we know that they are on philosophical grounds. Nor do I mean that a sense of fitness will do instead of close inquiry into the historical evidence. As I have repeatedly pointed out, the historical evidence cannot be estimated unless we have first estimated the intrinsic probability of the recorded event. It is in making that estimate as regards each story of the miraculous that our sense of fitness comes into play.

If in giving such weight to the sense of fitness I were doing anything new, I should feel rather nervous. In reality I am merely giving formal acknowledgement to a principle which is always used. Whatever men may *say*, no one really thinks that the Christian doctrine of the Resurrection is exactly on the same level with some pious tittle-tattle about how Mother Egarée Louise miraculously found her second best thimble by the aid of St Anthony. The religious and the irreligious are really quite agreed on the point. The whoop of delight with which the sceptic would unearth the story of the thimble, and the 'rosy pudency' with which the Christian would keep it in the background, both tell the same tale. Even those who think all stories of miracles absurd think some very much more absurd than others: even those who believe them all (if anyone does) think that some require a specially robust faith. The criterion which both parties are actually using is that of fitness. More than half the disbelief in miracles that exists is based on a sense of their *unfitness*: a conviction (due, as I have argued, to false philosophy) that they are unsuitable to the dignity of God or Nature or else to the indignity and insignificance of man.

In the three following chapters I will try to present the central miracles of the Christian Faith in such a way as to exhibit their 'fitness'. I shall not, however, proceed by formally setting out the conditions which 'fitness' in the abstract ought to satisfy and then dovetailing the Miracles into that scheme. Our 'sense of fitness' is too delicate and elusive a thing to submit to such treatment. If I succeed, the fitness – and if I fail, the unfitness – of these miracles will of itself become apparent while we study them.

14

THE GRAND MIRACLE

A light that shone from behind the sun; the sun
Was not so fierce as to pierce where that light could.
CHARLES WILLIAMS

The central miracle asserted by Christians is the Incarnation. They say that God became Man. Every other miracle prepares for this, or exhibits this, or results from this. Just as every natural event is the manifestation at a particular place and moment of Nature's total character, so every particular Christian miracle manifests at a particular place and moment the character and significance of the Incarnation. There is no question in Christianity of arbitrary interferences just scattered about. It relates not a series of disconnected raids on Nature but the various steps of a strategically coherent invasion – an invasion which intends complete conquest and 'occupation'. The fitness, and therefore credibility, of the particular miracles depends on their relation to the Grand Miracle; all discussion of them in isolation from it is futile.

The fitness or credibility of the Grand Miracle itself cannot, obviously, be judged by the same standard. And let us admit at once that it is very difficult to find a standard by which it can be judged. If the thing happened, it was the central event in the history of the Earth – the very thing that the whole story has been about. Since it happened only once, it is by Hume's standards infinitely improbable. But then the whole history of the Earth has also happened only once; is it therefore incredible? Hence the difficulty, which weighs upon Christian and atheist alike, of estimating the probability of the Incarnation. It is like asking whether the existence of Nature herself is intrinsically probable. That is why it is easier to argue, on historical grounds, that the Incarnation actually occurred than to show, on philosophical grounds, the probability of its occurrence. The historical difficulty of giving for the life, sayings and influence of Jesus any explanation that is not harder than the Christian explanation, is very great. The discrepancy between the depth and sanity and (let me add) *shrewdness* of His moral teaching and the rampant megalomania which must lie behind His theological teaching unless He is indeed God, has never been satisfactorily got over. Hence the non-Christian hypotheses succeed one another with the restless fertility of bewilderment. Today we are asked to regard all the theological elements as later accretions to the story of a 'historical' and merely human Jesus: yesterday we were asked to believe that the whole thing began with vegetation myths and mystery religions and that the pseudo-historical Man was only fadged up at a later date. But this historical inquiry is outside the scope of my book.

Since the Incarnation, if it is a fact, holds this central position, and since we are assuming that we do not yet know it to have happened on historical grounds, we are in a position which may be illustrated by the following analogy. Let us suppose we possess parts of a novel or a symphony. Someone now brings us a newly discovered piece of manuscript and says, 'This is the missing part of the work. This is the chapter on which the whole plot of the novel really turned. This is the main theme of the symphony'. Our business would be to see whether the new passage, if admitted to the central place which the discoverer claimed for it, did actually illuminate all the parts we had already seen and 'pull them together'. Nor should we be likely to go very far wrong. The new passage, if spurious, however attractive it looked at the first glance, would become harder and harder to reconcile with the rest of the work the longer we considered the matter. But if it were genuine then at every fresh hearing of the music or every fresh reading of the book, we should find it settling down, making itself more at home and eliciting significance from all sorts of details in the whole work which we had hitherto neglected. Even though the new central chapter or main theme contained great difficulties in itself, we should still think it genuine provided that it continually removed difficulties elsewhere. Something like this we must do with the doctrine of the Incarnation. Here, instead of a symphony or a novel, we have the whole mass of our knowledge. The credibility will depend on the extent to which the doctrine, if accepted, can illuminate and integrate that whole mass. It is much less important that the doctrine itself should be fully comprehensible. We believe that the sun is in the sky at midday in summer not because we can clearly see the sun (in fact, we cannot) but because we can see everything else.

The first difficulty that occurs to any critic of the doctrine lies in the very centre of it. What can be meant by 'God becoming man'? In what sense is it conceivable that eternal self-existent Spirit, basic Fact-hood, should be so combined with a natural human organism as to make one person? And this would be a fatal stumbling-block if we had not already discovered that in every human being a more than natural activity (the act of reasoning) and therefore presumably a more than natural agent is thus united with a part of Nature: so united that the composite creature calls itself 'I' and 'Me'. I am not, of course, suggesting that what happened when God became Man was simply another instance of this process. In other men a supernatural *creature* thus becomes, in union with the natural creature, one human being. In Jesus,

it is held, the Supernatural Creator Himself did so. I do not think anything
we do will enable us to imagine the mode of consciousness of the incarnate
God. That is where the doctrine is not fully comprehensible. But the difficulty which we felt in the mere idea of the Supernatural descending into the
Natural is apparently non-existent, or is at least overcome in the person of
every man. If we did not know by experience what it feels like to be a rational animal – how all these natural facts, all this biochemistry and instinctive
affection or repulsion and sensuous perception, can become the medium of
rational thought and moral will which understand necessary relations and
acknowledge modes of behaviour as universally binding, we could not conceive, much less imagine, the thing happening. The discrepancy between a
movement of atoms in an astronomer's cortex and his understanding that
there must be a still unobserved planet beyond Uranus, is already so
immense that the Incarnation of God Himself is, in one sense, scarcely more
startling. We cannot conceive how the Divine Spirit dwelled within the created and human spirit of Jesus: but neither can we conceive how His human
spirit, or that of any man, dwells within his natural organism. What we can
understand, if the Christian doctrine is true, is that our own composite existence is not the sheer anomaly it might seem to be, but a faint image of the
Divine Incarnation itself – the same theme in a very minor key. We can
understand that if God so descends into a human spirit, and human spirit so
descends into Nature, and our thoughts into our senses and passions, and if
adult minds (but only the best of them) can descend into sympathy with
children, and men into sympathy with beasts, then everything hangs
together and the total reality, both Natural and Supernatural, in which we
are living is more multifariously and subtly harmonious than we had suspected. We catch sight of a new key principle – the power of the Higher, just
in so far as it is truly Higher, to come down, the power of the greater to
include the less. Thus solid bodies exemplify many truths of plane geometry,
but plane figures no truths of solid geometry: many inorganic propositions
are true of organisms but no organic propositions are true of minerals;
Montaigne became kittenish with his kitten but she never talked philosophy
to him.[1] Everywhere the great enters the little – its power to do so is almost
the test of its greatness.

In the Christian story God descends to reascend. He comes down; down
from the heights of absolute being into time and space, down into humanity;
down further still, if embryologists are right, to recapitulate in the womb
ancient and pre-human phases of life; down to the very roots and seabed of
the Nature He has created. But He goes down to come up again and bring
the whole ruined world up with Him. One has the picture of a strong man

[1] *Essays*, I, xii, Apology for Raimond de Sebonde.

stooping lower and lower to get himself underneath some great complicated burden. He must stoop in order to lift, he must almost disappear under the load before he incredibly straightens his back and marches off with the whole mass swaying on his shoulders. Or one may think of a diver, first reducing himself to nakedness, then glancing in mid-air, then gone with a splash, vanished, rushing down through green and warm water into black and cold water, down through increasing pressure into the death-like region of ooze and slime and old decay; then up again, back to colour and light, his lungs almost bursting, till suddenly he breaks surface again, holding in his hand the dripping, precious thing that he went down to recover. He and it are both coloured now that they have come up into the light: down below, where it lay colourless in the dark, he lost his colour too.

In this descent and reascent everyone will recognise a familiar pattern: a thing written all over the world. It is the pattern of all vegetable life. It must belittle itself into something hard, small and deathlike, it must fall into the ground: thence the new life reascends. It is the pattern of all animal generation too. There is descent from the full and perfect organisms into the spermatozoon and ovum, and in the dark womb a life at first inferior in kind to that of the species which is being reproduced: then the slow ascent to the perfect embryo, to the living, conscious baby, and finally to the adult. So it is also in our moral and emotional life. The first innocent and spontaneous desires have to submit to the deathlike process of control or total denial: but from that there is a reascent to fully formed character in which the strength of the original material all operates but in a new way. Death and Rebirth – go down to go up – it is a key principle. Through this bottleneck, this belittlement, the highroad nearly always lies.

The doctrine of the Incarnation, if accepted, puts this principle even more emphatically at the centre. The pattern is there in Nature because it was first there in God. All the instances of it which I have mentioned turn out to be but transpositions of the Divine theme into a minor key. I am not now referring simply to the Crucifixion and Resurrection of Christ. The total pattern, of which they are only the turning point, is the real Death and Rebirth: for certainly no seed ever fell from so fair a tree into so dark and cold a soil as would furnish more than a faint analogy to this huge descent and reascension in which God dredged the salt and oozy bottom of Creation.

From this point of view the Christian doctrine makes itself so quickly at home amid the deepest apprehensions of reality which we have from other sources, that doubt may spring up in a new direction. Is it not fitting in too well? So well that it must have come into men's minds from seeing this pattern elsewhere, particularly in the annual death and resurrection of the corn? For there have, of course, been many religions in which that annual drama (so important for the life of the tribe) was almost admittedly the central theme, and the deity – Adonis, Osiris, or another – almost undisguisedly a personification of the corn, a 'corn-king' who dies and rose again each year. Is not Christ simply another corn-king?

Now this brings us to the oddest thing about Christianity. In a sense the view which I have just described is actually true. From a certain point of view Christ is 'the same sort of thing' as Adonis or Osiris (always, of course, waiving the fact that they lived nobody knows where or when, while He was executed by a Roman magistrate we know in a year which can be roughly dated). And that is just the puzzle. If Christianity is a religion of that kind why is the analogy of the seed falling into the ground so seldom mentioned (twice only if I mistake not) in the New Testament? Corn-religions are popular and respectable: if that is what the first Christian teachers were putting across, what motive could they have for concealing the fact? The impression they make is that of men who simply don't know how close they are to the corn-religions: men who simply overlook the rich sources of relevant imagery and association which they must have been on the verge of tapping at every moment. If you say they suppressed it because they were Jews, that only raises the puzzle in a new form. Why should the only religion of a 'dying God' which has actually survived and risen to unexampled spiritual heights occur precisely among those people to whom, and to whom almost alone, the whole circle of ideas that belong to the 'dying God' was foreign? I myself, who first seriously read the New Testament when I was, imaginatively and poetically, all agog for the Death and Rebirth pattern and anxious to meet a corn-king, was chilled and puzzled by the almost total absence of such ideas in the Christian documents. One moment particularly stood out. A 'dying God' – the only dying God who might possibly be historical – holds bread, that is, corn, in His hand and says, 'This is my body'. Surely here, even if nowhere else – or surely if not here, at least in the earliest comments on this passage and through all later devotional usage in ever swelling volume – the truth must come out; the connection between this and the annual drama of the crops must be made. But it is not. It is there for me. There is no sign that it was there for the disciples or (humanly speaking) for Christ Himself. It is almost as if He didn't realise what He had said.

The records, in fact, show us a Person who *enacts* the part of the Dying God, but whose thoughts and words remain quite outside the circle of religious ideas to which the Dying God belongs. The very thing which the Nature-religions are all about seems to have really happened once; but it happened in a circle where no trace of Nature-religion was present. It is as if you met the sea-serpent and found that it disbelieved in sea-serpents: as if history recorded a man who had done all the things attributed to Sir Launcelot but who had himself never apparently heard of chivalry.

There is, however, one hypothesis which, if accepted, makes everything easy and coherent. The Christians are not claiming that simply 'God' was incarnate in Jesus. They are claiming that the one true God is He whom the Jews worshipped as Jahweh, and that it is He who has descended. Now the double character of Jahweh is this. On the one hand He is the God of Nature, her glad Creator. It is He who sends rain into the furrows till the valleys stand so thick with corn that they laugh and sing. The trees of the wood rejoice before Him and His voice causes the wild deer to bring forth their young. He is the God of wheat and wine and oil. In that respect He is constantly doing all the things that Nature-Gods do: He is Bacchus, Venus, Ceres all rolled into one. There is no trace in Judaism of the idea found in some pessimistic and Pantheistic religions that Nature is some kind of illusion or disaster, that finite existence is in itself an evil and that the cure lies in the relapse of all things into God. Compared with such anti-natural conceptions Jahweh might almost be mistaken for a Nature-God.

On the other hand, Jahweh is clearly *not* a Nature-God. He does not die and come to life each year as a true Corn-king should. He may give wine and fertility, but must not be worshipped with Bacchanalian or aphrodisiac rites. He is not the soul of Nature nor of any part of Nature. He inhabits eternity: He dwells in the high and holy place: heaven is His throne, not His vehicle, earth is His footstool, not His vesture. One day He will dismantle both and make a new heaven and earth. He is not to be identified even with the 'divine spark' in man. He is 'God and not man': His thoughts are not our thoughts: all our righteousness is filthy rags. His appearance to Ezekiel is attended with imagery that does not borrow from Nature, but (it is a mystery too seldom noticed[2]) from those machines which men were to make centuries after Ezekiel's death. The prophet saw something suspiciously like a *dynamo*.

Jahweh is neither the soul of Nature nor her enemy. She is neither His body nor a declension and falling away from Him. She is His creature. He is not a nature-God, but the God of Nature – her inventor, maker, owner, and controller. To everyone who reads this book the conception has been familiar from childhood; we therefore easily think it is the most ordinary conception in the world. 'If people are going to believe in a God at all,' we ask, 'what other kind would they believe in?' But the answer of history is, 'Almost any other kind'. We mistake our privileges for our instincts: just as one meets ladies who believe their own refined manners to be natural to them. They don't remember being taught.

Now if there is such a God and if He descends to rise again, then we can understand why Christ is at once so like the Corn-King and so silent about

---

[2] I owe this point to Canon Adam Fox.

him. He is like the Corn-King because the Corn-King is a portrait of Him. The similarity is not in the least unreal or accidental. For the Corn-King is derived (through human imagination) from the facts of Nature, and the facts of Nature from her Creator; the Death and Rebirth pattern is in her because it was first in Him. On the other hand, elements of Nature-religion are strikingly absent from the teaching of Jesus and from the Judaic preparation which led up to it precisely because in them Nature's Original is manifesting Itself. In them you have from the very outset got in behind Nature-religion and behind Nature herself. Where the real God is present the shadows of that God do not appear; that which the shadows resembled does. The Hebrews throughout their history were being constantly headed off from the worship of Nature-gods; not because the Nature-gods were in all respects unlike the God of Nature but because, at best, they were merely like, and it was the destiny of that nation to be turned away from likenesses to the thing itself.

The mention of that nation turns our attention to one of those features in the Christian story which is repulsive to the modern mind. To be quite frank, we do not at all like the idea of a 'chosen people'. Democrats by birth and education, we should prefer to think that all nations and individuals start level in the search for God, or even that all religions are equally true. It must be admitted at once that Christianity makes no concessions to this point of view. It does not tell of a human search for God at all, but of something done by God for, to, and about, Man. And the way in which it is done is selective, undemocratic, to the highest degree. After the knowledge of God had been universally lost or obscured, one man from the whole earth (Abraham) is picked out. He is separated (miserably enough, we may suppose) from his natural surroundings, sent into a strange country, and made the ancestor of a nation who are to carry the knowledge of the true God. Within this nation there is further selection: some die in the desert, some remain behind in Babylon. There is further selection still. The process grows narrower and narrower, sharpens at last into one small bright point like the head of a spear. It is a Jewish girl at her prayers. All humanity (so far as concerns its redemption) has narrowed to that.

Such a process is very unlike what modern feeling demands: but it is startlingly like what Nature habitually does. Selectiveness, and with it (we must allow) enormous wastage, is her method. Out of enormous space a very small portion is occupied by matter at all. Of all the stars, perhaps very few, perhaps only one, have planets. Of the planets in our own system probably only one supports organic life. In the transmission of organic life, countless seeds and spermatozoa are emitted: some few are selected for the distinction of fertility. Among the species only one is rational. Within that species only a few attain excellence of beauty, strength or intelligence.

At this point we come perilously near the argument of Butler's famous *Analogy*. I say 'perilously' because the argument of that book very nearly admits parodying in the form 'You say that the behaviour attributed to the Christian God is both wicked and foolish: but it is no less likely to be true on that account for I can show that Nature (which He created) behaves just as badly.' To which the atheist will answer – and the nearer he is to Christ in his heart, the more certainly he will do so – 'If there is a God like that I despise and defy Him.' But I am not saying that Nature, as we now know her, is good; that is a point we must return to in a moment. Nor am I saying that a God whose actions were no better than Nature's would be a proper object of worship for any honest man. The point is a little finer than that. This selective or undemocratic quality in Nature, at least in so far as it affects human life, is neither good nor evil. According as spirit exploits or fails to exploit this Natural situation, it gives rise to one or the other. It permits, on the one hand, ruthless competition, arrogance, and envy: it permits on the other, modesty and (one of our greatest pleasures) admiration. A world in which I was *really* (and not merely by a useful legal fiction) 'as good as everyone else', in which I never looked up to anyone wiser or cleverer or braver or more learned than I, would be insufferable. The very 'fans' of the cinema stars and the famous footballers know better than to desire that! What the Christian story does is not to instate on the Divine level a cruelty and wastefulness which have already disgusted us on the Natural, but to show us in God's act, working neither cruelly nor wastefully, the same principle which is in Nature also, though down there it works sometimes in one way and sometimes in the other. It illuminates the Natural scene by suggesting that a principle which at first looked meaningless may yet be derived from a principle which is good and fair, may indeed be a depraved and blurred copy of it – the pathological form which it would take in a *spoiled* Nature.

For when we look into the Selectiveness which the Christians attribute to God we find in it none of that 'favouritism' which we were afraid of. The 'chosen' people are chosen not for their own sake (certainly not for their own honour or pleasure) but for the sake of the unchosen. Abraham is told that 'in his seed' (the chosen nation) 'all nations shall be blest'. That nation has been chosen to bear a heavy burden. Their sufferings are great: but, as Isaiah recognised, their sufferings heal others. On the finally selected Woman falls the utmost depth of maternal anguish. Her Son, the incarnate God, is a 'man of sorrows'; the one Man into whom Deity descended, the one Man who can be lawfully adored, is pre-eminent for suffering.

But, you will ask, does this much mend matters? Is not this still injustice, though now the other way round? Where, at the first glance, we accused God of undue favour to His 'chosen', we are now tempted to accuse Him of undue disfavour. (The attempt to keep up both charges at the same time had better be dropped.) And certainly we have here come to a principle very deep-rooted in Christianity: what may be called the principle of *Vicariousness*. The Sinless Man suffers for the sinful, and, in their degree, all good men for all bad men. And this Vicariousness – no less than Death and Rebirth or Selectiveness – is also a characteristic of Nature. Self-sufficiency, living on one's own resources, is a thing impossible in her realm. Everything is indebted to everything else, sacrificed to everything else, dependent on everything else. And here too we must recognise that the principle is in itself neither good nor bad. The cat lives on the mouse in a way I think bad: the bees and the flowers live on one another in a more pleasing manner. The parasite lives on its 'host': but so also the unborn child on its mother. In social life without Vicariousness there would be no exploitation or oppression; but also no kindness or gratitude. It is a fountain both of love and hatred, both of misery and happiness. When we have understood this we shall no longer think that the depraved examples of Vicariousness in Nature forbid us to suppose that the principle itself is of divine origin.

At this point it may be well to take a backward glance and notice how the doctrine of Incarnation is already acting on the rest of our knowledge. We have already brought it into contact with four other principles: the composite nature of man, the pattern of descent and reascension, Selectiveness, and Vicariousness. The first may be called a fact about the frontier between Nature and Supernature; the other three are characteristics of Nature herself. Now most religions, when brought face to face with the facts of Nature either simply reaffirm them, give them (just as they stand) a transcendent prestige, or else simply negate them, promise us release from such facts and from Nature altogether. The Nature-Religions take the first line. They sanctify our agricultural concerns and indeed our whole biological life. We get really drunk in the worship of Dionysus and lie with real women in the temple of the fertility goddess. In Life-force worship, which is the modern and western type of Nature-religion, we take over the existing trend towards 'development' of increasing complexity in organic, social, and industrial life, and make it a god. The anti-Natural or pessimistic religions, which are more civilised and sensitive, such as Buddhism or higher Hinduism, tell us that Nature is evil and illusory, that there is an escape from this incessant change, this furnace of striving and desire. Neither the one nor the other sets the facts of Nature in a new light. The Nature-religions merely reinforce that view of Nature which we spontaneously adopt in our moments of rude health and cheerful brutality; the anti-natural religions do the same for the view we take in moments of compassion, fastidiousness, or lassitude. The Christian doctrine does neither of these things. If any man approaches it with the idea that because Jahweh is the God of fertility our lasciviousness is going to be authorised or that the Selectiveness and Vicariousness of God's method will excuse us for imitating (as 'Heroes', 'Supermen' or social parasites) the lower Selectiveness and Vicariousness of Nature, he will be stunned and repelled by the inflexible Christian demand for chastity, humility, mercy and justice. On the other hand if we come to it regarding the death which precedes every rebirth, or the fact of inequality, or our dependence on others and their dependence on us, as the mere odious necessities of an evil cosmos, and hoping to be delivered into transparent and 'enlightened' spirituality where all these things just vanish, we shall be equally disappointed. We shall be told that, in one sense, and despite enormous differences, it is 'the same all the way up'; that hierarchical inequality, the need for self surrender, the willing sacrifice of self to others, and the thankful and loving (but unashamed) acceptance of others' sacrifice to us, hold sway in the realm beyond Nature. It is indeed only love that makes the difference: all those very same principles which are evil in the world of selfishness and necessity are good in the world of love and understanding. Thus, as we accept this doctrine of the higher world we make new discoveries about the lower world. It is from that hill that we first really understand the landscape of this valley. Here, at last, we find (as we do not find either in the Nature-religions or in the religions that deny Nature) a real illumination: Nature is being lit up by a light from beyond Nature. Someone is speaking who knows more about her than can be known from inside her.

Throughout this doctrine it is, of course, implied that Nature is infested with evil. Those great key-principles which exist as modes of goodness in the Divine Life, take on, in her operations, not merely a less perfect form (that we should, on any view, expect) but forms which I have been driven to describe as morbid or depraved. And this depravity could not be totally removed without the drastic remaking of Nature. Complete human virtue could indeed banish from human life all the evils that now arise in it from Vicariousness and Selectiveness and retain only the good: but the wastefulness and painfulness of non-human Nature would remain – and would, of course, continue to infect human life in the form of disease. And the destiny which Christianity promises to man clearly involves a 'redemption' or 'remaking' of Nature which could not stop at Man, or even at this planet. We are told that 'the whole creation' is in travail, and that Man's rebirth will be the signal for hers. This gives rise to several problems, the discussion of which puts the whole doctrine of the Incarnation in a clearer light.

In the first place, we ask how the Nature created by a good God comes to be in this condition? By which question we may mean either how she comes to be imperfect – to leave 'room for improvement' as the schoolmasters say in their reports – or else, how she comes to be positively depraved. If we ask the question in the first sense, the Christian answer (I think) is that God, from the first, created her such as to reach her perfection by a process in time. He made an Earth at first 'without form and void' and brought it by degrees to its perfection. In this, as elsewhere, we see the familiar pattern – descent from God to the formless Earth and reascent from the formless to the finished. In that sense a certain degree of 'evolutionism' or developmentalism' is inherent in Christianity. So much for Nature's imperfection; her positive depravity calls for a very different explanation. According to the Christians this is all due to sin: the sin both of men and of powerful, non-human beings, supernatural but created. The unpopularity of this doctrine arises from the widespread Naturalism of our age – the belief that nothing but Nature exists and that if anything else did she is protected from it by a Maginot Line – and will disappear as this error is corrected. To be sure, the morbid inquisitiveness about such beings which led our ancestors to a pseudo-science of Demonology, is to be sternly discouraged: our attitude should be that of the sensible citizen in wartime who believes that there are enemy spies in our midst but disbelieves nearly every particular spy story. We must limit ourselves to the general statement that beings in a different, and higher 'Nature' which is *partially* interlocked with ours have, like men, fallen and have tampered with things inside our frontier. The doctrine, besides proving itself fruitful of good in each man's spiritual life, helps to protect us from shallowly optimistic or pessimistic views of Nature. To call her either 'good' or 'evil' is boys' philosophy. We find ourselves in a world of transporting pleasures, ravishing beauties, and tantalising possibilities, but all constantly being destroyed, all coming to nothing. Nature has all the air of a good thing spoiled.

The sin, both of men and of angels, was rendered possible by the fact that God gave them free will: thus surrendering a portion of His omnipotence (it is again a deathlike or descending movement) because He saw that from a world of free creatures, even though they fell, He could work out (and this is the reascent) a deeper happiness and a fuller splendour than any world of automata would admit.

Another question that arises is this. If the redemption of Man is the beginning of Nature's redemption as a whole, must we then conclude after all that Man is the most important thing in Nature? If I had to answer 'Yes' to this question I should not be embarrassed. Supposing Man to be the only rational animal in the universe, then (as has been shown) his small size and the small size of the globe he inhabits would not make it ridiculous to regard him as the hero of the cosmic drama: Jack after all is the smallest character in *Jack the Giant-Killer*. Nor do I think it in the least improbable that Man is in fact the only rational creature in this spatio-temporal Nature. That is just the sort of lonely pre-eminence – just the disproportion between picture and frame –

which all that I know of Nature's 'selectiveness' would lead me to anticipate. But I do not need to assume that it actually exists. Let Man be only one among a myriad of rational species, and let him be the only one that has fallen. Because he has fallen, for him God does the great deed; just as in the parable it is the one lost sheep for whom the shepherd hunts. Let Man's pre-eminence or solitude be one not of superiority but of misery and evil: then, all the more, Man will be the very species into which Mercy will descend. For this prodigal the fatted calf, or, to speak more suitably, the eternal Lamb, is killed. But once the Son of God, drawn hither not by our merits but by our unworthiness, has put on human nature, then our species (whatever it may have been before) does become in one sense the central fact in all Nature: our species, rising after its long descent, will drag all Nature up with it because in our species the Lord of Nature is now included. And it would be all of a piece with what we already know if ninety and nine righteous races inhabiting distant planets that circle distant suns, and needing no redemption on their own account, were remade and glorified by the glory which had descended into our race. For God is not merely mending, not simply restoring a *status quo*. Redeemed humanity is to be something more glorious than unfallen humanity would have been, more glorious than any unfallen race now is (if at this moment the night sky conceals any such). The greater the sin, the greater the mercy: the deeper the death the brighter the rebirth. And this super-added glory will, with true vicariousness, exalt all creatures and those who have never fallen will thus bless Adam's fall.

I write so far on the assumption that the Incarnation was occasioned only by the Fall. Another view has, of course, been sometimes held by Christians. According to it the descent of God into Nature was not in itself occasioned by sin. It would have occurred for Glorification and Perfection even if it had not been required for Redemption. Its attendant circumstances would have been very different: the divine humility would not have been a divine humiliation, the sorrows, the gall and vinegar, the crown of thorns and the cross, would have been absent. If this view is taken, then clearly the Incarnation, wherever and however it occurred, would always have been the beginning of Nature's rebirth. The fact that it has occurred in the human species, summoned thither by that strong incantation of misery and abjection which Love has made Himself unable to resist, would not deprive it of its universal significance.

This doctrine of a universal redemption spreading outwards from the redemption of Man, mythological as it will seem to modern minds, is in reality far more philosophical than any theory which holds that God, having once entered Nature, should leave her, and leave her substantially unchanged, or that the glorification of one creature could be realised without the glorification of the whole system. God never undoes anything but evil, never does good to undo it again. The union between God and Nature in the Person of Christ admits no divorce. He will not *go out* of Nature again and she must be glorified in all ways which this miraculous union demands. When spring comes it 'leaves no corner of the land untouched'; even a pebble dropped in a pond sends circles to the margin. The question we want to ask about Man's 'central' position in this drama is really on a level with the disciples' question, 'Which of them was the greatest?' It is the sort of question which God does not answer. If from Man's point of view the re-creation of non-human and even inanimate Nature appears a mere by-product of his own redemption, then equally from some remote, non-human point of view Man's redemption may seem merely the preliminary to this more widely diffused springtime, and the very permission of Man's fall may be supposed to have had that larger end in view. Both attitudes will be right if they will consent to drop the words *mere* and *merely*. Where a God who is totally purposive and totally foreseeing acts upon a Nature which is totally interlocked, there can be no accidents or loose ends, nothing whatever of which we can safely use the word *merely*. Nothing is 'merely a by-product' of anything else. All results are intended from the first. What is subservient from one point of view is the main purpose from another. No thing or event is first or highest in a sense which forbids it to be also last and lowest. The partner who bows to Man in one movement of the dance receives Man's reverences in another. To be high or central means to abdicate continually: to be low means to be raised: all good masters are servants: God washes the feet of men. The concepts we usually bring to the consideration of such matters are miserably political and prosaic. We think of flat repetitive equality and arbitrary privilege as the only two alternatives – thus missing all the overtones, the counterpoint, the vibrant sensitiveness, the inter-inanimations of reality.

For this reason I do not think it at all likely that there have been (as Alice Meynell suggested in an interesting poem) many Incarnations to redeem many different kinds of creature. One's sense of *style* – of the divine idiom – rejects it. The suggestion of mass-production and of waiting queues comes from a level of thought which is here hopelessly inadequate. If other natural creatures than Man have sinned we must believe that they are redeemed: but God's Incarnation as Man will be one unique act in the drama of total redemption and other species will have witnessed wholly different acts, each equally unique, equally necessary and differently necessary to the whole process, and each (from a certain point of view) justifiably regarded as 'the great scene' of the play. To those who live in Act II, Act III looks like an epilogue: to those who live in Act III, Act II looks like a prologue. And both are right until they add the fatal word *merely*, or else try to avoid it by the dullard's supposition that both acts are the same.

It ought to be noticed at this stage that the Christian doctrine, if accepted, involves a particular view of Death. There are two attitudes towards Death which the human mind naturally adopts. One is the lofty view, which reached its greatest intensity among the Stoics, that Death 'doesn't matter', that it is 'kind nature's signal for retreat', and that we ought to regard it with indifference. The other is the 'natural' point of view, implicit in nearly all private conversations on the subject, and in much modern thought about the survival of the human species, that Death is the greatest of all evils: Hobbes is perhaps the only philosopher who erected a system on this basis. The first idea simply negates, the second simply affirms, our instinct for self-preservation; neither throws any new light on Nature, and Christianity countenances neither. Its doctrine is subtler. On the one hand Death is the triumph of Satan, the punishment of the Fall, and the last enemy. Christ shed tears at the grave of Lazarus and sweated blood in Gethsemane: the Life of Lives that was in Him detested this penal obscenity not less than we do, but more. On the other hand, only he who loses his life will save it. We are baptised into the *death* of Christ, and it is the remedy for the Fall. Death is, in fact, what some modern people call 'ambivalent'. It is Satan's great weapon and also God's great weapon: it is holy and unholy; our supreme disgrace and our only hope; the thing Christ came to conquer and the means by which He conquered.

To penetrate the whole of this mystery is, of course, far beyond our power. If the pattern of Descent and Reascent is (as looks not unlikely) the very formula of reality, then in the mystery of Death the secret of secrets lies hid. But something must be said in order to put the Grand Miracle in its proper light. We need not discuss Death on the highest level of all: the mystical slaying of the Lamb 'before the foundation of the world' is above our speculations. Nor need we consider Death on the lowest level. The death of organisms which are nothing more than organisms, which have developed no personality, does not concern us. Of it we may truly say, as some spiritually minded people would have us say of human Death, that it 'doesn't matter'. But the startling Christian doctrine of human Death cannot be passed over.

Human Death according to the Christians, is a result of human sin; Man, as originally created, was immune from it: Man, when redeemed, and recalled to a new life (which will, in some undefined sense, be a bodily life) in the midst of a more organic and more fully obedient Nature, will be immune from it again. This doctrine is of course simply nonsense if a man is nothing but a Natural organism. But if he were, then, as we have seen, all thoughts would be equally nonsensical, for all would have irrational causes. Man must therefore be a composite being – a natural organism tenanted by, or in a state of *symbiosis* with, a supernatural spirit. The Christian doctrine, startling as it must seem to those who have not fully cleared their minds of Naturalism, states that the relations which we now observe between that spirit and that organism, are abnormal or pathological ones. At present spirit can retain its foothold against the incessant counter-attacks of Nature (both physiological and psychological) only by perpetual vigilance, and physiological Nature always defeats it in the end. Sooner or later it becomes unable to resist the disintegrating processes at work in the body and death ensues. A little later the Natural organism (for it does not long enjoy its triumph) is similarly conquered by merely physical Nature and returns to the inorganic. But, on the Christian view, this was not always so. The spirit was once not a garrison, maintaining its post with difficulty in a hostile Nature, but was fully 'at home' with its organism, like a king in his own country or a rider on his own horse – or better still, as the human part of a Centaur was 'at home' with the equine part. Where spirit's power over the organism was complete and unresisted, death would never occur. No doubt, spirit's permanent triumph over natural forces which, if left to themselves, would kill the organism, would involve a continued miracle: but only the same sort of miracle which occurs every day – for whenever we think rationally we are, by direct spiritual power, forcing certain atoms in our brain and certain psychological tendencies in our natural soul to do what they would never have done if left to Nature. The Christian doctrine would be fantastic only if the present frontier-situation between spirit and Nature in each human being were so intelligible and self-explanatory that we just 'saw' it to be the only one that could ever have existed. But is it?

In reality the frontier situation is so odd that nothing but custom could make it seem natural, and nothing but the Christian doctrine can make it fully intelligible. There is certainly a state of war. But not a war of mutual destruction. Nature by dominating spirit wrecks all spiritual activities: spirit by dominating Nature confirms and improves natural activities. The brain does not become less a brain by being used for rational thought. The emotions do not become weak or jaded by being organised in the service of a moral will – indeed they grow richer and stronger as a beard is strengthened by being shaved or a river is deepened by being banked. The body of the reasonable and virtuous man, other things being equal, is a better body than that of the fool or the debauchee, and his sensuous pleasures better simply as sensuous pleasures: for the slaves of the senses, after the first bait, are starved by their masters. Everything happens as if what we saw was not war, but rebellion: that rebellion of the lower against the higher by which the lower destroys both the higher and itself. And if the present situation is one of rebellion, then reason cannot reject but will rather demand the belief that there was a time before the rebellion broke out and may be a time after it has been settled. And if we thus see grounds for believing that the supernatural spirit and the natural organism in Man have quarrelled, we shall immediately find it confirmed from two quite unexpected quarters.

Almost the whole of Christian theology could perhaps be deduced from the two facts (*a*) That men make coarse jokes, and (*b*) That they feel the dead to be uncanny. The coarse joke proclaims that we have here an animal which finds its own animality either objectionable or funny. Unless there had been a quarrel between the spirit and the organism I do not see how this could be: it is the very mark of the two not being 'at home' together. But is very difficult to imagine such a state of affairs as original – to suppose a creature which from the very first was half shocked and half tickled to death at the mere fact of being the creature it is. I do not perceive that dogs see anything funny about being dogs: I suspect that angels see nothing funny about being angels. Our feeling about the dead is equally odd. It is idle to say that we dislike corpses because we are afraid of ghosts. You might say with equal truth that we fear ghosts because we dislike corpses – for the ghost owes much of its horror to the associated ideas of pallor, decay, coffins, shrouds, and worms. In reality we hate the division which makes possible the conception of either corpse or ghost. Because the thing ought not to be divided, each of the halves into which it falls by division is detestable. The explanations which Naturalism gives both of bodily shame and of our feeling about the dead are not satisfactory. It refers us to primitive taboos and superstitions – as if these themselves were not obviously results of the thing to be explained. But once accept the Christian doctrine that man was originally a unity and that the present division is unnatural, and all the phenomena fall into place. It would be fantastic to suggest that the doctrine was devised to explain our enjoyment of a chapter in Rabelais, a good ghost story, or the *Tales* of Edgar Allan Poe. It does so none the less.

I ought, perhaps, to point out that the argument is not in the least affected by the value-judgements we make about ghost stories or coarse humour. You may hold that both are bad. You may hold that both, though they result (like clothes) from the Fall, are (like clothes) the proper way to deal with the Fall once it has occurred: that while perfected and recreated Man will no longer experience that kind of laughter or that kind of shudder, yet here and now not to feel the horror and not to see the joke is to be less than human. But either way the facts bear witness to our present maladjustment.

So much for the sense in which human Death is the result of sin and the triumph of Satan. But it is also the means of redemption from sin, God's medicine for Man and His weapon against Satan. In a general way it is not difficult to understand how the same thing can be a masterstroke on the part of one combatant and also the very means whereby the superior combatant defeats him. Every good general, every good chess-player, takes what is precisely the strong point of his opponent's plan and makes it the pivot of his own plan. Take that castle of mine if you insist. It was not my original intention that you should – indeed, I thought you would have had more sense. But take it by all means. For now I move thus ... and thus ... and it is mate in three moves. Something like this must be supposed to have happened about Death. Do not say that such metaphors are too trivial to illustrate so high a matter: the unnoticed mechanical and mineral metaphors which, in this age, will dominate our whole minds (without being recognised as metaphors at all) the moment we relax our vigilance against them, must be incomparably less adequate.

And one can see how it might have happened. The Enemy persuades Man to rebel against God: Man, by doing so, loses power to control that other rebellion which the Enemy now raises in Man's organism (both psychical and physical) against Man's spirit: just as that organism, in its turn, loses power to maintain itself against the rebellion of the inorganic. In that way, Satan produced human Death. But when God created Man he gave him such a constitution that, if the highest part of it rebelled against Himself, it would be bound to lose control over the lower parts: i.e. in the long run to suffer Death. This provision may be regarded equally as a punitive sentence ('In the day ye eat of that fruit ye shall die'), as a mercy, and as a safety device. It is punishment because Death – that Death of which Martha says to Christ 'But ... Sir ... it'll *smell*' – is horror and ignominy. ('I am not so much afraid of death as ashamed of it,' said Sir Thomas Browne.) It is mercy because by willing and humble surrender to it Man undoes his act of rebellion and makes even this depraved and monstrous mode of Death an instance of that higher and mystical Death which is eternally good and a necessary ingredient in the highest life. 'The readiness is all' – not, of course, the merely heroic readiness but that of humility and self-renunciation. Our enemy, so welcomed, becomes our servant: bodily Death, the monster, becomes blessed spiritual Death to self, if the spirit so wills – or rather if it allows the Spirit of the willingly dying God so to will in it. It is a safety-device because, once Man has fallen, natural immortality would be the one utterly hopeless destiny for him. Aided to the surrender that he must make by no external necessity of Death, free (if you call it freedom) to rivet faster and faster about himself through unending centuries the chains of his own pride and lust and of the nightmare civilisations which these build up in ever-increasing power and complication, he would progress from being merely a fallen man to being a fiend, possibly beyond all modes of redemption. This danger was averted. The sentence that those who ate of the forbidden fruit would be driven away from the Tree of Life was implicit in the composite nature with which Man was created. But to convert this penal death into the means of eternal life – to add to its negative and preventive function a positive and saving function – it was further necessary that death should be *accepted*. Humanity must embrace death freely, submit to it with total humility, drink it to the dregs, and so convert it into that mystical death which is the secret of life. But only a Man who did not need to have been a Man at all unless He had chosen, only one who served in our sad regiment as a volunteer, yet also only one who was perfectly a Man, could perform this perfect dying; and thus (which way you put it is unimportant) either defeat death or redeem it. He tasted death on behalf of all others. He is the representative 'Die-er' of the universe: and for that very reason the Resurrection and the Life. Or conversely, because He truly lives, He truly dies, for that is the very pattern of reality. Because the higher can descend into the lower He who from all eternity has been incessantly plunging Himself in the blessed death of self-surrender to the Father can also most fully descend into the horrible and (for us) involuntary death of the body. Because Vicariousness is the very idiom of the reality He has created, His death can become ours. The whole Miracle, far from denying what we already know of reality, writes the comment which makes that crabbed text plain: or rather, proves itself to be the text on which Nature was only the commentary. In science we have been reading only the notes to a poem; in Christianity we find the poem itself.

With this our sketch of the Grand Miracle may end. Its credibility does not lie in Obviousness, Pessimism, Optimism, Pantheism, Materialism, all have this 'obvious' attraction. Each is confirmed at the first glance by multitudes of facts: later on, each meets insuperable obstacles. The doctrine of the Incarnation works into our minds quite differently. It digs beneath the surface, works through the rest of our knowledge by unexpected channels, harmonises best with our deepest apprehensions and our 'second thoughts', and in union with these undermines our superficial opinions. It has little to say to the man who is still certain that everything is going to the dogs, or that everything is getting better and better, or that everything is God, or that everything is electricity. Its hour comes when these wholesale creeds have begun to fail us. Whether the thing really happened is a historical question. But when you turn to history, you will not demand for it that kind and degree of evidence which you would rightly demand for something intrinsically improbable; only that kind and degree which you demand for something which, if accepted, illuminates and orders all other phenomena, explains both our laughter and our logic, our fear of the dead and our knowledge that it is somehow good to die, and which at one stroke covers what multitudes of separate theories will hardly cover for us if this is rejected.

15

MIRACLES OF THE

OLD CREATION

The Son can do nothing of himself, but what
he seeth the Father do.
John 5:19.

I f we open such books as Grimm's *Fairy Tales* or Ovid's *Metamorphoses* or the Italian epics we find ourselves in a world of miracles so diverse that they can hardly be classified. Beasts turn into men and men into beasts or trees, trees talk, ships become goddesses, and a magic ring can cause tables richly spread with food to appear in solitary places. Some people cannot stand this kind of story, others find it fun. But the least suspicion that it was true would turn the fun into nightmare. If such things really happened they would, I suppose, show that Nature was being invaded. But they would show that she was being invaded by an alien power. The fitness of the Christian miracles, and their difference from these mythological miracles, lies in the fact that they show invasion by a Power which is not alien. They are what might be expected to happen when she is invaded not simply by a god, but by the God of Nature: by a Power which is outside her jurisdiction not as a foreigner but as a sovereign. They proclaim that He who has come is not merely a king, but *the* King, her King and ours.

It is this which, to my mind, puts the Christian miracles in a different class from most other miracles. I do not think that it is the duty of a Christian apologist (as many sceptics suppose) to disprove all stories of the miraculous which fall outside the Christian records, nor of a Christian man to disbelieve them. I am in no way committed to the assertion that God has never worked miracles through and for Pagans or never permitted created supernatural beings to do so. If, as Tacitus, Suetonius, and Dion Cassius relate, Vespasian performed two cures, and if modern doctors tell me that they could not have been performed without miracle, I have no objection. But I claim that the Christian miracles have a much greater intrinsic probability in virtue of their organic connection with one another and with the whole structure of the religion they exhibit. If it can be shown that one particular Roman emperor – and, let us admit, a fairly good emperor as emperors go – once was empowered to do a miracle, we must of course put up with the fact. But it would remain a quite isolated and anomalous fact. Nothing comes of it, nothing leads up to it, it establishes no body of doctrine, explains nothing, is connected with nothing. And this, after all, is an unusually favourable instance of a non-Christian miracle. The immoral, and sometimes almost idiotic interferences attributed to gods in Pagan stories, even if they had a trace of historical evidence, could be accepted only on the condition of our accepting a wholly meaningless universe. What raises infinite difficulties and solves none will be believed by a rational man only under absolute compulsion. Sometimes the credibility of the miracles is in an inverse ratio to the credibility of the religion. Thus miracles are (in late documents, I believe) recorded of the Buddha. But what could be more absurd than that he who came to teach us that Nature is an illusion from which we must escape should occupy himself in producing effects on the Natural level – that he who comes to wake us from a nightmare should *add* to the nightmare? The more we respect his teaching the less we could accept his miracles. But in Christianity, the more we understand what God it is who is said to be present and the purpose for which He is said to have appeared, the more credible the miracles become. That is why we seldom find the Christian miracles denied except by those who have abandoned some part of the Christian doctrine. The mind which asks for a non-miraculous Christianity is a mind in process of relapsing from Christianity into mere 'religion'.[1]

---

[1] A consideration of the Old Testament miracles is beyond the scope of this book and would require many kinds of knowledge which I do not possess. My present view – which is tentative and liable to any amount of correction – would be that just as, on the factual side, a long preparation culminates in God's becoming incarnate as Man, so, on the documentary side, the truth first appears in *mythical* form and then by a long process of condensing or focusing finally becomes incarnate as History. This involves the belief that Myth in general is not merely misunderstood history (as Euhemerus thought) nor diabolical illusion (as some of the Fathers thought) nor priestly lying (as the philosophers of the Enlightenment thought) but, at its best, a real though unfocused gleam of divine truth falling on human imagination. The Hebrews, like other people, had mythology: but as they were the chosen people so their mythology was the chosen mythology – the mythology chosen by God to be the vehicle of the earliest sacred truths, the first step in that process which ends in the New Testament where truth has become completely historical. Whether we can ever say with certainty where, in this process of crystallisation, any particular Old Testament story fails, is another matter. I take it that the Memoirs of David's court come at one end of the scale and are scarcely less historical than St Mark or Acts; and that the Book of Jonah is at the opposite end. It should be noted that on this view (*a*) Just as God, in becoming Man, is 'emptied' of His glory, so the truth, when it comes down from the 'heaven' of myth to the 'earth' of history, undergoes a certain humiliation. Hence the New Testament is, and ought to be, more prosaic, in some ways less *splendid*, than the Old; just as the Old Testament is and ought to be less rich in many kinds of imaginative beauty than the Pagan mythologies. (*b*) Just as God is none the less God by being Man, so the Myth remains Myth even when it becomes Fact. The story of Christ demands from us, and repays, not only a religious and historical but also an imaginative response. It is directed to the child, the poet, and the savage in us as well as to the conscience and to the intellect. One of its functions is to break down dividing walls.

The miracles of Christ can be classified in two ways. The first system yields the classes (1) Miracles of Fertility (2) Miracles of Healing (3) Miracles of Destruction (4) Miracles of Dominion over the Inorganic (5) Miracles of Reversal (6) Miracles of Perfecting or Glorification. The second system, which cuts across the first, yields two classes only: they are (1) Miracles of the Old Creation, and (2) Miracles of the New Creation.

I contend that in all these miracles alike the incarnate God does suddenly and locally something that God has done or will do in general. Each miracle writes for us in small letters something that God has already written, or will write, in letters almost too large to be noticed, across the whole canvas of Nature. They focus at a particular point either God's actual, or His future, operations on the universe. When they reproduce operations we have already seen on the large scale they are miracles of the Old Creation: when they focus those which are still to come they are miracles of the New. Not one of them is isolated or anomalous: each carries the signature of the God whom we know through conscience and from Nature. Their authenticity is attested by the *style*.

Before going any further I should say that I do not propose to raise the question, which has before now been asked, whether Christ was able to do these things only because He was God or also because He was perfect man; for it is a possible view that if Man had never fallen all men would have been able to do the like. It is one of the glories of Christianity that we can say of this question, 'It doesn't matter.' Whatever may have been the powers of unfallen man, it appears that those of redeemed Man will be almost unlimited.[2] Christ, reascending from His great dive, is bringing up Human Nature with Him. Where He goes, it goes too. It will be made 'like Him'.[3] If in His miracles He is not acting as the Old Man might have done before his Fall, then He is acting as the New Man, every new man, will do after his redemption. When humanity, borne on His shoulders, passes with Him up from the cold dark water into the green warm water and out at last into the sunlight and the air, it also will be bright and coloured.

Another way of expressing the real character of the miracles would be to say that though isolated from other actions, they are not isolated in either of the two ways we are apt to suppose. They are not, on the one hand, isolated from other Divine acts: they do close and small and, as it were, in focus what God at other times does so large that men do not attend to it. Neither are they isolated exactly as we suppose from other human acts: they anticipate powers which all men will have when they also are 'sons' of God and enter

[2] Matthew 17:20, 21:21, Mark 11:23, Luke 10:19, John 14:12, 1 Corinthians 3:22, 2 Timothy 2:12.
[3] Philippians 3:21, 1 John 3:1, 2.

into that 'glorious liberty'. Christ's isolation is not that of a prodigy but of a pioneer. He is the first of His kind; He will not be the last.

Let us return to our classification and firstly to Miracles of *Fertility*. The earliest of these was the conversion of water into wine at the wedding feast in Cana. This miracle proclaims that the God of all wine is present. The vine is one of the blessings sent by Jahweh: He is the reality behind the false god Bacchus. Every year, as part of the Natural order, God makes wine. He does so by creating a vegetable organism that can turn water, soil and sunlight into a juice which will, under proper conditions, become 'wine'. Thus, in a certain sense, He constantly turns water into wine, for wine, like all drinks, is but water modified. Once, and in one year only, God, now incarnate, short circuits the process: makes wine in a moment: uses earthenware jars instead of vegetable fibres to hold the water. But uses them to do what He is always doing. The miracle consists in the short cut; but the event to which it leads is the usual one. If the thing happened, then we know that what has come into Nature is no anti-Natural spirit, no God who loves tragedy and tears and fasting *for their own sake* (however He may permit or demand them for special purposes) but the God of Israel who has through all these centuries given us wine to gladden the heart of man.

Other miracles that fall in this class are the two instances of miraculous feeding. They involve the multiplication of a little bread and a little fish into much bread and much fish. Once in the desert Satan had tempted Him to make bread of stones: He refused the suggestion. 'The Son does nothing except what He sees the Father do': perhaps one may without boldness surmise that the direct change from stone to bread appeared to the Son to be not quite in the hereditary style. Little bread into much bread is quite a different matter. Every year God makes a little corn into much corn: the seed is sown and there is an increase. And men say, according to their several fashions, 'It is the laws of Nature,' or 'It is Ceres, it is Adonis, it is the Corn-King'. But the laws of Nature are only a pattern: nothing will come of them unless they can, so to speak, take over the universe as a going concern. And as for Adonis, no man can tell us where he died or when he rose again. Here, at the feeding of the five thousand, is He whom we have ignorantly worshipped: the *real* Corn-King who will die once and rise once at Jerusalem during the term of office of Pontius Pilate.

That same day He also multiplied fish. Look down into every bay and almost every river. This swarming, undulating fecundity shows He is still at work 'thronging the seas with spawn innumerable'. The ancients had a god called Genius; the god of animal and human fertility, the patron of gynaecology, embryology, and the marriage bed – the 'genial' bed as they called it after its god Genius. But Genius is only another mask for the God of Israel, for it was He who at the beginning commanded all species 'to be fruitful and multiply and replenish the earth'. And now, that day, at the feeding of the thousands, incarnate God does the same: does close and small, under His human hands, a workman's hands, what He has always been doing in the seas, the lakes and the little brooks.

With this we stand on the threshold of that miracle which for some reason proves hardest of all for the modern mind to accept. I can understand the man who denies miracles altogether: but what is one to make of people who will believe other miracles and 'draw the line' at the Virgin Birth? Is it that for all their lip service to the laws of Nature there is only one natural process in which they really believe? Or is it that they think they see in this miracle a slur upon sexual intercourse (though they might just as well see in the feeding of the five thousand an insult to bakers) and that sexual intercourse is the one thing still venerated in this unvenerating age? In reality the miracle is no less, and no more, surprising than any others.

Perhaps the best way to approach it is from the remark I saw in one of the most archaic of our anti-god papers. The remark was that Christians believed in a God who had 'committed adultery with the wife of a Jewish carpenter'. The writer was probably merely 'letting off steam' and did not really think that God, in the Christian story, had assumed human form and lain with a mortal woman, as Zeus lay with Alcmena. But if one had to answer this person, one would have to say that if you called the miraculous conception divine adultery you would be driven to find a similar divine adultery in the conception of every child – nay, of every animal too. I am sorry to use expressions which will offend pious ears, but I do not know how else to make my point.

In a normal act of generation the father has no creative function. A microscopic particle of matter from his body, and a microscopic particle from the woman's body, meet. And with that there passes the colour of his hair and the hanging lower lip of her grandfather and the form of humanity in all its complexity of bones, sinews, nerves, liver and heart, and the form of those pre-human organisms which the embryo will recapitulate in the womb. Behind every spermatozoon lies the whole history of the universe: locked within it lies no inconsiderable part of the world's future. The weight or drive behind it is the momentum of the whole interlocked event which we call Nature up-to-date. And we know now that the 'laws of Nature' cannot supply that momentum. If we believe that God created Nature that momentum comes from Him. The human father is merely an instrument, a carrier, often an unwilling carrier, always simply the last in a long line of carriers – a line that stretches back far beyond his ancestors into pre-human and pre-organic deserts of time, back to the creation of matter itself. That line is in God's hand. It is the instrument by which He normally creates a man. For He is the reality behind both Genius and Venus; no woman ever conceived a child, no mare a foal, without Him.

But once, and for a special purpose, He dispensed with that long line which is His instrument: once His life-giving finger touched a woman without passing through the ages of interlocked events. Once the great glove of Nature was taken off His hand. His naked hand touched her. There was of course a unique reason for it. That time He was creating not simply a man but the Man who was to be Himself: was creating Man anew: was beginning, at this divine and human point, the New Creation of all things. The whole soiled and weary universe quivered at this direct injection of essential life – direct, uncontaminated, not drained through all the crowded history of Nature. But it would be out of place here to explore the religious significance of the miracle. We are here concerned with it simply as Miracle – that and nothing more. As far as concerns the creation of Christ's human nature (the Grand Miracle whereby His divine begotten nature enters into it is another matter) the miraculous conception is one more witness that here is Nature's Lord. He is doing now, small and close, what He does in a different fashion for every woman who conceives. He does it this time without a line of human ancestors: but even where He uses human ancestors it is not the less He who gives life.[4] The bed is barren where that great third party, Genius, is not present.

The miracles of *Healing*, to which I turn next, are now in a peculiar position. Men are ready to admit that many of them happened, but are inclined to deny that they were miraculous. The symptoms of very many diseases can be aped by hysteria, and hysteria can often be cured by 'suggestion'. It could, no doubt, be argued that such suggestion is a spiritual power, and therefore (if you like) a supernatural power, and that all instances of 'faith healing' are therefore miracles. But in our terminology they would be miraculous only in the same sense in which every instance of human reason is miraculous: and what we are now looking for is miracles other than that. My own view is that it would be unreasonable to ask a person who has not yet embraced Christianity in its entirety to allow that all the healings mentioned in the Gospels were miracles – that is, that they go beyond the possibilities of human 'suggestions'. It is for the doctors to decide as regards each particular case – supposing that the narratives are sufficiently detailed to allow even probable diagnosis. We have here a good example to what was said in an earlier chapter. So far from belief in miracles depending upon ignorance of natural law, we are here finding for ourselves that ignorance of law makes miracle unascertainable.

Without deciding in detail which of the healings must (apart from acceptance of the Christian faith) be regarded as miraculous, we can however indicate the kind of miracle involved. Its character can easily be obscured by the somewhat magical view which many people still take of ordinary and

---

[4] Cf. Matthew 23:9.

medical healing. There is a sense in which no doctor ever heals. The doctors themselves would be the first to admit this. The magic is not in the medicine but in the patient's body – in the *vis medicatrix naturae*, the recuperative or self-corrective energy of Nature. What the treatment does is to simulate Natural functions or to remove what hinders them. We speak for convenience of the doctor, or the dressing, healing a cut. But in another sense every cut heals itself: no cut can be healed in a corpse. That same mysterious force which we call gravitational when it steers the planets and biochemical when it heals a live body, is the efficient cause of all recoveries. And that energy proceeds from God in the first instance. All who are cured are cured by Him, not merely in the sense that His providence provides them with medical assistance and wholesome environments, but also in the sense that their very tissues are repaired by the far-descended energy which, flowing from Him, energises the whole system of Nature. But once He did it visibly to the sick in Palestine, a Man meeting with men. What in its general operations we refer to laws of Nature or once referred to Apollo or Aesculapius thus reveals itself. The Power that always was behind all healings puts on a face and hands. Hence, of course, the apparent chanciness of the miracles. It is idle to complain that He heals those whom He happens to meet, not those whom He doesn't. To be a man means to be in one place and not in another. The world which would not know Him as present everywhere was saved by His becoming *local*.

Christ's single miracle of Destruction, the withering of the fig-tree, has proved troublesome to some people, but I think its significance is plain enough. The miracle is an acted parable, a symbol of God's sentence on all that is 'fruitless' and specially, no doubt, on the official Judaism of that age. That is its moral significance. As a miracle, it again does in focus, repeats small and close, what God does constantly and throughout Nature. We have seen in the previous chapter how God, twisting Satan's weapon out of his hand, had become, since the Fall, the God even of human death. But much more, and perhaps ever since the creation, He has been the God of the death of organisms. In both cases, though in somewhat different ways, He is the God of death because He is the God of Life: the God of human death because through it increase of life now comes – the God of merely organic death because death is part of the very mode by which organic life spreads itself out in Time and yet remains new. A forest a thousand years deep is still collectively alive because some trees are dying and others are growing up. His human face, turned with negation in its eyes upon that one fig-tree, did once what His unincarnate action does to all trees. No tree died that year in Palestine, or any year anywhere, except because God did – or rather ceased to do – something to it.

All the miracles which we have considered so far are Miracles of the Old Creation. In all of them we see the Divine Man focusing for us what the God of Nature has already done on a larger scale. In our next class, the Miracles of Dominion over the Inorganic, we find some that are of the Old Creation and some that are of the New. When Christ stills the storm He does what God has often done before. God made Nature such that there would be both storms and calms: in that way all storms (except those that are still going on at this moment) have been stilled by God. It is unphilosophical, if you have once accepted the Grand Miracle, to reject the stilling of the storm. There is really no difficulty about adapting the weather conditions of the rest of the world to this one miraculous calm. I myself can still a storm in a room by shutting the window. Nature must make the best she can of it. And to do her justice she makes no trouble at all. The whole system, far from being thrown out of gear (which is what some nervous people seem to think a miracle would do) digests the new situation as easily as an elephant digests a drop of water. She is, as I have said before, an accomplished hostess. But when Christ walks on the water we have a miracle of the New Creation. God had not made the Old Nature, the world before the Incarnation, of such a kind that water would support a human body. This miracle is the foretaste of a Nature that is still in the future. The New creation is just breaking in. For a moment it looks as if it were going to spread. For a moment two men are living in that new world. St Peter also walks on the water – a pace or two: then his trust fails him and he sinks. He is back in Old Nature. That momentary glimpse was a snowdrop of a miracle. The snowdrops show that we have turned the corner of the year. Summer is coming. But it is a long way off and the snowdrops do not last long.

The Miracles of Reversal all belong to the New Creation. It is a Miracle of Reversal when the dead are raised. Old Nature knows nothing of this process: it involves playing backwards a film that we have always seen played forwards. The one or two instances of it in the Gospels are early flowers – what we call spring flowers, because they are prophetic, although they really bloom while it is still winter. And the Miracles of Perfecting or of Glory, the Transfiguration, the Resurrection, and the Ascension, are even more emphatically of the New Creation. These are the true spring, or even the summer, of the world's new year. The Captain, the forerunner, is already in May or June, though His followers on earth are still living in the frosts and east winds of Old Nature – for 'spring comes slowly up this way'.

None of the Miracles of the New Creation can be considered apart from the Resurrection and Ascension: and that will require another chapter.

16

MIRACLES OF THE
NEW CREATION

Beware, for fiends in triumph laugh
O'er him who learns the truth by half!
Beware; for God will not endure
For men to make their hope more pure
Than His good promise, or require
Another than the five-stringed lyre[1]
Which He has vowed again to the hands
Devout of him who understands
To tune it justly here!

C. PATMORE, *The Victories of Love*

In the earliest days of Christianity an 'apostle' was first and foremost a man who claimed to be an eyewitness of the Resurrection. Only a few days after the Crucifixion when two candidates were nominated for the vacancy created by the treachery of Judas, their qualification was that they had known Jesus personally both before and after His death and could offer first-hand evidence of the Resurrection in addressing the outer world (Acts 1:22). A few days later St Peter, preaching the first Christian sermon, makes the same claim – 'God raised Jesus, of which we all (we Christians) are witnesses' (Acts 2:32). In the first Letter to the Corinthians, St Paul bases his claim to apostleship on the same ground – 'Am I not an apostle? Have I not seen the Lord Jesus?' (1:9).

As this qualification suggests, to preach Christianity meant primarily to preach the Resurrection. Thus people who had heard only fragments of St Paul's teaching at Athens got the impression that he was talking about two new gods, Jesus and Anastasis (i.e. Resurrection) (Acts 17:18). The Resurrection is the central theme in every Christian sermon reported in the Acts. The Resurrection, and its consequences, were the 'gospel' or good news which the Christians brought: what we call the 'gospels', the narratives of Our Lord's life and death, were composed later for the benefit of those

[1] i.e. the Body with its five senses.

who had already accepted the *gospel*. They were in no sense the basis of Christianity: they were written for those already converted. The miracle of the Resurrection, and the theology of that miracle, comes first: the biography comes later as a comment on it. Nothing could be more unhistorical than to pick out selected sayings of Christ from the gospels and to regard those as the datum and the rest of the New Testament as a construction upon it. The first fact in the history of Christendom is a number of people who say they have seen the Resurrection. If they had died without making anyone else believe this 'gospel' no gospels would ever have been written.

It is very important to be clear about what these people meant. When modern writers talk of the Resurrection they usually mean one particular moment – the discovery of the Empty Tomb and the appearance of Jesus a few yards away from it. The story of that moment is what Christian apologists now chiefly try to support and sceptics chiefly try to impugn. But this almost exclusive concentration on the first five minutes or so of the Resurrection would have astonished the earliest Christian teachers. In claiming to have seen the Resurrection they were not necessarily claiming to have seen *that*. Some of them had, some of them had not. It had no more importance than any of the other appearances of the risen Jesus – apart from the poetic and dramatic importance which the beginnings of things must always have. What they were claiming was that they had all, at one time or another, met Jesus during the six or seven weeks that followed His death. Sometimes they seem to have been alone when they did so, but on one occasion twelve of them saw Him together, and on another occasion about five hundred of them. St Paul says that the majority of the five hundred were still alive when he wrote the First Letter to the Corinthians, i.e. in about 55 AD.

The 'Resurrection' to which they bore witness was, in fact, not the action of rising from the dead but the state of having risen; a state, as they held, attested by intermittent meetings during a limited period (except for the special, and in some ways different, meeting vouchsafed to St Paul). This termination of the period is important, for, as we shall see, there is no possibility of isolating the doctrine of the Resurrection from that of the Ascension.

The next point to notice is that the Resurrection was not regarded simply or chiefly as evidence for the immortality of the soul. It is, of course, often so regarded today: I have heard a man maintain that 'the importance of the Resurrection is that it proves *survival*'. Such a view cannot at any point be reconciled with the language of the New Testament. On such a view Christ would simply have done what all men do when they die: the only novelty would have been that in His case we were allowed to see it happening. But there is not in Scripture the faintest suggestion that the Resurrection was new evidence for something that had *in fact* been always happening. The New Testament writers speak as if Christ's achievement in rising from the dead was the first event of its kind in the whole history of the universe. He is the 'first fruits', the 'pioneer of life'. He has forced open a door that has been locked since the death of the first man. He has met, fought, and beaten the King of Death. Everything is different because He has done so. This is the beginning of the New Creation: a new chapter in cosmic history has opened.

I do not mean, of course, that the writers of the New Testament disbelieved in 'survival'. On the contrary they believed in it so readily that Jesus on more than one occasion had to assure them that He was not a ghost. From the earliest times the Jews, like many other nations, had believed that man possessed a 'soul' or *Nephesh* separable from the body, which went at death into the shadowy world called *Sheol*: a land of forgetfulness and imbecility where none called upon Jehovah any more, a land half unreal and melancholy like the Hades of the Greeks or the Niflheim of the Norsemen. From it shades could return and appear to the living, as Samuel's shade had done at the command of the Witch of Endor. In much more recent times there had arisen a more cheerful belief that the righteous passed at death to 'heaven'. Both doctrines are doctrines of 'the immortality of the soul' as a Greek or modern Englishman understands it: and both are quite irrelevant to the story of the Resurrection. The writers look upon this event as an absolute novelty. Quite clearly they do not think they have been haunted by a ghost from Sheol, nor even that they have had a vision of a 'soul' in 'heaven'. It must be clearly understood that if the Psychical Researchers succeeded in proving 'survival' and showed that the Resurrection was an instance of it, they would not be supporting the Christian faith but refuting it. If that were all that had happened the original 'gospel' would have been untrue. What the apostles claimed to have seen did not corroborate, nor exclude, and had indeed nothing to do with, either the doctrine of 'heaven' or the doctrine of Sheol. Insofar as it corroborated anything it corroborated a third Jewish belief which is quite distinct from both these. This third doctrine taught that in 'the day of Jahweh' peace would be restored and world dominion given to Israel under a righteous King: and that when this happened the righteous dead, or some of them, would come back to earth – not as floating wraiths but as solid men who cast shadows in the sunlight and made a noise when they tramped the floors. 'Awake and sing, ye that dwell in the dust', said Isaiah, 'And the earth shall cast out the dead' (26:19). What the apostles thought they had seen was, if not that, at any rate a lonely first instance of that: the first movement of a great wheel beginning to turn in the direction opposite to that which all men hitherto had observed. Of all the ideas entertained by man about death it is this one, and this one only, which the story of the Resurrection tends to confirm. If the story is false then it is this Hebrew myth of resurrection which begot it. If the story is true then the hint and anticipation of the truth is to be found not in popular ideas about ghosts nor in eastern doctrines of reincarnation nor in philosophical speculations about the immortality of the soul, but exclusively in the Hebrew prophecies of the return, the restoration, the great reversal. Immortality simply as immortality is irrelevant to the Christian claim.

There are, I allow, certain respects in which the risen Christ resembles the 'ghost' of popular tradition. Like a ghost He 'appears' and 'disappears': locked doors are no obstacle to Him. On the other hand He Himself vigorously asserts that He is corporeal (Luke 24: 39-40) and eats broiled fish. It is at this point that the modern reader becomes uncomfortable. He becomes more uncomfortable still at the word, 'Don't touch me; I have not yet gone up to the Father' (John 20:17). For voices and apparitions we are, in some measure, prepared. But what is this that must not be touched? What is all this about going 'up' to the Father? Is He not already 'with the Father' in the only sense that matters? What can 'going up' be except a metaphor for *that*? And if so, why has He 'not yet' gone? These discomforts arise because the story the 'apostles' actually had to tell begins at this point to conflict with the story we expect and are determined beforehand to read into their narrative.

We expect them to tell of a risen life which is purely 'spiritual' in the negative sense of that word: that is, we use the word 'spiritual' to mean not what it is but what it is not. We mean a life without space, without history, without environment, with no sensuous elements in it. We also, in our heart of hearts, tend to slur over the risen *manhood* of Jesus, to conceive Him, after death, simply returning into Deity, so that the Resurrection would be no more than the reversal or undoing of the Incarnation. That being so, all references to the risen *body* make us uneasy: they raise awkward questions. For as long as we hold the negatively spiritual view, we have not really been believing in that body at all. We have thought (whether we acknowledged it or not) that the body was not objective: that it was an appearance sent by God to assure the disciples of truths otherwise incommunicable. But what truths? If the truth is that after death there comes a negatively spiritual life, an eternity of mystical experience, what more misleading way of communicating it could possibly be found than the appearance of a human form which eats broiled fish? Again, on such a view, the body would really be a hallucination. And any theory of hallucination breaks down on the fact (and if it is invention it is the oddest invention that ever entered the mind of man) that on three separate occasions this hallucination was not immediately recognised as Jesus (Luke 24:13-31; John 20:15, 21:4). Even granting that God sent a holy hallucination to teach truths already widely believed without it, and far more easily taught by other methods, and certain to be completely obscured by this, might we not at least hope that He would get the face of the hallucination *right*? Is He who made all faces such a bungler that He cannot even work up a recognisable likeness of the Man who was Himself?

It is at this point that awe and trembling fall upon us as we read the records. If the story is false, it is at least a much stranger story than we expected, something for which philosophical 'religion', psychical research, and popular superstition have all alike failed to prepare us. If the story is true, then a wholly new mode of being has arisen in the universe.

The body which lives in that new mode is like, and yet unlike, the body His friends knew before the execution. It is differently related to space and probably to time, but by no means cut off from all relation to them. It can perform the animal act of eating. It is so related to matter, as we know it, that it can be touched, though at first it had better not be touched. It has also a history before it which is in view from the first moment of the Resurrection; it is presently going to become different or go somewhere else. That is why the story of the Ascension cannot be separated from that of the Resurrection. All the accounts suggest that the appearances of the Risen Body came to an end; some describe an abrupt end about six weeks after the death. And they describe this abrupt end in a way which presents greater difficulties to the modern mind than any other part of Scripture. For here, surely, we get the implication of all those primitive crudities to which I have said that Christians are not committed: the vertical ascent like a balloon, the local Heaven, the decorated chair to the right of the Father's throne. 'He was caught up into the sky (*ouranos*)', says St Mark's Gospel 'and sat down at the right hand of God.' 'He was lifted up', says the author of Acts 'and a cloud cut Him off from their sight.'

It is true that if we wish to get rid of these embarrassing passages we have the means to do so. The Marcan one probably formed no part of the earliest text of St Mark's Gospel: and you may add that the Ascension, though constantly implied throughout the New Testament, is described only in these two places. Can we then simply drop the Ascension story? The answer is that we can do so only if we regard the Resurrection appearances as those of a ghost or hallucination. For a phantom can just fade away; but an objective entity must go somewhere – something must happen to it. And if the Risen Body were not objective, then all of us (Christian or not) must invent some explanation for the disappearance of the corpse. And all Christians must explain why God sent or permitted a 'vision' or 'ghost' whose behaviour seems almost exclusively directed to convincing the disciples that it was not a vision or a ghost but a really corporeal being. If it were a vision then it was the most systematically deceptive and lying vision on record. But if it were real, then something happened to it after it ceased to appear. You cannot take away the Ascension without putting something else in its place.

The records represent Christ as passing after death (as no man had passed before) neither into a purely, that is, negatively, 'spiritual' mode of existence nor into a 'natural' life such as we know, but into a life which has its own, new Nature. It represents Him as withdrawing six weeks later, into some different mode of existence. It says – He says – that He goes 'to prepare a place for us'. This presumably means that He is about to create that whole new Nature which will provide the environment or conditions for His glorified humanity and, in Him, for ours. The picture is not what we expected – though whether it is less or more probable and philosophical on that account is another question. It is not the picture of an escape from any and every kind of Nature into some unconditioned and utterly transcendent life. It is the picture of a new human nature, and a new Nature in general, being brought into existence. We must, indeed, believe the risen body to be extremely different from the mortal body: but the existence, in that new state, of anything that could in any sense be described as 'body' at all, involves some sort of spatial relations and in the long run a whole new universe. That is the picture – not of unmaking but of remaking. The old field of space, time, matter, and the senses is to be weeded, dug, and sown for a new crop. We may be tired of that old field: God is not.

And yet the very way in which this New Nature begins to shine in has a certain affinity with the habits of Old Nature. In Nature as we know her, things tend to be anticipated. Nature is fond of 'false dawns', of precursors: thus, as I said before, some flowers come before true spring: sub-men (the evolutionists would have it) before the true men. So, here also, we get Law before Gospel, animal sacrifices foreshadowing the great sacrifice of God to God, the Baptist before the Messiah, and those 'miracles of the New Creation' which come before the Resurrection. Christ's walking on the water, and His raising of Lazarus fall in this class. Both give us hints of what the New Nature will be like.

In the Walking on the Water we see the relations of spirit and Nature so altered that Nature can be made to do whatever spirit pleases. This new obedience of Nature is, of course, not to be separated even in thought from spirit's own obedience to the Father of Spirits. Apart from that proviso such obedience by Nature, if it were possible, would result in chaos: the evil dream of Magic arises from finite spirit's longing to get that power without paying that price. The evil reality of lawless applied science (which is Magic's son and heir) is actually reducing large tracts of Nature to disorder and sterility at this very moment. I do not know how radically Nature herself would need to be altered to make her thus obedient to spirits, when spirits have become wholly obedient to their source. One thing at least we must observe. If we are in fact spirits, not Nature's offspring, then there must be some point (probably the brain) at which created spirit even now can produce effects on matter not by manipulation or technics but simply by the wish to do so. If that is what you mean by Magic then Magic is a reality manifested every time you move your hand or think a thought. And Nature, as we have seen, is not destroyed but rather perfected by her servitude.

The raising of Lazarus differs from the Resurrection of Christ Himself because Lazarus, so far as we know, was not raised to a new and more glorious mode of existence but merely restored to the sort of life he had had before. The fitness of the miracle lies in the fact that He who will raise all men at the general resurrection here does it small and close, and in an inferior – a merely anticipatory – fashion. For the mere restoration of Lazarus is as inferior in splendour to the *glorious* resurrection of the New Humanity as stone jars are to the green and growing vine or five little barley loaves to all the waving bronze and gold of a fat valley ripe for harvest. The resuscitation of Lazarus, so far as we can see, is simple reversal: a series of changes working in the direction opposite to that we have always experienced. At death, matter which has been organic, begins to flow away into the inorganic, to be finally scattered and used (some of it) by other organisms. The resurrection of Lazarus involves the reverse process. The general resurrection involves the reverse process universalised – a rush of matter toward organisation at the call of spirits which require it. It is presumably a foolish fancy (not justified by the words of Scripture) that each spirit should recover those particular units of matter which he ruled before. For one thing, they would not be enough to go round: we all live in second-hand suits and there are doubtless atoms in my chin which have served many another man, many a dog, many an eel, many a dinosaur. Nor does the unity of our bodies, even in this present life, consist in retaining the same particles. My form remains one, though the matter in it changes continually. I am, in that respect, like a curve in a waterfall.

But the miracle of Lazarus, though only anticipatory in one sense, belongs emphatically to the New Creation, for nothing is more definitely excluded by Old Nature than any return to a *status quo*. The pattern of Death and Rebirth never restores the previous individual organism. And similarly, on the inorganic level, we are told that Nature never restores order where disorder has once occurred. 'Shuffling,' said Professor Eddington, 'is the thing Nature never undoes.' Hence we live in a universe where organisms are always getting more disordered. These laws between them – irreversible death and irreversible entropy – cover almost the whole of what St Paul calls the 'vanity' of Nature: her futility, her ruinousness. And the film is never reversed. The movement from more order to less almost serves to determine the direction in which Time is flowing. You could almost define the future as the period in which what is now living will be dead and in which what order still remains will be diminished.

But entropy by its very character assures us that though it may be the universal rule in the Nature we know, it cannot be universal absolutely. If a man says 'Humpty Dumpty is falling', you see at once that this is not a complete story. The bit you have been told implies both a later chapter in which Humpty Dumpty will have reached the ground, and an earlier chapter in which he was still seated on the wall. A Nature which is 'running down' cannot be the whole story. A clock can't run down unless it has been wound up. Humpty Dumpty can't fall off a wall which never existed. If a Nature which disintegrates order were the whole of reality, where would she find any order to disintegrate? Thus on any view there must have been a time when processes the reverse of those we now see were going on: a time of winding up. The Christian claim is that those days are not gone for ever. Humpty Dumpty is going to be replaced on the wall – at least in the sense that what has died is going to recover life, probably in the sense that the inorganic universe is going to be reordered. Either Humpty Dumpty will never reach the ground (being caught in mid-fall by the everlasting arms) or else when he reaches it he will be put together again and replaced on a new and better wall. Admittedly, science discerns no 'king's horses and men' who can 'put Humpty Dumpty together again'. But you would not expect her to. She is based on observation: and all our observations are observations of Humpty Dumpty in mid-air. They do not reach either the wall above or the ground below – much less the King with his horses and men hastening towards the spot.

The Transfiguration or 'Metamorphosis' of Jesus is also, no doubt, an anticipatory glimpse of something to come. He is seen conversing with two of the ancient dead. The change which His own human form had undergone is described as one to luminosity, to 'shining whiteness'. A similar whiteness characterises His appearance at the beginning of the book of Revelation. One rather curious detail is that this shining or whiteness affected His clothes as much as His body. St Mark indeed mentions the clothes more explicitly than the face, and adds, with his inimitable naïvety, that 'no laundry could do anything like it'. Taken by itself this episode bears all the marks of a 'vision': that is, of an experience which, though it may be divinely sent and may reveal great truth, yet is not, objectively speaking, the experience it seems to be. But if the theory of 'vision' (or holy hallucination) will not cover the Resurrection appearances, it would be only a multiplying of hypotheses to introduce it here. We do not know to what phase or feature of the New Creation this episode points. It may reveal some special glorifying of Christ's manhood at some phase of its history (since history it apparently has) or it may reveal the glory which that manhood always has in its New Creation: it may even reveal a glory which all risen men will inherit. We do not know.

It must indeed be emphasised throughout that we know and can know very little about the New Nature. The task of the imagination here is not to forecast it but simply, by brooding on many possibilities, to make room for a more complete and circumspect agnosticism. It is useful to remember that even now senses responsive to different vibrations would admit us to quite new worlds of experience: that a multi-dimensional space would be different, almost beyond recognition, from the space we are now aware of, yet not discontinuous from it: that time may not always be for us, as it now is, unilinear and irreversible: that others parts of Nature might some day obey us as our cortex now does. It is useful not because we can trust these fancies to give us any positive truths about the New Creation but because they teach us not to limit, in our rashness, the vigour and variety of the new crops which this old field might yet produce. We are therefore compelled to believe that nearly all we are told about the New Creation is metaphorical. But not quite all. That is just where the story of the Resurrection suddenly jerks us back like a tether. The local appearances, the eating, the touching, the claim to be corporeal, must be either reality or sheer illusion. The New Nature is, in the most troublesome way, interlocked at some points with the Old. Because of its novelty we have to think of it, for the most part, metaphorically: but because of the partial interlocking, some facts about it come through into our present experience in all their literal facthood – just as some facts about an organism are inorganic facts, and some facts about a solid body are facts of linear geometry.

Even apart from that, the mere idea of a New Nature, a Nature beyond Nature, a systematic and diversified reality which is 'supernatural' in relation to the world of our five present senses but 'natural' from its own point of view, is profoundly shocking to a certain philosophical preconception from which we all suffer. I think Kant is at the root of it. It may be expressed by saying that we are prepared to believe either in a reality with one floor or in a reality with two floors, but not in a reality like a skyscraper with several floors. We are prepared, on the one hand, for the sort of reality that Naturalists believe in. That is a one-floor reality: this present Nature is all that there is. We are also prepared for reality as 'religion' conceives it: a reality with a ground floor (Nature) and then above that one other floor and one only – an eternal, spaceless, timeless, spiritual Something of which we can have no images and which, if it presents itself to human consciousness at all, does so in a mystical experience which shatters all our categories of thought. What we are not prepared for is anything in between. We feel quite sure that the first step beyond the world of our present experience must lead either nowhere at all or else into the blinding abyss of undifferentiated spirituality, the unconditioned, the absolute. That is why many believe in God who cannot believe in angels and an angelic world. That is why many believe in immortality who cannot believe in the resurrection of the body. That is why Pantheism is more popular than Christianity, and why many desire a Christianity stripped of its miracles. I cannot now understand, but I well remember, the passionate conviction with which I myself once defended this prejudice. Any rumour of floors or levels intermediate between the Unconditioned and the world revealed by our present senses I rejected without trial as 'mythology'.

Yet it is very difficult to see any rational grounds for the dogma that reality must have no more than two levels. There cannot, from the nature of the case, be evidence that God never created and never will create, more than one system. Each of them would be at least extra-natural in relation to all the others: and if any of them is more concrete, more permanent, more excellent, and richer than another it will be to that other *super*-natural. Nor will a partial contact between any two obliterate their distinctness. In that way there might be Natures piled upon Natures to any height God pleased, each Supernatural to that below it and Subnatural to that which surpassed it. But the tenor of Christian teaching is that we are actually living in a situation even more complex than that. A new Nature is being not merely made but made out of an old one. We live amid all the anomalies, inconveniences, hopes, and excitements of a house that is being rebuilt. Something is being pulled down and something going up in its place.

To accept the idea of intermediate floors – which the Christian story will, quite simply, force us to do if it is not a falsehood – does not of course involve losing our spiritual apprehension of the top floor of all. Most certainly, beyond all worlds, unconditioned and unimaginable, transcending discursive thought, there yawns for ever the ultimate Fact, the fountain of all other facthood, the burning and undimensioned depth of the Divine Life. Most certainly also, to be united with that Life in the eternal Sonship of Christ is, strictly speaking, the only thing worth a moment's consideration. And in so far as *that* is what you mean by *Heaven*, Christ's divine Nature never left it, and therefore never returned to it: and His human nature ascended thither not at the moment of the Ascension but at every moment. In that sense not one word that the spiritualisers have uttered will, please God, ever be unsaid by me. But it by no means follows that there are not other truths as well. I allow, indeed I insist, that Christ cannot be at 'the right hand of God' except in a metaphorical sense. I allow and insist that the Eternal Word, the Second Person of the Trinity, can never be, nor have been, confined to any place at all: it is rather in Him that all places exist. But the records say that the glorified, but still in some sense corporeal, Christ withdrew into some different mode of being about six weeks after the Crucifixion: and that He is 'preparing a place' for us. The statement in St Mark that He sat down at the right hand of God we must take as a metaphor: it was indeed, even for the writer, a poetical quotation, from Psalm 110. But the statement that the holy Shape went up and vanished does not permit the same treatment.

What troubles us here is not simply the statement itself but what (we feel sure) the author meant by it. Granted that there are different Natures, different levels of being, distinct but not always discontinuous – granted that Christ withdrew from one of these to another, that His withdrawal from one was indeed the first step in His creation of the other – what precisely should we expect the onlookers to see? Perhaps mere instantaneous vanishing would make us most comfortable. A sudden break between the perceptible and the imperceptible would worry us less than any kind of joint. But if the spectators say they saw first a short vertical movement and then a vague luminosity (that is what 'cloud' presumably means here as it certainly does in the account of the Transfiguration) and then nothing – have we any reason to object? We are well aware that increased distance from the centre of this planet could not *in itself* be equated with increase of power or beatitude. But this is only saying that *if* the movement had no connection with such spiritual events, why then it had no connection with them.

Movement (in any direction but one) away from the position momentarily occupied by our moving Earth will certainly be to us movement 'upwards'. To say that Christ's passage to a new 'Nature' could involve no such movement, or no movement at all, within the 'Nature' he was leaving, is very arbitrary. Where there is passage, there is departure; and departure is an event in the region from which the traveller is departing. All this, even on the assumption that the Ascending Christ is in a three-dimensional space. If it is not that kind of body, and space is not that kind of space, then we are even less qualified to say what the spectators of this entirely new event might or might not see or feel as if they had seen. There is, of course, no question of a human body as we know it existing in interstellar space as we know it. The Ascension belongs to a New Nature. We are discussing only what the 'joint' between the Old Nature and the new, the precise moment of transition, would look like.

But what really worries us is the conviction that, whatever we say, the New Testament writers meant something quite different. We feel sure that they thought they had seen their Master setting off on a journey for a local 'Heaven' where God sat in a throne and where there was another throne waiting for Him. And I believe that in a sense that is just what they did think. And I believe that, for this reason, whatever they had actually seen (sense perception, almost by hypothesis, would be confused at such a moment) they would almost certainly have remembered it as a vertical movement. What we must not say is that they 'mistook' local 'Heavens' and celestial throne-rooms and the like for the 'spiritual' Heaven of union with

God and supreme power and beatitude. You and I have been gradually disentangling different senses of the word *Heaven* throughout this chapter. It may be convenient here to make a list. *Heaven* can mean (1) The unconditioned Divine Life beyond all worlds. (2) Blessed participation in that Life by a created spirit. (3) The whole Nature or system of conditions in which redeemed human spirits, still remaining human, can enjoy such participation fully and for ever. This is the Heaven Christ goes to 'prepare' for us. (4) The physical Heaven, the sky, the space in which Earth moves. What enables us to distinguish these senses and hold them clearly apart is not any special spiritual purity but the fact that we are the heirs to centuries of logical analysis: not that we are sons to Abraham but that we are sons to Aristotle. We are not to suppose that the writers of the New Testament mistook Heaven in sense four or three for Heaven in sense two or one. You cannot mistake a half sovereign for a sixpence until you know the English system of coinage – that is, until you know the difference between them. In their idea of Heaven all these meanings were latent, ready to be brought out by later analysis. They never thought merely of the blue sky or merely of a 'spiritual' heaven. When they looked up at the blue sky they never doubted that there, whence light and heat and the precious rain descended, was the home of God: but on the other hand, when they thought of one ascending to that Heaven they never doubted He was 'ascending' in what we should call a 'spiritual' sense. The real and pernicious period of literalism comes far later, in the Middle Ages and the seventeenth century, when the distinctions have been made and heavy-handed people try to force the separated concepts together again in wrong ways. The fact that Galilean shepherds could not distinguish what they saw at the Ascension from that kind of ascent which, by its very nature, could never be seen at all, does not prove on the one hand that they were unspiritual, nor on the other that they saw nothing. A man who really believes that 'Heaven' is in the sky may well, in his heart, have a far truer and more spiritual conception of it than many a modern logician who could expose that fallacy with a few strokes of his pen. For he who does the will of the Father shall know the doctrine. Irrelevant material splendours in such a man's idea of the vision of God will do no harm, for they are not there for their own sakes. Purity from such images in a merely theoretical Christian's idea will do no good if they have been banished only by logical criticism.

But we must go a little further than this. It is not an accident that simple-minded people, however spiritual, should blend the ideas of God and Heaven and the blue sky. It is a fact, not a fiction, that light and life-giving heat do come down from the sky to Earth. The analogy of the sky's role to begetting and of the Earth's role to bearing is sound as far as it goes. The huge dome of the sky is of all things sensuously perceived the most like infinity. And when God made space and worlds that move in space, and clothed our world with air, and gave us such eyes and such imaginations as those we have, He knew what the sky would mean to us. And since nothing in His work is accidental, if He knew, He intended. We cannot be certain that this was not indeed one of the chief purposes for which Nature was created; still less that it was not one of the chief reasons why the withdrawal was allowed to affect human senses as a movement upwards. (A disappearance into the Earth would beget a wholly different religion.) The ancients in letting the spiritual symbolism of the sky flow straight into their minds without stopping to discover by analysis that it was a symbol, were not entirely mistaken. In one way they were perhaps less mistaken than we.

For we have fallen into an opposite difficulty. Let us confess that probably every Christian now alive finds a difficulty in reconciling the two things he has been told about 'heaven' – that it is, on the one hand, a life in Christ, a vision of God, a ceaseless adoration, and that it is, on the other hand, a bodily life. When we seem nearest to the vision of God in this life, the body seems almost an irrelevance. And if we try to conceive our eternal life as one in a body (any kind of body) we tend to find that some vague dream of Platonic paradises and gardens of the Hesperides has substituted itself for that mystical approach which we feel (and I think rightly) to be more important. But if that discrepancy were final then it would follow – which is absurd – that God was originally mistaken when He introduced our spirits into the Natural order at all. We must conclude that the discrepancy itself is precisely one of the disorders which the New Creation comes to heal. The fact that the body, and locality and locomotion and time, now feel irrelevant to the highest reaches of the spiritual life is (like the fact that we can think of our bodies as 'coarse') a *symptom*. Spirit and Nature have quarrelled in us; that is our disease. Nothing we can yet do enables us to imagine its complete healing. Some glimpses and faint hints we have: in the Sacraments, in the use made of sensuous imagery by the great poets, in the best instances of sexual love, in our experiences of the earth's beauty. But the full healing is utterly beyond our present conceptions. Mystics have got as far in contemplation of God as the point at which the senses are banished: the further point, at which they will be put back again, has (to the best of my knowledge) been reached by no one. The destiny of redeemed man is not less but more unimaginable than mysticism would lead us to suppose – because it is full of semi-imaginables which we cannot at present admit without destroying its essential character.

One point must be touched on because, though I kept silence, it would none the less be present in most readers' minds. The letter and spirit of scripture, and of all Christianity, forbid us to suppose that life in the New Creation will be a sexual life; and this reduces our imagination to the withering alternative either of bodies which are hardly recognisable as human bodies at all or else of a perpetual fast. As regards the fast, I think our present outlook might be like that of a small boy who, on being told that the sexual act was the highest bodily pleasure should immediately ask whether you ate chocolates at the same time. On receiving the answer 'No,' he might regard absence of chocolates as the chief characteristic of sexuality. In vain would you tell him that the reason why lovers in their carnal raptures don't bother about chocolates is that they have something better to think of. The boy knows chocolate: he does not know the positive thing that excludes it. We are in the same position. We know the sexual life; we do not know, except in glimpses, the other thing which, in Heaven, will leave no room for it. Hence where fullness awaits us we anticipate fasting. In denying that sexual life, as we now understand it, makes any part of the final beatitude, it is not of course necessary to suppose that the distinction of sexes will disappear. What is no longer needed for biological purposes may be expected to survive for splendour. Sexuality is the instrument both of virginity and of conjugal virtue; neither men nor women will be asked to throw away weapons they have used victoriously. It is the beaten and the fugitives who throw away their swords. The conquerors sheathe theirs and retain them. 'Trans-sexual' would be a better word than 'sexless' for the heavenly life.

I am well aware that this last paragraph may seem to many readers unfortunate and to some comic. But that very comedy, as I must repeatedly insist, is the symptom of our estrangement, as spirits, from Nature and our estrangement, as animals, from Spirit. The whole conception of the New Creation involves the belief that this estrangement will be healed. A curious consequence will follow. The archaic type of thought which could not clearly distinguish spiritual 'Heaven' from the sky, is from our point of view a confused type of thought. But it also resembles and anticipates a type of thought which will one day be true. That archaic sort of thinking will become simply the correct sort when Nature and Spirit are fully harmonised – when Spirit rides Nature so perfectly that the two together make rather a *Centaur* than a mounted knight. I do not mean necessarily that the blending of Heaven and sky, in particular, will turn out to be specially true, but that that kind of blending will accurately mirror the reality which will then exist. There will be no room to get the finest razor-blade of thought in between Spirit and Nature. Every state of affairs in the New Nature will be the perfect expression of a spiritual state and every spiritual state the perfect informing of, and bloom upon, a state of affairs; one with it as the perfume with a flower or the 'spirit' of great poetry with its form. There is thus in the history of human thought, as elsewhere, a pattern of death and rebirth. The old, richly imaginative thought which still survives in Plato has to submit to the deathlike, but indispensable, process of logical analysis: nature and spirit, matter and mind, fact and myth, the literal and the metaphorical, have to be more and more sharply separated, till at last a purely mathematical universe and a purely subjective mind confront one another across an unbridgeable chasm. But from this descent also, if thought itself is to survive, there must be reascent and the Christian conception provides for it. Those who attain the glorious resurrection will see the dry bones clothed again with flesh, the fact and the myth remarried, the literal and the metaphorical rushing together.

The remark so often made that 'Heaven is a state of mind' bears witness to the wintry and deathlike phase of this process in which we are now living. The implication is that if Heaven is a state of mind – or, more correctly, of the spirit – then it must be only a state of the spirit, or at least that anything else, if added to that state of spirit, would be irrelevant. That is what every great religion *except* Christianity would say. But Christian teaching by saying that God made the world and called it good teaches that Nature or environment cannot be simply irrelevant to spiritual beatitude in general, however far in one particular Nature, during the days of her bondage, they may have drawn apart. By teaching the resurrection of the body it teaches that Heaven is not merely a state of the spirit but a state of the body as well: and therefore a state of Nature as a whole. Christ, it is true, told His hearers that the Kingdom of Heaven was 'within' or 'among' them. But His hearers were not *merely* in 'a state of mind'. The planet He had created was beneath their feet, His sun above their heads; blood and lungs and guts were working in the bodies He had invented, photons and sound waves of His devising were blessing them with the sight of His human face and the sound of His voice. We are never *merely* in a state of mind. The prayer and the meditation made in howling wind or quiet sunshine, in morning alacrity or evening resignation, in youth or age, good health or ill, may be equally, but are differently, blessed. Already in this present life we have all seen how God can take up all these seeming irrelevances into the spiritual fact and cause them to bear no small part in making the blessing of that moment to be the particular blessing it was – as fire can burn coal and wood equally but a wood fire is different from a coal one. From this factor of environment Christianity does not teach us to desire a total release. We desire, like St Paul, not to be un-clothed but to be re-clothed: to find not the formless Everywhere-and-Nowhere but the promised land, that Nature which will be always and perfectly – as present Nature is partially and intermittently – the instrument for that music which will then arise between Christ and us.

And what, you ask, does it matter? Do not such ideas only excite us and distract us from the more immediate and more certain things, the love of God and our neighbours, the bearing of the daily cross? If you find that they so distract you, think of them no more. I most fully allow that it is of more importance for you or me today to refrain from one sneer or to extend one charitable thought to an enemy than to know all that angels and archangels know about the mysteries of the New Creation. I write of these things not because they are the most important but because this book is about miracles. From the title you cannot have expected a book of devotion or of ascetic theology. Yet I will not admit that the things we have been discussing for the last few pages are of no importance for the practice of the Christian life. For I suspect that our conception of Heaven as *merely* a state of mind is not unconnected with the fact that the specifically Christian virtue of Hope has in our time grown so languid. Where our fathers, peering into the future, saw gleams of gold, we see only the mist, white, featureless, cold and never moving.

The thought at the back of all this negative spirituality is really one forbidden to Christians. They, of all men, must not conceive spiritual joy and worth as things that need to be rescued or tenderly protected from time and place and matter and the senses. Their God is the God of corn and oil and wine. He is the glad Creator. He has become Himself incarnate. The sacraments have been instituted. Certain spiritual gifts are offered us only on condition that we perform certain bodily acts. After that we cannot really be in doubt of His intention. To shrink back from all that can be called Nature into negative spirituality is as if we ran away from horses instead of learning to ride. There is in our present pilgrim condition plenty of room (more room than most of us like) for abstinence and renunciation and mortifying our natural desires. But behind all asceticism the thought should be, 'Who will trust us with the true wealth if we cannot be trusted even with the wealth that perishes?' Who will trust me with a spiritual body if I cannot control even an earthly body? These small and perishable bodies we now have were given to us as ponies are given to schoolboys. We must learn to manage: not that we may some day be free of horses altogether but that some day we may ride bare-back, confident and rejoicing, those greater mounts, those winged, shining and world-shaking horses which perhaps even now expect us with impatience, pawing and snorting in the King's stables. Not that the gallop would be of any value unless it were a gallop with the King; but how else – since He has retained His own charger – should we accompany Him?

17

EPILOGUE

If you leave a thing alone you leave it to a
torrent of change. If you leave a white post
alone it will soon be a black post.
G. K. CHESTERTON, *Orthodoxy*

My work ends here. If, after reading it, you now turn to study the historical evidence for yourself, begin with the New Testament and not with the books about it. If you do not know Greek get it in a modern translation. Moffat's is probably the best: Monsignor Knox is also good. I do not advise the *Basic English* version. And when you turn from the New Testament to modern scholars, remember that you go among them as a sheep among wolves. Naturalistic assumptions, beggings of the question such as that which I noted on the first page of this book, will meet you on every side – even from the pens of clergymen. This does not mean (as I was once tempted to suspect) that these clergymen are disguised apostates who deliberately exploit the position and the livelihood given them by the Christian Church to undermine Christianity. It comes partly from what we may call a 'hangover'. We all have Naturalism in our bones and even conversion does not at once work the infection out of our system. Its assumptions rush back upon the mind the moment vigilance is relaxed. And in part the procedure of these scholars arises from the feeling which is greatly to their credit – which indeed is honourable to the point of being Quixotic. They are anxious to allow to the enemy every advantage he can with any show of fairness claim. They thus make it part of their method to eliminate the supernatural wherever it is even remotely possible to do so, to strain natural explanation even to the breaking point before they admit the least suggestion of miracle. Just in the same spirit some examiners tend to overmark any candidate whose opinions and character, as revealed by his work, are revolting to them. We are so afraid of being led into unfairness by our instant dislike of the man that we are liable to overshoot the mark and treat him too kindly. Many modern Christian scholars overshoot the mark for a similar reason.

In using the books of such people you must therefore be continually on guard. You must develop a nose like a bloodhound for those steps in the argument which depend not on historical and linguistic knowledge but on the concealed assumption that miracles are impossible, improbable or improper. And this means that you must really re-educate yourself: must work hard and consistently to eradicate from your mind the whole type of thought in which we have all been brought up. It is the type of thought which, under various disguises, has been our adversary throughout this book. It is technically called *Monism*; but perhaps the unlearned reader will understand me best if I call it *Everythingism*. I mean by this the belief that 'everything', or 'the whole show', must be self-existent, must be more important than every particular thing, and must contain all particular things in such a way that they cannot be really very different from one another – that they must be not merely 'at one', but one. Thus the Everythingist, if he starts from God, becomes a Pantheist; there must be nothing that is not God. If he starts from Nature he becomes a Naturalist; there must be nothing that is not Nature. He thinks that everything is in the long run 'merely' a precursor or a development or a relic or an instance or a disguise, of everything else. This philosophy I believe to be profoundly untrue. One of the moderns has said that reality is 'incorrigibly plural'. I think he is right. All things come from One. All things are related – related in different and complicated ways. But all things are not one. The word 'everything' should mean simply the total (a total to be reached, if we knew enough, by enumeration) of all the things that exist at a given moment. It must not be given a mental capital letter; must not (under the influence of picture thinking) be turned into a sort of pool in which particular things sink or even a cake in which they are the currants. Real things are sharp and knobbly and complicated and different. Everythingism is congenial to our minds because it is the natural philosophy of a totalitarian, mass-producing, conscripted age. That is why we must be perpetually on our guard against it.

And yet ... and yet ... It is that *and yet* which I fear more than any positive argument against miracles: that soft, tidal return of your habitual outlook as you close the book and the familiar four walls about you and the familiar noises from the street reassert themselves. Perhaps (if I dare suppose so much) you have been led on at times while you were reading, have felt ancient hopes and fears astir in your heart, have perhaps come almost to the threshold of belief – but now? No. It just won't do. Here is the ordinary, here is the 'real' world, round you again. The dream is ending; as all other similar dreams have always ended. For of course this is not the first time such a thing has happened. More than once in your life before this you have heard a strange story, read some odd book, seen something queer or imagined you have seen it, entertained some wild hope or terror: but always it ended in the same way. And always you wondered how you could, even for a moment, have expected it not to. For that 'real world' when you came back to it is so unanswerable. *Of course* the strange story was false, of course the voice was really subjective, of course the apparent portent was a coincidence. You are ashamed of yourself for having ever thought otherwise: ashamed, relieved, amused, disappointed, and angry all at once. You ought to have known that, as Arnold says, 'Miracles don't happen'.

About this state of mind I have just two things to say. First, that it is precisely one of those counterattacks by Nature which, on my theory, you ought to have anticipated. Your rational thinking has no foothold in your merely natural consciousness except what it wins and maintains by conquest. The moment rational thought ceases, imagination, mental habit, temperament, and the 'spirit of the age' take charge of you again. New thoughts, until they have themselves become habitual, will affect your consciousness as a whole only while you are actually thinking them. Reason has but to nod at his post, and instantly Nature's patrols are infiltrating. Therefore, while counter-arguments against Miracle are to be given full attention (for if I am wrong, then the sooner I am refuted the better not only for you but for me) the mere gravitation of the mind back to its habitual outlook must be discounted. Not only in this enquiry but in every enquiry. That same familiar room, reasserting itself as one closes the book, can make other things *feel* incredible besides miracles. Whether the book has been telling you that the end of civilisation is at hand, that you are kept in your chair by the curvature of space, or even that you are upside down in relation to Australia, it may still seem a little unreal as you yawn and think of going to bed. I have found even a simple truth (e.g. that my hand, this hand now resting on the book, will one day be a skeleton's hand) singularly unconvincing at such a moment. 'Belief-feelings', as Dr Richards calls them, do not follow reason except by long training: they follow Nature, follow the grooves and ruts which already exist in the mind. The firmest theoretical conviction in favour of materialism will not prevent a particular kind of man, under certain conditions, from being afraid of ghosts. The firmest theoretical conviction in favour of miracles will not prevent another kind of man, in other conditions, from *feeling* a heavy, inescapable certainty that no miracle can ever occur. But the feelings of a tired and nervous man, unexpectedly reduced to passing a night in a large empty country house at the end of a journey on which he has been reading a ghost-story, are no evidence that ghosts exist. Your feelings at this moment are no evidence that miracles do not occur.

The second thing is this. You are probably quite right in thinking that you will never see a miracle done: you are probably equally right in thinking that there was a natural explanation of anything in your past life which seemed, at the first glance, to be 'rum' or 'odd'. God does not shake miracles into Nature at random as if from a pepper-caster. They come on great occasions: they are found at the great ganglions of history – not of political or social history, but of that spiritual history which cannot be fully known by men. If your own life does not happen to be near one of those great ganglions, how should you expect to see one? If we were heroic missionaries, apostles, or martyrs, it would be a different matter. But why you or I? Unless you live near a railway, you will not see trains go past your windows. How likely is it that you or I will be present when a peace-treaty is signed, when a great scientific discovery is made, when a dictator commits suicide? That we should see a miracle is even less likely. Nor, if we understand, shall we be anxious to do so. 'Nothing almost sees miracles but misery.' Miracles and martyrdoms tend to bunch about the same areas of history – areas we have naturally no wish to frequent. Do not, I earnestly advise you, demand an ocular proof unless you are already perfectly certain that it is not forthcoming.

APPENDIX A

ON THE WORDS 'SPIRIT'
AND 'SPIRITUAL'

The reader should be warned that the angle from which Man is approached in Chapter IV is quite different from that which would be proper in a devotional or practical treatise on the spiritual life. The kind of analysis which you make of any complex thing depends on the purpose you have in view. Thus in a society the important distinctions, from one point of view, would be those of male and female, children and adults, and the like. From another point of view the important distinctions would be those of rulers and ruled. From a third point of view distinctions of class or occupation might be the most important. All these different analyses might be equally correct, but they would be useful for different purposes. When we are considering Man as evidence for the fact that this spatio-temporal Nature is not the only thing in existence, the important distinction is between that part of Man which belongs to this spatio-temporal Nature and that part which does not: or, if you prefer, between those phenomena of humanity which are rigidly interlocked with all other events in this space and time and those which have a certain independence. These two parts of a man may rightly be called Natural and Supernatural: in calling the second 'Super-Natural' we mean that it is something which invades, or is added to, the great interlocked event in space and time, instead of merely arising from it. On the other hand this 'Supernatural' part is itself a created being – a thing called into existence by the Absolute Being and given by Him a certain character or 'nature'. We could therefore say that while 'supernatural' in relation to *this* Nature (this complex event in space and time) it is, in another sense, 'natural' – i.e. it is a specimen of a class of things which God normally creates after a stable pattern.

There is, however, a sense in which the life of this part can become *absolutely* Supernatural, i.e. not beyond *this* Nature but beyond any and every Nature, in the sense that it can achieve a kind of life which could never have been *given* to any created being in its mere creation. The distinction will, perhaps, become clearer if we consider it in relation not to men but to angels. (It does not matter, here, whether the reader believes in angels or not. I am using them only to make the point clearer.) All angels, both the 'good' ones and the bad or 'fallen' ones which we call devils, are equally 'Supernatural' in relation to *this* spatio-temporal Nature: i.e. they are outside it and have powers and a mode of existence which it could not provide. But the good angels lead a life which is Supernatural in another sense as well. That is to say, they have, of their own free will, offered back to God in love the 'natures' He gave them at their creation. All creatures of course live from God in the sense that He made them and at every moment maintains them in existence. But there is a further and higher kind of 'life from God' which can be given only to a creature who voluntarily surrenders himself to it. This life the good angels have and the bad angels have not: and it is absolutely Supernatural because no creature in any world can have it by the mere fact of being the sort of creature it is.

As with angels, so with us. The rational part of every man is supernatural in the relative sense – the same sense in which *both* angels and devils are supernatural. But if it is, as the theologians say, 'born again', if it surrenders itself back to God in Christ, it will then have a life which is absolutely Supernatural, which is not created at all but begotten, for the creature is then sharing the begotten life of the Second Person of the Deity.

When devotional writers talk of the 'spiritual life' – and often when they talk of the 'supernatural life' or when I myself, in another book, talked of *Zoë* – they mean this *absolutely* Supernatural life which no creature can be given simply by being created but which every rational creature can have by voluntarily surrendering itself to the life of Christ. But much confusion arises from the fact that in many books the words 'Spirit' or 'Spiritual' are also used to mean the *relatively* supernatural element in Man, the element external to *this* Nature which is (so to speak) 'issued' or handed out to him by the mere fact of being created as a Man at all.

It will perhaps be helpful to make a list of the sense in which the words 'spirit', 'spirits' and 'spiritual' are, or have been, used in English.

1. The chemical sense, e.g. 'Spirits evaporate very quickly.'

2. The (now obsolete) medical sense. The older doctors believed in certain extremely fine fluids in the human body which were called 'the spirits'. As medical science this view has long been abandoned, but it is the origin of some expressions we still use; as when we speak of being 'in high spirits' or 'in low spirits' or say that a horse is 'spirited' or that a boy is 'full of animal spirits'.

3. 'Spiritual' is often used to mean simply the opposite of 'bodily' or 'material'. Thus all that is immaterial in man (emotions, passions, memory, etc.) is often called 'spiritual'. It is very important to remember that what is 'spiritual' in this sense is not necessarily good. There is nothing specially

fine about the mere fact of immateriality. Immaterial things may, like material things, be good or bad or indifferent.

4. Some people use 'spirit' to mean that relatively supernatural element which is given to every man at his creation – the rational element. This is, I think, the most useful way of employing the word. Here again it is important to realise that what is 'spiritual' is not necessarily good. A Spirit (in this sense) can be either the best or the worst of created things. It is because Man is (in this sense) a spiritual animal that he can become either a son of God or a devil.

5. Finally, Christian writers use 'spirit' and 'spiritual' to mean the life which arises in such rational beings when they voluntarily surrender to Divine grace and become sons of the Heavenly Father in Christ. It is in this sense, and in this sense alone, that the 'spiritual' is always good.

It is idle to complain that words have more than one sense. Language is a living thing and words are bound to throw out new senses as a tree throws out new branches. It is not wholly a disadvantage, since in the act of disentangling these senses we learn a great deal about the things involved which we might otherwise have overlooked. What is disastrous is that any word should change its sense during a discussion without our being aware of the change. Hence, for the present discussion, it might be useful to give different names to the three things which are meant by the word 'Spirit' in senses three, four, and five. Thus for sense three a good word would be 'soul': and the adjective to go with it would be 'psychological'. For sense four we might keep the words 'spirit' and 'spiritual'. For sense five the best adjective would be 'regenerate', but there is no very suitable noun.[1] And this is perhaps significant: for what we are talking about is not (as *soul* and *spirit* are) a part or element in Man but a redirection and revitalising of all the parts or elements. Thus in one sense there is nothing more in a regenerate man than in an unregenerate man, just as there is nothing more in a man who is walking in the right direction than in one who is walking in the wrong direction. In another sense, however, it might be said that the regenerate man is *totally* different from the unregenerate, for the regenerate life, the Christ that is formed in him, transforms every part of him: in it his spirit, soul and body will all be reborn. Thus if the regenerate life is not a *part* of the man, this is largely because where it arises at all it cannot rest till it becomes the whole man. It is not divided from any of the parts as they are divided from each other. The life of the 'spirit' (in sense four) is in a sense cut off from the life of the soul: the purely rational and moral man who tries to live entirely by his created spirit finds himself forced to treat the passions and imaginations of his soul

---

[1] Because the 'spirit' in this sense is identical with the New Man (the Christ formed in each perfected Christian) some Latin theologians call it simply our *Novitas* i.e. our 'newness'.

as mere enemies to be destroyed or imprisoned. But the regenerate man will find his soul eventually harmonised with his spirit by the life of Christ that is in him. Hence Christians believe in the resurrection of the body, whereas the ancient philosophers regard the body as a mere encumbrance. And this perhaps is a universal law, that the higher you rise the lower you can descend. Man is a tower in which the different floors can hardly be reached from one another but all can be reached from the top floor.

N.B. In the Authorised Version the 'spiritual' man means what I am calling the 'regenerate' man: the 'natural' man means, I think, both what I call the 'spirit man' and the 'soul man'.

APPENDIX B

ON 'SPECIAL PROVIDENCES'

In this book the reader has heard of two classes of events and two only – miracles and natural events. The former are not interlocked with the history of Nature in the backward direction – i.e. in the time before their occurrence. The latter are. Many pious people, however, speak of certain events as being 'providential' or 'special providences' without meaning that they are miraculous. This generally implies a belief that, quite apart from miracles, some events are providential in a sense in which some others are not. Thus some people thought that the weather which enabled us to bring off so much of our army at Dunkirk was 'providential' in some way in which weather as a whole is not providential. The Christian doctrine that some events, though not miracles, are yet answers to prayer, would seem at first to imply this.

I find it very difficult to conceive an intermediate class of events which are neither miraculous nor merely 'ordinary'. Either the weather at Dunkirk was or was not that which the previous physical history of the universe, by its own character, would inevitably produce. If it was, then how is it 'specially' providential? If it was not, then it was a miracle.

It seems to me, therefore, that we must abandon the idea that there is any special class of events (apart from miracles) which can be distinguished as 'specially providential'. Unless we are to abandon the conception of Providence altogether, and with it the belief in efficacious prayer, it follows that all events are equally providential. If God directs the course of events at all then he directs the movement of every atom at every moment; 'not one sparrow falls to the ground' without that direction. The 'naturalness' of natural events does not consist in being somehow outside God's providence. It consists in their being interlocked with one another inside a common space-time in accordance with the fixed pattern of the 'laws'.

In order to get any picture at all of a thing, it is sometimes necessary to begin with a false picture and then correct it. The false picture of Providence (false because it represents God and Nature as being both contained in a common Time) would be as follows. Every event in Nature results from some previous event, not from the laws of Nature. In the long run the first natural event, whatever it was, has dictated every other event. That is, when God at the moment of creation fed the first event into the framework of the 'laws' – first set the ball rolling – He determined the whole history of Nature. Foreseeing every part of that history, He intended every part of it. If He had wished for different weather at Dunkirk He would have made the first event slightly different.

The weather we actually had is therefore in the strictest sense providential; it was decreed, and decreed for a purpose, when the world was made – but no more so (though more interestingly to us) than the precise position at this moment of every atom in the ring of Saturn.

It follows (still retaining our false picture) that every physical event was determined so as to serve a great number of purposes.

Thus God must be supposed in predetermining the weather at Dunkirk to have taken fully into account the effect it would have not only on the destiny of two nations but (what is incomparably more important) on all the individuals involved on both sides, on all animals, vegetables and minerals within range, and finally on every atom in the universe. This may sound excessive, but in reality we are attributing to the Omniscient only an infinitely superior degree of the same kind of skill which a mere human novelist exercises daily in constructing his plot.

Suppose I am writing a novel. I have the following problems on my hands: (1) Old Mr A. has got to be dead before Chapter 15. (2) And he'd better die suddenly because I have to prevent him from altering his will. (3) His daughter (my heroine) has got to be kept out of London for three chapters at least. (4) My hero has somehow got to recover the heroine's good opinion which he lost in Chapter 7. (5) That young prig B. who has to improve before the end of the book, needs a bad moral shock to take the conceit out of him. (6) We haven't decided on B.'s job yet; but the whole development of his character will involve giving him a job and showing him actually at work. How on earth am I to get in all these six things? ... I have it. What about a railway accident? Old A. can be killed in it, and that settles him. In fact the accident can occur while he is actually going up to London to see his solicitor with the very purpose of getting his will altered. What more natural than that his daughter should run up with him? We'll have her slightly injured in the accident: that'll prevent her reaching London for as many chapters as we need. And the hero can be on the same train. He can behave with great coolness and heroism during the accident – probably he'll rescue the heroine from a burning carriage. That settles my fourth point. And the young prig B.? We'll make him the signalman whose negligence caused the accident. That gives him his moral shock and also links him up with the main plot. In fact, once we have thought of the railway accident, that single event will solve six apparently separate problems.

No doubt this is in some ways an intolerably misleading image: firstly because (except as regards the prig B.) I have been thinking not of the ultimate good of my characters but of the entertainment of my readers: secondly because we are simply ignoring the effect of the railway accident on all the other passengers in that train: and finally because it is I who make B. give the wrong signal. That is, though I pretend that he has free will, he really hasn't. In spite of these objections, however, the example may perhaps suggest how Divine ingenuity could so contrive the physical 'plot' of the universe as to provide a 'providential' answer to the needs of innumerable creatures.

But some of these creatures have free will. It is at this point that we must begin to correct the admittedly false picture of Providence which we have hitherto been using. That picture, you will remember, was false because it represented God and Nature as inhabiting a common Time. But it is probable that Nature is not really in Time and almost certain that God is not. Time is probably (like perspective) the mode of our perception. There is therefore in reality no question of God's at one point in time (the moment of creation) adapting the material history of the universe in advance to free acts which you or I are to perform at a later point in Time. To Him all the physical events and all the human acts are present in an eternal Now. The liberation of finite wills and the creation of the whole material history of the universe (related to the acts of those wills in all the necessary complexity) is to Him a single operation. In this sense God did not create the universe long ago but creates it at this minute – at every minute.

Suppose I find a piece of paper on which a black wavy line is already drawn, I can now sit down and draw other lines (say in red) so shaped as to combine with the black line into a pattern. Let us now suppose that the original black line is conscious. But it is not conscious along the whole length at once – only on each point on that length in turn.

Its consciousness in fact is travelling along that line from left to right retaining point A only as a memory when it reaches B and unable until it has left B to become conscious of C. Let us also give this black line free will. It chooses the direction it goes in. The particular wavy shape of it is the shape it wills to have. But whereas it is aware of its own chosen shape only moment by moment and does not know at point D which way it will decide to turn at point F, I can see its shape as a whole and all at once. At every moment it will find my red lines waiting for it and adapted to it. Of course: because I, in composing the total red-and-black design have the whole course of the black line in view and take it into account. It is a matter not of impossibility but merely of designer's skill for me to devise red lines which at every point have a right relation not only to the black line but to one another so as to fill the whole paper with a satisfactory design.

In this model the black line represents a creature with free will, the red lines represent material events, and I represent God. The model would of course be more accurate if I were making the paper as well as the pattern and if there were hundreds of millions of black lines instead of one – but for the sake of simplicity we must keep it as it is.[1]

It will be seen that if the black line addressed prayers to me I might (if I chose) grant them. It prays that when it reaches point N it may find the red lines arranged around it in a certain shape. That shape may by the laws of design require to be balanced by other arrangements of red lines on quite different parts of the paper – some at the top or bottom so far away from the black line that it knows nothing about them: some so far to the left that they come before the beginning of the black line, some so far to the right that they come after its end. (The black line would call these parts of the paper, 'The time before I was born,' and, 'The time after I'm dead.') But these other parts of the pattern demanded by that red shape which Black Line wants at N, do not prevent my granting its prayer. For his whole course has been visible to me from the moment I looked at the paper and his requirements at point N are among the things I took into account in deciding the total pattern.

Most of our prayers if fully analysed, ask either for a miracle or for events whose foundation will have to have been laid before I was born, indeed, laid when the universe began. But then to God (though not to me) I and the prayer I make in 1945 were just as much present at the creation of the world as they are now and will be a million years hence. God's creative act is timeless and timelessly adapted to the 'free' elements within it: but this timeless adaptation meets our consciousness as a sequence and prayer and answer.

Two corollaries follow:

1. People often ask whether a given event (not a miracle) was really an answer to prayer or not. I think that if they analyse their thought they will find they are asking, 'Did God bring it about for a special purpose or would it have happened anyway as part of the natural course of events?' But this (like the old question, 'Have you left off beating your wife?') makes either answer impossible. In the play, *Hamlet*, Ophelia climbs out on a branch overhanging a river: the branch breaks, she falls in and drowns. What would you reply if anyone asked, 'Did Ophelia die because Shakespeare for poetic reasons wanted her to die at that moment – or because the branch broke?' I

[1] Admittedly all I have done is to turn the tables by making human volitions the constant and physical destiny the variable. This is as false as the opposite view; the point is that it is no falser. A subtler image of creation and freedom (or rather, creation of the free and the unfree in a single timeless act) would be the *almost* simultaneous mutual adaptation in the movement of two expert dancing partners.

think one would have to say, 'For both reasons.' Every event in the play happens as a result of other events in the play, but also every event happens because the poet wants it to happen. All events in the play are Shakespearian events; similarly all events in the real world are providential events. All events in the play, however, come about (or ought to come about) by the dramatic logic of events. Similarly all events in the real world (except miracles) come about by natural causes. 'Providence' and Natural causation are not alternatives; both determine every event because both are one.

2. When we are praying about the result, say, of a battle or a medical consultation the thought will often cross our minds that (if only we knew it) the event is already decided one way or the other. I believe this to be no good reason for ceasing our prayers. The event certainly has been decided – in a sense it was decided 'before all worlds'. But one of the things taken into account in deciding it, and therefore one of the things that really cause it to happen, may be this very prayer that we are now offering. Thus, shocking as it may sound, I conclude that we can at noon become part causes of an event occurring at ten a.m. (Some scientists would find this easier than popular thought does.) The imagination will, no doubt, try to play all sorts of tricks on us at this point. It will ask, 'Then if I stop praying can God go back and alter what has already happened?' No. The event has already happened and one of its causes has been the fact that you are asking such questions instead of praying. It will ask, 'Then if I begin to pray can God go back and alter what has already happened?' No. The event has already happened and one of its causes is your present prayer. Thus something does really depend on my choice. My free act contributes to the cosmic shape. That contribution is made in eternity or 'before all worlds'; but my consciousness of contributing reaches me at a particular point in the time-series.

The following question may be asked: If we can reasonably pray for an event which must in fact have happened or failed to happen several hours ago, why can we not pray for an event which we know *not* to have happened? e.g. pray for the safety of someone who, as we know, was killed yesterday. What makes the difference is precisely our knowledge. The known event states God's will. It is psychologically impossible to pray for what we know to be unobtainable; and if it were possible the prayer would sin against the duty of submission to God's known will.

One more consequence remains to be drawn. It is never possible to prove empirically that a given, non-miraculous event was or was not an answer to prayer. Since it was non-miraculous the sceptic can always point to its natural causes and say, 'Because of these it would have happened anyway,' and the believer can always reply, 'But because these were only links in a chain of events, hanging on other links, and the whole chain hanging upon God's will, they may have occurred because someone prayed.' The efficacy of prayer, therefore, cannot be either asserted or denied without an exercise of the will – the will choosing or rejecting faith in the light of a whole philosophy. Experimental evidence there can be none on either side. In the sequence M.N.O. event N, unless it is a miracle, is always caused by M and causes O; but the real question is whether the total series (say A–Z) does or does not originate in a will that can take human prayers into account.

This impossibility of empirical proof is a spiritual necessity. A man who knew empirically that an event had been caused by his prayer would feel like a magician. His head would turn and his heart would be corrupted. The Christian is not to ask whether this or that event happened because of a prayer. He is rather to believe that all events without exception are *answers* to prayer in the sense that whether they are grantings or refusals the prayers of all concerned and their needs have all been taken into account. All prayers are heard, though not all prayers are granted. We must not picture destiny as a film unrolling for the most part on its own, but in which our prayers are sometimes allowed to insert additional items. On the contrary; what the film displays to us as it unrolls already contains the results of our prayers and of all our other acts. There is no question *whether* an event has happened because of your prayer. When the event you prayed for occurs your prayer has always contributed to it. When the opposite event occurs your prayer has never been ignored; it has been considered and refused, for your ultimate good and the good of the whole universe. (For example, because it is better for you and for everyone else in the long run that other people, including wicked ones, should exercise free will than that you should be protected from cruelty or treachery by turning the human race into automata.) But this is, and must remain, a matter of faith. You will, I think, only deceive yourself by trying to find special evidence for it in some cases more than in others.

SURPRISED BY JOY

The shape of
my early life

Surprised by Joy – impatient as the wind
WORDSWORTH

To Dom Bede Griffiths, O.S.B.

Contents

PREFACE

This book is written partly in answer to requests that I would tell how I passed from Atheism to Christianity and partly to correct one or two false notions that seem to have got about. How far the story matters to anyone but myself depends on the degree to which others have experienced what I call 'joy'. If it is at all common, a more detailed treatment of it than has (I believe) been attempted before may be of some use. I have been emboldened to write of it because I notice that a man seldom mentions what he had supposed to be his most idiosyncratic sensations without receiving from at least one (often more) of those present the reply, 'What! Have *you* felt that too? I always thought I was the only one.'

The book aims at telling the story of my conversion and is not a general autobiography, still less 'Confessions' like those of St Augustine or Rousseau. This means in practice that it gets less like a general autobiography as it goes on. In the earlier chapters the net has to be spread pretty wide in order that, when the explicitly spiritual crisis arrives, the reader may understand what sort of person my childhood and adolescence had made me. When the 'build-up' is complete, I confine myself strictly to business and omit everything (however important by ordinary biographical standards) which seems, at that stage, irrelevant. I do not think there is much loss; I never read an autobiography in which the parts devoted to the earlier years were not far the most interesting.

The story is, I fear, suffocatingly subjective; the kind of thing I have never written before and shall probably never write again. I have tried so to write the first chapter that those who can't bear such a story will see at once what they are in for and close the book with the least waste of time.

C. S. LEWIS

THE FIRST YEARS

Happy, but for so happy ill secured.
MILTON

I was born in the winter of 1898 at Belfast, the son of a solicitor and of a clergyman's daughter. My parents had only two children, both sons, and I was the younger by about three years. Two very different strains had gone to our making. My father belonged to the first generation of his family that reached professional station. His grandfather had been a Welsh farmer; his father, a self-made man, had begun life as a workman, emigrated to Ireland, and ended as a partner in the firm of Macilwaine and Lewis, 'Boiler-makers, Engineers, and Iron Ship Builders'. My mother was a Hamilton with many generations of clergymen, lawyers, sailors, and the like behind her; on her mother's side, through the Warrens, the blood went back to a Norman knight whose bones lie at Battle Abbey. The two families from which I spring were as different in temperament as in origin. My father's people were true Welshmen, sentimental, passionate, and rhetorical, easily moved both to anger and to tenderness; men who laughed and cried a great deal and who had not much of the talent for happiness. The Hamiltons were a cooler race. Their minds were critical and ironic and they had the talent for happiness in a high degree – went straight for it as experienced travellers go for the best seat in a train. From my earliest years I was aware of the vivid contrast between my mother's cheerful and tranquil affection and the ups and downs of my father's emotional life, and this bred in me long before I was old enough to give it a name a certain distrust or dislike of emotion as something uncomfortable and embarrassing and even dangerous.

Both my parents, by the standards of that time and place, were bookish or 'clever' people. My mother had been a promising mathematician in her youth and a B.A. of Queen's College, Belfast, and before her death was able to start me both in French and Latin. She was a voracious reader of good novels, and I think the Merediths and Tolstoys which I have inherited were bought for her. My father's tastes were quite different. He was fond of oratory and had himself spoken on political platforms in England as a young man; if he had had independent means he would certainly have aimed at a political career. In this, unless his sense of honour, which was fine to the point of being Quixotic, had made him unmanageable, he might well have succeeded, for he had many of the gifts once needed by a Parliamentarian – a fine presence, a resonant voice, great quickness of mind, eloquence, and memory. Trollope's political novels were very dear to him; in following the career of Phineas Finn he was, as I now suppose, vicariously gratifying his own desires. He was fond of poetry provided it had elements of rhetoric or pathos, or both; I think *Othello* was his favourite Shakespearian play. He greatly enjoyed nearly all humorous authors, from Dickens to W. W. Jacobs, and was himself, almost without rival, the best *raconteur* I have ever heard; the best, that is, of his own type, the type that acts all the characters in turn with a free use of grimace, gesture, and pantomime. He was never happier than when closeted for an hour or so with one or two of my uncles exchanging 'wheezes' (as anecdotes were oddly called in our family). What neither he nor my mother had the least taste for was that kind of literature to which my allegiance was given the moment I could choose books for myself. Neither had ever listened for the horns of elfland. There was no copy either of Keats or Shelley in the house, and the copy of Coleridge was never (to my knowledge) opened. If I am a romantic my parents bear no responsibility for it. Tennyson, indeed, my father liked, but it was the Tennyson of *In Memoriam* and *Locksley Hall*. I never heard from him of the *Lotus Eaters* or the *Morte d'Arthur*. My mother, I have been told, cared for no poetry at all.

In addition to good parents, good food, and a garden (which then seemed large) to play in, I began life with two other blessings. One was our nurse, Lizzie Endicott, in whom even the exacting memory of childhood can discover no flaw – nothing but kindness, gaiety, and good sense. There was no nonsense about 'lady nurses' in those days. Through Lizzie we struck our roots into the peasantry of County Down. We were thus free of two very different social worlds. To this I owe my lifelong immunity from the false identification which some people make of refinement with virtue. From before I can remember I had understood that certain jokes could be shared with Lizzie which were impossible in the drawing-room; and also that Lizzie was, as nearly as a human can be, simply good.

The other blessing was my brother. Though three years my senior, he never seemed to be an elder brother; we were allies, not to say confederates, from the first. Yet we were very different. Our earliest pictures (and I can remember no time when we were not incessantly drawing) reveal it. His were of ships and trains and battles; mine, when not imitated from his, were of what we both called 'dressed animals' – the anthropomorphised beasts of nursery literature. His earliest story – as my elder he preceded me in the transition from drawing to writing – was called *The Young Rajah*. He had already made India 'his country'; Animal-Land was mine. I do not think any

of the surviving drawings date from the first six years of my life which I am
now describing, but I have plenty of them that cannot be much later. From
them it appears to me that I had the better talent. From a very early age
I could draw movement – figures that looked as if they were really running
or fighting – and the perspective is good. But nowhere, either in my
brother's work or my own, is there a single line drawn in obedience to an
idea, however crude, of beauty. There is action, comedy, invention; but there
is not even the germ of a feeling for design, and there is a shocking ignorance
of natural form. Trees appear as balls of cotton wool stuck on posts, and
there is nothing to show that either of us knew the shape of any leaf in the
garden where we played almost daily. This absence of beauty, now that
I come to think of it, is characteristic of our childhood. No picture on the
walls of my father's house ever attracted – and indeed none deserved – our
attention. We never saw a beautiful building nor imagined that a building
could be beautiful. My earliest aesthetic experiences, if indeed they were
aesthetic, were not of that kind; they were already incurably romantic, not
formal. Once in those very early days my brother brought into the nursery
the lid of a biscuit tin which he had covered with moss and garnished with
twigs and flowers so as to make it a toy garden or a toy forest. That was the
first beauty I ever knew. What the real garden had failed to do, the toy garden did. It made me aware of nature – not, indeed, as a storehouse of forms
and colours but as something cool, dewy, fresh, exuberant. I do not think
the impression was very important at the moment, but it soon became
important in memory. As long as I live my imagination of Paradise will
retain something of my brother's toy garden. And every day there were
what we called 'the Green Hills'; that is, the low line of the Castlereagh Hills
which we saw from the nursery windows. They were not very far off but
they were, to children, quite unattainable. They taught me longing –
Sehnsucht; made me for good or ill, and before I was six years old, a votary
of the Blue Flower.

If aesthetic experiences were rare, religious experiences did not occur at
all. Some people have got the impression from my books that I was brought
up in strict and vivid Puritanism, but this is quite untrue. I was taught the
usual things and made to say my prayers and in due time taken to church.
I naturally accepted what I was told but I cannot remember feeling much
interest in it. My father, far from being specially Puritanical, was, by nineteenth-century and Church of Ireland standards, rather 'high', and his
approach to religion, as to literature, was at the opposite pole from what
later became my own. The charm of tradition and the verbal beauty of Bible
and Prayer Book (all of them for me late and acquired tastes) were his natural delight, and it would have been hard to find an equally intelligent man
who cared so little for metaphysics. Of my mother's religion I can say

almost nothing from my own memory. My childhood, at all events, was not in the least other-worldly. Except for the toy garden and the Green Hills it was not even imaginative; it lives in my memory mainly as a period of humdrum, prosaic happiness and awakes none of the poignant nostalgia with which I look back on my much less happy boyhood. It is not settled happiness but momentary joy that glorifies the past.

To this general happiness there was one exception. I remember nothing earlier than the terror of certain dreams. It is a very common trouble at that age, yet it still seems to me odd that petted and guarded childhood should so often have in it a window opening on what is hardly less than Hell. My bad dreams were of two kinds, those about spectres and those about insects. The second were, beyond comparison, the worse; to this day I would rather meet a ghost than a tarantula. And to this day I could almost find it in my heart to rationalise and justify my phobia. As Owen Barfield once said to me, 'The trouble about insects is that they are like French locomotives – they have all the works on the outside.' *The works* – that is the trouble. Their angular limbs, their jerky movements, their dry, metallic noises, all suggest either machines that have come to life or life degenerating into mechanism. You may add that in the hive and the ant-hill we see fully realised the two things that some of us most dread for our own species – the dominance of the female and the dominance of the collective. One fact about the history of this phobia is perhaps worth recording. Much later, in my teens, from reading Lubbock's *Ants, Bees and Wasps*, I developed for a short time a genuinely scientific interest in insects. Other studies soon crowded it out; but while my entomological period lasted my fear almost vanished, and I am inclined to think a real objective curiosity will usually have this cleansing effect.

I am afraid the psychologists will not be content to explain my insect fears by what a simpler generation would diagnose as their cause – a certain detestable picture in one of my nursery books. In it a midget child, a sort of Tom Thumb, stood on a toadstool and was threatened from below by a stag-beetle very much larger than himself. This was bad enough; but there is worse to come. The horns of the beetle were strips of cardboard separate from the plate and working on a pivot. By moving a devilish contraption on the *verso* you could make them open and shut like pincers: snip-snap – snip-snap – I can see it while I write. How a woman ordinarily so wise as my mother could have allowed this abomination into the nursery is difficult to understand. Unless, indeed (for now a doubt assails me), unless that picture itself is a product of nightmare. But I think not.

In 1905, my seventh year, the first great change in my life took place. We moved house. My father, growing, I suppose, in prosperity, decided to leave the semi-detached villa in which I had been born and built himself a much larger house, further out into what was then the country. The 'New House', as we continued for years to call it, was a large one even by my present standards; to a child it seemed less like a house than a city. My father, who had more capacity for being cheated than any man I have ever known, was badly cheated by his builders; the drains were wrong, the chimneys were wrong, and there was a draught in every room. None of this, however, mattered to a child. To me, the important thing about the move was that the background of my life became larger. The New House is almost a major character in my story. I am a product of long corridors, empty sunlit rooms, upstair indoor silences, attics explored in solitude, distant noises of gurgling cisterns and pipes, and the noise of wind under the tiles. Also, of endless books. My father bought all the books he read and never got rid of any of them. There were books in the study, books in the drawing-room, books in the cloak-room, books (two deep) in the great bookcase on the landing, books in a bedroom, books piled high as my shoulder in the cistern attic, books of all kinds reflecting every transient stage of my parents' interests, books readable and unreadable, books suitable for a child and books most emphatically not. Nothing was forbidden me. In the seemingly endless rainy afternoons I took volume after volume from the shelves. I had always the same certainty of finding a book that was new to me as a man who walks into a field has of finding a new blade of grass. Where all these books had been before we came to the New House is a problem that never occurred to me until I began writing this paragraph. I have no idea of the answer.

Out of doors was 'the view' for which, no doubt, the site had principally been chosen. From our front door we looked down over wide fields to Belfast Lough and across it to the long mountain line of the Antrim shore – Divis, Colin, Cave Hill. This was in the far-off days when Britain was the world's carrier and the Lough was full of shipping; a delight to both us boys, but most to my brother. The sound of a steamer's horn at night still conjures up my whole boyhood. Behind the house, greener, lower, and nearer than the Antrim mountains, were the Holywood Hills, but it was not till much later that they won my attention. The north-western prospect was what mattered at first; the interminable summer sunsets behind the blue ridges, and the rooks flying home. In these surroundings the blows of change began to fall.

First of all, my brother was packed off to an English boarding-school and thus removed from my life for the greater part of every year. I remember well the rapture of his homecomings for the holidays but have no recollection of any corresponding anguish at his departures. His new life made no difference to the relations between us. I, meanwhile, was going on with my education at home; French and Latin from my mother and everything else from an excellent governess, Annie Harper. I made rather a bugbear of this mild and modest little lady at the time, but all that I can remember assures me that I was unjust. She was a Presbyterian; and a longish lecture which she once interpolated between sums and copies is the first thing I can remember that brought the other world to my mind with any sense of reality. But there were many things that I thought about more. My real life – or what memory reports as my real life – was increasingly one of solitude. I had indeed plenty of people to talk to: my parents, my grandfather Lewis, prematurely old and deaf, who lived with us; the maids; and a somewhat bibulous old gardener. I was, I believe, an intolerable chatterbox. But solitude was nearly always at my command, somewhere in the garden or somewhere in the house. I had now learned both to read and write; I had a dozen things to do.

What drove me to write was the extreme manual clumsiness from which I have always suffered. I attribute it to a physical defect which my brother and I both inherit from our father; we have only one joint in the thumb. The upper joint (that farthest from the nail) is visible, but it is a mere sham; we cannot bend it. But whatever the cause, nature laid on me from birth an utter incapacity to make anything. With pencil and pen I was handy enough, and I can still tie as good a bow as ever lay on a man's collar, but with a tool or a bat or a gun, a sleeve-link or a corkscrew, I have always been unteachable. It was this that forced me to write. I longed to make things, ships, houses, engines. Many sheets of cardboard and pairs of scissors I spoiled, only to turn from my hopeless failures in tears. As a last resource, as a *pis aller*, I was driven to write stories instead; little dreaming to what a world of happiness I was being admitted. You can do more with a castle in a story than with the best cardboard castle that ever stood on a nursery table.

I soon staked out a claim to one of the attics and made it 'my study'. Pictures, of my own making or cut from brightly coloured Christmas numbers of magazines, were nailed on the walls. There I kept my pen and inkpot and writing books and paint-box; and there

> *What more felicity can fall to creature*
> *Than to enjoy delight with liberty?*

Here my first stories were written, and illustrated, with enormous satisfaction. They were an attempt to combine my two chief literary pleasures – 'dressed animals' and 'knights-in-armour'. As a result, I wrote about chivalrous mice and rabbits who rode out in complete mail to kill not giants but cats. But already the mood of the systematiser was strong in me; the mood which led Trollope so endlessly to elaborate his Barsetshire. The Animal-Land which came into action in the holidays when my brother was at home was a modern Animal-Land; it had to have trains and steamships if it was to be a country shared with him. It followed, of course, that the medieval

Animal-Land about which I wrote my stories must be the same country at an earlier period; and of course the two periods must be properly connected. This led me from romancing to historiography; I set about writing a full history of Animal-Land. Though more than one version of this instructive work is extant, I never succeeded in bringing it down to modern times; centuries take a deal of filling when all the events have to come out of the historian's head. But there is one touch in the *History* that I still recall with some pride. The chivalric adventures which filled my stories were in it alluded to very lightly and the reader was warned that they might be 'only legends'. Somehow – but heaven knows how – I realised even then that a historian should adopt a critical attitude towards epic material. From history it was only a step to geography. There was soon a map of Animal-Land – several maps, all tolerably consistent. Then Animal-Land had to be geographically related to my brother's India, and India consequently lifted out of its place in the real world. We made it an island, with its north coast running along the back of the Himalayas; between it and Animal-Land my brother rapidly invented the principal steamship routes. Soon there was a whole world and a map of that world which used every colour in my paint-box. And those parts of that world which we regarded as our own – Animal-Land and India – were increasingly peopled with consistent characters.

Of the books that I read at this time very few have quite faded from memory, but not all have retained my love. Conan Doyle's *Sir Nigel*, which first set my mind upon 'knights in armour', I have never felt inclined to re-read. Still less would I now read Mark Twain's *Yankee at the Court of King Arthur*, which was then my only source for the Arthurian story, blissfully read for the sake of the romantic elements that came through and with total disregard of the vulgar ridicule directed against them. Much better than either of these was E. Nesbit's trilogy, *Five Children and It*, *The Phoenix and the Carpet*, and *The Story of the Amulet*. The last did most for me. It first opened my eyes to antiquity, the 'dark backward and abysm of time'. I can still re-read it with delight. *Gulliver* in an unexpurgated and lavishly illustrated edition was one of my favourites, and I pored endlessly over an almost complete set of old *Punches* which stood in my father's study. Tenniel gratified my passion for 'dressed animals' with his Russian Bear, British Lion, Egyptian Crocodile and the rest, while his slovenly and perfunctory treatment of vegetation confirmed my own deficiencies. Then came the Beatrix Potter books, and here at last beauty.

It will be clear that at this time – at the age of six, seven, and eight – I was living almost entirely in my imagination; or at least that the imaginative experience of those years now seems to me more important than anything else. Thus I pass over a holiday in Normandy (of which, nevertheless, I retain very clear memories) as a thing of no account; if it could be cut out of my past I should still be almost exactly the man I am. But imagination is a vague word and I must make some distinctions. It may mean the world of reverie, day-dream, wish-fulfilling fantasy. Of that I knew more than enough. I often pictured myself cutting a fine figure. But I must insist that this was a totally different activity from the invention of Animal-Land. Animal-Land was not (in that sense) a fantasy at all. I was not one of the characters it contained. I was its creator, not a candidate for admission to it. Invention is essentially different from reverie; if some fail to recognise the difference that is because they have not themselves experienced both. Anyone who has will understand me. In my day-dreams I was training myself to be a fool; in mapping and chronicling Animal-Land I was training myself to be a novelist. Note well, a novelist; not a poet. My invented world was full (for me) of interest, bustle, humour, and character; but there was no poetry, even no romance, in it. It was almost astonishingly prosaic.[1] Thus if we use the word imagination in a third sense, and the highest sense of all, this invented world was not imaginative. But certain other experiences were, and I will now try to record them. The thing has been much better done by Traherne and Wordsworth, but every man must tell his own tale.

The first is itself the memory of a memory. As I stood beside a flowering currant bush on a summer day there suddenly arose in me without warning, and as if from a depth not of years but of centuries, the memory of that earlier morning at the Old House when my brother had brought his toy garden into the nursery. It is difficult to find words strong enough for the sensation which came over me; Milton's 'enormous bliss' of Eden (giving the full, ancient meaning to 'enormous') comes somewhere near it. It was a sensation, of course, of desire; but desire for what? not, certainly, for a biscuit-tin filled with moss, nor even (though that came into it) for my own past. Ἰουλίαν ποθῶ[2] – and before I knew what I desired, the desire itself was gone, the whole glimpse withdrawn, the world turned commonplace again, or only stirred by a longing for the longing that had just ceased. It had taken only a moment of time; and in a certain sense everything else that had ever happened to me was insignificant in comparison.

The second glimpse came through *Squirrel Nutkin*; through it only, though I loved all the Beatrix Potter books. But the rest of them were merely entertaining; it administered the shock, it was a trouble. It troubled me with what I can only describe as the Idea of Autumn. It sounds fantastic to say that one can be enamoured of a season, but that is something like

---

[1] For readers of my children's books, the best way of putting this would be to say that Animal-Land had nothing whatever in common with Narnia except the anthropomorphic beasts. Animal-Land, by its whole quality, excluded the least hint of wonder.

[2] Oh, I desire too much.

what happened; and, as before, the experience was one of intense desire. And one went back to the book, not to gratify the desire (that was impossible – how can one *possess* Autumn?) but to re-awake it. And in this experience also there was the same surprise and the same sense of incalculable importance. It was something quite different from ordinary life and even from ordinary pleasure; something, as they would now say, 'in another dimension'.

The third glimpse came through poetry. I had become fond of Longfellow's *Saga of King Olaf*: fond of it in a casual, shallow way for its story and its vigorous rhythms. But then, and quite different from such pleasures, and like a voice from far more distant regions, there came a moment when I idly turned the pages of the book and found the unrhymed translation of *Tegner's Drapa* and read

> *I heard a voice that cried,*
> *Balder the beautiful*
> *Is dead, is dead —*

I knew nothing about Balder; but instantly I was uplifted into huge regions of northern sky, I desired with almost sickening intensity something never to be described (except that it is cold, spacious, severe, pale, and remote) and then, as in the other examples, found myself at the very same moment already falling out of that desire and wishing I were back in it.

The reader who finds these three episodes of no interest need read this book no further, for in a sense the central story of my life is about nothing else. For those who are still disposed to proceed I will only underline the quality common to the three experiences; it is that of an unsatisfied desire which is itself more desirable than any other satisfaction. I call it Joy, which is here a technical term and must be sharply distinguished both from Happiness and from Pleasure. Joy (in my sense) has indeed one characteristic, and one only, in common with them; the fact that anyone who has experienced it will want it again. Apart from that, and considered only in its quality, it might almost equally well be called a particular kind of unhappiness or grief. But then it is a kind we want. I doubt whether anyone who has tasted it would ever, if both were in his power, exchange it for all the pleasures in the world. But then Joy is never in our power and pleasure often is.

I cannot be absolutely sure whether the things I have just been speaking of happened before or after the great loss which befell our family and to which I must now turn. There came a night when I was ill and crying both with headache and toothache and distressed because my mother did not come to me. That was because she was ill too; and what was odd was that there were several doctors in her room, and voices, and comings and goings all over the house and doors shutting and opening. It seemed to last for hours. And then my father, in tears, came into my room and began to try to convey to my terrified mind things it had never conceived before. It was in fact cancer and followed the usual course; an operation (they operated in the patient's house in those days), an apparent convalescence, a return of the disease, increasing pain, and death. My father never fully recovered from this loss.

Children suffer not (I think) less than their elders, but differently. For us boys the real bereavement had happened before our mother died. We lost her gradually as she was gradually withdrawn from our life into the hands of nurses and delirium and morphia, and as our whole existence changed into something alien and menacing, as the house became full of strange smells and midnight noises and sinister whispered conversations. This had two further results, one very evil and one very good. It divided us from our father as well as our mother. They say that a shared sorrow draws people closer together; I can hardly believe that it often has that effect when those who share it are of widely different ages. If I may trust to my own experience, the sight of adult misery and adult terror has an effect on children which is merely paralysing and alienating. Perhaps it was our fault. Perhaps if we had been better children we might have lightened our father's sufferings at this time. We certainly did not. His nerves had never been of the steadiest and his emotions had always been uncontrolled. Under the pressure of anxiety his temper became incalculable; he spoke wildly and acted unjustly. Thus by a peculiar cruelty of fate, during those months the unfortunate man, had he but known it, was really losing his sons as well as his wife. We were coming, my brother and I, to rely more and more exclusively on each other for all that made life bearable; to have confidence only in each other. I expect that we (or at any rate I) were already learning to lie to him. Everything that had made the house a home had failed us; everything except one another. We drew daily closer together (that was the good result) – two frightened urchins huddled for warmth in a bleak world.

Grief in childhood is complicated with many other miseries. I was taken into the bedroom where my mother lay dead; as they said, 'to see her', in reality, as I at once knew, 'to see it'. There was nothing that a grown-up would call disfigurement – except for that total disfigurement which is death itself. Grief was overwhelmed in terror. To this day I do not know what they mean when they call dead bodies beautiful. The ugliest man alive is an angel of beauty compared with the loveliest of the dead. Against all the subsequent paraphernalia of coffin, flowers, hearse, and funeral I reacted with horror. I even lectured one of my aunts on the absurdity of mourning clothes in a style which would have seemed to most adults both heartless and precocious; but this was our dear Aunt Annie, my maternal uncle's

Canadian wife, a woman almost as sensible and sunny as my mother herself. To my hatred for what I already felt to be all the fuss and flummery of the funeral I may perhaps trace something in me which I now recognise as a defect but which I have never fully overcome – a distaste for all that is public, all that belongs to the collective; a boorish inaptitude for formality.

My mother's death was the occasion of what some (but not I) might regard as my first religious experience. When her case was pronounced hopeless I remembered what I had been taught; that prayers offered in faith would be granted. I accordingly set myself to produce by will-power a firm belief that my prayers for her recovery would be successful; and, as I thought, I achieved it. When nevertheless she died I shifted my ground and worked myself into a belief that there was to be a miracle. The interesting thing is that my disappointment produced no results beyond itself. The thing hadn't worked, but I was used to things not working, and I thought no more about it. I think the truth is that the belief into which I had hypnotised myself was itself too irreligious for its failure to cause any religious revolution. I had approached God, or my idea of God, without love, without awe, even without fear. He was, in my mental picture of this miracle, to appear neither as Saviour nor as Judge, but merely as a magician; and when He had done what was required of Him I supposed He would simply – well, go away. It never crossed my mind that the tremendous contact which I solicited should have any consequences beyond restoring the *status quo*. I imagine that a 'faith' of this kind is often generated in children and that its disappointment is of no religious importance; just as the things believed in, if they could happen and be only as the child pictures them, would be of no religious importance either.

With my mother's death all settled happiness, all that was tranquil and reliable, disappeared from my life. There was to be much fun, many pleasures, many stabs of Joy; but no more of the old security. It was sea and islands now; the great continent had sunk like Atlantis.

2

CONCENTRATION CAMP

Arithmetic with Coloured Rods.
Times Educational Supplement,
19 November 1954

Clop-clop-clop-clop ... we are in a four-wheeler rattling over the uneven squaresets of the Belfast streets through the damp twilight of a September evening, 1908; my father, my brother, and I. I am going to school for the first time. We are in low spirits. My brother, who has most reason to be so, for he alone knows what we are going to, shows his feelings least. He is already a veteran. I perhaps am buoyed up by a little excitement, but very little. The most important fact at the moment is the horrible clothes I have been made to put on. Only this morning – only two hours ago – I was running wild in shorts and blazer and sandshoes. Now I am choking and sweating, itching too, in thick dark stuff, throttled by an Eton collar, my feet already aching with unaccustomed boots. I am wearing knickerbockers that button at the knee. Every night for some forty weeks of every year and for many a year I am to see the red, smarting imprint of those buttons in my flesh when I undress. Worst of all is the bowler-hat, apparently made of iron, which grasps my head. I have read of boys in the same predicament who welcomed such things as signs of growing up; I had no such feeling. Nothing in my experience had ever suggested to me that it was nicer to be a schoolboy than a child or nicer to be a man than a schoolboy. My brother never talked much about school in the holidays. My father, whom I implicitly believed, represented adult life as one of incessant drudgery under the continual threat of financial ruin. In this he did not mean to deceive us. Such was his temperament that when he exclaimed, as he frequently did, 'There'll soon be nothing for it but the workhouse,' he momentarily believed, or at least felt, what he said. I took it all literally and had the gloomiest anticipation of adult life. In the meantime, the putting on of the school clothes was, I well knew, the assumption of a prison uniform.

We reach the quay and go on board the old 'Fleetwood boat'; after some miserable strolling about the deck my father bids us good-bye. He is deeply moved; I, alas, am mainly embarrassed and self-conscious. When he has gone ashore we almost, by comparison, cheer up. My brother begins to show me over the ship and tell me about all the other shipping in sight. He is an experienced traveller and a complete man of the world. A certain agreeable excitement steals over me. I like the reflected port and starboard lights on the oily water, the rattle of winches, the warm smell from the engine-room skylight. We cast off. The black space widens between us and the quay; I feel the throb of screws underneath me. Soon we are dropping down the Lough and there is a taste of salt on one's lips, and that cluster of lights astern, receding from us, is everything I have known. Later, when we have gone to our bunks, it begins to blow. It is a rough night and my brother is sea-sick. I absurdly envy him this accomplishment. He is behaving as experienced travellers should. By great efforts I succeed in vomiting; but it is a poor affair – I was, and am, an obstinately good sailor.

No Englishman will be able to understand my first impressions of England. When we disembarked, I suppose at about six next morning (but it seemed to be midnight), I found myself in a world to which I reacted with immediate hatred. The flats of Lancashire in the early morning are in reality a dismal sight; to me they were like the banks of Styx. The strange English accents with which I was surrounded seemed like the voices of demons. But what was worst was the English landscape from Fleetwood to Euston. Even to my adult eye that main line still appears to run through the dullest and most unfriendly strip in the island. But to a child who had always lived near the sea and in sight of high ridges it appeared as I suppose Russia might appear to an English boy. The flatness! The interminableness! The miles and miles of featureless land, shutting one in from the sea, imprisoning, suffocating! Everything was wrong; wooden fences instead of stone walls and hedges, red brick farmhouses instead of white cottages, the fields too big, haystacks the wrong shape. Well does the *Kalevala* say that in the stranger's house the floor is full of knots. I have made up the quarrel since; but at that moment I conceived a hatred for England which took many years to heal.

Our destination was the little town of – let us call it Belsen – in Hertfordshire. 'Green Hertfordshire', Lamb calls it; but it was not green to a boy bred in County Down. It was flat Hertfordshire, flinty Hertfordshire, Hertfordshire of the yellow soil. There is the same difference between the climate of Ireland and of England as between that of England and the Continent. There was far more weather at Belsen than I had ever met before; there I first knew bitter frost and stinging fog, sweltering heat and thunder-storms on the great scale. There, through the curtainless dormitory windows, I first came to know the ghastly beauty of the full moon.

The school, as I first knew it, consisted of some eight or nine boarders and about as many day-boys. Organised games, except for endless rounders in the flinty playground, had long been moribund and were finally abandoned not very long after my arrival. There was no bathing except one's weekly bath in the bathroom. I was already doing Latin exercises (as taught by my mother) when I went there in 1908, and I was still doing Latin exercises when I left there in 1910; I had never got in sight of a Roman author. The only stimulating element in the teaching consisted of a few well-used canes which hung on the green iron chimney-piece of the single schoolroom. The teaching staff consisted of the headmaster and proprietor (we called him Oldie), his grown-up son (Wee Wee), and an usher. The ushers succeeded one another with great rapidity; one lasted for less than a week. Another was dismissed in the presence of the boys, with a rider from Oldie to the effect that if he were not in Holy Orders he would kick him downstairs. This curious scene took place in the dormitory, though I cannot remember why. All these ushers (except the one who stayed less than a week) were obviously as much in awe of Oldie as we. But there came a time when there were no more ushers, and Oldie's youngest daughter taught the junior pupils. By that time there were only five boarders, and Oldie finally gave up his school and sought a cure of souls. I was one of the last survivors, and left the ship only when she went down under us.

Oldie lived in a solitude of power, like a sea-captain in the days of sail. No man or woman in that house spoke to him as an equal. No one except Wee Wee initiated conversation with him at all. At meal times we boys had a glimpse of his family life. His son sat on his right hand; they two had separate food. His wife and three grown-up daughters (silent), the usher (silent), and the boys (silent) munched their inferior messes. His wife, though I think she never addressed Oldie, was allowed to make something of a reply to him; the girls – three tragic figures, dressed summer and winter in the same shabby black – never went beyond an almost whispered 'Yes, Papa,' or 'No, Papa,' on the rare occasions when they were addressed. Few visitors entered the house. Beer, which Oldie and Wee Wee drank regularly at dinner, was offered to the usher but he was expected to refuse; the one who accepted got his pint, but was taught his place by being asked a few moments later in a voice of thunderous irony, 'Perhaps you would like a little *more* beer, Mr N.?' Mr N., a man of spirit, replied casually, 'Well, thank you, Mr C., I think I would.' He was the one who did not stay till the end of his first week; and the rest of that day was a black one for us boys.

I myself was rather a pet or mascot of Oldie's – a position which I swear I never sought and of which the advantages were purely negative. Even my brother was not one of his favourite victims. For he had his favourite victims, boys who could do nothing right. I have known Oldie enter the schoolroom after breakfast, cast his eyes round, and remark, 'Oh, there you are, Rees, you horrid boy. If I'm not too tired I shall give you a good drubbing this afternoon.' He was not angry, nor was he joking. He was a big, bearded man with full lips like an Assyrian king on a monument, immensely strong, physically dirty. Everyone talks of sadism nowadays but I question whether his cruelty had any erotic element in it. I half divined then, and seem to see clearly now, what all his whipping-boys had in common. They were the boys who fell below a certain social status, the boys with vulgar accents. Poor P. – dear, honest, hard-working, friendly, healthily pious P. – was flogged incessantly, I now think, for one offence only; he was the son of a dentist. I have seen Oldie make that child bend down at one end of the schoolroom and then take a run of the room's length at each stroke; but P. was the trained sufferer of countless thrashings and no sound escaped him until, towards the end of the torture, there came a noise quite unlike a human utterance. That peculiar croaking or rattling cry, that, and the grey faces of all the other boys, and their deathlike stillness, are among the memories I could willingly dispense with.[1]

The curious thing is that despite all this cruelty we did surprisingly little work. This may have been partly because the cruelty was irrational and unpredictable; but it was partly because of the curious methods employed. Except at geometry (which he really liked) it might be said that Oldie did not teach at all. He called his class up and asked questions. When the replies were unsatisfactory he said in a low, calm voice, 'Bring me my cane. I see I shall need it.' If a boy became confused Oldie flogged the desk, shouting in a crescendo, 'Think – Think – THINK!!' Then, as the prelude to execution, he muttered, 'Come out, come out, come out.' When really angry he proceeded to antics; worming for wax in his ear with his little finger and babbling, 'Aye, aye, aye, aye ...' I have seen him leap up and dance round and round like a performing bear. Meanwhile, almost in whispers, Wee Wee or the usher, or (later) Oldie's youngest daughter, was questioning us juniors at another desk. 'Lessons' of this sort did not take very long; what was to be done with the boys for the rest of the time? Oldie had decided that they could, with least trouble to himself, be made to do arithmetic. Accordingly, when you entered school at nine o'clock you took your slate and began doing sums. Presently you were called up to 'say a lesson'. When that was finished you went back to your place and did more sums – and so for ever. All the other arts and sciences thus appeared as islands (mostly rocky and dangerous islands)

Which like to rich and various gems inlaid
The unadorned bosom of the deep

– the deep being a shoreless ocean of arithmetic. At the end of the morning you had to say how many sums you had done; and it was not quite safe to

---

[1] This punishment was for a mistake in a geometrical proof.

lie. But supervision was slack and very little assistance was given. My brother – I have told you that he was already a man of the world – soon found the proper solution. He announced every morning with perfect truth that he had done five sums; he did not add that they were the same five every day. It would be interesting to know how many thousand times he did them.

I must restrain myself. I could continue to describe Oldie for many pages; some of the worst is unsaid. But perhaps it would be wicked, and it is certainly not obligatory, to do so. One good thing I can tell of him. Impelled by conscience, a boy once confessed to him an otherwise undetectable lie. The ogre was touched; he only patted the terrified boy's back and said, 'Always stick to the truth.' I can also say that though he taught geometry cruelly, he taught it well. He forced us to reason, and I have been the better for those geometry lessons all my life. For the rest, there is a possible explanation of his behaviour which renders it more forgivable. Years after, my brother met a man who had grown up in the house next door to Oldie's school. That man and his family, and (I think) the neighbours in general, believed Oldie to be insane. Perhaps they were right. And if he had fairly recently become so, it would explain a thing which puzzles me. At that school as I knew it most boys learned nothing and no boy learned much. But Oldie could boast an impressive record of scholarships in the past. His school cannot always have been the swindle it was in our time.

You may ask how our father came to send us there. Certainly not because he made a careless choice. The surviving correspondence shows that he had considered many other schools before fixing on Oldie's; and I know him well enough to be sure that in such a matter he would never have been guided by his first thoughts (which would probably have been right) nor even by his twenty-first (which would at least have been explicable). Beyond doubt he would have prolonged deliberation till his hundred-and-first; and they would be infallibly and invincibly wrong. This is what always happens to the deliberations of a simple man who thinks he is a subtle one. Like Earle's *Scepticke in Religion* he 'is alwaies too hard for himself'. My father piqued himself on what he called 'reading between the lines'. The obvious meaning of any fact or document was always suspect: the true and inner meaning, invisible to all eyes except his own, was unconsciously created by the restless fertility of his imagination. While he thought he was interpreting Oldie's prospectus, he was really composing a school-story in his own mind. And all this, I doubt not, with extreme conscientiousness and even some anguish. It might, perhaps, have been expected that this story of his would presently be blown away by the real story which we had to tell after we had gone to Belsen. But this did not happen. I believe it rarely happens. If the parents in each generation always or often knew what really goes on at their sons' schools, the history of education would be very different. At any rate, my brother and I certainly did not succeed in impressing the truth on our father's mind. For one thing (and this will become clearer in the sequel) he was a man not easily informed. His mind was too active to be an accurate receiver. What he thought he had heard was never exactly what you had said. We did not even try very hard. Like other children, we had no standard of comparison; we supposed the miseries of Belsen to be the common and unavoidable miseries of all schools. Vanity helped to tie our tongues. A boy home from school (especially during that first week when the holidays seem eternal) likes to cut a dash. He would rather represent his master as a buffoon than an ogre. He would hate to be thought a coward and a cry-baby, and he cannot paint the true picture of his concentration camp without admitting himself to have been for the last thirteen weeks a pale, quivering, tear-stained, obsequious slave. We all like showing scars received in battle; the wounds of the *ergastulum*, less. My father must not bear the blame for our wasted and miserable years at Oldie's; and now, in Dante's words, 'to treat of the good that I found there'.

First, I learned, if not friendship, at least gregariousness. There had been bullying at the school when my brother first went there. I had my brother's protection for my first few terms (after which he left to go to a school we may call Wyvern) but I doubt if it was necessary. During those last declining years of the school we boarders were too few and too badly treated to do or suffer much in that way. Also, after a certain time, there were no new boys. We had our quarrels, which seemed serious enough at the time; but long before the end we had known one another too long and suffered too much together not to be, at the least, very old acquaintance. That, I think, is why Belsen did me, in the long run, so little harm. Hardly any amount of oppression from above takes the heart out of a boy like oppression from his fellows. We had many pleasant hours alone together, we five remaining boarders. The abandonment of organised games, though a wretched preparation for the public school life to which most of us were destined, was at the time a great blessing. We were sent out for walks alone on half holidays. We did not do much walking. We bought sweets in drowsy village shops and pottered about on the canal bank or sat at the brow of a railway cutting watching a tunnel-mouth for trains. Hertfordshire came to look less hostile. Our talk was not bound down to the narrow interests which satisfy public school boys; we still had the curiosity of children. I can even remember from those days what must have been the first metaphysical argument I ever took part in. We debated whether the future was like a line you can't see or like a line that is not yet drawn. I have forgotten which side I took though I know that I took it with great zeal. And always there was what Chesterton calls 'the slow maturing of old jokes'.

The reader will notice that school was thus coming to reflect a pattern I had already encountered in my home life. At home, the bad times had drawn my brother and me closer together; here, where the times were always bad, the fear and hatred of Oldie had something of the same effect upon us all. His school was in some ways very like Dr Grimstone's school in *Vice Versa*; but unlike Dr Grimstone's it contained no informer. We stood foursquare against the common enemy. I suspect that this pattern, occurring twice and so early in my life, has unduly biassed my whole outlook. To this day the vision of the world which comes most naturally to me is one in which 'we two' or 'we few' (and in a sense 'we happy few') stand together against something stronger and larger. England's position in 1940 was to me no surprise; it was the sort of thing that I always expect. Hence while friendship has been by far the chief source of my happiness, acquaintance or general society has always meant little to me, and I cannot quite understand why a man should wish to know more people than he can make real friends of. Hence, too, a very defective, perhaps culpably defective, interest in large impersonal movements, causes and the like. The concern aroused in me by a battle (whether in story or in reality) is almost in an inverse ratio to the number of the combatants.

In another way too Oldie's school presently repeated my home experience. Oldie's wife died; and in term time. He reacted to bereavement by becoming more violent than before; so much so that Wee Wee made a kind of apology for him to the boys. You will remember that I had already learned to fear and hate emotion; here was a fresh reason to do so.

But I have not yet mentioned the most important thing that befell me at Oldie's. There first I became an effective believer. As far as I know, the instrument was the church to which we were taken twice every Sunday. This was high 'Anglo-Catholic'. On the conscious level I reacted strongly against its peculiarities – was I not an Ulster Protestant, and were not these unfamiliar rituals an essential part of the hated English atmosphere? Unconsciously, I suspect, the candles and incense, the vestments and the hymns sung on our knees, may have had a considerable, and opposite, effect on me. But I do not think they were the important thing. What really mattered was that I here heard the doctrines of Christianity (as distinct from general 'uplift') taught by men who obviously believed them. As I had no scepticism, the effect was to bring to life what I would already have said that I believed. In this experience there was a great deal of fear. I do not think there was more than was wholesome or even necessary; but if in my books I have spoken too much of Hell, and if critics want a historical explanation of the fact, they must seek it not in the supposed Puritanism of my Ulster childhood but in the Anglo-Catholicism of the church at Belsen. I feared for my soul; especially on certain blazing moonlight nights in that curtainless dormitory – how the sound of other boys breathing in their sleep comes back! The effect, so far as I can judge, was entirely good. I began seriously to pray and to read my Bible and to attempt to obey my conscience. Religion was among the subjects which we often discussed; discussed, if my memory serves me, in an entirely healthy and profitable way, with great gravity and without hysteria, and without the shamefacedness of older boys. How I went back from this beginning you shall hear later.

Intellectually, the time I spent at Oldie's was almost entirely wasted; if the school had not died, and if I had been left there two years more, it would probably have sealed my fate as a scholar for good. Geometry and some pages in West's *English Grammar* (but even those I think I found for myself) are the only items on the credit side. For the rest, all that rises out of the sea of arithmetic is a jungle of dates, battles, exports, imports and the like, forgotten as soon as learned and perfectly useless had they been remembered. There was also a great decline in my imaginative life. For many years Joy (as I have defined it) was not only absent but forgotten. My reading was now mainly rubbish; but as there was no library at the school we must not make Oldie responsible for that. I read twaddling school-stories in *The Captain*. The pleasure here was, in the proper sense, mere wish-fulfilment and fantasy; one enjoyed vicariously the triumphs of the hero. When the boy passes from nursery literature to school-stories he is going down, not up. *Peter Rabbit* pleases a disinterested imagination, for the child does not want to be a rabbit, though he may like pretending to be a rabbit as he may later like acting Hamlet; but the story of the unpromising boy who became captain of the First Eleven exists precisely to feed his real ambitions. I also developed a great taste for all the fiction I could get about the ancient world: *Quo Vadis, Darkness and Dawn, The Gladiators, Ben Hur*. It might be expected that this arose out of my new concern for my religion, but I think not. Early Christians came into many of these stories, but they were not what I was after. I simply wanted sandals, temples, togas, slaves, emperors, galleys, amphitheatres; the attraction, as I now see, was erotic, and erotic in rather a morbid way. And they were mostly, as literature, rather bad books. What has worn better, and what I took to at the same time, is the work of Rider Haggard; and also the 'scientifiction' of H. G. Wells. The idea of other planets exercised upon me then a peculiar, heady attraction, which was quite different from any other of my literary interests. Most emphatically it was not the romantic spell of *Das Ferne*. 'Joy' (in my technical sense) never darted from Mars or the Moon. This was something coarser and stronger. The interest, when the fit was upon me, was ravenous, like a lust. This particular coarse strength I have come to accept as a mark that the interest which has it is psychological, not spiritual; behind such a fierce tang there lurks, I suspect, a psychoanalytical explanation. I may perhaps add that my own planetary romances have been not so much the gratification of that fierce curiosity as its exorcism. The exorcism worked by reconciling it with, or subjecting it to, the other, the more elusive, and genuinely imaginative, impulse. That the ordinary interest in scientifiction is an affair for psychoanalysts is borne out by the fact that all who like it, like it thus ravenously, and equally by the fact that those who do not, are often nauseated by it. The repulsion of the one sort has the same coarse strength as the fascinated interest of the other and is equally a tell-tale.

So much for Oldie's; but the year was not all term. Life at a vile boarding-school is in this way a good preparation for the Christian life, that it teaches one to live by hope. Even, in a sense, by faith, for at the beginning of each term, home and the holidays are so far off that it is as hard to realise them as to realise heaven. They have the same pitiful unreality when confronted with immediate horrors. To-morrow's geometry blots out the distant end of term as to-morrow's operation may blot out the hope of Paradise. And yet, term after term, the unbelievable happened. Fantastical and astronomical figures like 'This time six weeks' shrank into practicable figures like 'This time next week', and then 'This time to-morrow', and the almost supernatural bliss of the Last Day punctually appeared. It was a delight that almost demanded to be stayed with flagons and comforted with apples; a delight that tingled down the spine and troubled the belly and at moments went near to stopping the breath. Of course this had a terrible and equally relevant reverse side. In the first week of the holidays we might acknowledge that term would come again – as a young man in peace time, in full health, acknowledges that he will one day die. But like him we could not even by the grimmest *memento mori* be brought to realise it. And there too, each time, the unbelievable happened. The grinning skull finally peered through all disguises; the last hour, held at bay by every device our will and imaginations knew, came in the end, and once more it was the bowler-hat, the Eton collar, the knickerbockers, and (clop-clop-clop-clop) the evening drive to the quay. In all seriousness I think that the life of faith is easier to me because of these memories. To think, in sunny and confident times, that I shall die and rot, or to think that one day all this universe will slip away and become memory (as Oldie slipped away into memory three times a year, and with him the canes and the disgusting food, the stinking sanitation and the cold beds) – this is easier to us if we have seen just that sort of thing happening before. We have learned not to take present things at their face value.

In attempting to give an account of our home life at this time I am troubled by doubts about chronology. School affairs can to some extent be dated by surviving records, but the slow, continuous unfolding of family life escapes them. Our slight alienation from our father imperceptibly increased. In part no one was to blame; in a very great part we were to blame. A temperamental widower, still prostrated by the loss of his wife, must be a very good and wise man indeed if he makes no mistakes in bringing up two noisy and mischievous schoolboys who reserve their confidence wholly for each other. And my father's good qualities as well as his weaknesses incapacitated him for the task. He was far too manly and generous to strike a child for the gratification of his anger; and he was too impulsive ever to punish a child in cold blood and on principle. He therefore relied wholly on his tongue as the instrument of domestic discipline. And here that fatal bent towards dramatisation and rhetoric (I speak of it the more freely since I inherit it) produced a pathetic yet comic result. When he opened his mouth to reprove us he no doubt intended a short well-chosen appeal to our common sense and conscience. But alas, he had been a public speaker long before he became a father. He had for many years been a public prosecutor. Words came to him and intoxicated him as they came. What actually happened was that a small boy who had walked on damp grass in his slippers or left a bathroom in a pickle found himself attacked with something like Cicero on Catiline or Burke on Warren Hastings; simile piled on simile, rhetorical question on rhetorical question, the flash of an orator's eye and the thundercloud of an orator's brow, the gestures, the cadences and the pauses. The pauses might be the chief danger. One was so long that my brother, quite innocently supposing the denunciation to have ended, humbly took up his book and resumed his reading; a gesture which my father (who had after all only made a rhetorical miscalculation of about a second and a half) not unnaturally took for 'cool, premeditated insolence'. The ludicrous disproportion between such harangues and their occasions puts me in mind of the advocate in Martial who thunders about all the villains of Roman history while meantime *lis est de tribus capellis* –

> *This case, I beg the court to note,*
> *Concerns a trespass by a goat.*

My poor father, while he spoke, forgot not only the offence, but the capacities, of his audience. All the resources of his immense vocabulary were poured forth. I can still remember such words as 'abominable', 'sophisticated' and 'surreptitious'. You will not get the full flavour unless you know an angry Irishman's energy in explosive consonants and the rich growl of his R's. A worse treatment could hardly have been applied. Up to a certain age these invectives filled me with boundless terror and dismay. From the wilderness of the adjectives and the welter of the unintelligible, emerged ideas which I thought I understood only too well, as I heard with implicit and literal belief that our Father's ruin was approaching, that we should all soon beg our bread in the streets, that he would shut up the house and keep us at school all the year round, that we should be sent to the colonies and there end in misery the career of crime on which we had, it seemed, already embarked. All security seemed to be taken from me; there was no solid ground beneath my feet. It is significant that at this time if I woke in the night and did not immediately hear my brother's breathing from the neighbouring bed, I often suspected that my father and he had secretly risen while I slept and gone off to America – that I was finally abandoned. Such was the effect of my father's rhetoric up to a certain age; then, quite suddenly, it became ridiculous. I can even remember the moment of the change, and the story well illustrates both the justice of my father's anger and the unhappy way in which he expressed it. One day my brother decided it would be a good thing to make a tent. Accordingly we procured a dust-sheet from one of the attics. The next step was to find uprights; the step-ladder in the wash-house suggested itself. For a boy with a hatchet it was the work of a moment to reduce this to a number of disconnected poles. Four of these were then planted in the earth and the sheet draped over them. To make sure that the whole structure was really reliable my brother then tried sitting on the top of it. We remembered to put away the ragged remains of the sheet but quite forgot about the uprights. That evening, when my father had come home from work and dined, he went for a stroll in the garden, accompanied by us. The sight of four slender wooden posts rising from the grass moved in him a pardonable curiosity. Interrogation followed; on this occasion we told the truth. Then the lightnings flashed and the thunder roared; and all would have gone now as it had gone on a dozen previous occasions, but for the climax – 'Instead of which I find you have cut up the step-ladder. And what for, forsooth? To make a thing like an abortive Punch-and-Judy show.' At that moment we both hid our faces; not, alas, to cry.

As will be seen from this anecdote one dominant factor in our life at home was the daily absence of our father from about nine in the morning till six at night. For the rest of the day we had the house to ourselves, except for the cook and housemaid with whom we were sometimes at war and sometimes in alliance. Everything invited us to develop a life that had no connection with our father. The most important of our activities was the endless drama of Animal-Land and India, and this of itself isolated us from him.

But I must not leave the reader under the impression that all the happy hours of the holidays occurred during our father's absence. His temperament was mercurial, his spirits rose as easily as they fell, and his forgiveness was as thorough-going as his displeasure. He was often the most jovial and companionable of parents. He could 'play the fool' as well as any of us, and had no regard for his own dignity, 'conned no state'. I could not, of course, at that age see what good company (by adult standards) he was, his humour being of the sort that requires at least some knowledge of life for its full appreciation; I merely basked in it as in fine weather. And all the time there was the sensuous delight of being at home, the delight of luxury – 'civilisa-tion', as we called it. I spoke just now of *Vice Versa*. Its popularity was surely due to something more than farce. It is the only truthful school story in existence. The machinery of the Garuda Stone really serves to bring out in their true colours (which would otherwise seem exaggerated) the sensations which every boy had on passing from the warmth and softness and dignity of his home life to the privations, the raw and sordid ugliness, of school. I say 'had' not 'has'; for perhaps homes have gone down in the world and schools gone up since then.

It will be asked whether we had no friends, no neighbours, no relatives. We had. To one family in particular our debt is so great that it had better be left, with some other matters, to the next chapter.

3

MOUNTBRACKEN AND

CAMPBELL

*For all these fair people in the hall were in
their first age; none happier under the
heaven; their king, the man of noblest
temper. It would be a hard task to-day to
find so brave a fellowship in any castle.*
GAWAIN AND THE GREEN KNIGHT

To speak of my nearer relatives is to remind myself how the contrast of
Lewis and Hamilton dominated my whole early life. It began, for me,
with the grandparents. Grandfather Lewis, deaf, slow-moving, humming his
psalm chants, much concerned for his health and prone to remind the family
that he would not be with them long, is contrasted with Grandmother
Hamilton, the sharp-tongued, sharp-witted widow, full of heterodox opinions (even, to the scandal of the whole connection, a Home Ruler), every
inch a Warren, indifferent to convention as only an old Southern Irish aristocrat could be, living alone in a large tumble-down house with half a
hundred cats for company. To how many an innocent conversational gambit
did she reply, 'You're talking great nonsense'? Born a little later, she would,
I think, have been a Fabian. She met vague small talk with ruthless statements of ascertainable fact and well-worn maxims with a tart demand for
evidence. Naturally, people called her eccentric. Coming down a generation
I find the same opposition. My father's elder brother 'Uncle Joe', with his
family of two boys and three girls, lived very close to us while we were at
the Old House. His younger son was my earliest friend, but we drifted apart
as we grew older. Uncle Joe was both a clever man and a kind, and especially
fond of me. But I remember nothing that was said by our elders in that
house; it was simply 'grown up' conversation – about people, business, politics, and health, I suppose. But 'Uncle Gussie' – my mother's brother, A. W.
Hamilton – talked to me as if we were of an age. That is, he talked about
Things. He told me all the science I could then take in, clearly, eagerly, without silly jokes and condescensions, obviously liking it as much as I did. He
thus provided the intellectual background for my reading of H. G. Wells.

I do not suppose he cared for me as a person half so much as Uncle Joe did; and that (call it an injustice or not) was what I liked. During these talks our attention was fixed not on one another but on the subject. His Canadian wife I have already mentioned. In her also I found what I liked best – an unfailing, kindly welcome without a hint of sentimentality, unruffled good sense, the unobtrusive talent for making all things at all times as cheerful and comfortable as circumstances allowed. What one could not have one did without and made the best of it. The tendency of the Lewises to re-open wounds and to rouse sleeping dogs was unknown to her as to her husband.

But we had other kin who mattered to us far more than our aunts and uncles. Less than a mile from our home stood the largest house I then knew, which I will here call Mountbracken, and there lived Sir W. E. Lady E. was my mother's first cousin and perhaps my mother's dearest friend, and it was no doubt for my mother's sake that she took upon herself the heroic work of civilising my brother and me. We had a standing invitation to lunch at Mountbracken whenever we were at home; to this, almost entirely, we owe it that we did not grow up savages. The debt is not only to Lady E. ('Cousin Mary') but to her whole family; walks, motor-drives (in those days an exciting novelty), picnics, and invitations to the theatre were showered on us, year after year, with a kindness which our rawness, our noise, and our unpunctuality never seemed to weary. We were at home there almost as much as in our own house, but with this great difference, that a certain standard of manners had to be kept up. Whatever I know (it is not much) of courtesy and *savoir faire* I learned at Mountbracken.

Sir W. ('Cousin Quartus') was the eldest of several brothers who owned between them one of the most important industrial concerns in Belfast. He belonged in fact to just that class and generation of which the modern man gets his impressions through Galsworthy's Forsytes. Unless Cousin Quartus was very untrue to type (he may well have been) that impression is grossly unjust. No one less like a Galsworthian character ever existed. He was gracious, childlike, deeply and religiously humble, and abounding in charity. No man could feel more fully his responsibility to dependants. He had a good deal of boyish gaiety about him; at the same time I always felt that the conception of duty dominated his life. His stately figure, his grey beard, and his strikingly handsome profile make up one of the most venerable images in my memory. Physical beauty was indeed common to most of the family. Cousin Mary was the very type of the beautiful old lady, with her silver hair and her sweet Southern Irish voice; foreigners must be warned that this resembles what they call a 'brogue' about as little as the speech of a Highland gentleman resembles the jargon of the Glasgow slums. But it was the three daughters whom we knew best. All three were 'grown up' but in fact much nearer to us in age than any other grown-ups we knew, and all three were strikingly handsome. H., the eldest and the gravest, was a Juno, a dark queen who at certain moments looked like a Jewess. K. was more like a Valkyrie (though all, I think, were good horsewomen) with her father's profile. There was in her face something of the delicate fierceness of a thoroughbred horse, an indignant fineness of nostril, the possibility of an excellent disdain. She had what the vanity of my own sex calls a 'masculine' honesty; no man ever was a truer friend. As for the youngest, G., I can only say that she was the most beautiful woman I have ever seen, perfect in shape and colour and voice and every movement – but who can describe beauty? The reader may smile at this as the far-off echo of a precocious calf-love, but he will be wrong. There are beauties so unambiguous that they need no lens of that kind to reveal them; they are visible even to the careless and objective eyes of a child. (The first woman who ever spoke to my blood was a dancing mistress at a school that will come in a later chapter.)

In some ways Mountbracken was like our Father's house. There too we found the attics, the indoor silences, the endless bookshelves. In the early days, when we were still only a quarter tamed, we often neglected our hostesses and rummaged on our own; it was there that I found Lubbock's *Ants, Bees and Wasps*. But it was also very different. Life there was more spacious and considered than with us, glided like a barge where ours bumped like a cart.

Friends of our own age – boy and girl friends – we had none. In part this is a natural result of boarding school; children grow up strangers to their next-door neighbours. But much more it was the result of our own obstinate choice. One boy who lived near us attempted every now and then to get to know us. We avoided him by every means in our power. Our lives were already full, and the holidays too short for all the reading, writing, playing, cycling, and talking that we wanted to get through. We resented the appearance of any third party as an infuriating interruption. We resented even more bitterly all attempts (excepting the great and successful attempt made by Mountbracken) to show us hospitality. At the period that I am now speaking of this had not yet become a serious nuisance, but as it became gradually and steadily more serious throughout our schooldays I may be allowed to say a word about it here and to get the subject out of our way. It was the custom of the neighbourhood to give parties which were really dances for adults but to which, none the less, mere schoolboys and schoolgirls were asked. One sees the advantages of this arrangement from the hostess's point of view; and when the junior guests know each other well and are free from self-consciousness perhaps they enjoy themselves. To me these dances were a torment – of which ordinary shyness made only a part. It was the false position (which I was well able to realise) that tormented me; to know that one was regarded as a child and yet be forced to take part in an essentially grown-up function, to feel that all the adults present were being half-mock-ingly kind and pretending to treat you as what you were not. Add to this the discomfort of one's Eton suit and stiff shirt, the aching feet and burning head, and the mere weariness of being kept up so many hours after one's usual bedtime. Even adults, I fancy, would not find an evening party very endurable without the attraction of sex and the attraction of alcohol; and how a small boy who can neither flirt nor drink should be expected to enjoy prancing about on a polished floor till the small hours of the morning, is beyond my conception. I had of course no notion of the social nexus. I never realised that certain people were in civility obliged to ask me because they knew my father or had known my mother. To me it was all inexplicable, unprovoked persecution; and when, as often happened, such engagements fell in the last week of the holidays and wrested from us a huge cantle of hours in which every minute was worth gold, I positively felt that I could have torn my hostess limb from limb. Why should she thus pester me? I had never done her any harm, never asked *her* to a party.

My discomforts were aggravated by the totally unnatural behaviour which I thought it my duty to adopt at a dance; and that had come about in a sufficiently amusing way. Reading much and mixing little with children of my own age, I had, before I went to school, developed a vocabulary which must (I now see) have sounded very funny from the lips of a chubby urchin in an Eton jacket. When I brought out my 'long words' adults not unnatu-rally thought I was showing off. In this they were quite mistaken. I used the only words I knew. The position was indeed the exact reverse of what they supposed; my pride would have been gratified by using such schoolboy slang as I possessed, not at all by using the bookish language which (inevitably in my circumstances) came naturally to my tongue. And there were not lacking adults who would egg me on with feigned interest and feigned seriousness – on and on till the moment at which I suddenly knew I was being laughed at. Then, of course, my mortification was intense; and after one or two such experiences I made it a rigid rule that at 'social func-tions' (as I secretly called them) I must never on any account speak of any subject in which I felt the slightest interest nor in any words that naturally occurred to me. And I kept my rule only too well; a giggling and gurgling imitation of the vapidest grown-up chatter, a deliberate concealment of all that I really thought and felt under a sort of feeble jocularity and enthusi-asm, was henceforth my party manner, assumed as consciously as an actor assumes his rôle, sustained with unspeakable weariness, and dropped with a groan of relief the moment my brother and I at last tumbled into our cab and the drive home (the only pleasure of the evening) began. It took me years to make the discovery that any real human intercourse could take place at a mixed assembly of people in their good clothes.

I am here struck by the curious mixture of justice and injustice in our lives. We are blamed for our real faults but usually not on the right occasions. I was, no doubt, and was blamed for being a conceited boy; but the blame was usually attached to something in which no conceit was present. Adults often accuse a child of vanity without pausing to discover on what points children in general, or that child in particular, are likely to be vain. Thus it was for years a complete mystery to me that my father should stigmatise as 'affectation' my complaints about the itching and tickling of new underclothes. I see it all now; he had in mind a social legend associating delicacy of skin with refinement and supposed that I was claiming to be unusually refined. In reality I was in simple ignorance of that social legend, and if vanity had come into the matter would have been much prouder of having skin like a sailor. I was being accused of an offence which I lacked resources to commit. I was on another occasion called 'affected' for asking what 'stirabout' was. It is, in fact, a 'low' Irish word for porridge. To certain adults it seems obvious that he who claims not to know the Low must be pretending to be High. Yet the real reason why I asked was that I had never happened to hear the word; had I done so I should have piqued myself on using it.

Oldie's school, you will remember, sank unlamented in summer 1910; new arrangements had to be made for my education. My father now hit upon a plan which filled me with delight. About a mile from the New House rose the large red-brick walls and towers of Campbell College, which had been founded for the express purpose of giving Ulster boys all the advantages of a public school education without the trouble of crossing the Irish Sea. My clever cousin, Uncle Joe's boy, was already there and doing well. It was decided that I should go as a boarder, but I could get an *exeat* to come home every Sunday. I was enchanted. I did not believe that anything Irish, even a school, could be bad; certainly not so bad as all I yet knew of England. To 'Campbell' I accordingly went.

I was at this school for so short a time that I shall attempt no criticism of it. It was very unlike any English public school that I have ever heard of. It had indeed prefects, but the prefects were of no importance. It was nominally divided into 'houses' on the English pattern, but they were mere legal fictions; except for purposes of games (which were not compulsory) no one took any notice of them. The population was socially much more 'mixed' than at most English schools; I rubbed shoulders there with farmers' sons. The boy I most nearly made a friend of was the son of a tradesman who had recently been going the rounds with his father's van because the driver was illiterate and could not keep 'the books'. I much envied him this pleasant occupation, and he, poor fellow, looked back on it as a golden age. 'This time last month, Lewis,' he used to say, 'I wouldn't have been going in to Preparation. I'd have been coming home from my rounds and a wee tea-cloth laid for me at one end of the table and sausages to my tea.'

I am always glad, as a historian, to have known Campbell, for I think it was very much what the great English schools had been before Arnold. There were real fights at Campbell, with seconds, and (I think) betting, and a hundred or more roaring spectators. There was bullying, too, though no serious share of it came my way, and there was no trace of the rigid hierarchy which governs a modern English school; every boy held just the place which his fists and mother-wit could win for him. From my point of view the great drawback was that one had, so to speak, no home. Only a few very senior boys had studies. The rest of us, except when seated at table for meals or in a huge 'preparation room' for evening 'Prep', belonged nowhere. In out-of-school hours one spent one's time either evading or conforming to all those inexplicable movements which a crowd exhibits as it thins here and thickens there, now slackens its pace and now sets like a tide in one particular direction, now seems about to disperse and then clots again. The bare brick passages echoed to a continual tramp of feet, punctuated with catcalls, scrimmages, gusty laughter. One was always 'moving on' or 'hanging about' – in lavatories, in store rooms, in the great hall. It was very like living permanently in a large railway station.

The bullying had this negative merit that it was honest bullying; not bullying conscience-salved and authorised in the *maison tolérée* of the prefectorial system. It was done mainly by gangs; parties of eight or ten boys each who scoured those interminable corridors for prey. Their sorties, though like a whirlwind, were not perceived by the victim till too late; the general, endless confusion and clamour, I suppose, masked them. Sometimes capture involved serious consequences; two boys whom I knew were carried off and flogged in some backwater – flogged in the most disinterested fashion, for their captors had no personal acquaintance with them; art for art's sake. But on the only occasion when I was caught myself my fate was much milder and perhaps odd enough to be worth recording. When I had come to myself after being dragged at headlong speed through a labyrinth of passages which took me beyond all usual landmarks, I found that I was one of several prisoners in a low, bare room, half-lit (I think) by a single gas-jet. After a pause to recover their breath two of the brigands led out the first captive. I now noticed that a horizontal row of pipes ran along the opposite wall, about three feet from the floor. I was alarmed but not surprised when the prisoner was forced into a bending position with his head under the lowest pipe, in the very posture for execution. But I was very much surprised a moment later. You will remember that the room was half dark. The two gangsters gave their victim a shove; and instantly no victim was there. He vanished; without trace, without sound. It appeared to be sheer black magic. Another victim was led out; again the posture for a flogging was assumed; again, instead of flogging, – dissolution, atomisation, annihilation. At last my own turn came. I too received the shove from behind, and found myself falling through a hole or hatch in the wall into what turned out to be a coal-cellar. Another small boy came hurtling in after me, the door was slammed and bolted behind us, and our captors with a joyous whoop rushed away for more booty. They were, no doubt, playing against a rival gang with whom they would presently compare 'bags'. We were let out again presently, very dirty and rather cramped, but otherwise none the worse.

Much the most important thing that happened to me at Campbell was that I there read *Sohrab and Rustum* in form under an excellent master whom we called Octie. I loved the poem at first sight and have loved it ever since. As the wet fog, in the first line, rose out of the Oxus stream, so out of the whole poem there rose and wrapped me round an exquisite, silvery coolness, a delightful quality of distance and calm, a grave melancholy. I hardly appreciated then, as I have since learned to do, the central tragedy; what enchanted me was the artist in Pekin with his ivory forehead and pale hands, the cypress in the queen's garden, the backward glance at Rustum's youth, the pedlars from Khabul, the hushed Chorasmian waste. Arnold gave me at once (and the best of Arnold gives me still) a sense, not indeed of passionless vision, but of a passionate, silent gazing at things a long way off. And here observe how literature actually works. Parrot critics say that *Sohrab* is a poem for classicists, to be enjoyed only by those who recognise the Homeric echoes. But I, in Octie's form-room (and on Octie be peace) knew nothing of Homer. For me the relation between Arnold and Homer worked the other way; when I came, years later, to read the *Iliad* I liked it partly because it was for me reminiscent of *Sohrab*. Plainly, it does not matter at what point you first break into the system of European poetry. Only keep your ears open and your mouth shut and everything will lead you to everything else in the end – *ogni parte ad ogni parte splende*.

About half-way through my first and only term at Campbell I fell ill and was taken home. My father, for reasons I do not quite know, had become dissatisfied with the school. He had also been attracted by accounts of a preparatory school in the town of Wyvern, though quite unconnected with Wyvern College; especially by the convenience that if I went there my brother and I could still do the journey together. Accordingly I had a blessed six weeks at home, with the Christmas holidays to look forward to at the end and, after that, a new adventure. In a surviving letter my father writes to my brother that I think myself lucky but he 'fears I shall be very lonely before the end of the week'. It is strange that having known me all my life he should have known me so little. During these weeks I slept in his room and was thus freed from solitude during most of those dark hours in which alone solitude was dreadful to me. My brother being absent, he and I could not lead one another into mischief; there was therefore no friction between my father and myself. I remember no other time in my life of such untroubled affection; we were famously snug together. And in the days when he was out, I entered with complete satisfaction into a deeper solitude than I had ever known. The empty house, the empty, silent rooms, were like a refreshing bath after the crowded noise of Campbell. I could read, write, and draw to my heart's content. Curiously enough it is at this time, not in earlier childhood, that I chiefly remember delighting in fairy tales. I fell deeply under the spell of Dwarfs – the old bright-hooded, snowy-bearded dwarfs we had in those days before Arthur Rackham sublimed, or Walt Disney vulgarised, the earth-men. I visualised them so intensely that I came to the very frontiers of hallucination; once, walking in the garden, I was for a second not quite sure that a little man had not run past me into the shrubbery. I was faintly alarmed, but it was not like my night-fears. A fear that guarded the road to Faerie was one I could face. No one is a coward at all points.

4

I BROADEN MY MIND

I struck the board, and cry'd,
'No more; I will abroad'.
What? shall I ever sigh and pine?
My lines and life are free: free as the rode,
Loose as the winde, as large as store.

HERBERT

In January 1911, just turned thirteen, I set out with my brother to Wyvern, he for the College and I for a preparatory school which we will call Chartres. Thus began what may be called the classic period of our school-days, the thing we both think of first when boyhood is mentioned. The joint journeys back to school with a reluctant parting at Wyvern station, the hilarious reunion at the same station for the joint journey home, were now the great structural pillars of each year. Growing maturity is marked by the increasing liberties we take with our travelling. At first, on being landed early in the morning at Liverpool, we took the next train south; soon we learned that it was pleasanter to spend the whole morning in the lounge of the Lime Street Hotel with our magazines and cigarettes and to proceed to Wyvern by an afternoon train which brought us there at the latest permitted moment. Soon too we gave up the magazines; we made the discovery (some people never make it) that real books can be taken on a journey and that hours of golden reading can so be added to its other delights. (It is important to acquire early in life the power of reading sense wherever you happen to be. I first read *Tamburlaine* while travelling from Larne to Belfast in a thunderstorm, and first read Browning's *Paracelsus* by a candle which went out and had to be relit whenever a big battery fired in a pit below me, which I think it did every four minutes all that night.) The homeward journey was even more festal. It had an invariable routine: first the supper at a restaurant – it was merely poached eggs and tea but to us the tables of the gods – then the visit to the old Empire (there were still music halls in those days) – and after that the journey to the Landing Stage, the sight of great and famous ships, the departure, and once more the blessed salt on our lips.

The smoking was of course, as my father would have said, 'surreptitious'; not so the visit to the Empire. He was no Puritan about such matters, and often of a Saturday night would take us to the Belfast Hippodrome. I recognise now that I never had the taste for vaudeville which he shared with my brother. At the time I supposed myself to be enjoying the show, but I was mistaken. All those antics lie dead in my memory and are incapable of rousing the least vibration even of reminiscent pleasure; whereas the pain of sympathy and vicarious humiliation which I felt when a 'turn' failed is still vivid. What I enjoyed was merely the etcetera of the show, the bustle and lights, the sense of having a night out, the good spirits of my father in his holiday mood, and – above all – the admirable cold supper to which we came back at about ten o'clock. For this was also the classical age of our domestic cookery, the age of one Annie Strahan. There were certain 'raised pies' set on that table of which a modern English boy has no conception, and which even then would have astonished those who knew only the poor counterfeits sold in shops.

Chartres, a tall, white building further up the hill than the College, was a smallish school with less than twenty boarders; but it was quite unlike Oldie's. Here indeed my education really began. The Headmaster, whom we called Tubbs, was a clever and patient teacher; under him I rapidly found my feet in Latin and English and even began to be looked on as a promising candidate for a scholarship at the College. The food was good (though of course we grumbled at it) and we were well cared for. On the whole I got on well with my schoolfellows, though we had our full share of those lifelong friendships and irreconcilable factions and deadly quarrels and final settlements and glorious revolutions which made up so much of the life of a small boy, and in which I came out sometimes at the bottom and sometimes at the top.

Wyvern itself healed my quarrel with England. The great blue plain below us and, behind, those green, peaked hills, so mountainous in form and yet so manageably small in size, became almost at once my delight. And Wyvern Priory was the first building that I ever perceived to be beautiful. And at Chartres I made my first real friends. But there, too, something far more important happened to me: I ceased to be a Christian.

The chronology of this disaster is a little vague, but I know for certain that it had not begun when I went there and that the process was complete very shortly after I left. I will try to set down what I know of the conscious causes and what I suspect of the unconscious.

Most reluctantly, venturing no blame, and as tenderly as I would at need reveal some error in my own mother, I must begin with dear Miss C., the Matron. No school ever had a better Matron, more skilled and comforting to boys in sickness, or more cheery and companionable to boys in health. She was one of the most selfless people I have ever known. We all loved her; I, the orphan, especially. Now it so happened that Miss C., who seemed old to me, was still in her spiritual immaturity, still hunting, with the eagerness of a soul that had a touch of angelic quality in it, for a truth and a way of life. Guides were even rarer then than now. She was (as I should now put it) floundering in the mazes of Theosophy, Rosicrucianism, Spiritualism; the whole Anglo-American Occultist tradition. Nothing was further from her intention than to destroy my faith; she could not tell that the room into which she brought this candle was full of gunpowder. I had never heard of such things before; never, except in a nightmare or a fairy tale, conceived of spirits other than God and men. I had loved to read of strange sights and other worlds and unknown modes of being, but never with the slightest belief; even the phantom dwarf had only flashed on my mind for a moment. It is a great mistake to suppose that children believe the things they imagine; and I, long familiar with the whole imaginary world of Animal-Land and India (which I could not possibly believe in since I knew I was one of its creators) was as little likely as any child to make that mistake. But now, for the first time, there burst upon me the idea that there might be real marvels all about us, that the visible world might be only a curtain to conceal huge realms uncharted by my very simple theology. And that started in me something with which, on and off, I have had plenty of trouble since – the desire for the preternatural, simply as such, the passion for the Occult. Not everyone has this disease; those who have will know what I mean. I once tried to describe it in a novel. It is a spiritual lust; and like the lust of the body it has the fatal power of making everything else in the world seem uninteresting while it lasts. It is probably this passion, more even than the desire for power, which makes magicians. But the result of Miss C.'s conversation did not stop there. Little by little, unconsciously, unintentionally, she loosened the whole framework, blunted all the sharp edges, of my belief. The vagueness, the merely speculative character, of all this Occultism began to spread – yes, and to spread *deliciously* – to the stern truths of the creed. The whole thing became a matter of speculation: I was soon (in the famous words) 'altering "I believe" to "one does feel"'. And oh, the relief of it! Those moonlit nights in the dormitory at Belsen faded far away. From the tyrannous noon of revelation I passed into the cool evening twilight of Higher Thought, where there was nothing to be obeyed, and nothing to be believed except what was either comforting or exciting. I do not mean that Miss C. did this; better say that the Enemy did this in me, taking occasion from things she innocently said.

One reason why the Enemy found this so easy was that, without knowing it, I was already desperately anxious to get rid of my religion; and that for a reason worth recording. By a sheer mistake – and I still believe it to have been an honest mistake – in spiritual technique I had rendered my private practice of that religion a quite intolerable burden. It came about in this way. Like everyone else I had been told as a child that one must not only say one's prayers but think about what one was saying. Accordingly, when (at Oldie's) I came to a serious belief, I tried to put this into practice. At first it seemed plain sailing. But soon the false conscience (St Paul's 'Law', Herbert's 'prattler') came into play. One had no sooner reached 'Amen' than it whispered, 'Yes. But are you sure you were really thinking about what you said?'; then, more subtly, 'Were you, for example, thinking about it as well as you did last night?' The answer, for reasons I did not then understand, was nearly always No. 'Very well,' said the voice, 'hadn't you, then, better try it over again?' And one obeyed; but of course with no assurance that the second attempt would be any better.

To these nagging suggestions my reaction was, on the whole, the most foolish I could have adopted. I set myself a standard. No clause of my prayer was to be allowed to pass muster unless it was accompanied by what I called a 'realisation', by which I meant a certain vividness of the imagination and the affections. My nightly task was to produce by sheer will-power a phenomenon which will-power could never produce, which was so ill-defined that I could never say with absolute confidence whether it had occurred, and which, even when it did occur, was of very mediocre spiritual value. If only someone had read to me old Walter Hilton's warning that we must never in prayer strive to extort 'by maistry' what God does not give! But no one did; and night after night, dizzy with desire for sleep and often in a kind of despair, I endeavoured to pump up my 'realisations'. The thing threatened to become an infinite regress. One began of course by praying for good 'realisations'. But had that preliminary prayer itself been 'realised'? This question I think I still had enough sense to dismiss; otherwise it might have been as difficult to begin my prayers as to end them. How it all comes back! The cold oil-cloth, the quarters chiming, the night slipping past, the sickening, hopeless weariness. This was the burden from which I longed with soul and body to escape. It had already brought me to such a pass that the nightly torment projected its gloom over the whole evening, and I dreaded bedtime as if I were a chronic sufferer from insomnia. Had I pursued the same road much further I think I should have gone mad.

This ludicrous burden of false duties in prayer provided, of course, an unconscious motive for wishing to shuffle off the Christian faith; but about the same time, or a little later, conscious causes of doubt arose. One came from reading the classics. Here, especially in Virgil, one was presented with a mass of religious ideas; and all teachers and editors took it for granted from the outset that these religious ideas were sheer illusion. No one ever attempted to show in what sense Christianity fulfilled Paganism or Paganism prefigured Christianity. The accepted position seemed to be that religions were normally a mere farrago of nonsense, though our own, by a fortunate exception, was exactly true. The other religions were not even explained, in the earlier Christian fashion, as the work of devils. That I might, conceivably, have been brought to believe. But the impression I got was that religion in general, though utterly false, was a natural growth, a kind of endemic nonsense into which humanity tended to blunder. In the midst of a thousand such religions stood our own, the thousand and first, labelled True. But on what grounds could I believe in this exception? It obviously was in some general sense the same kind of thing as all the rest. Why was it so differently treated? Need I, at any rate, continue to treat it differently? I was very anxious not to.

In addition to this, and equally working against my faith, there was in me a deeply ingrained pessimism; a pessimism, by that time, much more of intellect than of temper. I was now by no means unhappy; but I had very definitely formed the opinion that the universe was, in the main, a rather regrettable institution. I am well aware that some will feel disgust and some will laugh, at the idea of a loutish, well-fed boy in an Eton collar, passing an unfavourable judgement on the cosmos. They may be right in either reaction, but no more right because I wore an Eton collar. They are forgetting what boyhood felt like from within. Dates are not so important as people believe. I fancy that most of those who think at all have done a great deal of thinking in the first fourteen years. As to the sources of my pessimism, the reader will remember that though in many ways most fortunate, yet I had very early in life met a great dismay. But I am now inclined to think that the seeds of pessimism were sown before my mother's death. Ridiculous as it may sound, I believe that the clumsiness of my hands was at the root of the matter. How could this be? Not, certainly, that a child says, 'I can't cut a straight line with a pair of scissors, therefore the universe is evil.' Childhood has no such power of generalisation and is not (to do it justice) so silly. Nor did my clumsiness produce what is ordinarily called an Inferiority Complex. I was not comparing myself with other boys; my defeats occurred in solitude. What they really bred in me was a deep (and, of course, inarticulate) sense of resistance or opposition on the part of inanimate things. Even that makes it too abstract and adult. Perhaps I had better call it a settled expectation that everything would do what you did not want it to do. Whatever you wanted to remain straight, would bend; whatever you tried to bend would fly back to the straight; all knots which you wished to be firm would come untied; all knots you wanted to untie would remain firm. It is not possible to put it into language without making it comic, and I have indeed no wish to see it (now) except as something comic. But it is perhaps just these early experiences which are so fugitive and, to an adult, so grotesque, that give the mind its earliest bias, its habitual sense of what is or is not plausible.

There was another predisposing factor. Though the son of a prosperous man – a man by our present tax-ridden standards almost incredibly comfortable and secure – I had heard ever since I could remember, and believed, that adult life was to be an unremitting struggle in which the best I could hope for was to avoid the workhouse by extreme exertion. My father's highly coloured statements on such matters had sunk deeply into my mind; and I never thought to check them by the very obvious fact that most of the adults I actually knew seemed to be living very comfortable lives. I remember summing up what I took to be our destiny, in conversation with my best friend at Chartres, by the formula, 'Term, holidays, term, holidays, till we leave school, and then work, work, work till we die.' Even if I had been free from this delusion, I think I should still have seen grounds for pessimism. One's views, even at that age, are not wholly determined by one's own momentary situation; even a boy can recognise that there is desert all round him though he, for the nonce, sits in an oasis. I was, in my ineffective way, a tender-hearted creature; perhaps the most murderous feelings I ever entertained were towards an under master at Chartres who forbade me to give to a beggar at the school gate. Add to this that my early reading – not only Wells but Sir Robert Ball – had lodged very firmly in my imagination the vastness and cold of space, the littleness of Man. It is not strange that I should feel the universe to be a menacing and unfriendly place. Several years before I read Lucretius I felt the force of his argument (and it is surely the strongest of all) for atheism –

Nequaquam nobis divinitus esse paratam
Naturam rerum; tanta stat praedita culpa

Had God designed the world, it would not be
A world so frail and faulty as we see.

You may ask how I combined this directly Atheistical thought, this great 'Argument from Undesign' with my Occultist fancies. I do not think I achieved any logical connection between them. They swayed me in different moods, and had only this in common, that both made against Christianity. And so, little by little, with fluctuations which I cannot now trace, I became an apostate, dropping my faith with no sense of loss but with the greatest relief.

My stay at Chartres lasted from the spring term of 1911 till the end of the summer term 1913, and, as I have said, I cannot give an accurate chronology, between those dates, of my slow apostasy. In other respects the period is divided into two; about half-way through it a much loved under master, and the even more loved Matron, left at the same time. From that day onwards there was a sharp decline; not, indeed, in apparent happiness but in solid good. Dear Miss C. had been the occasion of much good to me as well as of evil. For one thing, by awakening my affections, she had done something to defeat that anti-sentimental inhibition which my early experience had bred in me. Nor would I deny that in all her 'Higher Thought', disastrous though its main effect on me was, there were elements of real and disinterested spirituality by which I benefited. Unfortunately, once her presence was withdrawn, the good effects withered and the bad ones remained. The change of masters was even more obviously for the worse. 'Sirrah', as we called him, had been an admirable influence. He was what I would now describe as a wise madcap: a boisterous, boyish, hearty man, well able to keep his authority while yet mixing with us almost as one of ourselves, an untidy, rollicking man without a particle of affectation. He communicated (what I very much needed) a sense of the gusto with which life ought, wherever possible, to be taken. I fancy it was on a run with him in the sleet that I first discovered how bad weather is to be treated – as a rough joke, a romp. He was succeeded by a young gentleman just down from the University whom we may call Pogo. Pogo was a very minor edition of a Saki, perhaps even a Wodehouse, hero. Pogo was a wit, Pogo was a dressy man, Pogo was a man about town, Pogo was even a lad. After a week or so of hesitation (for his temper was uncertain) we fell at his feet and adored. Here was sophistication, glossy all over, and (dared one believe it?) ready to impart sophistication to us.

We became – at least I became – dressy. It was the age of the 'knut': of 'spread' ties with pins in them, of very low cut coats and trousers worn very high to show startling socks, and brogue shoes with immensely wide laces. Something of all this had already trickled to me from the College through my brother, who was now becoming sufficiently senior to aspire to knuttery. Pogo completed the process. A more pitiful ambition for a lout of an overgrown fourteen-year-old with a shilling a week pocket money could hardly be imagined; the more so since I am one of those on whom Nature has laid the doom that whatever they buy and whatever they wear they will always look as if they had come out of an old clothes shop. I cannot even now remember without embarrassment the concern that I then felt about pressing my trousers and (filthy habit) plastering my hair with oil. A new element had entered my life: Vulgarity. Up till now I had committed nearly every other sin and folly within my power, but I had not yet been flashy.

These hobble-de-hoy fineries were, however, only a small part of our new sophistication. Pogo was a great theatrical authority. We soon knew all the latest songs. We soon knew all about the famous actresses of that age – Lily Elsie, Gertie Millar, Zena Dare. Pogo was a fund of information about their private lives. We learned from him all the latest jokes; where we did not understand he was ready to give us help. He explained many things. After a term of Pogo's society one had the feeling of being not twelve weeks but twelve years older.

How gratifying, and how edifying, it would be if I could trace to Pogo all my slips from virtue and wind up by pointing the moral; how much harm a loose-talking young man can do to innocent boys! Unfortunately this would be false. It is quite true that at this time I underwent a violent, and wholly successful, assault of sexual temptation. But this is amply accounted for by the age I had then reached and by my recent, in a sense my deliberate, withdrawal of myself from Divine protection. I do not believe Pogo had anything to do with it. The mere facts of generation I had learned long ago, from another boy, when I was too young to feel much more than a scientific interest in them. What attacked me through Pogo was not the Flesh (I had that of my own) but the World: the desire for glitter, swagger, distinction, the desire to be in the know. He gave little help, if any, in destroying my chastity, but he made sad work of certain humble and childlike and self-forgetful qualities which (I think) had remained with me till that moment. I began to labour very hard to make myself into a fop, a cad, and a snob.

Pogo's communications, however much they helped to vulgarise my mind, had no such electric effect on my senses as the dancing mistress, nor as Bekker's *Charicles*, which was given me for a prize. I never thought that dancing mistress as beautiful as my cousin G., but she was the first woman I ever 'looked upon to lust after her'; assuredly through no fault of her own. A gesture, a tone of the voice, may in these matters have unpredictable results. When the schoolroom on the last night of the winter term was decorated for a dance, she paused, lifted a flag, and, remarking, 'I love the smell of bunting,' pressed it to her face – and I was undone.

You must not suppose that this was a romantic passion. The passion of my life, as the next chapter will show, belonged to a wholly different region. What I felt for the dancing mistress was sheer appetite; the prose and not the poetry of the Flesh. I did not feel at all like a knight devoting himself to a lady; I was much more like a Turk looking at a Circassian whom he could not afford to buy. I knew quite well what I wanted. It is common, by the way, to assume that such an experience produces a feeling of guilt, but it did not do so in me. And I may as well say here that the feeling of guilt, save where a moral offence happened also to break the code of honour or had consequences which excited my pity, was a thing which at that time I hardly knew. It took me as long to acquire inhibitions as others (they say) have taken to get rid of them. That is why I often find myself at such cross-purposes with the modern world: I have been a converted Pagan living among apostate Puritans.

I would be sorry if the reader passed too harsh a judgement on Pogo. As I now see it, he was not too old to have charge of boys but too young. He was only an adolescent himself, still immature enough to be delightedly 'grown up' and naïf enough to enjoy our greater naïveté. And there was a real friendliness in him. He was moved partly by that to tell us all he knew or thought he knew. And now, as Herodotus would say, 'Goodbye to Pogo.'

Meanwhile, side by side with my loss of faith, of virtue, and of simplicity, something quite different was going on. It will demand a new chapter.

5

RENAISSANCE

So is there in us a world of love
to somewhat, though
we know not what in the world
that should be.

TRAHERNE

I do not much believe in the Renaissance as generally described by historians. The more I look into the evidence the less trace I find of that vernal
rapture which is supposed to have swept Europe in the fifteenth century. I
half suspect that the glow in the historians' pages has a different source, that
each is remembering, and projecting, his own personal Renaissance; that
wonderful reawakening which comes to most of us when puberty is complete. It is properly called a re-birth not a birth, a reawakening not a waken-
ing, because in many of us, besides being a new thing, it is also the recovery
of things we had in childhood and lost when we became boys. For boyhood
is very like the 'dark ages' not as they were but as they are represented in
bad, short histories. The dreams of childhood and those of adolescence may
have much in common; between them, often, boyhood stretches like an
alien territory in which everything (ourselves included) has been greedy,
cruel, noisy, and prosaic, in which the imagination has slept and the most
unideal senses and ambitions have been restlessly, even maniacally, awake.

In my own life it was certainly so. My childhood is at unity with the rest of
my life; my boyhood not so. Many of the books that pleased me as a child,
please me still; nothing but necessity would make me re-read most of the
books that I read at Oldie's or at Campbell. From that point of view it is all a
sandy desert. The authentic 'Joy' (as I tried to describe it in an earlier chapter)
had vanished from my life: so completely that not even the memory or the
desire of it remained. The reading of *Sohrab* had not given it to me. Joy is distinct not only from pleasure in general but even from aesthetic pleasure. It
must have the stab, the pang, the inconsolable longing.

This long winter broke up in a single moment, fairly early in my time at
Chartres. Spring is the inevitable image, but this was not gradual like
Nature's springs. It was as if the Arctic itself, all the deep layers of secular
ice, should change not in a week nor in an hour, but instantly, into a landscape of grass and primroses and orchards in bloom, deafened with bird

songs and astir with running water. I can lay my hand on the very moment; there is hardly any fact I know so well, though I cannot date it. Someone must have left in the schoolroom a literary periodical: *The Bookman*, perhaps, or the *Times Literary Supplement*. My eye fell upon a headline and a picture, carelessly, expecting nothing. A moment later, as the poet says, 'The sky had turned round.'

What I had read was the words *Siegfried and the Twilight of the Gods*. What I had seen was one of Arthur Rackham's illustrations to that volume. I had never heard of Wagner, nor of Siegfried. I thought the Twilight of the Gods means the twilight in which the gods lived. How did I know, at once and beyond question, that this was no Celtic, or silvan, or terrestrial twilight? But so it was. Pure 'Northernness' engulfed me: a vision of huge, clear spaces hanging above the Atlantic in the endless twilight of Northern summer, remoteness, severity ... and almost at the same moment I knew that I had met this before, long, long ago (it hardly seems longer now) in *Tegner's Drapa*, that Siegfried (whatever it might be) belonged to the same world as Balder and the sunward-sailing cranes. And with that plunge back into my own past there arose at once, almost like heartbreak, the memory of Joy itself, the knowledge that I had once had what I had now lacked for years, that I was returning at last from exile and desert lands to my own country; and the distance of the Twilight of the Gods and the distance of my own past Joy, both unattainable, flowed together into a single, unendurable sense of desire and loss, which suddenly became one with the loss of the whole experience, which, as I now stared round that dusty schoolroom like a man recovering from unconsciousness, had already vanished, had eluded me at the very moment when I could first say *It is*. And at once I knew (with fatal knowledge) that to 'have it again' was the supreme and only important object of desire.

After this everything played into my hands. One of my father's many presents to us boys had been a gramophone. Thus at the moment when my eyes fell on the words *Siegfried and the Twilight of the Gods*, gramophone catalogues were already one of my favourite forms of reading; but I had never remotely dreamed that the records from Grand Opera with their queer German or Italian names could have anything to do with me. Nor did I for a week or two think so now. But then I was assailed from a new quarter. A magazine called *The Soundbox* was doing synopses of great operas week by week, and it now did the whole *Ring*. I read in a rapture and discovered who Siegfried was and what was the 'twilight' of the gods. I could contain myself no longer – I began a poem, a heroic poem on the Wagnerian version of the Niblung story. My only source was the abstracts in *The Soundbox*, and I was so ignorant that I made Alberich rhyme with *ditch* and Mime with *time*. My model was Pope's *Odyssey* and the poem began (with some mixture of mythologies)

> *Descend to earth, descend, celestial Nine*
> *And chant the ancient legends of the Rhine ...*

Since the fourth book had carried me only as far as the last scene of *The Rheingold*, the reader will not be surprised to hear that the poem was never finished. But it was not a waste of time, and I can still see just what it did for me and where it began to do it. The first three books (I may, perhaps, at this distance of time, say it without vanity) are really not at all bad for a boy. At the beginning of the unfinished fourth it goes all to pieces; and that is exactly the point at which I really began to try to make poetry. Up to then, if my lines rhymed and scanned and got on with the story I asked no more. Now, at the beginning of the fourth, I began to try to convey some of the intense excitement I was feeling, to look for expressions which would not merely state but suggest. Of course I failed, lost my prosaic clarity, spluttered, gasped, and presently fell silent; but I had learned what writing means.

All this time I had still not heard a note of Wagner's music, though the very shape of the printed letters of his name had become to me a magical symbol. Next holidays, in the dark, crowded shop of T. Edens Osborne (on whom be peace), I first heard a record of the *Ride of the Valkyries*. They laugh at it nowadays, and, indeed, wrenched from its context to make a concert piece, it may be a poor thing. But I had this in common with Wagner, that I was thinking not of concert pieces but of heroic drama. To a boy already crazed with 'the Northernness', whose highest musical experience had been Sullivan, the *Ride* came like a thunderbolt. From that moment Wagnerian records (principally from the *Ring*, but also from *Lohengrin* and *Parsifal*) became the chief drain on my pocket money and the presents I invariably asked for. My general appreciation of music was not, at first, much altered. 'Music' was one thing, 'Wagnerian music' quite another, and there was no common measure between them; it was not a new pleasure but a new kind of pleasure, if indeed 'pleasure' is the right word, rather than trouble, ecstasy, astonishment, 'a conflict of sensations without name'.

That summer our cousin H. (you remember, I hope, Cousin Quartus' eldest daughter, the dark Juno, the queen of Olympus) who was now married, asked us to spend some weeks with her on the outskirts of Dublin, in Dundrum. There, on her drawing-room table, I found the very book which had started the whole affair and which I had never dared to hope I should see, *Siegfried and the Twilight of the Gods* illustrated by Arthur Rackham. His pictures, which seemed to me then to be the very music made visible, plunged me a few fathoms deeper into my delight. I have seldom coveted anything as I coveted that book; and when I heard that there was a cheaper edition at fifteen shillings (though the sum was to me almost mythological) I knew I could never rest till it was mine. I got it in the end, largely because my brother went shares with me, purely through kindness, as I now see and then more than half suspected, for he was not enslaved by the Northernness. With a generosity which I was even then half ashamed to accept, he sank in what must have seemed to him a mere picture-book seven and sixpence for which he knew a dozen better uses.

Although this affair will already seem to some readers undeserving of the space I have given it, I cannot continue my story at all without noting some of its bearings on the rest of my life.

First, you will misunderstand everything unless you realise that, at the time, Asgard and the Valkyries seemed to me incomparably more important than anything else in my experience – than the Matron Miss C., or the dancing mistress, or my chances of a scholarship. More shockingly, they seemed much more important than my steadily growing doubts about Christianity. This may have been – in part, no doubt, was – penal blindness; yet that might not be the whole story. If the Northernness seemed then a bigger thing than my religion, that may partly have been because my attitude towards it contained elements which my religion ought to have contained and did not. It was not itself a new religion, for it contained no trace of belief and imposed no duties. Yet unless I am greatly mistaken there was in it something very like adoration, some kind of quite disinterested self-abandonment to an object which securely claimed this by simply being the object it was. We are taught in the Prayer Book to 'give thanks to God for His great glory', as if we owed Him more thanks for being what He necessarily is than for any particular benefit He confers upon us; and so indeed we do and to know God is to know this. But I had been far from any such experience; I came far nearer to feeling this about the Norse gods whom I disbelieved in than I had ever done about the true God while I believed. Sometimes I can almost think that I was sent back to the false gods there to acquire some capacity for worship against the day when the true God should recall me to Himself. Not that I might not have learned this sooner and more safely, in ways I shall now never know, without apostasy, but that Divine punishments are also mercies, and particular good is worked out of particular evil, and the penal blindness made sanative.

Secondly, this imaginative Renaissance almost at once produced a new appreciation of external nature. At first, I think, this was parasitic on the literary and musical experiences. On that holiday at Dundrum, cycling among the Wicklow mountains, I was always involuntarily looking for scenes that might belong to the Wagnerian world, here a steep hillside covered with firs where Mime might meet Sieglinde, there a sunny glade where Siegfried might listen to the bird, or presently a dry valley of rocks where the lithe scaly body of Fafner might emerge from its cave. But soon (I cannot say how soon) nature ceased to be a mere reminder of the books, became herself the medium of the real joy. I do not say she ceased to be a reminder. All Joy reminds. It is never a possession, always a desire for something longer ago or further away or still 'about to be'. But Nature and the books now became equal reminders, joint reminders, of – well, of whatever it is. I came no nearer to what some would regard as the only genuine love of nature, the studious love which will make a man a botanist or an ornithologist. It was the mood of a scene that mattered to me; and in tasting that mood my skin and nose were as busy as my eyes.

Thirdly, I passed on from Wagner to everything else I could get hold of about Norse mythology, *Myths of the Norsemen, Myths and Legends of the Teutonic Race*, Mallet's *Northern Antiquities*. I became knowledgeable. From these books again and again I received the stab of Joy. I did not yet notice that it was, very gradually, becoming rarer. I did not yet reflect on the difference between it and the merely intellectual satisfaction of getting to know the Eddaic universe. If I could at this time have found anyone to teach me Old Norse I believe I would have worked at it hard.

And finally, the change I had undergone introduces a new difficulty into the writing of this present book. From that first moment in the schoolroom at Chartres my secret, imaginative life began to be so important and so distinct from my outer life that I almost have to tell two separate stories. The two lives do not seem to influence each other at all. Where there are hungry wastes, starving for Joy, in the one, the other may be full of cheerful bustle and success; or again, where the outer life is miserable, the other may be brimming over with ecstasy. By the imaginative life I here mean only my life as concerned with Joy – including in the outer life much that would ordinarily be called imagination, as, for example, much of my reading, and all my erotic or ambitious fantasies; for these are self-regarding. Even Animal-Land and India belong to the 'Outer'.

But they were no longer Animal-Land and India; some time in the late eighteenth century (their eighteenth century, not ours) they had been united into the single state of Boxen, which yields, oddly, an adjective *Boxonian*, not *Boxenian* as you might expect. By a wise provision they retained their separate kings but had a common legislative assembly, the Damerfesk. The electoral system was democratic, but this mattered very much less than in England, for the Damerfesk was never doomed to one fixed meeting place. The joint sovereigns could summon it anywhere, say at the tiny fishing village of Danphabel (the Clovelly of Northern Animal-Land, nestling at the foot of the mountains) or in the island of Piscia; and since the Court knew the sovereigns' choice earlier than anyone else, all local accommodation would be booked before a private member got wind of the matter, nor, if he reached the session, had he the least assurance that it would not be moved elsewhere as soon as he arrived. Hence we hear of a certain member who had never actually sat in the Damerfesk at all except on one fortunate occasion when it met in his home town. The records sometimes call this assembly the Parliament, but that is misleading. It had only a single chamber, and the kings presided. At the period which I know best the effective control, however, was not in their hands but in those of an all-important functionary known as the Littlemaster (you must pronounce this all as one word with the accent on the first syllable – like *Jerrybuilder*). The Littlemaster was a Prime Minister, a judge, and if not always Commander-in-Chief (the records waver on this point) certainly always a member of the General Staff. Such at least were the powers he wielded when I last visited Boxen. They may have been encroachments, for the office was held at that time by a man – or to speak more accurately, a Frog – of powerful personality. Lord Big brought to his task one rather unfair advantage; he had been the tutor of the two young kings and continued to hold over them a quasi-parental authority. Their spasmodic efforts to break his yoke were, unhappily, more directed to the evasion of his inquiry into their private pleasures than to any serious political end. As a result Lord Big, immense in size, resonant of voice, chivalrous (he was the hero of innumerable duels), stormy, eloquent, and impulsive, almost was the State. The reader will divine a certain resemblance between the life of the two kings under Lord Big and our own life under our father. He will be right. But Big was not, in origin, simply our father first batrachised and then caricatured in some directions and glorified in others. He was in many ways a prophetic portrait of Sir Winston Churchill as Sir Winston Churchill came to be during the last war; I have indeed seen photographs of that great statesman in which, to anyone who has known Boxen, the frog element was unmistakable. This was not our only anticipation of the real world. Lord Big's most consistent opponent, the gadfly that always got inside his armour, was a certain small brown bear, a lieutenant in the Navy; and believe me or believe me not, Lieutenant James Bar was almost exactly like Mr John Betjeman, whose acquaintance I could not then have made. Ever since I have done so, I have been playing Lord Big to his James Bar.

The interesting thing about the resemblance between Lord Big and my father is that such reflections of the real world had not been the germ out of which Boxen grew. They were more numerous as it drew nearer to its end, a sign of over-ripeness or even the beginning of decay. Go back a little and you will not find them. The two sovereigns who allowed themselves to be dominated by Lord Big were King Benjamin VIII of Animal-Land and Rajah Hawki (I think, VI) of India. They had much in common with my brother and myself. But their fathers, the elder Benjamin and the elder Hawki, had not. The Fifth Hawki is a shadowy figure; but the Seventh Benjamin (a rabbit, as you will have guessed) is a rounded character. I can see him still – the heaviest-jowled and squarest-builded of all rabbits, very fat in his later years, most shabbily and unroyally clad in his loose brown coat and baggy checked trousers, yet not without a certain dignity which could, on occasion, take disconcerting forms. His earlier life had been dominated by the belief that he could be both a king and an amateur detective. He never succeeded in the latter role, partly because the chief enemy whom he was pursuing (Mr Baddlesmere) was not really a criminal at all but a lunatic – a complication which would have thrown out the plans of Sherlock Holmes himself. But he very often got himself kidnapped, sometimes for longish periods, and caused great anxiety to his Court (we do not learn that his colleague, Hawki V, shared this). Once, on his return from such a misadventure, he had great difficulty in establishing his identity; Baddlesmere had dyed him and the familiar brown figure reappeared as a piebald rabbit. Finally (what will not boys think of?) he was a very early experimenter with what has since been called artificial insemination. The judgement of history cannot pronounce him either a good rabbit or a good king; but he was not a nonentity. He ate prodigiously.

And now that I have opened the gate, all the Boxonians, like the ghosts in Homer, come clamouring for mention. But they must be denied it. Readers who have built a world would rather tell of their own than hear of mine; those who have not would perhaps be bewildered and repelled. Nor had Boxen any connection with Joy. I have mentioned it at all only because to omit it would have been to misinterpret this period of my life.

One caution must here be repeated. I have been describing a life in which, plainly, imagination of one sort or another played the dominant part. Remember that it never involved the least grain of belief; I never mistook imagination for reality. About the Northernness no such question could arise: it was essentially a desire and implied the absence of its object. And Boxen we never could believe in, for we had made it. No novelist (in that sense) believes in his own characters.

At the end of the Summer Term 1913 I won a classical entrance scholarship to Wyvern College.

6

BLOODERY

Any way for Heaven sake
So I were out of your whispering.
WEBSTER

Now that we have done with Chartres we may call Wyvern College simply
Wyvern, or more simply still, as Wyvernians themselves call it, the Coll.
Going to the Coll was the most exciting thing that had yet happened in
my outer life. At Chartres we had lived under the shadow of the Coll. We
were often taken there to see matches or sports or the finish of the great
Goldbury Run. These visits turned our heads. The crowd of boys older than
oneself, their dazzling air of sophistication, scraps of their esoteric talk overheard, were like Park Lane in the old 'Season' to a girl who is to be a *débu-
tante* next year. Above all, the Bloods, the adored athletes and prefects, were
an embodiment of all worldly pomp, power, and glory. Beside them Pogo
shrank into insignificance; what is a Master compared with a Blood? The
whole school was a great temple for the worship of these mortal gods; and
no boy ever went there more prepared to worship them than I.

If you have not been at such a school as Wyvern, you may ask what a
Blood is. He is a member of the school aristocracy. Foreign readers must
clearly understand that this aristocracy has nothing whatsoever to do with
the social position of the boys in the outer world. Boys of good, or wealthy,
family are no more likely to be in it than anyone else; the only nobleman in
my House at Wyvern never became a Blood. Shortly before my time there
the son of a very queer customer had been at least on the fringe of Bloodery.
The qualifying condition for Bloodery is that one should have been at the
school for a considerable time. This by itself will not get you in, but newness
will certainly exclude you. The most important qualification is athletic
prowess. Indeed if this is sufficiently brilliant it makes you a Blood automatically. If it is a little less brilliant, then good looks and personality will
help. So, of course, will fashion, as fashion is understood at your school. A
wise candidate for Bloodery will wear the right clothes, use the right slang,
admire the right things, laugh at the right jokes. And of course, as in the
outer world, those on the fringes of the privileged class can, and do, try to
worm their way into it by all the usual arts of pleasing.

1292

At some schools, I am told, there is a sort of dyarchy. An aristocracy of Bloods, supported or at least tolerated by popular sentiment, stands over against an official ruling class of prefects appointed by the Masters. I believe they usually appoint it from the highest form, so that it has some claim to be an intelligentsia. It was not so at the Coll. Those who were made prefects were nearly all Bloods and they did not have to be in any particular form. Theoretically (though I do not suppose this would ever happen) the dunce at the bottom of the lowest form could have been made the captain – in our language, the Head – of the Coll. We thus had only a single governing class, in whom every kind of power, privilege, and prestige were united. Those to whom the hero-worship of their juniors would in any case have gone, and those whose astuteness and ambition would under any system have enabled them to rise, were the same whom the official power of the Masters supported. Their position was emphasised by special liberties, clothes, priorities, and dignities which affected every side of school life. This, you will see, makes a pretty strong class. But it was strengthened still further by a factor which distinguishes school from ordinary life. In a country governed by an oligarchy, huge numbers of people, and among them some very stirring spirits, know they can never hope to get into that oligarchy; it may therefore be worth their while to attempt a revolution. At the Coll the lowest social class of all were too young, therefore too weak, to dream of revolt. In the middle class – boys who were no longer fags but not yet Bloods – those who alone had physical strength and popularity enough to qualify them as leaders of a revolution were already beginning to hope for Bloodery themselves. It suited them better to accelerate their social progress by courting the existing Bloods than to risk a revolt which, in the unlikely event of its succeeding, would destroy the very prize they were longing to share. And if at last they despaired of ever doing so – why, by that time their schooldays were nearly over. Hence the Wyvernian constitution was unbreakable. Schoolboys have often risen against their Masters; I doubt if there has ever been or ever can be a revolt against Bloods.

It is not, then, surprising if I went to the Coll prepared to worship. Can any adult aristocracy present the World to us in quite such an alluring form as the hierarchy of a public school? Every motive for prostration is brought to bear at once on the mind of the New Boy when he sees a Blood; the natural respect of the thirteen-year-old for the nineteen-year-old, the fan's feeling for a film-star, the suburban woman's feeling for a duchess, the newcomer's awe in the presence of the Old Hand, the street urchin's dread of the police.

One's first hours at a public school are unforgettable. Our House was a tall, narrow stone building (and, by the way, the only house in the place which was not an architectural nightmare) rather like a ship. The deck on which we chiefly lived consisted of two very dark stone corridors at right angles to one another. The doors off them opened into the studies – little rooms about six feet square, each shared by two or three boys. The very sight of them was ravishing to a boy from a Prep. school who had never before had a *pied-à-terre* of his own. As we were still living (culturally) in the Edwardian period, each study imitated as closely as possible the cluttered appearance of an Edwardian drawing-room; the aim was to fill the tiny cell as full as it could hold with bookcases, corner cupboards, knick-knacks, and pictures. There were two larger rooms on the same floor; one the 'Pres' Room', the synod of Olympus, and the other the New Boys' Study. It was not like a study at all. It was larger, darker, and undecorated; an immovable bench ran round a clamped table. But we knew, we ten or twelve recruits, that not all of us would be left in the New Boys' Study. Some of us would be given 'real' studies; the residue would occupy the opprobrious place for a term or so. That was the great hazard of our first evening; one was to be taken and another left.

As we sat round our clamped table, silent for the most part and speaking in whispers when we spoke, the door would be opened at intervals; a boy would look in, smile (not at us but to himself) and withdraw. Once, over the shoulder of the smiler there came another face, and a chuckling voice said, 'Ho-ho! I know what *you're* looking for.' Only I knew what it was all about, for my brother had played Chesterfield to my Stanhope and instructed me in the manners of the Coll. None of the boys who looked in and smiled was a Blood; they were all quite young and there was something common to the faces of them all. They were, in fact, the reigning or fading Tarts of the House, trying to guess which of us were their destined rivals or successors.

It is possible that some readers will not know what a House Tart was. First, as to the adjective. All life at Wyvern was lived, so to speak, in the two concentric circles of Coll and House. You could be a Coll pre. or merely a House pre. You could be a Coll Blood or merely a House Blood, a Coll Punt (i.e. a pariah, an unpopular person) or merely a House Punt; and of course a Coll Tart or merely a House Tart. A Tart is[1] a pretty and effeminate-looking small boy who acts as a catamite to one or more of his seniors, usually Bloods. Usually, not always. Though our oligarchy kept most of the amenities of life to themselves, they were, on this point, liberal; they did not impose chastity on the middle-class boy in addition to all his other disabilities. Pederasty among the lower classes was not 'side', or at least not serious

---

[1] Here, and throughout this account, I sometimes use the 'historic present'. Heaven forfend I should be taken to mean that Wyvern is the same to-day.

side; not like putting one's hands in one's pockets or wearing one's coat unbuttoned. The gods had a sense of proportion.

The Tarts had an important function to play in making school (what it was advertised to be) a preparation for public life. They were not like slaves, for their favours were (nearly always) solicited, not compelled. Nor were they exactly like prostitutes, for the liaison often had some permanence and, far from being merely sensual, was highly sentimentalised. Nor were they paid (in hard cash, I mean) for their services; though of course they had all the flattery, unofficial influence, favour, and privileges which the mistresses of the great have always enjoyed in adult society. That was where the Preparation for Public Life came in. It would appear from Mr Arnold Lunn's *Harrovians* that the Tarts at his school acted as informers. None of ours did. I ought to know, for one of my friends shared a study with a minor Tart; and except that he was sometimes turned out of the study when one of the Tart's lovers came in (and that, after all, was only natural) he had nothing to complain of. I was not shocked by these things. For me, at that age, the chief drawback to the whole system was that it bored me considerably. For you will have missed the atmosphere of our House unless you picture the whole place from week's end to week's end buzzing, tittering, hinting, whispering about this subject. After games, gallantry was the principal topic of polite conversation; who had 'a case with' whom, whose star was in the ascendant, who had whose photo, who and when and how often and what night and where ... I suppose it might be called the Greek Tradition. But the vice in question is one to which I had never been tempted, and which, indeed, I still find opaque to the imagination. Possibly, if I had only stayed longer at the Coll, I might, in this respect as in others, have been turned into a Normal Boy, as the system promises. As things were, I was bored.

Those first days, like your first days in the army, were spent in a frantic endeavour to find out what you had to do. One of my first duties was to find out what 'Club' I was in. Clubs were the units to which we were assigned for compulsory games; they belonged to the Coll organisation, not the House organisation, so I had to go to a notice-board 'Up Coll' to get my facts. And first to find the place – and then to dare to squeeze oneself into the crowd of more important boys around the notice-board – and then to begin reading through five hundred names, but always with one eye on your watch, for of course there is something else to be done within ten minutes. I was forced away from the board before I had found my name, and so, sweating, back to the House, in a flurry of anxiety, wondering how I could find time to do the job to-morrow and what unheard-of disaster might follow if I could not. (Why, by the way, do some writers talk as if care and worry were the special characteristics of adult life? It appears to me that there is more *atra cura* in an average schoolboy's week than in a grown man's average year.)

When I reached the House something gloriously unexpected happened. At the door of the Pres' Room stood one Fribble; a mere House Blood, it is true, even a minor House Blood, but to me a sufficiently exalted figure; a youth of the lean laughing type. I could hardly believe it when he actually addressed me. 'Oh, I say, Lewis,' he bawled, 'I can tell you your Club. You're in the same one as me, B6.' What a transition from all but despair to elation I underwent! All my anxiety was laid to rest. And then the graciousness of Fribble, the condescension! If a reigning monarch had asked me to dine, I could hardly have been more flattered. But there was better to follow. On every half-holiday I went dutifully to the B6 notice-board to see whether my name was down to play that afternoon or not. And it never was. That was pure joy, for of course I hated games. My native clumsiness, combined with the lack of early training for which Belsen was responsible, had ruled out all possibility of my ever playing well enough to amuse myself, let alone to satisfy other players. I accepted games (quite a number of boys do) as one of the necessary evils of life, comparable to Income Tax or the Dentist. And so, for a week or two, I was in clover.

Then the blow fell. Fribble had lied. I was in a totally different Club. My name had more than once appeared on a notice-board I had never seen. I had committed the serious crime of 'skipping Clubs'. The punishment was a flogging administered by the Head of the Coll in the presence of the assembled Coll Pres. To the Head of the Coll himself – a red-headed, pimply boy with a name like Borage or Porridge – I can bear no grudge; it was to him a routine matter. But I must give him a name because the real point of the story requires it. The emissary (some Blood a little lower than the Head himself) who summoned me to execution attempted to reveal to me the heinousness of my crime by the words, 'Who are you? Nobody. Who is Porridge? THE MOST IMPORTANT PERSON THERE IS.'

I thought then, and I still think, that this rather missed the point. There were two perfectly good morals he could have drawn. He might have said, 'We are going to teach you never to rely on second-hand information when first-hand is available' – a very profitable lesson. Or he might have said, 'What made you think that a Blood could not be a liar?' But, 'Who are you? Nobody,' however just, seems hardly relevant. The implication is that I have skipped Club in arrogance or defiance. And I puzzle endlessly over the question whether the speaker really believed that. Did he really think it likely that an utterly helpless stranger in a new society, a society governed by an irresistible class on whose favour all his hopes of happiness depended, had set himself on the first week to pull the nose of The Most Important Person There Is? It is a problem which has met me many times in later life. What does a certain type of examiner mean when he says, 'To show up work like this is an insult to the examiners?' Does he really think that the ploughed candidate has insulted him?

Another problem is Fribble's share in my little catastrophe. Was his lie to me a hoax, a practical joke? Was he paying off some old score against my brother? Or was he (as I now think most likely) simply what our ancestors called a Rattle, a man from whose mouth information, true and false, flows out all day long without consideration, almost without volition? Some might think that, whatever his motive had originally been, he might have come forward and confessed his part when he saw what I was in for. But that, you know, was hardly to be expected. He was a very minor Blood, still climbing up the social stair; Burradge was almost as far above Fribble as Fribble was above me. By coming forward he would have imperilled his social position, in a community where social advancement was the one thing that mattered; school is a preparation for public life.

In justice to Wyvern, I must add that Fribble was not, by our standards, quite a fair representative of Bloodery. He had offended against the rules of gallantry in a manner which (my brother tells me) would have been impossible in his day. I said just now that the Tarts were solicited, not compelled. But Fribble did use all his prefectorial powers for a whole term to persecute a boy called, let us say, Parsley who had refused his suit. This was quite easy for Fribble to do. The innumerable small regulations which a junior boy could break almost unawares enabled a prefect to make sure that a given boy was nearly always in trouble, while the fagging system made it easy to see that he had no leisure at all at any hour of any day. So Parsley learned what it was to refuse even a minor Blood. The story would be more impressive if Parsley had been a virtuous boy and had refused on moral grounds. Unfortunately he was 'as common as a barber's chair', had been a reigning toast in my brother's day, and was now almost past his bloom. He drew the line at Fribble. But Fribble's attempt at coercion was the only instance of its kind I ever knew.

Indeed, taking them by and large, and considering the temptations of adolescents, so privileged, so flattered, our Bloods were not a bad lot. The Count was even kindly. The Parrot was nothing worse than a grave fool: 'Yards-of-Face' they called him. Stopfish, whom some thought cruel, even had moral principles; in his younger days many (I'm told) had desired him as a Tart, but he had kept his virtue. 'Pretty, but no good to anyone; he's *pie*' would be the Wyvernian comment. The hardest to defend, perhaps, is Tennyson. We did not much mind his being a shoplifter; some people thought it rather clever of him to come back from a tour of the town with more ties and socks than he had paid for. We minded more his favourite punishment for us rabble, 'a clip'. Yet he could truly have pleaded to the authorities that it meant merely a box on the ear. He would not have added that the patient was made to stand with his left ear, temple and cheek almost, but not quite, touching the jamb of a doorway, and then struck with full force on the right. We also grumbled a little in secret when he got up a tournament (either explicitly or virtually compulsory, I think) in a game called Yard Cricket, collected subscriptions, and neither held the tournament nor returned the cash. But you will remember that this happened in the Marconi period, and to be a prefect is a Preparation for Public Life. And for all of them, even Tennyson, one thing can be said; they were never drunk. I was told that their predecessors, a year before I came, were sometimes very drunk indeed in the House corridor at mid-day. In fact, odd as it would have sounded to an adult, I joined the House when it was in a stern mood of moral rearmament. That was the point of a series of speeches which the prefects addressed to us all in the House Library during my first week. It was explained with a wealth of threatenings that we were to be pulled Up or Together or wherever decadents are pulled by moral reformers. Tennyson was very great on that occasion. He had a fine bass voice and sang solos in the choir. I knew one of his Tarts.

Peace to them all. A worse fate awaited them than the most vindictive fag among us could have wished. Ypres and the Somme ate up most of them. They were happy while their good days lasted.

My flogging by pimply old Ullage was no unmerciful affair in itself. The real trouble was that I think I now became, thanks to Fribble, a marked man; the sort of dangerous New Boy who skips Clubs. At least I think that must have been the main reason why I was an object of dislike to Tennyson. There were probably others. I was big for my age, a great lout of a boy, and that sets one's seniors against one. I was also useless at games. Worst of all, there was my face. I am the kind of person who gets told, 'And take that look off your face too.' Notice, once more, the mingled justice and injustice of our lives. No doubt in conceit or ill-temper I have often intended to look insolent or truculent; but on those occasions people don't appear to notice it. On the other hand, the moments at which I was told to 'take that look off' were usually those when I intended to be most abject. Can there have been a freeman somewhere among my ancestors whose expression, against my will, looked out?

As I have hinted before, the fagging system is the chief medium by which the Bloods, without breaking any rule, can make a junior boy's life a weariness to him. Different schools have different kinds of fagging. At some of them, individual Bloods have individual fags. This is the system most often depicted in school stories; it is sometimes represented as – and, for all I know, sometimes really is – a fruitful relation as of knight and squire, in which service on the one part is rewarded with some degree of countenance and protection on the other. But whatever its merits may be, we never experienced them at Wyvern. Fagging with us was as impersonal as the labour-market in Victorian England; in that way, too, the Coll was a preparation for public life. All boys under a certain seniority constituted a labour pool, the common property of all the Bloods. When a Blood wanted his O.T.C. kit brushed and polished, or his boots cleaned, or his study 'done out', or his tea made, he shouted. We all came running, and of course the Blood gave the work to the boy he most disliked. The kit-cleaning – it took hours, and then, when you had finished it, your own kit was still to do – was the most detested *corvée*. Shoe-cleaning was a nuisance not so much in itself as in its attendant circumstances. It came at an hour which was vital for a boy like me who, having won a scholarship, had been placed in a high form and could hardly, by all his best efforts, keep up with the work. Hence the success of one's whole day in Form might depend on the precious forty minutes between breakfast and Morning School, when one went over the set passages of translation with other boys in the same Form. This could be done only if one escaped being fagged as a shoeblack. Not, of course, that it takes forty minutes to clean a pair of shoes. What takes the time is waiting in the queue of other fags in the 'boot-hole' to get your turn at the brushes and blacking. The whole look of that cellar, the darkness, the smell, and (for most of the year) the freezing cold, are a vivid memory. You must not of course suppose that, in those spacious days, we lacked servants. There were two official 'bootboys' paid by the Housemaster for cleaning all boots and shoes, and everyone, including us fags who had cleaned both our own shoes and the Bloods' shoes daily, tipped the bootboys at the end of each term for their services.

For a reason which all English readers will understand (others will hear something of it in the next chapter) I am humiliated and embarrassed at having to record that as time went on I came to dislike the fagging system. No true defender of the Public Schools will believe me if I say that I was tired. But I was – dog-tired, cab-horse tired, tired (almost) like a child in a factory. Many things besides fagging contributed to it. I was big and had possibly outgrown my strength. My work in Form was almost beyond me. I was having a good deal of dental trouble at the time, and many nights of clamorous pain. Never, except in the front line trenches (and not always there) do I remember such aching and continuous weariness as at Wyvern. Oh, the implacable day, the horror of waking, the endless desert of hours that separated one from bed-time! And remember that, even without fagging, a school day contains hardly any leisure for a boy who does not like games. For him, to pass from the form-room to the playing field is simply to exchange work in which he can take some interest for work in which he can take none, in which failure is more severely punished, and in which (worst of all) he must feign an interest.

I think that this feigning, this ceaseless pretence of interest in matters to me supremely boring, was what wore me out more than anything else. If the reader will picture himself, unarmed, shut up for thirteen weeks on end, night and day, in a society of fanatical golfers – or, if he is a golfer himself, let him substitute fishermen, theosophists, bimetallists, Baconians, or German undergraduates with a taste for autobiography – who all carry revolvers and will probably shoot him if he ever seems to lose interest in their conversation, he will have an idea of my school life. Even the hardy Chowbok (in *Erewhon*) quailed at such a destiny. For games (and gallantry) were the only subjects, and I cared for neither. But I must seem to care for both, for a boy goes to a Public School precisely to be made a normal, sensible boy – a good mixer – to be taken out of himself; and eccentricity is severely penalised.

You must not, from this, hastily conclude that most boys liked *playing* games any better than I did. To escape Clubs was considered by dozens of boys an obvious good. Leave off Clubs required the Housemaster's signature, and that harmless Merovingian's signature was imitable. A competent forger (I knew one member of the profession) by manufacturing and selling forged signatures could make a steady addition to his pocket money. The perpetual talk about games depended on three things. First, on the same sort of genuine (though hardly practical) enthusiasm which sends the crowds to the League Football Matches. Few wanted to play, but many wanted to watch, to participate vicariously in the triumphs of the Coll, or the House, team. Secondly, this natural feeling had the vigilant backing of all the Bloods and nearly all the Masters. To be lukewarm on such matters was the supreme sin. Hence enthusiasm had to be exaggerated where it existed and simulated where it did not. At cricket matches minor Bloods patrolled the crowd of spectators to detect and punish any 'slackness' in the applause; it reminds one of the precautions taken when Nero sang. For of course the whole structure of Bloodery would collapse if the Bloods played in the spirit of play, for their recreation; there must be audience and limelight. And this brings us to the third reason. For boys who were not yet Bloods but who had some athletic promise, Games were essentially a *moyen de parvenir*. There was nothing recreational about Clubs for them any more than for me. They went to the playing fields not as men go to the tennis-club but as stage-struck girls go to an Audition; tense and anxious, racked with dazzling hopes and sickening fears, never in peace of mind till they had won some notice which would set their feet on the first rung of the social ladder. And not then at peace either; for not to advance is to fall back.

The truth is that organised and compulsory games had, in my day, banished the element of play from school life almost entirely. There was no time to play (in the proper sense of the word). The rivalry was too fierce, the prizes too glittering, the 'hell of failure' too severe.

The only boy, almost, who 'played' (but not at games) was our Irish earl. But then he was an exception to all rules; not because of his earldom but because he was an untamable Irishman, anarch in grain, whom no society could iron out. He smoked a pipe in his first term. He went off by night on strange expeditions to a neighbouring city; not, I believe, for women, but for harmless rowdyism, low life, and adventure. He always carried a revolver. I remember it well, for he had a habit of loading one chamber only, rushing into your study, and then firing off (if that is the right word) all the others at you, so that your life depended on his counting accurately. I felt at the time, and I feel still, that this (unlike the fagging) was the sort of thing no sensible boy could object to. It was done in defiance both of masters and Bloods, it was wholly useless, and there was no malice in it. I liked Ballygunnian; he, too, was killed in France. I do not think he ever became a Blood; if he had, he wouldn't have noticed it. He cared nothing for the limelight or for social success. He passed through the Coll without paying it any attention.

I suppose Popsy – the pretty red-head who was housemaid on 'the Private side' – might also rank as an element making for 'play'. Popsy, when caught and carried bodily into our part of the House (I think by the Count), was all giggles and screams. She was too sensible a girl to surrender her 'virtue' to any Blood; but it was rumoured that those who found her in the right time and place might induce her to give certain lessons in anatomy. Perhaps they lied.

I have hardly mentioned a Master yet. One master, dearly loved and reverenced, will appear in the next chapter. But other masters are hardly worth speaking of. It is difficult for parents (and more difficult, perhaps, for schoolmasters) to realise the unimportance of most masters in the life of a school. Of the good and evil which is done to a schoolboy masters, in general, do little, and know less. Our own Housemaster must have been an upright man, for he fed us excellently. For the rest, he treated his House in a very gentlemanly, uninquisitive way. He sometimes walked round the dormitories of a night, but he always wore boots, trod heavily and coughed at the door. He was no spy and no kill-joy, honest man. Live and let live.

As I grew more and more tired, both in body and mind, I came to hate Wyvern. I did not notice the real harm it was doing to me. It was gradually teaching me to be a prig; that is, an intellectual prig or (in the bad sense) a High Brow. But that subject must wait for another chapter. At the tail-end of this I must repeat (for this is the overall impression left by Wyvern) that I was tired. Consciousness itself was becoming the supreme evil; sleep, the prime good. To lie down, to be out of the sound of voices, to pretend and grimace and evade and slink no more, that was the object of all desire – if only there were not another morning ahead – if only sleep could last for ever!

7

LIGHT AND SHADE

No situation, however wretched it seems, but has
some sort of comfort attending it.
GOLDSMITH

Here's a fellow, you say, who used to come before us as a moral and religious writer, and now, if you please, he's written a whole chapter
describing his old school as a furnace of impure loves without one word on
the heinousness of the sin. But there are two reasons. One you shall hear
before this chapter ends. The other is that, as I have said, the sin in question
is one of the two (gambling is the other) which I have never been tempted to
commit. I will not indulge in futile philippics against enemies I never met in
battle.

('This means, then, that all the other vices you have so largely written
about ...' Well, yes, it does, and more's the pity; but it's nothing to our purpose at the moment.)

I have now to tell you how Wyvern made me a prig. When I went there,
nothing was farther from my mind than the idea that my private taste for
fairly good books, for Wagner, for mythology, gave me any sort of superiority
to those who read nothing but magazines and listened to nothing but the
(then fashionable) Rag-time. The claim might seem unbelievable if I did not
add that I had been protected from this sort of conceit by downright ignorance. Mr Ian Hay somewhere draws a picture of the reading minority at a
Public School in his day as boys who talked about 'G.B.S. and G.K.C.' in the
same spirit in which other boys secretly smoked; both sets were inspired by
the same craving for forbidden fruit and the same desire to be grown-up. And
I suppose boys such as he describes might come from Chelsea or Oxford or
Cambridge homes where they heard things about contemporary literature.
But my position was wholly different. I was, for example, a great reader of
Shaw about the time I went to Wyvern, but I had never dreamed that reading
Shaw was anything to be proud of. Shaw was an author on my father's shelves
like any other author. I began reading him because his *Dramatic Opinions*
contained a good deal about Wagner and Wagner's very name was then a lure
to me. Thence I went on to read most of the other Shaws we had. But how his
reputation stood in the literary world I neither knew nor cared; I didn't know

there was 'a literary world'. My father told me Shaw was 'a mountebank' but that there were some laughs in *John Bull's Other Island*. It was the same with all my other reading; no one (thank God) had ever admired or encouraged it. (William Morris, for some unfathomable reason, my father always referred to as 'that whistlepainter'.) I might be – no doubt I was – conceited at Chartres for being good at my Latin; this was something recognised as meritorious. But 'Eng. Lit.' was blessedly absent from the official syllabus, so I was saved from any possibility of conceit about it. Never in my life had I read a work of fiction, poetry, or criticism in my own language except because, after trying the first few pages, I liked the taste of it. I could not help knowing that most other people, boys and grown-ups alike, did not care for the books I read. A very few tastes I could share with my father, a few more with my brother; apart from that, there was no point of contact, and this I accepted as a sort of natural law. If I reflected on it at all, it would have given me, I think, a slight feeling, not of superiority, but of inferiority. The latest popular novel was so obviously a more adult, a more normal, a more sophisticated taste than any of mine. A certain shame or bashfulness attached itself to whatever one deeply and privately enjoyed. I went to the Coll far more disposed to excuse my literary tastes than to plume myself on them.

But this innocence did not last. I was, from the first, a little shaken by all that I soon began to learn from my form-master about the glories of literature. I was at last made free of the dangerous secret that others had, like me, found there 'enormous bliss' and been maddened by beauty. Among the other New Bugs of my year, too, I met a pair of boys who came from the Dragon School at Oxford (where Naomi Mitchison in her teens had just produced her first play) and from them also I got the dim impression that there was a world I had never dreamed of, a world in which poetry, say, was a thing public and accepted, just as Games and Gallantry were accepted at Wyvern; nay, a world in which a taste for such things was almost meritorious. I felt as Siegfried felt when it first dawned on him that he was not Mime's son. What had been 'my' taste was apparently 'our' taste (if only I could ever meet the 'we' to whom that 'our' belonged). And if 'our' taste, then – by a perilous transition – perhaps 'good' taste or 'the right taste'. For that transition involves a kind of Fall. The moment good taste knows itself, some of its goodness is lost. Even then, however, it is not necessary to take the further downward step of despising the 'philistines' who do not share it. Unfortunately I took it. Hitherto, though increasingly miserable at Wyvern, I had been half ashamed of my own misery, still ready (if I were only allowed) to admire the Olympians, still a little overawed, cowed rather than resentful. I had, you see, no standing place against the Wyvernian *ethos*, no side for which I could play against it; it was a bare 'I' against what seemed simply the world. But the moment that 'I' became, however vaguely, a *we*

– and Wyvern not *the* world but *a* world – the whole thing changed. It was now possible, at least in thought, to retaliate. I can remember what may well have been the precise moment of this transition. A prefect called Blugg or Glubb or some such name stood opposite me, belching in my face, giving me some order. The belching was not intended as an insult. You can't 'insult' a fag any more than an animal. If Bulb had thought of my reactions at all, he would have expected me to find his eructations funny. What pushed me over the edge into pure priggery was his face – the puffy bloated cheeks, the thick, moist, sagging lower lip, the yokel blend of drowsiness and cunning. 'The lout!' I thought. 'The clod! The dull, crass clown! For all his powers and privileges, I would not be he.' I had become a Prig, a High-Brow.

The interesting thing is that the Public School system had thus produced the very thing which it was advertised to prevent or cure. For you must understand (if you have not been dipped in that tradition yourself) that the whole thing was devised to 'knock the nonsense' out of the smaller boys and 'put them in their place'. 'If the junior boys weren't fagged,' as my brother once said, 'they would become unsufferable.' That is why I felt so embarrassed, a few pages ago, when I had to confess that I got rather tired of perpetual fagging. If you say this, every true defender of the system will diagnose your case at once, and they will all diagnose it in the same way. 'Ho-ho!' they will cry, 'so *that's* the trouble! Thought yourself too good to black your betters' boots, did you? That just shows how badly you needed to be fagged. It's to cure young prigs like you that the system exists.' That any cause except 'thinking yourself too good for it' might awaken discontent with a fag's lot will not be admitted. You have only to transfer the thing to adult life and you will, apparently, see the full logic of the position. If some neighbouring V.I.P. had irresistible authority to call on you for any service he pleased at any hour when you were not in the office – if, when you came home on a summer evening, tired from work and with more work to prepare against the morrow, he could drag you to the links and make you his caddy till the light failed – if at last he dismissed you unthanked with a suitcase full of his clothes to brush and clean and return to him before breakfast, and a hamper full of his foul linen for your wife to wash and mend – and if, under this regime, you were not always perfectly happy and contented, where could the cause lie except in your own vanity? What else, after all, could it be? For, almost by definition, every offence a junior boy commits must be due to 'cheek' or 'side'; and to be miserable, even to fall short of rapturous enthusiasm, is an offence.

Obviously a certain grave danger was ever-present to the minds of those who built up the Wyvernian hierarchy. It seemed to them self-evident that, if you left things to themselves, boys of nineteen who played rugger for the county and boxed for the school would everywhere be knocked down and sat on by boys of thirteen. And that, you know, would be a very shocking spectacle. The most elaborate mechanism, therefore, had to be devised for protecting the strong against the weak, the close corporation of Old Hands against the parcel of newcomers who were strangers to one another and to everyone in the place, the poor, trembling lions against the furious and ravening sheep.

There is, of course, some truth in it. Small boys can be cheeky; and half an hour in the society of a French thirteen-year-old makes most of us feel that there is something to be said for fagging after all. Yet I cannot help thinking that the bigger boys would have been able to hold their own without all the complicated assurances, pattings on the back, and encouragement which the authorities gave them. For, of course, these authorities, not content with knocking the 'nonsense' out of the sheep, were always coaxing and petting an at least equal quantity of 'nonsense' into the lions; power and privilege and an applauding audience for the games they play. Might not the mere nature of boys have done all, and rather more than all, that needed doing in this direction without assistance?

But whatever the rationality of the design, I contend that it did not achieve its object. For the last thirty years or so England has been filled with a bitter, truculent, sceptical, debunking, and cynical *intelligentsia*. A great many of them were at public schools, and I believe very few of them liked it. Those who defend the schools will, of course, say that these Prigs are the cases which the system failed to cure; they were not kicked, mocked, fagged, flogged, and humiliated enough. But surely it is equally possible that they are the products of the system? that they were not Prigs at all when they came to their schools but were made Prigs by their first year, as I was? For, really, that would be a very natural result. Where oppression does not completely and permanently break the spirit, has it not a natural tendency to produce retaliatory pride and contempt? We reimburse ourselves for cuffs and toil by a double dose of self-esteem. No one is more likely to be arrogant than a lately freed slave.

I write, of course, only to neutral readers. With the wholehearted adherents of the system there is no arguing, for, as we have already seen, they have maxims and logic which the lay mind cannot apprehend. I have even heard them defend compulsory games on the ground that all boys 'except a few rotters' like the games; they have to be compulsory because no compulsion is needed. (I wish I had never heard chaplains in the Armed Forces produce a similar argument in defence of the wicked institution of Church Parades.)

But the essential evil of public school life, as I see it, did not lie either in the sufferings of the fags or in the privileged arrogance of the Bloods. These were symptoms of something more all-persuasive, something which, in the long run, did most harm to the boys who succeeded best at school and were happiest there. Spiritually speaking, the deadly thing was that school life was a life almost wholly dominated by the social struggle; to get on, to arrive, or, having reached the top, to remain there, was the absorbing preoccupation. It is often, of course, the preoccupation of adult life as well; but I have not yet seen any adult society in which the surrender to this impulse was so total. And from it, at school as in the world, all sorts of meanness flow; the sycophancy that courts those higher in the scale, the cultivation of those whom it is well to know, the speedy abandonment of friendships that will not help on the upward path, the readiness to join the cry against the unpopular, the secret motive in almost every action. The Wyvernians seem to me in retrospect to have been the least spontaneous, in that sense the least boyish, society I have ever known. It would perhaps not be too much to say that in some boys' lives everything was calculated to the great end of advancement. For this games were played; for this clothes, friends, amusements, and vices were chosen.

And that is why I cannot give pederasty anything like a first place among the evils of the Coll. There is much hypocrisy on this theme. People commonly talk as if every other evil were more tolerable than this. But why? Because those of us who do not share the vice feel for it a certain nausea, as we do, say, for necrophily? I think that of very little relevance to moral judgement. Because it produces permanent perversion? But there is very little evidence that it does. The Bloods would have preferred girls to boys if they could have come by them; when, at a later age, girls were obtainable, they probably took them. Is it then on Christian grounds? But how many of those who fulminate on the matter are in fact Christians? And what Christian in a society so worldly and cruel as that of Wyvern, would pick out the carnal sins for special reprobation? Cruelty is surely more evil than lust and the World at least as dangerous as the Flesh. The real reason for all the pother is, in my opinion, neither Christian nor ethical. We attack this vice not because it is the worst but because it is, by adult standards, the most disreputable and unmentionable, and happens also to be a crime in English law. The World will lead you only to Hell; but sodomy may lead you to jail and create a scandal, and lose you your job. The World, to do it justice, seldom does that.

If those of us who have known a school like Wyvern dared to speak the truth, we should have to say that pederasty, however great an evil in itself, was, in that time and place, the only foothold or cranny left for certain good things. It was the only counterpoise to the social struggle; the one oasis (though green only with weeds and moist only with foetid water) in the burning desert of competitive ambition. In his unnatural love-affairs, and perhaps only there, the Blood went a little out of himself, forgot for a few hours that he was One of the Most Important People There Are. It softens the picture. A perversion was the only chink left through which something spontaneous and uncalculating could creep in. Plato was right after all. Eros, turned upside down, blackened, distorted, and filthy, still bore traces of his divinity.

What an answer, by the by, Wyvern was to those who derive all the ills of society from economics! For money had nothing to do with its class system. It was not (thank Heaven) the boys with threadbare coats who became Punts, nor the boys with plenty of pocket-money who became Bloods. According to some theorists, therefore, it ought to have been entirely free from bourgeois vulgarities and iniquities. Yet I have never seen a community so competitive, so full of snobbery and flunkeyism, a ruling class so selfish and so class-conscious, or a proletariat so fawning, so lacking in all solidarity and sense of corporate honour. But perhaps one hardly needs to cite experience for a truth so obvious *a priori*. As Aristotle remarked, men do not become dictators in order to keep warm. If a ruling class has some other source of strength, why need it bother about money? Most of what it wants will be pressed upon it by emulous flatterers; the rest can be taken by force.

There were two blessings at Wyvern that wore no disguise; one of them was my form master, Smewgy as we called him. I spell the name so as to insure the right pronunciation – the first syllable should rhyme exactly with *Fugue* – though the Wyvernian spelling was 'Smugy'.

Except at Oldie's I had been fortunate in my teachers ever since I was born; but Smewgy was 'beyond expectation, beyond hope'. He was a grey-head with large spectacles and a wide mouth which combined to give him a froglike expression, but nothing could be less froglike than his voice. He was honey-tongued. Every verse he read turned into music on his lips: something midway between speech and song. It is not the only good way of reading verse, but it is the way to enchant boys; more dramatic and less rhythmical ways can be learned later. He first taught me the right sensuality of poetry, how it should be savoured and mouthed in solitude. Of Milton's 'Thrones, Dominations, Princedoms, Virtues, Powers' he said, 'That line made me happy for a week.' It was not the sort of thing I had heard anyone say before. Nor had I ever met before perfect courtesy in a teacher. It had nothing to do with softness; Smewgy could be very severe, but it was the severity of a judge, weighty and measured, without taunting –

He never yet no vileinye ne sayde
In all his lyf unto no maner wight.

He had a difficult team to drive, for our form consisted partly of youngsters, New Bugs with scholarships, starting there like myself, and partly of veterans who had arrived there at the end of their slow journey up the school. He made us a unity by his good manners. He always addressed us as 'gentle-men' and the possibility of behaving otherwise seemed thus to be ruled out from the beginning; and in that room at least the distinction between fags and Bloods never raised its head. On a hot day, when he had given us per-mission to remove our coats, he asked our permission before removing his gown. Once for bad work I was sent by him to the Headmaster to be threat-ened and rated. The Headmaster misunderstood Smewgy's report and thought there had been some complaint about my manners. Afterward Smewgy got wind of the Head's actual words and at once corrected the mis-take, drawing me aside and saying, 'There has been some curious misunder-standing. I said nothing of the sort about you. You will have to be whipped if you don't do better at your Greek Grammar next week, but naturally that has nothing to do with your manners or mine.' The idea that the tone of conversation between one gentleman and another should be altered by a flogging (any more than by a duel) was ridiculous. His manner was perfect: no familiarity, no hostility, no threadbare humour; mutual respect; decorum. 'Never let us live with *amousia*,' was one of his favourite maxims: *amousia*, the absence of the Muses. And he knew, as Spenser knew, that courtesy was of the Muses.

Thus, even had he taught us nothing else, to be in Smewgy's form was to be in a measure ennobled. Amidst all the banal ambition and flashy splen-dours of school life he stood as a permanent reminder of things more gra-cious, more humane, larger and cooler. But his teaching, in the narrower sense, was equally good. He could enchant but he could also analyse. An idiom or a textual crux, once expounded by Smewgy, became clear as day. He made us feel that the scholar's demand for accuracy was not merely pedantic, still less an arbitrary moral discipline, but rather a niceness, a deli-cacy, to lack which argued 'a gross and swainish disposition'. I began to see that the reader who misses syntactical points in a poem is missing aesthetic points as well.

In those days a boy on the classical side officially did almost nothing but classics. I think this was wise; the greatest service we can do to education to-day is to teach fewer subjects. No one has time to do more than a very few things well before he is twenty, and when we force a boy to be a mediocrity in a dozen subjects we destroy his standards, perhaps for life. Smewgy taught us Latin and Greek, but everything else came in incidentally. The books I liked best under his teaching were Horace's Odes, Aeneid IV, and Euripides' *Bacchae*. I had always in one sense 'liked' my classical work, but hitherto this had only been the pleasure that everyone feels in mastering a craft. Now I tasted the classics as poetry. Euripides' picture of Dionysus was closely linked in my mind with the whole mood of Mr Stephens' *Crock of Gold*, which I had lately read for the first time with great excitement. Here was something very different from the Northern-ness. Pan and Dionysus lacked the cold, piercing appeal of Odin and Frey. A new quality entered my imagination; something Mediterranean and volcanic, the orgiastic drumbeat. Orgiastic, but not, or not strongly, erotic. It was perhaps unconsciously connected with my growing hatred of the public school orthodoxies and conventions, my desire to break and tear it all.

The other undisguised blessing of the Coll was 'the Gurney', the school library; not only because it was a library, but because it was sanctuary. As the negro used to become free on touching English soil, so the meanest boy was 'unfaggable' once he was inside the Gurney. It was not, of course, easy to get there. In the winter terms if you were not on the list for 'Clubs' you had to go out for a run. In summer you could reach sanctuary of an afternoon only under favourable conditions. You might be put down for Clubs, and that excluded you. Or there might be either a House match or a Coll match which you were compelled to watch. Thirdly, and most probably, on your way to the Gurney you might be caught and fagged for the whole afternoon. But sometimes one succeeded in running the gauntlet of all these dangers; and then – books, silence, leisure, the distant sound of bat and ball ('Oh the brave music of a *distant* drum'), bees buzzing at the open windows, and freedom. In the Gurney I found *Corpus Poeticum Boreale* and tried, vainly but happily, to hammer out the originals from the translation at the bottom of the page. There too I found Milton, and Yeats, and a book on Celtic mythology, which soon became, if not a rival, yet a humble companion, to Norse. That did me good; to enjoy two mythologies (or three, now that I had begun to love the Greek), fully aware of their differing flavours, is a balancing thing, and makes for catholicity. I felt keenly the difference between the stony and fiery sublimity of Asgard, the green, leafy, amorous, and elusive world of Cruachan and the Red Branch and Tir-nan-Og, the harder, more defiant, sun-bright beauty of Olympus. I began (presumably in the holidays) an epic on Cuchulain and another on Finn, in English hexameters and in fourteeners respectively. Luckily they were abandoned before these easy and vulgar metres had time to spoil my ear.

But the Northernness still came first and the only work I completed at this time was a tragedy, Norse in subject and Greek in form. It was called *Loki Bound* and was as classical as any Humanist could have desired, with Prologos, Parodos, Epeisodia, Stasima, Exodos, Stichomythia, and (of course) one passage in trochaic *septenarii* – with rhyme. I never enjoyed anything more. The content is significant. My Loki was not merely malicious. He was against Odin because Odin had created a world though Loki had clearly warned him that this was a wanton cruelty. Why should creatures have the burden of existence forced on them without their consent? The main contrast in my play was between the sad wisdom of Loki and the brutal orthodoxy of Thor. Odin was partly sympathetic; he could at least see what Loki meant and there had been old friendship between those two before cosmic politics forced them apart. Thor was the real villain, Thor with his hammer and his threats, who was always egging Odin on against Loki and always complaining that Loki did not sufficiently respect the major gods; to which Loki replied

I pay respect to wisdom not to strength.

Thor was, in fact, the symbol of the Bloods; though I see that more clearly now than I did at the time. Loki was a projection of myself; he voiced that sense of priggish superiority whereby I was, unfortunately, beginning to compensate myself for my unhappiness.

The other feature in *Loki Bound* which may be worth commenting on is the pessimism. I was at this time living, like so many Atheists or Antitheists, in a whirl of contradictions. I maintained that God did not exist. I was also very angry with God for not existing. I was equally angry with Him for creating a world.

How far was this pessimism, this desire not to have been, sincere? Well, I must confess that this desire quite slipped out of my mind during the seconds when I was covered by the wild Earl's revolver. By the Chestertonian test, then, the test of *Manalive*, it was not sincere at all. But I am still not convinced by Chesterton's argument. It is true that when a pessimist's life is threatened he behaves like other men; his impulse to preserve life is stronger than his judgement that life is not worth preserving. But how does this prove that the judgement was insincere or even erroneous? A man's judgement that whisky is bad for him is not invalidated by the fact that when the bottle is at hand he finds desire stronger than reason and succumbs. Having once tasted life, we are subjected to the impulse of self-preservation. Life, in other words, is as habit-forming as cocaine. What then? If I still held creation to be 'a great injustice' I should hold that this impulse to retain life aggravates the injustice. If it is bad to be forced to drink the potion, how does it mend matters that the portion turns out to be an addictive drug? Pessimism cannot be answered so. Thinking as I then thought about the universe, I was reasonable in condemning it. At the same time I now see that my view was closely connected with a certain lop-sidedness of temperament. I had always been more violent in my negative than in my positive demands. Thus, in personal relations, I could forgive much neglect more easily than the least degree of what I regarded as interference. At table I could forgive much insipidity in my food more easily than the least suspicion of what seemed to me excessive or inappropriate seasoning. In the course of life I could put up with any amount of monotony far more patiently than even the smallest disturbance, bother, bustle, or what the Scotch call *kurfuffle*. Never at any age did I clamour to be amused; always and at all ages (where I dared) I hotly demanded not to be interrupted. The pessimism, or cowardice, which would prefer non-existence itself to even the mildest unhappiness was thus merely the generalisation of all these pusillanimous preferences. And it remains true that I have, almost all my life, been quite unable to feel that horror of nonentity, of annihilation, which, say, Dr Johnson felt so strongly. I felt it for the very first time only in 1947. But that was after I had long been re-converted and thus begun to know what life really is and what would have been lost by missing it.

8

RELEASE

As Fortune is wont, at her chosen hour,
Whether she sends us solace or sore,
The wight to whom she shows her power
Will find that he gets still more and more.

PEARL

A few chapters ago I warned the reader that the return of Joy had introduced into my life a duality which makes it difficult to narrate.
Reading through what I have just written about Wyvern, I find myself
exclaiming, 'Lies, lies! This was really a period of ecstasy. It consisted chiefly
of moments when you were too happy to speak, when the gods and heroes
rioted through your head, when satyrs danced and Maenads roared on the
mountains, when Brynhild and Sieglinde, Deirdre, Maeve and Helen were
all about you, till sometimes you felt that it might break you with mere richness.' And all that is true. There were more Leprechauns than fags in that
House. I have seen the victories of Cuchulain more often than those of the
first eleven. Was Borage the Head of the Coll? or was it Conachar
MacNessa? And the world itself – can I have been unhappy, living in
Paradise? What keen, tingling sunlight there was! The mere smells were
enough to make a man tipsy – cut grass, dew-dabbled mosses, sweet pea,
autumn woods, wood burning, peat, salt water. The sense ached. I was sick
with desire; that sickness better than health. All this is true, but it does not
make the other version a lie. I am telling a story of two lives. They had nothing to do with each other: oil and vinegar, a river running beside a canal,
Jekyll and Hyde. Fix your eye on either and it claims to be the sole truth.
When I remember my outer life I see clearly that the other is but momentary
flashes, seconds of gold scattered in months of dross, each instantly swallowed up in the old, familiar, sordid, hopeless weariness. When I remember
my inner life I see that everything mentioned in the last two chapters was
merely a coarse curtain which at any moment might be drawn aside to reveal
all the heavens I then knew. The same duality perplexes the story of my
home life, to which I must now turn.

Once my brother had left Wyvern and I had gone to it, the classic period
of our boyhood was at an end. Something not so good succeeded it, but this
had long been prepared by slow development within the classic age itself.

All began, as I have said, with the fact that our father was out of the house from nine in the morning till six at night. From the very first we built up for ourselves a life that excluded him. He on his part demanded a confidence even more boundless, perhaps, than a father usually, or wisely demands. One instance of this, early in my life, had far reaching effects. Once when I was at Oldie's and had just begun to try to live as a Christian I wrote out a set of rules for myself and put them in my pocket. On the first day of the holidays, noticing that my pockets bulged with all sorts of papers and that my coat was being pulled out of all shape, he plucked out the whole pile of rubbish and began to go through it. Boylike, I would have died rather than let him see my list of good resolutions. I managed to keep them out of his reach and get them into the fire. I do not see that either of us was to blame; but never from that moment until the hour of his death did I enter his house without first going through my own pockets and removing anything that I wished to keep private.

A habit of concealment was thus bred before I had anything guilty to conceal. By now I had plenty. And even what I had no wish to hide I could not tell. To have told him what Wyvern or even Chartres was really like would have been risky (he might write to the Headmaster) and intolerably embarrassing. It would also have been impossible, and here I must touch on one of his strangest characteristics.

My father – but these words, at the head of a paragraph, will carry the reader's mind inevitably to *Tristram Shandy*. On second thoughts I am content that they should. It is only in a Shandean spirit that my matter can be approached. I have to describe something as odd and whimsical as ever entered the brain of Sterne; and if I could, I would gladly lead you to the same affection for my father as you have for Tristram's. And now for the thing itself. You will have grasped that my father was no fool. He had even a streak of genius in him. At the same time he had – when seated in his own armchair after a heavy mid-day dinner on an August afternoon with all the windows shut – more power of confusing an issue or taking up a fact wrongly than any man I have ever known. As a result it was impossible to drive into his head any of the realities of our school life, after which (nevertheless) he repeatedly enquired. The first and simplest barrier to communication was that, having earnestly asked, he did not 'stay for an answer' or forgot it the moment it was uttered. Some facts must have been asked for and told him on a moderate computation, once a week and were received by him each time as perfect novelties. But this was the simplest barrier. Far more often he retained something, but something very unlike what you had said. His mind so bubbled over with humour, sentiment, and indignation that, long before he had understood or even listened to your words, some accidental hint had set his imagination to work, he had produced his own version of the facts, and believed that he was getting it from you. As he invariably got proper names wrong (no name seemed to him less probable than another) his *textus receptus* was often almost unrecognisable. Tell him that a boy called Churchwood had caught a fieldmouse and kept it as a pet, and a year, or ten years later, he would ask you, 'Did you ever hear what became of poor Chickweed who was so afraid of the rats?' For his own version, once adopted, was indelible, and attempts to correct it only produced an incredulous 'Hm! Well, that's not the story you *used* to tell.' Sometimes, indeed, he took in the facts you had stated; but truth fared none the better for that. What are facts without interpretation? It was axiomatic to my father (in theory) that nothing was said or done from an obvious motive. Hence he who in his real life was the most honourable and impulsive of men, and the easiest victim that any knave or imposter could hope to meet, became a positive Machiavel when he knitted his brows and applied to the behaviour of people he had never seen the spectral and labyrinthine operation which he called 'reading between the lines'. Once embarked upon that, he might make his landfall anywhere in the wide world: and always with unshakable conviction. 'I see it all' – 'I understand it perfectly' – 'It's as plain as a pikestaff,' he would say; and then, as we soon learned, he would believe till his dying day in some deadly quarrel, some slight, some secret sorrow or some immensely complex machination, which was not only improbable but impossible. Dissent on our part was attributed, with kindly laughter, to our innocence, gullibility, and general ignorance of life. And besides all these confusions, there were the sheer *non sequiturs* when the ground seemed to open at one's feet. 'Did Shakespeare spell his name with an E at the end?' asked my brother. 'I believe,' said I – but my father interrupted: 'I very much doubt if he used the Italian calligraphy *at all*.' A certain church in Belfast has both a Greek inscription over the door and a curious tower. 'That church is a great landmark,' said I, 'I can pick it out from all sorts of places – even from the top of Cave Hill.' 'Such nonsense,' said my father, 'how could you make out Greek letters three or four miles away?'

One conversation, held several years later, may be recorded as a specimen of these continual cross-purposes. My brother had been speaking of a reunion dinner for the officers of the Nth Division which he had lately attended. 'I suppose your friend Collins was there,' said my father.

B. Collins? Oh no. He wasn't in the Nth, you know.

F. (After a pause.) Did these fellows not like Collins then?

B. I don't quite understand. What fellows?

F. The Johnnies that got up the dinner.

B. Oh no, not at all. It was nothing to do with liking or not liking. You see, it was a purely Divisional affair. There'd be no question of asking anyone who hadn't been in the Nth.

F. (After a long pause.) Hm! Well, I'm sure poor Collins was very much
   hurt.

There are situations in which the very genius of Filial Piety would find it
difficult not to let some sign of impatience escape him.

I would not commit the sin of Ham. Nor would I, as historian, reduce a
complex character to a false simplicity. The man who, in his armchair, sometimes appeared not so much incapable of understanding anything as determined to misunderstand everything, was formidable in the police court and,
I presume, efficient in his office. He was a humorist, even, on occasion, a
wit. When he was dying, the pretty nurse, rallying him, said, 'What an old
pessimist you are! You're just like my father.' 'I suppose,' replied her
patient, 'he has *several* daughters.'

The hours my father spent at home were thus hours of perplexity for us
boys. After an evening of the sort of conversation I have been describing one
felt as if one's head were spinning like a top. His presence put an end to all
our innocent as well as to all our forbidden occupations. It is a hard thing –
nay, a wicked thing – when a man is felt to be an intruder in his own house.
And yet, as Johnson said, 'Sensation is sensation.' I am sure it was not his
fault, I believe much of it was ours; what is certain is that I increasingly
found it oppressive to be with him. One of his most amiable qualities helped
to make it so. I have said before that he 'conned no state'; except during his
Philippics he treated us as equals. The theory was that we lived together
more like three brothers than like a father and two sons. That, I say, was the
theory. But of course it was not and could not be so; indeed ought not to
have been so. That relation cannot really exist between schoolboys and a
middle-aged man of overwhelming personality and of habits utterly unlike
theirs. And the pretence that it does ends by putting a curious strain on the
juniors. Chesterton has laid his finger on the weak point of all such factitious equality: 'If a boy's aunts are his pals, will it not soon follow that a boy
needs no pals but his aunts?' That was not, of course, the question for us; we
wanted no pals. But we did want liberty, if only liberty to walk about the
house. And my father's theory that we were three boys together actually
meant that while he was at home we were as closely bound to his presence as
if the three of us had been chained together; and all our habits were frustrated. Thus if my father came home unexpectedly at mid-day, having
allowed himself an extra half-holiday, he might, if it were summer, find us
with chairs and books in the garden. An austere parent, of the formal school,
would have gone in to his own adult occupations. Not so my father. Sitting
in the garden? An excellent idea. But would not all three of us be better
on the summer-seat? Thither, after he had assumed one of his 'light spring
overcoats', we would go. (I do not know how many overcoats he had; I am
still wearing two of them.) After sitting for a few minutes, thus clad, on a

shadeless seat where the noon-day sun was blistering the paint, he not unnaturally began to perspire. 'I don't know what you two think,' he would say, 'but I'm finding this almost *too* hot. What about moving indoors?' That meant an adjournment to the study, where even the smallest chink of open window was rather grudgingly allowed. I say 'allowed', but there was no question of authority. In theory, everything was decided by the general Will. 'Liberty Hall, boys, Liberty Hall,' as he delighted to quote. 'What time would you like lunch?' But we knew only too well that the meal which would otherwise have been at one had already been shifted, in obedience to his lifelong preference, to two or even two-thirty; and that the cold meats which we liked had already been withdrawn in favour of the only food our father ever voluntarily ate – hot butcher's meat, boiled, stewed or roast ... and this to be eaten in mid-afternoon in a dining-room that faced south. For the whole of the rest of the day, whether sitting or walking, we were insepa-rable; and the speech (you see that it could hardly be called conversation), the speech with its cross-purposes, with its tone (inevitably) always set by him, continued intermittently till bedtime. I should be worse than a dog if I blamed my lonely father for thus desiring the friendship of his sons; or even if the miserable return I made him did not to this day lie heavy on my con-science. But 'sensation is sensation'. It was extraordinarily tiring. And in my own contributions to these endless talks – which were indeed too adult for me, too anecdotal, too prevailingly jocular – I was increasingly aware of an artificiality. The anecdotes were, indeed, admirable in their kind: business stories, Mahaffy stories (many of which I found attached to Jowett at Oxford), stories of ingenious swindles, social blunders, police-court 'drunks'. But I was acting when I responded to them. Drollery, whimsical-ity, the kind of humour that borders on the fantastic, was my line. I had to act. My father's geniality and my own furtive disobediences both helped to drive me into hypocrisy. I could not 'be myself' while he was at home. God forgive me, I thought Monday morning, when he went back to his work, the brightest jewel in the week.

Such was the situation which developed during the classic period. Now, when I had gone to Wyvern and my brother to a tutor to prepare for Sandhurst, there came a change. My brother had liked Wyvern as much as I loathed it. There were many reasons for this: his more adaptable temper, his face which bore no such smack-inviting signature as mine, but most of all the fact that he had gone there straight from Oldie's and I from a prepara-tory school where I had been happy. No school in England but would have appeared a heaven on earth after Oldie's. Thus in one of his first letters from Wyvern my brother communicated the startling fact that you could really eat as much (or as little) as you wanted at table. To a boy fresh from the school at Belsen, this alone would have outweighed almost everything else.

But by the time I went to Wyvern I had learned to take decent feeding for granted. And now a terrible thing happened. My reaction to Wyvern was perhaps the first great disappointment my brother had ever experienced. Loving the place as he did, he had looked forward to the days when this too could be shared between us – an *idem sentire* about Wyvern succeeding an *idem sentire* about Boxen. Instead he heard, from me, blasphemies against all his gods; from Wyvern, that his young brother looked like becoming a Coll Punt. The immemorial league between us was strained, all but broken.

All this was cruelly complicated by the fact that relations between my father and my brother were never before or since so bad as at this time; and Wyvern was behind that too. My brother's reports had grown worse and worse; and the tutor to whom he had now been sent confirmed them to the extent of saying that he seemed to have learned almost nothing at school. Nor was that all. Sentences savagely underlined in my father's copy of *The Lanchester Tradition* reveal his thoughts. They are passages about a certain glazed insolence, an elaborate, heartless flippancy, which the reforming Headmaster in that story encountered in the Bloods of the school he wished to reform. That was how my father envisaged my brother at this period: flippant, languid, emptied of the intellectual interests which had appeared in his earlier boyhood, immovable, indifferent to all real values, and urgent in his demand for a motor-bicycle.

It was, of course, to turn us into public-school boys that my father had originally sent us to Wyvern; the finished product appalled him. It is a familiar tragi-comedy and you can study it in Lockhart; Scott laboured hard to make his son a hussar, but when the actual hussar was presented to him, Scott sometimes forgot the illusion of being an aristocrat and became once more a respectable Edinburgh lawyer with strong views about Puppyism. So in our family. Mispronunciation was one of my father's favourite rhetorical weapons. He now always sounded the first syllable of Wyvern wrongly. I can still hear him growl, 'Wyvernian affectation.' In proportion as my brother's tone became languid and urbanely weary, so my father's voice became more richly and energetically Irish, and all manner of strange music from his boyhood in Cork and Dublin forced its way up through the more recent Belfastian crust.

During these miserable debates I occupied a most unfortunate position. To have been on my father's side and against my brother I should have had to unmake myself; it was a state of parties outside my whole philosophy of domestic politics. It was all very disagreeable.

Yet out of this 'unpleasantness' (a favourite word of my father's) there sprang what I still reckon, by merely natural standards, the most fortunate thing that ever happened to me. The tutor (in Surrey) to whom my brother had been sent was one of my father's oldest friends. He had been headmaster of Lurgan when my father was a boy there. In a surprisingly short time he so re-built and extended the ruins of my brother's education that he not only passed into Sandhurst but was placed among those very few candidates at the top of the list who received prize cadetships. I do not think my father ever did justice to my brother's achievement; it came at a time when the gulf between them was too wide, and when they were friends again it had become ancient history. But he saw very clearly what it proved about the exceptional powers of his teacher. At the same time, he was almost as sick as I of the very name of Wyvern. And I never ceased, by letter and by word of mouth, to beg that I might be taken away. All these factors urged him to the decision which he now made. Might it not after all be best to give me my desire? to have done with school for good and send me also to Surrey to read for the University with Mr Kirkpatrick? He did not form this plan without much doubt and hesitation. He did his best to put all the risks before me: the dangers of solitude, the sudden change from the life and bustle of a great school (which change I might not like so much as I anticipated), the possibly deadening effect of living with only an old man and his old wife for company. Should I really be happy with no companions of my own age? I tried to look very grave at these questions. But it was all imposture. My heart laughed. Happy without other boys? Happy without toothache, without chilblains, happy without pebbles in my shoes? And so the arrangement was made. If it had had nothing else to recommend it, the mere thought, 'Never, never, never, shall I have to play games again,' was enough to transport me. If you want to know how I felt, imagine your own feelings on waking one morning to find that income tax or unrequited love had somehow vanished from the world.

I should be sorry if I were understood to think, or if I encouraged any reader in thinking, that this invincible dislike of doing things with a bat or a ball were other than a misfortune. Not, indeed, that I allow to games any of the moral and almost mystical virtues which schoolmasters claim for them; they seem to me to lead to ambition, jealousy, and embittered partisan feeling, quite as often as to anything else. Yet not to like them is a misfortune, because it cuts you off from companionship with many excellent people who can be approached in no other way. A misfortune, not a vice; for it is involuntary. I had tried to like games and failed. That impulse had been left out of my make-up; I was to games, as the proverb has it, like an ass to the harp.

It is a curious truth, noticed by many writers, that good fortune is nearly always followed by more good fortune, and bad, by more bad. About the same time that my Father decided to send me to Mr Kirkpatrick, another great good came to me. Many chapters ago I mentioned a boy who lived near us and who had tried, quite unsuccessfully, to make friends with my brother and myself. His name was Arthur and he was my brother's exact contemporary; he and I had been at Campbell together though we never met. I think it was shortly before the beginning of my last term at Wyvern that I received a message saying that Arthur was in bed, convalescent, and would welcome a visit. I can't remember what led me to accept this invitation, but for some reason I did.

I found Arthur sitting up in bed. On the table beside him lay a copy of *Myths of the Norsemen*.

'Do *you* like that?' said I.

'Do *you* like that?' said he.

Next moment the book was in our hands, our heads were bent close together, we were pointing, quoting, talking – soon almost shouting – discovering in a torrent of questions that we liked not only the same thing, but the same parts of it and in the same way; that both knew the stab of Joy and that, for both, the arrow was shot from the North. Many thousands of people have had the experience of finding the first friend, and it is none the less a wonder; as great a wonder (*pace* the novelists) as first love, or even a greater. I had been so far from thinking such a friend possible that I had never even longed for one; no more than I longed to be King of England. If I had found that Arthur had independently built up an exact replica of the Boxonian world I should not really have been much more surprised. Nothing, I suspect, is more astonishing in any man's life than the discovery that there do exist people very, very like himself.

During my last few weeks at Wyvern strange stories began to appear in the papers, for this was the summer of 1914. I remember how a friend and I puzzled over a column that bore the headline 'Can England keep out of it?' 'Keep out of it?' said he, 'I don't see how she can get into it.' Memory paints the last hours of that term in slightly apocalyptic colours, and perhaps memory lies. Or perhaps for me it was apocalyptic enough to know that I was leaving, to see all those hated things for the last time; yet not simply (at that moment) to hate them. There is a 'rumness', a ghostliness, about even a Windsor chair when it says, 'You will not see me again.' Early in the holidays we declared war. My brother, then on leave from Sandhurst, was recalled. Some weeks later I went to Mr Kirkpatrick at Great Bookham in Surrey.

9

THE GREAT KNOCK

You will often meet with characters in nature so
extravagant that a discreet poet would not venture
to set them upon the stage.
LORD CHESTERFIELD

On a September day, having crossed to Liverpool and reached London, I made my way to Waterloo and ran down to Great Bookham. I had been told that Surrey was 'suburban', and the landscape that actually flitted past the windows astonished me. I saw steep little hills, watered valleys, and wooded commons which ranked by my Wyvernian and Irish standards as forests; bracken everywhere; a world of red and russet and yellowish greens. Even the sprinkling of suburban villas (much rarer then than now) delighted me. These timbered and red-tiled houses, embosomed in trees, were wholly unlike the stuccoed monstrosities which formed the suburbs of Belfast. Where I had expected gravel drives and iron gates and interminable laurels and monkey puzzlers, I saw crooked paths running up or down hill from wicket gates, between fruit trees and birches. By a severer taste than mine these houses would all be mocked perhaps; yet I cannot help thinking that those who designed them and their gardens achieved their object, which was to suggest Happiness. They filled me with a desire for that domesticity which, in its full development, I had never known; they set one thinking of tea trays.

At Bookham I was met by my new teacher – 'Kirk' or 'Knock' or the Great Knock as my father, my brother, and I all called him. We had heard about him all our lives and I therefore had a very clear impression of what I was in for. I came prepared to endure a perpetual luke-warm shower bath of sentimentality. That was the price I was ready to pay for the infinite blessedness of escaping school; but a heavy price. One story of my father's, in particular, gave me the most embarrassing forebodings. He had loved to tell how once at Lurgan, when he was in some kind of trouble or difficulty, the Old Knock, or the dear Old Knock, had drawn him aside and there 'quietly and naturally' slid his arm round him and rubbed his dear old whiskers against my father's youthful cheek and whispered a few words of comfort ... And here was Bookham at last, and there was the arch-sentimentalist himself waiting to meet me.

He was over six feet tall, very shabbily dressed (like a gardener, I thought), lean as a rake, and immensely muscular. His wrinkled face seemed to consist entirely of muscles, so far as it was visible; for he wore moustache and side whiskers with a clean-shaven chin like the Emperor Franz Joseph. The whiskers, you will understand, concerned me very much at that moment. My cheek already tingled in anticipation. Would he begin at once? There would be tears for certain; perhaps worse things. It is one of my life-long weaknesses that I never could endure the embrace or kiss of my own sex. (An unmanly weakness, by the way; Aeneas, Beowulf, Roland, Launcelot, Johnson, and Nelson knew nothing of it.)

Apparently, however, the old man was holding his fire. We shook hands, and though his grip was like iron pincers it was not lingering. A few minutes later we were walking away from the station.

'You are now,' said Kirk, 'proceeding along the principal artery between Great and Little Bookham.'

I stole a glance at him. Was this geographical exordium a heavy joke? Or was he trying to conceal his emotions? His face, however, showed only an inflexible gravity. I began to 'make conversation' in the deplorable manner which I had acquired at those evening parties and indeed found increasingly necessary to use with my father. I said I was surprised at the 'scenery' of Surrey; it was much 'wilder' than I had expected.

'Stop!' shouted Kirk with a suddenness that made me jump. 'What do you mean by wildness and what grounds had you for not expecting it?'

I replied I don't know what, still 'making conversation'. As answer after answer was torn to shreds it at last dawned upon me that he really wanted to know. He was not making conversation, not joking, not snubbing me; he wanted to know. I was stung into attempting a real answer. A few passes sufficed to show that I had no clear and distinct idea corresponding to the word 'wildness', and that, in so far as I had any idea at all, 'wildness' was a singularly inept word. 'Do you not see, then,' concluded the Great Knock, 'that your remark was meaningless?' I prepared to sulk a little, assuming that the subject would now be dropped. Never was I more mistaken in my life. Having analysed my terms, Kirk was proceeding to deal with my proposition as a whole. On what had I based (but he pronounced it *baized*) my expectations about the Flora and Geology of Surrey? Was it maps, or photographs, or books? I could produce none. It had, heaven help me, never occurred to me that what I called my thoughts needed to be 'baized' on anything. Kirk once more drew a conclusion – without the slightest sign of emotion, but equally without the slightest concession to what I thought good manners: 'Do you not see, then, that you had no right to have any opinion whatever on the subject?'

By this time our acquaintance had lasted about three and a half minutes; but the tone set by this first conversation was preserved without a single break during all the years I spent at Bookham. Anything more grotesquely unlike the 'dear Old Knock' of my father's reminiscences could not be conceived. Knowing my father's invariable intention of veracity and also knowing what strange transformations every truth underwent when once it entered his mind, I am sure he did not mean to deceive us. But if Kirk at any time of his life took a boy aside and there 'quietly and naturally' rubbed the boy's face with his whiskers, I shall as easily believe that he sometimes varied the treatment by quietly and naturally standing on his venerable and egg-bald head.

If ever a man came near to being a purely logical entity, that man was Kirk. Born a little later, he would have been a Logical Positivist. The idea that human beings should exercise their vocal organs for any purpose except that of communicating or discovering truth was to him preposterous. The most casual remark was taken as a summons to disputation. I soon came to know the differing values of his three openings. The loud cry of 'Stop!' was flung in to arrest a torrent of verbiage which could not be endured a moment longer; not because it fretted his patience (he never thought of that) but because it was wasting time, darkening counsel. The hastier and quieter 'Excuse!' (i.e. 'Excuse me') ushered in a correction or distinction merely parenthetical and betokened that, thus set right, your remark might still, without absurdity, be allowed to reach completion. The most encouraging of all was, 'I hear you.' This meant that your remark was significant and only required refutation; it had risen to the dignity of error. Refutation (when we got so far) always followed the same lines. Had I read this? Had I studied that? Had I any statistical evidence? Had I any evidence in my own experience? And so to the almost inevitable conclusion, 'Do you not see then that you had no right, etc.'

Some boys would not have liked it; to me it was red beef and strong beer. I had taken it for granted that my leisure hours at Bookham would be passed in 'grown-up conversation'. And that, as you know already, I had no taste for. In my experience it meant conversation about politics, money, deaths, and digestion. I assumed that a taste for it, as for eating mustard or reading newspapers, would develop in me when I grew older (so far, all three expectations have been disappointed). The only two kinds of talk I wanted were the almost purely imaginative and the almost purely rational; such talk as I had about Boxen with my brother or about Valhalla with Arthur, on the one hand, or such talk as I had had with my uncle Gussie about astronomy on the other. I could never have gone far in any science because on the path of every science the lion Mathematics lies in wait for you. Even in Mathematics, whatever could be done by mere reasoning (as in simple geometry) I did with delight; but the moment calculation came in I was helpless. I grasped the principles but my answers were always wrong. Yet though I could never have been a scientist, I had scientific as well as imaginative impulses, and I loved ratiocination. Kirk excited and satisfied one side of me. Here was talk that was really about something. Here was a man who thought not about you but about what you said. No doubt I snorted and bridled a little at some of my tossings; but, taking it all in all, I loved the treatment. After being knocked down sufficiently often I began to know a few guards and blows, and to put on intellectual muscle. In the end, unless I flatter myself, I became a not contemptible sparring partner. It was a great day when the man who had so long been engaged in exposing my vagueness at last cautioned me against the dangers of excessive subtlety.

If Kirk's ruthless dialectic had been merely a pedagogic instrument I might have resented it. But he knew no other way of talking. No age or sex was spared the elenchus. It was a continuous astonishment to him that anyone should not desire to be clarified or corrected. When a very dignified neighbour, in the course of a Sunday call, observed with an air of finality, 'Well, well, Mr Kirkpatrick, it takes all sorts to make a world. You are a Liberal and I am a Conservative; we naturally look at the facts from different angles,' Kirk replied, 'What do you mean? Are you asking me to picture Liberals and Conservatives playing peep-bo at a rectangular Fact from opposite sides of a table?' If an unwary visitor, hoping to waive a subject, observed, 'Of course, I know opinions differ—' Kirk would raise both hands and exclaim, 'Good heavens! I have no *opinions* on any subject whatsoever.' A favourite maxim was, 'You can have enlightenment for ninepence but you prefer ignorance.' The commonest metaphors would be questioned till some bitter truth had been forced from its hiding place. 'These fiendish German atrocities —' 'But are not fiends a figment of the imagination?' – 'Very well, then; these brutal atrocities —' 'But none of the brutes does anything of the kind!' – 'Well, what am I to call them?' 'Is it not plain that we must call them simply *Human*?' What excited his supreme contempt was the conversation of other Headmasters, which he had sometimes had to endure at conferences when he himself was Head of Lurgan. 'They would come and ask me, "What attitude do you adopt to a boy who does so-and-so?" Good Heavens! As if I ever adopted an attitude to anybody or anything!' Sometimes, but rarely, he was driven to irony. On such occasions his voice became even weightier than usual and only the distention of his nostrils betrayed the secret to those who knew him. It was in such fashion that he produced his *dictum*, 'The Master of Balliol is one of the most important beings in the universe.'

It will be imagined that Mrs Kirkpatrick led a somewhat uneasy life: witness the occasion on which her husband by some strange error found himself in the drawing-room at the beginning of what his lady had intended to be a bridge party. About half an hour later she was observed to leave the room with a remarkable expression on her face; and many hours later still the Great Knock was discovered sitting on a stool in the midst of seven elderly ladies ('ful drery was hire chere') begging them to clarify their terms.

I have said that he was almost wholly logical; but not quite. He had been a Presbyterian and was now an Atheist. He spent Sunday, as he spent most of his time on weekdays, working in his garden. But one curious trait from his Presbyterian youth survived. He always, on Sundays, gardened in a different, and slightly more respectable, suit. An Ulster Scot may come to disbelieve in God, but not to wear his week-day clothes on the Sabbath.

Having said that he was an Atheist, I hasten to add that he was a 'Rationalist' of the old, high and dry nineteenth-century type. For Atheism has come down in the world since those days, and mixed itself with politics and learned to dabble in dirt. The anonymous donor who now sends me anti-God magazines hopes, no doubt, to hurt the Christian in me; he really hurts the ex-Atheist. I am ashamed that my old mates and (which matters much more) Kirk's old mates should have sunk to what they are now. It was different then; even McCabe wrote like a man. At the time when I knew him, the fuel of Kirk's Atheism was chiefly of the anthropological and pessimistic kind. He was great on *The Golden Bough* and Schopenhauer.

The reader will remember that my own Atheism and Pessimism were fully formed before I went to Bookham. What I got there was merely fresh ammunition for the defence of a position already chosen. Even this I got indirectly from the tone of his mind or independently from reading his books. He never attacked religion in my presence. It is the sort of fact that no one would infer from an outside knowledge of my life, but it is a fact.

I arrived at Gastons (so the Knock's house was called) on a Saturday, and he announced that we would begin Homer on Monday. I explained that I had never read a word in any dialect but the Attic, assuming that when he knew this he would approach Homer through some preliminary lessons on the Epic language. He replied merely with a sound very frequent in his conversation which I can only spell 'Huh'. I found this rather disquieting; and I woke on Monday saying to myself, 'Now for Homer. Golly!' The name struck awe into my soul. At nine o'clock we sat down to work in the little upstairs study which soon became so familiar to me. It contained a sofa (on which we sat side by side when he was working with me), a table and chair (which I used when I was alone), a bookcase, a gas stove, and a framed photograph of Mr Gladstone. We opened our books at *Iliad*, Book I. Without a word of introduction Knock read aloud the first twenty lines or so in the 'new' pronunciation, which I had never heard before. Like Smewgy, he was a chanter; less mellow in voice, yet his full gutturals and rolling R's and more varied vowels seemed to suit the bronze-age epic as well as Smewgy's honey tongue had suited Horace. For Kirk, even after years of residence in

England, spoke the purest Ulster. He then translated, with a few, a very few explanations, about a hundred lines. I had never seen a classical author taken in such large gulps before. When he had finished he handed me over Crusius' *Lexicon* and, having told me to go through again as much as I could of what he had done, left the room. It seems an odd method of teaching, but it worked. At first I could travel only a very short way along the trail he had blazed, but every day I could travel further. Presently I could travel the whole way. Then I could go a line or two beyond his furthest North. Then it became a kind of game to see how far beyond. He appeared at this stage to value speed more than absolute accuracy. The great gain was that I very soon became able to understand a great deal without (even mentally) translating it; I was beginning to think in Greek. That is the great Rubicon to cross in learning any language. Those in whom the Greek word lives only while they are hunting for it in the lexicon, and who then substitute the English word for it, are not reading the Greek at all; they are only solving a puzzle. The very formula, '*Naus* means a ship', is wrong. *Naus* and *ship* both mean a thing, they do not mean one another. Behind *Naus*, as behind *navis* or *naca*, we want to have a picture of a dark, slender mass with sail or oars, climbing the ridges, with no officious English word intruding.

We now settled into a routine which has ever since served in my mind as an archetype, so that what I still mean when I speak of a 'normal' day (and lament that normal days are so rare) is a day of the Bookham pattern. For if I could please myself I would always live as I lived there. I would choose always to breakfast at exactly eight and to be at my desk by nine, there to read or write till one. If a cup of good tea or coffee could be brought me about eleven, so much the better. A step or so out of doors for a pint of beer would not do quite so well; for a man does not want to drink alone and if you meet a friend in the tap-room the break is likely to be extended beyond its ten minutes. At one precisely lunch should be on the table; and by two at the latest I would be on the road. Not, except at rare intervals, with a friend. Walking and talking are two very great pleasures, but it is a mistake to combine them. Our own noise blots out the sounds and silences of the out-door world; and talking leads almost inevitably to smoking, and then farewell to nature as far as one of our senses is concerned. The only friend to walk with is one (such as I found, during the holidays, in Arthur) who so exactly shares your taste for each mood of the countryside that a glance, a halt, or at most a nudge, is enough to assure us that the pleasure is shared. The return from the walk, and the arrival of tea, should be exactly coincident, and not later than a quarter past four. Tea should be taken in solitude, as I took it at Bookham on those (happily numerous) occasions when Mrs Kirkpatrick was out; the Knock himself disdained this meal. For eating and reading are two pleasures that combine admirably. Of course not all books are suitable for meal-time reading. It would be a kind of blasphemy to read poetry at table. What one wants is a gossipy, formless book which can be opened any-where. The ones I learned so to use at Bookham were Boswell, and a trans-lation of Herodotus, and Lang's *History of English Literature*. *Tristram Shandy*, *Elia* and the *Anatomy of Melancholy* are all good for the same pur-pose. At five a man should be at work again, and at it till seven. Then, at the evening meal and after, comes the time for talk, or, failing that, for lighter reading; and unless you are making a night of it with your cronies (and at Bookham I had none) there is no reason why you should ever be in bed later than eleven. But when is a man to write his letters? You forget that I am describing the happy life I led with Kirk or the ideal life I would live now if I could. And it is an essential of the happy life that a man would have almost no mail and never dread the postman's knock. In those blessed days I received, and answered, only two letters a week; one from my father, which was a matter of duty, and one from Arthur which was the high light of the week, for we poured out to each other on paper all the delight that was intoxicating us both. Letters from my brother, now on active service, were longer and rarer, and so were my replies.

Such is my ideal, and such then (almost) was the reality, of 'settled, calm, Epicurean life'. It is no doubt for my own good that I have been so generally prevented from leading it, for it is a life almost entirely selfish. Selfish, not self-centred: for in such a life my mind would be directed towards a thou-sand things, not one of which is myself. The distinction is not unimportant. One of the happiest men and most pleasing companions I have ever known was intensely selfish. On the other hand I have known people capable of real sacrifice whose lives were nevertheless a misery to themselves and to others, because self-concern and self-pity filled all their thoughts. Either condition will destroy the soul in the end. But till the end, give me the man who takes the best of everything (even at my expense) and then talks of other things, rather than the man who serves me and talks of himself, and whose very kindnesses are a continual reproach, a continual demand for pity, gratitude, and admiration.

Kirk did not, of course, make me read nothing but Homer. The Two Great Bores (Demosthenes and Cicero) could not be avoided. There were (oh glory!) Lucretius, Catullus, Tacitus, Herodotus. There was Virgil, for whom I still had no true taste. There were Greek and Latin compositions. (It is a strange thing that I have contrived to reach my late fifties without ever reading one word of Caesar.) There were Euripides, Sophocles, Aeschylus. In the evenings there was French with Mrs Kirkpatrick, treated much as her husband treated Homer. We got through a great many good novels in this way and I was soon buying French books on my own. I had hoped there would be English essays, but whether because he felt he could not endure mine or because he soon guessed that I was already only too proficient in that art (which he almost certainly despised) Kirk never set me one. For the first week or so he gave me directions about my English reading, but when he discovered that, left to myself, I was not likely to waste my time, he gave me absolute freedom. Later in my career we branched out into German and Italian. Here his methods were the same. After the very briefest contact with Grammars and Exercises I was plunged into *Faust* and the *Inferno*. In Italian we succeeded. In German I have little doubt that we should equally have succeeded if I had stayed with him a little longer. But I left too soon and my German has remained all my life that of a schoolboy. Whenever I have set about rectifying this, some other and more urgent task has always interrupted me.

But Homer came first. Day after day and month after month we drove gloriously onward, tearing the whole *Achilleid* out of the *Iliad* and tossing the rest on one side, and then reading the *Odyssey* entire, till the music of the thing and the clear, bitter brightness that lives in almost every formula had become part of me. Of course my appreciation was very romanticised – the appreciation of a boy soaked in William Morris. But this slight error saved me from that far deeper error of 'classicism' with which the Humanists have hoodwinked half the world. I cannot therefore deeply regret the days when I called Circe a 'wise-wife' and every marriage a 'high-tide'. That has all burned itself out and left no snuff, and I can now enjoy the *Odyssey* in a maturer way. The wanderings mean as much as ever they did; the great moment of 'eucatastrophe' (as Professor Tolkien would call it) when Odysseus strips off his rags and bends the bow, means more; and perhaps what now pleases me best of all is those exquisite, Charlotte M. Yonge families at Pylos and elsewhere. How rightly Sir Maurice Powicke says, 'There have been civilised people in all ages.' And let us add, 'In all ages they have been surrounded by barbarism.'

Meanwhile, on afternoons and on Sundays, Surrey lay open to me. County Down in the holidays and Surrey in the term – it was an excellent contrast. Perhaps, since their beauties were such that even a fool could not force them into competition, this cured me once and for all of the pernicious tendency to compare and to prefer – an operation that does little good even when we are dealing with works of art and endless harm when we are dealing with nature. Total surrender is the first step towards the fruition of either. Shut your mouth; open your eyes and ears. Take in what is there and give no thought to what might have been there or what is somewhere else. That can come later, if it must come at all. (And notice here how the true training for anything whatever that is good always prefigures and, if submitted to, will always help us in, the true training for the Christian life. That is a school where they can always use your previous work whatever subject it was on.) What delighted me in Surrey was its intricacy. My Irish walks commanded large horizons and the general lie of land and sea could be taken in at a glance: I will try to speak of them later. But in Surrey the contours were so tortuous, the little valleys so narrow, there was so much timber, so many villages concealed in woods or hollows, so many field paths, sunk lanes, dingles, copses, such an unpredictable variety of cottage, farmhouse, villa, and country seat, that the whole thing could never lie clearly in my mind, and to walk in it daily gave one the same sort of pleasure that there is in the labyrinthine complexity of Malory or the *Faerie Queene*. Even where the prospect was tolerably open, as when I sat looking down on the Leatherhead and Dorking valley from Polesden Lacey, it always lacked the classic comprehensibility of the Wyvern landscape. The valley twisted away southward into another valley, a train thudded past invisible in a wooded cutting, the opposite ridge concealed its bays and promontories. This, even on a summer morning. But I remember more dearly autumn afternoons in bottoms that lay intensely silent under old and great trees, and especially the moment, near Friday Street, when our party (that time I was not alone) suddenly discovered, from recognising a curiously shaped stump, that we had travelled round in a circle for the last half-hour; or one frosty sunset over the Hog's Back at Guildford. On a Saturday afternoon in winter, when nose and fingers might be pinched enough to give an added relish to the anticipation of tea and fireside, and the whole weekend's reading lay ahead, I suppose I reached as much happiness as is ever to be reached on earth. And especially if there were some new, long-coveted book awaiting me.

For I had forgotten. When I spoke of the post I forgot to tell you that it brought parcels as well as letters. Every man of my age has had in his youth one blessing for which our juniors may well envy him: we grew up in a world of cheap and abundant books. Your *Everyman* was then a bare shilling, and, what is more, always in stock; your *World's Classic, Muses' Library, Home University Library, Temple Classic,* Nelson's French series, Bohn, and Longman's Pocket Library, at proportionate prices. All the money I could spare went in postal orders to Messrs Denny of the Strand. No days, even at Bookham, were happier than those on which the afternoon post brought me a neat little parcel in dark grey paper. Milton, Spenser, Malory, *The High History of the Holy Grail,* the *Laxdale Saga,* Ronsard, Chénier, Voltaire, *Beowulf* and *Gawain and the Green Knight* (both in translations), Apuleius, the *Kalevala,* Herrick, Walton, Sir John Mandeville, Sidney's *Arcadia,* and nearly all of Morris, came volume by volume into my hands. Some of my purchases proved disappointments and some went beyond my hopes, but the undoing of the parcel always remained a delicious moment. On my rare visits to London, I looked at Messrs Denny in the Strand with a kind of awe; so much pleasure had come from it.

Smewgy and Kirk were my two greatest teachers. Roughly, one might say (in medieval language) that Smewgy taught me Grammar and Rhetoric and Kirk taught me Dialectic. Each had, and gave me, what the other lacked. Kirk had none of Smewgy's graciousness or delicacy, and Smewgy had less humour than Kirk. It was a saturnine humour. Indeed he was very like Saturn – not the dispossessed King of Italian legend, but grim old Cronos, Father Time himself with scythe and hourglass. The bitterest, and also funniest, things came out when he had risen abruptly from table (always before the rest of us) and stood ferreting in a villainous old tobacco jar on the mantelpiece for the dottles of former pipes which it was his frugal habit to use again. My debt to him is very great, my reverence to this day undiminished.

10

FORTUNE'S SMILE

The fields, the floods, the heavens, with one consent
Did seeme to laugh on me, and favour mine intent.
SPENSER

At the same time that I exchanged Wyvern for Bookham I also
exchanged my brother for Arthur as my chief companion. My brother,
as you know, was serving in France. From 1914 to 1916, which is the
Bookham period, he becomes a figure that at rare intervals appears unpre-
dicted on leave, in all the glory of a young officer, with what then seemed
unlimited wealth at his command, and whisks me off to Ireland. Luxuries
hitherto unknown to me, such as first-class railway carriages and sleeping
cars, glorify these journeys. You will understand that I had been crossing the
Irish Sea six times a year since I was nine. My brother's leaves now often
added journeys extraordinary. That is why my memory is stored with
ship's-side images to a degree unusual for such an untravelled man. I have
only to close my eyes to see if I choose, and sometimes whether I choose or
no, the phosphorescence of a ship's wash, the mast unmoving against the
stars though the water is rushing past us, the long salmon-coloured rifts of
dawn or sunset on the horizon of cold grey-green water, or the astonishing
behaviour of land as you approach it, the promontories that walk out to
meet you, the complex movements and final disappearance of the mountains
further inland.

These leaves were of course a great delight. The strains that had been
developing (thanks to Wyvern) before my brother went to France were forgotten. There was a tacit determination on both sides to revive, for the short
time allowed us, the classic period of our boyhood. As my brother was in
the R.A.S.C., which in those days was reckoned a safe place to be, we did
not feel that degree of anxiety about him which most families were suffering
at this time. There may have been more anxiety in the unconscious than
came out in fully waking thought. That, at least, would explain an experience I had, certainly once, and perhaps more often; not a belief, nor quite a
dream, but an impression, a mental image, a haunting, which on a bitter winter night at Bookham represented my brother hanging about the garden
and calling – or rather trying to call, but as in Virgil's Hell *inceptus clamor*

frustratur hiantem, a bat's cry is all that comes. There hung over this image an atmosphere which I dislike as much as any I ever breathed, a blend of the macabre and the weakly, wretchedly, hopelessly pathetic – the dreary miasma of the Pagan Hades.

Though my friendship with Arthur began from an identity of taste on a particular point, we were sufficiently different to help one another. His home-life was almost the opposite of mine. His parents were members of the Plymouth Brothers, and he was the youngest of a large family; his home, nevertheless, was almost as silent as ours was noisy. He was at this time working in the business of one of his brothers, but his health was delicate and after an illness or two he was withdrawn from it. He was a man of more than one talent: a pianist and, in hope, a composer, and also a painter. One of our earliest schemes was that he should make an operatic score for *Loki Bound* – a project which, of course, after an extremely short and happy life, died a painless death. In literature he influenced me more, or more permanently, than I did him. His great defect was that he cared very little for verse. Something I did to mend this, but less than I wished. He, on the other hand, side by side with his love for myth and marvel, which I fully shared, had another taste which I lacked till I met him and with which, to my great good, he infected me for life. This was the taste for what he called 'the good, solid, old books', the classic English novelists. It is astonishing how I had avoided them before I met Arthur. I had been persuaded by my father to read *The Newcomes* when I was rather too young for it and never tried Thackeray again till I was at Oxford. He is still antipathetic to me, not because he preaches but because he preaches badly. Dickens I looked upon with a feeling of horror, engendered by long poring over the illustrations before I had learned to read. I still think them depraved. Here, as in Walt Disney, it is not the ugliness of the ugly figures but the simpering dolls intended for our sympathy which really betray the secret (not that Walt Disney is not far superior to the illustrators of Dickens). Of Scott I knew only a few of the medieval, that is, the weakest, novels. Under Arthur's influence I read at this time all the best Waverleys, all the Brontës, and all the Jane Austens. They provided an admirable complement to my more fantastic reading, and each was the more enjoyed for its contrast to the other. The very qualities which had previously deterred me from such books Arthur taught me to see as their charm. What I would have called their 'stodginess' or 'ordinariness' he called 'Homeliness' – a key word in his imagination. He did not mean merely Domesticity, though that came into it. He meant the rooted quality which attaches them to all our simple experiences, to weather, food, the family, the neighbourhood. He could get endless enjoyment out of the opening sentence of *Jane Eyre*, or that other opening sentence in one of Hans Andersen's stories, 'How it did rain, to be sure.' The mere word 'beck' in the Brontës was a feast to him; and so were the schoolroom and kitchen scenes. This love of the

'Homely' was not confined to literature; he looked for it in out-of-door scenes as well and taught me to do the same.

Hitherto my feelings for nature had been too narrowly romantic. I had attended almost entirely to what I thought awe-inspiring, or wild, or eerie, and above all to distance. Hence mountains and clouds were my especial delight; the sky was, and still is, to me one of the principal elements in any landscape, and long before I had seen them all named and sorted out in *Modern Painters* I was very attentive to the different qualities, and different heights, of the cirrus, the cumulus, and the rain-cloud. As for the Earth, the country I grew up in had everything to encourage a romantic bent, had indeed done so ever since I first looked at the unattainable Green Hills through the nursery window. For the reader who knows those parts it will be enough to say that my main haunt was the Holywood Hills – the irregular polygon you would have described if you drew a line from Stormont to Comber, from Comber to Newtownards, from Newtownards to Scrabo, from Scrabo to Craigantlet, from Craigantlet to Holywood, and thence through Knocknagonney back to Stormont. How to suggest it all to a foreigner I hardly know.

First of all, it is by southern English standards bleak. The woods, for we have a few, are of small trees, rowan and birch and small fir. The fields are small, divided by ditches with ragged sea-nipped hedges on top of them. There is a good deal of gorse and many outcroppings of rock. Small abandoned quarries, filled with cold-looking water, are surprisingly numerous. There is nearly always a wind whistling through the grass. Where you see a man ploughing there will be gulls following him and pecking at the furrow. There are no field-paths or rights of way, but that does not matter for everyone knows you – or if they do not know you, they know your kind and understand that you will shut gates and not walk over crops. Mushrooms are still felt to be common property, like the air. The soil has none of the rich chocolate or ochre you find in parts of England: it is pale – what Dyson calls 'the ancient, bitter earth'. But the grass is soft, rich, and sweet, and the cottages, always whitewashed and single storeyed and roofed with blue slate, light up the whole landscape.

Although these hills are not very high, the expanse seen from them is huge and various. Stand at the north-eastern extremity where the slopes go steeply down to Holywood. Beneath you is the whole expanse of the Lough. The Antrim coast twists sharply to the north and out of sight; green, and humble in comparison, Down curves away southward. Between the two the Lough merges into the sea, and if you look carefully on a good day you can even see Scotland, phantom-like on the horizon. Now come further to the south and west. Take your stand at the isolated cottage which is visible from my father's house and overlooks our whole suburb, and which everyone calls The Shepherd's Hut, though we are not really a shepherd country. You are still looking down on the Lough, but its mouth and the sea are now hidden by the shoulder you have just come from, and it might (for all you see) be a landlocked lake. And here we come to one of those great contrasts which have bitten deeply into my mind – Niflheim and Asgard, Britain and Logres, Handramit and Harandra, air and ether, the low world and the high. Your horizon from here is the Antrim Mountains, probably a uniform mass of greyish blue, though if it is a sunny day you may just trace on the Cave Hill the distinction between the green slopes that climb two-thirds of the way to the summit and the cliff wall that perpendicularly accomplishes the rest. That is one beauty; and here where you stand is another, quite different and even more dearly loved – sunlight and grass and dew, crowing cocks and gaggling ducks. In between them, on the flat floor of the Valley at your feet, a forest of factory chimneys, gantries, and giant cranes rising out of a welter of mist, lies Belfast. Noises come up from it continually, whining and screeching of trams, clatter of horse traffic on uneven sets, and, dominating all else, the continual throb and stammer of the great shipyards. And because we have heard this all our lives it does not, for us, violate the peace of the hill-top; rather, it emphasises it, enriches the contrast, sharpens the dualism. Down in that 'smoke and stir' is the hated office to which Arthur, less fortunate than I, must return to-morrow; for it is only one of his rare holidays that allows us to stand here together on a week-day morning. And down there too are the barefoot old women, the drunken men stumbling in and out of the 'spirit grocers' (Ireland's horrible substitute for the kindly English 'pub'), the straining, overdriven horses, the hard-faced rich women – all the world which Alberich created when he cursed love and twisted the gold into a ring.

Now step a little way – only two fields and across a lane and up to the top of the bank on the far side – and you will see, looking south with a little east in it, a different world. And having seen it, blame me if you can for being a romantic. For here is the thing itself, utterly irresistible, the way to the world's end, the land of longing, the breaking and blessing of hearts. You are looking across what may be called, in a certain sense, the plain of Down, and seeing beyond it the Mourne Mountains.

It was K. – that is, Cousin Quartus' second daughter, the Valkyrie – who first expounded to me what this plain of Down is really like. Here is the recipe for imagining it. Take a number of medium-sized potatoes and lay them down (one layer of them only) in a flat-bottomed tin basin. Now shake loose earth over them till the potatoes themselves, but not the shape of them, is hidden; and of course the crevices between them will now be depressions of earth. Now magnify the whole thing till those crevices are large enough to conceal each its stream and its huddle of trees. And then, for colouring, change your brown earth into the chequered pattern of fields, always small fields (a couple of acres each), with all their normal variety of crop, grass, and plough. You have now got a picture of the 'plain' of Down, which is a plain only in this sense that if you were a very large giant you would regard it as level but very ill to walk on – like cobbles. And now remember that every cottage is white. The whole expanse laughs with these little white dots; it is like nothing so much as the assembly of white foam-caps when a fresh breeze is on a summer sea. And the roads are white too; there is no tarmac yet. And because the whole country is a turbulent democracy of little hills, these roads shoot in every direction, disappearing and reappearing. But you must not spread over this landscape your hard English sunlight; make it paler, make it softer, blur the edges of the white cumuli, cover it with watery gleams, deepening it, making all unsubstantial. And beyond all this, so remote that they seem fantastically abrupt at the very limit of your vision, imagine the mountains. They are no stragglers. They are steep and compact and pointed and toothed and jagged. They seem to have nothing to do with the little hills and cottages that divide you from them. And sometimes they are blue, sometimes violet; but quite often they look transparent – as if huge sheets of gauze had been cut into mountainous shapes and hung up there, so that you could see through them the light of the invisible sea at their backs.

I number it among my blessings that my father had no car, while yet most of my friends had, and sometimes took me for a drive. This meant that all these distant objects could be visited just enough to clothe them with memories and not impossible desires, while yet they remained ordinarily as inaccessible as the Moon. The deadly power of rushing about wherever I pleased had not been given me. I measured distances by the standard of man, man walking on his two feet, not by the standard of the internal combustion engine. I had not been allowed to deflower the very idea of distance; in return I possessed 'infinite riches' in what would have been to motorists 'a little room'. The truest and most horrible claim made for modern transport is that it 'annihilates space'. It does. It annihilates one of the most glorious gifts we have been given. It is a vile inflation which lowers the value of distance, so that a modern boy travels a hundred miles with less sense of liberation and pilgrimage and adventure than his grandfather got from travelling ten. Of course if a man hates space and wants it to be annihilated, that is another matter. Why not creep into his coffin at once? There is little enough space there.

Such were my outdoor delights before I met Arthur, and all these he shared and confirmed. And in his search for the Homely he taught me to see other things as well. But for him I should never have known the beauty of the ordinary vegetables that we destine to the pot. 'Drills,' he used to say. 'Just ordinary drills of cabbages – what can be better?' And he was right.

Often he recalled my eyes from the horizon just to look through a hole in a hedge, to see nothing more than a farmyard in its mid-morning solitude, and perhaps a grey cat squeezing its way under a barn door, or a bent old woman with a wrinkled, motherly face coming back with an empty bucket from the pigsty. But best of all we liked it when the Homely and the unhomely met in sharp juxtaposition; if a little kitchen garden ran steeply up a narrowing *enclave* of fertile ground surrounded by outcroppings and furze, or some shivering quarry pool under a moonrise could be seen on our left, and on our right the smoking chimney and lamplit window of a cottage that was just settling down for the night.

Meanwhile, on the continent, the unskilled butchery of the first German War went on. As it did so and as I began to foresee that it would probably last till I reached military age, I was compelled to make a decision which the law had taken out of the hands of English boys of my own age; for in Ireland we had no conscription. I did not much plume myself even then for deciding to serve, but I did feel that the decision absolved me from taking any further notice of the war. For Arthur, whose heart hopelessly disqualified him, there was no such question. Accordingly I put the war on one side to a degree which some people will think shameful and some incredible. Others will call it a flight from reality. I maintain that it was rather a treaty with reality, the fixing of a frontier. I said to my country, in effect, 'You shall have me on a certain date, not before. I will die in your wars if need be, but till then I shall live my own life. You may have my body, but not my mind. I will take part in battles but not read about them.' If this attitude needs excusing I must say that a boy who is unhappy at school inevitably learns the habit of keeping the future in its place; if once he began to allow infiltrations from the coming term into the present holidays he would despair. Also, the Hamilton in me was always on guard against the Lewis; I had seen enough of the self-torturing temperament.

No doubt, even if the attitude was right, the quality in me which made it so easy to adopt is somewhat repellent. Yet, even so, I can hardly regret having escaped the appalling waste of time and spirit which would have been involved in reading the war news or taking more than an artificial and formal part in conversations about the war. To read without military knowledge or good maps accounts of fighting which were distorted before they reached the Divisional general and further distorted before they left him and then 'written up' out of all recognition by journalists, to strive to master what will be contradicted the next day, to fear and hope intensely on shaky evidence, is surely an ill use of the mind. Even in peacetime I think those are very wrong who say that schoolboys should be encouraged to read the newspapers. Nearly all that a boy reads there in his teens will be known before he is twenty to have been false in emphasis and interpretation, if not in fact as well, and most of it will have lost all importance. Most of what he remembers he will therefore have to unlearn; and he will probably have acquired an incurable taste for vulgarity and sensationalism and the fatal habit of fluttering from paragraph to paragraph to learn how an actress has been divorced in California, a train derailed in France, and quadruplets born in New Zealand.

I was now happier than I had ever been. All the sting had been drawn from the beginning of term. Yet the homecoming at its end remained almost as joyful as before. The holidays grew better and better. Our grown-up friends, and especially my cousins at Mountbracken, now seemed less grown up – for one's immediate elders grow downwards or backwards to meet one at that age. There were many merry meetings, much good talk. I discovered that other people besides Arthur loved books that I loved. The horrible old 'social functions', the dances, were at an end, for my father now allowed me to refuse the invitations. All my engagements were now pleasant ones, within a small circle of people who were all intermarried, or very old neighbours, or (the women anyway) old schoolfellows. I am shy of mentioning them. Of Mountbracken I have had to speak because the story of my life could not be told without it; beyond that I hesitate to go. Praise of one's friends is near impertinence. I cannot tell you here of Janie M. nor of her mother, nor of Bill and Mrs Bill. In novels, provincial-suburban society is usually painted grey to black. I have not found it so. I think we Strandtown and Belmont people had among us as much kindness, wit, beauty, and taste as any circle of the same size that I have ever known.

At home the real separation and apparent cordiality between my father and myself continued. Every holidays I came back from Kirk with my thoughts and my speech a little clearer, and this made it progressively less possible to have any real conversation with my father. I was far too young and raw to appreciate the other side of the account, to weigh the rich (if vague) fertility, the generosity and humour of my father's mind against the dryness, the rather death-like lucidity, of Kirk's. With the cruelty of youth I allowed myself to be irritated by traits in my father which, in other elderly men, I have since regarded as lovable foibles. There were so many unbridgeable misunderstandings. Once I received a letter from my brother in my father's presence which he immediately demanded to see. He objected to some expressions in it about a third person. In defence of them I pleaded that they had not been addressed to him. 'What nonsense!' answered my father. 'He knew you would show me the letter, and intended you to show me the letter.' In reality, as I well knew, my brother had foolishly gambled on the chance that it would arrive when my father was out. But this my father could not conceive. He was not overriding by authority a claim to privacy which he disallowed; he could not imagine anyone making such a claim.

My relations to my father help to explain (I am not suggesting that they excuse) one of the worst acts of my life. I allowed myself to be prepared for confirmation, and confirmed, and to make my first Communion, in total disbelief, acting a part, eating and drinking my own condemnation. As Johnson points out, where courage is not, no other virtue can survive except by accident. Cowardice drove me into hypocrisy and hypocrisy into blasphemy. It is true that I did not and could not then know the real nature of the thing I was doing: but I knew very well that I was acting a lie with the greatest possible solemnity. It seemed to me impossible to tell my father my real views. Not that he would have stormed and thundered like the traditional orthodox parent. On the contrary, he would (at first) have responded with the greatest kindness. 'Let's talk the whole thing over,' he would have said. But it would have been quite impossible to drive into his head my real position. The thread would have been lost almost at once, and the answer implicit in all the quotations, anecdotes, and reminiscences which would have poured over me would have been one I then valued not a straw – the beauty of the Authorised Version, the beauty of the Christian tradition and sentiment and character. And later, when this failed, when I still tried to make my exact points clear, there would have been anger between us, thunder from him and a thin, peevish rattle from me. Nor could the subject, once raised, ever have been dropped again. All this, of course, ought to have been dared rather than the thing I did. But at the time it seemed to me impossible. The Syrian captain was forgiven for bowing in the house of Rimmon. I am one of many who have bowed in the house of the real God when I believed Him to be no more than Rimmon.

During the week-ends and evenings I was closely tethered to my father and felt this something of a hardship, since these were the times when Arthur was most often accessible. My week-days continued to supply me with a full ration of solitude. I had, to be sure, the society of Tim, who ought to have been mentioned far sooner. Tim was our dog. He may hold a record for longevity among Irish terriers since he was already with us when I was at Oldie's and did not die till 1922. But Tim's society did not amount to much. It had long since been agreed between him and me that he should not be expected to accompany me on walks. I went a good deal further than he liked, for his shape was already that of a bolster, or even a barrel, on four legs. Also, I went to places where other dogs might be met; and though Tim was no coward (I have seen him fight like a demon on his home ground) he hated dogs. In his walking days he had been known, on seeing a dog far ahead, to disappear behind the hedge and re-emerge a hundred yards later. His mind had been formed during our schooldays and he had perhaps learned his attitude to other dogs from our attitude to other boys. By now he and I were less like master and dog than like two friendly visitors in the same hotel. We met constantly, passed the time of day, and parted with much esteem to follow our own paths. I think he had one friend of his own species, a neighbouring red setter; a very respectable, middle-aged dog. Perhaps a good influence; for poor Tim, though I loved him, was the most undisciplined, unaccomplished, and dissipated-looking creature that ever went on four legs. He never exactly obeyed you; he sometimes agreed with you.

The long hours in the empty house passed delightfully in reading and writing. I was in the midst of the Romantics now. There was a humility in me (as a reader) at that time which I shall never recapture. Some poems I could not enjoy as well as others. It never occurred to me that these might be the inferior ones; I merely thought that I was getting tired of my author or was not in the right mood. The *longueurs* of Endymion I attributed wholly to myself. The 'swoony' element in Keats' sensuality (as when Porphyro grows 'faint') I tried hard to like, and failed. I thought – though I have forgotten why – that Shelley must be better than Keats and was sorry I liked him less. But my great author at this period was William Morris. I had met him first in quotation in books on Norse Mythology; that led me to *Sigurd the Volsung*. I did not really like this as much as I tried to, and I think I now know why: the metre does not satisfy my ear. But then, in Arthur's bookcase, I found *The Well at the World's End*. I looked – I read chapter headings – I dipped – and next day I was off into town to buy a copy of my own. Like so many new steps it appeared to be partly a revival – 'Knights in Armour' returning from a very early period of my childhood. After that I read all the Morris I could get, *Jason, The Earthly Paradise*, the prose romances. The growth of the new delight is marked by my sudden realisation, almost with a sense of disloyalty, that the letters WILLIAM MORRIS were coming to have at least as potent a magic in them as WAGNER.

One other thing that Arthur taught me was to love the bodies of books. I had always respected them. My brother and I might cut up stepladders without scruple; to have thumb-marked or dog's-eared a book would have filled us with shame. But Arthur did not merely respect, he was enamoured; and soon, I too. The set up of the page, the feel and smell of the paper, the differing sounds that different papers make as you turn the leaves, became sensuous delights. This revealed to me a flaw in Kirk. How often have I shuddered when he took a new classical text of mine in his gardener's hands, bent back the boards till they creaked, and left his sign on every page.

'Yes, I remember,' said my father. 'That was old Knock's one fault.'

'A bad one,' said I.

'An all but unforgivable one,' said my father.

II

CHECK

When bale is at highest, boote is at next.
SIR ALDINGAR

The history of Joy, since it came riding back to me on huge waves of
Wagnerian music and Norse and Celtic mythology several chapters
ago, must now be brought up to date.

I have already hinted how my first delight in Valhalla and Valkyries began
to turn itself imperceptibly into a scholar's interest in them. I got about as
far as a boy who knew no old Germanic language could get. I could have
faced a pretty stiff examination in my subject. I would have laughed at popular bunglers who confused the late mythological Sagas with the classic
Sagas, or the Prose with the Verse Edda, or even, more scandalously, Edda
with Saga. I knew my way about the Eddaic cosmos, could locate each of the
roots of the Ash and knew who ran up and down it. And only very gradually did I realise that all this was something quite different from the original
Joy. And I went on adding detail to detail, progressing towards the moment
when 'I should know most and should least enjoy'. Finally I woke from
building the temple to find that the God had flown. Of course I did not put
it that way. I would have said simply that I didn't get the old thrill. I was in
the Wordsworthian predicament, lamenting that 'a glory' had passed away.

Thence arose the fatal determination to recover the old thrill, and at last
the moment when I was compelled to realise that all such efforts were failures. I had no lure to which the bird would come. And now, notice my
blindness. At that very moment there arose the memory of a place and time
at which I had tasted the lost Joy with unusual fullness. It had been a particular hill-walk on a morning of white mist. The other volumes of the *Ring*
(*The Rheingold* and *The Valkyrie*) had just arrived as a Christmas present
from my father, and the thought of all the reading before me, mixed with the
coldness and loneliness of the hillside, the drops of moisture on every
branch, and the distant murmur of the concealed town, had produced a
longing (yet it was also fruition) which had flowed over from the mind and
seemed to involve the whole body. That walk I now remembered. It seemed
to me that I had tasted heaven then. If only such a moment could return! But

what I never realised was that it had returned – that the remembering of that walk was itself a new experience of just the same kind. True, it was desire, not possession. But then what I had felt on the walk had also been desire, and only possession in so far as that kind of desire is itself desirable, is the fullest possession we can know on earth; or rather, because the very nature of Joy makes nonsense of our common distinction between having and wanting. There, to have is to want and to want is to have. Thus, the very moment when I longed to be so stabbed again, was itself again such a stabbing. The Desirable which had once alighted on Valhalla was now alighting on a particular moment of my own past; and I would not recognise him there because, being an idolater and a formalist, I insisted that he ought to appear in the temple I had built him; not knowing that he cares only for temples building and not at all for temples built. Wordsworth, I believe, made this mistake all his life. I am sure that all that sense of the loss of vanished vision which fills *The Prelude* was itself vision of the same kind, if only he could have believed it.

In my scheme of thought it is not blasphemous to compare the error which I was making with that error which the angel at the Sepulchre rebuked when he said to the women, 'Why seek ye the living among the dead? He is not here, He is risen.' The comparison is of course between something of infinite moment and something very small; like comparison between the Sun and the Sun's reflection in a dewdrop. Indeed, in my view, very like it, for I do not think the resemblance between the Christian and the merely imaginative experience is accidental. I think that all things, in their way, reflect heavenly truth, the imagination not least. 'Reflect' is the important word. This lower life of the imagination is not[1] a beginning of nor a step towards, the higher life of the spirit, merely an image. In me, at any rate, it contained no element either of belief or of ethics; however far pursued, it would never have made me either wiser or better. But it still had, at however many removes, the shape of the reality it reflected.

If nothing else suggests this resemblance it is at least suggested by the fact that we can make exactly the same mistakes on both levels. You will remember how, as a schoolboy, I had destroyed my religious life by a vicious subjectivism which made 'realisations' the aim of prayer; turning away from God to seek states of mind, and trying to produce those states of mind by 'maistry'. With unbelievable folly I now proceeded to make exactly the same blunder in my imaginative life; or rather the same pair of blunders. The first was made at the very moment when I formulated the complaint that the 'old thrill' was becoming rarer and rarer. For by that complaint I smuggled in the assumption that what I wanted was a 'thrill', a state of my own mind. And

---

[1] i.e. not necessarily and by its own nature. God can cause it to be such a beginning.

there lies the deadly error. Only when your whole attention and desire are fixed on something else – whether a distant mountain, or the past, or the gods of Asgard – does the 'thrill' arise. It is a by-product. Its very existence presupposes that you desire not it but something other and outer. If by any perverse askesis or the use of any drug it could be produced from within, it would at once be seen to be of no value. For take away the object, and what, after all, would be left? – a whirl of images, a fluttering sensation in the diaphragm, a momentary abstraction. And who could want that? This, I say, is the first and deadly error, which appears on every level of life and is equally deadly on all, turning religion into a self-caressing luxury and love into auto-eroticism. And the second error is, having thus falsely made a state of mind your aim, to attempt to produce it. From the fading of the Northernness I ought to have drawn the conclusion that the Object, the Desirable, was further away, more external, less subjective, than even such a comparatively public and external thing as a system of mythology – had, in fact, only shone through that system. Instead, I concluded that it was a mood or state within myself which might turn up in any context. To 'get it again' became my constant endeavour; while reading every poem, hearing every piece of music, going for every walk, I stood anxious sentinel at my own mind to watch whether the blessed moment was beginning and to endeavour to retain it if it did. Because I was still young and the whole world of beauty was opening before me, my own officious obstructions were often swept aside and, startled into self-forgetfulness, I again tasted Joy. But far more often I frightened it away by my greedy impatience to snare it, and, even when it came, instantly destroyed it by introspection, and at all times vulgarised it by my false assumption about its nature.

One thing, however, I learned, which has since saved me from many popular confusions of mind. I came to know by experience that it is not a disguise of sexual desire. Those who think that if adolescents were all provided with suitable mistresses we should soon hear no more of 'immortal longings' are certainly wrong. I learned this mistake to be a mistake by the simple, if discreditable, process of repeatedly making it. From the Northernness one could not easily have slid into erotic fantasies without noticing the difference; but when the world of Morris became the frequent medium of Joy, this transition became possible. It was quite easy to think that one desired those forests for the sake of their female inhabitants, the garden of Hesperus for the sake of his daughters, Hylas' river for the river nymphs. I repeatedly followed that path – to the end. And at the end one found pleasure; which immediately resulted in the discovery that pleasure (whether that pleasure or any other) was not what you had been looking for. No moral question was involved; I was at this time as nearly non-moral on that subject as a human creature can be. The frustration did not consist in finding a 'lower' pleasure instead of a 'higher'. It was the irrelevance of the conclusion that marred it. The hounds had changed scent. One had caught the wrong quarry. You might as well offer a mutton chop to a man who is dying of thirst as offer sexual pleasure to the desire I am speaking of. I did not recoil from the erotic conclusion with chaste horror, exclaiming, 'Not that!' My feelings could rather have been expressed in the words, 'Quite. I see. But haven't we wandered from the real point?' Joy is not a substitute for sex; sex is very often a substitute for Joy. I sometimes wonder whether all pleasures are not substitutes for Joy.

Such, then, was the state of my imaginative life; over against it stood the life of my intellect. The two hemispheres of my mind were in the sharpest contrast. On the one side a many-islanded sea of poetry and myth; on the other a glib and shallow 'rationalism'. Nearly all that I loved I believed to be imaginary; nearly all that I believed to be real I thought grim and meaningless. The exceptions were certain people (whom I loved and believed to be real) and nature herself. That is, nature as she appeared to the senses. I chewed endlessly on the problem: 'How can it be so beautiful and also so cruel, wasteful and futile?' Hence at this time I could almost have said with Santayana, 'All that is good is imaginary; all that is real is evil.' In one sense nothing less like a 'flight from reality' could be conceived. I was so far from wishful thinking that I hardly thought anything true unless it contradicted my wishes.

Hardly, but not quite. For there was one way in which the world, as Kirk's rationalism taught me to see it, gratified my wishes. It might be grim and deadly but at least it was free from the Christian God. Some people (not all) will find it hard to understand why this seemed to me such an overwhelming advantage. But you must take into account both my history and my temperament. The period of faith which I had lived through at Oldie's had contained a good deal of fear. And by now, looking back on that fear, and egged on by Shaw and Voltaire and Lucretius with his *Tantum religio*, I greatly exaggerated that element in my memory and forgot the many other elements which had been combined with it. At all costs I was anxious that those full-moon-lit nights in the dormitory should never come again. I was also, as you may remember, one whose negative demands were more violent than his positive, far more eager to escape pain than to achieve happiness, and feeling it something of an outrage that I had been created without my own permission. To such a craven the materialist's universe had the enormous attraction that it offered you limited liabilities. No strictly infinite disaster could overtake you in it. Death ended all. And if ever finite disasters proved greater than one wished to bear, suicide would always be possible. The horror of the Christian universe was that it had no door marked *Exit*. It was also perhaps not unimportant that the externals of Christianity made no appeal to my sense of beauty.

Oriental imagery and style largely repelled me; and for the rest, Christianity was mainly associated for me with ugly architecture, ugly music, and bad poetry. Wyvern Priory and Milton's verse were almost the only points at which Christianity and beauty had overlapped in my experience. But, of course, what mattered most of all was my deep-seated hatred of authority, my monstrous individualism, my lawlessness. No word in my vocabulary expressed deeper hatred than the word *Interference*. But Christianity placed at the centre what then seemed to me a transcendental Interferer. If its picture were true then no sort of 'treaty with reality' could ever be possible. There was no region even in the innermost depth of one's soul (nay, there least of all) which one could surround with a barbed wire fence and guard with a notice No Admittance. And that was what I wanted; some area, however small, of which I could say to all other beings, 'This is my business and mine only.'

In this respect, and this only at first, I may have been guilty of wishful thinking. Almost certainly I was. The materialist conception would not have seemed so immensely probable to me if it had not favoured at least one of my wishes. But the difficulty of explaining even a boy's thought entirely in terms of his wishes is that on such large questions as these he always has wishes on both sides. Any conception of reality which a sane mind can admit must favour some of its wishes and frustrate others. The materialistic universe had one great, negative attraction to offer me. It had no other. And this had to be accepted; one had to look out on a meaningless dance of atoms (remember, I was reading Lucretius), to realise that all the apparent beauty was a subjective phosphorescence, and to relegate everything one valued to the world of mirage. That price I tried loyally to pay. For I had learned something from Kirk about the honour of the intellect and the shame of voluntary inconsistency. And, of course, I exulted with youthful and vulgar pride in what I thought my enlightenment. In argument with Arthur I was a very swashbuckler. Most of it, as I now see, was incredibly crude and silly. I was in that state of mind in which a boy thinks it extremely telling to call God *Jahveh* and Jesus *Yeshua*.

Looking back on my life now, I am astonished that I did not progress into the opposite orthodoxy – did not become a Leftist, Atheist, satiric Intellectual of the type we all know so well. All the conditions seem to be present. I had hated my public school. I hated whatever I knew or imagined of the British Empire. And though I took very little notice of Morris' socialism (there were too many things in him that interested me far more) continual reading of Shaw had brought it about that such embryonic political opinions as I had were vaguely socialistic. Ruskin had helped me in the same direction. My lifelong fear of sentimentalism ought to have qualified me to become a vigorous 'debunker'. It is true that I hated the Collective as much as any man can hate anything; but I certainly did not then realise its relations to socialism. I suppose that my Romanticism was destined to divide me from the orthodox Intellectuals as soon as I met them; and also that a mind so little sanguine as mine about the future and about common action could only with great difficulty be made revolutionary.

Such, then, was my position: to care for almost nothing but the gods and heroes, the garden of the Hesperides, Launcelot and the Grail, and to believe in nothing but atoms and evolution and military service. At times the strain was severe, but I think this was a wholesome severity. Nor do I believe that the intermittent wavering in my materialistic 'faith' (so to call it) which set in towards the end of the Bookham period would ever have arisen simply from my wishes. It came from another source.

Among all the poets whom I was reading at this time (I read *The Faerie Queene* and *The Earthly Paradise* entire) there was one who stood apart from the rest. Yeats was this poet. I had been reading him for a long time before I discovered the difference, and perhaps I should never have discovered it if I had not read his prose as well: things like *Rosa Alchemica* and *Per Amica Silentia Lunae*. The difference was that Yeats believed. His 'ever living ones' were not merely feigned or merely desired. He really thought that there was a world of beings more or less like them, and that contact between that world and ours was possible. To put it quite plainly, he believed seriously in Magic. His later career as a poet has somewhat obscured that phase in popular estimates of him, but there is no doubt about the fact – as I learned when I met him some years later. Here was a pretty kettle of fish. You will understand that my rationalism was inevitably based on what I believed to be the findings of the sciences, and those findings, not being a scientist, I had to take on trust – in fact, on authority. Well, here was an opposite authority. If he had been a Christian I should have discounted his testimony, for I thought I had the Christians 'placed' and disposed of forever. But I now learned that there were people, not traditionally orthodox, who nevertheless rejected the whole Materialist philosophy out of hand. And I was still very ingenuous. I had no conception of the amount of nonsense written and printed in the world. I regarded Yeats as a learned, responsible writer: what he said must be worthy of consideration. And after Yeats I plunged into Maeterlinck; quite innocently and naturally since everyone was reading him at that time and since I made a point of including a fair amount of French in my diet. In Maeterlinck I came up against Spiritualism, Theosophy, and Pantheism. Here once more was a responsible adult (and not a Christian) who believed in a world behind, or around, the material world. I must do myself the justice of saying that I did not give my assent categorically. But a drop of disturbing doubt fell into my Materialism. It was merely a 'Perhaps'. Perhaps (oh joy!) there was, after all, 'something else'; and (oh reassurance!) perhaps it had nothing to do with Christian Theology. And as soon as I paused on that 'Perhaps', inevitably all the old Occultist lore, and all the old excitement which the Matron at Chartres had innocently aroused in me, rose out of the past.

Now the fat was in the fire with a vengeance. Two things hitherto widely separated in my mind rushed together: the imaginative longing for Joy, or rather the longing which *was* Joy, and the ravenous, quasi-prurient desire for the Occult, the Preternatural as such. And with these there came (less welcome) some stirring of unease, some of the immemorial fear we have all known in the nursery, and (if we are honest) long after the nursery age. There is a kind of gravitation in the mind whereby good rushes to good and evil to evil. This mingled repulsion and desire drew towards them everything else in me that was bad. The idea that if there were Occult knowledge it was known to very few and scorned by the many became an added attraction; 'we few', you will remember, was an evocative expression for me. That the means should be Magic – the most exquisitely unorthodox thing in the world, unorthodox both by Christian and by Rationalist standards – of course appealed to the rebel in me. I was already acquainted with the more depraved side of Romanticism; had read *Anactoria*, and Wilde, and pored upon Beardsley, not hitherto attracted, but making no moral judgement. Now I thought I began to see the point of it. In a word, you have already had in this story the World and the Flesh; now came the Devil. If there had been in the neighbourhood some elder person who dabbled in dirt of the Magical kind (such have a good nose for potential disciples) I might now be a Satanist or a maniac.

In actual fact I was wonderfully protected, and this spiritual debauch had in the end one rather good result. I was protected, first by ignorance and incapacity. Whether Magic were possible or not, I at any rate had no teacher to start me on the path. I was protected also by cowardice; the reawakened terrors of childhood might add a spice to my greed and curiosity as long as it was daylight. Alone, and in darkness, I used my best endeavours to become a strict Materialist again; not always with success. A 'Perhaps' is quite enough for the nerves to work upon. But my best protection was the known nature of Joy. This ravenous desire to break the bounds, to tear the curtain, to be in the secret revealed itself, more and more clearly the longer I indulged it, to be quite different from the longing that is Joy. Its coarse strength betrayed it. Slowly, and with many relapses, I came to see that the magical conclusion was just as irrelevant to Joy as the erotic conclusion had been. Once again one had changed scents. If circles and pentagles and the Tetragrammaton had been tried and had in fact raised, or seemed to raise, a spirit, that might have been – if a man's nerves could stand it – extremely interesting; but the real Desirable would have evaded one, the real Desire would have been left saying, 'What is this to me?'

What I like about experience is that it is such an honest thing. You may take any number of wrong turnings; but keep your eyes open and you will not be allowed to go very far before the warning signs appear. You may have deceived yourself, but experience is not trying to deceive you. The universe rings true wherever you fairly test it.

The other results of my glance into the dark room were as follows. First, I now had both a fresh motive for wishing Materialism to be true and a decreased confidence that it was. The fresh motive came, as you have divined, from those fears which I had so wantonly stirred up from their sleeping place in the memories of childhood; behaving like a true Lewis who will not leave well alone. Every man who is afraid of spooks will have a reason for wishing to be a Materialist; that creed promises to exclude the bogies. As for my shaken confidence, it remained in the form of a 'Perhaps', stripped of its directly and grossly magical 'affect' – a pleasing possibility that the Universe might combine the snugness of Materialism here and now with ... well, with I didn't know what; somewhere or something beyond, 'the unimaginable lodge for solitary thinkings'. this was very bad. I was beginning to try to have it both ways: to get the comforts both of a materialist and of a spiritual philosophy without the rigours of either. But the second result was better. I had learned a wholesome antipathy to everything occult and magical which was to stand me in good stead when, at Oxford, I came to meet Magicians, Spiritualists, and the like. Not that the ravenous lust was never to tempt me again but that I now knew it for a temptation. And above all, I now knew that Joy did not point in that direction.

You might sum up the gains of this whole period by saying that henceforward the Flesh and the Devil, though they could still tempt, could no longer offer me the supreme bribe. I had learned that it was not in their gift. And the World had never even pretended to have it.

And then, on top of this, in superabundance of mercy, came that event which I have already more than once attempted to describe in other books. I was in the habit of walking over to Leatherhead about once a week and sometimes taking the train back. In summer I did so chiefly because Leatherhead boasted a tiny swimming-bath; better than nothing to me who had learned to swim almost before I can remember and who, till middle age and rheumatism crept upon me, was passionately fond of being in water. But I went in winter, too, to look for books and to get my hair cut. The evening that I now speak of was in October. I and one porter had the long, timbered platform of Leatherhead station to ourselves. It was getting just dark enough for the smoke of an engine to glow red on the underside with the reflection of the furnace. The hills beyond the Dorking Valley were of a blue so intense as to be nearly violet and the sky was green with frost. My ears tingled with the cold. The glorious week-end of reading was before me. Turning to the bookstall, I picked out an Everyman in a dirty jacket, *Phantastes, a faerie Romance,* George Macdonald. Then the train came in.

I can still remember the voice of the porter calling out the village names, Saxon and sweet as a nut – 'Bookham, Effingham, Horsley train.' That evening I began to read my new book.

The woodland journeyings in that story, the ghostly enemies, the ladies both good and evil, were close enough to my habitual imagery to lure me on without the perceptions of a change. It is as if I were carried sleeping across the frontier, or as if I had died in the old country and could never remember how I came alive in the new. For in one sense the new country was exactly like the old. I met there all that had already charmed me in Malory, Spenser, Morris, and Yeats. But in another sense all was changed. I did not yet know (and I was long in learning) the name of the new quality, the bright shadow, that rested on the travels of Anodos. I do now. It was Holiness. For the first time the song of the sirens sounded like the voice of my mother or my nurse. Here were old wives' tales; there was nothing to be proud of in enjoying them. It was as though the voice which had called to me from the world's end were now speaking at my side. It was with me in the room, or in my own body, or behind me. If it had once eluded me by its distance, it now eluded me by proximity – something too near to see, too plain to be understood, on this side of knowledge. It seemed to have been always with me; if I could ever have turned my head quick enough I should have seized it. Now for the first time I felt that it was out of reach not because of something I could not do but because of something I could not stop doing. If I could only leave off, let go, unmake myself, it would be there. Meanwhile, in this new region all the confusions that had hitherto perplexed my search for Joy were disarmed. There was no temptation to confuse the scenes of the tale with the light that rested upon them, or to suppose that they were put forward as realities, or even to dream that if they had been realities and I could reach the woods where Anodos journeyed I should thereby come a step nearer to my desire. Yet, at the same time, never had the wind of Joy blowing through any story been less separable from the story itself. Where the god and the *idolon* were most nearly one there was least danger of confounding them. Thus, when the great moments came I did not break away from the woods and cottages that I read of to seek some bodiless light shining beyond them, but gradually, with a swelling continuity (like the sun at mid-morning burning through a fog) I found the light shining on those woods and cottages, and then on my own past life, and on the quiet room where I sat and on my old teacher where he nodded above his little *Tacitus*. For I now perceived that while the air of the new region made all my erotic and magical perversions of Joy look like sordid trumpery, it had no such disenchanting power over the bread upon the table or the coals in the grate. That was the marvel. Up till now each visitation of Joy had left the common world momentarily a desert – 'The first touch of the earth went nigh to kill.'

Even when real clouds or trees had been the material of the vision, they had been so only by reminding me of another world; and I did not like the return to ours. But now I saw the bright shadow coming out of the book into the real world and resting there, transforming all common things and yet itself unchanged. Or, more accurately, I saw the common things drawn into the bright shadow. *Unde hoc mihi?* In the depth of my disgraces, in the then invincible ignorance of my intellect, all this was given me without asking, even without consent. That night my imagination was, in a certain sense, baptised; the rest of me, not unnaturally, took longer. I had not the faintest notion what I had let myself in for by buying *Phantastes*.

12

GUNS AND GOOD COMPANY

*La compagnie de tant d'hommes vous plaist, nobles,
jeunes, actifs; la liberté de cette conversation sans art,
et une façon de vie masle et sans cérémonie.*

MONTAIGNE

The old pattern began to repeat itself. The Bookham days, like a longer and more glorious holidays, drew to their end; a scholarship examination and, after that, the Army, loomed behind them like a grimmer term. The good time had never been better than in its last months. I remember, in particular, glorious hours of bathing in Donegal. It was surf bathing: not the formal affair with boards that you have now, but mere rough and tumble, in which the waves, the monstrous, emerald, deafening waves, are always the winner, and it is at once a joke, a terror and a joy to look over your shoulder and see (too late) one breaker of such sublime proportions that you would have avoided him had you known he was coming. But they gather themselves up, pre-eminent above their fellows, as suddenly and unpredictably as a revolution.

It was late in the winter term of 1916 that I went to Oxford to sit for my scholarship examination. Boys who have faced this ordeal in peace-time will not easily imagine the indifference with which I went. This does not mean that I underestimated the importance (in one sense) of succeeding. I knew very well by now that there was hardly any position in the world save that of a don in which I was fitted to earn a living, and that I was staking everything on a game in which few won and hundreds lost. As Kirk had said of me in a letter to my father (I did not, of course, see it till many years later), 'You may make a writer or a scholar of him, but you'll not make anything else. You may make up your mind to *that*.' And I knew this myself; sometimes it terrified me. What blunted the edge of it now was that whether I won a scholarship or no I should next year go into the army; and even a temper more sanguine than mine could feel in 1916 that an infantry subaltern would be insane to waste anxiety on anything so hypothetical as his post-war life. I once tried to explain this to my father; it was one of the attempts I often made (though doubtless less often than I ought) to break through the artificiality of our intercourse and admit him to my real life. It was a total failure. He replied at once with fatherly counsels about the necessity of hard work and concentration, the amount that he had already spent in educating me, the very moderate, nay, negligible, assistance he would be able to give me in later life. Poor man! He misjudged me sadly if he thought that idleness at my book was among my many vices. And how, I asked myself, could he expect the winning or losing of a scholarship to lose none of its importance when life and death were the real issues? The truth is, I think, that while death (mine, his, everyone's) was often vividly present to him as a subject of anxiety and other emotions, it had no place in his mind as a sober, matter-of-fact contingency from which consequences could be drawn. At any rate the conversation was a failure. It shipwrecked on the old rock. His intense desire for my total confidence co-existed with an inability to listen (in any strict sense) to what I said. He could never empty, or silence, his own mind to make room for an alien thought.

My first taste of Oxford was comical enough. I had made no arrangements about quarters and, having no more luggage than I could carry in my hand, I sallied out of the railway station on foot to find either a lodging-house or a cheap hotel; all agog for 'dreaming spires' and 'last enchantments'. My first disappointment at what I saw could be dealt with. Towns always show their worst face to the railway. But as I walked on and on I became more bewildered. Could this succession of mean shops really be Oxford? But I still went on, always expecting the next turn to reveal the beauties, and reflecting that it was a much larger town than I had been led to suppose. Only when it became obvious that there was very little town left ahead of me, that I was in fact getting to open country, did I turn round and look. There, behind me, far away, never more beautiful since, was the fabled cluster of spires and towers. I had come out of the station on the wrong side and been all this time walking into what was even then the mean and sprawling suburb of Botley. I did not see to what extent this little adventure was an allegory of my whole life. I merely walked back to the station, somewhat footsore, took a hansom, and asked to be driven to 'some place where I can get rooms for a week, please'. The method, which I should now think hazardous, was a complete success, and I was soon at tea in comfortable lodgings. The house is still there, the first on the right as you turn into Mansfield Road out of Holywell. I shared the sitting-room with another candidate, a man from Cardiff College, which he pronounced to be architecturally superior to anything in Oxford. His learning terrified me, but he was an agreeable man. I have never seen him since.

It was very cold and next day snow began to fall, turning pinnacles into wedding-cake decorations. The examination was held in the Hall of Oriel, and we all wrote in greatcoats and mufflers and wearing at least our left-hand gloves. The Provost, old Phelps, gave out the papers. I remember very little about them, but I suppose I was outshone in pure classics by many of my rivals and succeeded on my general knowledge and dialectics. I had the impression that I was doing badly. Long years (or years that seemed long) with the Knock had cured me of my defensive Wyvernian priggery, and I no longer supposed other boys to be ignorant of what I knew. Thus the essay was on a quotation from Johnson. I had read several times the Boswellian conversation in which it occurred and was able to replace the whole question in that context; but I never thought that this (any more than a fairish knowledge of Schopenhauer) would gain me any particular credit. It was a blessed state to be in, but for the moment depressing. As I left the Hall after that essay I heard one candidate say to his friend, 'I worked in all my stuff about Rousseau and the Social Contract.' That struck dismay into my soul, for though I had dabbled (not to my good) in the *Confessions* I knew nothing of the *Contrat Social*. At the beginning of the morning a nice Harrovian had whispered to me, 'I don't even know if it's Sam or Ben.' In my innocence I explained to him that it was Sam and could not be Ben because Ben was spelled without an H. I did not think there could be any harm in giving away such information.

When I arrived home I told my father that I had almost certainly failed. It was an admission calculated to bring out all his tenderness and chivalry. The man who could not understand a boy's taking his own possible, or probable, death into account could very well understand a child's disappointment. Not a word was now heard of expenses and difficulties; nothing but consolation, reassurance and affection. Then, almost on Christmas Eve, we heard that 'Univ.' (University College) had elected me.

Though I was now a scholar of my College I still had to pass 'Responsions', which involved elementary mathematics. To prepare for this I returned after Christmas for one last term with Kirk – a golden term, poignantly happy under the approaching shadow. At Easter I was handsomely ploughed in Responsions, having been unable as usual to get my sums right. 'Be more careful', was the advice that everyone gave me, but I found it useless. The more care I took the more mistakes I made; just as, to this day, the more anxiously I fair copy a piece of writing the more certain I am to make a ghastly clerical error in the very first line.

In spite of this I came into residence in the summer (Trinity) term of 1917; for the real object now was simply to enter the University Officers' Training Corps as my most promising route into the Army. My first studies at Oxford, nevertheless, still had Responsions in view. I read algebra (devil take it!) with old Mr Campbell of Hertford who turned out to be a friend of our dear friend Janie M. That I never passed Responsions is certain, but I cannot remember whether I again sat for it and was again ploughed. The question became unimportant after the war, for a benevolent decree exempted ex-Service men from taking it. Otherwise, no doubt, I should have had to abandon the idea of going to Oxford.

I was less than a term at Univ. when my papers came through and I enlisted; and the conditions made it a most abnormal term. Half the College had been converted into a hospital and was in the hands of the R.A.M.C. In the remaining portion lived a tiny community of undergraduates – two of us not yet of military age, two unfit, one a Sinn-Feiner who would not fight for England, and a few other oddments which I never quite placed. We dined in the little lecture room which is now a passage between Common Room and Hall. Small though our numbers were (about eight) we were rather distinguished, for we included E. V. Gordon, afterwards Professor of English at Manchester, and A. C. Ewing, the Cambridge philosopher; also that witty and kindly man, Theobald Butler, skilled in turning the most lurid limericks into Greek verse. I enjoyed myself greatly; but it bore little resemblance to normal undergraduate life and was for me an unsettled, excited, and generally useless period. Then came the Army. By a remarkable turn of fate this did not mean removal from Oxford. I was drafted into a Cadet Battalion whose billet was Keble.

I passed through the ordinary course of training (a mild affair in those days compared with that of the recent war) and was commissioned as a Second Lieutenant in the Somerset Light Infantry, the old XIIIth Foot. I arrived in the front line trenches on my nineteenth birthday (November 1917), saw most of my service in the villages before Arras – Fampoux and Monchy – and was wounded at Mt Bernenchon, near Lillers, in April 1918.

I am surprised that I did not dislike the Army more. It was, of course, detestable. But the words 'of course' drew the sting. That is where it differed from Wyvern. One did not expect to like it. Nobody said you ought to like it. Nobody pretended to like it. Everyone you met took it for granted that the whole thing was an odious necessity, a ghastly interruption of rational life. And that made all the difference. Straight tribulation is easier to bear than tribulation which advertises itself as pleasure. The one breeds *camaraderie* and even (when intense) a kind of love between the fellow-sufferers; the other, mutual distrust, cynicism, concealed and fretting resentment. And secondly, I found my military elders and betters incomparably nicer than the Wyvern Bloods. This is no doubt because Thirty is naturally kinder to Nineteen than Nineteen is to Thirteen: it is really grown-up and does not need to reassure itself. But I am inclined to think that my face had altered. That 'look' which I had so often been told to 'take off it' had apparently taken itself off – perhaps when I read *Phantastes*. There is even some evidence that it had been succeeded by a look which excited either pity or kindly amusement. Thus, on my very first night in France, in a vast marquee or drill hall where about a hundred officers were to sleep on plank beds, two middle-aged Canadians at once took charge of me and treated me, not like a son (that might have given offence) but like a long-lost friend. Blessings

upon them! Once, too, in the Officers' Club at Arras where I was dining
alone, and quite happy with my book and my wine (a bottle of Heidsieck
then cost 8 francs, and a bottle of Perrier Jouet, 12) two immensely senior
officers, all covered with ribbons and red tabs, came over to my table
towards the end of the meal, and hailing me as 'Sunny Jim' carried me off to
their own for brandy and cigars. They weren't drunk either; nor did they
make me drunk. It was pure good will. And though exceptional, this was not
so very exceptional. There were nasty people in the army; but memory fills
those months with pleasant, transitory contacts. Every few days one seemed
to meet a scholar, an original, a poet, a cheery buffoon, a raconteur, or at the
least a man of good will.

Some time in the middle of that winter I had the good luck to fall sick
with what the troops called 'trench fever' and the doctors P.U.O. (Pyrexia,
unknown origin) and was sent for a wholly delightful three weeks to hospital at Le Tréport. Perhaps I ought to have mentioned before that I had had a
weak chest ever since childhood and had very early learned to make a minor
illness one of the pleasures of life, even in peace-time. Now, as an alternative
to the trenches, a bed and a book were 'very heaven'. The hospital was a
converted hotel and we were two in a room. My first week was marred by
the fact that one of the night nurses was conducting a furious love affair with
my room-mate. I had too high a temperature to be embarrassed, but the
human whisper is a very tedious and unmusical noise; especially at night.
After that my fortune mended. The amorous man was sent elsewhere and
replaced by a musical misogynist from Yorkshire, who on our second morning together said to me, 'Eh, lad, if we make beds ourselves dom b—s won't
stay in room so long' (or words to that effect). Accordingly, we made our
own beds every day, and every day when the two V.A.D.'s looked in they
said, 'Oh, they've made their beds! Aren't these two good?' and rewarded us
with their brightest smiles. I think they attributed our action to gallantry.

It was here that I first read a volume of Chesterton's essays. I had never
heard of him and had no idea of what he stood for; nor can I quite understand why he made such an immediate conquest of me. It might have been
expected that my pessimism, my atheism, and my hatred of sentiment would
have made him to me the least congenial of all authors. It would almost seem
that Providence, or some 'second cause' of a very obscure kind, quite over-
rules our previous tastes when It decides to bring two minds together.
Liking an author may be as involuntary and improbable as falling in love. I
was by now a sufficiently experienced reader to distinguish liking from
agreement. I did not need to accept what Chesterton said in order to enjoy
it. His humour was of the kind which I like best – not 'jokes' imbedded in
the page like currants in a cake, still less (what I cannot endure), a general
tone of flippancy and jocularity, but the humour which is not in any way

separable from the argument but is rather (as Aristotle would say) the 'bloom' on dialectic itself. The sword glitters not because the swordsman set out to make it glitter but because he is fighting for his life and therefore moving it very quickly. For the critics who think Chesterton frivolous or 'paradoxical' I have to work hard to feel even pity; sympathy is out of the question. Moreover, strange as it may seem, I liked him for his goodness. I can attribute this taste to myself freely (even at that age) because it was a liking for goodness which had nothing to do with any attempt to be good myself. I have never felt the dislike of goodness which seems to be quite common in better men than me. 'Smug' and 'smugness' were terms of disapprobation which had never had a place in my critical vocabulary. I lacked the cynic's nose, the *odora canum vis* or bloodhound sensitivity for hypocrisy or Pharisaism. It was a matter of taste: I felt the 'charm' of goodness as a man feels the charm of a woman he has no intention of marrying. It is, indeed, at that distance that its 'charm' is most apparent.

In reading Chesterton, as in reading MacDonald, I did not know what I was letting myself in for. A young man who wishes to remain a sound Atheist cannot be too careful of his reading. There are traps everywhere – 'Bibles laid open, millions of surprises,' as Herbert says, 'fine nets and stratagems.' God is, if I may say it, very unscrupulous.

In my own battalion also I was assailed. Here I met one Johnson (on whom be peace) who would have been a lifelong friend if he had not been killed. He was, like me, already a scholar of an Oxford college (Queen's) who hoped to take up his scholarship after the war, but a few years my senior and at that time in command of a company. In him I found dialectical sharpness such as I had hitherto known only in Kirk, but coupled with youth and whim and poetry. He was moving towards Theism and we had endless arguments on that and every other topic whenever we were out of the line. But it was not this that mattered. The important thing was that he was a man of conscience. I had hardly till now encountered principles in anyone so nearly of my own age and my own sort. The alarming thing was that he took them for granted. It crossed my mind for the first time since my apostasy that the severer virtues might have some relevance to one's own life. I say 'the severer virtues' because I already had some notion of kindness and faithfulness to friends and generosity about money – as who has not till he meets the temptation which gives all their opposite vices new and more civil names? But it had not seriously occurred to me that people like ourselves, people like Johnson and me who wanted to know whether beauty was objective or how Aeschylus handled the reconciliation of Zeus and Prometheus, should be attempting strict veracity, chastity, or devotion to duty. I had taken it that they were not our subjects. There was no discussion between us on the point and I do not think he ever suspected the truth about me. I was at no pains to display it. If this is hypocrisy, then I must conclude that hypocrisy can do a man good. To be ashamed of what you were about to say, to pretend that something which you had meant seriously was only a joke – this is an ignoble part. But it is better than not to be ashamed at all. And the distinction between pretending you are better than you are and beginning to be better in reality is finer than moral sleuthhounds conceive. I was, in intention, concealing only a part: I accepted his principles at once, made no attempt internally to defend my own 'unexamined life'. When a boor first enters the society of courteous people what can he do, for a while, except imitate the motions? How can he learn except by imitation?

You will have divined that ours was a very nice battalion; a minority of good regulars ruling a pleasantly mixed population of promoted rankers (west country farmers, these), barristers, and university men. You could get as good talk there as anywhere. Perhaps the best of us all was our butt, Wallie. Wallie was a farmer, a Roman Catholic, a passionate soldier (the only man I met who really longed for fighting) and gullible to any degree by the rawest subaltern. The technique was to criticise the Yeomanry. Poor Wallie knew that it was the bravest, the most efficient, the hardest and cleanest corps that ever sat on horses. He knew all that inside, having learned it from an uncle in the Yeomanry when he was a child. But he could not get it out. He stammered and contradicted himself and always came at last to his trump card: 'I wish my Uncle Ben was here to talk to you. Uncle Ben'd talk to you. He'd tell you.' Mortals must not judge; but I doubt whether any man fought in France who was more likely to go straight to Heaven if he were killed. I would have been better employed cleaning his boots than laughing at him. I may add that I did not enjoy the short time I spent in the company he commanded. Wallie had a genuine passion for killing Germans and a complete disregard of his own or anyone else's safety. He was always striking out bright ideas at which the hair of us subalterns stood on end. Luckily he could be very easily dissuaded by any plausible argument that occurred to us. Such was his valour and innocence that he never for a moment suspected us of any but a military motive. He could never grasp the neighbourly principles which, by the tacit agreement of the troops, were held to govern trench-warfare, and to which I was introduced at once by my sergeant. I had suggested 'pooping' a rifle grenade into a German post where we had seen heads moving. 'Just as 'ee like, zir,' said the sergeant, scratching his head, 'but once 'ee start doing that kind of thing, 'ee'll get zummit back, zee?'

I must not paint the war-time army all gold. I met there both the World and the great goddess Nonsense. The world presented itself in a very ridiculous form on that night (my nineteenth birthday) when I first arrived 'up the line'. As I emerged from the shaft into the dug-out and blinked in the candle-light I noticed that the Captain to whom I was reporting was a

master whom I had liked more than I had respected at one of my schools. I
ventured to claim acquaintance. He admitted in a low, hurried voice that he
had once been a schoolmaster, and the topic was never raised between us
again. The impact of the Great Goddess was even funnier, and I met it long
before I had reached my own battalion. The troop train from Rouen – that
interminable, twelve-mile-an-hour train, in which no two coaches were
alike – left at about ten in the evening. Three other officers and I were allot-
ted a compartment. There was no heating; for light we brought our own
candles; for sanitation there were the windows. The journey would last
about fifteen hours. It was freezing hard. In the tunnel just outside Rouen
(all my generation remember it) there was a sudden wrenching and grating
noise and one of our doors dropped off bodily into the dark. We sat with
chattering teeth till the next stop, where the officer commanding the train
came bustling up and demanded what we had done with our door. 'It came
off, sir,' said we. 'Don't talk nonsense,' said he, 'it wouldn't have come off if
there hadn't been some horseplay!' – as if nothing were more natural than
that four officers (being, of course, provided with screwdrivers) should
begin a night journey in midwinter by removing the door of their carriage.

The war itself has been so often described by those who saw more of it
than I that I shall say here little about it. Until the great German attack came
in the spring we had a pretty quiet time. Even then they attacked not us but
the Canadians on our right, merely 'keeping us quiet' by pouring shells into
our line about three a minute all day. I think it was that day I noticed how a
great terror overcomes a less: a mouse that I met (and a poor shivering
mouse it was, as I was a poor shivering man) made no attempt to run from
me. Through the winter, weariness and water were our chief enemies. I have
gone to sleep marching and woken again and found myself marching still.
One walked in the trenches in thigh gum boots with water above the knee;
one remembers the icy stream welling up inside the boot when you punctured it on concealed barbed wire. Familiarity both with the very old and
the very recent dead confirmed that view of corpses which had been formed
the moment I saw my dead mother. I came to know and pity and reverence
the ordinary man: particularly dear Sergeant Ayres, who was (I suppose)
killed by the same shell that wounded me. I was a futile officer (they gave
commissions too easily then), a puppet moved about by him, and he turned
this ridiculous and painful relation into something beautiful, became to me
almost like a father. But for the rest, the war – the frights, the cold, the smell
of H.E., the horribly smashed men still moving like half-crushed beetles, the
sitting or standing corpses, the landscape of sheer earth without a blade of
grass, the boots worn day and night till they seemed to grow to your feet –
all this shows rarely and faintly in memory. It is too cut off from the rest of
my experience and often seems to have happened to someone else. It is even

in a way unimportant. One imaginative moment seems now to matter more than the realities that followed. It was the first bullet I heard – so far from me that it 'whined' like a journalist's or a peace-time poet's bullet. At that moment there was something not exactly like fear, much less like indifference: a little quavering signal that said, 'This is War. This is what Homer wrote about.'

13

THE NEW LOOK

This wall I was many a weary month in finishing,
and yet never thought myself safe till it was done.
DEFOE, *Robinson Crusoe*

The rest of my war experiences have little to do with this story. How I
'took' about sixty prisoners – that is, discovered to my great relief that
the crowd of field-grey figures who suddenly appeared from nowhere, all
had their hands up – is not worth telling, save as a joke. Did not Falstaff
'take' Sir Colville of the Dale? Nor does it concern the reader to know how
I got a sound 'Blighty' from an English shell, or how the exquisite Sister N.
in the C.C.S. has ever since embodied my idea of Artemis. Two things stand
out. One is the moment, just after I had been hit, when I found (or thought
I found) that I was not breathing and concluded that this was death. I felt no
fear and certainly no courage. It did not seem to be an occasion for either.
The proposition 'Here is a man dying' stood before my mind as dry, as factual, as unemotional as something in a text-book. It was not even interesting. The fruit of this experience was that when, some years later, I met Kant's
distinction between the Noumenal and the Phenomenal self, it was more to
me than an abstraction. I had tasted it; I had proved that there was a fully
conscious 'I' whose connections with the 'me' of introspection were loose
and transitory. The other momentous experience was that of reading
Bergson in a Convalescent Camp on Salisbury Plain. Intellectually this
taught me to avoid the snares that lurk about the word *Nothing*. But it also
had a revolutionary effect on my emotional outlook. Hitherto my whole
bent had been towards things pale, remote, and evanescent; the water-colour
world of Morris, the leafy recesses of Malory,[1] the twilight of Yeats. The
word 'life' had for me pretty much the same associations it had for Shelley in
The Triumph of Life. I would not have understood what Goethe meant by
des Lebens goldnes Baum. Bergson showed me. He did not abolish my old
loves, but he gave me a new one. From him I first learned to relish energy,
fertility, and urgency; the resource, the triumphs, and even the insolence,
of things that grow. I became capable of appreciating artists who would,

---

[1] The iron in Malory, the tragedy of contrition, I did not yet at all perceive.

I believe, have meant nothing to me before; all the resonant, dogmatic, flaming, unanswerable people like Beethoven, Titian (in his mythological pictures), Goethe, Dunbar, Pindar, Christopher Wren, and the more exultant Psalms.

I returned to Oxford – 'demobbed' – in January 1919. But before I say anything of my life there I must warn the reader that one huge and complex episode will be omitted. I have no choice about this reticence. All I can or need say is that my earlier hostility to the emotions was very fully and variously avenged. But even were I free to tell the story, I doubt if it has much to do with the subject of the book.

The first lifelong friend I made at Oxford was A. K. Hamilton Jenkin, since known for his books on Cornwall. He continued (what Arthur had begun) my education as a seeing, listening, smelling, receptive creature. Arthur had had his preference for the Homely. But Jenkin seemed to be able to enjoy everything; even ugliness. I learned from him that we should attempt a total surrender to whatever atmosphere was offering itself at the moment; in a squalid town to seek out those very places where its squalor rose to grimness and almost grandeur, on a dismal day to find the most dismal and dripping wood, on a windy day to seek the windiest ridge. There was no Betjemannic irony about it; only a serious, yet gleeful, determination to rub one's nose in the very quiddity of each thing, to rejoice in its being (so magnificently) what it was.

My next was Owen Barfield. There is a sense in which Arthur and Barfield are the types of every man's First Friend and Second Friend. The First is the *alter ego*, the man who first reveals to you that you are not alone in the world by turning out (beyond hope) to share all your most secret delights. There is nothing to be overcome in making him your friend; he and you join like rain-drops on a window. But the Second Friend is the man who disagrees with you about everything. He is not so much the *alter ego* as the anti-self. Of course he shares your interests; otherwise he would not become your friend at all. But he has approached them all at a different angle. He has read all the right books but has got the wrong thing out of every one. It is as if he spoke your language but mispronounced it. How can he be so nearly right and yet, invariably, just not right? He is as fascinating (and infuriating) as a woman. When you set out to correct his heresies, you find that he forsooth has decided to correct yours! And then you go at it, hammer and tongs, far into the night, night after night, or walking through fine country that neither gives a glance to, each learning the weight of the other's punches, and often more like mutually respectful enemies than friends. Actually (though it never seems so at the time) you modify one another's thought; out of this perpetual dog-fight a community of mind and a deep affection emerge. But I think he changed me a good deal more than I him.

Much of the thought which he afterwards put into *Poetic Diction* had already become mine before that important little book appeared. It would be strange if it had not. He was of course not so learned then as he has since become; but the genius was already there.

Closely linked with Barfield of Wadham was his friend (and soon mine), A. C. Harwood of The House, later a pillar of Michael Hall, the Steinerite school at Kidbrooke. He was different from either of us; a wholly imperturbable man. Though poor (like most of us) and wholly without 'prospects', he wore the expression of a nineteenth-century gentleman with something in the Funds. On a walking tour when the last light of a wet evening had just revealed some ghastly error in map-reading (probably his own) and the best hope was 'Five miles to Mudham (if we could find it) and we *might* get beds there,' he still wore that expression. In the heat of argument he wore it still. You would think that he, if anyone, would have been told to 'take that look off his face'. But I don't believe he ever was. It was no mask and came from no stupidity. He has been tried since by all the usual sorrows and anxieties. He is the sole Horatio known to me in this age of Hamlets; no 'stop for Fortune's finger'.

There is one thing to be said about these and other friends whom I made at Oxford. They were all, by decent Pagan standards (much more, by so low a standard as mine), 'good'. That is, they all, like my friend Johnson, believed, and acted on the belief, that veracity, public spirit, chastity, and sobriety were obligatory – 'to be attempted', as the examiners say, 'by all candidates'. Johnson had prepared me to be influenced by them. I accepted their standards in principle and perhaps (this part I do not very well remember) tried to act accordingly.

During my first two years at Oxford I was busily engaged (apart from 'doing Mods' and 'beginning Greats') in assuming what we may call an intellectual 'New Look'. There was to be no more pessimism, no more self-pity, no flirtations with any idea of the supernatural, no romantic delusions. In a word, like the heroine of *Northanger Abbey*, I formed the resolution 'of always judging and acting in future with the greatest good sense'. And good sense meant, for me at that moment, a retreat, almost a panic-stricken flight, from all that sort of romanticism which had hitherto been the chief concern of my life. Several causes operated together.

For one thing, I had recently come to know an old, dirty, gabbling, tragic, Irish parson who had long since lost his faith but retained his living. By the time I met him his only interest was the search for evidence of 'human survival'. On this he read and talked incessantly, and, having a highly critical mind, could never satisfy himself. What was especially shocking was that the ravenous desire for personal immortality co-existed in him with (apparently) a total indifference to all that could, on a sane view, make immortality desirable. He was not seeking the Beatific Vision and did not even believe in God. He was not hoping for more time in which to purge and improve his own personality. He was not dreaming of reunion with dead friends or lovers; I never heard him speak with affection of anybody. All he wanted was the assurance that something he could call 'himself' would, on almost any terms, last longer than his bodily life. So, at least, I thought. I was too young and hard to suspect that what secretly moved him was a thirst for the happiness which had been wholly denied him on earth. And his state of mind appeared to me the most contemptible I had ever encountered. Any thoughts or dreams which might lead one into that fierce monomania were, I decided, to be utterly shunned. The whole question of immortality became rather disgusting to me. I shut it out. All one's thoughts must be confined to

> the very world, which is the world
> Of all of us – the place where, in the end,
> We find our happiness, or not at all.

Secondly, it had been my chance to spend fourteen days, and most of the fourteen nights as well, in close contact with a man who was going mad. He was a man whom I had dearly loved, and well he deserved love. And now I helped to hold him while he kicked and wallowed on the floor, screaming out that devils were tearing him and that he was that moment falling down into Hell. And this man, as I well knew, had not kept the beaten track. He had flirted with Theosophy, Yoga, Spiritualism, Psychoanalysis, what not? Probably these things had in fact no connection with his insanity, for which (I believe) there were physical causes. But it did not seem so to me at the time. I thought I had seen a warning; it was to this, this raving on the floor, that all romantic longings and unearthly speculations led a man in the end –

> Be not too wildly amorous of the far
> Nor lure thy fantasy to its utmost scope.

Safety first, thought I: the beaten track, the approved road, the centre of the road, the lights on. For some months after that nightmare fortnight, the words 'ordinary' and 'humdrum' summed up everything that appeared to me most desirable.

Thirdly, the new Psychology was at that time sweeping through us all. We did not swallow it whole (few people then did) but we were all influenced. What we were most concerned about was 'Fantasy' or 'wishful thinking'. For (of course) we were all poets and critics and set a very great value on 'Imagination' in some high Coleridgean sense, so that it became important to distinguish Imagination, not only (as Coleridge did) from Fancy, but also from Fantasy as the psychologists understand that term. Now what, I asked myself, were all my delectable mountains and western gardens but sheer Fantasies? Had they not revealed their true nature by luring me, time and again, into undisguisedly erotic reverie or the squalid nightmare of Magic? In reality, of course, as previous chapters have told, my own experience had repeatedly shown that these romantic images had never been more than a sort of flash, or even slag, thrown off by the occurrence of Joy, that those mountains and gardens had never been what I wanted but only symbols which professed themselves to be no more, and that every effort to treat them as the real Desirable soon honestly proved itself to be a failure. But now, busy with my New Look, I managed to forget this. Instead of repenting my idolatry I vilified the unoffending images on which I had lavished it. With the confidence of a boy I decided I had done with all that. No more Avalon, no more Hesperides. I had (this was very precisely the opposite of the truth) 'seen through' them. And I was never going to be taken in again.

Finally, there was of course Bergson. Somehow or other (for it does not seem very clear when I re-open his books today) I found in him a refutation of the old haunting idea, Schopenhauer's idea, that the universe 'might not have existed'. In other words one Divine attribute, that of necessary existence, rose above my horizon. It was still, and long after, attached to the wrong subject; to the universe, not to God. But the mere attribute was itself of immense potency. When once one had dropped the absurd notion that reality is an arbitrary alternative to 'nothing', one gives up being a pessimist (or even an optimist). There is no sense in blaming or praising the Whole, nor, indeed, in saying anything about it. Even if you persist in hurling Promethean or Hardyesque defiances at it, then, since you are part of it, it is only that same Whole which through you 'quietly declaims the cursings of itself' – a futility which seems to me to vitiate Lord Russell's stirring essay on 'The Worship of a Free Man'. Cursings were as futile, and as immature, as dreams about the western garden. One must (like Carlyle's lady) 'accept' the universe; totally, with no reservations, loyally. This sort of Stoical Monism was the philosophy of my New Look. And it gave me a great sense of peace. It was perhaps the nearest thing to a religious experience which I had had since my prep. school days. It ended (I hope for ever) any idea of a treaty or compromise with reality. So much the perception of even one Divine attribute can do.

As for Joy, I labelled it 'aesthetic experience' and talked much about it under that name and said it was very 'valuable'. But it came very seldom and when it came it didn't amount to much.

Those early days of the New Look were on the whole happy ones. Very gradually the sky changed. There came to be more unhappiness and anxiety in my own life; and Barfield was living through

> *that whole year of youth*
> *when life ached like an aching tooth.*

Our generation, the generation of the returned soldiers, began to pass. Oxford was full of new faces. Freshmen began to make historical allowances for our warped point of view. The problem of one's career loomed larger and grimmer.

It was then that a really dreadful thing (dreadful to me) happened. First Harwood (still without changing his expression), and then Barfield, embraced the doctrines of Steiner and became Anthroposophists. I was hideously shocked. Everything that I had laboured so hard to expel from my own life seemed to have flared up and met me in my best friends. Not only my best friends, but those whom I would have thought safest; the one so immovable, the other brought up in a free-thinking family and so immune from all 'superstition' that he had hardly heard of Christianity itself until he went to school. (The gospel first broke on Barfield in the form of a dictated list of Parables Peculiar to St Matthew.) Not only in my seeming-safest friends but at a moment when we all had most need to stand together. And as I came to learn (so far as I ever have learned) what Steiner thought, my horror turned into disgust and resentment. For here, apparently, were all the abominations; none more abominable than those which had once attracted me. Here were gods, spirits, after-life and pre-existence, initiates, occult knowledge, meditation. 'Why – damn it – it's *medieval*,' I exclaimed; for I still had all the chronological snobbery of my period and used the names of earlier periods as terms of abuse. Here was everything which the New Look had been designed to exclude; everything that might lead one off the main road into those dark places where men wallow on the floor and scream that they are being dragged down into Hell. Of course it was all arrant nonsense. There was no danger of *my* being taken in. But then, the loneliness, the sense of being deserted.

Naturally, I attributed to my friends the same desires which, had I become an Anthroposophist, would have been operative in me. I thought they were falling under that ravenous, salt lust for the occult. I now see that, from the very first, all the evidence was against this. They were not that sort. Nor does Anthropo-sophy, so far as I can see, cater for that sort. There is a difficulty and (to me) a reassuring Germanic dullness about it which would soon deter those who were looking for thrills. Nor have I ever seen that it had a deleterious effect on the character of those who embraced it; I have once known it to have a very good one.

I say this, not because I ever came within a hundred miles of accepting the thing myself, but in common fairness, and also as tardy amends for the many hard, unjust and bitter things I once said about it to my friends. For

Barfield's conversion to Anthroposophy marked the beginning of what I can only describe as the Great War between him and me. It was never, thank God, a quarrel, though it could have become one in a moment if he had used to me anything like the violence I allowed myself to him. But it was an almost incessant disputation, sometimes by letter and sometimes face to face, which lasted for years. And this Great War was one of the turning points of my life.

Barfield never made me an Anthroposophist, but his counter-attacks destroyed for ever two elements in my own thought. In the first place he made short work of what I have called my 'chronological snobbery', the uncritical acceptance of the intellectual climate common to our own age and the assumption that whatever has gone out of date is on that account discredited. You must find why it went out of date. Was it ever refuted (and if so by whom, where, and how conclusively) or did it merely die away as fashions do? If the latter, this tells us nothing about its truth or falsehood. From seeing this, one passes to the realisation that our own age is also 'a period', and certainly has, like all periods, its own characteristic illusions. They are likeliest to lurk in those wide-spread assumptions which are so ingrained in the age that no one dares to attack or feels it necessary to defend them. In the second place he convinced me that the positions we had hitherto held left no room for any satisfactory theory of knowledge. We had been, in the technical sense of the term, 'realists'; that is, we accepted as rock-bottom reality the universe revealed by the senses. But at the same time we continued to make for certain phenomena of consciousness all the claims that really went with a theistic or idealistic view. We maintained that abstract thought (if obedient to logical rules) gave indisputable truth, that our moral judgement was 'valid', and our aesthetic experience not merely pleasing but 'valuable'. The view was, I think, common at the time; it runs through Bridges' *Testament of Beauty*, the work of Gilbert Murray, and Lord Russell's 'Worship of a Free Man'. Barfield convinced me that it was inconsistent. If thought were a purely subjective event, these claims for it would have to be abandoned. If one kept (as rock-bottom reality) the universe of the senses, aided by instruments and co-ordinated so as to form 'science', then one would have to go much further – as many have since gone – and adopt a Behaviouristic theory of logic, ethics, and aesthetics. But such a theory was, and is, unbelievable to me. I am using the word 'unbelievable', which many use to mean 'improbable' or even 'undesirable', in a quite literal sense. I mean that the act of believing what the behaviourist believes is one that my mind simply will not perform. I cannot force my thought into that shape any more than I can scratch my ear with my big toe or pour wine out of a bottle into the cavity at the base of that same bottle. It is as final as a physical impossibility. I was therefore compelled to give up realism. I had been trying to defend it ever since I began reading philosophy. Partly, no

doubt, this was mere 'cussedness'. Idealism was then the dominant philosophy at Oxford and I was by nature 'against Government'. But partly, too,
realism satisfied an emotional need. I wanted Nature to be quite independent
of our obser-vation; something other, indifferent, self-existing. (This went
with the Jenkinian zest for rubbing one's nose in the mere quiddity.) But now,
it seemed to me, I had to give that up. Unless I were to accept an unbelievable
alternative, I must admit that mind was no late-come epiphenomenon; that
the whole universe was, in the last resort, mental; that our logic was participation in a cosmic *Logos*.

It is astonishing (at this time of day) that I could regard this position as
something quite distinct from Theism. I suspect there was some wilful blindness. But there were in those days all sorts of blankets, insulators, and insurances which enabled one to get all the conveniences of Theism, without
believing in God. The English Hegelians, writers like T. H. Green, Bradley,
and Bosanquet (then mighty names), dealt in precisely such wares. the
Absolute Mind – better still, the Absolute – was impersonal, or it knew itself
(but not us?) only in us, and it was so absolute that it wasn't really much more
like a mind than anything else. And anyway, the more muddled one got about
it and the more contradictions one committed, the more this proved that our
discursive thought moved only on the level of 'Appearance', and 'Reality'
must be somewhere else. And where else but, of course, in the Absolute?
There, not here, was 'the fuller splendour' behind the 'sensuous curtain'. The
emotion that went with all this was certainly religious. But this was a religion
that cost nothing. We could talk religiously about the Absolute; but there was
no danger of Its doing anything about us. It was 'there'; safely and immovably 'there'. It would never come 'here', never (to be blunt) make a nuisance
of Itself. This quasi-religion was all a one-way street; all *eros* (as Dr Nygren
would say) steaming up, but no *agape* darting down. There was nothing to
fear; better still, nothing to obey.

Yet there was one really wholesome element in it. The Absolute was
'there', and that 'there' contained the reconciliation of all contraries, the
transcendence of all finitude, the hidden glory which was the only perfectly
real thing there is. In fact, it had much of the quality of Heaven. But it was a
Heaven none of us could ever get to. For we are appearances. To be 'there'
is, by definition, not to be we. All who embrace such a philosophy live, like
Dante's virtuous Pagans, 'in desire without hope'. Or like Spinoza they so
love their God as to be unable even to wish that He should love them in
return. I should be very sorry not to have passed through that experience. I
think it is more religious than many experiences that have been called
Christian. What I learned from the Idealists (and still most strongly hold) is
this maxim: it is more important that Heaven should exist than that any of
us should reach it.

And so the great Angler played His fish and I never dreamed that the hook was in my tongue. But two great advances had been made. Bergson had showed me necessary existence; and from Idealism I had come one step nearer to understanding the words, 'We give thanks to thee for thy great glory.' The Norse gods had given me the first hint of it; but then I didn't believe in them, and I did believe (so far as one can believe an *Unding*) in the Absolute.

14

CHECKMATE

The one principle of hell is – 'I am my own.'
GEORGE MACDONALD

In the summer of 1922 I finished Greats. As there were no philosophical posts going, or none that I could get, my long-suffering father offered me a fourth year at Oxford during which I read English so as to get a second string to my bow. The Great War with Barfield had, I think, begun at this time.

No sooner had I entered the English School than I went to George Gordon's discussion class. And there I made a new friend. The very first words he spoke marked him out from the ten or twelve others who were present; a man after my own heart, and that too at an age when the instantaneous friendships of earlier youth were becoming rather rare events. His name was Nevill Coghill. I soon had the shock of discovering that he – clearly the most intelligent and best-informed man in that class – was a Christian and a thoroughgoing supernaturalist. There were other traits that I liked but found (for I was still very much a modern) oddly archaic; chivalry, honour, courtesy, 'freedom', and 'gentillesse'. One could imagine him fighting a duel. He spoke much 'ribaldry' but never 'villeinye'. Barfield was beginning to overthrow my chronological snobbery; Coghill gave it another blow. Had something really dropped out of our lives? Was the archaic simply the civilised, and the modern simply the barbaric? It will seem strange to many of my critics who regard me as a typical *laudator temporis acti* that this question should have arisen so comparatively late in my life. But then the key to my books is Donne's maxim, 'The heresies that men leave are hated most.' The things I assert most vigorously are those that I resisted long and accepted late.

These disturbing factors in Coghill ranged themselves with a wider disturbance which was now threatening my whole earlier outlook. All the books were beginning to turn against me. Indeed, I must have been as blind as a bat not to have seen, long before, the ludicrous contradiction between my theory of life and my actual experiences as a reader. George MacDonald had done more to me than any other writer; of course it was a pity he had that bee in his bonnet about Christianity. He was good *in spite of it*.

Chesterton had more sense than all the other moderns put together; bating, of course, his Christianity. Johnson was one of the few authors whom I felt I could trust utterly; curiously enough, he had the same kink. Spenser and Milton by a strange coincidence had it too. Even among ancient authors the same paradox was to be found. The most religious (Plato, Aeschylus, Virgil) were clearly those on whom I could really feed. On the other hand, those writers who did not suffer from religion and with whom in theory my sympathy ought to have been complete – Shaw and Wells and Mill and Gibbon and Voltaire – all seemed a little thin; what as boys we called 'tinny'. It wasn't that I didn't like them. They were all (especially Gibbon) entertaining; but hardly more. There seemed to be no depth in them. They were too simple. The roughness and density of life did not appear in their books.

Now that I was reading more English, the paradox began to be aggravated. I was deeply moved by the *Dream of the Rood*; more deeply still by Langland; intoxicated (for a time) by Donne; deeply and lastingly satisfied by Thomas Browne. But the most alarming of all was George Herbert. Here was a man who seemed to me to excel all the authors I had ever read in conveying the very quality of life as we actually live it from moment to moment; but the wretched fellow, instead of doing it all directly, insisted on mediating it through what I would still have called 'the Christian mythology'. On the other hand most of the authors who might be claimed as precursors of modern enlightenment seemed to me very small beer and bored me cruelly. I thought Bacon (to speak frankly) a solemn, pretentious ass, yawned my way through Restoration Comedy, and, having manfully struggled on to the last line of *Don Juan*, wrote on the end-leaf 'Never again'. The only non-Christians who seemed to me really to know anything were the Romantics; and a good many of them were dangerously tinged with something like religion, even at times with Christianity. The upshot of it all could nearly be expressed in a perversion of Roland's great line in the *Chanson* –

Christians are wrong, but all the rest are bores.

The natural step would have been to inquire a little more closely whether the Christians were, after all, wrong. But I did not take it. I thought I could explain their superiority without that hypothesis. Absurdly (yet many Absolute Idealists have shared this absurdity) I thought that 'the Christian myth' conveyed to unphilosophic minds as much of the truth, that is of Absolute Idealism, as they were capable of grasping, and that even that much put them above the irreligious. Those who could not rise to the notion of the Absolute would come nearer to the truth by belief in 'a God' than by disbelief. Those who could not understand how, as Reasoners, we participated in a timeless and therefore deathless world, would get a symbolic shadow of the truth by believing in a life after death. The implication – that something which I and most other undergraduates could master without extraordinary pains would have been too hard for Plato, Dante, Hooker, and Pascal – did not yet strike me as absurd. I hope this is because I never looked it squarely in the face.

As the plot quickens and thickens towards its end, I leave out more and more of such matters as would go into a full autobiography. My father's death, with all the fortitude (even playfulness) which he displayed in his last illness, does not really come into the story I am telling. My brother was at that time in Shanghai. Nor would it be relevant to tell in detail how I became a temporary lecturer at Univ. for a year and was elected a fellow of Magdalen in 1925. The worst is that I must leave undescribed many men whom I love and to whom I am deeply in debt: G. H. Stevenson and E. F. Carritt, my tutors, the Fark (but who could paint him anyway?), and five great Magdalen men who enlarged my very idea of what a learned life should be – P. V. M. Benecke, C. C. J. Webb, J. A. Smith, F. E. Brightman, and C. T. Onions. Except for Oldie, I have always been blessed both in my official and my unofficial teachers. In my earlier years at Magdalen I inhabited a world where hardly anything I wanted to know needed to be found out by my own unaided efforts. One or other of these could always give you a clue. ('You'll find something about it in Alanus ...' – 'Macrobius would be the man to try ...' – 'Doesn't Comparetti mention it?' – 'Have you looked for it in Du Cange?') I found, as always, that the ripest are kindest to the raw and the most studious have most time to spare. When I began teaching for the English Faculty, I made two other friends, both Christians (these queer people seemed now to pop up on every side) who were later to give me much help in getting over the last stile. They were H. V. D. Dyson (then of Reading) and J. R. R. Tolkien. Friendship with the latter marked the breakdown of two old prejudices. At my first coming into the world I had been (implicitly) warned never to trust a Papist, and at my first coming into the English Faculty (explicitly) never to trust a philologist. Tolkien was both.

Realism had been abandoned; the New Look was somewhat damaged; and chronological snobbery was seriously shaken. All over the board my pieces were in the most disadvantageous positions. Soon I could no longer cherish even the illusion that the initiative lay with me. My Adversary began to make His final moves.

The first Move annihilated the last remains of the New Look. I was suddenly impelled to re-read (which was certainly no business of mine at the moment) the *Hippolytus* of Euripides. In one chorus all that world's end imagery which I had rejected when I assumed my New Look rose before me. I liked, but did not yield; I tried to patronise it. But next day I was overwhelmed. There was a transitional moment of delicious uneasiness, and then

– instantaneously – the long inhibition was over, the dry desert lay behind, I was off once more into the land of longing, my heart at once broken and exalted as it had never been since the old days at Bookham. There was nothing whatever to do about it, no question of returning to the desert. I had simply been ordered – or, rather, compelled – to 'take that look off my face'. And never to resume it either.

The next Move was intellectual, and consolidated the first Move. I read in Alexander's *Space, Time, and Deity* his theory of 'Enjoyment' and 'Contemplation'. These are technical terms in Alexander's philosophy; 'Enjoyment' has nothing to do with pleasure, nor 'Contemplation' with the contemplative life. When you see a table you 'enjoy' the act of seeing and 'contemplate' the table. Later, if you took up Optics and thought about Seeing itself, you would be contemplating the seeing and enjoying the thought. In bereavement you contemplate the beloved and the beloved's death and, in Alexander's sense, 'enjoy' the loneliness and grief; but a psychologist, if he were considering you as a case of melancholia, would be contemplating your grief and enjoying psychology. We do not 'think a thought' in the same sense in which we 'think that Herodotus is unreliable'. When we think a thought, 'thought' is a cognate accusative (like 'blow' in 'strike a blow'). We enjoy the thought (that Herodotus is unreliable) and, in so doing, contemplate the unreliability of Herodotus.

I accepted this distinction at once and have ever since regarded it as an indispensable tool of thought. A moment later its consequences – for me quite catastrophic – began to appear. It seemed to me self-evident that one essential property of love, hate, fear, hope, or desire was attention to their object. To cease thinking about or attending to the woman is, so far, to cease loving; to cease thinking about or attending to the dreaded thing is, so far, to cease being afraid. But to attend to your own love or fear is to cease attending to the loved or dreaded object. In other words the enjoyment and the contemplation of our inner activities are incompatible. You cannot hope and also think about hoping at the same moment; for in hope we look to hope's object and we interrupt this by (so to speak) turning round to look at the hope itself. Of course the two activities can and do alternate with great rapidity; but they are distinct and incompatible. This was not merely a logical result of Alexander's analysis, but could be verified in daily and hourly experience. The surest means of disarming an anger or a lust was to turn your attention from the girl or the insult and start examining the passion itself. The surest way of spoiling a pleasure was to start examining your satisfaction. But if so, it followed that all introspection is in one respect misleading. In introspection we try to look 'inside ourselves' and see what is going on. But nearly everything that was going on a moment before is stopped by the very act of our turning to look at it. Unfortunately this does not mean that introspection finds nothing. On the contrary, it finds precisely what is left behind by the suspension of all our normal activities; and what is left behind is mainly mental images and physical sensations. The great error is to mistake this mere sediment or track or by-product for the activities themselves. That is how men may come to believe that thought is only unspoken words, or the appreciation of poetry only a collection of mental pictures, when these in reality are what the thought or the appreciation, when interrupted, leave behind – like the swell at sea, working after the wind has dropped. Not, of course, that these activities, before we stopped them by introspection, were unconscious. We do not love, fear, or think without knowing it. Instead of the twofold division into Conscious and Unconscious, we need a threefold division: the Unconscious, the Enjoyed, and the Contemplated.

This discovery flashed a new light back on my whole life. I saw that all my waitings and watchings for Joy, all my vain hopes to find some mental content on which I could, so to speak, lay my finger and say, 'This is it,' had been a futile attempt to contemplate the enjoyed. All that such watching and waiting ever *could* find would be either an image (Asgard, the Western Garden, or what not) or a quiver in the diaphragm. I should never have to bother again about these images or sensations. I knew now that they were merely the mental track left by the passage of Joy – not the wave but the wave's imprint on the sand. The inherent dialectic of desire itself had in a way already shown me this; for all images and sensations, if idolatrously mistaken for Joy itself, soon honestly confessed themselves inadequate. All said, in the last resort, 'It is not I. I am only a reminder. Look! Look! What do I remind you of?'

So far, so good. But it is at the next step that awe overtakes me. There was no doubt that Joy was a desire (and, in so far as it was also simultaneously a good, it was also a kind of love). But a desire is turned not to itself but to its object. Not only that, but it owes all its character to its object. Erotic love is not like desire for food, nay, a love for one woman differs from a love for another woman in the very same way and the very same degree as the two women differ from one another. Even our desire for one wine differs in tone from our desire for another. Our intellectual desire (curiosity) to know the true answer to a question is quite different from our desire to find that one answer, rather than another, is true. The form of the desired is in the desire. It is the object which makes the desire harsh or sweet, coarse or choice, 'high' or 'low'. It is the object that makes the desire itself desirable or hateful. I perceived (and this was a wonder of wonders) that just as I had been wrong in supposing that I really desired the Garden of the Hesperides, so also I had been equally wrong in supposing that I desired Joy itself. Joy itself, considered simply as an event in my own mind, turned out to be of no value at all.

All the value lay in that of which Joy was the desiring. And that object, quite clearly, was no state of my own mind or body at all. In a way, I had proved this by elimination. I had tried everything in my own mind and body; as it were, asking myself 'Is it this you want? Is it this?' Last of all I had asked if Joy itself was what I wanted; and, labelling it 'aesthetic experience', had pretended I could answer Yes. But that answer too had broken down. Inexorably Joy proclaimed, 'You want – I myself am your want of – something other, outside, not you nor any state of you.' I did not yet ask, Who is the desired? only What is it? But this brought me already into the region of awe, for I thus understood that in deepest solitude there is a road right out of the self, a commerce with something which, by refusing to identify itself with any object of the senses, or anything whereof we have biological or social need, or anything imagined, or any state of our own minds, proclaims itself sheerly objective. Far more objective than bodies, for it is not, like them, clothed in our senses; the naked Other, imageless (though our imagination salutes it with a hundred images), unknown, undefined, desired.

That was the second Move; equivalent, perhaps, to the loss of one's last remaining Bishop. The third Move did not seem to me dangerous at the time. It consisted merely in linking up this new *éclaircissement* about Joy with my idealistic philosophy. I saw that Joy, as I now understood it, would fit in. We mortals, seen as the sciences see us and as we commonly see one another, are mere 'appearances'. But appearances of the Absolute. In so far as we really are at all (which isn't saying much) we have so to speak, a root in the Absolute, which is the utter reality. And that is why we experience Joy: we yearn, rightly, for that unity which we can never reach except by ceasing to be the separate phenomenal beings called 'we'. Joy was not a deception. Its visitations were rather the moments of clearest consciousness we had, when we became aware of our fragmentary and phantasmal nature and ached for that impossible reunion which would annihilate us or that self-contradictory waking which would reveal, not that we had had, but that we *were*, a dream. This seemed quite satisfactory intellectually. Even emotionally too; for it matters more that Heaven should exist than that we should ever get there. What I did not notice was that I had passed an important milestone. Up till now my thoughts had been centrifugal; now the centripetal movement had begun. Considerations arising from quite different parts of my experience were beginning to come together with a click. This new dovetailing of my desire-life with my philosophy foreshadowed the day, now fast approaching, when I should be forced to take my 'philosophy' more seriously than I ever intended. I did not foresee this. I was like a man who has lost 'merely a pawn' and never dreams that this (in that state of the game) means mate in a few moves.

The fourth Move was more alarming. I was now teaching philosophy (I suspect very badly) as well as English. And my watered Hegelianism wouldn't serve for tutorial purposes.[1] A tutor must make things clear. Now the Absolute cannot be made clear. Do you mean Nobody-knows-what, or do you mean a superhuman mind and therefore (we may as well admit) a Person? After all, did Hegel and Bradley and all the rest of them ever do more than add mystifications to the simple, workable, theistic idealism of Berkeley? I thought not. And didn't Berkeley's 'God' do all the same work as the Absolute, with the added advantage that we had at least some notion of what we meant by Him? I thought He did. So I was driven back into something like Berkeleyanism; but Berkeleyanism with a few top-dressings of my own. I distinguished this philosophical 'God' very sharply (or so I said) from 'the God of popular religion'. There was, I explained, no possibility of being in a personal relation with Him. For I thought He projected us as a dramatist projects his characters, and I could no more 'meet' Him, than Hamlet could meet Shakespeare. I didn't call Him 'God' either; I called Him 'Spirit'. One fights for one's remaining comforts.

Then I read Chesterton's *Everlasting Man* and for the first time saw the whole Christian outline of history set out in a form that seemed to me to make sense. Somehow I contrived not to be too badly shaken. You will remember that I already thought Chesterton the most sensible man alive 'apart from his Christianity'. Now, I veritably believe, I thought – I didn't of course *say*; words would have revealed the nonsense – that Christianity itself was very sensible 'apart from its Christianity'. But I hardly remember, for I had not long finished *The Everlasting Man* when something far more alarming happened to me. Early in 1926 the hardest boiled of all the atheists I ever knew sat in my room on the other side of the fire and remarked that the evidence for the historicity of the Gospels was really surprisingly good. 'Rum thing,' he went on. 'All that stuff of Frazer's about the Dying God. Rum thing. It almost looks as if it had really happened once.' To understand the shattering impact of it, you would need to know the man (who has certainly never since shown any interest in Christianity). If he, the cynic of cynics, the toughest of toughs, were not – as I would still have put it – 'safe', where could I turn? Was there then no escape?

The odd thing was that before God closed in on me, I was in fact offered what now appears a moment of wholly free choice. In a sense. I was going up Headington Hill on the top of a bus. Without words and (I think) almost without images, a fact about myself was somehow presented to me. I became aware that I was holding something at bay, or shutting something

[1] Not, of course, that I thought it a tutor's business to make converts to his own philosophy. But I found I needed a position of my own as a basis from which to criticise my pupils' essays.

out. Or, if you like, that I was wearing some stiff clothing, like corsets, or even a suit of armour, as if I were a lobster. I felt myself being, there and then, given a free choice. I could open the door or keep it shut; I could unbuckle the armour or keep it on. Neither choice was presented as a duty; no threat or promise was attached to either, though I knew that to open the door or to take off the corslet meant the incalculable. The choice appeared to be momentous but it was also strangely unemotional. I was moved by no desires or fears. In a sense I was not moved by anything. I chose to open, to unbuckle, to loosen the rein. I say, 'I chose', yet it did not really seem possible to do the opposite. On the other hand, I was aware of no motives. You could argue that I was not a free agent, but I am more inclined to think that this came nearer to being a perfectly free act than most that I have ever done. Necessity may not be the opposite of freedom, and perhaps a man is most free when, instead of producing motives, he could only say, 'I am what I do.' Then came the repercussion on the imaginative level. I felt as if I were a man of snow at long last beginning to melt. The melting was starting in my back – drip-drip and presently trickle-trickle. I rather disliked the feeling.

The fox had been dislodged from Hegelian Wood and was now running in the open, 'with all the wo in the world', bedraggled and weary, hounds barely a field behind. And nearly everyone now (one way or another) in the pack; Plato, Dante, MacDonald, Herbert, Barfield, Tolkien, Dyson, Joy itself. Everyone and everything had joined the other side. Even my own pupil Griffiths – now Dom Bede Griffiths – though not yet himself a believer, did his share. Once, when he and Barfield were lunching in my room, I happened to refer to philosophy as 'a subject'. 'It wasn't a *subject* to Plato,' said Barfield, 'it was a *way*.' The quiet but fervent agreement of Griffiths, and the quick glance of understanding between these two, revealed to me my own frivolity. Enough had been thought, and said, and felt, and imagined. It was about time that something should be done.

For of course there had long been an ethic (theoretically) attached to my Idealism. I thought the business of us finite and half-unreal souls was to multiply the consciousness of Spirit by seeing the world from different positions while yet remaining qualitatively the same as Spirit; to be tied to a particular time and place and set of circumstances, yet there to will and think as Spirit itself does. This was hard; for the very act whereby Spirit projected souls and a world gave those souls different and competitive interests, so that there was a temptation to selfishness. But I thought each of us had it in his power to discount the emotional perspective produced by his own particular selfhood, just as we discount the optical perspective produced by our position in space. To prefer my own happiness to my neighbour's was like thinking that the nearest telegraph post was really the largest. The way to recover, and act upon, this universal and objective vision was daily and hourly to remember our true nature, to reascend or return into that Spirit which, in so far as we really were at all, we still were. Yes: but I now felt I had better try to do it. I faced at last (in MacDonald's words) 'something to be neither more nor less nor other than *done*'. An attempt at complete virtue must be made.

Really, a young Atheist cannot guard his faith too carefully. Dangers lie in wait for him on every side. You must not do, you must not even try to do, the will of the Father unless you are prepared to 'know of the doctrine'. All my acts, desires, and thoughts were to be brought into harmony with universal Spirit. For the first time I examined myself with a seriously practical purpose. And there I found what appalled me; a zoo of lusts, a bedlam of ambitions, a nursery of fears, a harem of fondled hatreds. My name was legion.

Of course I could do nothing – I could not last out one hour – without continual conscious recourse to what I called Spirit. But the fine, philosophical distinction between this and what ordinary people call 'prayer to God' breaks down as soon as you start doing it in earnest. Idealism can be talked, and even felt; it cannot be lived. It became patently absurd to go on thinking of 'Spirit' as either ignorant of, or passive to, my approaches. Even if my own philosophy were true, how could the initiative lie on my side? My own analogy, as I now first perceived, suggested the opposite: if Shakespeare and Hamlet could ever meet, it must be Shakespeare's doing.[1] Hamlet could initiate nothing. Perhaps, even now, my Absolute Spirit still differed in some way from the God of religion. The real issue was not, or not yet, there. The real terror was that if you seriously believed in even such a 'God' or 'Spirit' as I admitted, a wholly new situation developed. As the dry bones shook and came together in that dreadful valley of Ezekiel's, so now a philosophical theorem, cerebrally entertained, began to stir and heave and throw off its gravecloths, and stood upright and became a living presence. I was to be allowed to play at philosophy no longer. It might, as I say, still be true that my 'Spirit' differed in some way from 'the God of popular religion'. My Adversary waived the point. It sank into utter unimportance. He would not argue about it. He only said, 'I am the Lord'; 'I am that I am'; 'I am.'

People who are naturally religious find difficulty in understanding the horror of such a revelation. Amiable agnostics will talk cheerfully about 'man's search for God'. To me, as I then was, they might as well have talked about the mouse's search for the cat. The best image of my predicament is the meeting of Mime and Wotan in the first act of *Siegfried*; *hier brauch' ich*

---

[1] i.e. Shakespeare could, in principle, make himself appear as Author within the play, and write a dialogue between Hamlet and himself. The 'Shakespeare' within the play would of course be at once Shakespeare and one of Shakespeare's creatures. It would bear some analogy to Incarnation.

nicht Spärer noch Späher, Einsam will ich ... (I've no use for spies and snoopers. I would be private. ...)

Remember, I had always wanted, above all things, not to be 'interfered with'. I had wanted (mad wish) 'to call my soul my own'. I had been far more anxious to avoid suffering than to achieve delight. I had always aimed at limited liabilities. The supernatural itself had been to me, first, an illicit dram, and then, as by a drunkard's reaction, nauseous. Even my recent attempt to live my philosophy had secretly (I now knew) been hedged round by all sorts of reservations. I had pretty well known that my ideal of virtue would never be allowed to lead me into anything intolerably painful; I would be 'reasonable'. But now what had been an ideal became a command; and what might not be expected of one? Doubtless, by definition, God was Reason itself. But would He also be 'reasonable' in that other, more comfortable, sense? Not the slightest assurance on that score was offered me. Total surrender, the absolute leap in the dark, were demanded. The reality with which no treaty can be made was upon me. The demand was not even 'All or nothing'. I think that stage had been passed, on the bus-top when I unbuckled my armour and the snowman started to melt. Now, the demand was simply 'All'.

You must picture me alone in that room at Magdalen, night after night, feeling, whenever my mind lifted even for a second from my work, the steady, unrelenting approach of Him whom I so earnestly desired not to meet. That which I greatly feared had at last come upon me. In the Trinity Term of 1929 I gave in, and admitted that God was God, and knelt and prayed: perhaps, that night, the most dejected and reluctant convert in all England. I did not then see what is now the most shining and obvious thing; the Divine humility which will accept a convert even on such terms. The Prodigal Son at least walked home on his own feet. But who can duly adore that Love which will open the high gates to a prodigal who is brought in kicking, struggling, resentful, and darting his eyes in every direction for a chance of escape? The words *compelle intrare*, compel them to come in, have been so abused by wicked men that we shudder at them; but, properly understood, they plumb the depth of the Divine mercy. The hardness of God is kinder than the softness of men, and His compulsion is our liberation.

15

THE BEGINNING

Aliud est de silvestri cacumine videre patriam pacis ...
et aliud tenere viam illuc ducentem.
ST AUGUSTINE, *Confessions*, VII, XXI

For it is one thing to see the land of peace from a
wooded ridge ... and another to tread the road
that leads to it.

It must be understood that the conversion recorded in the last chapter was
only to Theism, pure and simple, not to Christianity. I knew nothing yet
about the Incarnation. The God to whom I surrendered was sheerly non-
human.

It may be asked whether my terror was at all relieved by the thought that
I was now approaching the source from which those arrows of Joy had been
shot at me ever since childhood. Not in the least. No slightest hint was
vouchsafed me that there ever had been or ever would be any connection
between God and Joy. If anything, it was the reverse. I had hoped that the
heart of reality might be of such a kind that we can best symbolise it as a
place; instead, I found it to be a Person. For all I knew, the total rejection of
what I called Joy might be one of the demands, might be the very first
demand He would make upon me. There was no strain of music from
within, no smell of eternal orchards at the threshold, when I was dragged
through the doorway. No kind of desire was present at all.

My conversion involved as yet no belief in a future life. I now number it
among my greatest mercies that I was permitted for several months, perhaps
for a year, to know God and to attempt obedience without even raising that
question. My training was like that of the Jews to whom He revealed
Himself centuries before there was a whisper of anything better (or worse)
beyond the grave than shadowy and featureless *Sheol*. And I did not dream
even of that. There are men, far better men than I, who have made immortality almost the central doctrine of their religion; but for my own part I
have never seen how a preoccupation with that subject at the outset could
fail to corrupt the whole thing. I had been brought up to believe that goodness was goodness only if it were disinterested, and that any hope of reward
or fear of punishment contaminated the will. If I was wrong in this (the

question is really much more complicated than I then perceived) my error was most tenderly allowed for. I was afraid that threats or promises would demoralise me; no threats or promises were made. The commands were inexorable, but they were backed by no 'sanctions'. God was to be obeyed simply because he was God. Long since, through the gods of Asgard, and later through the notion of the Absolute, He had taught me how a thing can be revered not for what it can do to us but for what it is in itself. That is why, though it was a terror, it was no surprise to learn that God is to be obeyed because of what He is in Himself. If you ask why we should obey God, in the last resort the answer is, 'I am.' To know God is to know that our obedience is due to Him. In his nature His sovereignty *de jure* is revealed.

Of course as I have said, the matter is more complicated than that. The primal and necessary Being, the Creator, has sovereignty *de facto* as well as *de jure*. He has the power as well as the kingdom and the glory. But the *de jure* sovereignty was made known to me before the power, the right before the might. And for this I am thankful. I think it is well, even now, sometimes to say to ourselves, 'God is such that if (*per impossibile*) his power could vanish and His other attributes remain, so that the supreme right were forever robbed of the supreme might, we should still owe Him precisely the same kind and degree of allegiance as we now do.' On the other hand, while it is true to say that God's own nature is the real sanction of His commands, yet to understand this must, in the end, lead us to the conclusion that union with that Nature is bliss and separation from it horror. Thus Heaven and Hell come in. But it may well be that to think much of either except in this context of thought, to hypostatise them as if they had a substantial meaning apart from the presence or absence of God, corrupts the doctrine of both and corrupts us while we so think of them.

The last stage in my story, the transition from mere Theism to Christianity, is the one on which I am now least informed. Since it is also the most recent, this ignorance may seem strange. I think there are two reasons. One is that as we grow older we remember the more distant past better than what is nearer. But the other is, I believe, that one of the first results of my Theistic conversion was a marked decrease (and high time, as all readers of this book will agree) in the fussy attentiveness which I had so long paid to the progress of my own opinions and the states of my own mind. For many healthy extroverts self-examination first begins with conversion. For me it was almost the other way round. Self-examination did of course continue. But it was (I suppose, for I cannot quite remember) at stated intervals, and for a practical purpose; a duty, a discipline, an uncomfortable thing, no longer a hobby or a habit. To believe and to pray were the beginning of extroversion. I had been, as they say, 'taken out of myself'. If Theism had done nothing else for me, I should still be thankful that it cured me of the time-wasting and foolish

practice of keeping a diary. (Even for autobiographical purposes a diary is
nothing like so useful as I had hoped. You put down each day what you think
important; but of course you cannot each day see what will prove to have
been important in the long run.[1])

As soon as I became a Theist I started attending my parish church on
Sundays and my college chapel on weekdays; not because I believed in
Christianity, nor because I thought the difference between it and simple
Theism a small one, but because I thought one ought to 'fly one's flag' by
some unmistakable overt sign. I was acting in obedience to a (perhaps mistaken) sense of honour. The idea of churchmanship was to me wholly
unattractive. I was not in the least anti-clerical, but I was deeply anti-
ecclesiastical. That curates and archdeacons and churchwardens should
exist, was admirable. They gratified my Jenkinian love of everything which
has its own strong flavour. And (apart from Oldie) I had been fortunate in
my clerical acquaintances; especially in Adam Fox, the Dean of Divinity at
Magdalen, and in Arthur Barton (later Archbishop of Dublin) who had been
our Rector at home in Ireland. (He, by the by, had once suffered under
Oldie at Belsen. Speaking of Oldie's death, I had said to him, 'Well, we
shan't see *him* again.' 'You mean,' he answered with a grim smile, 'we *hope*
we shan't.') But though I liked clergymen as I liked bears, I had as little wish
to be in the Church as in the zoo. It was, to begin with, a kind of collective;
a wearisome 'get-together' affair. I couldn't yet see how a concern of that
sort should have anything to do with one's spiritual life. To me, religion
ought to have been a matter of good men praying alone and meeting by twos
and threes to talk of spiritual matters. And then the fussy, time-wasting
botheration of it all! the bells, the crowds, the umbrellas, the notices, the
bustle, the perpetual arranging and organising. Hymns were (and are)
extremely disagreeable to me. Of all musical instruments I liked (and like)
the organ least. I have, too, a sort of spiritual *gaucherie* which makes me
unapt to participate in any rite.

Thus my churchgoing was a merely symbolical and provisional practice. If
it in fact helped to move me in the Christian direction, I was and am unaware
of this. My chief companion on this stage of the road was Griffiths, with
whom I kept up a copious correspondence. Both now believed in God, and
were ready to hear more of Him from any source, Pagan or Christian. In my
mind (I cannot now answer for his, and he has told his own story admirably

---

[1] The only real good I got from keeping a diary was that it taught me a just appreciation of
Boswell's amazing genius. I tried very hard to reproduce conversations, in some of which very
amusing and striking people had taken part. But none of these people came to life in the diary at
all. Obviously something quite different from mere accurate reporting went to the presentation
of Boswell's Langton, Beauclerk, Wilkes, and the rest.

in *The Golden String*) the perplexing multiplicity of 'religions' began to sort itself out. The real clue had been put into my hand by that hard-boiled Atheist when he said, 'Rum thing, all that about the Dying God. Seems to have really happened once'; by him and by Barfield's encouragement of a more respectful, if not more delighted, attitude to Pagan myth. The question was no longer to find the one simply true religion among a thousand religions simply false. It was rather, 'Where has religion reached its true maturity? Where, if anywhere, have the hints of all Paganism been fulfilled?' With the irreligious I was no longer concerned; their view of life was henceforth out of court. As against them, the whole mass of those who had worshipped – all who had danced and sung and sacrificed and trembled and adored – were clearly right. But the intellect and the conscience, as well as the orgy and the ritual, must be our guide. There could be no question of going back to primitive, untheologised and unmoralised, Paganism. The God whom I had at last acknowledged was one, and was righteous. Paganism had been only the childhood of religion, or only a prophetic dream. Where was the thing full grown? or where was the awaking? (*The Everlasting Man* was helping me here.) There were really only two answers possible: either in Hinduism or in Christianity. Everything else was either a preparation for, or else (in the French sense) a *vulgarisation* of, these. Whatever you could find elsewhere you could find better in one of these. But Hinduism seemed to have two disqualifications. For one thing, it appeared to be not so much a moralised and philosophical maturity of Paganism as a mere oil-and-water coexistence of philosophy side by side with Paganism unpurged; the Brahmin meditating in the forest, and, in the village a few miles away, temple prostitution, *sati*, cruelty, monstrosity. And secondly, there was no such historical claim as in Christianity. I was by now too experienced in literary criticism to regard the Gospels as myths. They had not the mythical taste. And yet the very matter which they set down in their artless, historical fashion – those narrow, unattractive Jews, too blind to the mythical wealth of the Pagan world around them – was precisely the matter of the great myths. If ever a myth had become fact, had been incarnated, it would be just like this. And nothing else in all literature was just like this. Myths were like it in one way. Histories were like it in another. But nothing was simply like it. And no person was like the Person it depicted; as real, as recognisable, through all that depth of time, as Plato's Socrates or Boswell's Johnson (ten times more so than Eckermann's Goethe or Lockhart's Scott), yet also numinous, lit by a light from beyond the world, a god. But if a god – we are no longer polytheists – then not a god, but God. Here and here only in all time the myth must have become fact; the Word, flesh; God, Man. This is not 'a religion', nor 'a philosophy'. It is the summing up and actuality of them all.

As I have said, I speak of this last transition less certainly than of any which went before it, and it may be that in the preceding paragraph I have mixed thoughts that came later. But I can hardly be wrong about the main lines. Of one thing I am sure. As I drew near the conclusion, I felt a resistance almost as strong as my previous resistance to Theism. As strong, but shorter-lived, for I understood it better. Every step I had taken, from the Absolute to 'Spirit' and from 'Spirit' to 'God', had been a step towards the more concrete, the more imminent, the more compulsive. At each step one had less chance 'to call one's soul one's own'. To accept the Incarnation was a further step in the same direction. It brings God nearer, or near in a new way. And this, I found, was something I had not wanted. But to recognise the ground for my evasion was of course to recognise both its shame and its futility. I know very well when, but hardly how, the final step was taken. I was driven to Whipsnade one sunny morning. When we set out I did not believe that Jesus Christ is the Son of God, and when we reached the zoo I did. Yet I had not exactly spent the journey in thought. Nor in great emotion. 'Emotional' is perhaps the last word we can apply to some of the most important events. It was more like when a man, after long sleep, still lying motionless in bed, becomes aware that he is now awake. And it was, like that moment on top of the bus, ambiguous. Freedom, or necessity? Or do they differ at their maximum? At that maximum a man is what he does; there is nothing of him left over or outside the act. As for what we commonly call Will, and what we commonly call Emotion, I fancy these usually talk too loud, protest too much, to be quite believed, and we have a secret suspicion that the great passion or the iron resolution is partly a put-up job.

They have spoiled Whipsnade since then. Wallaby Wood, with the birds singing overhead and the bluebells underfoot and the Wallabies hopping all round one, was almost Eden come again.

But what, in conclusion, of Joy? for that, after all, is what the story has mainly been about. To tell you the truth, the subject has lost nearly all interest for me since I became a Christian. I cannot, indeed, complain, like Wordsworth, that the visionary gleam has passed away. I believe (if the thing were at all worth recording) that the old stab, the old bitter-sweet, has come to me as often and as sharply since my conversion as at any time of my life whatever. But I now know that the experience, considered as a state of my own mind, had never had the kind of importance I once gave it. It was valuable only as a pointer to something other and outer. While that other was in doubt, the pointer naturally loomed large in my thoughts. When we are lost in the woods the sight of a signpost is a great matter. He who first sees it cries 'Look!' The whole party gathers round and stares. But when we have found the road and are passing signposts every few miles, we shall not stop and stare. They will encourage us and we shall be grateful to the authority that set them up. But we shall not stop and stare, or not much; not on this road, though their pillars are of silver and their lettering of gold. 'We would be at Jerusalem.'

Not, of course, that I don't often catch myself stopping to stare at roadside objects of even less importance.